D1094873

ORPHANS IN GETHSEMANE

A Novel of the Past in the Present

Books by Vardis Fisher

THE TESTAMENT OF MAN

Darkness and the Deep
The Golden Rooms
Intimations of Eve
Adam and the Serpent
The Divine Passion
The Valley of Vision
The Island of the Innocent
Jesus Came Again
A Goat for Azazel
Peace Like a River
My Holy Satan
Orphans in Gethsemane

THE VRIDAR HUNTER TETRALOGY:

In Tragic Life
Passions Spin the Plot
We Are Betrayed
No Villain Need Be

OTHER NOVELS

Children of God
Dark Bridwell
April
Toilers of the Hills
Forgive Us Our Virtues
City of Illusion
The Mothers
Pemmican
Tale of Valor

SHORT STORIES

Love and Death

NON-FICTON

God or Caesar?
The Neurotic Nightingale

Vardis Fisher

ORPHANS IN GETHSEMANE

A Novel of the Past in the Present

ALAN SWALLOW, *Denver*

Library of Congress Catolog Card Number: 60-6113

To Opal Laurel Holmes and Alan Swallow—

who was a candle when the night was deepest

who was a haven when the home was lost

A WORD TO THE READER

I feel a little apologetic toward those familiar with my tetralogy, published many years ago, who may unwittingly buy this book unaware that they have read a considerable part of it. I can only beg their indulgence on the ground that I have rewritten the Vridar Hunter story, cutting it by a third or more, and concluding it.

I have felt for a long time that I must do this. One reviewer said that in the tetralogy Neloa held novels two and three together, but that in the fourth novel the story went to pieces. I suspect that it was Vridar who went to pieces: imagining that he had become adult, he mistook a light for an illumination. It surely is true that the fourth novel was the weakest of the four, though (but not at all surprisingly) it has been favored above the other three by many of the 'Vridars' who have written me. Some of them seem to have read it a number of times. All four novels had imperfections of style and method, most of which I hope are at least less egregious than they were.

In offering this 12th novel which concludes what (for want of a better term) I have called my Testament of Man series, it may be well to make my position plain. I stand on this, that if mankind is ever to build a civilization worthy of that devotion which it seems richly endowed to give, it will first have to accept in the full light of its mind and soul the historical facts of its past, and the mutilations and perversions which its hostility to those facts has made upon its spirit. Only in the forces, ideas, and traditions that have produced it, and are the essence of its being, can mankind find its sanctions and powers; but we must hope that it need not forever cherish, because of fear and ignorance, the atavism in these forces, ideas, and traditions, or continue to be so much an expression of their will, once the necessity in their origins is understood and respected.

This novel, and the eleven which precede it, upon which it rests, I have regarded from the first as largely an exploration in fields which a scientific age will steadily broaden and enlighten. I make only this claim, that to the historical facts and probabilities, as well as I have been able to abstract these from books by the highest authorities, I have not, except in one instance, knowingly been false. To illuminate the Solomon story at a critical point in history I did make him a greater man and king than the Higher Critics think he was.

I offer this novel, and the whole series, in the spirit of Goethe, when he wrote, "All I have written and published are but fragments of a great confession"; in the spirit of Stendhal, when he wrote, "I have had a fire lit, and write this, without lying, I hope without any illusions, with real pleasure, like a letter to a friend."

Hagerman, Idaho   Vardis Fisher
July 1, 1959

CONTENTS

BOOK I: APHRODITE PANDAMOS

BOOK II: OURANIA APHRODITE

BOOK I: APHRODITE PANDAMOS*

*Plato divided Aphrodite into the two principles: Aphrodite Pandamos: sensual love of body; Ourania Aphrodite: intellectual love of mind.

PART ONE

IPHIGENIA AND ORESTES

"When Iphigenia heals her brother and frees him of his guilt feeling by touching him, the analyst may well assure that Orestes' guilt feeling was originally the result of 'touching' his sister"—Reik.

I

He was a powerful young man, with great shoulders and hands. His blue eyes, usually warm and a little whimsical, now darkened, for he had heard only a moment ago a scream of agony and a beseeching cry for help. Upon a mountain path in Wyoming the young man went swiftly, blindly toward the sound. He stopped and listened. He heard the cry again. Plunging into a ravine, leaping over bushes and fallen trees, striking limbs from his way he ran until he came to a clearing where elk had slept. There before him was a sight that momentarily paralyzed him, leaving him cold and white. This is what he saw.

A huge grizzly bear and a man were fighting for life and death. The bear half-stood on its hind legs, with one paw on the man's back, the claws buried in flesh and spine. The man's right arm was free but red with blood; his right hand held a short knife; and with this he was stabbing the beast, in its eyes and throat. His left arm was down the bear's throat, buried almost to the shoulder; and from this shoulder blood ran into the beast's mouth. The man's right thigh was laid open in bleeding furrows.

For a moment the young man looked at the horrible spectacle before him. Then he sprang forward, yelling with wild frenzy, half witless with fear and rage. With one mighty thrust he plunged his rifle into the bear's mouth, down past the teeth and along the mangled arm. He shoved it down, two feet of steel barrel, and pressed the trigger. Then, leaving the gun sticking out of the creature's throat, he drew a hunting-knife with a blade eight inches long and drove it between two ribs, seeking the heart. The brute shuddered and fell back, shaking its head, shaking blood out of its blinded eyes. The wounded man, still conscious, though bleeding from shoulder to feet, pulled his mangled arm from the awful mouth and sank to the earth. His left arm was so torn and broken that the two bones of the fore-part were visible. His back and one thigh had been laid open. He was a big man. A little while ago he had been muscled and beating with health and power, but now he had fought his last fight. He strove to lean on his good elbow but sprawled on his back and gurgled. The young man knelt at his side.

"I'm a goner!" gasped the man. "Shoot me—here." He raised his good hand to his forehead.

The young man did not shoot. He looked round him and saw what until this moment he had missed. He saw two men up a tree, clinging to the trunk and staring down at him. Pulling the gun from the dead throat the young man loaded it and walked over to the tree. "You God damned cowards!" he roared. "I ought to shoot you both!"

The men yelped with fright and came down, begging him to spare their lives. One of them, small and furtive, was shaking and chattering. He said he had a wife and child. He said he had been afraid to come down. He had tried to come down

9

but had not been able to move. The other man was also trembling. He said he had tried to come down but as with the other it had seemed that he had grown to the tree. He had never been a coward before, he said, and his teeth clicked.

The young man turned away and went back to the one who was dying. This man was still conscious but there was the look of death in his face. The earth around him was red. Again he begged the young man to shoot him. The young man looked at him and deliberated. Big wounds were in this man from his neck to his knees and half his blood had spilled out. Convulsed, gasping, he begged for death— for a gun, a knife, or a blow on his head. The young man knelt in blood and offered the red wet gun barrel and the other tried to grasp it but his hand was weak. Then the young man placed the muzzle to the other's forehead and brought the good right hand up and helped the fingers to the trigger; and looked away. The trigger was pulled. The body stiffened and rolled over on the mangled arm and was still.

The young man turned to the other men but they had fled. He stared a moment at the dead beast with the knife in its heart. He looked at the dead man, wondering who he was, thinking of his great courage. He drew the knife out and with it dug a grave under the wide boughs of a fir tree. He rolled the body into the grave, spread grass and leaves over it, and covered it with sod. Upon the sod he piled fallen trees and a few stones, and on the smooth bark of a maple he carved this legend:

A Brave Man is Buried
Near This Spot

Then he wiped the blood from his gun and his hunting knife and turned west.

This young man's name was Joseph Charles Hunter and the time was early autumn in the year 1868. With only his gun and knife and a pouch of ammunition he was journeying alone from Missouri to the Pacific coast. Many had gone before him but the way was still dangerous and food was scarce. In crossing the arid reaches of western Nebraska and eastern Wyoming he had almost starved to death. For twenty-three days he had lived on nothing but roots and the stiff wind-beaten hides of old wolves that had died of hunger. He had found a stone, rounded into a basin; he had burned the hair off a hide; then, after cutting the hide into small pieces, he had boiled it for hours in the stone. Once he had surprised an Indian and shot him from his horse; and he had shot the horse and eaten the tender parts of the beast's loins and hams. He had roasted a chunk of flesh and carried it with him.

Still he pushed westward, sleeping in caves or under roofs of timber, shooting coyotes and lacing their green pelts to his feet, until he arrived at last, gaunt and emaciated, in the valley of the great salt lake. Though headed for the gold coasts he paused here for the winter, and in the small hamlet of Ogden met Rose O'Rourke, an Irish lass whose people had come westward with Brigham Young. Many men wooed her, and one Lehi Biddle, a man of power in the Church, to whom revelation had vouchsafed the privilege of another bride, was determined to make Rose his fifth wife. Joe eloped with the girl and took her north to the Snake River valley.

He was one of the earliest of the pioneers there, and one of the first settlers in what is now called Annis, Idaho. In the rich river valley he chose a hundred and

10

sixty acres; built a great house of many rooms, hewing and planing the logs himself; planted an orchard and prospered and grew fat. To him and Rose were born four daughters and eight sons. In 1904 Joe and his family were singled out as the handsomest family in the upper valley.

The first son and oldest child was born March 12, 1870, and was named for his father. He was the only one of twelve children who had any wish for schooling but he was removed from school in his twelfth year and placed to hard work. When not following a plow or harvesting hay, he was the family huntsman, and in his father's smokehouse during the next ten years there was always to be found the cured flesh of deer and elk. The son became an expert marksman, and marksmanship, after school was denied him, became the only thing in his life of which he ever boasted. When still a youth it was said of him that he could break an elk's neck at half a mile, and shoot the heads off wild geese at a hundred yards.

The Celt was strong in this son's blood. His childhood was lonely and he had no close friends. Within him lived the desire to know and secretly he dreamed of becoming an engineer. In his twenty-second year he went to school again, but he was such a huge fellow among the pupils of the sixth grade that taunts and jeers drove him back to the plow. The Celt in him was turned under, like the furrows he homesteaded, and the German in him became his master; but the Celt lived, became fallow and put forth its twisted and brutal life. Young Joe Hunter became a strange man whom none was to understand until he was old.

He took as his own a quarter section of land adjoining that of his father. Part of it was worthless meadow, a swamp of mosquitos and willows; and a still larger part was cedar-covered butte. On its one fertile corner he set an orchard and built a one-room log shack. Then he looked round him for a wife.

His brother Ike had married at eighteen. Ike was the handsomest of the eight sons; he was six feet tall, powerfully muscled, superbly built. Some thought he looked like Wild Bill Hickok. He loved to fight and drink and wench. He was a wild youth, dangerous in combat, violent in his passions; and more than forty years of marriage and slavery were never to tame his savage heart. He took as wife one of the Huntington girls: dark creatures with hot impetuous emotions, and Comanche Indian blood. Joe was told that he should marry one of these, Mary the eldest, who was pining for him. Joe looked at her, timidly approached, wooed. He engaged himself, disengaged, and withdrew to ponder. He returned and slipped to a window and saw Mary embracing another man.

A few miles from Annis lived the Branton family. Samuel Branton was English and Dutch, a cobbler and a strange recluse; his wife was English, a stern and proud woman, who held sexual ardor only slightly above murder. The Brantons were an aloof and haughty clan. The oldest son, Enoch, scorned farming and set up a store. He collected curious stones and flowers, books and musical instruments and butterflies; and he wrote verse until he had a bale of it hidden away. It was his dream to be a writer or an archietect, but he seduced a stupid girl who became his nemesis and drove him into a self-imposed exile of bitterness and loss.

The second son wasted his life and his earnings in a fruitless effort to invent perpetual motion. Another son pushed into the west, headed for the gold fields,

11

and was scalped by Indians. A fourth son worked out a cosmic system based on astrology and went insane. The daughters were ignorant, arrogant, and proud. Spurning men who tilled the earth, one married a saloon-keeper and mothered morons; another went east and married an Oklahoma banker; a third eloped with an itinerant actor and vanished; and the youngest, named Prudence, was unmarried and past twenty when Joe Hunter turned away from Mary Huntington, moaning with delight in another man's arms. This was in the autumn of 1893.

Marriage-mongers set the stage and prepared the hour for the meeting of Prudence and Joe. To Joe they said, "There's that Prudence, just the wife for you. You couldn't find a better womern here to hell and back . . . ." To Prudence they said, "Joe Hunter, he's the one you otta marry. Serious-like, the kind you want . . . ."

To these encouragements neither Prudence nor Joe said a word. They affected unconcern, but in the heart of each grew a strange tenderness for one they had never seen. They stored away knowledge of the unknown and loverless mate. Each learned of the other that he was poor and unschooled, yet hungered for knowledge and a better life; and that he had no close friends. For several weeks their courtship grew; and though they had not met they came to feel betrothed, yet heaped upon encouragement either silence or scorn. An image of the one stood in the other's mind, lived and became familiar, took from gossip its features and its life.

"She don't intrist me," Joe would say, and from one so reticent this was a great deal. But he thought of her afresh, and wondered if her hair was red or only golden. He liked red hair. In a later time he was to say that no woman could be lovely without red hair; and he was to think bitterly of Mary, whose hair was as straight and black as an Indian's.

"I don't intend to marry," said Prudence, and remembered that gossip gave to Joe the mustache of a highwayman. Two years earlier she had been hopelessly in love with a smooth and polished scoundrel, who had a silken beard, and a mustache that had shone like gold. When he begged for intimacy before marriage she slapped him hard and sent him away.

And so they lived for weeks, the soul of each drawn across seven miles, each hungering alone and waiting. One day Jack Hunter came to his brother and said, "Joe, she'll be at the dance tonight! She promised!"

"To hell with her," said Joe, whose ways and speech were blunt. He took his rifle and stalked deer in the north woods. He built a fire under a tree and roasted venison and ate; but thoughts of the dance and of the golden-haired Prudence lured him and drew him back. He told himself that all women were flirts, that wedlock was a dreary burden on manhood, that children were not worth their time. He thought of Mary and her carpet of black hair, spread over the arms of another man, and he hated women. But after a while he arose, chilled by his thoughts, and got himself ready, putting on coarse hunting clothes, wearing them as a visible protest, making an obsession of that bullheaded stubbornness that was to die with him.

Their meeting was a portent, a kind of symbol, of what their lives would be together. Each strove to hide and to spy on the other; but around and behind each were the match-mongers urging them into the lamplight and pointing out where the other was hiding.

12

"See her right over there!" voices whispered to Joe. "God damn it, man, step out so she can see you!" Joe shook hands off, pushed men aside, withdrew into sullen resentment; but all the while he was looking for golden hair. "See him over there!" women whispered to Prudence. "Go dance, and soon he'll be right after you!" The heart of Prudence beat wildly for this man but she would not dance. She remained hidden. Her eyes searched nevertheless for a man with hair as fine as silk, with a high forehead, with steady rain-gray eyes, and with a mustache the color of bronze.

Neither would move out of hiding; neither would speak. The match-makers became desperate. They stooped to cunning. Two of the men seized Joe by his arms and whispered that he should be where he could watch her, to see if her hair was really golden, to infer her character from the way she stood and the way she looked. Perhaps he would not want to marry her after all. Joe allowed himself to be taken. He moved behind a bodyguard of tall men, and across their shoulders he stared at Prudence. She was a stately woman, so tightly corseted that she seemed carved of stone. Her body, he thought, was well made, though he could not be sure what part of her bosom and buttocks was padding and what part was flesh. He studied her face. Her hair was not red; it was golden, like the color of over-ripe wheat. It was piled in an enormous mass upon her proud head. Her eyes were blue, but from the distance he could not tell that they were a cold blue. Her mouth was too full, her upper lip too long; her chin was large and aggressive. Her throat was full and perfect, her skin was a dazzling white. She was a handsome woman but not lovely: deep of bosom and deep of hip, but too queenly and frigid. He felt the coldness of her and the inflexible strength of her will; but he thought she might do, and he decided that here stood his wife.

He withdrew to consider. She was well made and he liked a well made woman. Her reputation as a cook stood high. He had heard that she was frugal. She seemed to be healthy. He supposed that she was intelligent; he could tell that she had poise; and out of her blue eyes looked the will to achieve. Thus the German, the stolid and blunt part of him, summarized her and found her good. But the Celt recoiled. The Celt saw in her too much of the North and too little of the South. He hardly knew whether to advance or retreat, and while he hesitated the matter was decided for him.

A giant approached him, Burns McGard, Samson of the McGard clan. Burns was his cousin. A heavy hand was laid on Joe's shoulder and a deep voice laughed at his woe. "Come along," said Burns. "You're gonna meet her now and if you don't go decent like I'll carry you."

Joe looked at the big bearded face. "If you say so I guess I gotta go," he said.

He went, with Burns at his side. A throng of men and women followed them; laughter died away and voices were hushed. This was the hour, this was the moment, that a whole community had waited for. Men craned their necks, women stood tiptoe. Burns strode boldly across the unplaned plank of the floor and made a great bow to Prduence.

"Miss Branton," he said, "I now interduce Mr. Joseph Hunter."

Prudence turned crimson and lost her voice. She tried to speak but could only cough and look shamed and strangled. Joe also was silent, and as red as the handkerchief around Burns McGard's throat.

13

"Well," said Burns, "you better shake hands. We want a-see a little friendliness atwixt a future husband and wife."

Prudence burned more deeply, the red flowing in a wave down her white throat. She offered a timid hand. Joe grasped it with his big stubbed fingers, held it a brief moment, and turned it free. "Glad to meet you," he said.

Then the people roundabout, stretched to their fullest height, breathless and tense, relaxed in a mighty cheer that swept the hall. After months of plans frustrated, dances given in vain, and argument and beseeching and threat, Prudence Branton and Joseph Hunter had been forced to meet and now stood face to face.

Their courtship was a strange one. It was a cool flowering within a shelter of reticence, with passion shut away and all conversation stripped to the bone. With two such persons it could not have been otherwise. As a child, Joe had been cuffed and knocked about; he had been the family drudge; he had seen his younger brothers given the love and understanding that he had never known. He had been laughed at for his desire to learn. The warm and impulsive part of him had not grown because it had found no light; he had become morbidly taciturn. He had grown perverse, making a holy thing of stubbornness, looking with suspicion on spontaneous joy. A warm and impulsive woman might have led him into the sun, but he set his heart on Prudence and in choosing her almost lost his soul.

Prudence Branton was not a cold woman in the deeper chambers of her being; but she had been taught by a stern and self-pitying mother that sexual passion was base and unclean, that the intimacy of flesh was a degrading experience, save only for the purpose of birth. She had been taught never to sit with her legs crossed, never to stand with her legs apart. She had been taught to beware of candies and powders and drinks, because into these sly men sometimes spilled dangerous drugs and potions, that would paralyze a woman's will and make her as wanton as a whore. But in spite of all her teachings Prudence could have been led, by a skillful lover, to profound discovery of her body and its power for joy. But neither of these would ever be a lover, wedded to the other . . . .

And so their courtship was a cool white flowering, and their infrequent hand-clasps were brief and as passionless as snow. Joe took her to the weekly dance; he took her home; and usually over the seven miles of gleaming road neither uttered a word. He was baffled by her aloofness and by her haughty face. At her front door he would pause, fumble vaguely among his emotions, and say at last, "Well, I guess I'll see you next Saturday night."

"Yes," Prudence would say, trembling in the bitter moonlight.

Joe would go away from her without looking back. He would say, "Goodnight," speaking ahead of him, and would vanish into the winter cold.

During the week he would think of her, sometimes with a sudden leap of his heart, but he never left his work to make an unexpected call. When warmer days came he borrowed an old one-horse buggy and they rode to dances in it. He always left the dance early, telling her that he needed to get sleep for the next day's labor. Sundays in springtime he played on the baseball team, and sometimes Prudence watched him play. He was the catcher, and he took the hard-driven ball with his naked hands. In a later time, when catchers used gloves, Joe would grunt with contempt. The world had changed, he would say, and men were not what men used to be.

They never spoke of love. Love indeed was a word Joe was never to use in all the years of his life. For all terms of endearment he had a blunt and perverse scorn. The German in his soul found them useless and silly. The only word of tenderness he was ever to use was the simple word *dear,* and this he never used until after he was married. Nor did he ever kiss her until after they were betrothed, and only rarely then, his stiff mustache sweeping across her lips. Sometimes he would pat her hand or struggle clumsily to help her with a wrap. Once he astonished and shocked her by declaring simply that he liked women with long legs and was glad that her legs were long.

Their betrothal came about this way. Spring had opened in delicate loveliness; the time was April, and a blue and fragrant afternoon. Joe had been elected captain of the baseball team. He was feeling his great strength and his need of love and a home. Turning to Prudence sitting by him in the rickety buggy he said, "Well, I guess we'll be married about the first of June." He did not look at her. He shouted at the horse, profaned a little, and laid a willow smartly on its rump. They rode four miles and no word was spoken. Joe did not help her down; one of his most violent contempts was for the man who wooed a woman with little gallantries. He preceded her to the house. It had not occurred to him that Prudence might not wish to marry him, or to marry at all. The whole matter had been settled for him when they first met.

On the porch he stopped and they both waited. Was there a light in her eyes, a warmer hunger on her mouth? If these were there Joe did not see them; he was gazing stubbornly at the calloused hide of his palms. All the while nevertheless he was wondering if he should kiss her, or if he should hasten home and set the plow to land. Prudence, a little amused, perhaps a little hurt, studied his face and waited.

"Joe?" she said at last, and touched his arm.

Joe looked up. He had never seen her face so soft and full of light. He became aware that she was trembling. Yielding to an impulse he put hands on her shoulders and looked into her eyes. He bowed his handsome head and his lips and mustache briefly touched her lips. Then he turned away without speaking and drove furiously home.

During this while, between an April afternoon and the first June morning, they spent more time together. But they never spoke of love. They never wooed, or lifted more than a small and unimportant excitement out of their hunger. They spoke of the home they hoped to have, of the children that would come, of how they would educate these children, no matter what it cost. It was in this one thing, shame for their ignorance, and their desire to lift their sons and daughters to a loftier estate, that they found their deepest intimacy. It was this that would cement their lives, that would drive them forth to a long life of hard labor and self-sacrifice; that would bring upon Joe the scorn of people for whom he was a miser; that would humble a proud and golden-haired woman, looked upon by her people as one degraded and lost; and that would lead these two, however mismated they were, how-

15

ever bedeviled by wounds and outraged pride, to an eventual wedlock as profound as their common dream . . . .

The first of June, a day of gray rain and driven clouds, they were married, and all the people in the valley came to their wedding. That evening Joe entered his one-room shack with his bride and locked the door. At daylight the next morning he was in his barren fields, hands on a plow. Rich in strength and health he entered his kingdom of labor, without bothering to eat breakfast, for there was deep shame in him and deep hurt; and Prudence Hunter, a bride of only a few hours, who had been raped more than wooed, lay face downward on the bed, weeping her heart out.

She was to weep often during her first years as wife but never once did she think of turning back to her people. She wept not only for her husband, whose ways were tactless and unwittingly brutal, and who looked with scorn on her sensitive flesh; she was to weep also for her husband's mother, the hostile and implacable Scotch-Irish Rose O'Rourke.

Rose had an indomitable spirit. Her black eyes and thin straight lips and lean athletic body asked for no mercy and gave none. She hated all her daughters-in-law as they came, but for Prudence she reserved her most venomous words and bitterest spite. She hated this daughter-in-law for her haughty carriage, her aloofness, her pride. She hated her for another reason. Rose liked bawdy tales, the lush gleanings of sexual indecorum, the dank and odorous jests of carnal love. She would tell such tales, no matter around whom, and laugh with shrill wild laughter until tears blinded her. Her children grew up, accustomed daily to obscene jest and leer; her two oldest daughters flowered in her image. For these odds and ends of passion, these rank and earthy burrowings into the animal in man, her husband had no taste at all. He did not protest. He just sat in florid emotional health, reading his Bible or the Mormon *Deseret News,* and giving no heed to his wife's lewd tales, gathered from a hundred tongues.

Prudence Branton had never in her own home heard an indelicate word. That home had been a kind of nunnery, scrupulously chaste and pure. Her mother would have turned out of doors any man or woman who voiced an unclean thought or spoke an unclean word. Her father, and Prudence also, were embarrassed even by such words as legs and desire, bull and stud and bitch, rutting and heat. These words had never been spoken in the Branton home.

The third day of her marriage Prudence got her second violent shock. She entered Rose's house and Rose gave her a curt and hostile nod and a searching stare out of black eyes. "Have a seat," she said at last. "Don't stand there like you was a stranger."

Prudence colored and took a seat. Rose folded her arms and stared.

"You Brantons," she said, after a hard bitter appraisal, "gives yourselves a lot of stud-airs. Nobody is bettern anybody else in this world. That's a lesson you ain't never learnt."

Prudence did not speak. What was there to say? This lean and aggressive woman, all nerve and devil and iron will, made her feel very unhappy and unwanted.

Suddenly there was a great din somewhere outside: a loud outcry of voices and

16

the beating of feet; and a crowd of people trooped in, big coarse men smelling of earth and barnyards, large roomy women with bold eyes and unbridled tongues. These were the McGards, Scotch and Irish of blood, full-bodied and tremendous in health and power and passion. They overwhelmed the parlor. They sprawled on tables and chairs and on the floor. Their language was a flood of coarse earthy thoughts, their emotions burst into broad humor, their laughter shook the house. Among them was Burns. Prudence liked this man: he was the giant of them all, and mighty and clean. But she distrusted the others: their undisciplined vigor, their zest for love and battle, the vulgar tides of their speech. Tense and alone, a proud and sensitive alien, she stared at them and was afraid. She felt in them contempt for manners, for the graces of movement, the refinements of talk. They seemed to have risen bodily out of the soil. Soil was in their ears, in their uncombed hair, and it was rich and black under their nails. They smelt of it and of sweat, of orchards and barns and coops, of cedar boughs and tobacco and whisky. The men squirted tobacco juice into the stove, out of windows, through the open door; the women sprawled in voluptuous ease or kicked their men on their rumps or choked with laughter. While Prudence watched, comparing these people and their ways with her own people, the talk veered suddenly to the indelicate.

It turned to one Bridget, soon to be married, and to Bridget's dreams. It became heavy with implication, drew an analogy from a bitch; romped through coarse words, some of which Prudence had never before heard; and then leapt and squealed to a climax, the import of which darkened her senses. The crowd roared like thunder, all but Burns. With her flesh afire and her emotions sickened, Prudence arose and fled.

But this was only the beginning. From her husband's people she was to hear tales that made the blood burn over her throat. She was to hear sex spoken of as if the whole earth were an enormous bedroom full of mating couples; to hear love dragged down from the cool heavens where she had enthroned it and spilled in ruttish pawings and obscene laughter. She was glad that her husband did not like these things. "You don't, do you?" she asked him, and he said, "No." Long years were to pass before she understood the Rabelaisian vein in him, or knew that he had crushed this part of him, fenced it off into dank night air, because of the cold rebuke in her eyes and mouth.

Prudence said their children would be brought up with clean minds. Was that not the way he felt? He guessed so, he said, but the next time he embraced her he was rougher than he had been, even on his wedding night.

To bring up her children with clean minds, and ignorant as long as possible of all sexual matters, became for Prudence her first law of life. Sex for her, even more than when she was virginal, became an unlovely necessity, an impure prelude to birth, and the most amazing of all the dark blunders of God. Her blue eyes were never to lose their cold purity. Her will was never to waver in its fixed purpose. She would rear her children to be ladies and gentlemen; baby-step by childhood-step she would train them in pure thoughts and deeds. She did not foresee what bitterness and agony of soul her stern way of life would lead to. She felt that God was with her, and that her pieties and scruples were the warmth of his great heart.

And when in July of this year she felt the first faint stirring in her womb, she set heel to her inexorable pride, accepted as well as she could her husband's people, and went forth to a life of self-sacrifice that was to have no parallels in her time and place.

II

On a violent windy night seven months later her first son was born. The birth almost cost her life. For weeks she was unable to rise from her bed. The child was a sickly yelping infant that wailed wretchedly day and night. After a few days he was taken from the breast and nourished with cow's milk. Proud of his health and strength, Joe looked at his son and wondered for what reasons he had been punished with a weakling. He had been forced to mortgage his farm, and now from sunrise until after dark he toiled like one driven but his soil was poor and during the first years of his married life his fare was bread and water gravy with potatoes, with now and then a little garden stuff or a chunk of wild meat.

At the insistence of Rose the first son was named Vridar; the name, she said, had been in the family for at least two hundred years. Grandmother, parents, uncles and aunts spelled and pronounced it in different ways, until eighteen years later the young man settled the matter for himself: he spelled it Vridar and pronounced it Vreedar. His middle name, also imposed on him by the resourceful Rose, was Valejo: in this twenty-fourth year in an effort to simplify his life he threw it away.

Vridar was born with a caul. From this circumstance his mother and grandmother took augury of great achievement. Rose said he might be a prophet; Joseph Smith, she said, was born with a veil over his face. "And I've hear," she said, "Jesus Christ was too." This caul became a matter of legend and had a profound and unhappy influence on the child's life.

Vridar was told in later times that he was a remarkable child. He distrusted these tales, suspecting that they were the seed and growth of a mother's wish. He was told that he talked at nine months, walked easily and well before his first birthday, and counted to a hundred at the age of two. At the age of three he knew his multiplication tables to the sixes; at four he could add and substract; at six he was reading the Bible. Of this precocious time he remembered little.

The earliest experience he could recall was at the age of three. Some visitors had come to the one-room shack where he was born, and for their amazement and her own joy the proud mother asked her son to count. He refused. He was coaxed and petted and cajoled, but he disliked the strangers with their gaping faces and intent eyes and he withdrew into dim lamplight and sullen silence.

His father said if he did not count he would take him outside and spank him. His mother begged him to be a nice little gentleman. But the child shook his head and said no. Then the father took the child with him into the enormous black night, and Vridar was filled with deep and uncontrollable fear. He was afraid of the dark and the silence and of his father's face and hands. Vridar was set down behind the shack and he stood there shaking with terror and wondering why his mother had deserted him. From a sagebush Joe broke a slender branch and turned

18

the child over his knees and began to smite him softly. Vridar made a queer sound, not of weeping but of terror too ruthless to be endured. When asked if he would count his assent was a wild scream. Joe carried him back into the house. Vridar counted to seventy and stopped and began to moan and tremble. He turned eyes on his mother but he saw no pity in them; she was a strange woman in a house that had become strange. When commanded to count again his spirit broke. Horror, awful and black, closed over him, and he fell into a convulsion, with slobber pouring from his mouth.

During these early years, he was told long afterward, convulsions were common to him. His mother admitted them but would not talk about them. They were convulsions caused by terror, but why he had been so terrified at an early age he was never to know. He became bitterly, desperately afraid of people and of life. He was afraid of the night, of his parents, of all his relatives.

His second memory was of an experience that happened a little later. His parents took him to a photographer. He was placed on a high stool in what seemed to him to be a huge dark room; and before him was a strange dark machine. He was afraid of it and of the tall dark man who stood behind it, talking to him of incredible birds. Murmuring in his black beard the dark man was asking him to be a nice boy. He told Vridar that he would see white birds; they would come out of the air any minute and would float above his head. A moment later he was telling him that the birds would fly out of the machine. "Look right here," he said, indicating the lens, "and watch for the white birds."

Scowling and intent, Vridar stared at the lens, wondering how white birds could fly out of so small a place. But his mother said they would. The man said they would. Vridar believed them and waited for the miracle. Then he heard a clicking sound. The man smiled and asked him if he had seen the birds. Vridar knew by the man's face that he had lied, that his mother had lied, that they both tricked him.

When Vridar was a man he looked at this photograph. It was of a strange, frightened and beautiful child. The eyes were large and dark and unhappy; the face was sullen and intent. "So this is what I was," he would think, trying to realize that he had grown from this child; trying to go back down the years and sit again on that high stool and watch for white birds. He felt tenderness and pity for that small lad with his frightened eyes. "All my life," he thought, "I've been looking for white birds. What a fool I have been! . . . "

His third memory of this blurred and haunted time was of his sister's homecoming. It was in February, 1901. His father took him and his brother Marion to their grandmother's and said they would spend the night there. Vridar was almost paralyzed with fear. He was afraid of Rose O'Rourke; though she thought he might be a prophet, she hated him and he knew that she hated him. She hated him most of all because he was precocious and her youngest son was dull. "He'll grow up," she said, "and give hisself studhorse airs."

He was horribly afraid but he said nothing to his father. This man, as Vridar saw him, was a silent grim giant, as cold as deep ice and as unfraid as the nightwinds. He heard his father go away and he heard the door close and the gate swing; and then he sat by the kitchen fire, with his brother by him, and listened to the sound of storm. He did not know why his father had brought him here. His mother had not explained.

Evening drew on, his aunts and uncles came in, and there was talk. His youngest uncle was a year older than himself, a rugged blue-eyed, fearless lad who had unspeakable contempt for his two nephews. He would take both Vridar and Marion and hurl them to earth and sit on them; stuff hay and dust down their backs and into their mouths and blow dust and manure chaff into their eyes; and he would taunt them, telling them that they were cowards, that the streak of yellow down their backs was a yard wide, saying that they were Brantons with studhorse airs and would never be worth a bitch's teat.

His aunt Kate, youngest of his father's sisters, now a girl of nine years, was the only one in the senior household whom Vridar liked. She was studious and quiet. A large girl, with lovely dark gray eyes and a kindly forthright way, she would now and then defend Vridar when insults and abuse drove him to tears and rage. She defended him tonight.

When Rose entered the kitchen she stared for a moment at her grandsons. Vridar felt the sharp hostility. He expected unkind words and the words came. "You brats," she said, "don't have to hog the fire. I'd think you'd let somebody else get warm. You think all the fires in God's world was made just for you?"

Stung, abashed and shamed, Vridar moved back, taking his brother with him. They went to a dim corner and stood there, and Vridar watched his grandmother. She was lean, quick, and as straight as an arrow. Her coal-black hair hung in a long rope to her waist. She now prepared the evening meal, devouring the room with long strides; hurling sharp words, reproaches, warnings, commands; and in all ways showing herself to be the aggressive and pitiless mistress of this great house. Vridar watched her and shivered by the wall. He stared at her thin tight mouth, at the sudden flickerings in her black eyes, at the dead snake of her hair. His brother looked at him, interrogating, mute, and then sighed.

When the table was laid, Rose turned to her grandsons. "You kids had your supper? It's just like that mother of yours to send you off hungry."

Vridar was enraged by the insult. Because he had not eaten since noon he faced a dilemma here: to tell the truth and allow the insult, or to lie. His mother had told him that lying was a crime against the Holy Ghost, which God would punish in most terrible ways . . . .

"I ast you a question!" Rose cried, pausing to glare at him. "Ain't you never learnt to answer your betters?"

Vridar lied. He said they were not hungry. The shrewd Rose turned the lie upon him and made it his shame. She asked Marion if he had eaten and he said no. "I guess you ain't et since noon, have you?"

"No maam," he said.

Rose turned to Vridar. "I hate liars," she said. "Just for that you go to bed hungry."

All but Vridar gathered round the table and ate. Marion's plate was heaped with meat and vegetables and preserves, biscuits and butter; Vridar had only bread and potatoes and water gravy in his own home. The blue-eyed uncle, whose name

20

was Michael, looked round at Vridar and leered. His aunt Agnes, a girl of nineteen, giggled lewdly and said, "You little liar, see what you're missun? Your old ma don't give you no meals like this."

"His false pride," said Rose. "He'll choke black in the face some day on his damn false pride."

"Stop pickun on him," said Kate.

Vridar stood by the cold wall, not daring to approach the stove again. He watched them feeding hungrily; he listened to their talk. Their talk like their eating was loud and devouring. It was lewd. It scattered into dark meanings and tumbled into snickering laughs. For they talked of his mother in the cold shack on the hillside; and Vridar, listening, trying to turn sense out of strange words, got only the notion that a baby's coming was a shameful thing.

"In the mornun," said Agnes, looking at him with eyes full of lewd things, "mebbe you'll have a baby sister. That please you?"

"I don't know," Vridar said, barely above a whisper.

"Or brother. That please you?"

"I don't know."

"Well, Judas God, can't you say anything but you don't know? Do you know your hindend from a hole in the ground?"

"Oh, leave him be!" said Kate.

"I'll bet he knows he's hungry," said Rose. "The little liar."

"We won't even give you any breakfast," said Agnes.

"Oh, shut up!" Kate said.

Vridar was trying to understand their malice and spite, their dislike, their joy in his hunger. He was troubled by the snickering insinuations laid at his mother's door.

Later that evening Agnes told him and Marion to come to bed. She took them up a dark cold stairway, to a gloomy bedroom in a vast dark house. She turned quilts back and told them to get their clothes off and crawl in. "And don't let the ghosts get you!" she whispered to Vridar, bending forward. "There's ghosts all over here and the Devil hisself is in that closet. Shall I open the door and show you?"

"No!" Vridar gasped and felt panic.

"Just be awful still and don't make no fuss. If you make a fuss the Devil will jump on you and choke you—like this," she said, and grasped Vridar's throat.

He threw himself away and screamed. "Don't!" he begged. "We'll be still!"

Shivering and horrified, Vridar took off his patched trousers and shirt. He had no underwear, no shoes. He and Marion climbed into the bed and Agnes snuffed out the light. Vridar heard her close the door. He heard her creaking steps down the stairway. Then everything was profoundly still.

The next eight hours were a nightmare of cold and of terrifying silence or of still more terrifying sounds. He never closed his eyes, save now and then to shut away the ghostly shadows. He was almost afraid to breathe. When Marion stirred so that the bed creaked, moving nearer his brother to seek his warmth; or when he coughed a little or breathed too loud, then Vridar shook with apprehension and begged him to be quiet. Now and then he would draw the covers down a little and

21

look out, with eyes half-shut; but the room was so murky and strange and awful and the light at the windows was so frozen and weird that he would draw the quilts over his head and lie so quietly that he could hear his own heart.

At the end of each hour a great clock struck in the house below. It made a fearful sound, as though the silence were being shattered like glass. He counted the time, lay as if dead through each long and horrifying hour, and prayed for daylight. When he looked out he saw shadows in weird postures on the walls and a ghostly pool of light in a corner; and once he saw a living thing etched for a moment in a shaft of moonglow. When daylight came, spilling in golden flood through the silence, Vridar loved it with the intensity of one who had been saved from death.

Quietly he slipped from the bed and in a whisper told Marion to dress. Then they slipped down the cold stairway and softly let themselves out. Once in his time of manhood Vridar entered this house, climbed the stairway and looked into this room; and the memory of this night was still so vivid and terrible that he shuddered and turned away.

When a hundred yards away from the house Vridar began to run, and he did not pause until he came, white and trembling, to his father's door. He did not tell his parents about this night, now or ever. His fear darkened within him and grew and was not confessed. On those times when he showed fear, by his agitated manner or white face, he lied about the cause of it or refused to speak at all. This cold February morning he had no encouragement to tell. His mother, white and ill, lay in bed with an infant at her breast. Vridar looked at the red and hairless and wrinkled babe and was filled with the wonder of it. Where had it come from? If it was a girl, as his grandmother had said it would be, then why was it a girl, and in what way did a girl differ from a boy?

He went outside and looked over at the great house, three hundred yards in the west, and thought of the Devil behind that closed door. He knew that the Devil was a creature of evil, and that evil was what any good boy was ashamed of. It was evil that sent people to hell, to that black and underground abode of fire and red lights and eternal moaning. Hell was somewhere below the earth, and the earth seemed to be a flat area, stretched like a quilt from sky to sky. When he listened he thought he could hear groans somewhere under his feet but he was too afraid to kneel with his ear to the ground.

A few weeks later his mother rose from the bed and moved again in her accustomed ways. She asked Vridar if he was glad to have a sister. He was not. He already understood that both parents were more interested in the new child than in their sons. Besides, he was interested not in the wrinkled howling babe but in the shadowland out of which it had come. In an awed whisper he asked about her, where she had lived till now, in what manner she had got here. The doctor had brought her, his mother said. He had brought her in a big white basket warmed deep with wool and bound in white fleece. But where did the doctor find her? Oh, she came down from heaven and entered the doctor's house. She had been a little angel, with eyes like stars and with golden wings. Heaven was a lovely place beyond the blue sky; and God lived there. Angels lived there, too, little angels like his sister, and big angels like men. When a mother wanted a child she asked for one in prayer and God sent an angel down.

Vridar looked at his sister and considered all this. Where, he asked, were her wings now? On her way down a big angel had come with her; and when she stood at the window, looking into the doctor's house, the angel took her wings back to heaven. If she were a good girl and lived in God's teachings she would return home after death and wear the wings again.

The wonder of this fable left Vridar in deep thought. He stared with awe at his sister. He thought of that heavenly place and of her descent on golden wings and of the miracle in her being here. He was told that the babies of all things came down from the sky, but not quite in the way his sister had come. In some strange manner, not to be understood from his mother's telling, horse babies and cow babies came down long ago and were buried in the earth. If a cow wanted a baby she found a likely spot and dug a big hole in the earth and discovered a baby calf.

Vridar spent an afternoon looking over the farm. Upon the hillside he found some deep holes, and he knew that cows and mares had dug these and had found their offspring. He told his mother what he had found but she did not want to talk about it. He should not be too curious, she said, and he should never ask questions of any but herself. When he became a man, he would understand more. God would teach him to understand.

During these years and for many years to come Joe Hunter and his family were undernourished. Joe raised a few potatoes but sold most of them. He raised a few acres of wheat, sold it for thirty cents a bushel, and barely covered his seed and harvesting. There was a little garden stuff, a little fruit; but for the most part they ate bread without butter, potatoes, gravy made without milk, and wild meat. Joe toiled sixteen hours every day. "The more I work like a dog," he said, "the less I make."

It was Prudence who earned what clothes they had and such food as they had to buy. She had a few chickens and a cow. She sold all the milk and butter and all the eggs. For the infant daughter, who was named Diana, she made diapers and dresses of flour sacks; for her two sons she made shirts and trousers from their father's old garments or from such garments as Rose gave her.

After seven years of marriage, seven years of hard and desparate toil, they found themselves in debt. They owed for the doctor's services, an old wagon, a set of harness. Convinced that if they remained here they would soon have no farm, nothing, but the rags on their backs, Joe determined to make a fresh start elsewhere, to seek a newer frontier. Two months after Diana's birth they piled their belongings on the wagon, tied the cow behind, and set out toward mountains and a great river in the east.

III

This new home, for which Joe paid seven dollars and a wornout horse, was on the South Fork of Snake River, close by the Antelope hills. It was a sunken basin of bottomland, river-girted and mountain-walled. Part was cottonwood island, part was swamp, and part was brush-covered hills. This move, neighbors said, when the family set out, was the last Joe Hunter would ever make. He would drag his wife and children off to some God-forsaken spot of wild beasts and loneliness and there they would all go crazy or starve to death.

Joe never asked if this new home, isolated from neighbors and far from roads and markets, would be a happy one for his children or for his proud wife who hated deep snows and solitude and the bleak outposts of human existence. Unsocial and short of speech, a pioneer by taste and habit, he despised crowded places: he loved the rough and untamed corners of earth, the violence of wind and storm, the smell of wild life, a spot walled in and lost. He liked his new home. To the making of it lovely and fertile he was to give the remainder of his life; it would become his one dominant passion, his religion and his god.

He was to love it as he loved nothing else on earth, but his wife and children were to hate it. He was to find peace here but they would find nightmare and horror. Vridar was already a miserably neurotic and sensitive lad; his first vision of the new home left him profoundly stirred. After the slow and dusty trek across miles of hills, where he saw and smelled only wild things, the wagon paused on a brink and they all looked down. Vridar looked down over aspen groves falling away and down like congealed floods of green; down across great fir trees and stone; and then still down, and down, to the bottomland and the river. He saw the river, broad and muddy and wild, and beyond it what seemed to be a tiny farm and a log house. It was there, Joe said, that the Bridwells lived, who would be their only neighbor in all this area roundabout. Beyond the Bridwells were black misty canyons, and stupendous mountain shoulders, rising two thousand feet.

Joe cut a heavily-branched tree and with a log-chain tied it behind the wagon. This would serve as a brake. Then they started down the steep narrow rain-gutted dugway. This road, leading down, was only a mile in length, but it seemed to Vridar that they went down mile after mile, down out of the hills and the sky, down into the very bottom of the world. Everything around him was jungle that looked wild and tameless. After a while he looked back up and saw only the torn horizon of the sky and the forests above him; he stared to right or left and saw only the tremendous architecture of mountains, vast slides of spilled stone, and canyons black with forests, misty and still. After a while he could see the land of his new home and it all seemed to be buried under impenetrable growth. And when at last they were down out of the hills and the sky, he saw the house.

It was a two-room log shack and already so old that it was rotting. Its earth roof was covered with thistle and sage. Its two doors swung on leather hinges; its two windows had broken panes, spun over with spider webs full of dead things. Between the unplaned boards of its floor were huge cracks, choked with accumulated dust. The rooms smelled of mice and rats and bats and nighthawks and of un-tenanted age.

This was his new home and already he was afraid of it and he hated it. Did he sense that these were to be lonely and terrifying years? He would gather from them a morbid fear of blood and death, of pain, of brutality, of loneliness; in all the years of his life he would never look back upon them without shuddering. He would find here the mystery of earth and sky in their dark and destroying moods, in their harvesting of violence and unreason. A few times he would be happy and his heart would leap and his breath would go out of him, when he felt kinship with the serene reaches of life and being. But for the most part, so far as memory would be able to recreate it, he would experience only bitter things. If he had been a normal boy, all this would not have been so. If he had had a different father, yes, and a different mother, he might not have been overwhelmed by terror and nightmare. But he was pale, timid, scrawny, and morbidly sensitive, and experiences that would have affected normal lads no more than their mother's kiss or their father's belches went deep into Vridar and shaped his life.

And none went deeper than his early visions of blood and death. While riding somewhere on the hills Joe found a lost sheep and fetched it home. Preparing to butcher it, he went to an old grindstone behind a smokehouse, taking with him a long butcher knife. He sharpened the knife while Vridar turned the stone; little by little he ground away the brown rust, until the blade gleamed like silver. He tested it with his thumb. He jerked his thumb away and muttered on oath, as though he had been betrayed. Then he went to the house, followed by his curious and apprehensive son.

Joe took a pail of water, an axe, an empty basin, and the knife and went out to the sheep. Seizing the beast by a leg he dragged it, snorting and struggling, out of its pen. He threw one leg over its back and stood astride it. Then with his left hand he pulled the head up against his belly while with his right hand be began to feel into the creature with the long blade, thrusting, turning, and sinking it deeper and deeper, until blood spurted and gushed and the beast fought with all its dying strength. The blade was shoved in until there was only the handle in Joe's bloody fist. Then Joe stepped back, wiped the knife on the sheep's wool and went to the house.

The beast made several plunges, fell upon its almost severed head, kicked violently with hind legs, and lay shuddering. Feeling faint and almost paralyzed, and hardly breathing, Vridar went timidly forward, drawn in spite of his will to see what his father had done. He knelt by the sheep and listened to the gurgling flow of blood: it was a spurting stream, warm, red and vivid, and the smell of it filled the air. Unable to move, struggling to understand, the child listened to the desperate spurting and looked at the wideopen eyes. He saw an awful change in the eyes. Vision left them, and life, and they became glazed, fearfully set on nothing, as they filled with darkness and death. Two thin crimson streams ran from the nose. The throat, with head flung back, was a red maw, a horrible wide gash, out of which stuck one end of the windpipe. The legs still kicked, then were quiet, then kicked again. A shudder ran through the body, ending in a violent spasm; and for a moment there was a kind of boiling red pool in the throat.

Glancing again at the eyes, and feeling very weak and sick, Vridar arose and was turning away when he heard his father coming. Then suddenly he ran, leaping blindly in terror—going desperately with that blade in his mind, turning, thrusting, turning. He could hear the blood-sounds and smell the blood-smell. He ran until he found a thicket and there he hid, his face buried, his body shaking with terror and grief. He tried to strike out of his thoughts, out of his soul, the picture of streaming red; the blood-sounds and the choked gurgling death-sounds; and the knife-movement, reaching in and in through wool and flesh and pain to a beating heart. What was life, what was death? How could a sheep, only a little while ago strong with health, eating grass, bleating for the lost herd—how was it possible that it now hung from a tree, grotesque and ghastly, its pelt stripped off, its head thrown to the flies, its blood soaked in the earth? Why did the living slay and eat one another? Did God approve? he wanted to ask, but did not dare. He wanted to ask if a thing died because its blood ran out. If that was true, then was blood not the most precious thing in life?

A month later he saw death again. Late one evening he heard a wagon coming down the long dugway; he listened to the sound of it in the deepening gloom, and presently it came out of black woods and toward him. On the front bolster sat a huge man. His hair was long and dark and matted, his face was sullen, his clothes were patched and threadbare. The man said he was after a load of poles and had come down to camp where there was water. Joe gave him permission, and the man set up a small tent, tethered his horses in deep grass, and built a fire to cook a simple meal. Wondering why his parents did not ask the stranger to the house, Vridar stood by a window and looked at the fire's flame, until it sank to glowing embers and was at last only a faint smoke.

During the night one of the man's beasts gave birth to a colt. Vridar learned this when the man strode to the house and asked for an axe. The man took the axe and went back to his camp; and Vridar, sensing that the fellow was up to no good, slipped around and hid in the trees to spy on him. The colt was trying to race on ungainly legs. It seemed to be very alert; it frisked back and forth on long awkward legs, as though to test its life and strength. While wondering where the hole was out of which the colt had been born, Vridar saw the man walk up to it, square off, fling the axe far back over his shoulder, and then deliver a crushing blow on the colt's forehead. Its legs folded under it and it dropped like a dead thing, its neck kinked and its nose in the dust. The man put his toe under the jaws, kicked the head out and struck another blow. Then he took the axe back to the house.

Trembling with rage and fear and hate Vridar went forth to look at the stricken beast, shuddering and kicking. He heard the hoarse gasping of its breath. He stared at the warm crushed skull. He looked at the eyes and they were glazed like the sheep's eyes. Then he ran back to the aspen grove and sat there, trying to get hold of the horrible facts of living and dying. But they eluded him, they went off into the darkness of his ignorance; and nothing remained but the crushed skull out there, the quivering young body, the blood and the sightless eyes. He was sitting very still and feeling very white and weak inside when the man came back and hitched up his team and drove away. Then Vridar went out and sat by the colt and put a compassionate hand on its warm body. He patted it, though he knew that it was dead. But with a start he realized that it was not dead, that the heart was still beating under his hand; it would seem to stop, then rise with a great effort and strike, and stop again. The eyes were dead. Everything was dead but that desperate heart, entombed in a dead breast. Afraid at last of this terrible, muffled, hidden sound Vridar went back to the trees, praying that by some miracle the colt would rise and run again. By some miracle the crushed bones would be made well and the eyes

26

awakened. He prayed to God for this, and it seemed to him that a great deep cleanness was filling the world; but when he looked out he saw only the colt lying there in the awful silence . . . .

A third time in two months he saw death. His father had found, on the hills above, a patch of luxuriant brome grass: determined to harvest it, he took his family up the long road, trailing an old mowing machine behind. While the father mowed and the mother picked wild berries, and Marion and Diana sat solemn and silent in the wagon, Vridar followed the machine. With him was their dog Towser, an indefatigable hound that chased everything that jumped from cover. He not only pursued squirrels until they dived into holes, chipmunks until they ran up trees, tall rangy hares until they vanished into distance; he went pellmell after flying birds, prairie chickens, soaring hawks. He chased the shadow of hawks, leaping after them over sagebrush, yelping with furious zest, or standing baffled when the shadows ran up trees or sailed over a forest top.

When the hay was nearly all mown there darted out suddenly a cottontail rabbit. Towser dived headlong in pursuit. Vridar watched the race, hoping the rabbit would be as fleet as the hares; but Towser was gaining at every leap, and when capture seemed imminent the rabbit redoubled, sprang into the patch of hay and disappeared. Towser went in, still yelping as if he were being clubbed at every jump. After a few moments the rabbit came out, with the dog at its heels, went desperately ahead for fifty yards; turned swiftly, hesitated for a moment, and then came straight toward Vridar. Only a few feet away it stopped, its soft eyes wide and terrified, its whole body shaking. It seemed unable to move. While Vridar stood breathless, himself unable to move or shout, the dog leapt to its prey, and the rabbit gave one ringing scream, like that of a human being. With his teeth in its back the dog was shaking it with all his power when Vridar ran forward and kicked the dog. Towser ran off, yelping with consternation and looking back with offended eyes. Vridar picked the rabbit up and felt under its soft fur the wild beating of its heart. He looked into its eyes and saw in them what he would never be able to efface from memory. Running to his mother he showed her the broken and quivering thing, and she said, "Oh, a rabbit? We'll have it for supper."

O God! he thought. Does she mean we will *eat* it? He hugged it to him and nursed it but it died in his arms; and that evening, fried until it was brown and dripping, it was served with the customary meal of bread and milk. But Vridar did not eat of the rabbit. He would as soon have eaten his own hand. Remembering those soft gentle eyes, so vivid with terror, and the scream which had been human, he watched his father tear off flesh with his teeth and crunch at the bones. He watched his mother chew at a piece of leg and lick the grease off her fingers.

"You sure you don't want any?" she asked her son.

"No," he said. He felt a vague sense of guilt, for somehow he had failed a creature when it turned to him for help.

These experiences were important in shaping his life. Others, no less terrible, lay ahead of him; and each stirred in him a profound kinship and an abiding compassion for all things that moved and breathed, that struggled against dark forces to live, yet were overtaken and drawn into silence. From them he took not only a

27

horror of death, which in later years was to become one of his most desperate problems, but also a morbid sensitivity that was to deepen his fear and his loneliness. He felt that he was a coward, even when so very young, and he hated the shame of it. He fought to conquer it. But in childhood, fear was to be almost his complete master, and in his defense the most that pride could say was this, although racked and goaded and sometimes paralyzed by it, he never confessed to anyone, not even to his mother, or ever admitted that he was or ever had been afraid. He despised himself as a weakling and he heaped upon himself scorn and ridicule; but the only confessions he ever made were on his knees to God. "Our Father," said the boy, clasping his hands and looking up at the sky, "help me to be brave and strong! Help me to be unafraid . . . ."

<h1 style="text-align:center">IV</h1>

Except the house and its dooryard this river bottomland was for Vridar as wild and terrible as the coyote's wailing, which became with the roaring of the river the commonest sound for him in these years. The hundred acres of swamp and meadow were a choked jungle, a green wilderness of birch and cottonwood and willow, and of springs which, his father said, had no bottom at all. There were dozens of these springs, hidden down there in the thickets. Each was a fearful spot.

Riding behind his father on a horse, Vridar went one day into this jungleland. After a while they had to dismount and grope along trails, arched over and darkened, lost under their low gloomy ceilings. So dense was the growth, and so borne down and tangled by its own weight, that they had to fall to hands and knees; and behind them the horse lowered its head and plunged crashing along the path. For what seemed miles to Vridar they hunted like beasts through this jungle, so sunless and cool and heavy with its damp earth-smells. They emerged at last and crossed a small meadow, knee-deep with swamp grasses, its hummocks dotted with ripe wild strawberries; and again they fought their way under the green acres, leaving the sun behind them, struggling through the dark mystery of scurrying beasts and wild animal odors.

Now and then Joe pointed to a spring and said a word or two about it. Into this one he had thrust a fifty-foot pole and it had gone down and out of sight. It had gone swiftly and silently as if greased. Into that one, he had been told, a man had fallen, and he had gone down and down, sucked by the quicksands and bogs, never to be seen again. Over there was another: Jim Brown, from whom he had bought this place, had been chasing a coyote. It had tried to leap the spring, had slipped on the far bank, and then had disappeared like a fish into a well.

"When you come down here for the cows," said his father, "you best be careful. Don't try to wade none of these-here cricks. There ain't no bottom in them."

When he came for the cows! Would he be expected to come for cows in this wasteland of terror? Vridar stared at the spring in which the coyote had found its grave: it was bedded thick with cattail, heavy with broad flat leaves, flowered with their brown spikes. The center of the spring was clear of growth; it was many jets of boiling sand that fell away in smooth flowing loveliness.

Each spring down there came to vivid and sinister life for the child; sometimes standing in the dooryard, he would look down across the meadowland, thinking of these terrors, each hiding dangerously under its breath of fog. He thought of the jungle paths, drenched with coyote and bobcat and mountain lion smells; lying under their leafy roofs; crawling endlessly through phantomland. On cooler nights these marshy acres steamed upward with fog, hanging clouddomes upon their wilderness; and it was then that his imagination fed richly, peopling this region with slinking shapes, while there rolled up to him the morass warmth and the odors of the unknown. He watched twilight deepen, saw it flow down in gray waves; saw it turn into the enormous dark wonder of night, until there stood from earth to sky the silence of an old well, with only the river-sounds in it. Then there would come the wailing of coyotes and the occasional scream of a lion. After he had gone to bed this jungleland would flow through his sleep, rolling over and over in soundless fog-softened gloom, until he was buried and suffocated, with the nightsky building upon his chest.

There was the river. The swampland was terrible because of its silence, the river because of its sound. It was a thunderous foreboding, flooding to the sea. It formed the east, north and west boundaries of his home. Between the house and the river on the north lay the kingdom of islands, grown deep with willow and cottonwood. From the high bank only a few yards from the house he could overlook the islands and see the river hurling its great muddy arc around by the Bridwell place. The waters came out of the east in tumbling gray floods. They boiled against ledges of stone, shot foaming towers skyward, rolled and curled and vomited in tides of mud. In high water they overspread the islands until tormented willows whipped back and forth in surge and foam.

One night he went with his mother to the bank and they gazed out over the dark and thundering waste. Trees stood spectral and swaying upon the flood. Moonlight spilled and was darkened, trembled gleamingly on the crests, fell like molten silver into the valleys of mud, broke and scattered like knife-blades and then caught fire from wave to wave. Below them an uplifted green tree rose and drowned and rose, and was driven midway in its trunk against a mighty cottonwood. It was riven and its white flesh shot upward; it was spun into a sucking whirlpool and drawn down and out of sight. Against a sheer ledge of stone in the west was hurled the river's flood-sound; and the ledge broke it and rolled it in tides from mountain to mountain.

It was a horrible river, his mother said, and she was afraid of it; but he was her manly one, her brave little man, and he would never be afraid. Oh, by the living God, no! He would always be brave. . . . Yes, Mother, yes! He would protect his little brother, his sister, and he would grow to be a strong man, afraid neither of rivers nor of wild things nor of the night . . . . Yes, dear God, yes!

He went to bed, hoping that he could be her brave little man; but the sound of the river bore in upon him, was a steady murmuring in the walls, was the wild language of the whole out-of-doors. He stuffed a piece of rag in either ear and drew the quilts over his head.

One afternoon a month later Vridar was playing with his brother. A creek ran

29

under the bank a few yards from the house and they had ventured to its edge. In the bank Vridar was making a dugway, for his deepest urge, even when so young, was to create things, and, having neither tools nor materials for anything else, he was building a road.

Suddenly in the jungle growth along the creek he heard a low savage growl and was paralyzed. Trees shook. The earth quaked under a hideous roaring and snarling and snapping of teeth. Turning as white as water lilies, Vridar gave one choked cry and seized his brother's hand and headed for the house. He clawed his way up the bank, tearing his flesh, whipping twigs into his eyes; and behind him came the wild hunger-sound and the sound of crashing timbers and of heavy feet. Gaining the bank's top, Vridar turned Marion free and together they raced like rabbits. They dived into the house but nobody was there. They ran from room to room, sobbing with terror; they tried to bolt the doors; they went to a window to look out. Then Vridar listened, and again heard the savage growls. These were coming to the house and the whole friendless sky was filled with the noise of their coming. Frantic, his flesh crawling with terror, his face bloodless, Vridar again tried to bolt the door. But the hasp was broken. The hungry beast was drawing near. The beast was at the north window and the window darkened and a terrific blow shook the house. With his breath coming in choked gasps, Vridar seized his brother's hand and rushed outside. The growls now were a thunderous roaring but he did not desert his brother; he had been taught to protect Marion at all costs, and he now dragged the stricken lad after him, stumbling and screaming. They got to the stable and found nobody there. They came out and clambered over corral bars and burrowed into a mound of wild hay. They dug far in, clawing like frantic dogs; and when the world was shut out and they were alone with darkness they listened for the hunger-sound. They could hear only the furious beating of their hearts.

They remained here for what seemed to Vridar a long time. His flesh still burned, terror was a live thing in his whole scalp; but he thought that perhaps they had been saved. He was about to peer out when a sudden great power shook the pile of hay. All the breath came out of him in one scream. Seizing his brother again, he tore blindly out and was going madly for the house when he heard a human laugh. He paused fearfully and turned. There in the corral, convulsed and red with joy, was a huge man. He was rolling over and over, shaking with laughter; joy was pouring like thunder out of his mouth. Vridar trembled and stared at him, and little by little the meaning of the laughter found his mind. He knew that he had been tricked. Terror sank within him, leaving him so weak that he had to sit down; and in place of terror came humiliation, bitter and deep. Then came rage, wild and insane. Leaping up, his dark eyes aflame with fury, he sought and found a club, and he ran toward the man, resolved to avenge this insult. The man struggled to his feet and retreated, his big face mirthless now, his eyes strangely kindled; and Vridar ran after him, praying to God that he could crush the man's skull. He chased him over the corral bars. He was pursuing him to the house when he was caught from behind and heard his mother's voice rebuking him. Then all control left him, all vision and will, and his emotions fell into a void. He screamed and fought while froth slithered from his insane mouth.

Hours later he was still white and spent. At the evening meal he sickened at the table and went outside. All night he moaned in his sleep, now fleeing like wind from a hunger-sound, now striking blow on blow at a great grinning face.

This man was Charley Bridwell, their neighbor. He came to be for Vridar a huge fat symbol of all that was fearless, cunning, devilish, and unhuman. When Charley came alone he swam the river and appeared drenched at the door; when he brought his wife with him he used a small boat. One day he came with his wife. Vridar saw a pale woman with sad blue eyes and a great mane of hair that fell almost to her knees. Her name was Lela. They came suddenly up from the creek and surprised Vridar galloping across the yard on a stickhorse.

"Whoa!" Charley roared. "Stop beatun that horse on his ears!"

"Sir?" said Vridar, for he had been taught to be very polite to his elders.

"How long," asked Charley reproachfully, "since you fed this nag? The son of a bitch looks as lean as a shitepoke." He was staring down at the four feet of choke-cherry limb. "Blood on her ears!" he cried. "God Almighty, you should never beat a horse on its ears."

Vridar stammered with shame. He felt that he was being mocked for pretending that a stick was a horse. He let the stick fall and stepped back.

"Holy Judas priest, look there!" cried Charley. "Your nag's so weak she can't stand up." He lifted the stick and stroked it. He looked round him and saw a hill-side of grass. "Better take her over there and stake her," he said.

"Yes sir," said Vridar, burning under this grave nonsense. He glanced at Lela and saw that she was not amused.

"Got any more horses?" asked Charley. "Anything you want broke?"

"No sir," said Vridar, following the man's gaze as it swept the yard.

"What about that wild bastard?" He indicated eight feet of pole leaning against the house. "You ever rode him?"

"No sir. That's just stove wood."

"Stove Wood? Well, by God, Stove Wood looks like a wild one to me. Get me a rope and I'll ride him until he steps on his tongue."

Vridar did not move. Shame was too hot within him. Charley found a piece of rope, looped it around one end of the pole, and then, as though expecting to be kicked, stroked the pole.

"I might get throwed high as a hawk," he said, turning a troubled face on Vridar. "I need saddle and spurs but I'll try him bareback. Here, hold his head while I get on."

Vridar moved forward, shamed, baffled, because he suspected that all this was utter silliness, intended to humiliate him. At Charley's command he grasped the top end of the pole and held it. Suddenly the pole was broken from his grasp, spun around, and struck against his legs.

"Look out!" Charley roared. "God damn my hide, did he kick you? Why, the lousy son of a bitch! I'll knock his ears off." He seized a club and smote Stove Wood with savage blows. "Never get behind a horse," he said to Vridar. "Some of them kick like hell and Friday."

He patted the smooth wood, meanwhile turning round and round, as though the

31

horse were unmanageably restive. Then he threw one leg over and was off in furious bucking. He plunged and vaulted and swore; he almost pitched forward on his head, almost fell backward, or nearly went spinning from side to side. Around the yard, crashing into bushes, clattering over a pile of tin cans and bottles, plunging in great leaps, and all the while with his hat beating Stove Wood over his ears or reaching back to flog his tail. Nearly unseated, he let off such a string of oaths as Vridar had never heard; rode pellmell at the boy and sent him scurrying to the door; bore down upon Lela until she cried with fright and begged him to be done with his nonsense; pitched rolling to the earth and tumbled over and over, still smiting with his hat; and recovered his feet and came galloping into the yard. He sprang off, pretending that he dismounted from a great height; he leaned Stove Wood against the house; he mopped his huge florid brow and turned to Vridar.

"Hickory God, that was a bucker from away back! Is there some donkey in him?"

Vridar writhed and hesitated. His mother had told him always to answer questions put to him by his elders. "No sir," he said.

Charley stroked his buttocks and scowled. "I'm blistered all to hell," he said. "Where's your old man who pretends he don't like whisky?"

Charley and his wife entered the house. Vridar stood looking at the pole and thinking of this strange man. He rather liked the prodigious nonsense but he felt that the whole experience had been intended as a rebuke to lads who rode stick-horses. He never rode a stick-horse again.

Some time later he shyly entered the house. The day was Sunday, and before the Bridwells came Prudence had been reading to Joe from a dime novel. When Vridar entered she still had the book in her hands. Charley, sitting by an open window so that he could spit his tobacco juice across the sill, turned to Vridar with a wide cunning grin.

"How's Stove Wood? Did you feed him some oats?"

The lad glanced at his parents. They were amused and he hated them for being amused.

"Son," his mother said, "Mr. Bridwell was speakun to you. Why don't you answer him?"

"No sir," said Vridar, feeling sullen and murderous. Why did his own mother have to grin at his shame and command him to answer silly questions!

"You should water him," Charley said. "I imagine he's cooled off enough."

"Stop teasing the boy," said Lela. "He thinks you're a big fool."

Vridar looked at her, his eyes deep with gratitude. She was the kind of mother a boy should have. He loved her . . . . But his own mother was speaking again and her words chilled him. It would be shameful, she said, for her son to think anybody a fool; for all grown people he had only obedience and respect. Vridar knew the words to be a horrible lie. Charley was again grinning at him and his eyes were green and shrewd.

"Any more wild beasts been chasun you?"

Vridar hesitated. Why had he come in here to be insulted and mocked.

"Son, Mr. Bridwell asked you a question."

The boy looked at Mr. Bridwell and his eyes darkened. "No sir," he said.

The reply brought a jolly roar from Charley, and in the laughter Prudence joined. Joe grinned. Only the face of Lela was sad and unamused. Vridar wanted to withdraw but he did not know how to excuse himself. Sick with inner shame and rage he waited for the next question, the next command. It was Lela who turned gently to his rescue.

"Will you go to the bank," she said, "and look across the river. See if my boys are waving a white cloth for me to come home."

"Yes maam," Vridar said, and was gone. He went to the bank but he did not expect to see a white cloth. He knew that this kind woman had been letting him escape and he loved her gentleness. After a while he returned softly to the house and sat by the open window. Language poured out and died in the vast desolate air. He could see Charley's stream of tobacco juice when it came out and the stain of it on the earth. He could hear Charley asking Joe why he pretended not to like whisky and he wondered what whisky was. After a little he went to the north window and crawled into the bedroom and lay on a bed. He stared at the rotting aspen poles of the ceiling and at the long gray bellies of earth sagging between the poles. From the next room came words but no meaning, only shrill sounds or the pouring wind of Charley's laugh; and feeling weary Vridar turned on his belly and fell asleep.

He was awakened by tickling on a white patch of rump that showed through his ragged trousers. For a moment he did not understand. Then there burst over him in a wave of hot shame a full realization of what the tickling meant. He sprang up, burning, and faced Charley Bridwell. Beyond Charley stood his parents and Lela. His mother's face and throat were red.

Vridar had not known that the hole was in his trousers. He would have been humiliated if he had known. Now shame beat in his temples and surged like fire in his blood. He retreated, one hand reaching behind him, finding the awful certainty of the hole, his eyes on Charley's open grin or his mother's embarrassed face.

"Turn around," Charley said. "While you was asleep a rat chawed a hole in your pants."

"I won't!" the boy cried, wishing he could fall into a well and be lost forever.

"Son!" said Prudence. "Is that the way you speak to your betters?"

"Let me see," said Charley, advancing, his grin evil. "Mebbe it wasn't a rat. By God, mebbe it was a bear."

"Leave me alone!" Vridar cried, now backed to the wall.

"Let him be," said Lela. "He's sick of you."

"But I want a-see," Charley persisted. "Rats is gettun too damn bold when they come right in and eat a boy's rump." He looked round him, as if to see rats. He sniffed the air; he fell to hands and knees and stared under the bed. "I'n smell his tracks," he said.

"Come home," said Lela. "You'll have the boy hating you."

Charley was led outside. Vridar's parents filled the open door. The lad drew a sudden deep breath, hoping that the worst was over. He was exploring guiltily with a hand, fingering the hole's size, drawing cloth together to cover it, when he saw Charley's grinning face. The man was on hands and knees outside and was looking in, his head between Joe's legs. For a long moment the legs framed a horrible vision of cunning and joy. Then the face went away and Vridar saw daylight.

Later, Prudence called her son to her side and looked at him with blue eyes, severe and cold. She reproved him for his want of manners. No matter, she said, how vexed he became, or how much his temper was baited or his patience ridden, he must always be a polite little gentleman to his superiors. She said she could never stand a sassy child. "Do you understand me?"

"Yes maam," he said, hating her.

Hereafter he must be more careful, for it was a wicked and shameful thing to show certain parts of his body. Ah, God, how deep this was to go into him! Before no one, man, woman or child, was he ever to expose those—those certain parts. Some boys and a few girls were shameless and they played in dark and wicked ways. He must never associate with such children. He must never listen to nasty tales or believe what other people might tell him; and he must have faith, now and always, in the purity of women and the goodness of God. If boy or man ever whispered to him of an uncleanness, he must come at once to her and tell all that had been said. In this way he would keep his heart and mind pure and would grow up to be a noble and righteous man. Did he understand all that she meant?

"Yes maam," he said. He was remembering how his father, sitting at the table, would belch, or roll over to one ham and fart. He was remembering his mother's face in such moments, and he wished that he had been born without intestines and anus, for certainly nothing in the world, her face told him, not even adultery or murder, was as sinful as that part of a person's body. Ah, God, how deep this would go into him and how terrible his struggle would be!

"Promise me you'll always be truthful and pure."

"Yes maam."

"And never play with nasty little boys or listen to their nasty little tales."

"Yes maam—I mean no maam."

"Now take your pants off and crawl into bed and I will patch the hole."

He lay in bed, virtuously covered to his chin, and thought of all the dark implications in the last hour. These admonitions had been made before, time after time. Time after time he had promised these things. He had promised obedience, truthfulness, purity of heart and soul; to be a little gentleman in all ways; to cherish women as the holiest of all God's creations; and to protect them against the world's horde of men and boys who wanted to commit he could not imagine what awful crimes against them. He had promised never to fight, unless driven to it in defense of virtue; never to use unclean words or think unclean thoughts; never to lie, steal, or shame God. Now, as he lay under this fearful decalogue, counting its commandments one by one, he felt abandoned and lost.

This evening, as in all former evenings within memory, he knelt in prayer:

> Now I lay me down to sleep,
> I pray the Lord my soul to keep.
> If I should die before I wake
> I pray the Lord my soul to take.

To this prayer in later years he would add a few simple requests. He would ask God to bless his parents, his brother and sister, and all the people of earth; he would ask under his breath for a pair of shoes, a sled, a book; but these things never came.

In bed he lay in a room smelling of old and forgotten things. He lay in night-silence, but for the sounds of the river and the coyotes, with the night air coming through the window and blowing over him in fragrant waves; and again he remembered all that he had promised to be. He would be a good man, sheltered by the dim immensities of justice and right; but in his heart there was doubt, and a strange loneliness that trembled and darkened. Was it a faint intimation, a shadow thrown before, of all the desperate effort, the sunless years and regrets, the nightmares of terror to which his promises would lead him? No matter: it pushed like darkness into his thoughts. He thought of the terrible spot out of which came his body's wastes and he wished that he could somehow seal it off and never use it again. He wished he could cut off the thing out of which came his body's water. If these things were so shameful, why had God made them? He thought of what his father did and of the red shame and humiliation in his mother's face; and he hated himself and was afraid of himself. He drew quilts over his face and began to weep. Hours later he was buried and dreaming, his two hands clenched, his cheeks wet—and with a tightness in that shameful spot of him, a tightness that would always be there . . . .

V

Vridar's father stood two inches under six feet and weighed only a hundred and seventy-five pounds, but for the child he was a dreadful giant, with a black scowl and fits of rage in which he swept everything before him. Joe did not admit, now or ever, that he was a brutal and stubborn man; and the more his wife reproached him for bad judgment or cruel ways or sullen silences, the more he persisted in his errors. It was indeed, as Vridar was to realize long afterward, the scorn and con-sternation which he aroused in her that drove him to deeds still more violent. As a gesture to her of his resentment and hurt he outraged his own soul.

It was in his second summer here that Vridar first saw his father's dark and blaspheming wrath. From grazing herds out on the Antelope hills, Joe, with the permission of the owners, had brought in a dozen cows to milk. He built a corral for them on the river bank, overlooking the house; and early every morning, late every evening, he milked them with his wife's help. Vridar was the calf-tender. It was his task to admit a calf, watch it suck until the cow "gave her milk down," and then drive the calf back into its pen. But some of the calves were big lusty brutes, and though Vridar tugged at them desperately to take them away, they only shut their eyes and lowered their frames and sucked with renewed vigor.

"This way," said his father; and with forefinger and thumb he seized the calf's tender nose, and with his other hand twisted its tail, thus forcing it into the pen.

Vridar tried this method but his strength was too small. One morning with super-human effort he got a calf to the pen gate, but there the hungry beast evaded him and went plunging back to its mother. It accosted her with a heaving milk-hungry

35

blow of its head. She kicked swiftly, powerfully, and drove a full pail of milk into Joe's belly. The impact knocked him over, sent him sprawling out in soft dung, and drenched him with milk from head to feet. He came up roaring with rage and pain and threat. His first thundering words were a rebuke to his son. Then, scattering milk and foam and dung as he went, he rushed to the corral side and grasped a pole as thick as his arm. Alarmed, his wife stood up from her milking-stool and cried, "Now for God's sake, don't beat that cow!" But Joe gave no heed. A picture of awful wrath, his eyes like gray fire, he strode back, his legs chopping stiffly ahead of him; and he brought the pole down crushingly on the cow's skull. The pole broke in two like a reed and the cow dropped as though she had been hit with a sledge of iron. She plunged, kicking out with her feet; she recovered her legs and ran; and Joe went after her, swinging the half of his club still in his grasp. "So!" he bellowed. "I'll learn you to so, you God damn son of a bitch! . . . ."

He chased the terrified beast from corner to corner, commanding her to so, threatening to knock her daylights out. Such profanity roared out of him that the other cows began to quake and the calves stood spellbound. Vridar ran to the corral side and climbed over and peered in. His mother, very white and very angry, was imploring Joe to show a lick of sense; but Joe never paused in his mad pursuit. He overtook the cow, gave her a crushing blow across her ribs, and told her she would so hereafter or be knocked from hell to breakfast. Cornered again, she looked at him with bulging eyes and blew mucus from her nose. Her body shook like grass in a wind.

"You lousy son of a bitch, so now!" Joe thundered. He approached her, his club ready for a blow. The cow shuddered but did not move. Joe turned and looked round him, his eyes blinded with rage. "Where's my bucket? Where'd that God damn kid go to?"

"Here I am!" cried Vridar, and came up the corral poles like a squirrel.

"Why don't you get a move on when I speak?"

Vridar fetched the bucket and milking stool. Joe sat on the stool before the trembling beast. He set the bucket between his legs, grasped teats with both hands and yanked. The cow stared round at him but she did not move and she never kicked again.

He saw his father also as a giant behind a plow, a black cross on his back under suspenders where the sweat came through. He saw him bent day after day swinging a mattock, chopping his way foot by foot into the wilderness of brush, uprooting and piling the serviceberry and chokecherry and aspen and buffalo bush, making the acres clean for wheat and hay. The father would rise before daylight and Prudence with him. Together, carrying a lantern, they would do the milking and the chores. Then, while she prepared a simple breakfast, Joe would go out to his grubbing-hoe and labor. After an hour he would come in and eat, sit in silence a few moments picking at his teeth and dreaming his dreams, put a quid of tobacco in his mouth and rise and toil again, until again he ate, then toil again until he slept.

Often he would go out after dark to work and Vridar would see him there, framed in a room of yellow light, lifting the blade over his right shoulder and burying it to the hilt in root and earth, dragging the brush out into shadows, returning

36

to the light. Now and then he ventured out to watch his father. He tried to help a little, to pull tops away from the stroke, to throw chunks of root out to the brush heap, to paw earth away so that his father could strike a cleaner blow. And all the while he wondered about this man and about men.

Or Vridar would sit by a window and stare out into the fearful gloom, thinking of its night-mystery and silence and sounds. The lantern threw a strange brightness upon bushes, giving a deep blackness to their green leaves, streaking their trunks with sorcerous gleam. Beyond the light the darkness was intense, its body thinning upward and catching a faint glow from the stars. When the moon rose a great magic drenched everything, and out of the far night dark shadows became visible, long tunnels under trees, and leafy corridors and vast chambers full of transfixed silence. Fireflies shone like match ends and went out. Nightbirds left a sound of water among thick leaves. Winds rode across, spilling whispers and moans and sighs, and beating like heavy breath against the stone ledges.

It was a terrible nightland. In daylight its meaning seemed stark and clear: its meaning of still trees, of bushes full of locusts and wood-smells, of earth frank and warm in a bed of golden sun; but in nighttime everything changed. Then all life became drunk with courage. Winds smote the trees, pouring in rivers of darkness; and the trees flailed out with huge green arms, beating at nothingness but unafraid. Clouds stalked the mountain tops and wrapped fleece around the nest of eagle and hawk. Animals went abroad, the coyote and skunk and wolf and lion and bear, leaving a path of wild smell under the tangled growth. Shadows moved in droves as the moon drowned itself in one cloud and another; and the river waters rolled like black ink.

But of all this wonderland of night, with its deeper and more intense life than that of daytime, his father was unafraid. He bent over his hoe, giving no heed to sharp sounds or to sudden darkenings of earth or to the hungry treading of winds or to the wailing of coyotes that sometimes were visible in the shadows. If a cow lay out he would go into the black meadowland and bring her home. Without lantern or gun, with no guide but his keen eyes, he would search for hours, prowling among the wolf-smells in the terrifying night. As Vridar watched him swing the hoe and wipe sweat from his eyes, or stand erect for a moment to get a pain out of his back, he thought his father must be the boldest man in all the world.

Now and then the boy saw another side of him. One afternoon Joe sat on the floor and asked his wife to read, not from the Bible, which Vridar was now reading, but from a romantic tale called *Orange Blossoms*. Its heroine was Monica, a glorious creature of youth and courage, who found in the book's first half more thorns than roses. Read a little while, Joe said, and he would go back to his labor. In a voice that rose on the crises or sank softly into the mournful depths Prudence read from the book; and Vridar moved close to hear. This tale was an allegory for him of the dreadful struggle between virtue and vice. Virtue was the radiant Monica, with dark eyes and windblown curls; and Vice was all the horrible evils that dug graves at her feet. He listened, breathless, with compassion or hate beating in him; with sobs racking him when Monica bowed in grief; with rapture shouting through him when she stood in triumph.

He noted meanwhile his father's emotion. He saw the man stare at his calloused palms, pick at dead skin, bite his nails. He saw Joe's eyes lift slowly to the book when the drama deepened and saw the emotion round his mouth; saw him look down again when the crisis passed. In a dramatic scene, where Monica fought visible devils and still kept herself pure, the son saw the muscles twitch in his father's face and his strong hands turn rigid. He saw a mist of tears in his eyes. That evening when Vridar entered the house he found his father staring guiltily into the book. Joe shut the book suddenly and went outside.

In all his early years he never saw his father kiss his mother, never heard him use an endearing word. He felt nevertheless that Joe had impulses toward kindliness, that his heart was tender and warm, that something had chilled him and filled his soul with frost. His mother too, during these years, was a strange person, imperious, swift, competent and cold. Vridar could not remember a single time when she had kissed him. He felt deeply, and the feeling deepened, that he was wanted by neither parent. But he accepted his mother as a stern oracle who knew all wisdom and the full heart of God. When her will spoke, it was like steel on steel; when she turned to work, it melted like snow under her hands.

He watched her milk cows, beating earth and manure from udders and flanks, squeezing teats with her strong fingers. When he tried to milk, his wrists ached, but his mother never paused, moving quickly from cow to cow, until her pail overflowed with foam. He saw her chop wood, swinging the heavy axe like a man; saw her carry water from the spring, four gallons of it in either hand; saw her build hencoops, excavate dugouts in the hillside, break poles across her knees.

Daily he watched her make cheese, pour warm rich milk into a washtub, add to it a strange-smelling liquid that she called runnet, and let the milk thicken into curd. Then she dipped off the pale whey. She sank to knees and crushed the curd in her hands. Her cheese-press was a tin pail, a round piece of wood an inch thick sawed from a log, and a long pole. She would put a cloth sack into the pail, fill it with curd, fold the cloth and set the piece of wood upon it. Then she would take the pail outside. She would lay the pole across it with one end under the house and weight the other end with stones. Putting boards and branches over it to protect the cheese from the dog and cats she would leave it in press all night. In the morning she would bang the pail until the cheese slipped out and then butter it and store it away in a cool place.

During this summer and for many years afterward she peddled cheese far away to the valley folk, riding alone eighty or a hundred miles in a lumber wagon and soliciting from house to house. She made four or five journeys every year. She was gone four or five days or a week. She would camp by the roadside, tethering her horses to ditch banks where the grass was lush, sleeping between two quilts spread on the earth. In the valley she became known as that queer Mrs. Hunter, lost far away in that Black Canyon hole and slaving like a man to send her children to school. How bitter and lonely these journeys were, how deeply her pride suffered from humiliation and scorn, how terribly she hated her drudgery Vridar was never to sense until long afterward. But he knew his own loneliness and terror when she went away. With anxieties darkening his mind he would watch her pile cheese into the wagon and cover it over and then climb to the box seat.

"Be my brave little man," she would say, looking down at him. "Don't let brother or sister out of your sight." She would gather the reins and look around at her cargo, and say: "Mother will bring you something nice if we can afford it." Her face was pale and proud; her eyes looked sternly at the task ahead.

Then Vridar would turn away to hide his tears and choke back his fright. With his heart breaking he would watch the wagon go up the gray road and out of the dugway hills. He would listen to its sound, loving its friendliness, knowing that his mother was with it; when unable at last to hear anything at all, he would be enfolded by horrible loneliness. He would run up the road, hoping to catch another glimpse of the wagon; but nothing was there, nothing but a wilderness of hills and trails and empty sky. He would turn back, feeling homeless and abandoned.

Painfully conscious of his duty to keep close watch over his brother and sister, he would keep them near the house, the only friendly thing anywhere. He would steal inside and stare at the clock and try to add up the hours that had to be endured. His father was out of sight somewhere, bent over the mattock; but after the intolerable eternity of a forenoon Joe would come to the house and eat. He prepared a cold lunch. He called the children and the boys came stealthily, afraid to make a sound. Diana, now two years old, was set on a chair and they all ate in silence. Then Joe would smoke a pipeful of tobacco that he had already chewed, or he would lie back a few minutes and doze, or with a stub of pencil he would make figures on a piece of bark. Then he would go back to his grubbing hoe.

The afternoon was a nightmarish time of silence and waiting. The yellow lazy sun seemed to stand still, and the large hand of the clock took hours to move from one figure to the next. Everything was breathless in the awful quiet, everything but the flies. These creatures droned on the house walls, buzzed lazily from face to hand, from hand to leg. For Vridar, sitting hour after hour choked with dread, there came to be something horribly insane in the droning of flies. The monotonous sound of them and their purposeless movements so depressed him that he felt himself slipping, felt himself being dissolved into the silence, felt that all reality was flowing away into the yellow sunshine and the sky's hush. The horror of it became so unbearable that he would have to move, lest he lose all touch with life. To shatter the silence he would have to speak. "Marion," he would say, and his voice would seem strange to him. Under his breath he would say the word over and over until it became as meaningless and empty as the droning; and with sweat starting from him he would try to shout some word, any word, to break the silence. He would walk around, muttering words, changing to other words when the first had been sucked of their meaning, trying to make things seem real.

But in the hot lifelessness of midafternoon the silence would become so oppressive, so heavy and deep, that he was no longer able to shatter it with words; and then he would find the cat or the dog and strive for peace by watching them. It seemed to make no difference to them that his mother was gone. Or he would go out to find his father, carrying Diana and leading Marion, and he would watch Joe labor, with sweat soaking him and the sun's heat scalding his neck. But the father never

39

spoke. Bent over the hoe, driving at roots with his great power, flinging sweat from his eyes, straightening to ease his back, he never even looked at his children. And Vridar would go again to the house to wait for darkness and sleep. When evening came Joe would vanish into meadowland to fetch the cows; and Vridar would watch him go and when there was no sign of him he would moan with fright, his mind seeing only one thing, his father sinking down and down into a bottomless bog. He would light the lamp even before the sun had set because he wanted its friendliness before darkness came.

After his father returned Vridar would carry pails to the corral and help a little with the milking. Marion and Diana would sit in a corner, as quiet as the posts. Then they would all go to the house and Joe would strain the milk through a cloth into pans. He would pour milk into four bowls, slice and scatter bread on the table, and again they would eat, with walls staring gloomily out of lamplight, with darkness filling the door.

A little later Vridar would lie in his high bunk. The lamp's flame had been blown like a yellow leaf into darkness and the house was deep with the intensity of night. Through the north window he could see the bright loneliness of stars. He could hear his father's loud snores. Drawing quilts over him he would think of his mother, somewhere far away in purple valleyland with the smell around her of cheese and eggs. All day she had ridden slowly and joltingly across the hills, high above the river's underearth sound; and now she was lying somewhere between two quilts, thinking of the humiliations that lay ahead. Her tales lived again . . . .

"I wonder if you folks would like some cheese today. It's full-cream cheese. Only fifteen cents a pound and they weigh about five pounds. Would you like to sample one?"

"We ain't no great hands for cheese, not much. Seems like a kind a luxury, cheese does. But I'm willun to taste anything once . . . . Why, yes, it ain't so darned bad. Mary, come taste this-here cheese. Fifteen cents a pound did you say?"

"In case you took two—"

"By God, is that a worm hole? Mary, why the hell ain't you comun to taste this cheese?" Or if it was a woman who met Prudence at the door: "Cheese? No, we ain't no taste for cheese. If it was apples—"

"Mebe you'd like to sample it. It's full-cream. I don't make cheese out of skim milk."

"No, we ain't no taste for cheese. Sometime, if you have apples or spuds . . . ."

Another woman, sharper of tongue: "Cheese! Did you ask I want a-buy cheese? Listen, I'll tell you a thing. The last woman sold me cheese, it had worms in it and it stunk. Was that you? She had a long chin like yourn and a mole with hair in it."

"No"—gently, standing on her pride. "It's my first trip in this section."

"It don't matter, cheese is all alike. Flies get to it, maggots pop out all over . . . . No, I don't want a-taste it"—and the door was slammed.

The men were nicer, Prudence said, after telling of her experiences. They were polite, even when they didn't buy. But the women! Sometimes, said Prudence, she did not meet a lady in twenty miles.

On and on, back and forth, the scenes trooped through Vridar's mind: words and phrases, bright with wonder, shone for a moment and were clouded, and he recalled and rephrased them, to make them shine again. Multitudes lined the roadways, some friendly, some insolent and lewd; and beyond them all, riding an old rickety wagon from house to house, was his mother, her face hurt and proud, a slave-woman peddling her wares. He could hear the dark flowing of the waters, the dark hunting of nightwinds. He could see one lonely star in the dim cold north. An hour passed, another hour, and he did not sleep, for he lived only for his mother's return.

The afternoon of the fourth day he looked across the meadow's bogs and mists and into the west. Somewhere, far away in the purple haze, she was coming home! Entering the house he opened the clock door and turned the big hand twice around the circle. The short hand moved from three to five. He went outside, trying to believe that two hours had passed. But he could not deceive himself. He turned the clock back and felt more afraid, wondering if this was the fourth day or only the third, or maybe even only the second! He moved the clock hands back and forth, confusing himself and the hours, seeking some miracle to make time leap ahead. Marion came up and stared at him with weird eyes. When the right eye looked straight ahead the left gazed inward, with the iris half out of sight. He was cross-eyed, his mother said, because when two years old he had skinned his nose and for weeks had looked at the scab.

"Will she come today?" he whispered, looking at his brother.

"I don't know," Vridar said, also whispering.

Diana was playing in a pile of dirt; her hands and face were black with it and she had earth round her lips and on her tongue. He knew that her pants were filled with her own dung because he could smell her. The father changed her now and then but when Prudence was away, most of the time Diana toddled around with her pants hanging full or sat down in it to play. Why, Vridar wondered, had God made such a horrible thing as manure!

He carried water from the spring and poured it into a slop bucket and began to scrub the floors. He spilled water on the boards and swept the water into the cracks. It rose in black bubbles, exploded and sank. He carried more water and swept again, and out of the cracks came hordes of spiders and insects to scurry over the floor. After the rooms smelled wet and clean he wondered what else he could do, to excite his mother's wonder and invite her praise. She called him her manly little man and he hated her for it. Sometimes he dried her dishes, found dry kindling to make easy fires, swept cobwebs from corners, and even tried to make the beds; and she smiled at him and called him her little man and her helper.

Now he shook the grate and took ashes from the stove; filled the pails with clear cool water; tidied the beds and wiped a part of the dust off window panes; and Marion, watching him, slipped up to ask: "Will she bring us some lickerish?"

"I don't know."

When the sun like a bucket of blood sat on the western rim and the meadowlands began to darken, Vridar kindled the lamp. He could see two small open spaces in the dugway and these he watched, or he listened for the sound of wheels. Time and again he thought he heard the heavy chug-chug of hub against shoulders or saw something move on the patch of road. By the window he sat to watch the road and Marion stood by him; and Marion whispered, "I hope it's lickerish." Joe came in from his labor and took milk pails and went to the corral. At supper he said, "I don't reckon your ma's comun today."

Vridar's food choked in his throat. He looked at his father: at the ragged mustache fringed white with milk, his dark silky hair still damp with sweat, his wide open mouth when he sucked in huge spoonfuls of soaked bread. Then Joe looked at the clock. "That-air time can't be right," he said. In the slow deliberate way he had he leaned far back, grasped a thick strap hanging from his watch pocket, and dragged forth a watch almost as large as his hand. In drawing the watch forth he distorted his face as though in severe pain, for this was another of his queer ways.

"It ain't right," he said. He looked at his watch, at the clock, again at his watch. "It's fast," he said. Slowly, distorting his face, he shoved the watch back into its home, looked once again at the clock, and resumed his eating, sucking the wet bread into his mouth with a sloppy roar. Milk dripped from his mustache into his three-quart bowl.

When the meal was done, Joe gave off two or three loud belches, as he usually did after eating, and tore straws from the dirty old broom to clean his pipe. He had made a fire, and now on hands and knees he searched for a dry piece of wood and cut wide white shavings, and with these, one after another, he tried to fire the tobacco of his old quids. He puffed heartily, his eyes quiet and soft in firelight, his cheeks caving in and then blowing out, his thick forefinger tamping the tobacco down and down. When firing his pipe or cleaning it, Joe Hunter was a tremendous vision of patience and calm.

Outside, on the ends of house logs, on the grindstone seat, in a hundred odd places were his old quids, sucked dry of juice and given to the sun. He left them sometimes for days before he gathered and smoked them. Vridar had tasted them once, curious to know what tobacco was like, but they had seemed to him as flavorless as dry bark. Joe's plug of chewing tobacco he kept hidden.

"I thought I heared a wagon then," he said, and thrust another shaving into the stove.

Vridar went to the window and looked into the dark world. He listened but could hear nothing.

Vridar did not doubt, for his father's ears, he had learned, were as keen as the dog's. His heart leapt, his blood poured through him in liberated frenzy. He ran to the door, paused on the black threshold, and stepped outside. Towser now sprang to life. He jumped out of sleep, gave two sharp barks, and stood listening, his ears pointed into the night. Vridar listened, too, and after a moment he heard, far away in the opaque hush, far up in the terrible silence, the sound of wagon wheels. He almost fainted. Relief swept in and through him like clean bright air; the sunken terror of four long days and nights was driven out on his breath; and he wanted to cry, to cry until his heart broke. He heard the sound again. It was coming along the benchland rim, and oh, what a warm trail it was making in the night! What a friendly thing it was, as its wheels searched the ruts in darkness, rolling home!

Unable to endure his relief he ran behind the house and burst into tears. Joy filled his eyes with sweet blindness and drew all of life into this moment of homing sound. Choking his sobs back, he listened and heard it again and he wanted to run forth and meet it and kiss its big home-coming wheels. But he did not venture forth. Carefully drying his eyes and wiping the tear stains from his cheeks he strove to quiet his shaking body, while he stared out at the skyland of shadow, out of which his mother would come. The sound became loud on the tableland, half way to the mountaintop. It was continuous now, a steady rumbling of iron on iron. Never in later years was he to hear the sound of a wagon in nighttime without wanting to go forth and touch the wheels and hug them to his heart.

Now it was coming down the lane of shadow. Then, at last, at last, the horses emerged, black and steaming; and then—most incredible of miracles!—the wagon drew up with a crunching of brakes and stopped. It was here: he could smell it and see it! His mother was home! . . . . And Joe meanwhile sat calmly inside, trying to fire stubborn tobacco with a fresh litter of shavings.

Prudence climbed down, drenched with dust and night air and valley smells. She entered the house, and Vridar, who had been lurking in shadow, followed her.

"You're kinda late gettun home," said Joe, drawing great clouds from his pipe.

Prudence took off a wrap and shook it and the room smelled of road dust and the night. Joe tamped tobacco into the pipe, jerked his finger away and scowled as if the pipe had tricked him. But that was only another way he had. Prudence stood by the fire and looked around until her gaze fell on Vridar.

"How did mother's little man get along?"

"All right," he said.

"Did you get lonesome?"

"No maam," he said.

All his loneliness and fright seemed unimportant now. He was ashamed of them. In the demeanor of his bold and aggressive parents there was no encouragement to confession, no place for terror and nightmare. And so he pretended, now and hereafter, that he was what his mother wanted him to be: a brave little man, patient, fearless, able, and soberly matured in his emotions and thoughts. For was he not his brother's keeper and his mother's pride!

His parents went to the wagon and carried stuff inside: boxes full of clean store-smells: smells of brown paper and seasoned wood; the strong clean odor of a pair of overalls, of oats in which eggs had been stored, of a plug of tobacco, of sugar, oatmeal, and flour. He wanted to touch these things, to realize their wonder and newness, but he stood back, silent, watching, polite. Out of a cool depth at last Prudence drew a small paper bag and handed it to him. It held five sticks of licorice. He knew what to do. He had been taught that when dividing with another he must always give the better half.

He got a knife and went with Marion where they could sit in lamplight. They looked at the magnificent gift and each took two sticks; then Vridar cut the fifth stick in two and considered the two halves. One was round from end to end but a part of the other was flat. Which was the larger? Unable to decide he offered Marion his choice.

Marion took the pieces and stared at them. He laid them side by side and saw that their length was the same. He turned them over and over, measuring, weighing.

"Which you want?" asked Vridar in a whisper.

Marion did not know. "Which you think is biggest?"

"They're about the same." Vridar took the pieces and studied them. "Mebe the flat one's a little bigger," he said.

Again Marion tried to measure, examine, weigh. "This," he said, choosing the round one.

Vridar was pleased. He thought the flat one was slightly larger. Still, he would feel shame to the end of his life if he cheated his brother. He drew a deep breath and renounced. "No," he said, "you take the flat one."

Each lad clutched his own sticks and looked at those in his brother's hand. Then Vridar faced the severest duty of all. He had to treat his parents. Once before he had treated his father and the man had taken an enormous bite. Feeling dark misgivings, Vridar put his three pieces in the paper bag and went to his parents. "Mother," he said, his voice very polite, "will you have some lickerish?"

She looked into the bag. "You didn't cheat your little brother, did you?"

"No maam. I give him his choice."

"You must always give people their choice. Mother doesn't want her boy to be a stingy little man . . . . Well, you just cut mother off a little piece."

He did not like that at all. How was he to know what she thought a little piece? What if he cut it too small or too large? He went way with the knife and pondered this tremendous dilemma. He marked on one stick what he thought would be a generous piece. With sinking heart he cut it off. He took it to his mother and hoped she would not think him stingy.

"Oh, I don't want so much. Just a wee nibble."

When the father came in after stabling the horses Vridar approached him with his four pieces in the bag.

"What is it?" asked Joe, who knew very well what it was.

"Lickerish," said Vridar. He was amused. He had learned that his father always scowled when offered anything. He always pretended that he did not want those things which he wanted most. If he did not want a thing he never scowled.

"He's treatun you," said Prudence. "Why do you want a-scowl that way?"

Joe's scowl deepened, as it always did when rebuked. He stared into the bag and reached down with a big hand. He drew out the full stick, went to the stove to spit out his quid, tongued around his mouth to clean it and then bit off half the piece of licorice. He returned the other piece to the bag and began to chew, making dreadful facial contortions as if his teeth hurt.

"You might thank him," Prudence said.

Something like pain and contempt darkened the father's gray eyes. A little later when Marion made another offering Joe arose without speaking and left the house.

When the lads were tucked into bed their licorice was under their pillows, now secure in their own right with all gift-making done. Marion whispered that he would give Vridar a little of his but Vridar said no, he did not care. He did care, deeply; all his licorice had been mutilated, for there was not a piece that had not been bitten or whittled. Still, his mother was home and this was a great and shining joy. She would not go again until the cupboard was full of cheese and the oat-box level with eggs. He reached over to pat his brother's hand.

"I don't care," he said. He was thinking of his father, somewhere out in the dark. He knew that Joe had been deeply offended and had gone away to be alone. "I don't care," he said again. "If he had took all of it I wouldn't care."

VI

September came and great winds filled the bowl of their home. The winds sieved the tempest and sowed the ground with white. They harvested the lonely altitudes and scattered the chilled seed, heaped it in windrows, turned green bushes into white sheaves, and built white haystacks in glen and cove. They burst against the stone ledges and left great firs gasping for breath. They swept over the meadow springs, bore mist upward in smoky whorls, and went roaring eastward into Black Canyon and Burns.

Vridar wondered out of what invisible world these wild winds came. They fell like sky-floods of breathing or came up the river gorge, a wall of twilight first and then a howling wreckage of sound. When he asked his mother, she said God sent the winds forth and forgot to recall. This, it seemed to Vridar, was a tremendous oversight that offered to human beings an excuse for their own missteps in memory. But why, he asked, had God sent them forth? Had he not foreseen, from the great height where he sat, overlooking all worlds and all space, that winds would knock trees down, blow the earth from house roofs, and thresh the kernels out of ripening wheat? Prudence said he would understand such things when he was big. When he was big! Ah, what boundless knowledge awaited him! Then he would know:

Why the sky was blue, grass green, and maples red; whether the sun, which his mother said was God's daylamp, burned coal oil and had a wick; why it came up in the east and sank in the west, and whether God blew it out like a lamp or let it shine all night; why chickens walked on two legs, dogs on four, and why they never learned to talk; and why some things had feathers and some had hair; whether all prayers were heard and why some were never answered; whether God ever slept, and if the seasons of the year were in heaven, too; if the wings of angels were made of feathers like the wings of birds, and if God's eyes were blue like his mother's, gray like his father's, or brown like his own; whether they ate bread and milk for supper in the afterworld; if the bottomless springs in the meadow came out in China and if the lost pole and man and coyote had fallen clear through the earth; if stars were put there to light the night, why some them were so dim; why horses ate grass, pigs grain and swill, cats meat and gravy; why God was a man and not a woman and how long it had taken him to write the Bible; why roosters chased hens and climbed to their backs and then strutted pompously around them; why eggs were laid from the hen's craw, as his mother said, and why chickens were hatched from eggs, instead of being dug like calves and colts out of the earth . . . .

45

To most of his questions his mother gave fabulous answers, hiding the truth in parable and myth. She told him that answers to all questions were to be found in the Bible. There were two Bibles among the books his parents had brought here: one was small and fat with print so fine it was hard to read; the other was huge and illustrated, with big friendly letters. During the long cold winter he read the Bible, pasturing himself in its allegories as he sat hour after hour by the dim window or the pale lamp. He read over and over the first chapter of Genesis until he was drunk with the awful power, with the stupendous magnitude of that lordly gesture out of darkness, that wreaking of form and light upon the face of the deep. He could look out and see the firmament, the curved blue dome that was heaven, dividing the waters from the waters. He tried to imagine the instantaneous waking of each herb and tree, animal and fowl, when the word to live was spoken; and of the great miracle in the second chapter when man was raised from dust. The garden called Eden, his parents said, was in Missouri, and not in Asia, as so many people believed. The statement that the third river turned into Assyria was an error. It was the Ohio or the Mississippi. He marveled at Adam's ingenuity in finding names for all the creatures of air, earth and sea, and at God's creation of woman out of a rib. Had God given another rib to Adam? Prudence imagined that he had, but Joe said, scowling at her, that he had not; and prodding at his ribs he counted them one by one. On his right side he counted twelve but on his left only eleven; and he stared at his wife who was counting her own.

"I got twelve on each side," Prudence said.

"Well, wife, of course!" cried Joe with huge impatience. "You're a womern, ain't you?"

Prudence reddened. "Well, if I got twenty-four so have you. Couldn't God who is all-powerful make another rib for Adam?"

Joe considered this and prodded himself again. It would be a lot of sense, he said, to make another rib; for if God had intended to do that, why did he take one from Adam to begin with? Prudence called Vridar to her side, and she counted his ribs, each as unfleshed as a slat. She said he had twelve on his left side. Joe expressed his incredulity and scorn with a grunt. He wanted to count Vridar's ribs but he did not call the lad to him. He only stared at him.

"Your father wants to count your ribs," Prudence said.

Vridar went over timidly and Joe's big rough hands moved up and down over his bones. Then Joe turned away, satisfied, but he did not speak.

"Well?" said Prudence.

Joe ignored her. The matter was forever settled in his mind.

"How many has he got?" she asked impatiently.

"Why, wife," he said, "he's got leven on the left side. Ain't that what I said all along?"

Many a verse left Vridar deep in thought: And they were both naked, the man and his wife, and they were not ashamed. That he thought incredible. Still, it was God's utterance and therefore true. His own body was like fire, his blood beat in degradation when his young pale flesh was exposed; but the man and the woman, they were naked and unashamed! When he came to II Kings, xviii, 27 he gasped as if he had been drenched with frost: hath he not sent me to the men which sit on the wall, that they may eat their own dung and drink their own piss with you? Deeply horrified and shocked he turned the book over to be sure that he was reading the Bible. His face burned crimson as he read the verse again. To drink their own piss? What in the world could this mean!

And what did the tree of knowledge mean, with its fruit that opened eyes and made people like unto gods? What, he asked his mother, was this fruit, this good and pleasant thing that made people wise, of which Adam and Eva ate? She read the verses and pondered. "I don't know," she said. "Your father, mebbe he knows. He's read deeper in religion than I have."

"What fruit?" asked Joe, scowling at his wife.

"Why, the fruit Eve et. The tree of knowledge."

"Why, wife, nobody knows. When Eve et it God took it out of the garden and it ain't never growed since."

Vridar stored the answer away and read again. He approved Abel but sympathized with Cain. He got lost among the genealogies and ages and deaths of the patriarchs. There were giants in the earth in those days. How long, he asked his mother, did men live now? Eighty years, she said, was a ripe old age. Then why had they lived so long in the days of the giants?

"Because, my son, they were good. It's sin kills people off."

"Then old people are good people and the wicked die young?"

Well, no, she said, thinking of some scoundrels with gray beards.

Ah, Lord, it was a wicked world then, and God's wrath fell like thunder. Fifteen cubits upward did the waters prevail, and the mountains were covered. He thought of the mountains north of his home and tried to imagine the depth of water that in Noah's time must have washed the stars. How much was a cubit? he asked. Prudence came over, her hands bedded in dough. "Spell it, son."

"C-u-b-i-t."

Prudence said she thought it was about a mile. Fifteen miles of water, piled mountain on mountain upward, with nothing in sight but the sky and one ark! Truly the wrath of God was great. He strove to imagine the earth after the waters fell back, soaked with the heaving floodtides of a hundred and fifty days. He trembled at the rainstorm of fire that fell on Sodom. His breath stopped when he read that Lot's wife turned into salt. Did she still stand there on the plains of Zoar? His father said she did.

"But that can't be right," said Prudence. "A salt woman? Why, the rain would have washed her away after all these years."

Joe was annoyed, as he always was when his biblical lore was laid under doubt. He looked pityingly at his wife. "I guess," he said, "that God Almighty could keep that salt-womern there, iffen he can rain brimstone and cause floods and make a man stay alive in a whale's belly!"

That settled the matter. The salt-woman was still there on the plains of Zoar.

Again and again Vridar came to words that made his cheeks burn. There was the word ass which he had learned was a foul and unutterable word. But when he understood that Abraham had mounted an ass and ridden away to burn his son

47

Isaac, he decided that ass was not what his father's people thought it was. Still, the word bothered him and he never lingered long over a page where it occurred. He was trying to suck the great history of all its wisdom. Most of it he understood, or his father explained it for him; but when he read of the Firstborn and the Younger, who made their father drunk and then lay with him, he sensed a meaning that he did not dare ask about. Thus were both the daughters of Lot with child by their father: what deep and inscrutable secret was hidden there? These daughters bare sons, whatever that could mean . . . . And there was the verse about a damsel, fair to look upon: a virgin, neither had any man known her: and she went down to the well and filled her pitcher, and came up. What was meant by saying that no man had known Rebekah? Had she lived in hiding all her life? Other verses were even darker. There was the story of Judah and Shuah: and he took her, and went in unto her. And she conceived, and bare a son; and he called his name Er. He read the verses over and over and at last turned to his mother.

"What?" asked Prudence, reading under the pointed finger.

"This—it says he took her and went in unto her. And she c-o-n-c-e-i-v-e-d. What does that mean?" He looked up at his mother and saw that her face and throat were turning red and that in her blue eyes were secret things. His own face began to burn. Again she told him that he would understand when he was big.

He read further, and found Judah going in unto another woman, unto Tamar, his daughter-in-law. There was sin here certainly, for Judah commanded her to be burned. Then came this incredible passage: And it came to pass in the time of her travail, that, behold, twins were in her womb. And it came to pass, when she travailed, that the one put out his hand: and the midwife took and bound upon his hand a scarlet thread, saying, This came out first. And it came to pass, as he drew back his hand, that, behold, his brother came out: and she said, How hast thou broken forth? this breach be upon thee: therefore his name was called Pharez. And afterward came out his brother, that had the scarlet thread upon his hand. . . .

He pondered these verses until his senses ached and his mind reeled with the imminence of horrible discovery. He read other passages of like import; and though he came near the truth, touched its shadow, felt its deep pulse, it fell away and all was darker than before. There was sin in those days, as well as giants; there was the impetuous clamoring of unchaste blood.

But it was not the obscure things that interested him most. It was to the giants, to Moses and Joshua, to David and Samson, that he gave the beating life of his heart. They stepped like titans out of the pages; he could hear their great breath and feel their mighty will. Ah, what lordly conquerors they were! When he and Marion were in bed he would tell his brother some heroic saga of those ancient days, when warriors smote their enemies and God ravaged the earth with frogs. Against the night, deep and cold with winter, he projected the legends, until the darkness was that upon Egypt and the winds were the tumult over Israel. The boys would enter the bedroom and climb to the high frozen bed; they would bury themselves and breathe into the icy quilted interior, until it was a little warm; when, under the cover, in the gloom of bed-smell and growing heat, Vridar would tell the tales . . . .

He told about Moses, who was thrown into a pond and floated around there;

and the daughter of the Pharaoh, she came down and fished him out. "Then Moses, one day he slewed a Gyptian, he buried him in the sand. Then Moses got a stick, and the Lord, he said to Moses, throw that stick on the ground, and Moses did, and lo, it was a snake."

"You mean he'd been carryun a snake?"

"No, God, he turned it into a snake and told Moses to take it by the tail, and Moses did, and lo, it was only a stick."

"Then it wasn't a snake after all?" said Marion, disappointed.

"It was a stick and then a snake and then a stick. Then God, he got mad at the Gyptians and he said to Moses, hit your stick and turn the rivers into blood, and all the ponds and all the water in buckets. And Moses hit, and the water was blood and all the fish died, and the Gyptians dug all over for water to drink but there wasn't any. Then God, he spoke, and Moses made millions of frogs come and they crawled into beds and everywhere and there wasn't anything but frogs. Then the frogs died and the whole land stunk. Still the Pharaoh he wouldn't give in."

"Who was he?" asked Marion.

"He was a king somewhere. Then God spoke again, and Moses turned all the dust into lice. Then grasshoppers, they come in millions and et all the bushes and trees and all the grain, and there were so many grasshoppers, the daylight it was like darkness. The Pharaoh said, I've been a bad sinner, and God sent a wind and blowed the grasshoppers away. Then Pharaoh, he went back on his word, and God sent darkness all over and it was so thick you could feel it, and the Pharaoh, he give in a little more."

"He must a-been stubborn," whispered Marion.

"He got more stubborn. God killed all the firstborn, babies and cattle and every-thing—"

"What's a firstborn?"

"Me. You're a secondborn."

"If you'd been there would God killed you?"

"No. I ain't a Gyptian. Well, then Pharaoh was sorry and said they could go. They went in a big journey and God went before them; in the daytime he was a pillar of cloud and in the nightime he was a pillar of fire. They went a long time and Moses was singun. They come to the Red Sea and right in the middle the sea the Gyptians all got stuck and was drownded."

"Then what?" asked Marion, shivering.

"Then God he give them commandments and I learned most of them. It says him what curseth his father and mother he shalt die."

"Did God say that?"

"God said that to Moses. I read anothern. It says if a man, if he has a son won't obey his father and mother, then his father must take him out and stone him to death."

"God said that?" gasped Marion.

"That's what he said."

Buried deep in quilts they thought about God and his words. Had he ever wanted to curse his father? Vridar asked himself. He pushed the quilts backward and

49

struggled upward until his head emerged, and looked across the room where his parents lay. He could hear his father's snoring, the sound of a man sunk fathoms deep in sleep. But his mother, he knew, would be awake, because Joe's snoring annoyed and disturbed her. Softly he let himself down to the floor and tiptoed to the other bed.

"What's the matter, son?"

"I just want a-kiss you," he said.

She drew his frail shivering body to her and held him a moment. He kissed her forehead, her cheek. He wanted to kiss his father but he did not dare. He had never kissed his father and his father had never kissed him.

"Now run back," said his mother. "You'll freeze."

"Yes maam."

"Mebbe I should go," Marion whispered, when Vridar was back in bed.

"All right. Hurry."

And Marion went, as his brother had gone, bearing the small atonement of a kiss.

Another time Vridar told the tale of Joshua: how he commanded the sun to stand still upon Gibeon, and the moon in the valley of Ajalon; how God aided him against the five kings, smiting them with hailstone from Azekah to Makkedah; and of the one and thirty kings whom he smote beyond the Jordan. . . . Of how Jael, a sly and wicked woman, persuaded Sisera to lie and sleep, and then drove a nail into his temple and spiked him to the ground . . . . And of Jephthah's vow to the Lord, and his daughter's upon the mountain; and of her virginity and lamentations and death. Though what virginity was, said Vridar, spelling the word, he did not know and his mother would not tell him. "But he burnt her."

"His own daughter?" gasped Marion.

He told of Daniel thrown into a den of lions; of Jonah, cast to the sea and held for three days in a whale's belly; of Job, lord of virtue in hours of anguish, triumphant over doubt and boils; of David who, with five smooth stones, went out to face Goliath the giant and killed him. In the illustrated Bible was a picture of David, clothed in leopard skin, standing with one foot on the giant and holding the severed dripping head in his hand. Vridar had stared long at the bloody neck and huge black beard and the eyes glazed and staring out of death.

One January night when the world was frozen darkness full of the insanity of winds, he told about his favorite, the mighty Samson. Few nights in childhood were to remain more vividly in memory; and when, in later times, he heard this giant's name, he felt again the warm deep bedding, he saw the glacial rigidity of window and north wall, he heard the violence of the winds. "Now Samson, he was big and he had long black hair and he lived in the camp of Dan. Then he went down to Timnath, only on the way he met a lion and he grabbed it and tore it plumb in two. Then he got married and on his way back he saw honey in the lion and he et some of the honey."

"You mean he killed a lion?" asked Marion.

"He was a giant. Then they took his wife away and Samson he got awful mad and he caught two hundred foxes and set them all on fire and they run out and burnt up all the corn. Then the—the P-h-i-l-l-i-s-t-i-n-e-s—that was his enemies, they said, who done that? and one of them said Samson did and they took his wife and burnt her. Then Samson got madder. He hit them hip and thigh and he done a great slaughter. Then he lived in the top of a rock . . . ."

The house shuddered under the winds; the night screeched round the corners, roaring down upon the trees. Vridar was silent, thinking of Samson outside, wreaking vengeance upon a host of men. The men scattered and howled with the wind's voice, and the blind earth shook under its white death.

"Then Samson," said Vridar, whispering, "he met a woman name D-e-l-i-l-a-h; and she said what makes you so strong? He said to bind him with seven green twigs and he wouldn't be strong. She bound him but he busted them like thread; and she asked what can I do to make you weak? And Samson said to bind him with new ropes and he would be weak. She bound him with ropes and he busted them like threads. Then she was mad and said he did not love her, and Samson told her his long hair had never been cut and if it was cut he would be weak like other men. Our father believes that," said Vridar.

"That why his hair is long?"

"Yes. It makes him strong as a bull."

They were quiet, listening to the desolating anger of the night and the winds and the whipped body of darkness. Vridar looked at the panes, glazed deep with the witchery of ice. He had become afraid. He called to his mother and she came to the door, the door opened, and a flood of yellow light and warmth fell in.

"What is it, son?"

"I just wanted to know was you there."

The door was closed, the yellow vanished in a folding wing of light, and again there was the blackness and chill of the room. What happened then? Marion asked; and Vridar said that Samson yanked a building down and all the people were killed and Samson was killed too.

Again and again in these winter nights so deep with darkness and cold Vridar whispered under the bedclothes of the lordly conquerors who smote hip and thigh, rolled the seas back, stopped the sun, and smeared themselves with the blood of their foes. The white northern peaks were the border of Abel-meholah; the river was the Jordan; Rattlesnake Point was the rock of Oreb, and the marsh below it was the winepress where the Lord's troops cut off the head of Zeeb. The grain field, clothed in white, was the realm of Boaz, where Ruth gleaned; and the meadow, now an area of gleaming swords and spears, was the land of Gibeah, where Jonathan led and slew, and the hosts quaked and beat themselves and melted away. His home was a great white well, full of the night and of Israel.

Under the reading of each tale the geography changed: valleys opened out of darkness, shone with a wealth of tents and olive trees, faded into the plains of Samaria; lepers rose in twilight and swarmed over the deserted Syrian camp and disappeared skyward in shrieking pestilence; the Arnon flowed under green ice and spread into the pastures of the twenty-third psalm; and then all would turn into a pavilion of deep waters and clouds, and the sky would thresh in hailstones and coals of fire.

This wonderland, where right went forth with the sword and God invoked gray

51

plague or lightning tempest, he peopled at will, from the creeping things of the sixth day to the bulls of Bashan. Tabernacles stood here, towered with ice and frost; hills melted like wax in the Lord's glory; the floods of pain lifted up their voice. People ate ashes that were like bread and mingled their drink with weeping; and angels walked with proud and perfect heart. The beams of chambers were built upon waters, clouds rolled in wild chariots, and God walked on the wings of the wind. Flaming acres were laid throughout the land. Rocks opened and rivers gushed. A hill swallowed Dathan and wonders grew thick in the land of Ham. And over it all, above the shifting deserts or trembling rocks, above the moaning of sin and the waste of death, the Lord moved like sunlight and his words were lamps. For thy word is a lamp unto my feet, and a light unto my path. For thy mind is a temple, a great windowed room in the earth's darkness, with lit corridors under the shadow-roof of life, while glories flower in the storm . . . .

He told his mother one day that he knew what he wanted to be when he grew up. She looked at him in the strange way she had because she knew he was a strange child; and she asked him what he wanted to be.

"A prophet," he said.

She stared at him, remembering the caul, remembering that Rose had told her that Joseph Smith was born with a veil. She encouraged him. She said that in the last hundreds of years there had been only one prophet, Joseph Smith, who founded a church in which alone there was truth. He was a strange child, she said, looking at him with strange troubled eyes, noting his thin pinched face, his frail body, and his large eyes, always darkened and intense. She touched his hair and said there was something she had never told him, that she would tell him some time. How would he know if he was to be a prophet?

"God will show you in a vision."

Vridar read again. He was now in the second chapter of Isaiah. And nations would beat their spears into plowshares, their swords into pruninghooks; and they would learn war not any more. They would enter into the rock, hide themselves in the dust, and shake with fear at the majesty of God. Ah, here was the kind of prophet he wanted to be! He would smite the lofty looks of men and bow down their haughtiness: the cedars of Lebanon, the oaks of Bashan, and all the ships of Tarshish. He would stand on the housetops and say, Crawl into the stones and bow yourselfs down! This is the rod of mine anger, the staff of mine indignation! Woe to ye, hypocrites, because—because [he read again] the Holy One is a flame, and it shall come to pass that ye shall all be burnt alive! The wolf shall dwell with the lamb, and the leopard shall lie down with the kid; and the lion shall eat straw like the ox . . . . Yes, he would be a prophet: the Snake River would be smitten into seven streams, and all the Babylons of earth would wither under his voice. He read wolfishly, storing away in his mind all the things that the prophets did, memorizing the mightiest of their words. He would praise God in the way of Isaiah: I will exalt thee, for thou hast done wonderful things! For thou hast made of a city a heap; of a defenced city a ruin: a palace of strangers to be no city; it shall never be built.

His mother encouraged him, remembering the caul; his father stared at him with dubious eyes. The boy's heart sang. To himself he would whisper, Here, O Lord, is

52

a prophet and his name in Vridar! He will swallow up death in victory, for he will be a mighty one . . . .

In a later year he dreamed a dream and spoke to the Lord again. He read the Bible until his heart was full, until his conscience reeled under the burden of worlds to be saved, sin to be smitten, cities to be destroyed. But between this hour and that afternoon when he would try to shake a mountain there fell two long years, and the one who would be a prophet sank under fresh terrors.

VII

Spring came with its miracle of renewal, and the sun seemed to linger as if unwilling to set. The evenings were voluptuous and deeply sweet. Beauty awoke and budded, flowered in meadow and island and hillside, built its leafy ceilings and its green paths. Day by day Vridar watched the naked trees and the shrubs clothe themselves with life. He went into the awakening, smelling the broken snows and hearing the stammering rapture of streams. He found wild flowers, yellow sunleaf and blue skyleaf, each a tiny wonder pushing out of the sod. He saw blackbirds made of darkness and flight, swallows of milkfoam and raingray, hawks of remoteness and silence and rhythm. He saw robins sunburnished, doves cloudbreasted, and flickers firecrowned. He heard the rising throaty roar of the river and under it the broad windwash of the firs, and under them the small lipwhisper of leaves. He smelled dripping willow and rosebush and the river's floating gardens of ice; the clean steaming health of springs and the strong odor of marsh and frogpond and bog; the loamy sweetness of new furrows and the yellow warmth of the sun. He felt the wind on him, flowing over in cool enveloping waves and spilling its mischief in his hair; and the cloaking shadows and the searching frankness of sun, and all the great plateau of life under his naked feet.

With every sense he drank the season in. He walked in fancy and beauty clothed him. Beauty gave him golden trousers of sunlight, hats of cloudscarf, shoes of odorous soil. In a later time he would await his favorite season in many places but he would never see it shower upon the earth such mammoth armfuls of loveliness as it bestowed with blind extravagance upon this sunken bottomland. Summer he shrank from because of its hordes of murmuring flies and its passionless aloofness and the fixed intensity of its heat; autumn because of its carpets of desolation and the naked bones of its trees and its loneliness; and winter for its white deserts and screaming winds. But spring was all tenderness and faith. Its great pulse gushed and ran and out of everything came beauty. The sky for him was a blue allegory and each tree a green parable; and the sun was a warm legend out of Palestine. He loved it. He trusted it. April and violet and bluebird: it was a time to smell and breathe and feel. Ah, spring, spring!

But one day he was called out of wonderland and dreaming to look again on the terrible man who was his father. Joe had gone fishing. After dark he had returned with a five-pound rainbow trout, a lovely thing with a spine of blue and a belly of gold. He gutted it and laid it on the table and went to the chores. Prudence was outside and the children were with her. An hour later they all entered the house.

Upon the table, crunching and tearing at the fish, was the cat. The beast leapt down with blood on her whiskers and trotted away on padded feet. Joe swore an oath that shook the house. He stood for several moments looking at the mutilated fish and rage filled him; and then he swung, his eyes gleaming and his mouth ugly.

"Where'd she go?" he thundered.

"Now don't lose your temper," said his wife. "You should a-covered it with a pan."

"Oh by the God all-Judas! Can't a man step outside without that son of a bitch—"

"Now don't shout that way! It's done and it can't be helped."

"I'll learn her!" Joe cried. He stooped, looking under the iron stove, under the aspen-legged table; peering into corners and the woodbox; beating with his feet to frighten the cat from hiding.

"It's no use to beat her," said Prudence. "You should learn to cover things up."

"I should learn hell! I should do this and I should do that! Like I ain't got enough to do without botherun with that God-damned thief."

"Well, you don't have to swear. Your children are here, remember."

He seized the broom and went into the next chamber; he knocked around furiously under the beds and behind boxes. The cat darted out from hiding and sprang through the kitchen and into the woodbin.

"Scat!" Joe was thundering in the next room. "Scat you son of a bitch!"

Prudence quickly opened the door, hoping the cat would escape; but Joe came forth now, roaring with fury, and saw the trembling beast in the woodbox. He rushed over and seized her hind legs and carried her head downward outside.

In the front yard was a thick cedar post, set deep in the earth. Joe went to this post, and Vridar, close on his heels, saw what he did. Holding the cat by its hind legs he threw it back over his shoulder and then with all his great strength he smote it against the cedar. It was crushed against wood and wrapped around it like a rope, so that its mouth met its heels. When it struck a strange squawk came out of it.

Joe tossed the beast out into darkness and went inside and sat at the table to eat his bowl of bread and milk. Under the rage in his face there was now something like shame. Prudence was silent. A little later Vridar slipped outside to see if the cat was dead. On hands and knees he moved around until his hands found the soft fur. The body was warm but there seemed to be no life. It seemed to be a mass of broken flesh and bone; there was thick blood on the nose and mouth. He crawled into bed, feeling sick and lonely and terrified. Between his parents in the next room no word was spoken. Silently they came to bed and nothing was left but the crushed thing outside and the quiet and the night.

He was amazed the next morning when he entered the kitchen. There was the cat, looking very chastened and sad, licking milk from a saucer. She still had blood on her nose. Thereafter she moved slowly, as if overtaken by old age; she slept and purred and snored; but she became a strange creature that fell into sudden hissing fits. She would rush round and round snarling and spitting and striking at nothing with spiked paws; and then she would crawl away and sleep. She was never caught snooping again.

The next experience revealed another side of his father. Vridar now had a saddle-nag, a swaybacked wornout hack with a huge bony melancholy head, eyes vacant with idiocy and an ulcer in the top of her neck. One hip was lower than the other and most of her teeth were gone. Joe spoke of her as the plug with the hip knocked down. But for Vridar she was quite a steed. She was the only thing he owned in the world, and he loved the sleepy old grotesque, and he called her Alice.

There was a fence between the corrals and the house, and in it was what in this part of the world was called a Mormon gate. It was made of three or four barbed wires, fastened to two or three stays, and tied at one end to a post and at the other to a pole. When the gate was closed this pole stood in a loop of wire and had another loop over its top. The top end of this gate pole had been cut from dry aspen and was as sharp as a spike.

Towser one afternoon, restless and with nothing to do, trotted out to the barn and found the horses free. He nipped experimentally at their heels and liked his work. Then he singled Alice out and devoted himself to her. He turned his jaws sidewise, bit her ancient heels and with superb agility dodged her blows. He ran to her face, affronted her with insolent barks, snapped at her nose and seized it when her angry head came down. Little by little he worked her into a torment and himself into a fine frenzy of joy; then he chased her round and round. Conquered at last, she went off in a lumbering trot, with Towser dipping into her bleeding heels at every step. No human being was in sight. After a half hour of such frolic he had her haggard with despair. She plunged into the stable but he routed her. She came at him head down and nostrils blowing but he dodged nimbly and seized her graying tail. She trotted again, gathering momentum as she went, and careened into a terrified lope.

At this moment Joe and his family came on the scene. Joe shouted at the dog, but Towser, with the tail in his mouth and his blood fired by triumph, was being jerked frantically after flying heels. He threw his head from side to side, as if trying to jerk the tail out, and from his mouthful of hair came muffled victorious growls. In this way they went across the stubble and headed for the gate. When she reached the gate the old nag was sprinting with all her might, and, unable to stop or to turn, she tried to leap. She sprang into the air and came down violently on the sharp pole. There was a ripping of wire and an anxious yelp from the dog and then all was still. The beast remained there, impaled.

Joe raced forward in the stiff-legged way he had and Vridar ran after him. When he drew near, the boy saw blood running down the smooth unbarked pole and the wild terror in the old creature's eyes. Joe grasped the pole at its bottom and dragged it from the loop of wire to let the mare down. Then he drew the pole from her belly. It came out, almost two feet of it, bloody and dripping; and in the nag's side Vridar saw a ragged gaping wound. Suddenly without warning the beast gave a hoarse choked scream and began to run. She went back over the stubble field, striking the earth with great blows; and behind her, falling out of her like heavy gray rope, were her guts.

Vridar was forever to see this picture, graven deep in memory: a beast going at full speed with her guts spilling out, with her guts yanked behind her, thirty or forty feet of them, like gray clothrope: jerked in loops over the stubble and over bunches of grass and across piles of manure and into the corral; and his father running desperately after her, yet with his mind cool and thinking.

"Get a tub!" he shouted, even while he ran. "Warm water! Needle and thread!"

Calling Vridar to stay with his brother and sister, Prudence ran to the house, seized a galvanized tub, dumped into it the kettle's boiling contents and water from the reservoir, added cool water from pails, ran for a sack-needle and a ball of thread, and with more than a woman's strength half-carried and half-dragged the tub to the corral. Single-handed, Joe had thrown the beast down and was sitting on her neck. Her guts were all over the yard. Her big eyes were dumb with fright and pain and her mouth was rimmed with foam.

"Set here!" cried Joe, and Vridar leapt to obey.

He and his mother sat on the beast's neck. Joe fetched a heavy log and laid it across her neck and gave another command. He told Vridar to grasp her tail and hold it as much on the ground as he could. He went to the stable and came running with a rope: this he looped in a firm hitch over both hind legs and the other end he made secure to a corral post. He was moving swiftly, without fumble or lost power, and his son stared at him with wondering eyes. This was not the man who crushed the cat.

Joe now rolled his sleeves up and quickly washed his hands and arms, and then gathered the long gray rope into the tub. The tub was full of it. It looked like a horrible dead snake, coiled there but its two ends went into the beast's side. It was covered with dust and dry manure, weed seeds and twigs and old straw. Inch by inch Joe washed and examined it; tore off Prudence's apron to wipe it and shoved it back into the bleeding hole. He said he guessed it wasn't torn at all. He said her old guts were tough. Vridar turned away, sickened by the warm smell: blood-smell and the odor of the open belly. He puked a little and choked the sickness down; he watched again, fascinated by the loops and coils and by his father's deft hands. The beast did not wince. Her ribbed side moved up and down. Her legs looked stiff and dead. Inch by inch, yard by yard, the piled mass was inspected, rinsed like clothes, wiped until it shone like the gray back of a fish. With his wet bloody fist Joe poked it into the hole, thrusting it in until his arm disappeared to his elbow; drew his arm out, gathered a new handful, and pushed it in and out of sight. When the work was only half done the mass inside burst out, filling the hole with puffed tubes.

"Help me," he said to Prudence.

She moved over and strove to keep the guts inside, covering the wound with her two hands, holding in place what had been washed and cleaned. Joe stuffed more into the hole, and Prudence tried to keep it from bursting out. She said she couldn't hold it all, and Joe looked at the tub and considered. A fourth of the guts were still there. He got a pole four feet long and lifting the top hind leg he set the pole under it, so that the two legs were spread far apart. Vridar knew that he was trying to make more room in the beast.

After what seemed hours of patient toil the four busy hands shoved the remainder into the belly, and Prudence kept it from boiling out. Joe doubled and redoubled the black thread until he had about twenty strands, each a yard long.

He put these through the needle's eye, tied the strands into a knot and knelt to sew the wound. He pushed the big needle through the ragged hide and tied the thread and sewed the hole up. Prudence meanwhile seized hair on either side of the wound and drew the torn edges together; and Joe's big hands worked back and forth, pushing the needle in and out. He shook blood from his fingers as he worked. When the task was done and there was nothing to see but the irregular seam in the belly, Joe took the pole away and lowered the leg slowly, watching the seam as he did so to see if pressure would burst the thread. He let the leg down until it rested on the other leg and he knelt to look at the seam. He said he guessed it was all right. Then they waited while he went to the house for carbolic acid. Gathering some of the dirty water into a palm, he poured acid into it and bathed the wound. Vridar saw that his mother was trembling and white. He looked at his calm father and sensed what in a later time he was to understand fully, that the man should have been a surgeon.

They all went around and looked at the beast's eyes. They were big stupid eyes, stricken with pain and fear. When they went away the mare raised her head a little and looked after them.

For three days and nights she lay there in the corral. Joe carried water and poured it down her throat. He poured milk down her, too, and tried to make her eat tender grass and bran mash. But she would not eat. She would raise her head, hour after hour, and look back at her side. She would hold the gaze several moments, her eyes glazed with agony; then she would let her head fall. It would fall with a thud, as if her neck had suddenly been broken. She would lie for a little while and lift her head again to stare at the center of her pain, and again drop her skull like a dead thing. Before dark each night Vridar would go out to look at her. He would stand a little way off, his eyes wet, his whole body shaken by that one mute and repeated gesture. He asked God to save her life but he knew she was dying, little by little, through the long night. He would go out in the morning to look at her and he would try to understand. All night, he would think, she lay there; she lifted her head and looked at herself and let her head fall. All night, all night . . . . .

The fourth day he found her dead. Her tongue hung out. Her eyes were open and glassy and fixed. He went up to her and touched her with gentle compassion. And then he went away to hide his grief.

His next memorable experience was even more horrible than that of the cat or the mare. It happened in the corral where Alice died and in a black starless night. Close by the corral was his mother's hencoop, a dugout in the earth roofed with poles and dirt. Thieves had entered it. They had left hens spread out in feathered death, half-grown chicks sucked of their blood. These thieves were weasels and skunks.

"We must do something!" she cried, enraged by her loss. Joe thought of the matter and said they would sleep in the corral. And so they carried bedding out and made two beds on rye hay. Vridar was afraid out here, afraid of the night, and haunted by memory of the mare who had died only a little way from his bed. But he made no complaint, though every strange sound sent a wild searching up his spine and made his scalp burn.

One night he was awakened by the cackling of hens. "Mother!" he cried. "Mother!"

"What is it?" she asked, sitting up darkly in the night.

Joe leapt out of bed in his heavy underwear and grasped a shotgun. Prudence arose too, wearing a long white gown and looking like a ghost. Vridar pulled on his trousers and slunk after them. At the coop door Joe peered in and said, "I'n smell him. Wife, light a match."

He lifted the gun and Prudence struck a match. Vridar, staring, saw in the sudden pale interior two black eyes and a white ghostliness in an arched back. There was a thundering roar and then darkness.

"Another match," said Joe, and cocked the other barrel.

An awful stench swept out of the coop and stung their eyes. Another match flared. The skunk was dead, Joe said, and turned away.

"Well, don't rush off! There might be more."

"Good God, wife, you want a-stay in this stink?"

"Oh, I guess a little stink won't hurt you. I'll strike a match and you look."

Joe peered in and said the work was done. The beast lay there, as dead as a doorknob, as dead as nails. They returned to bed, taking the foul stench with them. It followed Vridar into the quilts; it filled his breath all night and stung his eyes. It went with him the next morning to the house and for days it was rank and pungent in the corral.

The next night Joe shot four skunks, blowing their guts all over the hencoop; and the next morning he cornered a litter of weasels and beat them into pulp. The next night a terrible thing came out of darkness, the mountains ringing with its cry. Vridar was awakened and came bolt upright, as if lifted by his hair. He had heard an awful wild screaming sound and he could still hear it in memory. His mother was also sitting up.

"Son, did you hear that sound?"

"Yes," he said, trembling.

They both listened but could hear only the roar of the river. Prudence lay back down but Vridar sat, shivering, straining his ears and eyes; and after a few minutes the sound fell again, a screaming sound so wild and horrible and full of pain that Vridar was paralyzed. Out in the night, piled in blackness to the stars, was a monster with a human cry. He saw his mother sit up and he heard her talking to his father and he heard Joe's protests and growls. Then the sound fell again. It was an unearthly pouring of pain and torture from some creature's throat. Joe now sat up, poking at his eyes and rumbling with distress and broken sleep. Vridar wanted to move over to the bed of his parents but he was rigid. He now heard something in the far night, like a sound of great blindness beating the earth. And then the scream came again—and again.

"What is it?" cried Prudence and she sounded hysterical.

"Be still," said Joe.

He got to his feet and walked away into the darkness. Vridar saw him there, spectral and tense; and again he heard the beating of earth, a weird frenzied

58

galloping, and the scream again. Prudence arose and asked Joe what it was, and he said, "Shut up! How you expect a man to hear anything?"

He was standing there, listening, when out of the night the thing bore down upon them, sudden and swift and wild; a light came, a huge white beast with eyes like fire, with mane beating like sheets in the wind. In a blur of terror Vridar was aware of great sounds, of another long maddened scream, hoarse and ringing, and of his father, waving spectral arms and shouting, "Hey-there! Hey-there!" Dawn was coming. Things were emerging from the murk. Joe seemed to be fighting, to be struggling desperately and madly with a beast; but Vidar was told afterward that this was not so. He saw the beast rise, white and river-drenched; saw it sit on its rump, mowing the air with its forelegs; saw the rolling gleam of its crazed eyes and the snorts of foam from its throat. He saw it turn round and round while sitting, its legs beating at the gloom; and he heard its hoarse scream again—and again. It seemed that his father smote the creature; it seemed that the monster fell and writhed and then shot upward, vast and ghostlike. He saw it whirl, as though reeling from a blow, and go crashing over the corral fence and vanish like a white streak. The sound of its galloping hooves rose and fell, smiting the earth. Its scream came again but was now far down in the meadow. Then there was silence as deep as night.

Prudence came over to her sons, both of whom were rigid. She held a club. Vridar tried to speak but his tongue was riven to his mouth. He tried to move but could not. The thing was gone now, Prudence said. Vridar made a choking sound. Prudence went over and sat by Joe and they both stared down toward the meadow. Again and again Vridar thought he could hear the awful cry and the whole earth moaning with pain. He watched daylight fill the world. Black immensities stood in the east, paling little by little, becoming the gloom of mountain peaks and islands of fog. The stable and hencoop were now distinct. Over in the house the south window was a strange dimness and then a rimmed glow and at last a gray light. Fogs rose from the meadow and filled the sky with their waste. Roosters began to crow.

Days passed before Vridar dared to whisper of this awful experience. The monster of the night, his mother said, was a turpentined horse. It had beaten its brains out in the meadowland and was now a rotting corpse down there in the jungle. What, he wanted to know, was a turpentined horse? She would not tell him, for the way of it, she said, had been brutal and vile. The horse was a stray perhaps that had been thieving in some haystack or wheatfield. His father said that the Bridwell boys had done it.

Vridar thought often of the night's experience but its meaning was dark, dark. He was haunted for weeks by that awful vision of agony and dying. Years later he learned that the beast had had a quart of turpentine poured through its anus and into its guts; but now he knew only that the deed had been malicious and cruel. He thought endlessly about the Bridwell boys, wondering what they were like; and one day he heard that his family was going to boat across the river to visit their neighbor. Little he dreamed that he was to meet the strangest boy he was ever to know.

59

VIII

They left the boat, plowed through a tangle of hawbush, and chokecherry and briar and emerged on the Bridwell place. It was a more tameless domain than Hunter bottom, because bears prowled there and wolves came down to bivouac the house and rattlesnakes lay everywhere. Or they did at least before Jed waged war upon them and destroyed their kingdom.

Charley came forth to meet them. "Hello!" he cried, grinning with hearty welcome. "God all-Judas, march right in."

The parents marched in with the father carrying Diana, but Vridar and Marion were ambushed by Jed and Thiel. Vridar stared fascinated at these wild river-lads, thinking of the horse. Thiel had reddish hair, freckles, and a foolish grin. Jed was intent and dark. He had a long deep scar above one eye.

"What's your name?" Jed asked.

"Vridar."

"Vridar! Judas priest, how do you spell it?" Vridar spelled it and Jed asked: "What's his name?"

"Marion."

"That's a girl's name." Jed was staring at Marion. "The holy jumped-up Jesus, what's wrong with his eyes?"

"Never mind. You're not to talk about his eyes."

"He's crosseyed, by God."

"Don't you call him crosseyed!" cried Vridar, beginning to tremble.

"I'n look crosseyed," said Jed. "Watch." The boys watched and he rolled his eyes horribly until they were like clots of blood. In a later time, Vridar heard, Jed rolled his irises out of sight and Charley had to beat him on the head to make his eyes return.

"Can you do it?" asked Jed.

"I don't know."

"Are you afraid to try? Well, you little son of a bitch, come on and I'll show you things." Jed spit with disgust. He scowled at Vridar and thumbed his nose. "You know what that means? It means you're a son of a bitch twice over."

Vridar had begun to shake. He had been taught to defend his brother, his sister, and the virtue of women; to brook no insults to the eyes of the one, or the purity of the others. His mother had been called a bitch. With all the courage he had he advanced on Jed and yelled hoarsely, "You take it back!"

"What?" asked Jed, astonished.

"You—you called my mother a bitch!"

Jed's next words were unprintable. Then: "I said it meant son of a bitch but I never said your old ma is a bitch. And listen," he said, his face turning hard, "don't stick your back up at me or I'll belt your eyes out."

"Well, you can't call my mother bad names."

"I'm sorry," said Jed, frowning thoughtfully at this pale lad. "Your mother's a nice woman. Well, Christ, whata we do now?"

60

Down by the stable an hour later Jed gravely explained the secrets of procreation and birth. He said Joe Hunter stuck his thing into Vridar's ma and that was the way Vridar was made. Vridar thought it another outrageous insult and he was troubled by words Jed used that he had never heard. "That's how," Jed told him. "When you're all tucked in like a baby that's what your old man does. You was carried around inside your ma for months. Do you believe it?"

"No," Vridar said. He thought the story was incredibly silly.

"Your old man will do it again," said Jed. "Watch your ma and see if she swells up."

Vridar stared at Jed, unable to take his gaze off him. Except his brother and uncle Mike, these were the only small children he had ever talked with. He distrusted them and was afraid of them. Thiel's face during the telling had been a yellow freckled grin, a loose and insolent leer; but Jed's face was a proud and scowling darkness. The one looked at Vridar with contempt for his ignorance, the other with grave pity.

"By God," said Jed, "you're the ignorantest person I ever saw."

After Vridar had been boated home, riding fearfully over the hills and valleys of the river, he drew his mother aside and told her what Jed had told him, using Jed's own words. He saw the color flow like red shadow up her throat and over her face and saw something strange and hard in her blue eyes. He wondered why she looked so shamed and crimson. She said the Bridwell lads were nasty little beasts. She would tell their father about this. And all the while Vridar waited for denial. He wanted her to say that his father did not— did not—but no, she was as rigid as stone. He became afraid of her.

"It ain't true, is it?" Vridar whispered.

She looked at him with strange bright eyes and there was something in her eyes that he did not like. It filled him with dismay and anger. No, she said, it was not true; hadn't she told him not to listen to nasty little boys?

"Yes maam," he said.

"Next time you meet such boys just run away from them, for they are wicked and sinful."

Convinced now that Jed had lied, he felt enormous relief. He was able again to respect his father. "I'm glad it ain't true," he said. Nevertheless he watched his mother as the weeks passed, to see if she was swelling up, as Jed had said she would; and he spied guiltily on his sister, hoping to discover what a girl was like. But his mother seemed to grow more lean under her hours of toil, and Vridar almost forgot the matter until the following year. But he was not to be left in peace. Other experiences razed his soul.

It was now his task to bring the cows home. During the spring months they pastured in the meadowland, emerging from the jungle at twilight and bawling for their calves. Then they would come in single file up the creek and past the house. But in June they were turned upon the hills. From the corral a gray sagebrush lane a half-mile in length followed the river-bank to the farm's eastern end. After the morning milking was done, the boy drove the beasts up this lane, let them through the gate, and closed the gate behind them. Sometimes a cow would rise on her hind legs and half-ride another cow; or steers that had wandered in from the hills would do so. Vridar wondered what such riding meant. Were the beasts too lazy to walk?

Driving them to the gate and walking the half-mile back did not frighten him much, though often he saw badgers or coyotes. Towser went with him and the dog was alert and tireless in pursuit of wild things. He disemboweled porcupines, never getting a quill in his mouth; chased badgers into holes and yelped and dug in an effort to follow; and when he leapt to the race coyotes melted in the distance. But going after the cows was another matter. Every day was a time of dread, an anxious watching of clock and sun. Two of the cows wore bells and during the afternoon he would listen, praying to hear the friendly sound. He would stare up at the mountainside, hoping to see a moving form there; but it was green jungle-growth, thick and dark. When the sun was only an hour high he would begin to quake, and by talking to himself he would try to arouse courage and quiet his heart. But his heart would beat in his ears and loneliness and fear would choke him.

"Son," his mother would say, "ain't it about time you run along? I haven't heard the bell today. Mebbe they're clear out on top."

Clear out on top! This would mean that he would have to climb more than half a mile up the steep mountain, through forests of aspen and fir; that he would then have to go over the densely wooded hills, searching from hill to hill, sometimes mile after mile, knowing that wild beasts were everywhere around him, including the wolf and the lion. But his mother never knew his heartbreak. With all his strength and pride he kept up the ghastly pretense of being her brave little man. She never guessed with what foreboding he turned away, calling the dog to him, to climb the steep sunless trail to the ledge-top; how he kept a clutch on the dog's neck, fearing to let it out of sight; how he would tremble when the house was far and lost, and over him and all around him were silence and forest and sky and the smells of wild things.

On the first benchland, halfway up the mountain, the hills rolled away east and west. Hundreds of feet above it were the plateaus of Antelope, vast in their reach and loneliness and friendless in their mood. From the rim he could look down to the river and to the Bridwell home beyond but he could not see his own house: only the cottonwood islands and a part of the meadowed wilderness. North and east were great peaks and canyons deep and black and clouds sunk in fogbanks. On naked feet, with one hand grasping the dog's leash, he would run from hill to vale through the whispering acres of bush and tree. He would stop to listen, his heart drumming and his lungs burned raw; and again he would run. Listening again with his whole quivering body, he would imagine the sound of a cowbell; and weeping with joy and relief he would race toward it, only to find there nothing at all. It seemed to him sometimes that he heard bells on all sides: the loneliness would become a nightmare of bells, insistent and vivid or far away and soft, luring him on and on. He would watch the sun, dreading its swift descent; he would look at the dog, eager to see if ears lifted; and now and then he would kneel and hug the creature, trying to draw into his shaking soul a part of the beast's fearlessness. He would talk to the dog, and this habit of talking to animals or to himself in an effort to shatter the dark weight of silence became fixed in his early years. He would try to talk quietly but his words would falter and moan and sob. "Towser—don't—you hear—no bell! . . . Towser—listen! . . . O Towser! . . ." And Towser would pant with tongue hanging out, or try to leap after a chipmunk that challenged from bush to tree.

One evening he set out late and in panic. He had been kept at the grindstone, helping his father sharpen a sickle. He watched the sun, sinking into its basin of night; looked at his father's face so wholly unaware of his child's problem; at the forested mountain to see if any cows were moving there. He wanted to say, "Father, I should go now," but he did not dare. He wanted to say, "The sun's almost down! I must go!" But he shrank from thought of the grunt and the contemptuous glance that would dismiss his anxiety. And so he cranked the stone and watched the sun and counted the knives that remained, and became steadily more frightened and apprehensive. Knife after knife, turn after turn, and still no end in sight! Joe always took his time. He would rise from the seat, spit a stream of tobacco juice, shake himself to get the pain out of his back, and with maddening slowness test the knife on his thumb. He would frown if he found it dull and very slowly apply it again to the stone. And the boy hated him.

When at last the task was done, Vridar dashed to the house and called the dog but no dog came. His mother was nowhere in sight. The cows had to be found. "Towser!" he called, his voice desperate. "Here Towser!"

Joe came up and looked at the sun. "You'd better get a move on," he said.

With his emotions darkening, Vridar ran south and took the trail. Trembling and panting he climbed with frenzied strength, never once pausing to look back. When through a clearing he could see out on his right he looked at the sun, now ominously low, and redoubled his speed. He ran across the hills; stopped, shaking, to listen, and heard only his furious heart. He began to shout, hoping to scare all enemies away and to break the awful silence. From hill to hill, trail to trail, he ran, shouting with all his might. To the topmost brink, along the fearful road, where his staring eyes saw fresh tracks; and to another hill; a quivering moment of listening and the vivid sound of a bell, far away, and again his naked feet running; another hill and another, now gray with twilight; another listening, and the bell again that was no bell at all. A bowl of red sunlight, a burning disc, and then only the vanishing glow; a golden veil spreading to the tall peaks and golden pools at the very top; slowly closing like shutters and then only the twilight gray. Running back up the road, another listening full of terrified heart; a pattering of bare feet through sagebrush depth and swift going to the far eastern brink. A looking down across a night-dark flank to the river, to the acres of cottonwood, to the sheer black precipice on the south—and again the sound of a bell. A going down over lava rock path, leaping from stone to stone; down through the night-acres of wilderness, through the silence with the river-sound pouring through it; down over earth cloudy with dusk and full of under-breath leaf-whispers and the scurrying of small things. Down to the first brink and a breathless searching through the gloom and the horrifying thought of climbing back, back into the dark and up to the hills and the road. And then the bell again, as vivid as a snapped twig.

He knew he had heard it and now the anxieties burst from him, pouring out in

63

relief and prayer; and he leapt down the mountain, vaulting over sage and bush, almost losing control and pitching headlong—down and down. Limbs ripped his clothes, roots and stones gouged his feet but he did not care. He wanted only to see the big friendly bodies of the cows and their quiet eyes. But near the mountain's bottom he leapt over a darkness of buckbrush and landed on the thick scattered glass of a broken bottle. He did not know at once that he had been hurt. When he struck the glass he felt a dull rending of one foot but he thought he had struck a chunk of wood. He reached down to the pain and felt a wet warmth and then saw that his hand was red. Dropping to earth he pulled his foot up to look at it; the bottom had been cut across, laid wide open, and blood was pumping out of it.

Night had come and he was a mile from home. He went blind with fright and began to babble but all the time he realized where he was, alone, and that he would have to aid himself. Sobbing with fear he dragged forth a big unclean rag that he used as a handkerchief and bound it on his foot, and saw the blood soak through and run. He tore his shirt off and made a bandage of it, using the sleeves as strings. Then, on hands and knees, and babbling like a creature with all reason gone, he started the journey home, dragging the bleeding foot after him. Night had come, a deep night without stars.

Finding a trail, he would rise to his good foot and waver a moment and then try to hop on it. But this way of going he soon learned made the blood spurt afresh; and again he would crawl, moving frantically through the darkness. Now and then he would stop and draw his foot to his lap and try to examine it; but he could tell only that the shirt was soaked with blood. Rod by rod he crept homeward, now pausing to hug his foot up, now yelping with renewed terror; but when at last he saw the corral before him, empty of cows, his fright yielded to shame. He hid under a bush and drew the hurt foot to him. The bandages were stickily sopped and the red colored his trousers and his hands. He crawled again but he now made no sound. He went down the hill and into the lamplight of the dooryard, and there he wiped his tears away before creeping into the house.

His father said, "Where in hell's the cows?"

"I—I don't know!" Vridar gasped. He held the foot on his lap, hoping that the wound would be terrible enough to excite forgiveness and compassion.

"What's the trouble?" asked Joe. "You hurt yourself?"

"Uh-uh-yes! A little!" Joe knelt and began to take the bandage off. "Don't!" Vridar cried. "It's stuck!"

"Don't be such a damn baby. Let me see."

Vridar began to gurgle. When Joe saw that the handkerchief and shirt were drenched he stood up and called his wife. This suggested to Vridar that the wound was worse than he had supposed and he began to sob.

"Stop your bawling," said Joe. "You think that'll help it?"

"No sir."

Prudence had come running. Seeing the bloody rags, she knelt by her son and asked how he had hurt himself. He said he did not know; the mountain was dark and he could not see. With warm water and gentle hands she removed the rags. When Vridar saw the ugly ragged wound he began to sob again. Joe meanwhile was

64

chewing a great quid, because tobacco was his cure-all. He drew it from his mouth, mushy with juice, and laid it on the wound and pushed it in; and Prudence brought a white clean cloth to bind the foot. A little later the parents went to bring the cows in and to milk, and Vridar was left sitting on a chair, with a deep pulsing throb shooting through him.

Two hours later he was in bed. Prudence kissed his forehead and asked if he felt pain. He said no. He lied. He lied because his parents made such a small matter of these things. He had seen his mother split her finger open with a sharp knife, almost the full length of it, soak it in cold water, fill it with iodine, bind it in a corset of cloth, and return to her work. A year ago his father, while cleaning a shotgun, had blown nearly all the flesh off one palm and almost shot his wife; and Vridar had seen him calmly fill the wound with tobacco and draw a dirty glove on his hand and go to the chores. No: blood and pain mattered little to them. He felt very unworthy and small and mean. In this life there was no place for him. But here he was, this wild frontier outpost was his home and he would have to be as brave as he could be. When terrors fell upon him he would have to choke them down and hide them from sight.

IX

Long years later, when looking back, Vridar would ask himself, Was there nothing but terror? Was it all nightmare? He would try to recall moments of tenderness, hours when his soul was not lacerated and nights when he was not choked with dread. But there was little to remember that was pleasant, little but the coming of spring, his rich dreaming among ancient legends and the holiness of one Christmas night; these and his listening to novels of passion and hope, his intense love of wild flowers and trees, and his unutterable joy when his mother came home after peddling cheese. All else was desolate and dark. These were the years that made him the man he was to be. These were the years that he hated, that he was always to hate, and look back upon with shame. To understand the man that he came to be it is necessary to go farther with him into terror and loneliness . . . .

The winters he remembered as warm shelter under bleak sky and storm. He read the Bible again, storing his mind with its wealth of symbols; he studied at his mother's knee. Wrapped now and then in his father's old rags and shoes, he would go outside in falling snow, and he learned to love its soft beauty and quiet. Sometimes his father crossed the river to kill deer and elk and carry the red flesh home. The big slabs of it hung in the smokehouse twenty yards from the front door. Joe would tell of his adventures but in a few words only; and though Prudence would question for an hour, she could never draw the whole story out of him.

"Wife, I told you. I told you all there is."

"But you say this strange animal tossed you as high as pine trees. What was it?"

"Wife, if I knowed I'd tell you. It might a-been a moose but it was biggern a moose."

"And you just grabbed its horns and it tossed you so high you could see over tall tree tops. That don't sound reasonable to me."

"I don't care how it sounds to you. That's how it was."

"And it had two legs shot off?"

"You heard me say both its hind legs was plumb shot off."

Joe said he had thought the creature helpless. Setting his rifle by a tree, he had advanced, intending to seize the horns and throw the beast down. He did grasp the horns. He knew nothing more until he was a hundred feet in the air, looking over the tallest trees. That was how it happened; there was nothing more to be said.

Vridar was to learn in a later time that Joe stubbornly exaggerated and embellished his tales, if they fell on skeptical ears, until they were wholly incredible. Of this incident with the beast he was never able to learn the truth. Nor of another which happened in the same winter: Joe staggered to the house one evening, frozen in an armor of ice; and sheathed with ice also were his rifle and two wild chickens. He had a fantastic fresco of ice in his beard and hair. But for many days he would not tell out of what danger he had emerged. If Prudence asked what had happened, he would say, "Wife, never mind," and he would read the Bible. He liked to be begged, entreated.

One evening he told. He evinced at least a willingness to tell, but his wife's eagerness made him withdraw into an hour of silence. What happened? she asked, staring at this strange person whom she was never to understand. Joe pretended not to hear, and he read meanwhile in a low mumbling voice: "And the king loved Esther above all the womern, and she ob—ob—tained grace . . . ." When he came to a word that baffled him, he would scowl at it and sink into silence, as though it had offended him. Under his breath he would experiment with the word, rolling it over and trying to pronounce it; and he would read again in a sulking monotone.

"Why don't you read so we'll all hear?"

Such a challenge would send him again into silence. His lips would move over the words; but later, if he thought no one was listening, he would begin to mumble aloud, only to retreat into hush if spoken to.

"What happened? Why don't you tell us?"

That was the question he had been waiting for. But he gave no heed. If Prudence persisted until he could no longer ignore her, he would pretend to be enraged.

"Wife, can't you let a man read his Bible?"

She would turn on him, scornful, baffled. "Oh, read! I don't think you want to. You just want to be stubborn."

That was the kind of tactless retort that whetted the perverse side of him. He would withdraw into underbreath perusal. He would emerge again into sound and mumble as before.

"Well, keep it to yourself. It don't matter to me if you never tell."

That was better. It was a clear sign of her defeat. Joe laid the Bible down and looked at her. "Wife, what is it you want me to tell?"

"Nothun. Just keep it locked up in your stubborn mind."

"Me stubborn, wife? Just say what you want to hear."

"Keep it. You're the stubbornest man ever drew the breath of life."

"There ain't a stubborn bone in my body. I'd tell if I knowed what you want to hear."

The children sat up, alert, for they knew the tale was coming. Their father always had to have a prelude of bickering and taunts.

"I was crossun the river, if that's what you mean. Mush ice tipped the boat over. I guess I swum out or I wouldn't be here, would I?"

Prudence gave him a long angry stare. "Ice tipped the boat over! Well, what was you fussun about to let it be tipped over?"

"Fussun, hell! Ain't you never heared tell a boat tippun over?"

"And then you swum out. You said you didn't know a thing till you come to on the bank."

"I don't recollect tellun you that. But it's the truth."

"Well, good Lord! Why don't you tell the whole story like it should be told?"

"God a-mighty, wife, I did. The boat tipped over and I swum out. I never knowed a thing till I found myself sittun on the bank."

"Why didn't you know anything? Did the boat hit you on the head?"

"No," he growled, "the boat never hit me on the head."

"Then what happened to you?"

"If I had knowed that I would a-told you, wouldn't I?"

"No. You'd just be as stubborn as you can." She was looking at him. "And you swum out with the rifle and chickens in your hand. All the time you didn't know anything. Is that it?"

Joe looked at her as if she were too childish for words. "How'd you think, wife, the gun and chickens would a-got here if I didn't?"

One Christmas eve the children hung their stockings and Vridar never forgot the miracle. He rose early the next morning and slipped quietly into the kitchen, and there beheld his stocking—his mother's really, for he had none of his own—bulging with the charity of Santa Claus. He crept back to bed and told Marion of the incredible wonder. Later they sat on the floor and reached deep into the store-smells. Vridar drew forth a big red apple, a handful of peanuts, a handful of candy, two sticks of licorice, a cap, and a small mouth organ. In all his life he had never seen such treasure as this.

He allotted to himself each day a half-piece of candy and three peanuts. He blew at the mouth organ until he learned to play, off key, two or three of the simple melodies he had heard his mother humming. Now and then he would let Marion blow the instrument, watching him with an attentive scowl. "Don't blow so hard!" he would cry, distracted. "Look, you get it full of spit!" And Marion, abashed, would hand the thing to his brother and Vridar would hide it away.

But the Christmas of the winter when Joe fell out of the boat Prudence told her children that Santa Claus was very poor. Matters had not gone well with him the past year. Vridar had written a letter to him, asking for a sled or air-gun, a pair of shoes, a few books, and a harmonica for his brother. None of these came. Indeed, this Christmas was one of the darkest and clumsiest disillusionments of his life. He drew forth from the stocking a handful of peanuts, and the cap and harmonica of the year before. It was the same old cap, dirty and almost wornout, and the same old mouth organ, now squeaking in most of its keys and dead in four. He looked at these things, wondering if a trick had been played.

67

Watching him, his mother said, "What did be bring?" He was staring with dismay at the old harmonica and cap, or up at her with interrogating eyes. "Well!" she said. "Did he put the old things back in your stocking!" He was still looking at her. He saw her stare waver and break and saw something in her eyes that was like guilt. "I told you he was poor this year," she said. "There's hard times all over, I guess." She said maybe Santa Claus would do better next time. She did not meet his eyes again. He kept watching her but she did not meet his eyes.

Then he rose, overwhelmed by humiliation and doubt, and went into the other room. He stood by the window and looked out at the white world. He knew somehow that the whole experience had been mean and false. He would rather have had only the peanuts or nothing at all than to have suffered the shame of tiptoeing to the stocking only to find there the familiar and old. He knew that there had been a lie in his mother's eyes and voice, but he was not ready to admit it; he hoped that it would turn out to have been a mistake. Perhaps this was not Christmas day. But he knew it was Christmas day. Perhaps he had not emptied the stocking of all its treasure. But he had, he had. He had turned it inside out, outside in.

There had been no white birds, there had been no Santa Claus: this was what his mother's voice and eyes had meant. There was no use trying to fool himself now. There was no long-bearded man who went with reindeers and whose mission was of charity and good will. The man was a myth, a parable, a lie. For days thereafter he refused to meet his mother's gaze for he knew that she had tricked him. She would try to draw him to her and ask what troubled him but he would break away. He was like the Brantons, she said, proud and highstrung, a child who was all sweet idealism and humble faith. The words enraged him but he did not let her know. He slunk away, howling inwardly that he was not humble faith and that she had not deceived him at all. He had never believed in white birds or Santa Claus or Jesus or George Washington on the Delaware! These tales were the spinning of human spiderlips for simple folk. And the Bible, what was it but a stupendous saga of nonsense!

Still, such doubts desolated him and left him blowing tears from his nose. He wanted to be assured beyond the reach of taunt and meanness that life was beautiful and good, that all human motive and purpose was clean, that the dark and the dross were only the brief ills of folly and pride. And under his disillusionment he did believe these things. The thunders of incredulity would shake his world but he was a stubborn or a tenacious crusader, and he clung to the flesh of every belief, every simple childhood teaching, until life stripped it to the hard and unpitying bone.

Six weeks after the Christmas episode another nebulous legend had its hide peeled off and he saw the raw truth. It was one of the most horrible disillusionments of his life. One of his chores was to carry water to the chickens. He hated the smell of hens and their dung and their coops, and in later years he was seldom to eat their flesh without remembering it; but he loved the smell of stabled beasts and their wintry breath and the sound of their strong teeth on oats and hay. He loved the smell of cold air and naked trees and clean straw and woodpile.

He went to the coops, carrying a steaming pail. He poured water into the pans and looked for a moment at the frozen chickens, each a feathered grotesque standing on frost-bitten feet. On his return he went by the corral because he liked to look at the cows. The larger one, named Bess, was huge and red and placid, with a perfect white star in her forehead. The other they called Pyde: she was small and energetic and lean. He saw Pyde first, lying in snow and manure chewing her cud. Then he looked at Bess and stood transfixed.

For perhaps ten minutes he stared without movement or sound and almost without breathing. It was an incredible thing that he saw—life emerging into life, form impaled upon form, wonder pulsing into birth. With all his might he looked and rubbed at his eyes trying to erase the picture; but the picture rose to four shaking legs and tottered and blinked and made a sound. With this new truth in his brain and heart, Vridar turned and ran. He fell from the path and plowed toward the house in snow waist-deep. At the woodpile he stopped, hardly conscious of what he had done, of what he had seen, and trying to believe that he had seen nothing at all. He stared back at the corral. His thoughts reeled and churned and his blood surged, thick with shame, his eyes still seeing that picture, that one ghastly and incredible picture of a calf coming out of a cow. He seized an armful of wood and stumbled into the house, and to hide his confusion and amazement he got the Bible and pretended to read. But he could not read. His world had gone mad, with its purpose riddled, its divinity ransacked and debased, its purity peeled away to the rotten core.

An hour later he was still clutching the Bible and turning its pages and striving to understand. What did it mean? he asked, and bewilderment was like the winds around him. He tried to remember the tale as his mother had told it, so many times. Babies were angels with wings and an unborn soul; they lived in an angel-kingdom; a mother prayed to God and a baby was sent down. A doctor took it and laid it in the mother's arms. Yes, that was the story she had told, and that with all his heart he had believed. And calves, they were dug out of earth; they slept in the warm ground and waited until they were smelled and lifted out. But this that he had seen! . . . Babies had wings and they flew round and round the blue heaven, feeding on honey and milk; and the others, they nested in the earth, or like chicks they came from eggs that were laid from the mother's mouth. But this other, this life coming out of life! Ah, good Lord!

Then the line, leaping from memory, burning like a comet through his brain: the one put out his hand; and the midwife took and bound upon his hand a scarlet thread, saying, This came out first. . . He shot the words back and forth among his frenzied thoughts, saw them ringed with flame; felt them ebb and flow like a pulse until all through him their meaning searched like fire . . . . And afterward came out his brother. This was the Bible speaking, and the Bible was the word of God. Out in the corral he had seen the word of God, had seen his astounding way of raising life from dust.

He remembered next the words of Jed Bridwell: of the father and mother and the things they did and how babies came to be. They all agreed. Jed and the Bible and the corral, they all told the same raw and terrible truth. And his mother, she had lied! She had lied about birds, about Santa Claus, about birth! And now he remembered other things: how sometimes at night he heard the bed of his parents squeaking, and, looking over, saw a strange movement up and down under the covers, and heard strange sounds as though of passion or of pain. Yes, great God, and there was still another thing! His mother had so convinced him that all women were pure and holy and that most men were wicked that this boy had not believed up to this age that his mother voided, that she emptied bowels and bladder. But now in a blinding flash of horror he knew that she did! He knew that his whole life had been a lie!

Feeling violently sick he went into the bedroom and lay on the bed and retched. His mother heard him and came and he turned from her and hid his face. He despised her now. His resentment was sullen, murderous; his hatred was deep. All his life she had tricked him. Most bitter of all, he had defended her under the pitiless stare of Jed and the lewd freckled scorn of Thiel. More bitter still, he had come to her, he had told her what the boys had said, in his complete and abysmal ignorance using their very words; and again she told him of angel wings and of calves nesting in the warm earth. Beyond this no humiliation could go. After this he would never trust her again. He would search every intonation and accent, every wavering of eye and guiltiness of voice, for hint of her fabulous lies and her crafty designs. She could go down on her knees and supplicate, she could beseech and weep, but he would never believe her again. Never! And more than this, infinitely more than this, he would never let her know that he did not believe.

X

A crucial period in Vridar's life fell between spring and fall of his tenth year. Twice his spirit was desolated by his father's wrath; twice there was wreaked upon him the vengeance of Jed Bridwell; and once he narrowly escaped death. It was in this summer, too, that he was seized by his first nightmare.

Joe's first rage fell in the month of June and came about this way. When Vridar's nag died, his father bought for him a small scrawny pony, paying for it two dollars and thirty cents. Vridar called the creature Dick. Dick was old, so old that death filled his movements and looked out of his eyes. Like Alice, the slain mare, he could not be flogged into a gallop; like her he was little more than bones, no matter how much he ate. Standing on four legs he was little more than grotesque belly, skinny neck, and graying skull. But he was harnesswise, Joe said, for on top of his neck was a bunch of white hair.

One morning Joe harnessed Dick and hitched him with another horse to the hay wagon. The collar hanging from his neck looked as if he could jump through it; the harness sagged in great loops and the breeching and bellyband almost touched the ground. Vridar was so dismayed that he whispered to his mother, and she asked Joe why he had hooked that poor little thing up. Joe's eyes darkened, as they always did when his wife rebuked him. The three of them climbed to the wagon and Joe gathered the reins and yelled, "Hain't up there!"

"I asked you why you hooked up this scrawny little thing?"

Joe spit juice and growled. "God a-mighty, wife, it won't hurt him nery a bit. What you think I feed the son of a bitch for?"

"But he can't work with a big horse!"

"Wife, don't you think I know my mind? Hain't up there!" he yelled again. The mare moved but Dick did not budge. The mare pulled the wagon against his rump, and Dick rolled his old eyes evilly and sat back on the doubletree. "He's balky," Joe said. "I knowed it."

"Mebe he hasn't been broke," said Prudence.

"God damn it, wife, you talk like I was a plumb greenhorn! He's got white hair on his neck."

"Oh, white hair! A horse has white hair in his forehead because he's been hooked to a wagon, I guess."

"Hain't up!" cried Joe. He seized a pitchfork and jabbed the tines into Dick's stubborn rump. "Hain't along there, you son of a bitch!" Dick reared again, waded into the air with front legs, and plunged forward. Up the field they went, Dick frantic with desperate leaps, the mare trotting serenely. They stopped between piles of hay and Joe sprang down. He pitched the hay up and Vridar tramped it down and Prudence drove to the next piles. Each time Dick was called on to move he looked round him, his eyes yellow and evil, and then leapt like a thing out of his mind. In this way they moved down the field until the wagon was loaded. Dick's consternation had grown as his burden became heavier. Each time before moving, his eyes had looked round him, desperately and wickedly, and his manner had become darker with threat. When Joe climbed up and took the reins, Dick turned as rigid as stone and Joe reached back for the pitchfork.

"Now don't lose your temper!" Prudence cried.

But his temper had been lost. It had gone out of him on one savage oath and off with the winds. He thrust the fork down, gleaming tines first, and thrust the sharp points deep into Dick's ancient hide. The beast winced and snorted and doubled back. Joe now began to roar. He shoved a full inch of tines into Dick's shuddering flesh. Dick came backward as though his hind legs had been snapped off. He sat down. Joe moved to thrust again but his wife seized his arm.

"Stop it!" she cried. "If you want to kill him do it in a decent way!"

Joe turned on her with eyes streaked and wild with fury. "Leave go my arm!"

"No! You can't set there like a fool and jab him to death!"

"I'll cut his God damned balky heart out!" He turned and Vridar saw his face, convulsed, violent, a hideous snarl from hair to chin.

"Get a gun and shoot him if you want to! But I won't let you torture him!"

Joe hurled the fork backward and stood up. He slid off the load and went on devouring strides to the barn, his feet wolfing the earth, his arms swinging with hands knotted.

"What'll he do now?" Vridar whispered.

"God only knows, son. Kill him, I guess."

Vridar saw that her face was white. He looked down at his stubborn and outraged steed and thought, This is the end of him! In a few minutes he would get a bullet between his eyes and he would squeal and sink down and be forever dead. His first pony had been gutted, his second would be shot.

Then he saw that his father wasn't bringing a gun or an axe. He was bringing the other horse, with a singletree and a log chain dragging behind. Joe returned as he had gone, on stiff angry legs, his face as grim as a skull-mouth. He threw the

71

chain around Dick's neck and caught it with the hook. He swung the horse and looked up at his wife. He smote the horse's ribs and the chain tightened; the hook came instantly under Dick's throat, between his lean jawbones, and he was pulled out, with his neck and body almost as taut as the chain, with his cynical eyes almost popping out of his head. In this manner, using Dick as a trace, the load of hay was pulled to the corral. Vridar stared down at the strange sight; it seemed to him that Dick's neck steadily lengthened, that it became twice as long as it had ever been, and that his body lengthened too. His hind legs now found the earth, now lost it; he was almost rolled over in the air, belly up; for the horse pulled the load singly and Dick was the only trace.

When the barn was reached, Joe unhooked the chain. Dick fell to his knees, sucking air into his lungs, for the chain had choked all the breath out of him. Joe gave him a smashing blow in his washboard side and sent him sprawling. Then Dick staggered to his feet, shook his wretched head, and drooped.

Later Vridar went out to look at him. The chain had torn hair and some hide from the pony's neck. But he did not seem to mind. He would chew for a moment, with hay sticking out of his aging mouth; he would fill his pot-belly with a great sigh and eat again. But his eyes were evil: cynical with memories and unfriendly and old. Vridar put a cheek to his hair and patted his razorback and called him gentle names. But the hack only chewed hay in the lifeless and defeated manner that was his: pausing now, as if tired, as if meditating on old follies, and now chewing again.

The next afternoon Vridar had his first nightmare, though many times before he had felt this strange power reaching into him. The day was full of enormous yellow warmth. Feeling ill, the boy lay on a bed, trembling. He could hear only the droning of flies and the sultry clucking of a hen. The droning invaded his mind and hummed over and over in feverish monotonous rhythm. An intolerable sky-weight was pushing down from above and filling his arms. One arm lay on his chest and it became a great puffed nothingness there, pressing out and up until the size of it filled the sky. It was an immense thing, attached and yet cut off, a part of the earth but still his own. He moved it slowly: the sickness and weight remained, though the vastness of it moved, changed and was still changeless. He smote the arm against him and for a moment it was full of the countless needles of a limb asleep—of an arm with the blood half-drained out of it. Its puffed immensity of horror fell away for an instant and he could feel the outline of bone and flesh. Then the strange unreality came back, creeping in and growing, until again its weight and volume lay from end to end of his life. He turned to one side, to the other; he smote himself again and again; but this deep possessing force had the patience of flies. Their droning rose out of it, its language and meaning, until their sound, too, expanded into a vast monotony. He fought against being taken, being stood upon by this monstrous nothingness, being puffed like a bloated sheep, until he was only an enormous and tired and dim consciousness, growing out and up and filling space. But he fought in vain. The power was oppressive and persistent. It engulfed him, drew him within; laid its smothering weight like piled blankets upon his body and mind; crept into his legs and loins; and at last he was rigid and unable to move. He could hear and see, but he could not move his eyes. Mixed in with the droning now were other sounds, murky with their own sultry emptiness and far away. He knew the bed was under him but he could not feel it, and the space below him seemed to be miles deep. He began to pray for one thing, that somebody would speak his name. Only the sound of his name, he seemed to realize, could shatter this enormous stupor, could bring him back into time and space. After fifteen minues or fifteen years of lying prone, with the horrible power entering and possessing him, he could feel no relationship to space or time. He could not think of past or future or of anything but this dread that held him rigid. His own body completely filled the universe. All sounds were within it, somehow in his flesh, like a murmuring of idiocy; the droning was in his bones and the clucking in the great room of his heart. Yet all the while he knew that he lay on a bed and that his mother was somewhere near. He heard her voice. At last he heard her speak to him. She asked if he was asleep, but he was unable to answer or move. He could not move his tongue or turn his head.

The sensation that gripped him became steadily more terrible as if it would burst him apart; as if he would fall, he who was all space and all time; as if he would expand until he was what had been before God made the world: he, the deep and the night, with only darkness upon him . . . .

"Son, are you asleep?"

Her voice was less than a voice now. It was almost nothing at all. And his head was swelling, it was an inconceivable round magnitude; and the weight grew in depth upon depth, in horror upon silence. He was paralyzed and he was wide-eyed with terror.

"Son, why don't you answer me? I can see your eyes open."

Then—yes, his eyes were open: he understood that—then he heard the beating of his heart. It was an awful sound. It was very slow and heavy, each blow like the muffled falling of something very huge. It was the sound of death. He had memory of it as though he had listened to it for ages; as though he had reached through or far under the sound of space, to its deep dark sob and beat. Each blow was a moment, the only moment. On the gigantic expanse of his brow he felt something cool. He tried to move the arm that was crushing his chest, the arm that had grown into him like a log into mud; but he could not move it or feel its limits. And all the while he was enormously alive and conscious. He felt that he would soon be rent apart, split open into the uncreated, upon which there would be only the formless void. With another desperate effort he strove to move, but he could not move, not even his eyelids. Yet he felt that he had heaved mountains, only to have them flow back and over him to suffocate and smother him. The coldness upon him was growing into huge ponds. The noise of his slow breath was spreading into wide foggy thunder . . . .

"Vridar, why don't you answer me?"

In one sharp moment the spell broke. He was lying on the bed, his face and body soaked with sweat, his hands clenched. Seeing his distress, Prudence came over.

"Why, son," she said, looking at the horror in his eyes, "What's the matter?"

"I—I don't know!" he gasped.

Prudence said it was something he had eaten. They would go out where the father was grubbing; and Vridar went with her, shaking, walking close, guiltily touching her dress to be sure that she was real. He glanced up at the desolate yellow sky. He looked at his father, so strong and bold, and he wanted to touch him. Bathed with sweat and still trembling and white, he watched his father labor, and when cow-time came he was too ill and feeble to go. Prudence gave him bitter aloes, Joe's cure for all internal sickness, and sent him to bed. Vridar called to his brother and begged him to come to bed with him, for he was too horribly afraid to be alone.

"If you wake up in the night," Vridar whispered, "say my name. Just speak my name."

"Why?"

"I want you to. Just say my name and touch me. And don't tell anyone I asked you to."

"All right," said Marion.

After a while Vridar said softly, "Marion, you asleep?" There was no reply. He became terrified. "Marion, wake up!"

The brother stirred. "What you want?"

"Don't sleep yet!"

And so they lay awake in silence, the one trying to fall asleep, the other to stay awake.

Long years afterward Vridar tried to discover what had caused these cataleptic trances. He supposed that possibly the reason was a very low blood pressure and metabolism. Or was it? He had suffered convulsions as a babe. He was to suffer nightmares for years, but he never told anyone until after he was grown. When his mother saw him shaken and white and covered with sweat, she would give him a cathartic and send him to bed, convinced that he had eaten the wrong thing. In these years, his mind and soul filled with the Bible, he supposed that God was punishing and testing him, as he had tested Job; and from this thought he drew a little comfort. These experiences deepened his mysticism, his superstitions, his dread. When lying rigid he saw the shadow of God's hand. To rescue himself from the feeling that he was vile and worthless, a craven coward and a contemptible weakling, he dreamed of himself as a new prophet.

One day he crawled under a huge chokecherry bush to meditate on himself and his destiny. His thoughts were of John, crying in the wilderness; of his camel's hair and his girdle, and the locusts and wild honey which he ate. Vridar thought, too, of entering a wilderness but when he peered down at the meadowland with its jungle and fog he realized that his prophethood would have to be nearer home. Just the same, he thought he would be willing to have the daughter of another Herod seek his head, if he, too, like the bearded man of the Jordan, could cry the coming of one who would again teach a gospel of love and peace.

His thoughts turned next to faith. Was his stronger than a grain of mustard seed? If so, he could prepare the way, for his father had said that the world was again bogged in sin and Christ's second coming was at hand. Perhaps when the bitter work was done and his head had been carried off on a charger, he would see the sky open to him and the spirit of God descending like a dove; and hear the great voice saying,

This is Vridar in whom I am well pleased. Ah, great heavens, how deep his need was to feel that he was not worthless!

He went over to the river-bank, wondering if he dared to test his faith. Among the mountains in the north was a round bald one, a thousand feet in height. Dared he try to move it with prayer? Kneeling, and looking at a cloud-scarf high in the east, he began to pray. He admitted first the power and the glory of the Father, and then asked him to test his faith; for, "If it is great enough it can move mountains, like the Bible says. I want to know if it is great enough. . . ." He turned a little to see if the bald peak was wavering. It was not. It looked as eternal and changeless as the sun. Still, he had not asked God to move it, and he clasped his hands and prayed again. Then he waited with held breath, wondering how long the moving would take. He turned again and saw the mountain as before and felt dashed. But possibly it had moved a little: it seemed to be farther west, nearer the river; and beyond he saw a grove of aspen that surely had not been visible before. But no, no, it had not moved at all, and he was a presumptuous simpleton to be kneeling here and asking God to move mountains!

He stretched out on his back and looked at the lazy yellow sun, and in this hour something happened to him. He would never know what it was. He would never know whether he wantonly lied or fell into a trance; but afterward he believed that he had seen a glorious vision. The heavens opened and he looked in; and he saw against a background of red and white clouds a great lamb that stared at him, and the lamb had seven eyes and seven tails. Roundabout the lamb was a mist of white angels, and among these was a throne, and upon the throne sat a white god. He heard, then, a roaring like that of water, and thunder rolled out of the west, and behind it came four horses, one red and one black, one green and one blue. They raced round and round the throne until the stars shook and fell like rain, and the sky was turned back like a scroll, and the sun was as black as ink and the moon was a round thing of blood. The four beasts ran up to the throne, screaming like the horse in agony, and knelt on the cloud-carpet of heaven. Hail began to fall and it was like frozen blood; it dripped upon trees and withered them; and the red streams flowed upon chaos. The beasts sprang up and their heads were then the heads of wolves, thin spires of flame shot from their eyes, and their breath was as black as the sun.

High above he saw a splendor walking, clothed all in white, with a crown of fire and a sword of fire in its hand. It smote with the sword, and plagues fell, pestilence avalanched downward in clouds of sickness, and devils ran frantic through fogland. He heard the voice of seven thunders, like the river's roar. He heard the white splendor speak, and the stars fell like autumn leaves and the imps pitched headlong into open burning graves. Upon the earth bodies lay dead, and folk danced round them, rejoicing and giving gifts; and then the bodies rose and shook off their sickness and went like a river of arrows to God. Among them Vridar saw himself, with Marion clinging to him; he felt himself borne upward in quivering light, until he came at last to the temple's own door. Angels swarmed round him and gave him a huge book and he ate it, and its taste was that of honey. He walked to the white throne and knelt and a crown was placed on his head.

75

Later he sat thinking about the vision. Had he seen the sky open or had he dreamed? He did not know. Was he an impostor or had God glorified him? He felt purged, cleaned out, as though pure light had been flowing through him; but he felt guilty, too, and shamed. He rose and went to the house and looked at his mother with intent fable-clouded eyes. She said he looked very strange, very queer, and she wanted to know what had happened; but like his father, he wanted to be entreated. He was eager to tell of this vision, even though it now stood in conscience like a grotesque folly.

"Son, you look very strange. What has happened?"

He felt stupid and false but he felt glorified. He wanted to tell. He said he had seen a vision.

"A vision! Son, what are you saying?"

"I saw a vision," he said stubbornly. Let her doubt, if she must: Judas doubted and Peter lied, and even Thomas could not recognize the son of God.

Prudence sat and drew him to her. "Tell mother. What did you see?"

"I saw a vision," he said, "but I don't want to tell."

She stared at him, remembering the caul. Caressing his hair and his thin pale cheeks, she begged him to tell, and her voice was gentle and a little awed. God alone knew what kind of son she had borne!

In a low voice he told her about the vision, feeling in one moment ecstasy, in the next shame. The legend became more convincing to him as he spoke; words captured it and made it real. He was trembling. His voice stammered over the fable, his heart beat in its power. When he had told his story he looked at her face and saw that it was filled with awed hush.

"It wasn't a dream, my son?"

"No maam. It wasn't a dream."

"You strange child!" she murmured and touched his hair.

He did not know, and in subsequent tellings he was to know with less and less certainty, what the truth had been. Had God called him to prophethood and a mission on earth? By this early age he had read the Bible through twice; he was filled with its legends, its great burden of sin, its angry and outraged prophets, invoking upon their people the wrath of God. God even had seven vials of wrath, though what a vial was he did not know; but he did know, for his mother had told him this so many times, that the world was more horribly wicked than in the days of Isaiah. Certainly there was need of a prophet now.

He heard his parents talking about him while lying in bed. Joe's amazement came out of him in grunts and rumblings. The next day he stared at his son but he did not speak. Had he sired a prophet? He doubted that he had, though in his Church there had been prophets since Joseph Smith.

When she went next to the valley, Prudence told Vridar's grandmother of the vision. Rose O'Rourke's fame as nurse, midwife, and interpreter of dreams had spread far beyond her home. Young and old brought their dreams to her. She would fix the narrator with her black eyes, draw her thin lips into a hard line, and then seem to doze as she slowly nodded her head. She would be silent a little while after the telling was done, and then with astonishing glibness tell exactly what the dream

76

had meant. She said that Vridar might be a prophet all right; she had never thought that he would be good for anything else. He was born with a caul and he was a queer one.

Prudence told Joe what his mother had said. "I'm jooberus," he said, "that womern don't know so much. I don't recollect as how anything she ever prophersied has come true." With a thumb and finger he was rubbing up and down his big nose while staring at his son. When he moved his hand up toward his brows, he could not see Vridar and he seemed to be speculating behind his hand; and then his thumb and finger would slide down his nose and his gray eyes would look over his hand at Vridar. "I'm jooberus about ma," he said.

"She said Vridar must always take care of his brother. That's one thing it meant."

Vridar had been told many times that he must be his brother's keeper, and with remorseless holiness he shouldered his duty, exhorting, chastising, and teaching. Out by the smokehouse one day Joe was tinkering with a handplow. He had built a fire and laid the plowshare in it, together with some bolts; and when the iron was redhot he laid it across a stone and beat it with a hammer to sharpen its edge. Vridar stood by and watched.

When the work was done Joe kicked the redhot bolts out of the fire and scattered them in grass to cool. Marion at this moment, barefooted and curious, came running toward them. The father yelled a warning, but Marion charged across the red bolts and gave a horrible scream and went pellmell, hopping on one leg. To the sole of a lifted foot stuck one of the bolts, burned to its depth in flesh. The smell of burning flesh filled the air.

Vridar ran after him. Marion paused, looked down at his foot, and was paralyzed with amazement and pain. He shook his foot and the bolt fell. Then he ran again, howling with all his might. A little later after the smoking furrow had been filled with soda and lard, he sat on a chair and sobbed and moaned. When the lads were in bed, Vridar rebuked and admonished.

"If you'd listen to me," he whispered, "you wouldn't get hurt."

"You-you get hurt!" Marion sobbed.

That sobered Vridar a little. "Yes," he admitted, remembering his own foot. "But mother says you should listen to me."

"Oh, it hurts!" moaned Marion. "I want cold water on it!"

"But that isn't good for it. Why do you want to do what ain't good for you?"

"I want it should stop hurtun!"

"You have to suffer some," said Vridar, convinced that pain was the first law of life. "When you do wrong you suffer. It's the same when you sin."

"Oh, shut up!" howled Marion. "It hurts I tell you!"

Prudence opened the door and looked in. "What's the trouble?"

"His foot hurts," said Vridar. "I tell him he'll always have trouble if he don't listen to me."

Prudence came over and kissed Marion's cheek. "Yes, dear son. Mother wants your brother to take care of you. You won't get hurt if you do what he says."

"He gets hurt!" Marion howled.

"Son, that's no way to speak to your mother."

77

"Yes maam. But I tell you it hurts!"

"Mother knows it does. I'll put more soda on it in a little while." Then she went out.

"See what I told you," said Vridar.

"Oh, shut up! I don't want a-listen to you!"

And so it was with them. The one brother, feeling his holiness, exhorted and cared for, and the other, hating him, became his shadow. The one with the queer eyes became a queer and lonely and deeply introverted child. The other nourished his delusions until many years later when gargantuan laughter shook his world. But even before that time his missionary zeal was to be leveled again and again to bitter emptiness and dust.

His notion of prophethood suffered its most devastating eclipse under the hands of Jed Bridwell; but before that hour he had his first narrow escape from death.

XI

The Bridwell boys could swim like otters. Vridar had seen them in the river; they would go under and be gone for what seemed to him a long time, when suddenly a rump would emerge, or a hand or a foot would wigwag a greeting. Vridar, feeling more and more that he was even less than a girl, wanted to learn to swim, too.

One morning he went with his brother and sister to the creek. His mother had told him never to go close to water, but he had been reading about the exploits of Kit Carson and Daniel Boone. He told Marion he would show him how deep he could wade. He had never waded above his knees; now he walked in almost to his crotch. He was feeling very heroic. "See how deep I am!" he said.

"That ain't so deep," said Marion, who had watched the Bridwell boys.

Feeling bolder, Vridar advanced, and suddenly stepped into a deep hole. He wore a big straw hat and the hat was the only thing about him now visible. Marion did not move. He decided that this was indeed real wading. "Look!" he said to Diana, and Diana, a chubby little girl, looked.

Vridar meanwhile was fighting for his life. There was nothing under him or around him but water. He clawed at it with desperate hands, sucked it into his lungs, felt it on his blind staring eyes; and he had no doubt at all that this would be his end. Through his mind during his churning and strangling passage downstream ran his mother's warning and her command. Then memory of this and a thousand spurts of thought darkened a little, as water filled him, as water seemed to boil into him and bear him down. Blindly he clutched for overhanging willows, remembering that the creek was lined with them. He tried to shout but the water poured into him with roaring weight and he choked and fought as his senses darkened. This was the end. . . .

When he came to he was kneeling on the bank, vomiting water from his lungs, his eyes wild and bulging. Marion and Diana had not moved. They thought their brother had accomplished a most daring feat. Vridar had found a limb and drawn himself half-dead and unaware to the bank. He did not remember the limb. Coughing and gasping and rolling his eyes, he realized at last that Marion had seen nothing to

78

alarm him, that he had thought the vanishing a part of a plan. Vridar looked up, his eyes wet and yellow with fear. Each effort to speak brought strangled gasps and spurts of water out of him. He shook with memory of that bottomless nothingness under his feet. Nevertheless he would pretend. Turning on his brother a sick and ghastly grin he gasped, "How did I do?"

"Fine," said Marion. "Only your hat stuck out."

Vridar shuddered and wondered if God had saved him. He turned to the creek, tempted to try again, but the darkly shadowed and crawling waters made him tremble. Affecting bravado and begging his brother and sister not to tattle, he took his frail and drenched body to the house, crossing the stream on a footpole. His mother was away gathering wild berries. He dried his clothes and sat on the doorstep, thinking about himself; he would have abjured his visions and his prophethood if he could have been like Jed.

One Sunday the family again crossed the river to visit, and Vridar stared with horror into the fast-flowing depths of the river. They feasted on a huge roast of bear flesh, raw turnips, ripe serviceberries, and cream. After the meal the children went to the garden and orchard, where they ate carrots and radishes. Jed marched around like a showman. He hardly knew what to make of these meek and timid lads.

"Hain't you never seen a girl?" he asked, scowling at Vridar.

"No."

"Then by the Judas god I'll show you one."

He seized his sister Beth, a big girl with warm sensuous eyes. He struggled with her and dragged her to the earth and sat on her. He pulled her dress up and Vridar began to redden with shame. He wanted to flee but he did not flee. He wished to see Beth but his face had become as red as chokecherry leaves in autumn. Jed was fighting and clawing and Beth was clawing and calling terrible names. Her dress was torn, her hair was mopped in the dust. With all his might Jed exposed her, forcing her legs apart and calling on Vridar to look; and Vridar peered, but his vision was blinded with shame and he could see nothing. Beth got to her feet, crimson and murderous, and went to the house. Vridar followed and stole over to his mother and whispered to her of what had happened. Charley saw him whisper and understood.

A half-hour later Jed and Thiel staggered up from river-brush, naked to their waist and red with blood. Their father had beaten them with a green hawthorn limb. Sick and shamed, Vridar slunk away and went to the boat and waited for his parents. His mother's face when she came was white and strange. His father's face was dark.

Never in all his years was Vridar to forgive himself this betrayal of Jed. In Jed's eyes when the boy entered the house, bloody and dripping and undone, Vridar had seen something that boded no good for him. Still, it was not this that troubled him most; it was the feeling that he had been unspeakably mean. His mother had told him that he should confess everything, but he began to understand that not all things were to be confessed. He hoped that Jed would forgive. But Jed never forgave and he never forgot. A little later he took his vengeance.

Vridar was still a small boy but he had known heavy work. He had followed a handplow until he was an exhausted quivering of flesh and bone. He had tramped long hours behind a harrow. The day was September 8, a day that in a later time was to become the bitterest of his life, and he was harrowing in the upper field a half-mile from the house. He was afraid, even before Jed came; he had seen a bear come down the dugway and fell a path through the ripened grain, and he had seen a mountain lion sit on the river's bank and scream. And so as he trudged it was apprehensively that he looked round him to see if any danger threatened. On a mountainside not far away he saw gray forms and shouted to frighten them but they only stood and looked at him. And a moment later he saw peering around a thicket the intent and scowling face of Jed. Vridar stopped the team and waited, not knowing whether Jed came as enemy or friend.

Jed approached, followed by Thiel, both drenched because they had swum the river. They looked at Vridar and he saw only hatred and malice in their eyes. Thiel fixed him with a freckled and derisive grin. Jed was savage and dark.

"Well," said Jed, "how's mama's god-damned little tattletale today?" Slowly he drew forth a pocket knife and opened a bright blade. He told Thiel to throw Vridar down. Thiel grasped the boy and hurled him to the earth, and Vridar heard Jed saying, "I'm going to cut your thing off and your balls with it. . . ." Then Vridar went mad. He babbled and screamed and heard Jed whetting the blade on a harrow tooth. He heard Jed say again what he was going to do. He felt Jed ripping his trousers open and he felt Jed's hands on his organs. Then all reason, all power to hear and understand, left the boy, and he became a raving maniac, fighting with the strength of ten. He tore free, beating at a world of dark faces and blood and knives. But again he was seized and thrown down and earth was stuffed into his mouth and pushed down his throat, until his eyes stood out like those of a crushed mouse. Frenzy poured from him, hurling the mud from his lungs and from his nose; and then he fainted and lay like one dead.

When he came to, the team and harrow were gone. Jed and Thiel were gone. He was alone in a wide field under an empty sky; and upon the mountain trail the gray shadows were trotting back and forth. Limp and shaken and half-blinded, he followed the harrow path, reaching down to learn if he had been unmanned, thinking of his father's rage, staggering and babbling with idiocy and fear. He found the team entangled in brush, the harness ripped and the harrow broken. He walked round and round them, unable to think or see, loathing himself and praying for death. Then still gurgling and spitting mud out, he stumbled to the house. When his mother saw him, she cried and was rigid. He stood before her, his hair matted with earth and his ears full of it, his teeth caked with it, his trousers torn, his face deathly white; and his crazed babbling chilled her.

For an hour he was unable to speak. If she asked questions, he heard dimly and dimly understood, but when he tried to answer nothing came out of him but hideous grief and terror. He nodded his head like an idiot; he started up, screaming with sudden fear; and then he shook and gurgled and tried to see if there was blood on his hands. Without letting her see, he would reach down to his belly and his loins; and he would stare blindly through black mist, trying to see if there was blood.

He trembled and moaned all night, but the next day he would not tell the truth. He said something frightened the team and it ran away. That was all. His betrayal

80

of Jed and Jed's hour of vengeance were a base part of his life that must never be told.

But Jed Bridwell was not done with vengeance yet. He swam the river and struck a second time. The harrow had been repaired and the harness mended and Vridar had gone back to work. He would rather have died but he had to go. Around such stern people as his parents his fear was contemptible and homeless. Was he not the brave little man, his brother's keeper, his mother's pride! He had to go.

But he went with awful blundering revulsion in his heart. The buildings were out of sight. He could see only the mountains, kingly with loneliness, and the river, a violent and unresting death. He watched round him for Jed's face or for sign of lion and bear.

One afternoon his father went with him and grubbed brush at the field's edge. Vridar loved him for this. He felt the man's courage and power like sunlight on the earth. Charley Bridwell came over that afternoon. Vridar rested the team and went over to the men.

"Ain't you ashamed?" asked Charley, grinning at him.

"Yes sir," said Vridar, convinced that he had much to be ashamed for.

"A big guy like you, workun that little team to death! See how they droop!"

Vridar looked at his father, wondering what he should say. He must be polite, but what else he hardly knew.

"Don't you?" Charley asked.

"Don't I what, sir?"

"Drive them heckety-belt."

"No sir, I just make them walk."

"Why, good God, I saw you beatun the grease out of them. You had a club in your hand as big as a bridge beam."

Vridar was looking at Charley and thinking of the brutal flogging he had given his sons. The man was a riddle. He looked kind and jolly, but he did the most unkind and unjolly things. His green eyes were cruel.

Charley now drew from his pocket a pint of whisky and turned to Joe. "A little nip?" he asked. "It might help you cut that root in two."

Joe scowled at the bottle and said nothing. Vridar knew by the scowl that he wanted a drink. He had seen his father once before slyly behind a bush when he thought only Charley could see.

"Warm your disposition a little," said Charley, proffering the bottle. "It might put a grin on your face."

"I never cared much for the stuff," said Joe. He scowled, as if the bottle had affronted him, and Vridar turned away, knowing that his father hesitated because his son stood near. Vridar also wanted a drink. He had found one of Charley's old bottles and had drunk the last drops and breathed deep of the marvelous odor. Pretending now not to be curious, he went behind a bush and peered through. He saw his father take the bottle, saw him scowl at it as if it were a senseless thing, saw him tip it and drink. He saw his father shudder and make a dreadful face, as though he had drunk bitters; and all the while Vridar perceived the pleasure behind an absurd mask of disgust. Charley offered him another drink, and though Joe's

81

glance lingered on the bottle he declined. He said he didn't like the stuff, and this, Vridar knew, was a monstrous lie. Returning to the team he tramped round and round the field, wondering about whisky and hoping to have some day a bottle of his own. It was a hot windless afternoon that became more and more oppressive and sinister.

It was his way when assigned a task to try to find a shortcut to its end. In later summers when he raked the hay he would divide a ten-acre field in a half-dozen plots so that none would seem to be of appalling size. He felt wretched and defeated when he saw ahead of him a task that filled more than an hour. When weeding potatoes he would take not one row but five or six down the field; and then, becoming still more anxious, he would hoe a few rows a little distance and return and hoe other rows, trying to do the entire patch at once. He felt that he was stupid in this, and, feeling stupid and deluded, he would fall into blind rage and weep.

He was weeping now while circling the enormous field. The harrowed margin, it seemed to him, was no wider than it had been hours ago. The horses enraged him because they were so tranquil and lazy, moving like a witless mechanism that was running down. He crossed the middle, cutting the field in two; he divided the halves again, and again divided, until he had the land sectored into squares and triangles. He shouted at the horses and hurled clods at them. He went aimlessly, mixing up the sectors and trying to lose them, hoping by some miracle to harrow them all at once. But after hours of deluded effort, he had only a crazy patchwork, and he turned home at quitting-time, hating himself and everything in sight.

The next day Joe did not come out to grub. This summer he herded cattle on the Antelope hills, gathering them from valley herds and charging a dollar for the care of each beast. For those lost, unless he found the dead beast and cut the brand out, he had to pay. His only saddle horse was a beautiful and wicked mare that he called Brown Doll. She had evil eyes and an evil unconquerable will. Every time he mounted her she bucked, madly and desperately; but Joe was a skilled rider and was proud of the fact that he had never been thrown. The family would go out to watch him mount. He would saddle the mare, drawing the cinch so tight that it was buried in her flesh, and he would blindfold her eyes. Then he would mount and jerk the blindfold away and ride the plunging beast out into a field. Lathered with sweat and shaken and spent, she would return, meek and conquered; but the next day she would buck again with the same desperate will.

While walking round the field Vridar thought of her. He had developed the habit of making himself the hero of gorgeous fantasies.

"Saddle the beast," he said, addressing incredulous men. "I'll ride him for fair and all."

"But you'll be killed," said one. "Nobody ain't never rode that critter yet. You'll be throwed over the moon."

"Saddle him up," said Vridar. "I'll ride him with hell and high leather!"

"But, man, he'll throw you over the stars. He throwed Jim Martin highern a hawk's wing and he never did come down."

"And Jess Bitt," said another. "He put such a kink in old Jess's neck that he didn't know his hindend from his face."

"Get the saddle on," said Vridar, adjusting his spurs. "I'll ride the son of a bitch until he sets on his rump and prays. Get the blindfold on."

"I tell you no man ain't never rode him. He'll throw you highern the Holy Ghost. This critter—"

The fantasy died suddenly in a yelp of consternation. Fifty yards away and coming swiftly toward him was Jed Bridwell. Vridar stopped, paralyzed, and watched the avenger drawing near. He saw his morbidly intent face and his black eyes. Suddenly Vridar broke within and ran, but Jed was fleeter; Jed pounced upon him and flung him reeling to the plowed earth. "Leave me alone!" Vridar yelled, staggering up to face him.

"You little son of a bitch!" said Jed. "Look!" He jerked his wet shirt up and showed fresh welts on his back. "My old man beat me again and you're the reason, and this time, by God, I'm really going to cut your outfit off!"

"I'm not the cause! Honest to God I'm not the cause!"

"You told him something, you stinkun little bastard you!"

"Honest I never! I swear to God!"

"I care nothun about God," said Jed, staring at the boy, now shaking and white. "And even if you didn't, you will, so I come to fix you. Get your pants down."

Vridar withdrew, tense, quivering, his eyes bright with dread. "Don't!" he moaned out of a dry and aching throat. "Please don't!"

"Stop that shakun around. God damn, what a coward! Come here."

"No!"

"Come here," he roared, "before I belt your eyes out!" Vridar advanced and looked at the dark remorseless eyes: there was no friendliness in them, no humor or pity: nothing but courage and hate. "Now watch," said Jed, and he rolled his eyes until they were like clots of blood. "Now you do it."

"I can't."

"I suppose you still suck your mother's tit. Well, I come to cut your balls off. Then you won't ever be able to do it to a woman. You won't even have anything to piss out of." Vridar retreated again, faltering backward, and Jed sprang like a cat and hurled him down. Vridar fought blindly and babbled but suddenly there came to him like a burst of dawn the thought that he would be a prophet, yet here he was, being mauled like a common clown.

"Let me up!" he panted. "If you don't God will strike you dead!"

"I'll fill your belly with dirt," said Jed, and stuffed a clod into Vridar's mouth. Again Vridar was struggling like a mad thing. He would not suffer this indignity, he would not have God outraged in such fashion as this. He shrieked and clawed and then with all his strength struck free and got up.

Jed stared at him. "All right, now we'll have a decent fight."

"Listen!" yelled Vridar, trembling with wrath and outrage. "You wouldn't dare touch me if you knowed who I am!"

"I know who you are, you dirty little stink! You're a liar and a bastard and a coward."

83

"I'm a prophet!" Vridar gasped.

Jed stared again. "Well, good God, what in hell's a prophet?"

"God give me a sign," said Vridar, still shaking.

"Well, you tit-sucking prophet, you just as well begin to pray." Jed reached for his knife.

"You leave me alone!"

Jed advanced, and Vridar asked God to help him now. He asked God to knock this boy as witless as the Philistines under Samson's jawbone. "Don't touch me!" he said in a solemn whisper.

Jed leapt again and broke Vridar to the earth. He knelt on him and pinned his arms in the soft deep soil and stuffed earth into his mouth, until he saw Vridar's face darken and his eyes bulge. Then Jed turned, astride, and began to dig for Vridar's organs and to yank at them. He got hold of the penis and pulled and yanked; and Vridar, strangled and choking, was fighting like mad. The plowed earth was like a soft mattress, and Vridar on his back was half-buried and unable even to strike free with his arms, which were imprisoned under Jed's lower legs. He was spitting dirt and coughing and strangling, and Jed meanwhile had reached lower to find the testes and was yanking at them so savagely that in the dark and despair of his mind Vridar thought they were torn off.

Then suddenly Jed leapt up and ran softly to the river bank and sank under it and disappeared. Vridar struggled until he was on hands and knees and then he choked and coughed, trying to get the earth out of his throat and lungs. He stood up at last, white and undone, and gently felt down with one hand to his parts.

XII

And so the boy lived in loneliness and fear. For five years here he saw no one but his family, the man who killed the colt, and the Bridwells. The world was lost in faint memory, and he was lost in this enormous hole that had a personality of its own. He came to think of it and to feel it, not as earth and river and stone ledge and forest, but as something alive in its own way, with its moods of solitude or violence, its emotions of anger, sadness, and hate. The sun and the stars and the winds, the flowing waters and the midnight, all these for him were alive with power to act and feel. He looked forward to the time when he would leave this spot and enter school.

That time was coming, he knew, because his parents spoke of it often, and they dreamed and planned and built. A few dollars had been hoarded away. A vision as bright and indestructible as the sun stood in their speech year after year, pervading even their moods of silence; for they had a dream of what their children would be. It united them in single and ceaseless toil. It fed them hope, lifted them in dark moments and shone in their eyes and ways. No matter how isolated and poor, no matter what people called them fools, for their children nothing less than college would be good enough.

Vridar caught the spirit of their mood when he heard them talk of what their children would be. They would be doctors or lawyers or school teachers, and not common slaves like their parents, their grandparents, and their great-grandparents before them. Of the Hunter and Branton clans in this part of the world, they would be the first to enter high school, the first to enter college, the first to step into life trained for power and a clean home. Vridar never questioned all this; for him it would have been sacrilege to question it. His parents were spending their bone and blood to get him on a high place, above dirt and ragged clothes, above days whose working hours were from dawn till midnight. His own secret wish was to be a carpenter, not because Jesus was, no, but because his deepest joy came from creating things. Or he would be a poet.

But he would be a lawyer, his parents said, and he wondered what a lawyer was. He would soon enter school. Already his shoes had come, his first since the tiny ones he wore as a babe; but he had not worn them yet. He took them to bed and looked at them, for they were wonderful things. He would slip them on, taking care to wash his feet and not to get dirt on the soles. He had also a blue suit, made from his grandfather's Civil War uniform; and Marion had one like it. He had a cap, some handkerchiefs and stockings, and some shirts. All these his mother had made, toiling far into the night. Yes, he would go to school soon, though no way had yet been found. It appeared unexpectedly the next July.

Down the long dugway one Sunday came a whitetopped buggy, squeaking under a load of the Hunter clan. When Vridar saw it rolling down the lane, bringing the first visitors in all these years, he was beside himself with excitement. He dashed into the house, shouting that people were coming, and back to the yard, mouth agape, eyes widening upon the vision, his body feeding hungrily on these strangers. Rose was there, still lean and athletic and sharp of speech.

"Hello," she said. "Where's your ma?"

"In the house!" he gasped.

"My God, you're skinny," said Rose, and stepped down to the doubletree and then to the earth. She beat dust out of her clothes. The buggy rocked as its humanity overflowed and spilled out. Prudence came now, patting her great mass of golden hair, looking with shame at her torn stockings and patched shoes.

"You'll have to excuse the way I look," she said.

"You're all right, Prudy!" a man bellowed. "You look like a spring daisy."

This man was large, vital, grinning, with a monstrous nose. Vridar stood apart, listening to the chatter and observing the way they clasped hands. He recognized another now, his aunt Agnes, a lovely and voluptuous woman, with large breasts filling her blouse. Vridar's thoughts went back to the time when he had seen his mother's breasts; she had been weaning Diana, and she would take out a large white mound and put some bitter juice around the nipple. Then Diana would suck, and Vridar, watching her, had felt that he had been cheated; felt that there was some great and magnificent beauty in this part of a woman; wished deeply to touch the breasts and taste them. He was staring enraptured at his aunt's bosom when she cried:

"Shut your mouth, for God sake! You catchun flies?" Then she twittered, turned in a warm sensuous movement, and fell into the arms of a young man. He had

85

bushy brows, small wicked eyes, and hair growing up from his chest and sticking above his shirt.

"My dish of honey and cream!" he said, half-serious, half-mocking, and kissed her. He kissed her by pushing his lips out and rubbing them into her red mouth. Vridar thought the caress unspeakably lewd and he hated both of them.

They all trooped into the house, shouting and guffawing, violent and coarse and raw. Vridar wanted to follow, but instead he went guiltily to a window and peered in.

"Hey, you sneak, stop that goppun and come inside!" Red with shame, he went to the door and hesitated. "Come in," said his aunt. "What you want a-sneak around for?"

He stepped inside and hugged the wall, and all the visitors turned to look at him.

"Tell her to go to hell," said the hairy man. "Tell her to shut her trap before you knock her eyes out."

Vridar looked at his mother. She was flushed, nervous, bewildered.

"Well," said his aunt, "has a cat got your tongue?"

The lad writhed and hugged the wall, his hands behind him, his naked feet rubbing one another.

"Tell her," said the hairy man, "to jump in a well."

The aunt giggled and choked and burst into high laughter. "I dreamt I was a well last night," she said, and gave the man an apple-cheeked warm-mouthed leer. "But it was you jumped in."

This jest threw the visitors into a roar. Rose's voice leapt in high faltering screeches; the big-nosed man bellowed until he rocked on his stool; and Agnes lost her breath entirely in shrill altitudes of hysteria. Vridar glanced at his mother and saw that her face was red; at his father, and saw the man trembling in a deep silent chuckle. He hugged the wall closer and waited.

"Shame on you," said the hairy man. "You make the kid blush."

"He'll get used to it," Agnes said. "He'll be fallun in a well hisself some time. Won't you?"

"No maam," he said, wondering what she meant. He knew by his mother's face that the jest had been obscene, but its meaning was as dark as a well's own darkness.

In an effort to fend off further indecencies, Prudence now spoke. She asked Rose if she had any apples to sell. But with a honeymoon imminent, these visitors were not to be sidetracked with apples.

"Ever night lately," said Agnes, "I been dreamun."

"Oh, sure," said the hairy man, wetting his lips.

"About a long one-eyed thing."

"O God!" cried Rose, and beat her lap in a spasm of joy.

How were crops in the valley? asked Prudence swiftly kneading pie dough. Were they cutting hay yet?

"What's in the well?" asked the hairy man, again wetting his lips. "The old oaken bucket?"

"Call it a bucket but it didn't feel like a bucket."

The big-nosed man roared again, subsided, and coughed out the dead end of a laugh.

"Agnes," said Prudence sharply, "will you come help me?"

Agnes rose with voluptuous laziness and yawned. She leaned backward, and Vridar saw the full outline of her breasts. When she approached the hairy man, he yanked her sprawling to his lap and reached down into her bosom. The next moment with his finger he probed at her abdomen and made a fierce amorous sound full of z's. She lay prone, abandoned, her arms and hair falling to the floor, one of her breasts almost out of her blouse.

"Agnes!" Prudence cried. "I want your help, please."

Agnes fumbled upward, yawning, crying, oh-oh, by God.

"You big lazy Swede," said the hairy man, "go make yourself useful. A hell of a wife you'll be."

"Swede? You're the only Swede around here, you hairy old stud."

"I thought you was a Dane," said Rose, staring at him with indignant reproach. "I never knowed a Swede worth his salt."

"Oh?" said the hairy man, looking at her, grinning. "There ain't no better men nen Swedes. You're a Swede yourself."

"Me?" yelled Rose, horrified. "I'm Irish-Scotch, Mr. Swensen. There's none of your pig-eyed Swede in me."

"There is in me," he said, still grinning. "A hundred and eighty pounds, all Swede. It was my ancestors discovered America."

"You fool! Tell me now Klumbus was a Swede!"

"Listen, you whisky-drinkun shanty Irish! My ancestors discovered America a thousands years before your Klumbus was wrapped up in his his didy. Ain't you never read no history?"

Rose narrowed her eyes and rocked back and forth, in the way habitual to her when baffled. She set her lower lip over her upper lip and kept it there a long time. Again and again she looked at him, her eyes bitter and resentful and her mouth giving him the lie.

Two hours later the adults were eating, and not since leaving his grandmother's had Vridar seen such a feast. There was fried chicken, gravy made of cream, mashed potatoes, bowls of fruit and fragrant pies. This was the third time in his life that he had seen pies, and he stared at them until his eyes watered. Still standing by the wall, because in the etiquette of his mother's world, when there were visitors children waited until the elders had eaten, he watched the table and saw delicious things gobbled up one by one. Great God, there would be nothing left but chicken bones and bread and milk!

He had been taught that it was ill-mannered to accept a second helping of dessert. It was wholly proper to eat all you could of bread and potatoes and common things; but it was mean and vulgar to ask for another serving of fruit or pie or cake. And so he was outraged when he heard these gluttons praise the pie and hand their plates over for a second piece. So overcome that he resolved not to eat at all, he went outside and Marion followed him.

"Did you see them?" he asked his brother.

"What?" whispered Marion.

"Why—" Vridar choked. "The gluttons, they took two pieces of pie!"

"Yes," said Marion, but his rage was only sympathetic. In spite of teaching, he thought it wise for a lad to eat what he could get.

"They're like pigs!" said Vridar.

"Mebbe they'll leave a little," said Marion.

"It's the principle!" said Vridar. "I don't care if I get no pie. It's to see them hog it down like they had no manners."

"I know something," said Marion. "Mother put some pie away for us."

"She did?"

"A whole pie in the cupboard."

"But it isn't that," said Vridar, feeling a little better. "They don't have any manners."

After the hungry but now surfeited pack had left the table, Vridar hoped they would all die of bellyache. These were his relatives, and a pretty bunch they were, the gluttonous loud-laughing earthy brutes! As a rebuke to their greed, he accepted only a small piece of pie, and he stared angrily at his brother who was stuffing a whole quarter-section into his mouth. Marion saw the reproving eyes. He choked a little and faltered and looked at his fingers, lathered with cream.

"Can't you use a spoon?" Vridar asked. "That's no proper way to eat."

"Why, shame," said Prudence, who overheard. "Use your spoon, son."

"Yes maam," said Marion and spooned the rich food. Glancing at his brother and seeing his frown, Marion arrested a spoonful in midair and looked at it. He dropped it to his plate, cut it in two, and turned to see if Vridar approved.

"That's better," Vridar said.

With a sigh Marion spooned again.

The next day Vridar saw something that made his eyes almost pop out of his skull. Because of the behavior of his mother, he sensed that something was in the air which she did not want him to see; but remembering her lies and resolved not to be outwitted again, he kept out of her sight. In the buggy team was a stallion. From his hiding-place Vridar saw the beast led forth, prancing and snorting, to one of Joe's horses; and almost at once the prancing beast rose to its hind legs and covered the other and Vridar saw it chewing at the mare's neck. Then he saw under its belly the mighty staff, almost as long and considerably thicker than a baseball bat; and with utter amazement he saw the staff enter the mare. He heard his aunt Agnes shrieking and saw her fall into the arms of the hairy man. He saw his mother look around her and knew that she was looking for her sons. Then he saw the staff come out and the beast dismounted and the staff fell downward almost to the ground. For more than an hour he sat still as death, thinking of what he had seen, of what Jed had told him, and of the passages in the Bible. And the man went in unto her! . . . .

The second evening, after the Hunters had gone, Prudence and Joe talked quietly, sitting by the stove, and then she spoke to her sons. She said next winter they would go to school. Their Aunt Agnes was to be married soon and would live on the cedared butte in Annis, in the one-room shack where they were born. They would live with her and go to school.

"Are you pleased?" she asked Vridar.

"Yes maam," he said, thinking of her lies and of the two breasts.

But he was not pleased. He was dismayed. Live with this woman who had never spoken to him save with taunt and insult! Live with that lewd hairy Swede! He slunk away to bed and lay in troubled thought. He was glad to be going away, away from the wintry loneliness and the summer madness of this hole; but he shuddered when he thought of seven or eight months with those two. He knew that there was no pity or tenderness in them. He knew that their ways were not his. They were vital and coarse, aggressive, zestful, and foul of speech. If he had a nightmare, they would laugh him to shame. They would laugh at his love of books and his wish to be a writer. But he would have to go. He would never be a lawyer if he did not go.

"Marion," he said under the covers, "what do you think?"

"About what?"

"Us with Aunt Agnes."

"I don't like her," Marion said.

"Do you like him?"

"Not him, either."

For a little while Vridar was silent. Then: "I wish we didn't have to go."

"Mebe we won't."

"No, we have to. We have to be lawyers or doctors some day."

"Won't we get homesick down there?"

"I guess so," said Vridar and choked. He tried to hold the tears back; he turned over and stretched his limbs and his aching throat; but the tears came. They welled up, hot and bitter. Marion also began to weep. "Don't cry!" Vridar sobbed and clasped his brother's hand. "Marion, don't cry."

"I—I can't help it!" Marion gasped. "Don't you cry and I won't!"

"All r-r-right! Marion, d-don't cry now!"

"Don't you c-cry t-t-too!"

"Now. I'm not crying now."

Marion squeezed his brother's hand and moved over close to him. "Let's say we don't want to go!" he whispered.

"But we—we have to go." He drew a great sigh. "We—we have to be a doctor or a lawyer some day. Mother says that."

"Vridar, are you—you crying now?"

"N-no."

"Vridar?"

"Yes."

"I'm afraid."

"I'm afraid, too."

They drew close to one another, their hands clasped, each fighting to hush his grief. Later, when Prudence came in, the boys were asleep, but their cheeks were wet and their pillows were wet under their cheeks.

XIII

In a jolting wagon with only a slab across the bed for a seat, Prudence and her sons rode across the Antelope hills. Vridar was staring into the blue valley ahead. Far away he could see in haze a group of mountains called the Big Buttes; and when the Antelope foothills were reached, he could see two round and shimmering blurs which his mother said were the Little Buttes. On the west slope of the north one was the house where he was born.

The wheels searched the ruts, turning the dust up like clouds of flour. The horses were powdered with it and had its grit mixed in the gray lather between their thighs. It ran in white streams down the spokes. It was like dirty snow on the traces and reins and doubletree. It swirled upward in storms and threw a yellow mist over the sun. Vridar shook it out of his hair and wiped its layers off his face and tasted its sand on his lips and teeth. He understood now why his mother after returning from peddling cheese had always looked so old and gray.

They left the foothills and entered the level irrigated acreage of Poplar. Trees stood here, lordly poplars in row on row, planted by the first Mormon settlers; orchards were by the wayside, canal banks burgeoned with the hues of autumn, and frontyard gardens smelled of autumn flowers. By a sweet stream they stopped and fed the beasts and ate buttered bread and cheese. They had been journeying since daylight. Hitching the team, they drove again, through lanes north and then west and then north; over a land of gravel which his mother called Rudy; into a more fertile region and past the small dusty town of Rigby and on and on. Darkness was falling when they entered the community of Annis, after a journey of more than thirty miles. They passed a faded structure, roomy and blind like a barn, and Prudence said this was the school where they would study. The boys looked at it and shuddered. Then they rounded the butte, with the wheels cutting deep into its dark gravel and white sand, and entered a gate with an orchard on its right and drew up before a house. Agnes Swensen framed herself in the doorway.

"I thought you wasn't comun till October," she said.

"I want my boys in school," said Prudence, climbing wearily down and beginning to unhitch the team. "School has started, hasn't it?"

"Honey dear, has school started yet?"

Honey dear stirred himself and came to the door. He looked at Prudence, as if feeling that he should help her, but reluctant to. "Hello," he said and came over to the team.

Vridar was watching his mother's face. It was distressed, offended, proud. While watering the beasts at an old well, Borg Swensen looked round and saw Vridar and gave him a foretaste of what was to come. "Hey, don't stand there goppun! Get some wood to your aunt if you want some supper." Vridar gathered wood and took it to the house.

90

Early the next morning Prudence walked with her two sons to school. She hoped that Vridar could enter the fifth grade, Marion the second, but the teacher questioned her and said no. Marion would have to enter the first and Vridar the third. He was a tall emaciated man with sharp cold eyes pinched together, a huge overhanging nose, and a purring threat in his voice. One long bloodless hand covered with yellow fuzz softly caressed the tiny chin hiding back under his mouth.

"Home teaching," he said, "is never what it should be. You say he's never studied no grammar? Then he'll have to enter the third."

Vridar saw that his mother was scornful and baffled. He became scornful, too. He hated grammar, whatever it was, and resolved never to learn it.

"He's a very unusual child," said Prudence quietly.

The teacher's smile was faint and weary. He looked hard at Vridar. "I'd say, Mrs. Hunter, he looks like most boys. All mothers think their sons are the best sons in the world."

"I know!" said Prudence sharply. "It ain't because he's my son. If—"

"But grammar. Between you and I, Mrs. Hunter, your own is not very good. But of course you can take him to another school."

On the way back Prudence did not speak, and even after her team had been harnessed and hitched she was still angry and trembling. Vridar was trembling, too, because the hour of parting had come. He was desperately lonely and afraid. He wanted to be taken home, to live forever in wild and ignorant isolation. But he had to be brave, he had to be the manly little man. When his mother stooped for his kiss, tears blinded him; agony gripped his throat and heart but he made no protest. He wanted to ask when she would come again and if she would write, but he could not even whisper, he could make no sound. She climbed to the slab seat and gathered the reins and looked down.

"Be good boys to your aunt," she said. "Do what she tells you and be polite."

Then she drove away. Ah, God! the boy thought, weeping, and clasping the hand of Marion, who was weeping too. It was all Vridar could do to keep from running after her. She went through the gate and around the butte and was gone. He tried to remain rooted, but grief and fear shook him and he began to run.

"Hey!" shouted a voice. "Get the hell back here!" Vridar stopped, his heart breaking. He came back and faced his aunt. "Don't try some of your sneakun tricks," she said. "I'm your boss now."

He tried to say yes maam but the words stuck in his throat. Marion was standing off alone, his eyes full of tears and fright. Remembering that he was his brother's keeper, Vridar went over and took Marion's hand and looked again at his aunt.

"Don't dig your shoes in the ground that way! You tryun to wear them out?"

With an effort he met her gaze. "No maam," he said.

The one room of this shack was small. In the northeast corner stood an old iron stove, in the northwest corner a handmade cupboard, and between the two was a table against the logs. In the southeast corner was the Swensen bed, an out-of-shape iron thing with paint scaling off its legs. In the southwest corner was the boys' bed on the floor, a bed of four quilts which their mother had made. This house was floored with slabs, spiked round side down to the beams; its surface was uneven and it was full of enormous cracks. Vridar's bed, he discovered, was uneven too, as though laid on a huge washboard. At home he had slept on wild goose and duck feathers, burrowing down into voluptuous softness; but here his unfleshed body was tortured as if it lay on a rockpile. His mother had brought a tick and had told him to fill it at his grandfather's strawstack; but his aunt said she would not have straw spilling in her house, and she hung the tick as a curtain between the two beds.

"That's so you won't see nothun ain't good for you," said said, her eyes mocking him. "And don't let me catch you snoopun. Just sleep like a log."

He knew what she meant. She never caught him snooping, but he often lay awake and heard their love-making. He heard their heavy breath and her gasping and the creaking of bedsprings. After a few days he lay awake for another reason.

For the care of their sons his parents had given to the sister and brother-in-law a milk cow, an elk and a deer, and a five-gallon keg of blackstrap molasses. Borg had said it was too much. Just the same the boys were so starved that they were skeletons when spring came. Soon after they arrived, they suffered an indignity that they never forgot or forgave.

For supper that evening Agnes had cooked a big vegetable stew, and, having no bowls, she set it on the table in a large pot. She served the boys, spooning potatoes and cabbage and soup and a little meat to their tin plates; and they ate this and wished for more. But they did not ask for more. They looked hungrily at the pot and waited. Possibly Marion's stare was a little bolder, for it was against him that Agnes exploded.

"Good God, ain't you full yet? You eat like a pig! Has your mother starved you all your born days?"

This rebuke was enough for Vridar; he pushed his plate back and strove to look satisfied.

"Ain't you had enough, too?" Agnes asked Marion.

"No maam," he said.

With a cry of rage she seized the huge pot and turned it bottomside up on Marion's plate. The contents filled his plate, overflowed on the table, and spilled in streams to his lap. He was drenched with food and too amazed to move.

"Now eat it!" she cried, her gray eyes like fire. "Eat ever bit of it!"

Borg looked round him, a little disconcerted, and tried to laugh; but Vridar could tell by the man's eyes that he thought it a good joke. Withdrawing to a corner, he watched his brother, heroically stuffing himself until he groaned. If Marion paused, his aunt would shout at him and command him to eat; and he ate until he was blind with food and grief. Then he was told to get to the well and clean himself off, and to fetch pail and mop and scrub the floor. All this he meekly did.

But it was not for experiences like this that Vridar lay awake, though they haunted him and made him hate. It was because he and Marion were always given the coarsest fare, dry bread and potatoes and the bitter molasses, while for her husband and self Agnes cooked delicious things. She never suspected that Vridar knew this. She never ate them when she thought he could see. She cooked them when he was away at school, and she hid them in a trunk under the bed. But his keen nose smelled them out. When his aunt stepped outside to go to the woodpile or the well, he would swiftly explore, and find pudding or pie or cake.

These things were eaten after the boys had gone to bed. Their aunt would ask, "Are you asleep yet?" and at first if he was not asleep Vridar told her so. Her fury then was so sudden and bitter that he knew she had some purpose in mind. He deceived her thereafter, and when she asked, "Are you kids asleep?" he gave no sound. Not quite satisfied, she would ask again or perhaps come over to look at their closed eyes; then, convinced that they slept, she would softly bring the food from its hiding-place. Husband and wife would eat together and laugh in low murmurs, as if they shared a secret between them, and a treasure, too. Vridar took Marion into his confidence, and he also would listen, while pretending to sleep. They heard teeth bite into pie crust and they smelled the richness. For seven months, they deceived their aunt and uncle, and for seven months with one exception they ate dry bread, potatoes, molasses and now and then a little meat.

Sometimes the aunt and uncle talked, believing that the small ears did not hear. "I'd never take kids again," she said one evening, her words muffled by pie. "I'll hate all the little bastards but my own."

The man chuckled. "They're sure sheepish little lubbers," he said.

"It's the Branton. There ain't nothun sheepish in my people."

"You know, honey girl, we ain't gettun enough for this. You see that God damn milk cow Joe give us?"

"Oh well, Joe's too stingy to drink all the water he wants. It's moren I thought we'd get."

"They're a hell of a pack of bother. Will they be here till school's out?"

"I guess. That's what their mother said."

Night after night, their hands clasped, the lads heard their talk, and their hearts darkened with hate against them. But of the abuse, the starvation, and the insults their parents were never to know until long after their boys were grown.

They came from school to hard words and chores. "It takes you a hell of a while to get home!" their aunt would cry. "Where you been?"

"We come right home," said Vridar.

"Well, get your chores done."

One day Borg called Vridar to turn the grindstone. The man would press on the sickle, Vridar knew, more than was necessary, and he would make the boy turn long after the knives were sharp. Vridar would glance up to see the evil and malice in Borg's eyes.

"You ain't tired yet, are you?"

"No sir."

"A hell of a man you'll be." Borg bent down and offered his arm. "Here, feel some muscle."

"Yes sir, I can see."

"Put your hand here." Vridar suspected treachery but he placed his hand. It was caught between muscles that were like stone. He yelped with pain and Borg shook with cunning laughter. "Think you'll ever be a man like me?"

"I hope so, sir."

93

"A puny little stick like you? Well, crank away, kid, I'll be done in a few more hours."

Vridar turned again, using both hands, and glancing up from time to time to see the hair thrusting from Borg's chest, like that pushing out of his grandmother's old sofa. Borg was proud of his hairy chest and arms and legs.

"Kid, I got hair on my belly. Think you'll ever have hair on your belly?"

"I don't know."

"You'll do well, son, if you have any on your chin."

Borg sometimes made a strange frenzied sound. He would rub his hard knuckles over the lad's scalp and make the sound; and in bed, too, he made it while wooing his wife. She would shriek with delight and beg him to stop.

It was not alone from his uncle and aunt that Vridar suffered. His grandmother and his youngest uncle, Mike, also gave him unholy hell. Rose said the Branton stuck out on him like warts; it was deceit in his eyes; it was a kind of slinking coyotish thing in his movements and speech. His love of books was only the Branton in him, trying to lord it over his betters. Mike was yellow-haired, blue-eyed, and bold. He hated school. He had contempt for his nephews, and this contempt he expressed every time he saw them. "Come on and fight," he would say. "I'n lick you both." When Vridar would not fight, Mike would tie one of his own hands behind him. "I'n lick you both with one hand." Then he would pounce on the boys and hurl them down and press their enraged faces into manure. This humiliation, repeated again and again, so sickened Vridar and so lacerated his self-esteem that one day he resolved to fight if set on again, to fight desperately until he died.

At school he found an old mouth organ out in the sagebrush. Mike said it was his. Vridar thought his uncle lied and he began to run, with Mike at his heels. He plunged into his grandmother's home, hoping to find justice there.

"It's mine!" Vridar shouted, holding the worthless thing up for Rose to see. "I found it and it's mine!"

"Give it to me!" said Rose, and snatched it from Vridar's hand.

"I'll beat his daylights out!" yelled Mike, panting and furious. "He stole it!"

"I didn't!" said Vridar, staring covetously at the organ. All the other boys had things in their pockets but Vridar and Marion. They had nothing, not even a marble. Vridar now tried to seize it and got a stinging blow on his face.

"Are you just a damn little thief?" asked Rose, scowling at him. "What else you been stealun, I'd like to know!"

"It's a lie to say I stole it! I found it!"

"You call your grandma a liar? Son," she said, turning to Mike, "fetch me a stick. I'll blister his hindend for him."

Mike darted in search of a green limb, but Vridar did not wait. He bolted outside and went howling with grief and outrage to his aunt's house.

Hearing him coming, she framed herself in the doorway. "What's all the racket about?" she demanded. "Good God, you sound like you was about to be killed!"

Vridar ran away from her and hid behind a stinkbush to weep out of him the insult and the shame. After a while he dried his eyes and sat thinking about people.

He hated his father's people, all of them, and decided that when he was grown he would change his name to Branton.

But if his humiliations were bitter, he saw himself avenged on his uncle and aunt by a power greater than his own. He saw them quarrel until they were both shot with rage; heard them threaten to kill one another; heard them promise to die. During the first weeks they kept their violent tempests out of sight, but later they cast shame and pride to the winds and roared and shrieked until the house shook. Agnes said she would go outside and freeze, she would jump into the well, she would take his razor and cut her throat; and by all the stars he begged her to do so.

A typical scene occurred in December when the snow outside was two feet deep. The quarrel started this way. Second only to her sister Villette, Agnes had been the belle of this area, with many wooers, one of whom tried to shoot himself after she married Borg. Borg himself had been a gay rake, for whom girls had made valentines and daisy chains. Memory of what they had been and of people whom they could have married was constantly in their speech. If one threw a taunt the other's insult was twice as mean.

"I could a-had my pick of men!" Agnes cried. "I didn't have to marry a pig-eyed Swede!"

"Oh-ho! Pig-eyed Swede! Listen, you fat-assed cow, I could have married Lily Bott and she had you beat forty ways from Christ! That woman knew how to do it in bed."

"Ohhh!" gasped Agnes, sucking her breath in. "You beast."

And the quarrel was on. This evening Borg had brought for his wife a letter which the postman had left with Rose. Agnes opened it and read while Borg and the lads watched. She caught her breath and turned red and tried to run outside.

"No you don't!" said Borg, hurling her back. "Let me read it."

Borg seized her and they struggled, with Agnes spitting at him and howling and screeching until he hurled her to the bed and crushed her down. While she lay there panting and moaning, he read the letter and then tore it in tiny strips and fed it to the fire. She leapt up to stop him but was too late, and then faced him, quivering with fury.

"You pig-eyed Swede!"

He fixed her with an evil grin. "So this is the guy you been bustin your heart for!"

"No!"

"You lie. And you'll always be his sweetheart, will you?—his little honey doll? By God, ain't that sweet! And he'll never forget you, no, oh no! And if you ever get sick of me—"

"He don't mean nothun to me. Stop talkun that way."

"You fat lying bitch! What'd you marry me for, you hippercrite? Huh?" He was yelling at her now. "I'll choke your God damn eyes out one of these days!" He stared round him, baffled, as if wondering whether to choke her now or later.

"Borg, don't be a fool." She came toward him, timid, supplicating. "I ain't done no wrong."

"No, by God, to hear you tell it! You been a lily-white angel all your life!" He was looking at her with a furious scowl. "I guess you could tell a lot of stories."

95

"Borg! I was a virgin—"

"Oh no you wasn't. I know a virgin when I bed her down." He was not shouting now. His voice was so sinister, so ominous that she cowered and shrank back. "I'll beat your brains out, by God. When I marry a woman she's mine and not the whore of every son of a bitch in the country."

"Borg, I won't let you call me such names!"

"I'll call you any God damn name I can think of. The trouble is I can think of nothun bad enough. You was a whore before I knowed you. I wasn't the first man you slept with."

"That's a lie, I cross my heart to God! You stop talkun that way or I'll leave you!"

"Go on, get the hell out. Pack your duds. Don't just say you'll do it. Do it. Do it before I throw you out on your ass."

She began to wail. She sat on the bed, twisting her hands and crying to him that she would kill herself.

"Get into bed!" he yelled. When she did not obey him at once, he roared like a fiend. He said he would break her neck. He said he would knock her brains out if she had any brains. Then he saw the two boys cowering in a dark corner, looking at him, and he roared at them. "Don't stand there with your eyes stuck out, you little bastards! Get to bed!"

The lads tore at their clothes and kicked their shoes off and went quaking into the quilts. Agnes was undressing. She was moaning and clutching blindly at buttons and hooks. Borg told her to hurry or he would set the house afire and burn her alive. Then he began to undress. He took his big boots off and hurled them at the north wall. One struck a pan of milk and knocked it clear to the window. He pitched his shirt after the shoes, telling her all the while what he would do. She could not write love-letters under his very nose. He would go find this man and knock all his teeth clear into his belly.

"What's he look like?" he demanded.

"Oh, I don't know!" she chattered, pulling on a nightgown.

"God damn it, you screwed him and don't know what he looks like?"

"I never! I hope that lie chokes you!"

"Dark complected," said Borg, sneering. "Black hair on his belly, huh? I think I seen the son of a bitch once. When I see him again I'll hit him so hard he'll roll from here to London." He stood up in his underwear, hair pushing out between the buttons. He walked over to the lamp and blew it out. Then the bed creaked under his weight.

Vridar thought the quarrel was finished. It had only begun. Something happened in the bed and Agnes came clawing out like a cat. Peering out, Vridar saw her white nightgown in the gloom. He heard her sobbing dark threats. She had stood all that any woman could stand and she would kill herself, now, tonight.

"Do it!" shouted Borg. "Go jump in the well!" She was fumbling about in darkness. "Jump in the well, that's easiest, and when you're good and dead I'll drag you out."

"I'll kill myself!" she wailed. "I'll cut my throat!"

"Sure, cut your God damn throat."

She was now pawing in the cupboard. "I'll cut my throat!" she shrieked at him, and Vridar saw something gleaming in her hand.

"Sure," he said.

"I got your razor!" she cried. "I'll go out now and kill myself!"

"Hang your dress on a bush so I'n find you."

She opened the door, with the blade still in her hand, and looked outside. She wavered there, undecided, and bitter air filled the room.

"Shut the door!" he bellowed. "Go on and kill yourself!"

She went then, with nothing on but a nightdress. The door was closed. Her naked feet made a sound in the frozen snow and the sound grew more distant and all was silence. Borg at last left the bed and lit the lamp and sat on a chair, looking at the door, listening.

"Vridar!" he cried.

"Yes sir?" said Vridar, sitting up.

Borg did not look at him. His eyes were fixed on the door. "You think she'll do it?"

"Do what?"

"Kill herself, you lubber. By God, I'll bet she's right on the doorstep, listenun." He went over and swung the door wide. Only darkness was there. He closed it and sat. "Do you?"

"Yes sir, she might."

"Did you see she took the razor?"

"Yes sir, she took it."

"Don't lie to me!" He went to the cupboard and looked in. "By God, I guess she did," he said, and sat again. There was silence. His underwear was unbuttoned and Vridar could see the matted yellow hair on his chest and belly. Slipping his boots on Borg hesitated by the door and then went outside. Many minutes passed. Then Vridar heard the sound of feet, the door was flung open, and Borg staggered inside, carrying his wife. He pitched her into the bed and built up the fire. All night Vridar heard her sobs.

But the next day they suffocated one another with love. There was no school and the boys saw what they did. Borg would dance amorously round his bride, neighing like a stud, caressing her thighs, bending her backward and thrusting a leg between her own. They kissed with such violent passion that Vridar could only stare and hold his breath. They clung to each other as if grown together; they breathed honeyed endearments and gazed deep into the eyes of each. She called him her darling-sweet and her hero-man; he called her his angel-lily and his bunch-of-love. He said her hips and breasts and lips and everything about her had been tailored for him and suited him right down to a gnat's hindend. He gave long amorous moans and exploded smacking kisses into her ears. He kissed her legs and the back of her neck and pulled her dress down and chewed at her breasts.

"I'm your ram," he said. "Ever see a buck ram a ewe? That's what our word ramming means. I ain't so ignerant."

97

Gasping and panting under his wooing, Agnes saw the lads watching her. "Hey, in God's name, what you here for? Get outside!"

"Let them see us," said Borg. "They'll be married some day. They should know how to warm a woman up."

"Scat!" said Agnes. "Ain't you got no manners a-tall?"

The boys slunk outside into the cold. Then Vridar stood on the doorstep and listened and heard the bed creaking.

XIV

Violent though his home life was this winter, it was his life in school that caused a deeper anguish. It was a school of bullies, and they were after him all the time. If he hid, he was discovered and dragged forth; if he wept and begged to be left alone, the glee of his persecutors knew no bounds. Because of his suit made from the Civil War uniform, he was called Little Boy Blue. "The cows is in the hay!" they would shout at him. "Fod God sake blow your horn!"

The three who tormented him most were big gawky lewd fellows. One was Charles Dinsmore, freckled, grinning, relentless. Another was Olaf Sorenson, a blue-eyed, pudgy-cheeked Dane. The third was Lew Brode, loose of mouth, obscene of speech, and irresistible to some girls. The three of them were in the sixth grade and had been for years. It was Dinsmore whom Vridar hated and feared most; the others sometimes forgot him, but Dinsmore was always on his trail.

When Vridar and Marion came to school, they were usually met at some distance from the schoolhouse by Dinsmore and his henchmen. Coming up the road, Vridar would be alert, his heart drumming in his ears; and then he would see the gang coming toward him. Clasping Marion's hand, he would stop and look round him for a way out, but there was never a way out.

"Here's the little boy blues!" Dinsmore would cry. "God, did you ever see such sweet little fellers?"

"Let's take their didies off," said one.

"Give them a nipple," said another. "By God, they ain't weaned yet."

"Such sweet little fellers!" said Dinsmore, and pretended to be convulsed with grief. Then Lew Brode, the best actor of the lot, would affect to be overcome; he would moan and pound at his chest, or fall to his knees in prayer.

"Be still!" he would sputter, as if tears choked him. "I'll ask God to fetch their horns back . . . . O God, our father, who art a big blue man, listen to my grief! All of us now assembled in revrunt prayer, kneelun here in the holy dust with our hearts a-bustin with tears, we ask thee to fetch these sweet little fellers another horn! The cows is in the hay and all bloated to hell and gone! Give em another horn, you old fibblesnoot! . . . ."

"Don't ever come to school again," said Dinsmore to Vridar, "without your horn. God will put it anunder your pillow."

"Now," said Lew, "take your little panties down. We want to see if your auntie changed your didies. Something stunk horrible in school yesterday."

This sally brought great gales of mirth. Fifty grinning faces were lewd with anticipation, fifty pairs of eyes were malicious and intent.

"See if they've got their marbles," said one.

"Sure," said another, "take their pants down."

"Shshsh!" said Dinsmore. "Don't scare these little fellers. I'll see if they've got their marbles." He approached Vridar, his eyes devilish. "Take your pants down and show papa."

"Leave us alone!" Vridar cried, panting with shame and hate.

Then Dinsmore would hurl Vridar down and expose him; and solemnly he would say, while they all pushed in to look: "This kid ain't got no marbles. He's a steer."

"Then we just as well cut his thing off too."

And the schoolbell would clang. So nearly every morning they were met with some fresh lewdness that made Vridar frantic. And inside the schoolhouse matters were only a little improved.

The building was enormous and bleak like a barn. The row of desks on the north wall was occupied by the first grade, the row on the south wall by the eighth grade, and between these two the other grades were ranged, so that the room when full was terraced in heads and shoulders, save for a number of big louts who were still in the fifth or sixth grades. One of these was a large man more than twenty years old named Alfred Bott. He had been in the fifth grade for years and came to school to escape from work.

The hundred or more pupils were taught by one teacher. His name was Wallace Ross. In the front of the room he sat behind a desk, and facing him was a circle of benches to which, in turn, he called each grade for recitation. He had small eyes of the color of shadowed ice, a humped unfleshed nose, and an absurdly small mouth. His voice was rasping and shrill. When he stood up, he looked like a wooden cross with a man's suit hanging upon it. He never smiled.

From the first bell until the last this school was a fantastic farce. The great shysters in the fifth and sixth grades hurled chalk and erasers and paper wads soaked with ink at the teacher, or gave sudden loud groans, or blew their noses with prolonged frenzy. On hearing a sudden lewd snort, Ross would leap to his feet and stand trembling in his loose clothes while glaring at the grinning faces. "Who made that noise?" he would ask, his thin voice quavering. Nobody, of course, would reply. Then he would stand there and scowl, his eyes like beads of ice and his nose like a small plowshare. "Alfred Bott, was that you?" "No sir," Bott would say, his tone ominously respectful. "Charles Dinsmore, was that you?" "No sir." "I'd like to know what you mean! This isn't a hogpen and you're not a bunch of hogs!"

He would glare them into such silence that the room was utterly still. Then he would sit down; but from time to time he would look up swiftly, searchingly, his pale lips aquiver. Dinsmore would look round him and grin. Lew Brode would pout his lips amorously at Ruby Beam, the school's whore. And meanwhile Olaf would be patiently rolling the cheese of his lunch into a round yellow ball. He would wait until Ross was quiet and reassured. Then his right hand would come back, swift and strong, and the yellow bullet would strike the schoolmaster on his green cravat. Ross would move as if stung but he would not leap up at once. For a little while he would not look at anyone. He would stare down at his cravat, now stained with cheese, or at his lean hands, as though wondering how much strength they held. Then he would rise to his feet, slowly, like one suddenly grown old, and look at the big louts. He would come up the aisle and stop by Sorenson, now busy trying to divide 17 into 837, and look down at him. While he stood there looking at Sorenson, Bott would begin to blow his nose. Into a red unclean handkerchief he would snort great blasts, pinching his nostrils as he blew, so that the sound would come out in violent barks. When the master turned to him, he would say quietly, with that same ominous respect: "I got a bad cold." And again he would honk with all his might.

Trembling with fury, Ross would return to his desk and sit.

One November afternoon Lew precipitated a riot. In front of him sat Annie Cluff, a very pale blonde; her eyes were the color of skimmed milk and her hair of ripe oats. She was the amorous friend of Ruby Beam. She had pinched sloping shoulders, and legs which, Lew had scribbled in a legend on the privy wall, used her stomach for a crotch. She was past sixteen but was also still in the fifth grade.

Lew wooed her hour after hour, day after day. With the toe of his shoe he would reach forward and caress her thigh, whereupon she would shake with giggles and wink at Ruby. He would bend forward and kiss the silky yellow hair on her neck. He would clap hands over her eyes and draw her head back and thrust his red wet tongue into her ear. Vridar perceived that she liked this wooing: her pale face would drench with blood and her eyes gleam with sensuous warmth.

Lew wrote and sent notes to the big lubbers around him, and one of them fell into Vridar's hands. It said: I'm horny about burnets. Watch Annie for I aim to make a burnet out of her.

All those in the room who shared the secret watched and waited. Annie suspected some devilment but no one would let her read a note. She would glance back at Lew or move uneasily and twitter, but he affected to be sunk in a book. Under his desk, though, his hands were busy, pouring black ink from bottles passed stealthily down the aisle into his lunch pail. As part of the plan, Dinsmore was to leave the room and then knock on the door and call the teacher outside. He raised a hand and snapped his fingers.

"Mr. Dinsmore," said Ross severely, "do you wish to ask a question?"

"I want a-know can I go outside?"

"You went outside only a little while ago."

"Yes sir, but I got bowel trouble because I took epsom salts last night."

The room whooped with mirth. As red as pickled beets, Wallace Ross stood up. He began to speak but laughter rolled upon him in tides. At last he said, "You can go."

A few minutes later a great pounding shook the door. Ross stared at it apprehensively and then went softly over and peered out. Then he stepped outside. Lew fetched his lunch pail up and spilled a pint of black ink on Annie's oat-colored hair. She leapt up, clawing and screaming. Ink made black paths down her face and throat, ran into her mouth, spread like a shadow over her yellow dress. The big louts in the room went mad with joy. Olaf simply rolled out of his seat into the aisle and sprawled, roaring like a stuck hog. Alfred Bott with a mighty wrench tore his desk from its spikes and kicked it bottom side up. A big ruddy fellow whose name was Vernon West hurled his inkwell at the blackboard and sent his arithmetic and pencils and notebooks after it. Lew ran to an east window, kicked the glass out with his foot, and leapt down.

After this outrage, the school trustees met in secret council. They expelled Lew and Alfred, whose fathers had no influence in the community, placed Dinsmore and Olaf on probation but passed over Vernon with a gentle rebuke because his father was one of the trustees. But this was not the end of the matter. Lew came to the schoolground to play marbles or woo the girls or on privy walls to add new legends to the old. Weeks later Alfred Bott waited for Ross after school was dismissed and struck him a terrible blow on his mouth. When Ross spoke thereafter, his pupils could see a darkness where two teeth had been.

Such violent horseplay, however much it distressed Vridar, was not his principal concern. In the third row on his left sat Dinsmore, and between him and Dinsmore were two lads who became his bitter enemies, both older than he. Sid Hawk was a handsome scowling youngster who reminded Vridar of Jed Bridwell. Duke Beam had the jaws and eyes and mind of an ape. Duke's hostility Vridar never understood; Sid's rested on a curious fact.

When Vridar first entered this school, his Uncle Mike and Sid Hawk had fought eleven times. Mike had always been the victor. After he was beaten but not conquered, Sid would declare in a softly ominous voice that they would fight again. When his face was healed and the black was gone from his eyes, he would go to Mike and say, "I'm ready to fight again." The whole school would hum with excitement and most of the pupils would follow the warriors to a level area on the butte. There Sid and Mike would fight. They fought a standup and knockdown battle, with no wrestling or biting or gouging. Mike would knock his foe down, for he was imperturbably cool and struck clean powerful blows; and Sid would rise again and again, his eyes fearful to look at and his mouth twisted with hate. At last, despairing again of triumph, he would say quietly, "I've got enough this time but we'll fight again."

"Any time," Mike would say, and put on his coat.

Sid had a brother of Vridar's age, named Jupiter, a slow and dull but husky lad. Because Mike was his uncle, Vridar was called upon by the code of this school to see that Jupiter did not interfere. He quaked with fear when he saw Mike and Sid going to the hill to battle again, but he had to go; his self-esteem was like a lash, he had to stand by to see that Jupiter did not leap in. Desperately he would say, "Stay out, for if you fight I'll fight!"

Jupiter never fought, though Dinsmore and others taunted him with cowardice, eager to see what Vridar would do. After Mike and Sid had concluded their battle, the mob would close in howling for a wrestling match between the two smaller lads. In these matches Vridar always won. Jupiter was strong but awkward and fumbling; Vridar was quick and alert. But it is was grit and pride born of desperation that put him on top. He would maneuver until he got Jupiter down and then blind with anxiety and rage he would clutch the boy around his neck and try to strangle him.

101

Jupiter would grin and struggle and pant; he would rest a little while and struggle again; and Vridar would cling like madness, moaning in his breath and sobbing deep in his being. The mob would be yelling at Jupiter. "Get up, Jupe, God damn you! Why do you let a skinny wart like that hold you down? You damned awkward grunting lubber get up from there! . . ." Vridar hated these voices. They gave to Jupiter a new and lusty strength and again he would grunt and kick and try to get his fingers in Vridar's nostrils or ears or eyes. Vridar would be weeping quietly in sunken galling frenzy that was like fire in his brain. He would ask Jupiter to say he was down but Jupiter would shout, "No, I ain't!" Then Vridar would try to choke him and crush him to death. He would push his chin against Jupiter's chest or throat and rub hard until the lad would howl with astonishment and pain; he would put his face against the boy's face and grind their cheek bones together, hurting himself but enduring it in the hope that pain would break the other's will. When Jupiter said down at last, Vridar would stagger to his feet, white and spent and barely able to stand.

And so it was his triumph and the triumph of Mike that bred Sid's hate. Vridar liked him nevertheless, for he was intelligent and proud and he fought in a clean bright way. Duke on the other hand was as witless as a cow. He fought brutally, his strong uneven teeth chewing at ears and hands, his fingers probing for eyes while with his feet he tried to kick his foe's genitals, Vridar knew his way because he had seen him fight a boy named John. When the fight was done John's ears dripped red and his mouth was torn and one eye was puffed and blind and half-out of his skull.

In school Duke wrote Vridar a multitude of notes, challenging and insulting. One said, "basturd cowerd you your ma stinks and your pa is a horss theef and all your peepul is liers and hores will you fight now?" Another said," you sucked tits til you was six year old and you stink like shit and I can smel you a mile away I will poke your cowerd eyes out and bust your guts wide open you pukin stink will you fight now?" Vridar had to read these notes, for if he scorned them he heard the derisive chuckle of Sid Hawk. He read them and shook and felt that his days were building to a horrible crisis. If he glanced at Duke, the lad would thumb his nose and cross his eyes and hiss, "You shitass coward!" He would hiss, "You tit-sucker!"

"Be careful," Dinsmore would whisper, "or he'll bawl for his ma."

One day Vridar felt the steady baffled insolence of Duke's eyes. These eyes had been watching him for an hour, and all the while Dinsmore and Sid were encouraging Duke and feeding his dull mind with fresh insults. "Hey!" Duke whispered, but Vridar pretended not to hear. Suddenly Duke swung and put both feet against Vridar and sent him sprawling into the aisle. Vridar struck his head on a desk and made a great racket. The teacher came down, his icy eyes agleam and his small mouth puffed out.

"What's the matter with you? he asked. "Can't you sit in your seat?" Vridar crawled back, rubbing his skull. The master looked round him. "What happened here?"

"He just went to sleep," said Dinsmore. "He went to sleep and fell over."

"Is that the truth?" Ross asked. He grasped Vridar by his collar and marched him to the blackboard and made him stand there, his face to the wall, until school was dismissed.

Vridar became so desperately afraid of Duke that he rarely left the schoolhouse. During recess and the noon hour he would remain inside by a window, looking out at the games. Duke would come up and thumb his nose and thrust out his fat tongue. He would make a line on the earth and yell, "Cross that and watch me bust your gizzard!"

Sick of the humiliation and shame and of school and of life, Vridar would return to his desk and read. Everywhere he felt or thought he felt contempt. He thought he saw it in the eyes of boys, yes, and in the eyes of girls, and this was the worst bitterness of all. He loathed himself. He despised his thin white face and the fright in the darkness of his eyes and the tremulous lines of his mouth; so much so indeed that he never looked in a mirror save to comb his hair. Then he would mock himself; he would thumb his nose at his image and stare at it with a derisive sneer; and he would smite his cheek a burning blow. Sometimes when self-loathing made him sick he would rise from his desk, resolved to go outside even if he had to face death. He would slip out and watch a group playing marbles, but when he saw Duke coming he would gasp and run, with no power to control his legs or clench his hands; and Duke would chase him like a scared rabbit into the house.

So the matter stood until his humiliation and self-contempt possessed him like nausea and he wished himself dead. Not forever could he live this way. An end would have to come, a turning point, a crisis of rage and blood. He would have been willing to be beaten senseless if that was the price of peace. But he lacked the courage to force the bitter thing to a crisis, and when the crisis came it was thrust upon him.

Across from the school in a house shaded by great trees lived his father's brother, who was called Dock, and Dock's wife. Her name was Ruth. Vridar had seen her once, a sad lovely woman with grief and a terrible silence in her eyes. She had fled from home and people to marry this man, and now among strangers in a strange world she was slowly dying. Vridar was told that she had leakage of the heart.

One afternoon there were sounds in the gloomy house and school children ran over to the fence. From a window Vridar saw them go and he ran out and joined them. Dock, with a man on either side, was walking up and down among the naked trees, howling insanely with grief. The men were trying to give him courage and cheer. Vridar understood then that the strange silent woman was dead. Profoundly stirred, he looked at his uncle and saw the man striking out with his arms while he bellowed with anguish, or knelt to weep like a child. Vridar heard some women say that Dock had loved her with all his heart and soul and would never marry again. Then the three men went into the house and there was nothing to see or hear. The pupils turned away and went back to their games but Vridar stood here, thinking of this man's grief and of the strange woman who was dead. He began to weep. A sharp voice brought him to his senses and he swung to look into the evil eyes of Duke Beam.

"Now I got you!" cried Duke, eager for battle. "By God, you'll fight now!"

"Leave me alone!" Vridar shouted, looking desperately round him.

"You stinkun coward, you'll be a sight for sad eyes when I'm done with you!"

Vridar turned and ran. He went like the wind and the clumsy Duke was left far behind, but at the schoolhouse door was Dinsmore with his gang. They barred Vridar's way and taunted him and said he would have to fight now. The boy looked back and saw Duke coming, his fists ready and his eyes ablaze. Vridar ran again. Fear seized him and bore him as if on wings. He ran around the building and dived into the coal shed and slammed the door shut. Frantically he began to pile coal against the door. He heard the mob-feet. He heard the loud obscene challenges of Duke.

There was a great din outside while Vridar, shaking with terror, tried to barricade himself. "Come out!" the voices were shouting, and battering rams smote the door. The door rocked, its leather hinges ripping and its barricade of coal tumbling back. Then the door crashed down, and there within Vridar stood, a pale desperate boy facing a mob. Duke plowed forward, his eyes lusting for battle, and in this moment Vridar was remembering what Borg had said: "If you ever fight be sure to shut your fists like this—tight, see?—and put your thumbs this way. Close your hands as tight as you can and then when you hit you won't bust no bones . . . ." He was closing his hands tight and clasping his thumbs against his fingers, for he knew now that he would have to fight and he was resolved to fight until he died.

He stepped forth and his eyes were so desperate with the unalterable purpose of his mind that some of the boys fell back. Duke gaped with amazement; and as Vridar stepped through the door he was watching the lad's eyes and he saw a change in them. He advanced slowly, remembering that Borg had said that when you brought your right fist back you rolled backward with the right shoulder and when you struck you then turned in a rolling movement with all your body behind the blow. Duke was slowly retreating and Vridar was following, and when he came close he brought his right fist back and rolled with his shoulder, and in the next moment as swift as lightning he struck, rolling with the blow and putting all his weight behind it. He smote Duke full on the mouth and the boy dropped as if felled by a club. Then Duke rolled backward, yelping like a dog, and a moment later got to his feet and ran.

Vridar was never troubled again by Duke Beam, but Dinsmore and his gang redoubled their persecution. Vridar would come to school and find his inkwell full of urine. They once took his shoes off and filled them with dung, and they would take his pants down and tell him they intended to cut off his marbles. His mother, they said, was a whore and he was not his father's child. They wrote him into vile legends on the privy walls and linked in ribald verse his name with the names of girls. They teased others too but they were most relentless with him. Lying in bed at night he wondered why. He learned to hate them so desperately and bitterly that he promised himself over and over that when a grown man he would become an expert fighter and he would seek them all out and beat them to death. This thought comforted him a little. Some day . . . .

He would look at them, thinking of that distant time when he would knock them senseless. Lest he forget their names he wrote them all down, ranking them in their order of catastrophe:

Charl Dinsmore
Olaf Sorenson
Lew Brode
Sid Hawk
Bush O'Brien

Bush had never molested him; it was a premonition that caused him to add this name. He felt that trouble stood ahead, somewhere, some time, between him and Bush O'Brien. And in this he was right.

XV

But these first seven months in school were not all anguish and humiliation. The last two were an idyl of glory. He fell in love. From the privy walls as well as from the lips of boys and girls he had learned the coarse vigorous language of sex. He would read the foul legends and stare at the crude drawings and ponder them and they would become strange things in his dreams. Birth, he knew, sprang from the sudden mating of flesh with flesh, and that the mating was pleasurable he read in the eyes of Ruby and Annie and the big louts who lay with them.

A conflict was growing within him. It fed on the experiences of this winter and became in a later time almost too bitter to be endured. His mother had taught him in her stern way that all women and girls were pure, were angels of a kind, until debauched by men; and that he should respect and cherish them and defend them against insult. Insult of girls and women, he had come to perceive, was mysteriously related to love and mating and birth. The boys here, it seemed to him, were forever insulting the girls, and the girls, or at least a few of them, liked it. That boys would insult them he had been taught to expect, but that girls would like it he was left to discover for himself. What kind of girls, he wondered, could Ruby and Annie and Susie Pross be, that they should go out of their way, as they so obviously did, to invite vulgar speech and caress! What kind were they that they should speak with such contempt of virgins, and unblushingly use all the words recorded on the privy walls!

Quite as amazing for Vridar was the fact that the big louts ignored the shy chaste maids and ran after those who were wanton. He found that he himself was more than curious. He suffered unmistakable pangs of rage and dismay when he saw one of the girls being hugged and kissed, or watched her sneak off into the brush with an eager boy at her side. Not, he told himself, with self-righteous disdain, that he would stoop to such infamy against a girl! Still . . . . He had no desire to kiss Ruby's bold red mouth or take the plump sinuous Susie in his arms! No, by all the angels, no! Nevertheless he ached to see what was done, while assuring himself that these lewd boys and girls had come from the loins of Cain. He would stare until his eyes filled with mist. When in a hidden place he saw a girl bend backward under a kiss he would hate her. And he hated Delbert Brode.

This lad, about Vridar's age, was distinguished in common opinion as the handsomest boy in school, with his curly golden hair as soft as silk, his gentian-blue eyes, his long dark lashes, and his shapely nose and mouth. For a little while he was Ruby's beau. Ruby, two or three years older, with bold eyes the color of wet gray marble and red cheeks and mouth, was in the opinion of every one the toughest girl in school. On the privy walls was the name of every boy who had known her favors. Ruby said in her simple frank way that she intended to become a whore.

Her two friends Annie and Susie were not so lovely. Annie was the blonde upon whom Lew poured the ink. Her chin and mouth were small; her pale eyes were so absurdly far apart that her face was a grotesque triangle. Susie was plump and abandoned and full of the devil and mischief. But she was still a virgin, said the legends on the walls.

Ruby lived a half-mile up the lane running east. Sometimes after school the three girls set off together, followed by a crowd of boys. The boys would yell after them and the girls would yell back. Now and then Vridar slunk along, shamed by his unclean interest but eager to see and hear. He listened to the running fire of lewd talk. If the girls stopped, he would move in close, to stare at their mouths and eyes, their breasts and hips. With her unwelcome suitors Ruby was cruel and ruthless. One of these was Alfred Bott's big gawky brother named Bill. Bill was crazy about her. He told everyone that he would give his right hand and one of his eyes to lie with her once.

One afternoon he was bolder in his pursuit. He ran ahead of the crowd, yelling and acting witless, and pausing now and then to look back with a foolish grin. He shouted insults at Ruby until she stopped and faced him. "You—you—" he said.

"You God damn halfwit!" said Ruby. "You horny old pig-feeder!" She said worse things than that. Ruby used all the words on the privy walls and used them as if she had been born with them in her mouth.

The boys liked to see Bill abused. "Tell him what else he is!" they said.

"He's the runt pig that got the little tit."

"Tell him some more!"

Ruby was looking at Bill. "You quit followun me," she said, her eyes glowing with contempt. She flung at him words that made Vridar's ears burn. "I ain't your whore yet, you halfwitted pimp, and I won't never be."

Mouth agape, Bill was leering like an idiot. "You just do what a whore does," he said.

"Yeah, you dumb stud! Well, I won't with you, so hit the grit."

The boys liked this talk. They liked her bold words and ways. They stared at her with famished eyes, tongues licking out and bodies quivering. The next day on the privy wall Vridar saw a fresh legend: there was Ruby, naked and prone with her legs spread, and Bill tied to a post, eating hay. Vridar stared at the picture a long while.

He gave more time to these amorous doing than to his studies. If Ruby or Susie glanced at him, he felt sudden rapture, even though the girl was not aware of him at all. He listened when one of the big boys told what Ruby looked like without clothes. In a north field where a canal ran she sometimes went swimming, and boys would sneak over on hands and knees to spy on her. Vridar also wanted to see a naked girl—not a pure sweet girl, ah no, for to look at her would be sinful; but a wicked lost girl like Ruby. He went so far as to slip away one day to learn where the canal was.

But though these matters shook him and left him sunk in wonder, he soon forgot them in the glory of another girl's coming. Rescued from lewd meditation, he was delivered body and soul to the holiness of his first love. It was early in April and Marion was sick and Vridar went to school alone. The road from Borg's ran around the butte, climbed in deep white sand to the level area where Mike and Sid fought, and then fell downward into the long straight lane past the schoolhouse. At the top another lane ran north. Vridar had trudged up the hill this morning and had paused to rest, when a hundred yards away on the north road he saw the girl coming toward him. As she drew near, he thought she was such a vision as he had never seen. Then the girl came up and stopped, and for the first time Vridar and Neloa stood face to face.

She was not seven yet, Vridar learned afterward, but she was tall enough for nine or ten. He would also learn that she was Danish and Irish and American Indian. The power that held him now was her face and hair. Her eyes were a deep dark brown, with depth lying upon depth in luster and softness, and with something in them that seemed to him to be lonely and sad. Her cheeks and mouth had the color of health. Her eyebrows were two black arches. Her young body was slender and straight and proud. Her hair, very dark and very heavy, fell in a broad mane down her back and almost to her knees.

They looked at each other for several moments and neither spoke. Then the girl went ahead of him and down the road, with the dark mane lying down her back. She entered the schoolhouse. After hesitating, Vridar went softly in and saw her talking with Ross. He could not hear what she said but he thought her voice was sad and lonely like her eyes. The next few weeks he looked at her whenever he could. Before school closed, he loved her with blind and unreasoning fervor and set her up as his symbol and his ideal. She was to become more deeply than he would realize for a long time the center of his heart and his world.

The reasons for this passion at so young an age he was never fully to understand. Was it because of the loneliness and the want of love and tenderness in his life? Was it in part because of his new and impassioned interest in girls? Or was it some elusive and impalpable depth that he felt in Neloa Doole? Was he deceived in his belief that she moved like a queen, aloof, proud, and unapproachable? He never saw her playing with other girls. So far as he could tell she had no interest in the world around her, but lived for some strange reason in a world of her own.

In the schoolroom she sat two rows on his right and three seats ahead. With a long ruler he could have touched the glory of her hair. He stared at her endlessly, with a sweet choked pain in his heart, and inexorably and without reason he built her into his dream. Sometimes she wore her hair in a long braided tail but usually it fell loosely down her back and spread on the seat around her. It was so long that sometimes it touched the floor. She seldom looked up from her book, and finding her so studious Vridar would feel shame for his own laziness and drag his speller forth. Now and then he would write a note to her. The note would say, "Dear friend

Neloa, I think you are the nicest girl in the room. I know that you never use the words that some of the other girls use, but are sweet and pure. Will you let me be your friend?" Or in a bolder moment he would write: "I would like to walk home with you if you would let me. Will you?" He would read his notes again and again and decide that they were pretty silly and he would tear them up. They did not say what he wanted to say.

At a little distance from the school in a raw unpainted building lived some of her people. The men were dark and straight and looked like Indians. During the noon hour Neloa always went into this building and remained there until the bell clanged. Vridar would go softly over, feeling guilty and mean, and try to peer in. The windows were very high but by piling stones on stones he could stand and tiptoe and see Neloa inside. She would sit in a chair and seem neither to talk nor move. He saw unclean ragged babies crawling over the bare floor, and dirty garments and dishes and two round chamber pots under a far bed. These things sickened him a little. She annoyed him by going into such a place.

During the morning or afternoon recess, she went outside but she did not play. She would watch the others, her face very sober and her eyes, it seemed to Vridar, very sad and dark. Sometimes the boys tried to flirt with her but she would spurn them. Then Vridar was happy and proud. She was his girl, even though unaware of him, and some day she would be his wife.

Her most persistent wooer was Archie Brode, brother of Delbert and Lew. He was ten years old; he had a pale grinning face and very crooked teeth. If his gentler wooing got no response, he would yank at her hair or try to steal a button from her dress. "Oh, stop it!" she would say, looking at him with contempt that would have withered Vridar. But Archie was not withered. Day after day he was on her trail.

Vridar thought she hated him, but one day he came on them suddenly and was amazed. They were almost hidden from sight between the coal shed and the house and they were alone. Neloa was smiling at Archie and talking to him. This was not much but it was more than Vridar could stand, and he shook with jealous rage while he looked at them. It seemed that Archie had been out in the sagebrush and had gathered a bouquet of wild flowers for her. She had a yellow one in her black hair. Then Archie tried to kiss her and she cried: "Stop it!"

"But you should ought to kiss me for the flowers."

"I won't."

"Then let me kiss your cheek."

"No."

"Let me kiss your hand."

"No."

"Ah, just one little kiss, just one!"

"No, I said."

Archie then grasped her hand and tried to kiss it, and though she pushed him away she was smiling. Vridar, already a lad of intuitive insights, knew that she liked this wooing, and he held his breath, afraid that she was not quite as pure as he had hoped she would be. He was two years older than Archie or he would have gone over to slap the boy's face. As it was he waited, spying on them, praying that she would walk away, proud and unapproachable, a queen among girls. Then Archie saw Vridar and swung.

"Hey, you! You spyun on us, you sneak?"

Vridar did not know whether to stand his ground or retreat. What a bitter humiliation, to be caught spying on the girl he loved!

"You, there!" cried Archie. "What you sneakun around here for?"

"I'm not sneakun," said Vridar, now burning with shame. He moved toward them, trembling with anger and abased pride. "Why don't you leave her alone? Can't you see she don't like you?"

"Who don't like me? You mean her? She's crazy about me."

Vridar looked at Neloa and saw that her eyes were not friendly. She looked at him like one who had never seen him before and cared never to see him again. "She ought to slap your face," said Vridar, feeling more and more ridiculous.

"And who are you, to tell her? You're the one she ought to slap, you sneak!"

"I'm not a sneak!" cried Vridar, knowing full well that he was. Ah God, what a fool he had made of himself! He could not remain here and face her eyes, yet he did not know how to withdraw. Desperately he said, "She doesn't want to kiss you. Can't you tell it?"

"Oh, the hell she don't! Well, she's already kissed me, so now what?"

"I don't believe it. I think you're a liar."

"Hey!" said Archie, his eyes opening wide. "Did you call me a liar?"

"I said she doesn't want to kiss you. She ain't that kind of a girl."

"You can't call me a liar! My brother, he'll lick the hell out of you."

"All right, fetch him around." This was more than Vridar had expected, but he would have died rather than have been a coward before this girl. "Fetch him around, I said."

"Don't fret, I will. And now go away because she doesn't want you here. You can tell she don't like you."

"Who said she don't!"

"Ask her and see. You'n tell the way she looks at you."

Vridar felt that he had lost. She would never care for him now. She would look upon him as a spy, and he had been a spy and an utter and pathetic fool. He turned away, desolate with self-contempt; and when school was out he hastened to the butte and hid under a cedar to spy again. He wanted to see if Neloa would let Archie walk her home.

First there came the big rangy Botts, swinging theirs books from a piece of rope; and then William and Duncan Jasper, two dark sullen brothers who minded their own business and bore no insults; and then Hankie McGard, Vridar's distant cousin, and his sister Jewel. Then came Delbert Brode, walking home with Sadie Scott, a gay and charming lass. Then . . . . Vridar moved so quickly that he knocked his head on the cedar and for a moment was dizzy. Yes, then there came Archie and Neloa, side by side! Archie was carrying her books and talking to her, and Vridar could see her turn now and then to smile at him. He stared after them until they disappeared up the north lane; then, feeling that he had lost everything dear in life, he turned home, utterly wretched and miserable.

109

His aunt stood in the doorway. She had a huge swollen belly and Vridar thought she looked grotesque. Nearly every day now she sang vulgar ditties:

> When you get married and after you've carried
> an ounce of baby-seed
> just lift up the lid and take out a kid
> all bright and guaranteed! . . .

"You're late again!"

Yes, he was late. He glanced at her belly and then up at her eyes. "I came right home," he said.

"Like hell you did. Well, get the wood and water in . . . . Move, don't stand there!"

The next day he could not read his school books or think of anything but Neloa. He would not give her up. His pride and self-pity and his wounded self-esteem goaded him to absurd and foolhardy courage. He resolved to fight Archie's brother, for he must wipe out those insults by the coal shed, he must prove to Neloa that though a spy he was no coward.

When after school Neloa went down the road alone Vridar followed her, and then saw Archie coming at full speed. Vridar clenched his fists and waited.

"Listen," he said, when Archie came up, "you leave her alone!"

"What?" said Archie, staring at him.

"You leave her alone. She's my girl."

"Oh, the hell she is! Did she tell you that?"

"Yes."

"You're a liar. She hates you."

Trembling with rage, Vridar seized the lad and threw him down. Archie howled as if he were being killed, and Vridar clutched the lad's throat and hissed in his face, "Say you'll leave her alone!"

"I won't! I tell you she hates you! She told me so!"

Vridar took a handful of dust and rubbed it over Archie's distorted and outraged face. He seized Archie's ears and bounced the boy's head up and down. "Say you'll leave her alone!"

Archie was weeping. "Let me up!" he screamed. "My brother will beat you for this!"

Vridar became more and more desperate. He felt shame for sitting astride a smaller lad and smearing him with earth and yanking his ears. But he had to make him yield. He begged Archie to leave her alone, and when Archie began to struggle Vridar twisted the boy's arm until he yelped with pain.

"Say you won't go around her any more!"

"You're hurtun me!" cried Archie, bawling and weeping.

"Say it!"

"All right, I say it!"

Vridar got to his feet. Then Archie stood up and shook dust from his clothes. He looked at Vridar, and in the boy's eyes Vridar saw malicious gloating.

"All right, you take her home," said Archie. "Iffen she'll let you."

110

"She'll let me," said Vridar, looking up the road. Neloa had stopped and seemed to be waiting.

"You're afraid to."

"No, I'm not afraid to."

"Then let's see you do it."

Vridar went up the road, but slowly, for he knew that Archie was right. He was afraid. More than anything in life he wanted to walk at this girl's side and look at her and worship her. But his legs were stiff and heavy and he seemed unable to quicken his pace. From the fence posts larks sang, and birds skipped ahead of him. The sky was soft and blue and the field on his right was odorous with spring growth. Neloa had gone over the butte now and was out of sight. Vridar began to run and he ran until he could see her again. She crossed the canal bridge and was in the shaded beauty of the lane; and once or twice he saw her look back. What should he do! After another few hundred yards she would pass through her home gate and be lost to him, and she would be laughing at him and Archie would be laughing. Tomorrow Archie would tell her how Vridar had mauled him and what he had said to Vridar. He began to walk more swiftly but everything around him was becoming strangely unreal and remote. He could hear his heart and his breath. He was walking in a nightmare, a desperate boy who was afraid to overtake her and see the pity or the amusement in her eyes. Again she looked back at him. Then she left the road and entered a field and he saw her pluck a wild flower and a spray of green. She seemed to be making a tiny bouquet. Vridar stopped. The sound of his heart now filled the whole sky. Again she was looking at him. She returned to the road and stood there, looking at her flowers. O God, Vridar thought, what a coward I am! He began to pray. "Our Lord, give me strength and tell me what to do! . . ."

She was walking again, but slowly, and again she looked back. Ah, what a wretched and ridiculous thing he was! She must be laughing at him now, telling herself that he was stupid and silly! She would laugh at him tomorrow when Archie told her what had happened. He fumbled ahead, his feet kicking up dust, or pretending to stumble when there was nothing to stumble over; his eyes trying to find interest in the birds and fields around him; his mind trying to say, The crops there will be fine this year; or, That looks like very fine soil. Ah God, how absurd! For now he was seeking an excuse, a way out. Could he pass her and say, My aunt sent me to borrow something from a neighbor up the road? Could he cover his shame with some such lie as that?

He was only fifty feet behind her now. She was walking pensively and she seemed to be looking for wild flowers to her right or left. Vridar looked also. With sudden ridiculous interest he would stare intently as if he had seen something strange. But he had seen nothing at all, nothing at all. What a clown he was! What a stupid and contemptible fool he was! If he had any sense he would go home. But instead he walked more swiftly, asking himself desperately what he would say to her. Should he say, Neloa, can I walk with you? But that would be too silly for words. Should he lie? Neloa, I have to go up to a neighbor's. No, not that. Should he tell her the truth? Should he say, Neloa, I love you and I want to be near you but I'm afraid to? And what would she think then?

Perceiving with alarm that her home was only a little distance away he felt his heart and breath stop. She would be gone in a moment and never again would he be with her where birds sang and flowers bloomed. He began to run. He felt horribly stupid and futile but he had to run. He could not lose her now. He went at a ridiculous jogtrot, like a machine, his thoughts falling away into darkness and his heart sounding as loud as his feet. He came up to her and slowed to a walk. She turned to look at him. His face was like fire and his mouth seemed filled with hot swollen tongue. She did not speak. He did not look at her. And so they walked, Neloa smelling of her flowers or glancing at him, Vridar burning with love and shame. Had lad ever walked with lass in a way like this! Ah, but it was glory to be here, so near to her and alone with her! It was glory to burst his heart, and indeed his heart felt as though it would break open and spill. She glanced at him again. He knew, he felt her gaze, but he did not dare to meet her eyes. On the contrary he had fallen into his preposterous acting: he peered searchingly at a hedgerow or tree, or looked up with sudden interest at the sky, or strained his ears when he heard a bird call. Or he kicked at the dust and paused now and then to look down, as if he had uncovered diamonds . . . .

They came to her home gate. She raised the latch and hesitated for just a moment and then went inside. She looked back at him, but he was too suffocated with shame to look at her. She went up the walk and paused just a moment at the door and entered the house. He was alone now. He dodged back out of sight and ran up the lane on wild guilty feet, never pausing until he was far away from her. Then he hid behind a tree and tried to think. O Lord, O Lord, what a fool he had been! How she must be laughing at him and how Archie would laugh! How they would laugh together when he told her and she told him what Vridar had done! Yes, they would, they would, but he had walked with her in a sweet fragrant lane and they had been alone. Even if she loved Archie, even if she married him, he had walked with her when his heart was on fire, and not all of life surely, perhaps not even death, could ever rob him of that!

XVI

His mother came in the wagon to take her boys home. She kissed them in her strange way and asked how they had got along. There had been no trouble, Agnes said. They had been very good boys.

"We got along dandy, didn't we?" She was looking at Vridar.

"Yes maam," he said.

"They look awful pale and skinny," Prudence said.

"Well," said Agnes, "they studied too hard. They sure had plenty to eat. Didn't you?" She looked again at Vridar.

"Yes," he said but he did not look at her.

They rode in the jolting wagon up the lanes toward home, and far in the east

Vridar could see the great purple mountains. Their mother said they seemed to be very quiet. "You didn't have any trouble, did you?"

"N-no," said Vridar.

"Your aunt wasn't mean to you, was she?"

He glanced at Marion and hesitated. "No maam," he said.

"Did you get along in school all right?"

"I—I guess so."

When they were on the Antelope hills and he remembered his bitter years of loneliness, the old mood returned. The old dread entered him, the premonition of nightmare, and he thought again of the scenes of violence and blood and death. And when at last they came to the brink and he looked down over the acres of aspen and fir and jungle into the bottomland and saw the mighty river dark and heaving with its spring floods he was afraid. He wanted to turn back. He did not want to live again where terror had been the principal emotion in his life. Life in Annis had been starved and haunted and solitary, but it had been better than this.

He climbed down and helped his mother roughlock the wagon and then rode down and down into the dusk. Old exeriences leapt at him. There in another twilight he had run breathless over the hills, listening for the friendly sound of a bell . . . . Yonder he had jumped over the bush and cut his foot, and down that road had dragged himself on hands and knees. In the dooryard somewhere down in the night he had waited so many times for the sound of a homing wagon; in the gloomy house smelling of mice he had lain in nightmare and prayed to hear his name. Oh, he hated it all, hated it with passion that shook him! But it was his home and he was here again and there was nothing to be said.

His father came out and said hello to his sons and unhitched the team. He smelled of earth and the hogpen and of the juice of trees. The old deep silence stood around him. After the team was stabled they went into the house and with a piece of rag Prudence cleaned the dirty lamp chimney. She kindled the wick and as of old the room was full of feeble yellow light and shadows.

"You glad to be home?" she asked Vridar.

"Yes," he said.

The father was looking at him and at Marion with sober eyes. Diana, now a girl of six, came out of the dark bedroom and looked at her brothers. She was plump and round-faced and had gray eyes like her father's.

"Well," said Prudence, bustling around, "mother will have us a nice supper in a minute. We mustn't eat just bread and milk the first night our scholars are home."

She had often called the boys her scholars. She was proud of them, and in his strange reticent way Joe was proud, too. Vridar was thinking of their own lonely winter here, snowbound, shut away from all human life. He thought of their patience and toil and their unwavering dream for their sons and he felt a little ashamed. Later, when they sat at the table, he strove to talk, to chat lightly about his winter in school, but the words stuck in his throat. They seemed to be lies, nothing but lies. He said they had learned a lot, but he knew that was a lie. He said they liked their studies and that was a lie. He looked at his father and saw that the man's eyes were shining with pride. His mother's eyes were shining with pride.

113

When he sensed how complete their trust was, how deep and still their joy, he sickened and could barely eat. For it was all a lie. His months away from them had been a lie from end to end, a dark period of torture and human meanness and spite and greed and obscene words, of waste and loss. It had not been the glorious thing which he saw in their eyes. No, but he must never tell them, he must let them keep their dream.

"Was your grandmother good to you?" asked Prudence.

He faltered but he said yes, she had been good. Then he had to leave the table. He had to go to the water pail for a drink.

"He says Agnes and Borg was good to them," she said to Joe.

"I kallated they would be," Joe said.

At the water pail Vridar choked and set the cup down.

But this summer, while not without its canker and scourge, was happier than Vridar had expected it to be. It was the happiest of all his summers in childhood. When looked back upon from a later time he saw it as a rather pleasant interlude between dreadful years that went before it and the deeper wounds and heartbreak that came after.

Joe admitted a partner to his plan to civilize this wild bottomland. For a team and a harness and a few dollars, he sold a half-interest to his cousin Nephi McGard. A week after the boys came home Nephi drove in with his family, looked around him for an hour or so and set to work. He was a tall man but was sunken in his chest and very thin. His hair was black and bushy and as coarse as wire. His heavy tangled eyebrows hung like small hedges over his pale unfriendly eyes. His mustache was tobacco-juiced, ragged and unsightly because Nephi was forever licking it into his mouth and chewing off the hair. With his tongue and lower lip he would draw a part of it down and chew a while and then spit the hair out. When released the mustache would spring up like the roached mane of a horse from a stroking hand. His mouth was sinister and cruel and full of yellow teeth. Vridar was never to see the man smile.

His wife Becky was short, plump, and as solid as a bridge pier. Her hair was a bleached golden; her skin was sandy and sprinkled with freckles. These doubled in size after she had been an hour in the sun. On her arms was a heavy growth of fine yellow hair. Like the flesh of her cheeks or of her arms, her mouth looked as firm and unkissable as a piece of gristle. Her voice was high-pitched, a kind of drawling whine; and when angered she barked in a shrill falsetto that filled Vridar with mirth.

It was not the parents, though, in whom he was interested. They brought with them their two youngest children, Hankie and Jewel. Vridar had seen them at school and had recognized them as distant cousins but he had rarely spoken to them. Hankie was fourteen but very small for his age; he was tawny like his mother; like her he was covered with freckles and he had her thin voice. By turns he was timid or arrogant, whimpering or aggressive, baffled or sly. Vridar disliked him.

But he rather liked Jewel, though she was homely as sin. Her mouth was so absurdly large that when she ate she seemed to be devouring with her whole face. Her hair was dirty and yellow. But she was fun-loving and generous, and she

114

played and talked with prodigious zest. Her smile, her laughter, her words were open and frank. She was eight years old but like her brother was small for her age.

At a little distance from Joe's house Nephi built a shanty of unbarked slabs. It had only an earth floor, a slab door swung on leather hinges, and a crazy misfit of a window that often fell out. Nephi was no carpenter, Joe said; if a good wind came along his shack would tumble down.

This summer as formerly Joe herded cattle on the Antelope hills. Nephi was his partner in this and the two rode on alternate days. When Becky was not cooking or beating the squirrels and rats out of her shanty, she would look over the western mountains, thinking of all her people whom she had left. "What a God-forsaken hole this is!" she would cry. "Only people with no sense would live here!"

"Oh, I don't know," Prudence would say, nettled. "It's beautiful, it's quiet, and there's no neighbors to bother you."

"What about that lazy stinkun old bum across the river?"

"He's all right. He means well. He just forgets to pay back."

"Prudence, you'll be craziern a hoot-owl if you go on living here."

"Mebbe. Sometimes I do feel pretty queer." Then she would laugh in her strange way as she always did when speaking of loneliness. "But if I go crazy there's a place they put crazy folks in."

"You give me the chills. It is like you was down in a grave here, down in a grave, waitun for someone to shovel the earth on you."

"You'll get used to it. People can get used to anything."

"Not me," said Becky. "I wouldn't live here all my born days to save my own soul."

"If you think it's lonesome now wait till wintertime. Snowed-in for months and not another person in sight."

Vridar would listen to these talks and then dash away to see if Hankie had robbed another bird's nest. Robbing nests was second among Hankie's joys. With an awl he would make two small holes in the eggs and let the meat run out, and then string the shells on a white cord. After he had been here two weeks he had a rope of shells a yard long: the greenish blue of robin and bluebird, the buff faintly spotted of the ruby-crowned kinglet, the blotched grayish of the blackbird, the pure white of the dove, the spotted brown and purple of the meadowlark: all these and more he found and bled and added to his chain.

Vridar had been taught that robbing the nests of birds was as wicked as theft or adultery. When he learned what Hankie was doing, he flew into a rage and ordained himself as guardian in the kingdom of birds. He went to Hankie and delivered an ultimatum.

"Don't rob any more bird nests," he said. "If you do I'll bust you wide open."

"Oh, do tell!" Hankie croaked. "Just mind your own damn business. My pa, he owns half this."

"Remember what I said. I mean it."

"Go to hell!" said Hankie.

Thereafter Hankie became more furtive in his thefts. He would slip away and climb ledges for the nests of hawks and rock wrens. Far up on a cliff were three nests which Vridar had found and which he kept an eye on. One held four lovely wren eggs; another held three swallow eggs, white and speckled with lilac; and the third built in a hollow stump was the nest of a hawk. One day Vridar saw the egg-thief climb this ledge and he followed him; he saw Hankie prowling back and forth, searching everywhere; and then at last he saw him come to the wren's nest and lift the eggs out.

In a few moments Vridar was there, yelling, "You put them back!"

Instead of putting them back, Hankie ran, with Vridar in hot pursuit. Vridar chased the boy clear to the dooryard and there heard him imploring Prudence's aid; and for reasons that Vridar was never to divine his mother took the eggs and hid them away.

"He robbed a nest!" he cried to her. "I saw you take the eggs!"

"Son, don't shout at me that way."

"I want the eggs to take them back!"

"I said not to speak to your mother that way."

"But you're helping him to steal!"

"Son!"

"But I know you are. I saw you."

"Hankie promised he would hatch them. Then he will take the baby birds back to the nest."

"O God!" said Vridar. "Do you believe that?"

"I always believe a person till I catch him in a lie. We'll wait and see."

Vridar waited to see. Several times every day Hankie would strut about the yard, carrying the eggs in his hand and blowing on them. He would blow breath on them a few minutes and then take them to Prudence and she would put them away. This was such a preposterous piece of villainy in which his mother was a conniver that Vridar would stare at her and remember bitterly how she had in times past lied to him.

He went to Hankie and said, "If you don't hatch them I'll beat your head off." Hankie was afraid of him. Hankie had seen him knock Duke Beam down.

Two weeks passed and the eggs were not hatched and Hankie no longer blew on them. He had thrown them away. When Vridar learned this, he caught the lad out by the woodpile and seized him and hurled him down. Hankie fought and yelped and screamed. "Shut up!" Vridar hissed, and smote the boy in his nose. Hankie now yelled as though he were being knifed. Nephi and Becky came running, and behind them were Prudence and Joe.

"What you mean?" Nephi bellowed. "Let my boy up from there!"

Vridar was astride Hankie, sitting on the boy's stomach. He looked up at his mother. "He didn't hatch the eggs," he said. "I knew he wouldn't and you knew it."

Nephi grasped Vridar and lifted him as a cat lifts her kittens and shook him. "You God damn little fiend!" he said.

Vridar liked being called a fiend. He had always been such a timid quaking boy that he would rather have been a fiend than to have gone to heaven. He strove to multiply his rage. He struck at Nephi and howled as he imagined a fiend would howl, and then clawed desperately toward Hankie to smite him again. Prudence came forward and took him from Nephi's violent hands.

"Come with me!" she said.

"I won't! I'll beat the damn daylights out of him! He can't rob any more nests!"

"Son! Have you gone crazy?"

"I hate him!" Vridar yelled, determined to exploit this moment for its full heroism and glory. Only once before had he been the victor, save when wrestling with Jupiter. He had been mauled and exposed and stuffed with earth; he had had his face pressed into dung; he had been chased like a frightened hare into a coal bin. This was his hour of triumph. He wanted them all to think that he was greedy for battle . . . .

But he was slapped and rebuked and hustled off to bed. The sun still shone in the room. He could hear Hankie playing outside. Nevertheless he was quite content; he had wreaked vengeance upon a thief; in a real honest-to-God fight he had thrown him down and slugged him.

For days thereafter he was like a hound on Hankie's trail. He breathed dire threats and laid down whole decalogues for Hankie's behavior and promised to knock him senseless if he filched again. Hankie was afraid, but he was cunning and stubborn and devious. He sneaked away at most unexpected times. He added little by little to the length of his egg-chain. But the one egg which he coveted most, that of the killdeer, he had not been able to find, and one afternoon he went again to the cottonwood island. Vridar followed him and hid to watch.

Hankie waded in marshland and in the tule and peered under rotted logs. He found something at last; Vridar knew this by the way the boy looked all around him and then stooped and filled his hands. Vridar leapt out, yelling with all his crusading might, and Hankie took to his heels. He was fleet when scared; finding himself outdistanced, Vridar seized and hurled a pebble. It struck Hankie's head and it felled him. Vridar was horrified. Divine zeal had carried him too far.

Hankie was writhing on the ground but after a few moments he struggled up and went sobbing and screaming to the house. Now and then he would pause like a rooster about to crow and let off a shrill piercing wail. Vridar followed, choked with fear and remorse, for on Hankie's head he could see blood, could see the bright color of it running down the boy's neck. When Hankie entered the dooryard, he redoubled his screams and his mother came out like a big hornet. Prudence came running, too. Then Joe and Nephi came running from the corral.

"It's him!" Hankie yelled, pointing an accusing finger at Vridar. "He snuck up and hit me with a rock!"

Becky now examined her son's head. A bloody gash two inches long was in his scalp, and his hair was clotted and sticky.

"Son," said Prudence, "why did you do this?"

"Why?" yelled Becky. "Why does the beast keep pickun on my little boy, and why do you let him?"

Nephi's face was a sullen gaping snarl. "I tell you, Joe," he roared, "I won't stand this no longer! If you can't make that God damned little fiend mind I can!"

"Don't get your shirt off," said Joe quietly.

117

Vridar wanted his father to say, My son will lick your son and I'll lick you. But he knew that Joe would never say that. Nephi was stuttering with amazement and rage.

"What you intend to do? Just let him go on till he kills my boy? No, by God, you won't."

"Cam yourself," said Joe. "He ain't hurt much."

"Ain't hurt?" Becky yelled. "Look at that gash, will you?"

Hankie began to yelp afresh. A bawling strangled sound flowed out of him and he gurgled and choked and hissed.

"Why did you hit him?" Prudence asked, looking sternly at her son.

"Because," said Vridar, "he robbed another nest."

"You lie!" Hankie yelled. "I was catchun minnies!"

"He wasn't. He took a killdeer's eggs."

"He's a liar!" gasped Hankie.

"So my son can't even go out and ketch minnies," said Nephi, scowling at Joe. "By God, is that how you see it?"

"Do tell!" cried Becky.

Knowing that he had humiliated and shamed his parents, Vridar was eager to shoulder the odium of this misfortune. He said he was sorry. He said it was all his fault. He said he would never bother Hankie again.

"More lies!" growled Nephi. "If you was my kid I'd larrup your skin off!"

Prudence now awoke like a tigress, her eyes ablaze. "Listen, you old persley!" This was her word of contempt for him. "Don't call my son a liar. He never lies."

"No?" said Nephi, sneering. "He's just a God damn little angel, ain't he? He's a sneak and a liar, that's what he is."

Prudence advanced to him, her whole body shaking with fury. "If I was a man," she cried in his face, "I'd learn you how to talk to a lady! I'd beat you in a inch of your life" She swung sharply and spoke to Vridar. "Come!" she said and entered the house.

For an hour his mother sat by the window, trembling and looking out. Joe went back to his work. Vridar was suffering remorse and shame, and the next day he wanted to learn if Hankie was all right. He wanted to ask forgiveness. But after waiting around most of the day and seeing no sign of Hankie, he went at last to the shanty and knocked on the slab door. There was no response, though he knew that the family was inside. There were cracks between the slabs and he now peered through, trying to see Hankie, but everything inside was dark and quiet. He did not see Nephi rise and go to the water pail and slink around the wall to the door. Vridar was still peering when the door was kicked violently open, striking his face, and the next moment Nephi hurled upon him a full pail of water. Gasping and humiliated and bitter with shame Vridar ran to the big fir tree and hid. He rubbed a hand over his face and found a little blood, for the door had struck his nose. He took his clothes off and spread them in the sun to dry. Then he sat, naked and hidden, hating this man and wishing that some power would debase and humiliate him. Two days later his wish was fulfilled.

Joe and Nephi had been building a derrick, using Douglas fir logs as a base and spiking and bolting them. This frame was twenty feet square. Across its center they used a fifth heavy log as a crossbeam and bolted it securely, and then with team and cable and pulleys erected the frame on its edge and temporarily braced it to hold it there. The bottom of the thirty-foot derrick pole, with a heavy arm swinging from its top, they made secure to the crossbeam and braced it solidly from the four corners of the frame. They were then ready to erect the derrick.

Joe did not observe that Nephi was kneeling at the top end of the arm tinkering with a pulley. He spoke to the team and the chain went taut, and the reared frame was pulled earthward; and as the frame was drawn down, swiftly the pole went erect, dragging after it the long arm, swinging from a cable. Nephi was caught off guard. The whole thing happened so quickly that the derrick snapped upward and the frame rocked back and forth, and Nephi, who in a moment of alarm grasped the cable, was jerked aloft and left swinging up there thirty feet above the earth. He began to roar with astonishment and rage. The arm with its bottom end against the pole, held there by two plank jaws, and with its top end swinging from the cable moved easily in a great arc; and as it swung back and forth Nephi clung to its top like a huge insect. He tried to seize the arm and raise himself to its wood but it was freshly peeled and it was slippery and wet. A few moments he clung there with both hands grasping the wire rope just below the top pulley. He was holding on desperately. He was trying to throw a leg up and over the arm. Then his hands weakened and suddenly he came down like a shot bird, with the wire rope hissing between his palms. He struck the earth a frightful blow. He was bellowing with agony and rage.

Joe ran to him and said, "You hurt yourself?"

Nephi was writhing on the ground, his face distorted. He was feeling of his legs and groaning and turning on his back and rolling, his face a dreadful thing to look at. And then, sitting up, he roared: "Look at them hands!" He turned his palms upward. There was a black smoking furrow across each; the wire had burned through hide and flesh almost to the bone.

For days he sat around, his hands bandaged in huge poultices of soda and grease. Vridar's hatred melted into compassion. His pity was splendidly alive one day when Charley Bridwell came over. Nephi disliked Charley. His dislike shone in his cruel eyes and was venom in his words. Seeing Nephi squatting dolefully by his shack, his hands swathed in rags, Charley went over, grinning and spitting tobacco juice. "Did someone step on your hands?" he said.

Nephi did not speak. He blinked sullen eyes and began to chew his mustache.

"What you got all them diapers on your hands for?"

Nephi growled. "Go on," he said, "and borrow what you came to borrow. But don't ask me to give you no flour nor sugar nor nothun."

This thrust at the big jolly parasite who had borrowed from Vridar's parents a hundred times and paid nothing back seemed to make him wince a little. He spit a stream of juice and chuckled. Turning to Vridar he asked: "You been playing rough with him?"

"He hurt himself," said Vridar. "He slid down a cable."

"You mean he has fun all by himself just sliding down cables?"

119

Vridar thought the jesting was in poor taste. If only Charley could see the frightful furrows across Nephi's palms!

Again looking at the huge fat man, Nephi growled: "Go on and borrow your stuff! Old Joe will give you his home if you ask for it."

"I'd take it," said Charley, "if I could boat it across the river. As for you, take my advice and get your hands out of them pillows. Give them some air."

"Go borrow your stuff that you never pay back and leave me alone!"

Charley slouched over to Vridar and in a loud whisper which Nephi could hear he said: "Next time don't play so rough. I think you've hurt the kid."

After Charley entered the house to borrow flour and sugar, Vridar hid behind a bush and watched Nephi. He felt deeply sorry for him, sitting there day after day with the flesh rotting from his hands. He wanted to say a kind word. But in two experiences that followed his compassion again froze into hate.

The first of these involved Marion. In the hay harvest Vridar and Hankie alternated in loading or driving the derrick-horse. It was Marion's chore to bring fresh water from the spring, two hundred yards distant. After a load had been drawn in and forked to the stack, the men would wipe sweat from their faces and turn to the water pail. Marion disliked his chore. Each time he had to bring a two-gallon pail because Nephi after drinking would pour the remainder of the water over his head and hands and into his straw hat. Marion asked his mother if one pailful would not be enough for two loads of hay. She said it would.

And so Marion poured the two gallons into smaller pails and set one away in the shade of a bush. When the next load was off, Nephi bellowed for water and Marion took the pail to him. Nephi tipped it to his mouth and sniffed and perceived that it was warm; and with a gesture of rage he hurled the can of water at Marion's feet.

"God damn it!" he said. "You lazy good-for-nothun brat, do you think a man can drink that swill?" Marion did not speak. He looked at his father but Joe did not speak. "Hit the grit!" Nephi roared. "Bring some fresh water!"

Marion hit the grit but instead of going for water he ran to the house. He told his mother what Nephi had done, that he had thrown the pail at him and had sworn at him. Like a tigress again, Prudence came to the corral, with Marion trotting behind her. She went up and faced Nephi, hands on her hips.

"What's this my son tells me?" she asked, her eyes blazing. "Did you dump his water out?"

"By God, yes. You think I'll drink slop?"

"Listen, persley," she said, "you can't talk that way to my boys! After this if you want water your own son can carry it! My son has waited on you long enough and before I'd let him carry another drop you can choke black in the face!" Then she went wrathfully to the house, with Marion again trotting after her. Vridar looked at his father. Joe seemed to be embarrassed; he was very quiet, but in his gray eyes there was a shadowed gleam.

Nephi turned to Hankie. "Bring some fresh water," he said.

"Me?" Hankie yelped. "Why should I do it moren him?" He looked at Vridar.

"None of your lip," said Nephi. "Hit the grit."

In that experience Vridar saw the soul of the man, but it was for the next experience that he despised him most. Among the duties of the men as cowpunchers of the herds was that of dehorning and branding and castrating. On the Antelope hills they had no corral, but Joe was skilful with a lariat and they rode down the smaller calves and earmarked them and operated on the smaller bulls. The larger beasts were driven down the mountain and into the cow-pen above the house.

One morning they brought a small herd. Vridar went up to see them, for he liked the savage eyes and the lordly courage of bulls. He liked to watch them fight. The deep necks, the great flashing horns, the fearless eyes, and the will to win: these fed his wish to be a prize-fighter and a mighty man. He did not know what was to be done with these beasts. In previous times he had not been pressed into this service of fire and blood. Today he was.

Joe and Nephi had an assortment of brand-irons, and these now lay in the road. By them was a heap of sagebrush and dry aspen and cottonwood. Joe made a big fire and laid the irons on the flame. Hankie, he said, was to keep the fire going; Vridar was to bring the irons. Hanging from a corral pole was a common wood saw, and when his father picked this up Vridar perceived that the dehorning would come first.

Nephi was in the corral, chasing round and round after a beast. He would toss the rope and miss and toss again, until at last Joe said, "Let me show you," and took the rope. He twirled it in a clean loop and spun it through the air and neatly captured the two horns. Nephi then seized the rope with him and the two men ran to a post. With another rope Joe captured the beast's hind legs and the men stretched it out and forced it to drop. When ready for the saw, the animal was stretched so taut that it was half-choked and its eyes bulged. Nephi sat on the beast's neck and Joe took the saw.

This operation was enough to sicken Vridar, as it came to him in sound and sight and smell. There was the sound of the steel teeth cutting slowly into bone; eating deeper and deeper, with the noise becoming muffled and sunken as the teeth found blood; and the sound of agonized bawling and the heavy grim breathing of the two men. There was the sight of the poor brute, stretched out and half-choked, its flanks quivering and its eyes wild and half out of its skull. There were the smell of blood, warm and impalpable, and the smell of bone, smoking under the saw. And after the beast was freed and had staggered to shaking legs, there was the horrible picture of it, its noble antlers gone, its horn nebs open and raw and bleeding, with blood washing down into its stricken eyes.

Vridar was sick long before the brutal task of dehorning was done. He watched only the first; then he turned away and stuffed fingers in his ears, but he could hear the frenzied bawling and the remorseless sound of the saw eating into bone; and he could imagine the trembling and agony of the wretched thing and he could smell the blood.

The branding came next and was more horrible still. After a beast was thrown down and had its big horns sawed off, Vridar had to grasp an iron and run at full speed. The iron when he lifted it was flaming red; and as he ran with it sparks flew and hissed, shadows pulsed in the red metal, and heat flowed up the handle and

121

burned through his gloves. Quickly Joe would seize the iron and thrust a foot against the beast's flank, hold the throbbing iron for a moment above the heaving ribs, and suddenly press it down. And he would not press it only once: as though he loved the torture, he would lift it and press, lift it and press, burning through flesh and into the bone. And Vridar hated him for it. Black smoke rose in clouds, drenched with the reek of burning hair and flesh. The creature bawled with such agony as Vridar had never heard, while Nephi stood on its head and the iron melted into bone. And when the iron was lifted the last time, there on the ribs was a great brand, as large as a man's two hands, black and stinking and hideous; a broad deep wound of fried meat and showing through this the brown seared bones.

Seventeen of them were branded this way, some with a huge W or X, some with U P or Y Z, some with H—. The whole corral, the whole yard and lane, was full of the odor of burned meat and bone and burned hair. By the time the branding was done Vridar was almost too sick to stand. His mouth looked like that of a person forty-eight hours dead. He wanted to run away and hide but he had to stay here, for there were big bulls to be operated on, and this task, his father said, would take the strength of all.

The largest of the bulls came first, a full-grown beast, one of the lords of the Antelope herds. His hind legs were caught in a loop and jerked together and the rope was made fast to the bottom of a post. The bull snorted and plunged, reaping the air with his great horns and blowing mucus from his nose. His front legs were trapped in a third rope. Nephi and Joe heaved at this rope, running now to the right and now to the left; and the feet were jerked from earth and the bull plowed violently and dropped like a ton of stone. With still other ropes he was trussed and bound. Nephi sat on the deep neck, but cautiously, for he knew that if the head-rope broke he might be gutted. Then Joe took the saw and the debasement began.

For what seemed to Vridar an hour the saw ate into the strong gleaming horns. There was again the smell of blood and bone, and the boy leaned against the corral poles, feeling that he would vomit. He felt as weak as if his veins had been opened. Dizziness swept him and he tried to shake it off; a horrible darkness engulfed his mind. He struggled upward, drawing a long clean breath, and again heard the cutting of the saw. Only by fighting desperately and kicking and pinching himself could he keep his faintness under control; until at last the two horns were thrown away and Joe picked up his knife. Vridar glanced once and saw the great wound laid open; then there came back to him all the times when Jed Bridwell or the boys in Annis had threatened to castrate him, and he seemed to feel his organs shriveling, seemed to feel them drawing up into his body, to be hidden there and safe. They castrated other bulls. Joe would hurl the big testicles from him, and they lay all around him in the corral dung or out in the lane. After a while the poor beasts stood with blood running from their bellies and skulls, their heads drooping, their eyes such eyes as Vridar could not look at. He could not see the ordeal through to the end; he slipped away, so faint and sick that he could barely see, and went down to the creek to lave his white face with cool water.

So these were men! These were men who believed in the gentle Jesus and all the Christian dogmas, who waged war on one another, who sawed and cut and burned until the poor creatures could no longer even bawl but were half-dead; these were men who did these things with no more emotion than they might feel when lighting their pipes or lacing their shoes! But what kind of men were these and what kind of thing was man? Was there no gentler and better way than this awful butchery? Quietly he reached down to feel himself, for in his loins was the sensation that his own organs had been cut away. This sensation was so strong that he could hardly believe his hands.

Hours later he slipped up to the corral. The fire was dead now. The irons lay in a pile, still warm, with burnt flesh and hair on them. Scattered roundabout were the horns. But all the bulls' organs were gone and he knew why; he knew that Nephi had gathered them up and taken them to the house to eat. He knew that his father had wanted to eat them; and once he had brought a few to the door and Prudence had thrown them in his face. He had heard Hankie say that the eating of testicles gave to men an almost uncontrollable passion for women . . . . Yes, all the organs were gone.

The cattle were up the lane now; but alone, each standing solitary with drooping heads, were the bulls, their horns and vitality gone. Vridar went up to look at the largest one, at the great beautiful creature that had been lord of a herd but was now only a steer. The brute looked as if he would never move again. The regal fire had passed from his eyes and all the noble splendor was gone from his head. He had walked a few steps and paused, and walked again, for behind him were pools of blood. There was a pool under his belly now and from the wound blood was not dripping but still running. Vridar moved nearer to look at the eyes but the eyes seemed dead. The head sank, with clots in the hair and the froth of old rage on the mouth. Then the beast looked at him but in a feeble way, without interest or strength. Flies buzzed round the big holes where his horns had been; flies swarmed under his belly and flew in hordes round his mouth and eyes . . . .

Again sick with rage and pity and hating such butchery as this and the dark wrong of it; and hating his father and Nephi and men and himself and life, and all things and purpose, whatever their reason, that reduced a kingly beast to such a mean and abject and impotent state; and hating in human beings the lust and greed that broke all things to their will and wreaked upon all things their hungers and passions, Vridar slipped down and hid under the bank. He remained here so long, trying to understand, trying to fathom the black underworld of human passion and will, that darkness came and with darkness his mother's voice.

"In a minute," he said. "I'll come in a minute." Then he bowed to his knees in despair and was sick, sick. . . .

XVII

Although he made a great show of his manliness and boasted of his way with girls, Hankie McGard was for Vridar a queer boy. He made mud pies, dressed forked sticks in rags and called them his family, and crooned over a big fir knot shaped like a human face, saying he was rocking his baby to sleep. He not only

123

made mud pies down by a hole where frogs squatted with their sides gently heaving; he made mud cakes too, and pastries of all sorts and huge puddings stuffed with moss and watercress. After shaping a cake he would embellish it with white wood shavings which he called cocoanut shreds and with red poisonous berries which Vridar's father said would kill a mule; and over it all he would sprinkle white sand, declaring it was sugar or salt, depending on which you wanted.

Taking black mud in his freckled hands he would mix it patiently and thoroughly with sprigs of grass and tassels of moss; he would pat it and garnish it and smell of it; and then he would stand it in the sun to bake. He had a board lying under a willow by the pond and upon this he spread his cookery; loaves and macaroons, doughnuts, bonbons, and tarts and puffs. He had pies whose filling was grated potatoes, filched from his mother's sack, and sheep wool which he had gathered from barbed wire fences in the valley; and common dry dung and pine needles and cedar berries and wild roses and asters. He had puddings, immense black things, stuffed with cress and tree fungus and alfalfa bloom. After standing a few days these cracked open and exposed to view a mattress-looking tangle of withered things.

Hankie also bottled what he called fruits and vegetables. As soon as he came here he began to hoard old cans and pots and broken glassware. When his canning season came round, he gathered fragrant catnip and the seed-pods of wild mustard; the fruit of wild carrot and the plumelike curls of pigweed seed; the huge purple thistles of artichokes, the firm florets of yarrow, the hard berries of kinnikinic and stinkbush, and the petals of innumerable flowers. All these were his fruits, he said, and with Jewel's aid he solemnly canned them. Some of them, like the thistle, he cooked, stirring them in an old rusted bake-oven on a tiny fire; others he bottled fresh in cold water; and still others he put away in hot water because these, he said, were peas and beans.

Feeling a little foolish Vridar also canned. His mother let him have a few fruit jars and various empty medicine bottles and salt- and pepper- and coffee-cans. All these he filled. Those containers which he could not seal he banked with mud, pretending with Hankie that this was sealing-wax. Sometimes the boys tasted their concoctions; one, a stinking and fermenting mixture of harebell and berries and fir juice Hankie said was very good indeed. He said it tasted like gooseberry jam. One day he ate so abundantly of his vile assortments that his parents thought he would die.

Hankie said he knew how to make magpies talk and for days he strove to capture one. He set traps, hung looped strings athwart posts, and made deadfalls thinly covered with leaves; but the birds were too smart for him. Then he took Jed Bridwell into his dream. Jed had captured nearly everything that flies, from hawks to hummingbirds, and one day he brought two magpies to Hankie, swimming the river on his back and holding the creatures above him. Now, said Hankie, he would make them talk, and taking them with him he vanished into a thicket and Vridar and Jed followed.

"How'n you make them talk?" asked Jed, scowling at him.

"Don't ask me no questions," said Hankie pompously, "and I'll tell you no lies."

Hankie drew a knife and opened a blade. He tied a string to the leg of one bird and tethered the flapping thing to a bush. He pried open the beak of the other, grasped its tongue and pulled it out. He thrust the blade into the tongue and split it from its tip almost to the bird's throat. Then he staked this one and operated on the other.

"They'll talk in a week," he said. "It takes a few days for them to learn."

"They'd better talk," said Jed, "or I'll knock your brains out."

"Oh, I know what I know!" Hankie shouted, his voice running up into a thin whine. "I seen magpies what talks."

Jed was peering at the birds, now beating their wings and drooling red foam. "You freckled bugger!" he said, turning to Hankie. "For a cent I'd belt you one right now."

"Just you wait and see! Just wait and see, I tell you!"

Vridar had been standing back, sickened by what Hankie had done. He had no love for magpies; they were thieves that pillaged hencoops and the nests of song-birds. Yet this was no decent way to treat them. They should be killed, he thought, and not left to starve and beat their wings, with blood oozing from their bills. But he dared make no protest with the unpitying Jed standing near.

He did not tell his mother what had been done. For tattling he had been brutally chastised twice and he would never tattle again. Several times a day he would slip into the thicket to look at the captives. Hankie took food to them and water but they never ate or drank and their lovely gloss faded and they squatted more and more instead of standing on their legs. Then one day they were dead with butchered tongues hanging from their mouths.

Hankie and Jewel would catch horseflies, preferably the huge black ones, whose bite was so severe that it made a big beast wince. They would break off dry stems of grass and after thrusting one end into the fly's anus they would set it free and it would go almost straight up like an arrow as far as the eye could see. Or they would liberate two at once to see which would climb faster. Sometimes they inserted a straw too long for the fly to carry and it would struggle waveringly to climb and then fall to the earth.

Hankie preyed endlessly on frogs, for his father's favorite dish, he said, was poached frog-legs. He would forage in marsh and mire, gathering legs for Sunday dinner. Vridar would watch him seize the luckless creatures and cut their hind legs off, leaving the frogs alive; and when he protested, Hankie said it was all right. They would grow new legs, he said. "Judas priest, I'll bet I've cut the legs offen this one a dozen times!" But Vridar knew better. He had seen the amputated things lying dead on banks or floating belly up among the tule. He wanted to tell his mother about this boy's brutal ways, but he would never tattle again.

Besides, he had been guilty of a cruel thing and the shame of it would always live in him. With bow and a nail-tipped arrow he had shot a rooster through and through, with the arrow sticking out on either side. Then hot with guilt he pursued the thing, hoping to save its life. He dived after it under fences and chased it across fields; and the arrow all the while was dipping and rising and dipping. In a thicket he caught it at last and felt the throb of its heart and blood. Gently he broke the arrow and pulled it out and set the rooster free. It staggered as if drunk; it fell back and shut its eyes; and then it sat on its rump and refused to move.

"Kill it," Hankie said. "Your ma won't never know."

But Vridar said no, he would save its life, and he hid it away in a gunnysack. He daubed it with liniment, sprinkled it with antiseptic powders and fed it bitter aloes, until it smelled like a medicine chest. He forced food and drink down its sick throat. He hugged its pale head to him and murmured over it and shared its pain. But like the magpies it died. He then dug a grave and put it into a cardboard box and buried it, and now and then he would go in atonement to look at the grave.

He was also a guilty witness of cock-fighting. Among his mother's chickens were some Minorca roosters. She had other kinds but it was the Minorca cocks that Vridar admired; they were warlike and fierce and they fought till they died. A trim black rooster with gleaming spurs and a proud strut had vanquished every cock but one. The boys brought them together and tormented them until they were in fighting rage. The cocks then fought until both were bloody from head to tail. They dug with their sharp spurs and struck with their hard bitter beaks, until neither could stand; and then they fought while sitting or lying. They made queer throaty sounds and on the eyes of both Vridar saw the film of death. Still Hankie pushed them together and prodded and urged them; and they would struggle up and falter at each other with weary wings, or strike with beak and trample with spurs. When the fight was done they were both blind and their heads were like clots of blood.

The next day both cocks were dead.

Another experience which became a shameful memory he was forced to against his wish. Nephi had brought with him several cats. Four big indolent tabbies littered and the dooryard was alive with kittens. Joe hated cats and said they would have to be killed. His whole damned ranch, he said, would be nothing but cats, for the kittens would have kittens before long.

"Well, why don't you kill them?" Prudence asked.

"Oh, wife, like I ain't enough to do without that! Have Vridar kill them."

"Do you want to?" she asked, looking at her son.

"No," he said. How stupid was she to image that he wanted to kill things!

"Well, I guess you'll have to. Just put them all in a gunnysack with some rocks and throw them in the crick."

But he put the task off until his father roared again. "I thought he was to kill them God damn cats!"

"But what will persley say?"

"Wife, do you think I care what that-air man says? Throw them in the crick."

The next day Vridar stealthily gathered the kittens without letting the McGards see and in a gunnysack carried them to the creek. There he faltered. He took them out and looked at them. They were such soft furry little things, so full of fun and playfulness: they scattered over him, climbing to his shoulders and head, or they slapped and hissed and rolled like balls of down. He loved them and played with them and wished that they did not have to die. But grimly at last, feeling mean and

126

despicable, he put them all into the sack and some stones with them and tied the sack. And again he faltered. He wanted to take them out again and watch them play and fondle them; but he knew that he would be doing this over and over until his father roared again. He tossed the sack out and it wavered for a moment and then sank, with a wealth of bubbles rising to the surface. Unable to endure the thought of all the fear and agony in that watery grave, Vridar flung his clothes off and leapt in. The hole was deep. He went under, flailing with his arms and kicking up cyclones with his feet. He felt himself drowning again. Fighting for his life and forgetting why he had leapt in, he threshed to the bank, gasping and spent, and crawled out. He ran and got a long willow and with this reached into the depth to find the sack and drag it to him. But he knew that they were dead now, though he remembered that he had torn a hole in the sack and he hoped that by some miracle they had escaped.

And one did escape. Two years later there prowled through the jungleland a huge cat, swift and wild, but with the markings of those he had thrown in. Once Vridar saw it, looking at him with vivid green eyes, the sole survivor of seventeen.

He had hardly recovered from this experience when he spent a wretched day and an unforgettable night. With a few tools he was down on the creek building a longer and sturdier footbridge, and dreaming of some day making mighty bridges and dams and structures that would have in them the strength which he did not have. He was hacking at a tree when his sister came down to watch. He told her to stand back or she might be hit by the axe, but she stood right behind him, watching the white chips fall. She was a bold and foolhardy girl who had never known the meaning of fear. In the previous summer she had seized a wild colt's tail and the beast had kicked her, knocking her end over end. On her forehead she had a red scar in the shape of a horseshoe.

"Stand back, I said! Do you want to get hit?"

"I'm back," she said.

He resumed the chopping. He did not observe that she had stepped even closer, and when he swung the axe back over his shoulder the blade struck her elbow and split it open.

"Ouch," she said.

"Did I hit you?" he asked, looking at her. Then he saw the blood pumping out of her arm. Frantic, he ran for the house, yelling for help. His parents came running and with them were Nephi and Becky.

"Now what has your kid done?" Nephi growled to Joe.

Diana came slowly up the hill with one hand clasped over the spurting elbow. Blood had spread over her pink dress and it dripped from her fingers but she was calm and self-possessed. While Nephi muttered that Vridar would kill everybody on the place before he was done with it, Joe gathered his daughter to his arms and carried her to the house. Vridar ran away to hide and to meditate on the enormity of his blunders. The sky had darkened and thunder choked far away, and lightning was making white snake-dens in the west. This was Hankie's evening to go for the cows.

127

But when cowtime came Hankie looked at the sky and refused to budge. "I went last night," he said.

"You did not," said Vridar.

"You're a liar."

"And you're a liar too."

"Here!" cried Prudence. "What do you mean calling each other such names? Now which one went last night?"

"I did," Hankie said.

"He knows better," said Vridar. "I went."

Prudence turned to Marion. "Which one went?"

"Vridar."

"You're another liar," said Hankie.

Becky had come to the door. "What's all the trouble about?"

"Didn't I go for the cows last night?" her son asked.

"Yes."

"He didn't," said Vridar. "I went."

"Son," said Prudence, "you go. It's not worth an argument."

"But I won't go. I went last night."

"Son, don't give me your lip. Run along now."

Vridar went muttering to the stable, observing that the sky was becoming steadily more black and dreadful. I'll get even, he thought. "That little son of a bitch!" He shuddered a little, for never before had he profaned aloud. Some day he would curse rings around the sun and curdle sweet milk. Jeff McGard, he had heard, could turn sweet milk into sour; and when Jad Thurgenstowen really got warmed up he started thunderstorms. "The bastard!" Vridar muttered, trying to imagine what Hankie would look like when he was done with him. His teeth would be knocked out. His cheeks would be freckled pulp and his nose would hang over on one side. "The God damn mud pie coward!" he said.

In the stable was a mare which the boys shared between them, a shaggy bony old thing that reminded Vridar of his pony Alice. He climbed to her sharp back and rode south but at the mountain's base he sprang off and led her. The path up was so sharp and steep and rocky that a beast could barely climb it when unburdened. Great boulders jutted out and pitfalls hid under leaves, for this trail was an old flood-bed down which the spring waters rushed, eating all the earth away from stones. Barefooted, Vridar went ahead, leading the nag. When she came to a difficult place she would shut her eyes and hang back, and then he would jerk at her, trying to make her move. "You old son of a bitch!" he cried. Bracing himself he yanked and yanked and swore. "God damn you anyhow!" The sky was black now from end to end and lightning was spilling in white sheets.

The mare awoke suddenly and raised her shaggy old head and leapt. Unprepared for this, Vridar had no time to get out of her way and a big rugged hoof came down like stone on his naked foot. At first, though the pain was intense, he did not cry for help. He smote at the head of bone and pulled at her ears, or with all his strength tried to shove her back. But she stood solid and impassive as though she would never move again. He looked down at his foot and saw blood. Again

128

he pushed against her and wrenched at her nostrils and beat on her skull, trying to make her move. But she would not move; she stood, sleepy and sagging, with a good part of her weight on the boy's foot, and so far as he could tell she would stand there forever. Alarmed, he began to roar. He began to howl as if he were being slain, and all the while he was pounding on her skull or trying with desperate effort to drag his foot out.

Then suddenly his howling stopped. Across the tops of the aspens he saw his parents running toward him, saw Nephi leap up from mending a harness and saw Becky sprint across the dooryard. The whole world was racing toward him, convinced that he was dying, though there was nothing more serious than a horse standing on his foot. His father was running stiff-legged, his face uplifted to the mountain, and Prudence outdistanced him and ran ahead. Ashamed and horrified, Vridar bent over and twisted and pulled and wrenched, and little by little freed his foot, with the skin peeling off it as it came out. He glanced at it and saw that it seemed to be flattened out like a crushed stinkbug. When he put his weight on it flashes of pain shot through it and up his leg. But he had to get out of here. Desperately he got behind the beast and flogged her and forced her up the path to the brink; and then he mounted her and still flogging her galloped away. After he had gone a half-mile he pulled his foot up to examine it: there was sharp pain when he wiggled his toes, there was blood, and he supposed there were broken bones. But what were broken bones in this world! More terrible than broken bones were his parents back there, crying his name and searching for his dead body, while Nephi watched them with contempt in his eyes. "The son of a bitch!" Vridar muttered and galloped again.

When he gained the upper benchland, rain was lying in misty sheets down the western sky and out of its gloom a wagon was moving toward him. He waited until the wagon drew near, when in the dusk he could see the colorful raiment of John and Jim, two Bannock Indians. Three years ago they had been told that a man far up the river killed enough elk and deer every winter to make moccasins for the whole tribe. Thereafter each summer they had come in a rickety old derelict of a wagon, with wheels of uneven sizes, front or rear, and with a cottonwood tongue wired to the hounds. Because the axles were never greased they squealed like a herd of pigs. The wagon was drawn by the two most gaunt, starved and hideous beasts Vridar had ever seen; one had had an eye knocked out, the other had huge swellings on three of its legs. Their teeth had been worn to their gums, so that when they chewed hay or grass they slobbered and sneezed and now and then stopped eating altogether, with hay hanging from their mouths. Along either side of each were raw sores, gouged by the wire with which John and Jim patched their traces. Their gray tails looked like a handful of hair sprayed from a dark cudgel . . . .

With them John and Jim usually brought their squaws, two enormous fat creatures with coppery rolls on their jowls; with red and purple and green blankets wrapped around their deep shoulders; with smoked elkskin on their feet. But the bucks were handsome men, tall and straight, with a mane of black hair and strong white teeth. Their speech was only grunts or a few monosyllables or the fierce wild seeking of their eyes.

129

To their camp one evening Vridar had gone with his father. Joe sat with them by their fire, for he liked Indians and knew their ways; and Vridar stood back, curious and afraid, his eyes watching them. Sitting crosslegged the squaws like two robed heaps stared at the flames, never speaking, never looking up. John and Jim rolled cigarettes and smoked them one after another and drank black coffee from tin cups; and Joe sat near them, chewing tobacco and squirting its juice on the fire. Vridar was fascinated and allured by these people. There was about them so much that he could not define, but the vividness and power of which he could feel: the deep silence, the wild-animal smell, the tenseness and rigidity of their emotions, the ancient and inscrutable quiet of their faces, and the jungle-dark of their eyes. He had read books about Indians. His grandfather had been an Indian fighter, and his father when young had spent much time among them. Looking at them squatting by the fire, Vridar thought of their wild and nomadic ways, of their cunning and ferocity and fortitude; but he felt that they were homeless and lost now, like forest things in a cage . . . .

Tonight in the rain and the gloom he waited. The wagon wrenched crazily from side to side and the horses were only grotesque skeletons; and there in the box sat the four stoic nomads, looking neither to right nor left. They came up, the wagon shaking like a drunken thing.

"Hello," Vridar said, afraid of them.

They did not speak. He saw John look at Jim and he heard him grunt. A little while they sat there, just staring at Vridar. The squaws were huddled under colors that were now gray with dust. John had a gorgeous feather in his hair. Thunder choked and roared, and a wet wind drove the waves of mist. Then John shook the reins and reached back for a club and smote the weary beasts across their hips. They staggered, and rattled the harness of wire and chain and broken buckles, and the wagon went squealing down the hill.

After finding the cows and chasing them to the corral Vridar went to the cottonwood grove where the Indians camped to see what they were doing. John was standing on the river bank, fishing; Jim lay prone in the wagon with his hands under his head; and up the mountain at some distance the squaws were gathering brush for a fire and looking for edible roots. Thunder crashed again like the wreaking fury of dynamite, the dusk flowered in blinding glare. Vridar was galloping homeward, glancing back now and then to see if the Indians pursued, when a violent crash fell around him, followed at once by an awful brilliance that filled the world. Then there was a great hissing whiteness that swept in a river of flame up a huge dry fir. The mare stopped, reeling under him and for a moment blind. He felt a sudden warmth and the smoke of dead boughs, and smelt the strong wood-odor of flaming tree. In one stroke it had been fire-gutted from root to top and was now a seething darkness, with a million jewels like fireflies in its twigs. The sky broke again and a cloud of rain fell. It rode down the wind in wild gray sheets, whipping the trees into wet furies and rolling up the river like a leaning wall of dusk. He galloped into it, with flame bursting in white floods around him and with thunder sounding like a concourse of huge organs. Thickets of rain lashed at his face and the wet jungles of it drenched the land with night. Wind hissed over bushes and shrieked in frenzy around trees and fell before him into pools of moaning. Water soaked him now and was running in cold paths down his neck and back. Drops stung his face like hot frying grease and his hair was a dripping mat.

He was frightened but he liked this wild ride. He liked the clean stinging vividness of the rain, the fragrant darkness of it, and its convulsed delirium overhead. Its broad ravening tumult or the biting insolence of sudden squalls which would leap out and beat against him sent his blood racing and made him feel bold and fearless. He fancied himself as Paul Revere, galloping pellmell to arouse a nation; or as a scout dashing through a wilderness of arrows to warn of the approach of redskins. The mare's hooves struck rhythm in puddle and mud, and behind in the dark was a trail of galloping sound. The drama of this journey, with its blow and splash and clatter, its menace and threat, became a meaning so splendid and tameless and free that he began to shout. He yelled at the armies of trees and the battalions of brush and goldenrod whipping in the wind. "Come on!" he cried, for he was Sheridan now. He waved to them and said, "Come on, come on!"

But the night that followed did not enfold him with glory. After wading in the corral barefooted in manure six inches deep; after standing in the remorseless deluge before one cow and another, pumping milk from their udders and smelling their wet unclean hides and being struck across his face with their foul wet tails; and after going shivering to the house and eating bread and milk while listening to the roar of storm, he saw no glamor in anything. The floor was streaked with rain and mud and dung. Marion and Diana were huddled in a corner, wretched and silent. His father and mother in dripping ragged coats squashed about with water squirting from their shoes, with water shining on their cold red faces and hands. He told them the Indians had come but they seemed not to hear.

"We must see about the little chickens!" Prudence cried. "They'll all be drowned!"

"Wife, I should a-thought you'd a-seen to them when you saw the rain comun!"

"Oh, you should a-thought wonders! You said there wouldn't be any rain. The moon wasn't right, you said."

Joe lit a lantern and Prudence rubbed her frozen hands. She told the children to go to bed, and then the parents went out into the black wind-shaken roaring night. The room was dark now, with rain and wind smiting the rattling windows and over the house, with the wind striking in recoiling shrieks and falling back in desolate deep-breath moaning. Upon the dirt roof was the mud-sob of water, and water like shadows was creeping down the walls. Vridar went to his bed and felt over the quilts. There was only one puddle yet. He shook it to the floor and called to his brother and sister. They all undressed in the dark wet silence, and when Vridar saw his sister faintly in the gloom he peered at her but there was nothing to see.

"Turn your head!" she cried, for she had been watching him.

"My head was turned," he said, but he lied.

When she was in bed he went over to her and she asked angrily, "What do you want?"

"To see how your arm is. Does it hurt?"

131

"Leave me alone."

He returned, limping, to his bed and crawled in, ashamed of his impulse. The wind was howling from a thousand wild throats and the house was shaking in the storm. Now and then sudden white blindness would fill the room and Vridar could see everything as plain as in daylight. When the parents came in, Prudence took elk and deer hides and spread them over the beds. They were as stiff as boards and smelled of strong wild places.

"Is your bed wet anywhere?"

"Only in one place," he said.

"Diana, you feel any leaks on you?"

"I feel one," said Marion. "It's down by my feet."

Prudence brought the lantern in. She looked the beds over and then cried to Joe.

"Now what?" he growled, looming in the doorway.

"The roof is leaking like a sieve!"

"Well, wife," he said, staring up at the ceiling, "what can I do?"

"You'n help," she said, and she brought all the pots and pans from the kitchen. She set them on the beds and around the room where rain was dripping, and she told the children to be careful or they would upset the pans. She said to wake her up if they felt water on them. Then she blew out the lantern and Vridar could hear his parents undressing; and a few moments later when a white flash came he saw them grotesquely silhouetted in their underclothes.

Vridar lay quietly and listened to the roar of storm and the dripping of rain in pans. Now and then the room awoke in a long quivering brilliance. He could hear the far-away barking of thunder or its sudden sharp burst and then he waited for the flash that would come next, followed again by thunder. His father had said the lightning was very close if the thunder came at once. He could smell the odor of lightning and of rain and of the wild hair under which he was bedded; and in the whole house he could smell the corral dung. He wondered if the whole roof might melt under the rain and fall. Then he fell asleep, thinking of the Indians trying to keep dry under the rain-swept trees.

He was awakened some time later and saw a nightgowned figure moving about the room. His mother was emptying the pans that were full; she would take them to the door and hurl the water out and set the pans again. From a few of the roof-holes the water no longer dripped but fell in gurgling streams. The rain outside was a steady monotonous downpour, with the thunder far away now and with the lightning falling in faint ghostly pulsations. Rising to an elbow, he felt over the elk and deer skins: basined in each was a pool of water and mud. When he moved his feet he struck water under the quilts, and he heard it dripping from the bedding to the floor. He stirred again and discovered that there was water under his back. The whole bed seemed to be soaked.

"You wet?" his mother asked, coming over.

"A little."

"Wife, what's all the fuss?" asked Joe, peering over a deer skin.

"Everything is soaked!" she cried angrily. "Why don't you get up and help?"

"If it's soaked," he said, "it's soaked. Come on to bed."

"You bring your family to a God-forsaken place and you lay there and don't care." She felt under bedding to see if her sons were dry. When her hands came close to Vridar's loins he moved away, embarrassed by her searching.

"I'm all right," he said.

"Joe, there ain't a dry thing left in the house!"

"It'll be daylight soon," said Joe.

Prudence told the boys to crawl out, and they stepped to the floor and stood shivering on its wet boards. She jerked the skins off, hurling water on the floor, and turned the tick bottomside up.

"They can't sleep this way," she said. "Their bed is soaked."

Joe rumbled. "Wife, why don't you come to bed?"

"Why don't you get up and help?"

"It's daylight soon," he said.

She went to Diana's bed and explored and said it was dry. She told her sons to crawl in there. They crawled in, with Vridar next to Diana, and Prudence covered them over with the skins. Then she returned to her bed.

Vridar lay on his back, listening to the storm. Diana was asleep, with her wounded elbow drawn to her breast. Feeling the warmth of her Vridar turned to look at her face and saw it like a wan full moon. Above him there seemed to be no leak, but elsewhere he could hear mud dropping and the sudden eagerness of water when a roof-puddle melted through. The room was white and blind and a moment later thunder crashed; and he saw his bed as a tumbled wet mass of quilts and ticking, paler where dry, darker where drenched. In the same instant he saw the dripping walls and the floor littered with puddles and pans and the ragged wet ceiling. Then darkness, the ghostly window, and the sound of rain hitting tin. At first after the pans had been emptied the sound of each drop was crisp and ringing; but after water covered the pan bottoms the sounds were a kind of liquid purling and tinkling, until the room became full of rain-music.

While he lay quietly, trying to be lulled into sleep, he heard a sudden gutting sound overhead; and a moment later a bucketful of mud and rain fell, striking the elk skin over his chest. He sat and spilled the water to right and left. When he lay back he stared up at the pale night-hole in the roof. He could see raindrops form at its edge, run together and distend as if breathing; and then he could see the shining gem grow downward, like a bulb of melted glass, and hang for a moment from a slender neck that steadily lengthened, and fall. The night-opening grew in size as rain ate into its crumbling banks; and other chunks of mud dropped to the skin.

Joe was snoring. Vridar had learned that his father's snores were one of the curses of his mother's life. Air seemed to roar into Joe in great foggy sucking consonants, as if his nose were alternately pinched and opened; and the air came out of him in a hissing moan and then in guttural chokings. Vridar listened to his father and looked up at the menace of the roof, wondering if a ton of earth might fall and entomb him in mud. Now and then he sat up to shake water from the bed. Down the hillside path which led from the corral to the house he could hear a raging torrent, and beyond it, the broad terrible journeying of river waters. Diana stirred

133

and smote at her face; a trickle had broken through and struck her. Vridar laid a deer skin over her head and she sighed and slept.

The window was becoming ghostly with the first morning light. Shadows now paled on the drenched walls; the wet floor gleamed. While Vridar was waiting and watching, he saw the window darken, and then an Indian, looking in.

"Mother!" he said.

"Son, what's the matter?"

"An Indian is there by the window."

"Joe, wake up!"

Joe choked on a snore and growled. "Now what in hell's the trouble?"

The Indian left the window and pounded on the door. Leaping out of bed, Prudence drew her garments from under the tick and began to dress. From under his own tick Vridar pulled his shirt and trousers into the bed to warm them. Joe yawned and pushed his legs over the bed's edge and sat up, looking warm and sleepy in his heavy underwear. He picked up cotton socks and looked at them and rubbed them between his hands, as he always did, to shake out of them their sweat and dirt. The stink and dust of them when he did this would fill the room and his wife would reproach him; and Joe would only scowl and rub his socks harder.

Perceiving that Vridar was awake, he drew a quilt around him, for he never showed himself to his sons, even in his underwear. Vridar had seen one mighty calf, almost hairless and as thick as a tree trunk. Joe was proud of his lower legs. He thought a man with thin lower legs was no good at all.

Vridar dressed and went into the other room. His mother was there, making a fire in a wet stove; and in the doorway stood John and Jim. Their moccasins were muddy and wet but otherwise they were dry. Joe came from the other room with the skins. He took them out to the dooryard, for the rain had stopped now, and the Indians looked at them, pawing them over and over. Joe spoke to them in their own language and at last they gave him four pairs of buckskin gloves.

"They don't want much," he said, entering the house.

"What?" asked Prudence angrily.

"God a-mighty," he said.

"I suppose they want eggs and milk and flour and tobacco and matches—"

"Wife, that ain't what I mean. One of their horses is dead and they want a horse."

"A horse!" she said, staring at him. "Well, I hope you're not fool enough to give them a horse." She thrust savagely at the fire. "Go help them up the dugway and tell them to get home the best way they can."

Followed by Vridar, Joe took a hammer, an axe, some wire, and a horse and went with the Indians up the lane. During this distance of almost a mile not a word was spoken. They found the squaws sitting under a tree by a campfire. They saw one of the gaunt beasts, lying dead, and the other standing near, drooping, forlorn, with rain-streaked hide.

Joe cut two aspens, knocked the tongue from the wagon and put in its stead two thills. He hitched his own horse, a big powerful beast, between the shafts, after putting on him the old wired harness; he piled the hides on the wagon; then, with Jim riding the forlorn scarecrow and John and the squaws and Vridar walking in

134

the mud, Joe went up the dugway. At the top he removed his horse and put the harness on Jim's beast and hitched it to the wagon. Then he told the Indians to hit the grit.

The four of them crawled to the wagon box and sat huddled under blankets, under a dark wet sky; and ahead of them the skeleton staggered from side to side, trying to draw the load. "I'm jooberus," said Joe, "they won't get fur with that-air outfit. But mebbe they'll get fur enough to bother some other person."

After a few minutes he bit off a quid and stared at a hill, where the starved wreck was struggling in mud, slipping and skidding and falling to its knees, while on the wagon three nomads sat patiently and a fourth smote with a club.

"The lazy red buggers," said Joe. "Why don't they get off and push?"

Then Joe turned down the mountain. Vridar stood for a few minutes and watched. The pathetic skeleton was reeling and plunging now under the bitter blows of a hawthorn whip. It would fall down and struggle to its trembling legs and try again; but the load was too much for it when the path lay uphill and the footing was mud. The squaws got down and pushed but neither of the bucks did, and one of them continued to smite with the stick. Little by little the wagon was drawn and shoved to the hill's crest. Then the squaws climbed up and sat again under their brilliant blankets, and the journey fell downward and out of sight.

XVIII

In all the years of his childhood and youth Vridar's parents toiled from daylight until long after dark. When the labor of the day was done the chores remained to do: the milking, the straining of milk through a rag and the setting of it in pans, the feeding and watering of beasts, the herding of fowl into their coops and the locking of doors; and still other odds and ends. Sometimes when the chores were done it was midnight, and just at daylight and sometimes before the parents were again dressed and ready.

Leaving the house, Joe would set out through morning dusk for the hills where his horses grazed. He would climb the mountain and find their tracks and follow them, and sometimes he would walk for miles before they were found. He would return after an hour or two hours or three and water and harness them; and then he would come to the house and eat. He had his land to till and harvest and the herds on which to ride; and as though all this were not enough, he undertook to operate a sawmill.

Prudence was as busy as Joe and a lot faster and more efficient. After rising she would go to her chickens, and then with Vridar's help would milk a dozen or more cows. When these chores were done she cooked the breakfast; then made a cheese, a long and back-breaking task; then cooked the noon meal and rushed from the table to build hencoops, wash clothes, scrub floors and help Joe with his own tasks. She had to make a half-dozen journeys to the valley to peddle her eggs, butter and cheese from house to house. And because Joe set up a sawmill, new burdens were laid upon her.

Three miles up Black Canyon, which looked upon Hunter Bottom from the east there had been a sawmill years ago, and it was for this that the long dugway down the mountain had been made. The tall flume was still there, the mill-wheel and saw and belts, the cabins and piles of sawdust. A hundred yards of brown cable still spanned the river, but the ferryboat had been carried away by spring floods.

For what was left of the old mill and its equipment Vridar's parents gave two hundred dollars, all that they had saved from twelve years of toil. Somewhere up the river lodged on an island Joe had found an old ferryboat; he caulked and tarred it and rode it down, guiding it with a huge sweep on a fulcrum. With superhuman effort he threaded its rusty pulleys with the cable, built landing piers of fir and stone, and got the mill in shape. Hearing of the low price he asked for lumber, ranchers came with wagons from the valley to haul it away. It became the mother's task to ferry them across the river.

When she heard wheels on the dugway, she would drop her work and run, not walk, the distance of more than half a mile to the ferry. Some days she had to make several journeys. She would return, her face dripping with sweat and her mouth white with fatigue, and pick up her unfinished task. She would bend over washtub or cheese-rack, when, hearing wheels again, she would trot up the long dusty lane.

For her older son she was a miracle of patience and endurance and will. It passed into legend among valley folk that she could kill a dozen men, that no other woman had ever slaved as she slaved, that she and her husband were money-grubbing skin-flints. But these people did not know that ahead of her stood a vision: a dream of educated children, living clean lives far from corral and hogpen and chicken coop. Watching her toil or sometimes hearing her moan in her sleep, Vridar felt unworthy of such sacrifice. He might become a lawyer or a professor or possibly even a great writer, but he could never repay such devotion or make her slavery worth its cost. He felt her pain when she winced under the taunts of Nephi.

"It's a purty comedown for you," he said one day. "You was allus so stuckup. Us men down in Annis wasn't good enough for you. By God, see you now in this hole, slavun your guts out!"

"Well, persley," she would say, wiping sweat away with a forearm, "let's see whose children go farthest. Let's see which is better educated, yours or mine."

"I don't take no stock in college," he said, his eyes glinting under his shaggy brows. "And I don't imagine your kids will be any smartern mine."

"We'll wait and see."

Hearing these words, Vridar resolved to write his name high. What else could he do, with parents like these! He would go to Nephi some day and he would say to him, "Well, I'm a professor now. I saw your Hankie the other day and he's a plain dirt-grubber like you." Or he would say: "I'm an author now and I write books. I doubt if your Hankie could understand them."

But if he marveled in this year and in so many years to come at the frenzied ambition of his mother, his father astonished him hardly less. Joe did the work of two or three men. If he had a spare moment he would seize the mattock and add another small patch to the cleared area of his farm, or go, as in former years, after dark, taking the lantern with him, to bend like an inexhaustible machine over the roots. He also sometimes went at a trot. They both ran so much, Prudence and

Joe, that Charley Bridwell, coming to borrow food which he never paid back, would roar with laughter and tell them they were digging their graves.

"You need four legs and four arms," he said to Joe. "Then you could pitch hay and grub at the same time. Here, let's set in the shade and have a drink . . . "

In late July Vridar went with his father to help at the mill, and here he saw the man as the mightiest toiler he had ever known, the mightiest he was ever to know. And here he came again very close to death.

Black Canyon, which opened in a wide mouth on Snake River, and lay upward for seven miles to a misty divide, was named for its dark flanks of Douglas fir. It was for Vridar a fearful place; and even in later years when he was grown he was never able to shake free of the spell it had laid on him. A wild cold stream cascaded mile after mile over its great stones. On his first ride up its jungle-bottom he saw five bears, each fearless and mildly curious; smelled the wild life of it and heard the strange sounds in its growth. His father pointed to four rotting walls: there, he said, an old prospector once lived, but he went crazy and blew his brains out. His bones were still there, buried under the fallen roof. His skull was not buried, though; elk hunters had used it, and when Joe saw it last it had tomato seeds sticking to the bone.

The mill site was an uneven half-acre with an earth ledge above. At the foot of this stood the flume, a square tower of planks, fifty feet high. In its depth was the wheel, and close by, with a great belt on its shoulder, was the saw. Across the creek which roared deep here under a tangle of brush were two cabins, one of fir-logs, dirt-roofed, and one of slabs. They smelled of age and darkness and mice.

In the dirt-roofed one which had two rooms lived Agnes and Borg. Agnes had come as cook, Borg as lumberjack. Joe had also hired two other men: Jeb McGard, a rough silent giant of the McGard clan, filthy and hairy; and Vridar's uncle Dock. Dock had married again and had homesteaded on the Antelope hills. Vridar and his father slept in the slab shack.

The boy spent two weeks here and each day added a new wonder to his life. He liked the cold pure water, tasting and smelling of snow and of the many shrubs along its banks; he liked the sharp clean air and the fragrant lumber and sawdust and the forested mountainsides. His appetite became wolfish. His unfleshed bones took on weight and strength.

Vridar's place of work was the sawdust pit under the saw. Leading to the creek was a gangway of boards, upon which with a one-wheel cart he bore sawdust to the water and dumped it in. Above him sang the great gleaming saw, as his father swung a lever and the teeth ate a clean narrow canyon through a log. He liked the swift precision of the work here: the broad belt riding over the shoulder and down into the mill's darkness, where the turbine was hidden; the powerful log-carriage, the levers and iron runways and rods, and the cloudburst of yellow dust. He liked the sounds: the creaking of heavy machinery, the music of the saw as it gathered speed, the gurgling flow of water. When a lever was drawn and the flume's power was released to the belt the saw flashed and all its white teeth for a moment shone like racing daggers; and then the teeth became a blur of incredible speed and hummed like a human throat when they struck the log. In the pit he could feel the saw's wind, and smell the fragrant gutting of fir. He loved this work.

But not all his hours were so pleasant as those with the sawdust. The creek's banks by the cabins were mantled with cool walls of tangled growth. One day he was standing on the footbridge, watching the play of shadows on the stream below, when his aunt came up and looked at him. She said she did not like all the weedy growth on the cabin side of the creek and asked him if he would pull it up. At once he set to work. He did not see her turn and wink at Borg. Some of the shrubs shot stinging pains into his hands when he seized them and fell like flaking fire on his naked arms; but he went ahead until he had cleared the area and then looked up at her.

"Is that all right?" he asked.

He saw that she was grinning with malicious joy. He saw cruelty distorting her full ripe mouth. Beyond her in the doorway stood Borg and he was grinning, too, and Vridar knew that somehow he had been tricked.

"Look at your hands," she said, giggling at him.

He looked at his hands. A reddish rash of blood-sickness had spread over them and his arms, and his flesh was burning and itching, as if full of powdered glass. He scratched the back of one hand and the itching spread in scalding pricking heat. He looked at her again.

"I guess you thought that was a smart trick," he said.

"Why, you silly, I never knowed it would do that. Did you, Borg?"

"You lie," Vridar said.

He went up the creek and hid. Sitting on cool stones under a shelter of thimble-berry vines, he thrust his arms into the water and the pain was drawn out. But when he took his arms from the water the itching was much worse than before. The rash had now gathered into blotches. He blew breath on it, cooling the fever, but the pain steadily increased. I'll get even with her! he thought, tears of humiliation washing down his cheeeks. The pain now seemed to shoot up his arms and reach his heart. He went back and faced her.

"A hell of a fine aunt you are!" he cried, glaring at her and wishing he could obliterate the devilish triumph in her eyes.

"I didn't know it would do that," she said.

"You lie and you know you lie!"

"Don't shout that way or you'll wake the baby up."

"To hell with your baby!" he said, wishing that he could smite her to the heart. "I hope your sons are murderers and your daughters are whores!"

"Vridar! Is that the way you talk to your aunt?"

"You're no aunt of mine and you never will be!"

Vridar slept with his father and memory of these nights was forever galling. Joe lay on his back, his arms folded over his chest, as if he were dead, save that he snored violently at the roof. Five minutes after he lay down he was buried fathoms deep, and nightlong he never turned over or stirred. Vridar was restless and wakeful. His habit when sleeping with Marion was to turn again and again, now lying on one side, now on the other, or now on his belly. But in bed with his father he did not dare to move. If he did Joe would growl at him and demand to know what in hell was wrong; or he would look over at his son with threatening eyes. And so Vridar sank into a kind of paralysis, his body stiffening into such aches that the long night became excruciating torture. The first night after poisoning his hands he did not sleep at all. He had shown the itching rash to his father, but Joe had merely glanced at it and said it would be well in a few days. After timidly undressing and sliding into his small part of the bed he found the agony more than he could endure without moving. He would rub quietly at his burning flesh.

"Now what's the matter?" Joe growled.

"It itches."

"Go to sleep. It'll be all right."

For as long as he could endure it, Vridar lay utterly quiet. He hardly breathed. Cramps gripped his leg-bones. He wanted to cough but he did not dare to, and he gurgled a little and choked. He wanted to go to the creek and soak his wounds. He wanted to scratch his arms. When after what seemed to him ages he began stealthily to draw an arm forth or to straighten a paralyzed leg or to turn from one side to the other Joe would swallow a great snore and grunt. Striving then to move quickly while his father was adjusting himself, Vridar seized the covers and turned.

"Now what in hell is it?" Joe roared.

"Nothing."

Joe grunted and drew a deep sigh. "Go to sleep," he said.

The next morning Vridar dressed his aching limbs and went outside and saw Borg clowning. By the footbridge was a huge fir stump with a flat top. Stark naked, Borg was standing on this and shouting, and Agnes was watching him from the doorway. He smote his hands over his broad hairy chest and made a drumming sound, and then suddenly snorted and neighed like a stallion approaching a mare. He ran hands through the hair over his body and pulled at it and clutched and yanked, all the while half-sitting, half-rising, half-sitting again. Amorous sounds roared out of him as in turn he imitated the stud and the bull and slapped his buttocks and pranced round and round. He stretched to tiptoe and craned his neck and crowed. He kicked backward, as if at a mare, and pretended to be nipping at her with his teeth; and he pranced and snorted and whinnied.

"I been suckun raw eggs!" he yelled. "Fetch me a woman in heat!"

Agnes snickered. Joe, out by the saw lacing a belt, paid no attention at all. Vridar had hidden and was peering out. Jeb sat on a pile of lumber and looked thoughtful.

"You're sure a hairy son of a bitch," he said. "You got more hair nen me."

Borg was neighing and prancing. With both hands he clutched his genitals and cupped them, drawing them up his belly, and hopped round and round.

"I keep my old missus lookun at the ceiling all the time!" he said. "She ain't no match for me."

"You're sure a hairy son of a bitch," said Jeb. "You got a cat beat all holler."

"I'm a man!" Borg roared. "I'm all he-lion and wolf-meat!" He was now whistling like a bull elk. Vridar saw that the man's organ was standing up. Then he saw

Borg jump down and spat his hinder at Jeb and go prancing and neighing toward his wife, who fled shrieking before him.

Every morning thereafter Borg got on the stump and clowned, and Agnes watched him from the door.

One day a horrible accident occured. Vridar had been in the pit during most of the forenoon, shoveling the yellow sawdust and looking up at the two men above him. He wondered which was the more powerful. His father was very strong. It was Joe's proud boast, if one quiet statement can be called a boast, that he could walk off with more green lumber than any other man he had known. Jeb was stronger perhaps. He weighed two hundred and forty pounds and was all muscle and bone. His tough knotted palms were like great sunbaked hams. When he bent over and heaved at a log, scorning to use a canthook, muscles bulged upward under his shirt and rolls of beef ringed his neck. But he was not the mightiest of the McGard clan. It was Burns, Vridar remembered, the titan of them all, whose feats of strength had passed into legend.

Jeb kicked ordinary logs around as if they were poles. Using a two by six plank as a lever, he would snap it in two and Joe would growl at him; and when he stepped on the carriage the beams trembled. Many of the logs were crooked, with huge curved butts, and from these slabs were sliced off sometimes a foot in depth; but Jeb laid hold of them and carried them away. Ah Lord, Vridar thought, if only some day I am a man like that!

He did not see the accident. He was bent over, shoveling dust. He heard a shout and then a strange singing in the saw, and the hiss of flying splinters. When he looked up the power had been thrown off and the belt was flapping to a stop. Halfway across the saw lay a riddled slab. By the saw stood Jeb.

His left hand, Vridar perceived next, had been struck. The fingers were shredded bone and flesh. Jeb stood there quietly, looking at his hand. A little way up the road Dock had been skidding logs and he now left his team and came running; and for what seemed to Vridar a long time the three men stood in silence, looking at the dripping hand. It was Jeb who spoke.

"Looks like it's done for," he said. "Them fingers ain't no good now." He shook his hand a little and blood spattered round him and his fingers dangled like red rags. Dock drew a deep breath. "God a-mighty!" he said.

Vridar felt sick. The men stood, silent, looking at the shreds of flesh and bone. Jeb turned to Joe.

"Well," he said, "I guess you got a-get a new offbearer. I'll have to chop them fingers off." He looked round him and with his good right hand picked up an axe. He set off toward the creek and Vridar followed the men, eager to see what was done.

Dock was crying to Jeb: "God a-mighty, man, mebbe them fingers ain't plumb worseless! Don't chop them off!" But Jeb seemed to pay no heed. He went to the flat stump upon which Borg pranced and whinnied. And what Jeb did now, Vridar decided long afterward, was the most amazing instance of sheer grit that he had ever witnessed. Jeb laid his mangled hand on the stump. Dock grasped his arm.

140

"Don't be a plumb loonytick! Joe, you aim to let him chop them off?"

"I guess he knows his own mind," said Joe.

"Don't do it, Jeb! We can go to a doctor like God kicked us in the end! Show some sense, man!"

"Joe," said Jeb, "fetch me some water." Joe hastened to the cabin and returned with a pailful. "Just throw some on," Jeb said, still speaking quietly, "so I'n see where to cut." Joe poured water over the red pulp. Blood flowed away and bones came out stark and white. "A little more water, Joe, so I can see. Douse it on." Joe hurled a washing stream and Jeb raised the axe, balanced for a moment and brought the blade down. Four fingers were severed at the hand-joints. He raised it again and chopped off the thumb. "Now bring me a horse," he said and entered the cabin.

He came out in a few moments with the hand bundled in rags. Red spots were already showing through. Dock meanwhile had brought a horse, and Jeb now mounted the beast and galloped down the canyon and out of sight. Vridar knew that he would swim the horse across the river, riding its back as it swam. Upon the stump lay the fingers and thumb. Joe tossed them into the creek. Two years later when Vridar came again to the sawmill the wood was still dark with the stain.

Joe and Dock entered a cabin and sat and looked at the floor. Agnes asked them questions but they did not look up.

"God a-mighty, Joe," Dock said at last He stirred in his chair and bit off a quid. "I seen grit in my life but that takes the cake, by God if it don't."

Joe said nothing. Dock went to the door and squirted a brown stream and came back, wiping his mouth. "Them McGards," he said, "they're all toughern a skinned hoot-owl. Joe, in all your borned life did you ever see such plumb God damn grit?"

"No," said Joe, "I never did."

Dock was silent a few moments. "Say, how much McGard is there in us anyhow?"

Two days later Vridar experienced his narrowest escape from death. The mill penstock leaked. From cracks between the planks the gunnysacking had fallen out in many places or had rotted and shrunk, and when the penstock was full, water spurted out in countless streams, wasting the mill's power. Joe asked his son if he would descend into the penstock and caulk it.

Vridar said he would. How could he refuse, remembering Jeb! The penstock was empty now. Up the canyon above, the creek had been shut off from the millrace and was storing itself in a deep pond. Joe brought a wedge of maple, a hammer and a great armful of rags. There were steps, he said, that led down into the flume but some of them were weak and Vridar would have to be careful. The father got a long rope. He tied the rope to the top of the penstock and flung the other end down. Vridar peered into the wet and darkness of the hole; it was four or five feet feet square and deep and black like a well. It was a dreadful thing. It smelled of old soaked planks and drowned things and mud. Across one corner boards had been spiked, to serve as a ladder, and Vridar could tell looking down that the distance between any two of them was about three feet. He could tell that some were split

141

at the ends where the spikes had been driven and looked as if they would not support a songbird.

"If I wasn't afeared them steps," said Joe, "I'd go down. But I guess they'll hold you all right." He dropped the bundle of rags into the depth and sent the hammer and wedge after it. "Keep aholt the rope when you go down. Some of them steps might not hold you."

Vridar was frightened. It had always made him feel dizzy and ill when he looked down a sheer wall from a height. But he had to go, even if he were to break his neck. Thinking of Jeb, he threw his legs over the brink, grasped the rope with both hands, and started down. But he did not look down, lest he sicken and fall. He looked up at the square of sky. With naked feet he explored and found each step in turn. The first three or four had supported him, but then one splintered and left its spikes and fell and suddenly he was dangling while hanging by his hands.

"They won't hold me!" he screamed up the penstock.

"Don't get afeared," said Joe quietly. "The next, it's strong enough mebbe."

Holding his breath and putting all his strength into his hands Vridar slid down the rope inch by inch and found the next step. It held. He drew a sucking breath and rested.

"Is the next all right?" Joe asked.

"Yes, I guess so!"

The boy stood a few moments trying to control his shaking legs, meanwhile clutching the rope with all his might. He knew that if he were to fall from this height he would be killed. Then he reached far down with one foot, found the next step, tested it with part of his weight, and lowered his other foot; and in this way yard by yard with his eyes fixed on the patch of sky he went down and down until he stood in mud. It looked like a half-mile to the top. His father's face had vanished; Vridar shouted up to him but there was no answer, save a blinding echo in the walls. He dug into mud and found the hammer and wedge; he seized the rags and set to work. The worst leaks were at the bottom. While he worked he was chilled with apprehension. Though this flume was as cold as an ice-bin, sweat poured out of him and his heart raced. He tore rags feverishly, laid them along the cracks and wedged them in. Some of the cracks were so large that he could see daylight. When a good part of the caulking was done, he knelt in mud and tried to see the great wheel. He wondered how water made it turn. He reached down until he could touch it and it felt like a great stone half-buried in mud.

After he had sealed all the cracks within reach he climbed to the first step, braced himself with an arm and elbow and drove gunnysacking into the light-slits around him. He climbed to the second step, to the third. From his waist hung a belt of rags; he carried the wedge between his teeth. He had been working perhaps an hour when he heard a sound. Looking up he saw nothing but the window of sky. He shouted, but heard only his own voice, shattered in a multitude of echoes. He listened, and heard the sound again. It was like a deep wind rising, or like a herd of trampling feet. The booming of it was now coming in waves, shuddering in the walls and pouring great whisperings down into the hole. Sensing imminent danger, yet unable to see it or to guess what it was, he stared up at the patch of sky and waited, his hands clutching the rope. He heard the sound drawing steadily near. It was like—it was like the rolling of waters, the tumbling rush of oncoming waves. Then, great God, in one appalling moment of certainty he knew what it was: the dam had broken and the waters of the pond were rolling upon him!

With a yell of terror he flung the wedge and hammer from him and climbed frantically to the next step. Looking up and shouting with all his might he started to climb; and then the sound broke into a booming washing and spilling, and a sheet of water shot out above and darkened the sky and came down in piles of thunder. It struck him with a terrific blow of roar and wave and knocked him from the step to the mud bottom. Wild with fear he groped blindly under the crushing deluge; he found the rope and seized it and again started to climb. He glanced up but the flood smote his face; in the one instant of vision before water blinded his eyes he saw the plunging column above him, with its edges churning out in foam and spray. He was on the first step now, with the violent tons striking his head and shoulders, with the water boiling upward from the mud bottom, rising to his waist and then to his neck. Water crushed him against the wall and spumed into his gasping mouth and stung his eyeballs and was like great rough hands on his shoulders. I must keep cool! he thought, knowing that death was everywhere around him. He tried to shout as he climbed again but under his terror was the one thought that he must keep his head. He had shut his eyes because when he opened them and tried to look up, water smote them like a palm of iron. He kept his face close to the steps and realized as he climbed that the higher he went up the more the steps were back under and away from the floods pouring down. By hugging the corner he could breathe, with the waters breaking on his shoulders and back and shooting over him. His hands on the rope were desperate and rigid. I must keep cool! he kept thinking, as step by step he struggled upward through the avalanche of nightmare.

When he was twenty feet or so from the bottom, a step gave way and dropped; and he was left hanging to the rope, with a part of the mighty stream hurling against him. He swung through it and struck the opposite wall and swung back, knowing all the while that if his hands lost their grip he would die. He slid down a little to the step below and then rested until the water boiling upward reached his neck; and then climbed hand over hand to the next step and rested there a moment; and climbed again. He thrust his face back into the corner and panted and shook. He felt the water boiling against his face and climbed again and still again, with no sound in his ears but the deafening crash of water on water, with no feeling of water on his flesh but only of terror and fire. He rested an instant and breathed and then climbed, until at last when he reached the top he was spent and choked and half-drowned. The water had followed him up; and now, clutching the rope and with only his head out, he rested a moment, gasping and sobbing; then with the last of his strength he drew himself up and over the edge. He staggered and fell in the stream and was almost carried away in the downward roar. He clawed toward the bank and clutched a willow and lay for a little while, with only his face out. His eyes were shut and he was sucking air like fire into his lungs. He drew himself to the bank and tried to stand but his legs broke and he fell. On hands and knees he began to cough water from his lungs; and dimly, as though in a dream, he knew that the penstock was

143

full now. He could hear the boiling maelstrom at the top and water overflowing the banks.

Then a flood shot down to the piled logs and the millyard. Joe came running and clambering up the bank, shouting his son's name; but Vridar was too weak to answer, too weak to move. Joe came up the bank and saw his son and looked down at him, drenched and white and half-dead.

"You all right?" he asked.

Weakly Vridar glanced up at him, and in the bitterness of his heart he was thinking, What kind of father is this, who would put his son to such risks! Then he stretched out on his belly and gasped and choked, trying to get the water out of him, and the fear and the terror.

XIX

In September Nephi prepared to move. He said he might return, though he had made no money in this infernal hole. He would try it once more. "I'm that big of a fool," he said. Joe said if he wanted to sell out they could arrange it. "No," said Nephi, "I'll try it once more. I'm that big a fool, with no sense at all."

After the wagon had gone up the dugway and the last sound of it had died, the place for Vridar was unutterably desolate. Again there was the old dread over swamp and hill and the old loneliness in the sky. His mother felt the change, too; she was more silent now. Across the river patches of maple were turning scarlet; all around him autumn was burning toward death in the dark red of chokecherry leaf, in the pale wintry yellow upon aspens and the frost upon goldenrod.

Hankie had said he would see Vridar in school but Vridar did not know and his thought went far away to Neloa. Nothing had been said about school for the boys this year. The matter, Vridar felt, was not to be spoken of. Perhaps there was no money to spend, or perhaps the dream was dead.

September passed and October came in on a white snowstorm; and he knew that school had started long ago. But his parents were still silent. All day and part of every night Joe rode the mountains and hills, searching for beasts lost from the herds. He rode far away, east and west, north and south; and now and then he found one or two and drove them to the ranch. When he came in late at night, Prudence would glance at his face and read there his success or failure. But they rarely spoke. Meals were eaten in silence and in silence the family went to bed.

During this autumn Vridar was trying to do a man's work. Fallow land had to be plowed. Snow was on the ground now, several cold dry inches of it, and the earth was hardening in frost; but day after day he followed a handplow, walking the furrows with red naked feet. When the day's labor was done, he had to help milk cows and pitch manure from the stable and bed and feed the beasts. Then he ate cold bread and milk and went wearily to sleep.

October passed and gray lonely November came. School was two months old now. Neloa and Archie would be walking home in these autumn afternoons, across the cedared butte and down a white lane. And here he was, dressed in rags, naked to his knees, plowing and milking and shoveling manure, and hating this work with all his strength. He would never be a lawyer, a writer or a professor. There seemed to be no love here and very little hope. Prudence was as silent and stern as the naked lodges, Joe rode and came home and rode again, his face growing haggard with defeat. Then he said he would ride no more. He had searched from hell to breakfast but no more beasts were to be found, though more than twenty were still missing.

"If you don't find them," his wife cried, "we won't make a thing this year!"

"I know it," he said, his eyes bleak with loss.

"We won't even be able to pay for what we've lost!"

"Wife, I know it. Don't you think I figgered it out?"

"Then how'll we put the boys in school?"

"We'll find a way. They'll have to batch."

"Batch! You mean live all alone and take care of themselves?"

"Wife, you don't have to shout like I was plumb deaf. I do all any man can."

"Well, our management ain't right somehow. We slave like niggers and we're still behind. I work—" She broke off and turned away, and for the first time in his life Vridar saw tears in her eyes.

"Wife, you don't work no hardern me. I do all any man can."

"Oh yes, we both slave our hearts and guts out and what have we got? Less than we had when we started!"

Joe was silent, his gray eyes hard and bright and his mouth like stone.

"Our boys will go to school, even if we have to mortgage. Is that right?"

"That's right," he said.

And so the matter was settled. Their dream still lived.

They went to school in Poplar, an area of ranches where Snake River valley lay against the Antelope hills. For almost seven months they would live alone, though every second week in the winter season Joe would fight through blizzards to bring them food. Their house was an old gloomy deserted thing of two rooms, with a dirt roof, cottonwood walls, and no floor but the earth. It had a wooden bunk with boards instead of springs; a small scabbed iron stove, with wire hinges on its doors; a table made of rough plank, a box of dishes, a roll of bedding and two broken chairs. Its two dreary windows had no curtains and no shades. His mother had made curtains but Vridar used them for dish-towels.

Vridar was cook. Without variation their breakfast was a bowl of oatmeal, with sugar but with no milk or cream; and sometimes a slice of bread. Sometimes they had butter but oftener they had none. Their lunch was a sandwich of bread and elk meat. Their supper was bread and meat, fried potatoes or water gravy, and usually a little fruit. Sometimes the bread was of Vridar's own making, heavy and soggy and tasteless.

This winter they nearly starved and they nearly froze, but their parents never knew it. The father would ask how they were getting along and Vridar would always reply, "All right, I guess." He would rather have died than have complained. For his parents had too many worries now and were sacrificing to their limit. Besides, they were proud of their sons and this pride sustained him. To be worthy

145

of them he would have to be the most phenomenal child in Idaho, even though loneliness choked him and hunger stripped him to his bones.

Nevertheless he bitterly hated his father for the man's wolfish appetite. When Joe came, bringing all the butter the ranch had, a can of milk, a big roast of elk meat, and a dozen fragrant brown loaves of bread, he was cold and hungry and he always ate as if he would never be done. Vridar, sitting back and watching him, would grow rigid with grief. Joe would break a loaf in two, spread on the half more butter than Vridar would use in a week, cut deep into the roast and eat like a starved beast. He would turn and ask, "Ain't you boys hungry?" and Vridar would lie, though his mouth watered and hunger gnawed in him like a rat. The boys could not afford to eat tonight. If the father had been less gluttonous they might have eaten a little; but as he made great inroads on their meager supplies Vridar could only stare resentfully and hope that the man's next mouthful would be his last.

"I guess you et before I come," said Joe, slicing off another big chunk from the roast.

"Yes," Vridar said. He glanced at Marion, whose eyes were bright, whose tongue was licking at his starved mouth.

Father, Father! Vridar thought, and shook with despair.

After Joe had finished and had sunk back groaning; after he had rolled from side to side to release his gas; after he had got busy rubbing dry quids in his palms and stoking his pipe with tobacco dust, Vridar would go to the table and set the food away. He would stare at a small piece of bread, all that remained of a huge loaf; at the mound of butter with a big hole in its side; at the roast of elk, of which it seemed to him at least five pounds had been devoured. The father would eat again before going home. Vridar liked to have him here, but his appetite devastated what for the boys would have been enough for two or three days.

"You got a good teacher?" Joe asked, blinking in tobacco fog.

"I think so."

"What is his name, Vreed?"

The use of his name stirred Vridar. Joe never used it save when trying to be fatherly. "Art Flint."

"Oh. I've knowed him a long time. He has a college learnun. You like him, Marion?"

"Yes," Marion said.

Joe blinked at his sons, looking proud and at peace. He was striving, Vridar realized, to draw them into talk, to bridge that gulf which had always lain between them. But Vridar's mind was on food and the threat of hunger in the second week.

"Anything you need?" Joe asked, tamping at his pipe with a calloused thumb.

"No, I guess not," Vridar said.

They needed many things: pencils and writing-paper; a pot without rags in its bottom; more covering for the bed. They needed a lamp to study by, for they had only the feeble lantern, brought from the ranch.

"Your mother, she said you need anything write it down."

He wrote nothing down. He thought of her, now alone with Diana in that snow-

146

bound hole, wondering what her sons needed for their comfort and studies. Joe closed his eyes and puffed at his pipe. The boys hugged the fire, shivering, because it was a small fire, and a loud cold wind was driving against the house. A big watch in Joe's pocket talked in faint monotony of time. The windows shone dimly like squares of ice. Then Joe yawned and knocked his pipe out.

"Well, I guess it's bedtime."

The father's voice troubled Vridar. It was the voice of a man who had tried vainly to recognize his sons.

In this school, which was a mile away, the boys were not met as in Annis by a group of lewd youths bent on malicious fun; but like most schools this one had its bully. His name was Ollie Bitt. Ollie was a little older than Vridar. He had large pale eyes, a wide mouth, and a freckled sallow face. When he grinned, as he often did, his mouth was drawn into his left cheek, giving to his face a sneering evil look, and his left eye was almost closed. He had a brother, Doag, a year younger than Vridar. Their mother was dead. Their father was a small vivid man, with eyes like a hawk's, and a reputation as a fighting man. It was said he had killed a man with a shovel.

When the boys first went to school, Vridar paused at the gate, wondering if a gang of roughnecks here would make his life wretched. But he saw no one who looked threatening, and with a sigh he swung the gate and went in.

This school like that of Annis was a one-room building, with only one teacher for the eight grades. The classes in turn went to the front and recited there. Across from Vridar sat a girl with an abnormally high forehead that made her look half-bald. She stared at Vridar a great deal and he felt that he must have unclean ears or dandruff showing in his hair. The thought had never occurred to him that a girl might find him interesting for himself. If he met her gaze, she would turn on him a warm friendly smile.

But it was another who took his heart, a Danish lass whose name was Helen. Her home was large and handsome and just across the canal from the shack in which the boys lived. Her father was a big man, a blacksmith and a drunkard. Her mother was blonde, warm, alluring, with silken yellow hair and blue eyes like Helen's. Helen was about Vridar's age and full of light and mischief. When Vridar first looked at her, the bright sunshine of her face and the pagan laughter of her eyes electrified him, left him witless and agape, with his heart caught. From that moment he thought of her as his girl.

But everyone knew that Helen's beau was Alvin Kress. Two years older than Vridar, he was a chunky youth with sexual images in his eyes. Ollie did not bully Alvin. Ollie fixed his whole interest on Vridar. He would walk round him with a hand to his snickering mouth and wink at the other boys; or he would stare as if amazed at Marion's eyes. All this Vridar put up with, telling himself that there was no insult as long as it was not openly flung. As long as Ollie did no more than to leer and nudge and whisper, honor would not demand a fight; and Vridar hoped and prayed that a fight would never come. He tried to be unobtrusive, inoffensive, and meek but he knew all the while that a crisis was coming, because Ollie became bolder and more insolent and his taunts became more direct. In the third week the crisis came.

During the noon-hour Vridar and Marion were standing by a wall when Doag came up and squared off before Marion and said: "What's the matter your eyes?"

Marion glanced up at his brother, and Vridar began to tremble, knowing that the hour had come. He turned sick with fear and rage.

"Answer me!" Doag yelled.

"Leave him alone," said Vridar.

"I wasn't talkun to you," he said. "Keep your damn jib shut or my brother will shut it for you." Doag was staring at Marion, and other boys now came up, including Ollie, with the grinning leer in his cheek and his cold eyes on Vridar. Doag was working up a rage. He had clenched his fists, and he now kicked at Marion and said, "What's the matter your eyes? You bastard, can't you talk?" Ollie was snickering. "Answer me what's the matter your eyes or I'll bust you a whack!"

Desperate now, Vridar looked at the faces, knowing that there was no escape. Boys hedged him in on all sides. He knew that a fight was imminent. In a voice that came out of furious anguish he cried to Doag, "Leave him alone!"

"Hey you!" said Ollie, pushing toward Vridar. "If you want to talk to anyone talk to me!"

Vridar gave no reply. He was unwilling to answer anything but a direct and unmistakable insult.

"I'll tell you," said Doag, moving so close that his breath struck Marion's face. "You're crosseyed. You're a crosseyed little bastard."

There was silence. Vridar knew that the insult had been flung, but he was so weak with nausea that for a moment he could not speak. He saw all the intent eyes, watching to see what he would do. He gasped, as though he had been slapped, and turning a white face to Doag said in a hoarse whisper, "Take it back!"

Ollie sprang forward. He was not grinning now. "What's that you said?" he demanded, his eyes venomously green.

Vridar turned and met his gaze. He was afraid of this boy who had threshed half the other boys in school, but his code of honor was stronger than death, and bitterer than death would be shame if he yielded. He tried to speak calmly but it seemed to him that his voice croaked. "I said for him to take it back!"

"So you pick on him because he's smaller! Why don't you tell me to take it back?"

Vridar licked his dry lips and looked into Ollie's green eyes. "You haven't said it yet."

"All right, by God, I say it now! Your brother's a crosseyed bastard!"

Doag stepped back and Ollie took his place. Vridar had been praying that a fight would not come, but here he was, face to face with the school's bully, who had thrown an insult in his teeth. Vridar was a strange lad in moments like this. He had almost no faith in his own physical powers. He believed that almost any boy could knock the daylights out of him, even though he had triumphed over Duke and Hankie. He was afraid, but his self-esteem had been so outraged by humiliation and loneliness, and his pride was so stubborn when driven to the wall that he preferred death to defeat. In this moment and in many that would come he renounced life, convinced that he had no chance to win, yet ready to die rather than lose.

His resolve showed itself in a strange way. He became insane, really, with life gutted of all meaning, with nothing in his heart or mind but a frenzied wish to fight until he was dead. The madness shone in his eyes. It made a fearful thing of his white lips. It shuddered through and through him in fury and terror until he was appalling to look at. He now stepped forth, trembling, his eyes agleam, and thrust a clenched hand against Ollie's chest. "You take it back!" he said.

Ollie retreated a little. He glanced round to see what the other boys made of this. He said he would not take it back, but his voice faltered.

"Then you'll fight!" Vridar howled at him. "You coward! You God damned stinking son of a bitch of a coward!" The words were pouring out of him. With all meaning gone but the one thought that he must wipe out the insult, he ran toward Ollie with his fists swinging and that astonished boy took to his heels. He ran across the yard, with Vridar in hot pursuit; he plunged to the road and over to the canal bank and disappeared. Vridar came back, trembling, astonished, shamed. Boys now looked at him with awe, for he had chased the bully clear out of the yard. Girls pointed to him and whispered. But Vridar was not for a moment conscious of all that. He hoped that he had acquitted himself honorably, as his mother would wish him to, but he felt rather ridiculous and stupid. He had seen too much of pain and brutality and dying to want to drive his fists into any lad's face.

Ollie now became his friend. Vridar distrusted the boy and tried to avoid him, but Ollie persisted, now giving him a few marbles, and then one day overwhelming him by laying before him two pairs of skates, one for him and one for Marion. He also usurped Vridar's position as Marion's guardian; and if he saw a boy peering at Marion's eyes his ultimatum was sharp and final.

"Don't look at him that way," he would cry, "or I'll knock your teeth out!"

Three times this autumn he threshed a big gawky youth named Mike Andern. Mike always wept with despair and ran but Ollie would overtake him and leap on him and with bitter hard fists smite him to the earth. Vridar felt the injustice in these beatings but he said nothing. Besides, Mike hated Vridar for reasons which he was unable to learn.

In December Ollie accused Mike of stealing marbles. Mike denied the theft. Then, knowing what was coming, he looked round him, ready to flee.

"Give them back," said Ollie, "or I'll lick you hardern last time."

"I ain't got your marbles!"

"You lie!"

"I don't!" Mike began to whimper. He rolled big brown eyes; his mouth and chin sobbed.

"Come out to the road," Ollie said.

"I won't! I'll tell Jim on you!" Jim was his older brother, no longer in school.

Ollie sprang at him and Mike fled. Hare-and-hound fashion they streaked across the yard, with most of the boys yelling after them. Missing the gate, Mike plunged at a fence and got tangled in barbed wire. He struggled there, sobbing and yelling, and Ollie stood by, fists clenched, waiting. Then Mike's inflamed eyes saw Vridar looking at him.

"Why don't you fight him?" he howled. "You're afraid of him!"

"So are you," said Ollie. "He'n lick you. He'n lick anyone in school."

"He can't!"

"He'll lick you now if you'll get out of there."

This sudden turn of events horrified Vridar. Without engaging in combat or threshing anyone, he had achieved a reputation, and now, it appeared certain, this reputation was to be knocked head over heels. Ollie came up to him and told Vridar to take off his coat. Vridar did not want to be a hero, but out of nothing at all he had been made a hero and he would have to play the part. In the eyes of the boys around him he saw what was expected. They stepped back to form a circle, never doubting that he would fling off his coat. But he was sick with fear and disgust and could not move to save his life.

Mike had freed himself of wire and was looking at Vridar. He had been threshed so many times by Ollie that if he had to fight again he wanted a new foe. Vridar glanced at Ollie and saw in that boy's eyes a doubt of him. This he could not endure; it was worse than death. He stripped his coat off.

With a stick Ollie made a furrow in the snow. "Tell him to cross that line," he said to Vridar. "If he does, hit him so hard you'll kill him."

Vridar's eyes had lit up with insane desperation. He advanced to the line and he tried to speak but words would not come. Nevertheless, his hands were knotted, he was ready to fight.

"There's the line!" Ollie said. "Cross it if you darst!"

Mike had got to his feet and was looking at Vridar. He hesitated. He stepped forward, once, twice, advancing to the line, and faltered and turned away.

"I don't want to fight," he said.

"You yellow-belly!" Ollie howled triumphantly. "I'll bet you my flint taw he'n lick you! I'll bet you my skates!"

Other boys, eager to gather profit, offered wagers also. They would bet agates and steel taws, pocket-knives and bean-flippers, or even their caps and shoes. Vridar was appalled by all these offers. It looked as if the whole world would be staked on his prowess.

But Mike refused to bet. He had edged along the fence, muttering to himself, saying that Jim would come over and clean up the whole school. Then, when no one was expecting the move, he took to his heels again.

Thereafter Vridar was the silently acclaimed champion of the school. He knew what a bitter irony it was! He, who turned sick when he saw blood spilling from throat or testicles; who wished to be every lad's friend and not a swaggering bully-boy; and who hated whatever it was in boys and men that made them want to beat one another—he, of all persons, was the school's hero! And Ollie, acting as if he were Vridar's manager, searched high and low for a boy of Vridar's age bold enough to fight him. He found none. They were all Vridar's friends now, all but Alvin Kress. And he would have had no trouble with Alvin, no fight, if it had not been for his blind infatuation with Helen. In the school's small library he had found a book of poems, and one of them he had read over and over, until he knew it by heart.

"Helen, thy beauty is to me . . ."
And so it was to him.

XX

Lying east and west between the school and the shack where the boys lived was the Poplar canal. When winter came it froze over, with patches of ice as smooth as glass. Helen skated upon it, to and from school; and because her home was close to Vridar's, while Alvin's was miles away, he sensed his advantage and learned to skate. Once in a while he thought of Neloa but she was far away now. Here, in every hour of his life, was this tantalizing lass with the golden hair and the blue eyes. He told himself that he loved her and would marry her some day; and then tried to do a fancy turn and sprawled flat on his face.

After he had learned well enough to stroke without spilling, he awaited his time. With skates in his desk and his feet itching to feel the ice under him, he shot pure worshipful glances at the girl; and Mae Kohler with the high forehead watched him and perceived where his interest stood. One day when he knocked a pencil from his desk, Mae quickly recovered it, and then looked at him, her eyes absurdly devoted. She offered the pencil but when he reached for it she drew it back. She was trying to be demure and alluring but he thought her preposterous and silly.

"Give it to me!" he whispered, scowling at her.

She shook her head. She wrote a note and tossed it at his feet. He picked it up and found one question, drawn in large bold letters: What will you give me for it? He deliberated a few moments and wrote an answer: What do you want? When he tossed the note to Mae he saw that Helen was watching him. Ah, good Lord, now she would think he had been flirting!

When school was dismissed he ran with skates to the canal, put them on, and stroked furiously homeward. After covering half the distance, he sat on a bank and waited. Helen would come. He had gone ahead because twice he had tried to overtake her and failed. She skated superbly, dipping and curving as if she moved on wings.

While he waited he tried to pretend that he was not waiting at all. He pulled his cap off and brushed his hair; he wiped his mouth and teeth; he bored into his ears, wondering if they were clean. She once told him he had dirty ears. Seeing, next, some grease spots on his trousers he scrubbed at them with snow, reflecting meanwhile on the woes of cooking. These stains were from sizzling potatoes. He observed that there were spots on his shirt, and dough under his fingernails. The dough he tried to bite out, and the spots he rubbed with a piece of ice.

He was sitting there, industriously scrubbing at elk fat, when Helen came in sight like a golden rhythm. His heart began to race and his hands to tremble. Her hair was flowing behind her and her skates were singing on the ice.

"Hello," she said, gliding up and spinning. "You broke your skate?"

151

"I guess so," he said. He hoped it was broken. He turned it over and over.

"Let's see it," she said.

In his eagerness he dropped it. He stooped to recover it and his skated foot shot out from under him and he fell flat. Burning with humiliation, he clawed to his feet and struck snow from his clothes. Helen was laughing, with hands to her mouth.

"You was thinkun of Mae," she said. "That's why you fell down."

"I wasn't," he said, glancing at her eyes.

"Well, you big silly, put it on."

He did not like this. He sat and fumbled with the skate and wondered what he should do about being called silly. He was hating her, but then she knelt to help him, her hair sweeping his cheeks and her hands touching his own. He trembled so at her nearness and touch that she was surprised.

"Why do you shiver? Are you cold?"

"No," he said, in an absurd choked voice.

"Then why do you shake?"

"It's just your imagination."

"Oh, is it!" She laid a warm palm on his hand.

"Don't!" he said.

She then cupped his chin and made him look up. She met his dark worshipful eyes. "You're funny," she said, and turned away.

They skated up the canal, Helen leading in graceful curves, Vridar stroking desperately to overtake her. In an excess of love and folly he would attempt longer strides and his feet would race ahead and floor him. He would then see Helen looking back, laughing, with hands to her mouth. When they came to her home, which stood a little way from the canal, Vridar was bruised and wet and sullen. She looked at him and pouted her lips. Her blue eyes were drenched with laughter.

"I'll tell you what," she said.

He waited, his eyes feeding hungrily on her hair and lips and the curves of her breasts. "What?" he said.

"Look, can you do this?" She cut an H in the ice.

"Some day I will."

She skated round and round him, tantalizing, mocking. "Now watch," she said, and wrote her name in the ice, riding on one foot and inscribing with the toe of the other skate. "Now you write your name under it."

"I can't," he said. With pleasure he observed that the two e's were not well-formed.

"Watch," she said, and skated backward, her eyes mocking him.

He was annoyed by her skill. He hated her because she was laughing at him. "I have to go home," he said.

"All right, then why don't you go?"

"I will in a minute," he said. Her mockery infuriated him. He scowled at her in a luxury of self-pity.

"You better go," she said, skating round and round him.

"I thought you were going to tell me something."

She skated up and looked at him—at his eyes first and then over his face and again at his eyes. "But you said you had to go home."

Good Lord, how he hated her! He wished the ice would break and drop her out of sight.

"I'll tell you what," she said. "Some time I'll come over and cook your supper."

"Will you?" he gasped, astounded by this gate into heaven.

"Or mebbe Mae will."

"You know I don't like Mae!"

"Just the same, I saw you write a note to her. I guess you said, Mae, I love you."

He knew she was playing with him. Turning away with tragic resignation, he sat on the bank and took his skates off. He wanted to say something that would sting her, something about Alvin, but he could not be that mean. "I have to go now," he said and climbed the bank.

"So you don't want me to tell you!" she called after him.

He stopped and considered. His pride had suffered outrage, but when a man was in love, ah Lord, what could he do! Scowling at her he said: "What?"

"Oh, what I have to tell."

Wretched and undecided, he stood and waited. She was skating round and round, now and then glancing up at him. Should he stride away or should he debase his pride still more? Would she tell him if he did not ask again? He knew she would not. And so at last with an effort he said, trying to speak with dignity: "What is it you have to tell me?"

"But you don't want to know."

"That is a lie!"

"You're fickle," she said. "I saw you write that love-letter to Mae."

"It wasn't a love-letter."

"Mebbe that's the lie," said Helen.

He moved toward her a little and again choked his pride down. "I do want to know." He waited a moment and said: "Helen, I do want to know." He had never spoken her name before. Since memorizing the Poe lyric he had decided that it was the loveliest of all names. She turned toward him again and for a moment he thought her eyes were wet. Or perhaps his own were wet. He could not be sure.

She looked up at him and tossed her golden hair back. "What I had to tell you," she said, "is, after supper I'm comun out to skate. . . . Well, that's all I had to tell."

"And you want me to come?"

She knelt and tossed her head forward, and hair like yellow silk spread over the ice around her. With the skates in her hand she stood up and tossed the hair in a wave backward and went to the house. Vridar looked after her until the door closed. Then he turned and ran.

He dashed into the house and found Marion shivering in the cold. "Come!" Vridar cried. "Let's get the wood!" They went over snowdrifts and gathered willows and sage. They carried them to the house and built a fire. Then Vridar cooked their supper.

Out of a tin can he dug a spoonful of frozen elk grease and dropped it to a hot skillet; mixed flour with it and cooked the grease and flour into a brown paste; and then poured water in and stirred vigorously, for if he did not the flour ran into lumps. Marion meanwhile was laying the table. "Cut the bread!" Vridar cried, and ran to a window to see if Helen had appeared. He put a small piece of butter in the lid of a baking-powder can and put the lid on the stove. The butter melted into warm softness. He took from the oven some tough fried elk, only half warmed through, and standing by the table and shivering in the gloom the two boys ate. They tore and chewed at the tough meat. They poured hot water gravy, thin and tasteless, over slices of frozen bread. When Vridar had choked down his unappetizing supper he ran to the window to look out. Helen was coming to the canal. He told his brother to hurry and Marion stuffed his mouth full of gravy-soaked bread. Then Vridar washed the few dishes and Marion dried them. They had no soap. Grease stuck to the washpan, rimming it with dirty gray streaks; grease shone on the slippery plates; it was deep in the pores of Vridar's hands.

Seizing hi scap and coat and skates, Vridar bolted through the door and raced toward the canal, trying to dislodge elk meat from his teeth as he ran. Helen was nowhere in sight. After putting his skates on, he threshed up the canal until he came to a turn; retraced his path and went down; and so raced back and forth until he found her at last, standing under sheltering trees. Now all the boldness went out of him. He looked at her with witless devotion, observing that she was fur-coated and mittened and muffed.

"Why were you so late?" she asked, frowning at him.

"I had to make a fire and cook. You know that."

"When you marry your wife will cook."

"That will be you," he said.

"Oh no," she said. "I intend to marry a man with money."

Money! Good Lord, he had no money! "I'll have money some day," he said.

"I'll marry you," said Helen, "if you can catch me."

She skated away and he pursued with all his might. When he passed under overhanging willows, a limb smote his face and sent him plunging to a bank where he came down in a heap. God damn! he thought, hating his awkwardness and his blundering ways.

"What's the trouble?" called Helen, standing ahead of him in the night.

He was too furious to speak. He thought of renouncing her and going home, but when she vanished again he stroked awkwardly and desperately into the dusk, his eyes straining to catch sight of her. A mile up the canal he found her under another tree.

"You should try to catch Mae," she said. "She's slow, like you." And now she mimicked his plodding toiling way. He looked at her and he was telling himself again that she was making a fool of him when suddenly she skated over and felt his hands. "Where's your mittens?"

"I haven't any."

"Take mine. I'll use the muff."

When he refused the mittens, she grasped his shoulders and tried to shake him.

He liked her hands on his shoulders. "I won't take them," he said, hoping she would shake him again.

"I should box your ears," she said. "You're like a baby." For a moment she looked into his adoring eyes. Then she moved closer, warm and sweet and womanly, and closed her hands over his ears. He was shaking with rapture when she said: "Good heavens, what big ears you have! Here, feel mine."

He fumbled into her hair and found a small warm ear. She reached up and took his hand away. Again she looked into his eyes, and in her eyes he saw mirth and sly gentle knowledge of him.

"What'll we do now?" she said.

"I don't know," he said, and gazed round him, as if looking for something to do. He did not want to skate. He wished only to be near her and to have her touch him. He began to beat his hands on his thighs, and when again she offered the mittens he refused them.

"Well, if you won't, I'll not coax you."

She was off then, on long rhythms in the dusk. He pursued, his arms swinging and his skates chopping, but she was a vanishing shadow and then she was gone. Feeling very ridiculous in his efforts to overtake her, he gave up the chase and skated round and round. If she did not come back, why, that would be all right too, but each circle carried him in her direction.

In a little while she came back and said, tartly, coldy, that she was going in now. Vridar expostulated. He said the time was still early and a moon was coming up. But without saying goodnight, without looking at him, she went up the bank and to the house, and he was left alone, drooping and bitter and sad, as he skated round and round, watching her doorway and hoping she would come again.

They skated often together in the weeks that followed, and all over Poplar it was said that these two were in love. Vridar luxuriated in this legend. Neloa was far away now on an old horizon in a forgotten land; and though he sometimes thought of her his heart and soul were given to this exasperating little flirt with her golden hair and blue eyes and alluring ways. When they were old enough they would marry and they would love one another deeply and they would die in the same hour.

He never kissed her during these weeks. He wanted to, but kissing, it seemed to him, was a little obscure and a little obscene. He had seen kissing as a gesture of meeting or farewell. He had seen it as a sign of passion between Agnes and Borg. He did not permit himself to think of Helen save in a pure and worshipful way. She was such a symbol for him of all that was good and tender in life that he adored even her mittens and her skates.

Helen's mother sometimes sat by a window and watched them on the canal. Vridar had seen her smile. Once on the cruel sotted face of her husband Vridar had seen a smile, when the man stood on the bank and looked at them. He knew there was something about his idyl with Helen that people found good. He knew that no other school children talked about them. On the privy walls he read, Vridar loves Helen, or, Helen is Vridar's girl. He read these over and over, his breath sinking deep into him, and murmured Poe's lovely lines.

One afternoon when they were skating Helen came to him and laughed. She

155

pointed to her home window. "See mama," she said. "You know what she told me?"

"What?"

"Guess."

"I can't guess. Helen, tell me."

"She says we're in love."

"We are," he said gravely.

"She says when we're old enough we'll marry."

"We will," he said, gazing at her with intense devotion.

She laughed merrily, teasingly and circled round him. "You know what she asked me?"

"No."

"She asked had you ever kissed me yet."

"She did! And what did you tell her?"

"Why, you silly, I told her the truth."

"You mean you said I never had?"

She skated again, leaving him to ponder the matter. Had he blundered in not kissing her? Was she laughing at him now? "Helen," he said imperiously, "come here!"

"Go to grass."

"Come here!" he said, speaking like a husband.

She stopped and looked at him. "If you can catch me, I'll let you kiss me." And she was off like the wind.

He pursued furiously until exhausted; and when at last she stopped and waited and let him come up to her he did not kiss her. He trembled and looked away.

"I broke my skate," she said. He looked down at her skates and then into her eyes, and wondered what it was that he saw there. Then she laughed mockingly and cried gaily, "Oh, but I didn't!" and was off again.

On Helen's birthday early in March came the climax and the end of Vridar's idyl with Helen. Her mother gave a party. Among those invited were Vridar and Marion.

When the boys went to the house that evening, Vridar scraped his shoes on the stone steps and looked at himself. He had on his only suit, coarse and ill-fitting; a shirt which he himself had washed and ironed; and a sprig of green moss in his buttonhole. He wore this because he had read in a novel about a gay and reckless man who never wooed without something sweet and tender in his buttonhole, and a smile on his face. Vridar was trying to smile but then looked at his old shoes, scuffed, run down at the heels, and laced with green cord. He knew that he must look very preposterous, and so he stood on the doorstep a little while, scraping his shoes and waiting for the courage to knock. He was still waiting when the door was opened and a flood of light fell out and Helen's mother spoke.

"Come in," she said, smiling at him.

Vridar stumbled inside and the brilliant room wrought confusion in his soul. Never had he seen such furnishings, such gorgeous colorful curtains and drapes, such chairs bulging with velvet—or with what seemed to be velvet anyway—and such a carpet of silky splendor. There were four lamps in the room, each a great shining thing of silver or gold. He counted them and thought of the dirty lantern in the cold shack across the canal.

Helen, the mother said, would be out in a minute. The boys stood like gawky trespassers in the room's center. Vridar looked at a chair and wondered if anyone ever sat on such richness; he glanced down at his ugly shoes, planted shamelessly on the clean deep rug.

"Won't you boys set down?"

"Yes maam, thanks," he said.

Marion walked over and sank half-buried among luxurious cushions. Vridar went to a chair, too, but he thought it would be sacrilege to sit on it. While he was deliberating the matter and growing hot with embarrassment, Helen came in. She was a vivid radiance. He hardly knew her. Her dress was of flowing silken stuff a shade or two darker than her hair, and her hair hung in a loose golden sheaf down her back. Around her forehead she had a blue ribbon a shade paler than her eyes. Her slippers were of yellow satin with blue buckles, and she had a pale blue bracelet on her left arm. Never in his life had Vridar seen such loveliness, or known that a girl could be so lovely. He blushed for his boldness, his presumption, in daring to love one so tender and sweet: he, a pig-feeder, a cow-milker; he who lived on water gravy and his own soggy doughgods; he, a poacher in fairyland! He wished he could hide his feet and he wondered if his neck and ears and face were clean.

Helen, too, seemed embarrassed. She sat across from him like a small golden goddess; she glanced at him once or twice but she did not speak.

"You should entertain your guests," her mother said, looking in from another room. "You ain't afraid of each other, are you? You don't act like this out on the ice."

Vridar essayed a polite laugh but it seemed to him to be only a quavering croak. Drawing his feet back, he strove to hide them under the chair. He peered at a shirt cuff and saw with horror that he had burned it brown. Trying again to laugh, he decided that it would be best to look inscrutable and wise. But in a few moments he was furtively chewing at his fingernails.

Then the other guests arrived. Sarah Mills entered, her cheeks like round red apples and her mouth like flame. Behind her came Mae and Ardella Kohler, the first prim and sedate, the other bubbling and twinkling; and Mary Kress, Alvin's homely, freckled wide-mouthed sister; and Katie Andern, a dowdy little thing with black eyes . . . The boys trooped in, among them the Bitt brothers and Mike and Alvin. They surrounded Helen and offered her gifts, each neatly wrapped in a box; and Vridar, seeing this, though he would die of shame. He had not known that they were expected to fetch gifts. He had never heard of such a thing. And he had moreover no presents and no money to buy them with. His cheeks burned until he could feel their heat.

His shame was to go still deeper. Helen now unwrapped the presents, taking each from its box, and they were passed from hand to hand. Alvin turned to Vridar and said, "Now let's see his" because Alvin's gift was the loveliest of all, a dozen linen handkerchiefs edged with old lace and embroidered with her first name.

157

"Whose?" asked Helen, excited by the gifts.

"His," Alvin said, pointing to Vridar. "What did he bring?"

Splotched red, Vridar now wished he could drop into the earth. All eyes turned to him and nobody spoke.

"Well," cried Alvin at last, "why don't you show us what you fetched her?"

Dying of shame, Vridar was unable to speak. It was Helen who saved the wretched lad from further embarrassment. "Oh," she said, "he didn't bring his tonight. He's having me something made to order special."

There were cries of astonishment. This was a wonder indeed, having a thing made to order! What was it? they wanted to know. That, Helen said, was a secret; they would find out in time.

They now turned away from Vridar. Cold with sweat he was calling himself a clown and a fool; but under his shame and his bitter self-contempt was a new vision of love. He would have died for her now. He would have been happy to die for her now.

An hour later they were all playing a game. The loser, if a girl, had to kiss a boy chosen by the hostess; and, if a boy, he had to kiss a girl or have his head ducked in the kitchen sink. Vridar hated the game. His shyness made him awkward and stupid. He was trying to hide his awkward shoes. He was afraid Alvin would be kissing Helen . . .

"It's him!" a voice cried. "He lost."

"You want to kiss a girl or get your head ducked?"

"Helen, he wants to kiss her but it won't be fair to name her."

"Well, say! Which do you want?"

"You mean me?" asked Vridar, bewildered.

"Cripes almighty," said Alvin, "he's asleep!"

"You lost," said Mae, simpering at him.

They were all looking at him. "You want to kiss a girl?"

"What girl?" he asked stupidly.

"The girl Ardelle names. She's hostess now."

Furious color was darkening Vridar's cheeks. He glanced over where Helen's mother sat in a deep chair and she smiled at him. He looked then at Helen and saw that she pretended to be smoothing her dress.

"He wants to kiss Helen!" someone bawled.

"It wouldn't be fair to name her."

"He's to be punished. Make him kiss a homely girl."

"Well, my God," said Alvin, "has the cat got your tongue?"

"Which you choose?" Ardelle said.

Sweat was standing on Vridar's forehead. It would be utter folly to say he wanted his head ducked; no boy had chosen this. He wanted to kiss Helen. Still . . .

"Let's duck him!" said Mike, and seized Vridar's arm.

Vridar shook the hand off and moistened his lips. He glanced at Helen. He said he would kiss a girl and felt as if he had mortgaged his life.

Now all eyes turned to Ardella.

"Ardie, cripes almighty, hurry up and choose!"

158

"Make him kiss Helen."

"No, good Lord, that's what he wants to do! Make him kiss Mae."

"Sure, Mae, she wants him to."

"Be still," said Ardella, and looked in turn at the girls. Vridar waited, his mind dark with panic. Ardella then looked at him. "Mae," she said.

A great shout went up. Mae was grasped and pushed forward, blushing and shrieking but eager to be kissed. Rough hands shoved Vridar toward her.

"Kiss her!" Mike howled. "Kiss her or get ducked!"

"Don't!" said Vridar, trying to shake off the hands. Mae stood before him, trembling, eager, waiting.

"Good God, hurry up!" said Alvin.

Vridar turned on him with murderous fury. "Shut your mouth!"

"Hey, don't tell me to shut my mouth!"

"Boys, boys!" said Helen's mother, laughing.

Ollie slipped up and whispered in Vridar's ear: "Christ amighty, kiss her! It won't kill you!"

Blindly then Vridar stepped forward, but his kiss fell on Mae's chin.

A little later Alvin lost and Mae was now the hostess.

"Which you want?" Mike asked.

"You know which *I* want," said Alvin, staring boldly at the girls. His manner infuriated Vridar. It seemed to him that Alvin was looking at the girls as though they were all dying to kiss him. His eyes were pale, eager, insolent. He turned to Mae. "Who's the lucky girl?"

"Lucky!" Vridar cried, and was ashamed.

Alvin turned to him, scowling. "Shut your jib!"

Mae looked at Vridar, at Helen, at Vridar again. "Helen," she said.

Instead of clamor this time there was sudden quiet. Alvin moved forward and grasped Helen's arm. "Here, get yourself kissed," he said. She raised her face to him and their lips met.

From this point on the evening for Vridar was a nightmare of self-pity and outrage. He withdrew from the game. After a while Ollie came to him and said, "He thinks you're afraid. Sock him a jolt."

"Who?" Vridar asked but he knew.

"When the party's over," said Ollie, "hit him a smack."

"I don't want any trouble," Vridar said. He had withdrawn from the play to avoid a quarrel, but in spite of his self-effacement the quarrel came.

Marion had been playing. Twice he had lost and twice he had kissed a girl. He now lost again and the hostess said he should kiss Helen. But when Marion advanced to kiss her, Alvin grasped the boy and hurled him back.

"He can't kiss her," he said, appealing to the hostess. "She don't want to kiss him. And if she don't want a-kiss a crosseyed little bum she don't have to."

Hearing the insult, Vridar began to tremble. There was silence. Vridar stood up, but before he could speak or move or strike, Helen's mother came to Alvin, all the laughter gone from her eyes. She told him he ought to burn with shame. To Marion she said, "Go on and kiss her," and Marion did.

159

But the matter had not been settled for Vridar. Alvin would have to recant. Ollie slipped over and asked, "You heard what he said?" Vridar nodded, helpless with misery. "You intend to make him take it back?" Again Vridar nodded. Ollie was silent, his cold blue eyes studying Vridar's face. "When?"

"Tonight, I guess."

"We'll leave early," Ollie said. "We'll wait by the barn."

And so a little later four boys said goodnight and went outside. They went to the barn and stepped inside and waited there in darkness. The longer Vridar waited, the more sick he felt in all his heart and soul, until he despised himself and wished again that he had never been born. He heard feet coming down the road. He heard Ollie say that there would be no butting in, that while Vridar knocked the daylights out of Alvin he would keep the others off. Vridar tried to thank him, for it was wonderful to have a friend so loyal and bold. Then he saw Alvin and Mike and Arnold coming. They were passing the barn and still Vridar did not move. He tried to move but seemed to be paralyzed.

"There he is," said Ollie. "Call him over."

Vridar made a tremendous effort. "You!" he cried hoarsely. "Just a minute, you!"

The boys came over and looked into the barn's shadows. "What you want?" Alvin said.

Ollie said, "It's Vridar, he wants to see you."

"Oh, the hell he does! Well, here I am and I ain't runnun."

There was anger in his voice, and arrogance, and these gave Vridar a little strength. He felt something dark and savage stir in his heart. He remembered Alvin's lips on Helen's, and then there came up in him hatred that was black and courage that was blind. He stepped outside and Alvin squared off and looked at him.

"Well, you stinkheel, did you want to see me?"

"I guess," said Vridar, and he knew that his voice was shaking, "I guess you remember what you said tonight."

"Well, what did I say?"

"About my brother."

"He means about his eyes," Ollie said.

"Oh, sure!" said Alvin. He laughed. "Yes," he said sneeringly, "I remember. I said he's a crosseyed son of a bitch!"

That was what Vridar had hoped for—words that would come like a blow. The words released him from paralysis. Suddenly, swiftly the world lost all meaning and he went mad. He was never able to remember what he did. He could never recall that he gave a cry, a kind of insane gurgling yell; or that he leapt like a savage thing and struck and struck again. He could not remember that he had been dragged off like a screaming wildcat, or that Ollie was pleading in his ear, begging him to withhold his violent arms and not strike again. He did remember one moment when he saw Alvin lying on the earth, with blood running from his nose and mouth and soaking his white shirt and his hands.

160

XXI

Again Vridar stood on the brink of his home and looked down. He was weary and footsore, for with Marion he had walked the fifteen miles from Poplar, with the old dread returning as he walked. There was the river, its floods rolling eternally to the sea; and beyond it the Bridwell place, with its shack and its river-jungle and its wild odors; and the deep dark valley of Burns Canyon and over on the right, Black Canyon, both ominously misty and still. It was all so terrible, yet so full of beautiful life. Loveliness lay in soft depth upon depth here, in forest and flowering bush and deep grasses. He looked down, trying to understand the meaning of the place and of himself in it. Annis was dull and gray, Poplar was flat; but here before him, filled with the river's thunder and framed in the desolation of mountains and silence was a harbor of all moods. All the elemental passions of life were drama- tized here. From sky to earth there might be in one hour a mute brooding quiet like his own despair; but in the next the west might open, the sky would be a wilder- ness of lightning-paths, and storm would howl from precipice to peak. There could be peace like the peace in deep and abandoned wells; or foreboding and dark omen, like night-shadows upon moving waters; or menace and vengeance like the river's sucking madness where whirlpools beat in violence upon stones. There was beauty in the fires, loveliness in flowering chokecherry, in harebell, mallow, paintbrush and columbine; but there was grim and deformed ugliness in the river-banks, gnawed year after year by the rushing waters, until trees roared in their foundations and shuddered and split and crashed; in the gnarled cedar-dwarfs trying to draw life out of sand and stone; in the remorseless down-moving erosions of slide-rock and the haggard loneliness of old trees. There was witchery here when rainbows stood row on row from mountain to mountain. There were the enchanting sunsets when purple and golden towers grew on the western rim. There was sorcery when life darkened with its own intense secret, and the owl's cry was the horn of loneliness. There were sultry afternoons with their wraiths of silence shimmering upon the monotonous hours; and at midnight the ghoulish terrors of long-after-dark.

It was a beautiful but a haunted place. It got hold of you and wormed into your blood and became part of your bone. You could go away and travel half-around the world but it would always go with you, calling you back. That was what Charley had said. Some places, he said, just grabbed on to you and you were in quicksand. Remembering Charley's words Vridar felt that if he spent many more summers here he would be forever lost. His breath would be only the atmosphere of this bottomland and in his eyes would be images of these solitary peaks. He would be both soft and hard, like this place; both beautiful and distorted, happy and yet lonely, aggressive but still afraid. All its virtues and vices would swim in his blood, until he would be a strange person, a detached part of this home-bowl, no matter where he went. And all that he sensed now, standing here, he came to be. Ahead of him now to be fought desperately lay the bitterest struggle of his life. This story could be closed here, its darkest part left untold; or it could ignore, as so many stories do, that gethsemane through which all youth must pass. But nobody would understand then the strange man that he was to be and the strange things he was to do. His journey now fell downward until his eighteenth year and became a nightmare of the dark.

He had a premonition of all this as he stood with his brother, looking down. "I hate it, I hate it," he said; and Marion said: "I hate it, too." And then they went down the dugway to their home. Their mother was out at a hencoop. When they called she came running, with a sick and drooling hen in her arms. She gave them a quick kiss, as a mother might whose heart was buried and whose deeper emotions had never felt the air and sun. "I guess you're hungry," she said.

While eating, Vridar studied her face. She seemed to have aged, to have gathered a part of the white winter to her face and hair, since he last saw her, seven months ago. Her eyes, he thought, were sad. He glanced once at her hands; these, once soft and lovely, were now horny and gnarled. They were hands that gripped the axe, molded cheese, squeezed the teats of cows, feeling nothing year after year but the hard surface of toil. He saw that her shoes were rags of leather, her stockings full of holes, her dress stained with chicken filth. And yet this was the proud woman who had said she woud never marry a farmer.

Joe came in, with Diana trailing him. He said, "Oh, hello," and that was all. Diana's greeting was not effusive. She said hello and looked at her brothers. She sat, and Joe sat, and the shack was full of the old silence. Vridar felt in a strange and terrible way that these were not his people and this was not his home.

Nephi came a little later with his wife and son and daughter. Hankie had changed. He seemed to be more furtive and sly, but bolder also. He profaned when alone with Vridar, spitting the oaths with great gusto and queerly smacking his lips. He hinted of knowledge of secret delights. Vridar was now thirteen and Hankie was fifteen, a pale boastful runt who considered himself a man. "I know somethink to make you shiver with joy," he said, leering at Vridar and blinking his pale eyes. Most boys knew it, Hankie said, and Vridar wondered what it could be. "If you don't want to know," Hankie cried with sudden fury, "you can go to hell!"

"Don't put on airs," Vridar said.

"I don't put on airs!" said Hankie in his high thin voice. He started and cried: "The holy gods and little orphunts!"

"Now what's the mater?" asked Vridar.

"Shsh! There comes your ma."

Vridar wished to know the secret but Hankie was very mysterious and annoying. Vridar might blab to his ma, Hankie said, and strutted, blowing out his sallow cheeks. Or perhaps he was too young. "This is somethink for a man to know. It puts hair on your chest. You got any hair yet?"

"No," said Vridar, thinking of Borg.

"Well, come into the bushes and I'll show you my hair." Hankie drew his shirt up and exposed his belly. It had a sparse growth of yellow fuzz. "That's the signs of a man," he said.

When, Vridar demanded, was the secret to be told.

"I ain't sure you should know it. You don't darst swear and cuss the lickety hell out of creation." Hankie was looking at him. "Let's hear you cuss a streak."

162

"Why should I?"

"Because life is a riddle that gets a man het up."

"Oh, good Lord!" said Vridar. "You swagger around but you're only a little wart."

"The Christ all-Jesus God damn low-down snort-eyed jumpun-up-Judas son of a bitch! You're afraid. You're afraid of girls."

"Who said I am?"

"I said it. You're afraid my sister but you think I'm afraid of yourn? And I'll tell you somethink," said Hankie, his lewd face coming to life. "I aim to teach your sister somethink or rather. How old is she?"

"Seven."

"That's old enough," said Hankie and tongued his lips. "You ever done it to your sister yet?"

"Done what?"

"You know what I mean. I've done it to Jewel. I'll show you some day."

But before that shameful hour visitors came to the Hunter place. Vridar had never seen them before. They were relatives, his mother said, of an aunt-in-law and they had Indian blood in them. A wagonload of them rolled down the dugway and swarmed in the dooryard. Two men, both very tall and dark and straight, went to the river to fish, leaving their fat unclean wives to talk to Prudence. There were three girls of about Vridar's age, with small black eyes, the eyes of a porcupine, and black hair hanging in tails, and wet lewd mouths. At once they set upon Vridar and badgered him for hours, hurling profane or obscene taunt or chanting obscene rimes. He would remember their words. He would remember:

> You lie, you link, you fart, you stink,
> you suck your daddy's rubber dink.

In unison they chanted these lines, their mouths wide and grinning, their eyes searching him for shame. From the house to the corral, up the lane, across fields, back to the house they followed him, chanting the words. Or they would jeer, "Fraidy cat, fraidy cat!" and hiss and snicker. "Hey, you mother's sissy, wait a minute! You afraid?"

He looked back and the three of them made a face at him.

"Why don't you run? You think we'll hurt you? You think we'll throw you down and do things to you?"

That was exactly what he thought. He had seen it in their eyes. And he was wondering about them and about his mother, who had told him so many times that girls were as pure as angels and that he must protect them . . .

"Fraidy cat, fraidy cat, why are you runnun away like that? Because he's afraid of a girl, that's it! Look at the fraidy cat hit the grit!"

He was crawling through a fence and then he cut across a field, and they ran around to intercept him. He rather liked the notion of their doing things to him. It thrilled him for some inexplicable reason that he knew to be shameful; but when he tried to put it away the emotion came back and overflowed his heart.

"Hey, you silly fool, why do you run?" Yes, he was running all right. He was being very ridiculous. They took up another chant: "You fool, you fool, ain't you never been to school? Hey there, what do you think you are?—and what do you think a girl is for? . . ."

Vridar wanted to run but forced himself to walk, afraid that someone might see him fleeing from girls. When he reached the house they were still pursuing. When he went down to the creek they followed. Hankie was standing apart, watching.

"Don't run!" Hankie yelled. "Let them chase me and I'll show them somethink!"

"He's afraid!" the girls called to Hankie. "He still sucks his mother's tit!"

Vridar crossed the footbridge and went to the island; and when they came running after him he swung to face them. "What do you want?" he said angrily.

"Why you afraid of girls?"

"I'm not."

"You lie. If you ain't afraid then come over here."

He went over and stood before them. He looked into their black malicious eyes. "What do you want?"

They fell against one another, giggling. "Who said we wanted anything?"

"Then why do you follow me?"

"Because we hate you," one said. "We hate you like poison and snakes."

Vridar was baffled. He looked up at the bank and saw Hankie grinning.

"They want somethink!" Hankie said.

"What?" asked Vridar, gazing stupidly at Hankie.

"You ask them what!"

"Go behind a bush and wipe your nose!" said one of the girls to Hankie.

"Go away and play with yourself!"

"Go to hell!" shouted Hankie. "You bitches! You hag-toothed wall-eyed bow-legged—"

"Ah, go on and play with yourself! That's all you do anyway!"

"I'll come down there," Hankie howled, "and bust your gizzards out! You Indians! You squaws!"

"Look up at him!" cried the boldest girl. "He picks his nose and eats it!"

"You squaws!" Hankie screamed. "You God damn squaws!"

The girls were all looking at him. "You play with yourself!" one said. "That's why you're a runt!"

It was during these weeks that life aroused in Vridar a morbid curiosity about sex. He had been curious for years. The girls in Annis, the legends on privy walls, the visions of copulation and of birth, the tales of Jed Bridwell; all these and his own emotions in many times and places had led him to thoughts that were mysterious, dark, and he had no doubt shameful. He had developed an extraordinary interest in the female breast. He had become almost obsessed with the signs of woman that were not the signs of man.

His nipples had become sore. He would look at them and wonder if he was ill. Feeling that it was something that he ought to hide, he neverthless spoke of it to his mother, saying that he must be sick. She looked at him and felt his ears. He had no fever, she said. She looked at his tongue.

"Where do you feel sick?"

"Well—" Why in God's name had he mentioned the matter! "Well, I'm sore."

"Where?"

He writhed and hesitated. "Here," he said, "and here." He looked up at her He saw her face redden, he saw the old shame come into her eyes. There was nothing to worry about, she said. He was undergoing a change. Every boy did at his age, and every girl, too. But it was best not to think about it or talk about it. Some day he would understand but he could not understand now. He was too young.

"Just don't think about it," she said, and he felt the shame in her voice.

But he did think about it. Becoming even more shy than he had been, he would go off alone and brood on the matter, feeling that he was doomed. There was evil in his blood. He had sinned. But he could not remember when or where or how. He had heard of sin that rotted flesh, that burst out in boils, that turned blood into black stagnant lymph. And while he sought to understand, life around him seemed to be all strange sexual allegory. It startled him with sudden postures; out of experiences formerly commonplace and meaningless stood its inscrutable symbolisms. The second morning after he went to his mother he saw an amazing thing.

Joe had a mare with a bad sore on its leg. To this, one night, he applied a huge poultice of what he called Spanish fly. Vridar watched him. He looked at the mare after the bandage had been bound and wired. Then he did his chores and went to bed.

The next morning Joe took the poultice off and tossed it to the yard. It was an ugly thing mixed with hair and blood and it had a rank smell.

A little while later a big sow fell into most extraordinary capers. She pursued Vridar, her huge drooling jaws agape, her small dull eyes strangely filled with light. She squealed and roared and came head-on. He ran and climbed to the barn roof and looked down at her. She looked up, her mouth open and her eyes intent. Then she whirled and went off like a demented thing; she saw the dog approach and chased the dog. She pursued the astonished creature until it vanished into a thicket. She ran round and round and then came loping back to the corral. A moment later she saw a big tumbleweed rolling out in a field and she went madly after it. She overtook it and stopped, apparently baffled; when, howling afresh and shaking her wet mouth from side to side, she headed for the barn. She went into it and found it empty and came roaring outside. She would stand and look until she saw a moving object and then she would go squealing after it.

Vridar thought she had gone mad, like a dog with rabies; and yet, he doubted this. He felt in her mood and in her desperate behavior something that was not lunacy at all. It was hunger, an uncontrollable passion of a most ravening kind. He could see her down in the meadow now. She was running round and round a horse; now stopping, as if patiently waiting; now squealing between its legs; and now going furiously to another beast. When Vridar went to the house he saw Nephi and

Hankie, both grinning lewdly. He was about to enter the house when a voice stopped him.

His mother was saying to his father: "You should a-known better! Why did you throw it out where she could get it? You knowed she would eat it, the blood would make her do that!"

"Well, wife, I guess no harm is done."

"No harm! It's nice for our children to see, isn't it? If they ask what the trouble is what would you say?"

"I'd tell the truth. I guess it wouldn't kill them!"

"The truth! You'd fill their minds with a lot of bad notions!"

The sow was still running round and round the horse. Nephi and Hankie were grinning.

"Wife, you don't have to act like a crazy womern!"

Vridar was still wondering what kind of demon had got into the sow when Hankie explained. Hankie said the stuff she had eaten made females very passionate. It had the same effect on women, he said. There were men who fed the stuff to girls, and the girls then squealed and screamed and threw themselves after men, as the sow had done after anything that moved. Vridar said he did not believe it, but he recalled his mother's angry words and her shame. And then he saw another thing that amazed him.

The sow was out behind the barn, and the dog was there, trying to do what Vridar had imagined no dog ever did. He hid in a thicket and watched. After the dog had covered the sow and was making movements against her, Vridar would call, "Towser, what are you doing?" The dog at once would get down, looking abashed, looking slinking and shamed, and turn away, his tail lying against his belly. He would go off a little distance and stand, looking guiltily round him, as though stricken with abasement, yet eager to return. And when he could see no one or hear further rebuke he would come back, his slinking shame falling from him as he neared his quest. He would mount again and Vridar would watch him; and again Vridar would shout at him; and again Towser would sneak off, his head down, his tail humiliated. A half-dozen times or more Vridar called, and Towser withdrew, only to return when all had become silence.

This experience opened to Vridar a large and terrible world. Life in spite of its riddles had been rather neatly ordered, with the right and the wrong of it as clearly divided as light and dark. But what was this? There had been dawn and dusk, two borderlands that blurred. But now dusk was everywhere. Out of their own area and passions beasts prowled into the strange and mated with those not of their kind. What was love, if it could be fulfilled in these dark and horrible ways? Was hunger as tall and mysterious as the night, and did it fill the whole world, seeking its fulfillment where it could? If all this was so, had God ordained it? Was all this a part of his plan?

An attempt to undertsand deepened the boy's distress and added to his shyness and loneliness and distrust. He read the Bible again, but its parables seemed only the more awful, now that he knew the secret of birth. He read other books, one of which, a novel called *The Yoke,* fired his erotic impulses and sent him groping. All

166

life was pressing in and overpowering him, for nothing was literal any more. *Nothing was literal any more!* It was all a fabulous and untranslatable tale. Death was a fable, and so was love; and sin too, and birth. But he could not understand the fables. If there were clean and beautiful meanings in them, he could not find the meanings and draw their health and loveliness into his soul. They were only fog-spirals, wreaths of smoke, shimmerings in the impalpable blue; only dawn witchery, with Nephi's face and Hankie's face grinning in the dusk, and beyond them his mother's face, red with shame, and all the mother's lies that she had told. Nothing in life was literal any more.

While he floundered, with nobody to turn to, there came into his life for one golden July afternoon the most incredible girl he was ever to meet. Her name was Bonnie Adams. She came across the river with Charley and his wife and at once fixed her interest on Vridar. The bold stare of her gray eyes, probing, unashamed, and somehow eager and determined, shone so unwaveringly upon him that he became confused. He blushed, he looked away, he went away to hide, but she followed him. She came up close and looked for a moment at his mouth, over his face, and then into his eyes.

"What's your name?"

"Vridar."

"I knowed what it was. How old are you?"

"Thirteen."

Again she appraised him. She was about fourteen and of his height. Her mouth was warm with color, her lips were soft. There was something in her eyes that thrilled him and made him back off.

"You afraid of me?" she asked.

"No," he said, but he did not meet her eyes.

"You know Jed Bridwell."

"Yes."

"He's my man now but somehow or rather I'm tired of him. You like Jed?"

"I guess so."

"He hates you. He says you're a coward. Are you?"

Vridar resented the catechism. Again he met her eyes.

"What you afraid of most?"

"The river, I guess."

"Good Christ. Can't you swim?"

"No."

"The holy gods. What else you afraid of? Girls?"

He lied. "No."

"All right, then let's go fishun. You got two poles?"

He went behind the house as if to see if poles were there. But he knew that poles were there. He wanted time really to think about this girl and to decide if he should flee from her. She jerked poles from their spikes.

"What you use for bait?"

"Minnies," he said. "Or grubworms or grasshoppers or muckets."

"Muckets? In July?" She laughed, a low laugh, sensuous, amused, pitying. "These the best hooks you got?"

He drew close to her, ostensibly to look at the hooks but really to see if he was afraid. She swung suddenly and gave him a frank open smile. "What you thinkun?"

"Me?" he asked, doubly confused.

"You wouldn't dare tell, would you? Was it about me here?—" she placed a hand "or here?" His face turned crimson. "Well, let's go."

She gave the poles to him and together they went up the hill and past the corral and to the high river bank. Vridar glanced back and saw Hankie staring after him. He felt rather lordly then but his face still burned. He looked across the river and thought someone in the Bridwell yard was watching them.

"Let's go on," he said, eager to get out of sight. But Bonnie said no. She wanted to stand here and be seen.

"You know what Jed told me? He said if you—"

Good Lord, had she spoken the word! Yes, he knew that she had: she had said that if he did this word to her, Jed would kill both of them. Vridar began to shiver. He plunged down the bank.

They went to the island and were sheltered by trees and Vridar felt more secure. If he had known that Jed was trailing him like a panther a hundred yards behind, he would have run for his life. As it was, he was flooded with rapture when the girl clasped his arm; and he tried to think of himself as a rather world-weary youth who knew all about girls and was bold in his manner toward them. After a while he ventured to look at her. She was smiling, and this disconcerted him. He hastily surveyed himself; glanced down with horror to see if his trousers were buttoned; wiped at his mouth, which he suspected might be unclean; and then left her to walk through a pond and take the mud off his feet. When he returned to her and walked again at her side, Bonnie destroyed with one statement the strength and self-ease which he had been so desperately trying to assume. In a voice as calm as dead water she told him what she would permit him to do. She used the four-letter word which was written everywhere on privy walls, and which from his mother Vridar had learned was the vilest word anywhere. But he was not to tell Jed that she had allowed him to do this with her. "He'd kill us both," she said.

Then she explained. Burning like fire, he heard her confess that Jed was her lover and that for many days now she had been doing this secret thing with him. For this afternoon she offered herself to Vridar, for one embrace, or possibly for two, if she liked the way he managed it.

"But only if you promise never to tell. Jed would as leave kill you as a skunk." She waited for Vridar to speak and then asked impatiently: "Well, do you promise or not?"

He was not able to speak. He felt like something withering in a shroud of flame. He knew that his face was as red as flame and that sweat was bursting from his forehead.

She stopped and looked at him. "Well! Can't you talk?"

He glanced at her, his face grotesque with shame and fright. He licked at his dry lips and choked.

"Why is your face so God damn red?" she asked, looking at him with astonishment. "You mean you ain't never done that with a girl?"

Desperately he went to the river and cast his unbaited hook in. She came and stood by his side and looked at him but he refused to look at her. He moved his pole up and down and stared intently as if a fish had nibbled, and all the while he was striving to collect his wits. Bonnie began to talk.

He was afraid, she said. He was afraid of what Jed would do. But there was no reason for Jed to know. "He's jealous as a married man," said Bonnie. "You know what he wants? He wants me to marry him and run away."

Unable to speak or to look at her Vridar yanked fiercely at his line and brought the hook above the water.

"The holy stinkun Moses!" she cried.

Vridar turned. He thought Jed must be near.

"You're fishun without any bait, you fool."

He colored even more deeply. He drew the line in and clutched the hook and said feebly, "I guess a fish took it."

She was looking at him again and he could feel in her the derision, the contempt, the pity. She stepped over and looked at the water and said a big fish was close to the bank. Vridar then went over to see the fish, and in the next moment she pushed him with all her might and sent him headlong in. It was an eddy of still water, but deep, and he struggled and fought to keep from drowning and at last clutched at willows and drew himself out. He climbed to the bank drenched and humiliated and looked round him but Bonnie was gone.

After this experience Vridar felt that he had been a fool that no kindness under heaven could ever forgive. He could not forget Bonnie's astonishment at his ignorance and timidity and her hard contemptuous eyes. Day by day he saw the lewd and sneering face of Hankie. I'm a fool! he thought, and he strove to understand how and why. A few days after Bonnie came, he awoke suddenly from deep sleep. He thought a hand had touched him. He would have sworn that a voice had spoken his name. And when he looked out into the gloom, Bonnie Adams was there, standing close by the bed, looking down at him. He saw her as clearly as he had ever seen anything in life. She was reaching out with one hand and this hand came steadily nearer. He was terrified and yet calm. Telling himself that this could not be, that he imagined this image in the night, he closed his eyes very tight and saw nothing. He opened them quickly and there she stood, reaching toward him, looking at him with tender concern. The hand came nearer and nearer and he saw her body bend after it; until at last he could almost feel it, and with a smothered yell of terror buried himself under quilts. There he lay quietly, listening to the pumping of his heart. When at last he felt bold enough to look out, Bonnie was gone, the darkness was empty and still.

He was never able to understand this. For years he would believe that she had been there, in actual flesh, reaching toward him. He was to have other visions like this one and in all of them he was to be wide awake. Time and science would change his belief; they would convince him that he had seen nothing at all; but to the day of

169

his death nothing in his life would ever be more real or vivid than these apparitions out of sleep.

This one, the first of many, wrought in him a curious change. It intensified his feeling of worthlessness, his shame for his ignorance, his wish to be bold. She had returned, it seemed to him, to taunt him, to mock his dull timidity and his pious distrust. He resolved to share that knowledge whatever it might be that crowned Hankie and set him apart, that gave such candid passion to Bonnie, and to Jed his own reckless and dark empire. Was it this that had made Ruby Beam so alluring, and Dinsmore and Lew so fearless? Was it these proscribed things that gave to life its abundant color and breath and being?

Something had been reaching out of him for years, but he had thrust it back into his heart where it had lain in shameful quivering darkness. He had been good, O Lord, he had been good! He had lifted his thoughts to his mother's face and to heaven, and for all this he was getting only sterile anguish, only his ridiculous blushing without knowing why he blushed. If a thing was right, then why was it right? If wrong, then why? What was sin and what was God? Beyond the deed itself where lay its sanction?—and beyond the guilty act where and why lay the curse? Goaded, tormented, driven in turn to profanity or prayer, he went to Hankie and demanded to know what he had to tell.

"But you didn't want a-know," said Hankie, like one long and grievously put upon.

"Then I didn't. I do now."

"Only fools change their mind," said Hankie, looking at Vridar with the pity that Vridar hated.

"Oh, in Christ's name!" Vridar stared at him, remembering that this lad's favorite dish was a porridge of potatoes and sugar and milk.

"You realize, I guess," said Hankie, screwing his mouth up, "it's a secret only men know. And women. If I tell you—"

"You're not a man!"

"Oh, do tell! Well, you listen! I'n knock a girl up and you got a-be a man to do that. I could get married and have a family tomorrow."

Vridar looked at the scrawny frail body and the pale sallow face.

"Now," Hankie went on, "this is somethink you ain't to tell. Did you know the girls do it?"

"Girls?"

"Sure, God a-mighty. They do it all the time. My sister does it. We'll learn your sister how."

The matter for Vridar was becoming darker. Hankie now dwelt on this name or that, among the Annis children, telling of the love-life of each. Ruby Bean did not, he asserted with an oath; but had she any need to? Hadn't she lain in the bushes with a dozen men? But most girls did, yes, most of them did.

Now Hankie spoke of another matter. This pleasure, of which he would soon tell, was very dangerous; and if Vridar doubted that he could go to the asylum at Blackfoot and see for himself. It could turn a man crazy. It could give him warts and boils and cancers. Or it could make an idiot of him whose tongue would be

thick. He mentioned names—the name of one who had been hauled away screaming to the asylum; and of another who went raving off like steam and killed himself.
"I tell you," he said, looking at Vridar with aloof weariness, "so you'll be warned.
There's times I feel crazy as a bat. I hear ghosts walkun . . . . Well, you still want
to know?"

Vridar hesitated. He looked up at the sky, up out of this prison-hole, and asked
himself if he wanted to know. What would his mother think of him? Then he
remembered his ignorance, his shame and Bonnie's words.

"First," he said, "tell me this. Does Jed Bridwell—I mean—? And Bush O'-
Brien?"

Sure, said Hankie. Every boy worth his salt, and every girl, too. Why, by the holy
Judas priest, it was Bush who taught him!

"Then I want to know."

Hankie stretched to the sky and yawned. Tomorrow or the next day, he said; or
the next: a man had to be careful not to overspend his powers, if he did not want
to be toted off to Blackfoot.

Three days later Hankie called to Vridar and went into meadowed jungleland.
Already Vridar was feeling deep guilt. Again and again he glanced back, thinking
of Lot's wife who turned sinful eyes to the rear, feeling deeper than his need of
pleasure his need of faith. They crept into a dark shelter that smelled of sunless
days and the night. Hankie took his trousers down and rubbed something on his
palms; and Vridar observed that the boy's organ seemed to be curved under with a
kind of hook on it. He watched Hankie's face, and his hands, and when he saw the
passion that flushed and at last convulsed the face and heard the boy's hoarse
breathing, he shut his eyes, feeling dizzy and sick, as this new and more dreadful
truth came into him and filled him.

XXII

Of this new emotion, incredibly vivid and sweet, and so profound in its passionate
surge and reach and consummation, he was never done with thinking. Memory of
it swam in shimmering wonder through his days and laid a great glory upon his
sleep. It semed to capture and hold the entire subtle pulse of being, all of joy and
hope and yearning, and almost all of faith. It thrust roots deep into the inscrutable
warm darkness, moved down and enveloped the core; flowered like tremendous
suns of beauty that fed at the breast of peace. Why, then, was it so evil?

Under the first caress the rapture came in from all sides and shook him with
waves of sweet emotion; and these grew in intensity and power like a deepening
stream, until he could feel all around him the vast and imminent flood. His heart,
even his brain, melted into infinite tenderness, into a power unspeakably clean and
good, until compassion was the soul of it. Depth rose on depth, height relaxed and
fell, like valley dissolving into valley; and from all boundaries, from every remote
and alien place, the tides converged and closed, as if all space and time would be
distilled into the clear burning rapture of the crisis. Then breath left him, and

171

through his heart and through and through his quivering flesh he was riven with tenderness; and the flood burst and he was drowned.

If there could be such holiness in it, why was it evil? From his first experiences Vridar took an intense and spiritual cleanness; but this he lost, this became an ugly degradation, and his fight to recover it became the fight of his life. The emotion in these early whiles was naked and beautiful and so infinitely tender that he could only marvel at how cleansed he felt. There was nothing ugly in the heart of it and no feeling of guilt in the crisis. From prayer in former times that had purged him with frenzy and tears he had felt something akin to it. There was something akin to it in the holiness of his first Christmas night; in that hour when he first read about Jesus; in that afternoon when through a mist he had looked at three rainbows; in that breathless time when he walked with Neloa Doole. He forgot all that Hankie had said about lunacy and guilt. He forgot his own nightmares, and these now fell away from him during the first days; and the nameless dread fell away and the loneliness of his home. But this was only for a little while. His pure vision of holiness came to an end.

Because Hankie in spite of his pompous unconcern had only a lewd and guilty attitude toward the matter. His was a gesture toward manhood. This Vridar soon discovered and much more besides. One day Jewel entered the plot.

In this wide-mouthed girl Vridar had felt something that he could not define. He had sensed that her life harbored many secrets. He was not greatly astonished when he learned that Hankie was intimate with his sister, though this was not quite the way of it. He tried to be.

One day Hankie said they would all go to the shelter under the great fir on the river bank. There were five of them that day; Hankie said they would play husband and wife. "You be Jewel's husband," Hankie said to Vridar. "Diana, she's my wife now." For two hours the children played there. Diana would lie on her back and submit to one of Hankie's sober and futile attempts and then rise and brush her dress down; and Hankie would demand of his sister that she be his wife also. For he was a Mormon, he said, and Mormon men sometimes had many wives. Then Jewel would submit. Remembering the biblical verse, Vridar realized that Hankie was trying to go in unto her. But after submitting for only a few moments Jewel would struggle up, saying that there were other matters that properly concerned a wife; and she would run away while Hankie howled after her, "You don't have to cook yet! You pinhead, come back here!"

"It's suppertime," Jewel would say. "I have to find mushrooms for the steak." And from a wet bank she would uproot toadstools. "Get some wood," she said to her brother. "Then make a fire."

Sometimes they would play by the spring where Hankie had his outlandish assortment of mud pies and cakes, canned berries and cockleburs and weed seed. They would hum industriously for a little while, the girls mixing mud dough, Hankie chasing and impaling butterflies; and then thoughtfully, like a wife conscious of all her duties, Jewel would say, "It's time to play married again." And off she would go, followed by the others, to the hidden shelter under the river bank. Vridar tried to embrace both his sister and Jewel but he acted the way Towser had

172

acted with the sow. He was so filled with shame and so afraid of his mother that he could not force himself to learn what a girl looked like, but fumbled stupidly and blindly, trying to guide himself with his hands. Hankie after trying one girl or the other would then thrust Vridar aside, saying, "Here, she's my wife!" And Vridar would withdraw, shamed, as the dog had. Marion stood back and watched.

In September the McGards left this place and never returned. After they had gone, Vridar again walked in the ways of loneliness, deeper now because of deeper guilt. The mountainside turned yellow; the vales across the river where maples stood became blood-red. Life here as in former years was drawn into inexorable silence. Joe swung the mattock or labored at the mill; Prudence tended her poultry and cows and day by day buttered her aging cheese; and Vridar toiled in the fields like a man. Whether he would go to school this year he did not know. He asked no questions, for he had been taught that children were to be seen and not heard. He despised Hankie but he felt lost without him. No matter where he went he remembered that in this spot, under that tree, climbing that ledge he had been in a happier time. Here he had sat with Hankie and helped to shape bows and arrows. There he had walked with Bonnie, and though distressed then, he knew in looking back that in the experience there had been something good. Upon that aspen set apart he had carved his name and the name of Neloa.

In all these memories he found only sadness now, only a wretched self-pitying melancholy, only a haunting sense of beauty that had died. Sometimes he would weep, sometimes he would fall into blind rage, hating himself and hating life. And all the while each rapturous experience left him more alone and afraid. He had developed a passionate interest in his sister, and though he felt shameful and wicked he persisted in it. After the McGards left he would persuade her to go with him to fetch the cows. He wanted to see her naked flesh, and he wanted to play husband and wife with her again.

In an evening of dusk far up on the mountainside, he urged her to take off her clothes. She demurred; she said he was very silly and queer. But he was cunning and artful; he played with her, throwing her gently down and exciting her; and before the matter was done, he got his way. Unable longer to resist him she stripped off and stood unclothed. He could not see clearly because the twilight had deepened. He asked her to lie down for him and play as they had played under the tree, but she said no and she ran away.

"Don't tell mother!" he cried after her. He ran and overtook her and she stopped and completed her dressing.

"Why not?" she said.

"She might be mad. Promise you won't tell."

"Mebbe I will," she said, looking at him curiously.

He tried to bribe her, to intimidate her, and then appealed to her sense of loyalty as a sister: did she want their mother to punish him?

"But why should she?"

"She might think it was wrong."

Diana considered this. "Is it?" she asked.

"Promise you won't tell."

"I won't promise."

Envisaging a dreadful scene with his mother, he became deseperate. He followed her home, begging her not to tell, trying to persuade her with bribes, to frighten her with threats; but Diana only walked rapidly ahead of him, saying nothing at all.

She told. The next day she confessed to Prudence not only this but the husband and wife playing under the tree. With her face as red as chokecherry leaves, Prudence called Vridar to her and took him into the house and closed the door. For several moments she sat in awful calm and looked at him.

"Son," she said at last, and her voice was the voice of Jeremiah, "what have you been doing with your sister?"

He tried to meet her eyes. He did for a moment and then gulped and choked. They were eyes that were cold, angry, and estranged.

"Son, look at me!"

He tried to but he could not. Remembering all the lies she had told him, he began to feel insulted and outraged.

"Son, have you ever lied to me?"

Had he? He could not remember. He thought again of her lies to him. He looked up and met her gaze and said: "Have you ever lied to me?"

She was shocked and horrified. Was her own son calling his mother a liar?

"You have lied to me," he said.

"What are you saying!"

"I'm saying you lied to me. You lied about where babies come from."

"I said what was best for you. I want to know, have you ever lied to me?"

"I guess not," he said, knowing well that he had.

"You know what God does to liars?"

"Yes maam," he said, wondering what God did.

"Do you know that God is listenun to you?"

"Yes maam."

"Then tell me what you did to your sister."

Again, desperately, he met her eyes. "Why should I? She has told you."

"I want you to tell me."

He felt thirsty and wished he might have a drink. He started toward the pail.

"Son, come back here."

"I just wanted a drink!" he cried.

"You can drink later. Now tell me what you did."

Good Lord, did she want him to use the words on privy walls! "Well—" he said.

"Go on, I can't spend the whole day here."

"Well, I—I rassled around with her and tore her dress. That's all."

"Son!"

O God, how he hated her! What did she want him to say? "I looked at her!" he blurted.

"Why?"

"I—I wanted to see what a girl is like."

There was silence. He stared at the floor and wiped at his eyes and could hear the beating of his heart. He knew that she was looking at him. He knew that her face was stern and pitiless and not the face of a mother.

Then suddenly she asked a question and it overwhelmed him. She used the four-letter word on the privy walls. She used the word Bonnie had used. Had he ever, she asked, done that with his sister, and the question was sharp, merciless, and cold. He choked and looked up and met her gaze.

"No," he said.

"Son, don't lie to me!"

Almost gasping he said: "If you already know why do you ask me?"

"I want you to tell."

"I didn't do it."

"Son!"

"I didn't!" he cried.

"Don't lie to your mother."

"I didn't," he said, his voice quieter now. "I didn't do what it says in the Bible."

"In the Bible!" Again he had shocked her. "Do you know the Bible is the word of God?"

"That's what you have told me."

"The Bible does not use nasty words and talk about these nasty things."

He looked straight into her eyes and said: "It uses the word piss."

"Son!"

"And the Bible," he went on, realizing that he had momentarily vanquished her, "says the man went in unto her. I didn't go in unto my sister."

"Son, the Bible doesn't say such things. It's some other book you've read."

"Oh no it isn't." He had read the Bible several times. He knew what it said, even if his parents did not. He could even quote the words to her. Again meeting her gaze he spoke. "The Bible says, hath he not sent me to the men which sit on the wall, that they may eat their own dung, and drink their own piss with you? The Bible says that daughters lay with their father and were with child by him. It says—"

"I don't believe it," said Prudence, staring at her son.

"Do you tell me I lie? Do you want me to show you these things?"

"I will ask your father."

Vridar drew a long breath. "I did not go in unto my sister," he said. "If she says I did she lies."

"Did you try to?"

"Yes—but not really."

She now told him that he had been a very wicked boy, that God would punish him for his sin, and that she must punish him also, as God's instrument. She told him to go out and cut a green chokecherry branch and bring it to her. He groped from the house, with tears and confusion and hate blinding him, and went to the chokecherry bushes. Because he could not see he felt around for a green limb and broke it off; and then went back into the house, with nothing before him but a world of water and mist and rainbows.

It was not a severe flogging; it left no marks on his back. But its effect on him was worse than bitter blows could have been. It wrought in his soul a violent

175

distortion, and laid between mother and son an estrangement that not all of time would ever heal. With every burning stroke he took into his heart, not a clear sense of error but a ghastly dread of the sweet, the beautiful, the unexplained. Nothing was right, nothing was godly but pain, loneliness, shame, and self-denial. That was the meaning of the chokecherry limb. The soft, the alluring, the rapture and the tenderness, these were of the Devil, these were to be cast out. There was sin in the world, his mother said, and it seemed to be decoyed in everything of loveliness and light; and virtue, upon which God smiled, was to be seen in the stern and remorseless face of his mother . . .

After she had punished him, he slunk away, hating her, and with horrible bitterness in his soul. And beyond her, more even than her, he hated the Bible.

XXIII

And so it was that this boy lived. Each summer repeated the toil and anguish of the summer before; each winter found him with his brother, in Poplar or Annis, keeping his own house and cooking his own food and going to school. But it was not all bitterness and heartache. There were a few hours of love and glory, when he felt like something more than a contemptible sinner and a craven fool.

There was an April day when the eighth grade was reciting, and from where he sat Vridar could hear the teacher intoning the words of an ode to a nightingale. He became drunk with the warmth and sensuous beauty and color of Keats, with the magic of strange seas and casements, with the bird's ecstatic soaring above the reach of meanness and death. Again he resolved to become a poet. He read every book of poetry he could lay hands on, and day after day scribbled wretched verse of his own. The Psalm of Life moved him like a bugle; a poem to a waterfowl made him sob; The Chambered Nautilus left him purged and exalted; and Invictus was like a window in a dark sky. He read Gray, Poe, Edmund Vance Cook, Field, Bunner, Lanier, Sill, Longfellow, Bryant, and Whittier.

His own verse, monotonously flawless in meter, dismayingly sterile in theme, was songs of love, exhortations to faith and hope, paeans to courage, and apostrophes to God. He treasured the things and read them over and over, wondering if some day he would stand shoulder to shoulder with Shakespeare and Milton. For many weeks nobody knew that he wrote. He hid his stuff away. But one evening his mother found his hidden treasure and read every childish line of it and was amazed. Here was a poet indeed, and her own son! With that aloof pride that nothing could kill, she confessed to him that some of her people had been poets. She read the verses to Joe, and the father grunted and looked distressed: he wanted his son to be a lawyer or a doctor or a professor: in creating poets, God, he supposed, had a purpose in mind but the purpose eluded him.

There came to the place one day a Jim Whaker who in the legends about him was a brilliant and well-educated man. Once upon a time he had taught school. After eating, he sat back and filled his pipe; and Prudence, remembering the wonder, came to her son. She asked him to bring his poetry and read it. Vridar wanted to, but he demurred and tried to beg off; until, when his mother insisted, he brought forth a handful of verses.

"Mr. Whaker," she said, trying to conceal her pride, "I wonder if you would read these. I want to know what you think."

Mr. Whaker turned his lean face toward her. He took a wet pipestem from his yellowing teeth. "Why, yes," he said. He took the papers, drew spectacles from his pocket and set them on his long hooked nose, and began to read. Now and then he grunted or seemed to mutter in his breath, or he would stare meditatively at his pipe. Vridar meanwhile stood back, quivering with suspense and awaiting this great man's judgment. Mr. Whaker knocked the pipe on his heel and looked up at the sagging roof-poles.

"Who wrote this?" he asked at last.

"Just a minute," said Prudence, grotesquely playful. "Tell us first what you think."

"Mrs. Hunter, I'll tell you what I think. I've read lots of poetry in my day, but I've never read anything bettern this. Not a single solitary thing," he said, and seemed to be startled. He adjusted his spectacles and read again. "No sir, I never did."

Vridar was trembling. The words were honey but he felt that the man was a fraud.

"You really mean that?" asked Prudence.

"Yes," he said. He read again, and again seemed to be startled. "By George, yes, I mean it." He took his glasses off and laid the verses down. He looked at her. "Who wrote it?"

"He did," said Diana, and pointed at Vridar.

Vridar now felt as if the whole world had fixed its gaze on him. His cheeks were afire. The great man was looking at him. The great man arose and crossed the room and touched his hair. "Some day," he said, "you'll be a famous man." He turned to Prudence. "That's true," he said, and looked startled, as though someone had pinched him.

But even though the words were honey, Vridar felt in his soul that this man was pompous and false. A half-hour later neverthless he was hidden in a thicket, writing an incoherent panegyric to spring. Reading it and finding it good, in a burst of frenzy he wrote what he called an ode. Ah, what a man he would be!—yet here he was, milking cows and shoveling manure, he whom God had ordained to poetry.

There came another man, named Tim Prune. He was very long and lean, with black furtive eyes and a sunken weather-beaten face. His enormous beaked nose had flaring nostrils, filled with coarse untidy hair. His mouth was big and tearful and loose. He was a bachelor, he said, who had a need to hide from whisky and women, the twin curses of life. In an isolated spot like this he could rebuild his shattered health and again step forth to fight and win. He was a poor lost soul, Prudence cried, and almost wept. If he had a few dollars, said Tim, he could buy a few traps and a grubstake and come here and trap and restore his soul to God. Out of her savings Prudence gave him money and out of her heart she blessed him. Tim climbed the mountain and disappeared.

177

Tim was back after a few days, dragging his long weary legs and making sounds of grief. By the fire that evening he told his tale. He had been robbed. He had gone to the valley, with the money sewed in his underclothes, but some thugs had set upon him and knocked him as dizzy as typhoid and had stolen everything but his socks. For hours he had lain unconscious, as naked as a babe and as friendless as a little lamb whose mother would not own it. A farmer had found him and a farmer's wife had given him clothes.

"She was an angel," he said. "May the good God Almighty bless that woman. That's what I ask ever day my life. She was like you, Mrs. Hunter," he said, and blew his nose in a deluge of grief and remorse.

The story was retold and embellished, and Vridar saw that his mother's eyes were wet. His own intuitions were becoming sharper; he felt that this man was an impostor, a long crafty liar, a drunkard and a sneak. But Prudence consoled Tim with pious thoughts. There was always a turn ahead, she assured him; when things looked blackest, then the sky cleared. She asked Vridar to read some of his poetry.

The boy rebelled. In the realm of poetry, he was convinced, this Tim Prune was a dark infidel and a fraud. But after much coaxing he fetched some verses and read them, a singsong exhortation to courage and faith. By the time the verses were read Tim was bawling aloud. He was roaring great guffaws of sentimental agony; he was wiping tears from his sunken cheeks and slobbering like a child. And Prudence was weeping, too. Tears were running down her stern face as she rocked with silent grief. Then Diana began to cry. Vridar glanced at his father, sitting back in a corner smoking his pipe. There was something faint but unmistakable in the man's eyes and round his mouth. Vridar thought it was amusement and pity.

There was the enchanting and guilty hour with Betty Mill. Betty and Rod were brother and sister who lived up the canal from Vridar's Poplar home. They had been orphans from childhood and now, both grown, they lived together and tilled a small farm. Rumors had whispered of incest. Rumors said they slept in the same bed and were in all respects as husband and wife. Betty now and then baked a rich brown loaf or a cake or pudding and brought it to the lads; or she would fetch a jar of fruit or jellies and nuts, or the roasted half of a chicken, or apples that smelled of a deep cellar. She would caress Vridar's hair and pinch his cheeks.

She was a voluptuous woman, full-bodied and sensuous, vivid and warm. She had eyes that made Vridar think of dark ripe cherries, and the most alluring dimples he had ever seen. Sometimes when she stooped so that her blouse fell he could see the dazzling white curves of her breasts.

One evening she and her brother came when Vridar was in bed, feeling spent and ill. After getting wood and building a fire, Rod went with Marion to skate, and Betty sat on the bed by Vridar.

"You're not very sick, are you?"

"I guess not," he said.

She laid a palm on his cheek and counted his pulse. "No fever," she said, smiling at him. Then she took his hands and laid them against her breasts. "Why are you always so bashful? Are you afraid of girls?"

178

"No," he said, but he drew his hands away, pretending that he had to blow his nose. He snorted furiously into a big rag.

"Have you ever kissed a girl?"

"Yes."

"Did you like it?"

"I—I—" he said and blushed.

"I used to see you skate with Helen. Did you ever kiss her?"

He wanted to lie, but he said no, he had never kissed Helen.

Betty again took his hands and drew them to her. She bent toward him, smiling. "Would you like to kiss me?"

His heart, his surging blood told him that he would like to but he knew that it would be sinful. He could see her mouth like a flower waiting for him. "It wouldn't be right!" he gasped and tried to free his hands.

"Of course it would," she said softly, looking into his eyes.

"Don't" he said, struggling, and she released his hands. She was quiet a moment and he thought he had offended her.

But then she said: "Don't be afraid of me." She clasped his hands again. She pressed his hands to her belly and drew them up to her breasts. "Do you like that?" she asked.

"Yes," he said, feeling his blood race. He drew a deep sigh that ended in a gasp. Betty leaned forward and put his arms around her neck and her face against him.

"Just be quiet," she said. "Then you won't be afraid."

He was as quiet as he could be. Her lips were touching his cheek and the loosened mass of her hair was all over him. He could feel her slow breathing. He could feel the quick furious beating of his own heart.

"You afraid now?" she whispered.

"No!" he said, caught up and undone.

"You want to kiss me now?"

Yes, he wanted to, but he was remembering what his mother had told him, that lusting after a woman was the most dreadful of all sins. He asked her to wait a little longer, and then tried to thrust his head farther back. She patted him; her lips and tongue were against his cheek. Her gentleness and her reassuring caresses took all the fight out of him. He melted into the hour and surrendered, too confused and blissful to try to think any longer about sin and what his mother had said. He liked the way she was moving her lips and tongue over his cheek.

"Ready now?" she whispered.

She arose and framed his face in her hands and slowly bent forward, the deep richness of her possessing and enfolding him. Her arms reached under and gathered him, her arms drew his face to the white wonder of her bosom; and for him she was moving not as a woman but as an embodiment of pleasure, voluptuous and eternal and very sweet. Softly she drew his head up and pressed her lips upon his. They were softer than he had ever thought lips could be, and warm and hungry and seeking. Then for a moment he could feel her tongue.

"Afraid now?" she whispered, caressing his hair.

He could not speak. He seemed to have sunk into something that ran far under

179

the currents of speech, into a fragrant impalpable depth that was like holiness, that was like peace. She kissed him again, using her lips and her tongue and so filling him with rapture that he was utterly helpless. He had never known that kissing a woman could be like this. She kissed him with passion so sudden and fierce that she crushed his lips and drew all the breath out of him. In the next moment she had said good-night and was gone.

She came again and again, bringing him delicious things to eat; but he plotted his life so that she could never catch him alone. He wanted to be alone with her and to feel again the incredible wonder of her mouth. He wanted to go to bed with her but he was afraid. More than that, he could not believe that any woman could find him attractive, for he seemed to himself to be more frail and scrawny, more stupid and awkward and dull than he was. The next winter he went to school in Annis. He never saw Betty again.

It was in Annis that he was to store in his soul the brightest memory of these years. There he met Neloa again. He was fifteen this year. He did not know how old she was; he thought she was twelve or thirteen but she was tall for her age. Her olive cheeks seemed more richly dyed now, her eyes more velvety in their soft depths, her manner more aloof and inscrutable. He stared at her endlessly in school. He dreamed of her night after night. He would have made any sacrifice and suffered any shame for one word of encouragement, one intimate understanding glance, one word of love from this unapproachable maid. She did not know that he lived. She was never aware of his feeble clumsy efforts to capture her interest. He put himself in her way and kept close to her on the school grounds and guiltily trailed her half-way home; but she never looked at him, or if she looked she did not see.

In this fashion he lived through many months, breathing her name, idolizing her quiet, enthroning her among the perfect and the pure. In virtue and grace and charm, in poise and innocence she seemed far beyond anything he was or could ever be. He felt unworthy of her, almost too mean and contemptible to touch her dress. She paid no attention to any of the boys, and so Vridar persuaded himself that she had no interest in them, that all her thoughts rose nobly beyond their reach. He resolved that some day she would be his wife.

At the end of this year the school had a contest. Children from other schools round-about came to Annis to compete in spelling, geography, and arithmetic. Two contestants were chosen from each school. From the Annis school Vridar was one. The other was Neloa Doole.

Of his first fifteen years the hours in this contest were his highest glory and his deepest sense of his own worth. Under the guidance of his teacher, a soft-voiced woman who took pride in his scholarship, and under the envy of other pupils, his ego throve prodigiously and for a little while his self-contempt was sloughed away. Besides the envy and his teacher's belief that he would spell every other boy and girl black and blue, that he would add and multiply with a speed never before seen in this valley, that he would name the cities and countries, the mountains and rivers of the earth as though he had been born with the words in his mouth—besides all this was the fact that Neloa would stand at his side. Realization of this robbed him of appetite and sleep. It made him apply himself like one driven to the learning of words and names. And when the hour arrived at last he was so pale and starved and excited that he shook like a leaf.

People from the hamlets filled the schoolhouse, sitting huge and gawky in seats too small, the women overflowing with starch and ribbon, the men smelling of new overalls. On a front bench with the teacher by him, whispering instructions or patting his hands, and with Neloa almost within arm's reach, still aloof and inscrutable, Vridar waited and was afraid. He had glanced behind him and had known that a hundred pairs of eyes were watching him, and praying for him a cool and decisive triumph. He glanced at his opponents, boys and girls sitting roundabout, and it seemed to him that they were sharply alert and enviably at ease. All the while he was saying to himself, God, help me to be cool!

Arithmetic came first. With the contestants turned away the teachers wrote on the blackboard long columns of figures. The contestants were turned to the board with their eyes blindfolded, and at a signal the blinds were jerked away and they set to work. When one finished his addition he was to swing and call the sum.

Forgetting himself now, Vridar worked swiftly, his mind leaping ahead, his mind adding like a machine, as if it had been set free and he had no power over it. In breathless haste he turned and shouted his sum: "Two million, four hundred and seventeen thousand, two hundred and thirty-nine! "Correct!" a judge said, and Vridar turned to the next column. "Eight million, nine hundred and sixteen thousand, six hundred and ten!"

"Correct!"

Applause swept the hall. He was out of himself now. He was working like one in a dream, his mind and hands in conspiracy, the rest of him dazed and lost.

"Three billion, forty-seven million, one hundred and ninety-eight thousand, and two!"

"Correct!"

After him he heard other voices calling sums. He heard the sounds but he did not understand. All his wits had been drawn into sharp and brilliant focus. He won the arithmetic contest without an error, and the schoolhouse rattled under the shout and roar.

The geography contest he lost. There were only two survivors, he and another lad, when the word Reno was flung at him. He had never heard of it. He had learned the name of no city with fewer than ten thousand people. Realizing that he was ignorant of the place, he hesitated, looked at his teacher, reddened, and went to his seat.

Instantly came the answer: "Nevada!"

Menan had won.

For the spelling contest twelve boys and girls stood in a line across the room. Neloa was at Vridar's side. Down her back her hair hung in a great wave almost to her knees. A delicious color was in her cheeks and mouth, a shining intensity in the lustrous dark of her eyes. This was the proudest moment in Vridar's first fifteen years. When her sleeve touched him, he felt rapture in him like fire; when she looked into his eyes, as she did once, the world closed over him and his senses

181

drowned. He was only vaguely aware of farmers sitting with chins cupped, mouths open, eyes intent and still. On the front row before him sat the teachers and judges.

At the end of twenty minutes four contestants remained: a boy from Menan, a girl from Lewisville, and Vridar and Neloa. The word now offered was erysipelas. It was the Menan boy's turn. Without hesitating—he had floored two opponents with hippopotamus and benefited—he spelled the word.

"E-r-e-s-i-p-e-l-a-s."

"Wrong!" said a judge. "Take your seat."

It was Lewisville's turn. The girl hesitated and looked at her teacher and gulped. "E-r-e-s-i-p-p-e-l-a-s."

"Wr—" the judge began and stopped. He looked at his list of words. "No, that ain't right, neither. Take your seat."

Vridar knew the word but he did not care about that. He was praying that Neloa knew it, for it was her turn next. She spelled it with a y and with one p, but the last syllable she spelled as lus.

"Wrong!" cried the judge triumphantly, for he was from Menan. "Take your seat."

Neloa shrugged. She tossed her head, drew her lips into a pucker of disdain, and went to a bench. She was looking at Vridar now. All the eyes in the hall were looking at him. He could have heard a pin drop. His teacher was leaning forward, her lower lip caught betwen her teeth. Vridar spelled the word but it was no triumph for him, because Neloa had failed.

People crowded around him to grasp his hand and look at him with proud bright eyes. His teacher was so happy that she wept. But all of Vridar's thoughts were for Neloa. She had slipped away and as soon as he could free himself he went to find her. She was outside, standing alone in the dark.

"I'm sorry," he said, wondering how he could comfort her. "I wish you had won instead of me."

"What do I care!" she said, and shrugged under her broad mane. There were tears in her eyes, but there was something more than tears; and if he had been a wiser lad he might have seen now the character of the girl on whom he had set his heart. But he was too conscious of being alone with her to see anything, and while he stood here, fumbling for words, her mother came and took her away.

From a few other experiences he harvested joy and pride and self-esteem; or once in a while the ascetic, already thriving within his frame, was temporarily abashed by the good sensuous things of life. There was a feast at his grandmother's —a great goose gleamingly succulent with oil, stuffed with rich spiced dressing, odorous with hunger-smells; and all around it were bowls of snowwhite potatoes with butter melting in their dimples, of parsnip and jellied beets, of candied yams drowned in their own rich blood. There were pickles and relishes of more kinds and colors than he could remember, each delicioiusly aged and seasoned. There was an enormous fruitcake, with lemon rind and citron, with currants and nuts sticking out all over it; and another cake built in layers and covered deep with beaten sugar and eggwhite and cream; and a third, higher still, drenched with chocolate that had run down upon the plate in brown pools. There were bowls of

182

preserves and jellies: currant and gooseberry and quince and peach, strawberry and pear and apple, each lusciously thick and fragrant in its syrup. There was a bowl of rosy apples, candied whole; and a five gallon jar of preserved peaches, by which he stood, breathing its aroma and whetting his appetite.

After all these came the pies. He never learned how many kinds there were. He remembered four. There was the homemade mince in deep broad tins, with the fragrance of raisins and spices and wine rising in heat waves from their patterned tops. There was the lemon which, when cut, showed a bright yellow wall two inches thick. There was the pumpkin, opulently fat and full, its crust breaking into flakes that melted on the tongue; and there was the cream, made with all of Rose's materials and skill, banked high with white whip and crowned with red cherries.

After the feast was done and everyone had eaten until he patted his belly and grunted and yawned, Rose brought forth baskets of apples, smelling as Betty's had of cool deep cellars; baskets of nuts and pails of candies; and two foaming buckets of beer.

Vridar ate until his eyes were glazed, and his belly was like the drum of a bloated steer. He could not sit in comfort, he could not stand; and when he moved from place to place, moaning with gluttony, his grandmother thought he was hungry and urged him to eat more. He went outside, feeling as if he would die, believing that he would never eat again.

And there was from year to year, in spite of terror and grief and shame, his wonder in the glory of earth. He was never done with breathing of flowers, of the chokecherry in bloom, of the serviceberry's acres of pink and white; of dandelion and pentstemon and scarlet gilia, of cool carpets of moss, of the fir and the juniper. In many times and places he watched the hummingbird, flashing like a jewel above clusters of monkshood, gleaming in cinnamon and orange and green, probing tubes of the painted cup and vanishing like a thread of fire. Or the oriole with its black necktie on a yellow vest, weaving its home of fibers and horsehair, lining it with cottonwood down and flagtail wool. Or he would listen while lying in a shaded spot to the gorgeous stanzas of the meadowlark, ringing skyward in two octaves, until the sky was full of flutes. Or he would sit in morning dusk under the rhythms of swallows.

He did not know how thoroughly his prison-home, with its variety of habits and moods, its passions and humors and secrets, was shaping his character and soul. He hated the place but he felt bound to it. For nine years it had been the center of his universe, with all directions leading from it; and so strongly did he sense this that when away from it he felt uprooted and lost. He did not understand his problem at all. He strove to. With prayer and tears, desperately, ceaselessly, he tried to put aside his dread and his loneliness and find faith and peace. His struggle became so intense and mad that in the next years he went as far into darkness as a human being can go and return to the light.

XXIV

Feeling that he had sinned almost beyond the mercy and forgiveness of God, he determined to save his soul. He would do this with mental scourging, with bitter scorn and self-contempt. He would do it in part with self-denial. He became frugal in his habits, more shy and self-effacing in his moods; and when impulses awoke in him, calling him to fulfillment, he tried to deny and crush them. He liked to be near the old, the maimed or diseased, the forlorn and tragic, believing from his New Testament reading that these were nearer to God. Thoughts of women, of feasting, of revelry he tried to bury in darkness. Two or three times every day he sank to his knees in prayer.

But these denials only made him more wretched. The air seemed sweeter, the sky bluer, and the ways of wickedness more alluring when he felt most irrevocably lost. Flowers stood round him, bushes drooped under their riches, streams murmured with song, and his hunger for life would choke him. He would think again and again of the command of Jesus: suffer little children to come unto me. He did not know that suffer here meant allow. He thought it meant misery. He thought that if little children must suffer to find Jesus, he would have to suffer much more.

In spite of his resolutions and his will, he was drawn again and again to the ways of pleasure. He went like one in a trance, his conscience rebelling, his blood clamoring to go. The mood would come upon him in a strange way. Of the guilty sly moment out of which it was born and of its first stealthy growth he was unaware; when it entered consciousness, it was too lusty to be put aside. He fought it. He moaned and prayed and sometimes broke into sweat. Running to a wall he would count there the number of his virtuous days, struck from the calendar one after one. He had rows of lines—

—each a desperate record of his faltering footsteps toward heaven. But counting them gave him no strength after this hunger, this madness, had seized him. It was irresistible and he would turn away, his will quivering in its will.

The stages of this obsession were two. There was the time first of all when the impulse flowered up out of his subconscious being and became intimate and warm and growing in strength. It would grow in sensuous heat until it suffocated him. It was then that he fought against it and became afraid. It was then that he ran from place to place, trying to throw it off, yet realizing that if no aid came that was stronger than his own will he would again fall. It was then while running that he would go to the wall to count the lines, hoping that these symbols of his stronger periods would give him strength.

Or he would go to his mother during this first stage, praying that her stern face would abash the obsession that held him. Or he would call to Marion and suggest that they do this or that. But all the while the Thing was in his blood, eager but patient, with no diminishing of strength. As long as he rushed feverishly about, seeking escape, he was able almost to forget it, almost to believe that it had gone.

It was during this time that sweat would pour out of him and desperation would constrict his throat.

There came then the second stage. There stood up in his mind, bold and clear, the realization that again he had been conquered. But he did not yield at once. The yielding was little by little, almost imperceptibly degree by degree, as his will was sucked of its strength. There was nothing he could do now. He still hoped that some power would intervene, some force pull him back. Feeling himself on the brink he would pray for a will mightier than his own; and when at last, with his own will gone, he turned away for a hiding-place, he hoped that his mother would call him or that visitors would come or that he would fall and break a leg. He hoped he would fall—and walked with greater care; hoped that he would be seen—and went more stealthily from shelter to shelter! Because in him now, blind and all-conquering, was the delicious passion of a rising hunger, singing in him like music, overflowing his emotions and mind. He could not have turned back, or paused, under threat of death. It was as if he were drawn by an invisible mesh, as if his legs were not his own. Creeping into hiding, shaking like one tortured, dripping sweat, he would make one last wild abandoned gesture and offer up to pleasure his soul.

A little later he would come out, white and abject, loathing himself with loathing that sickened him. But in his heart there was the bright seed of another resolution, another promise to God. The Thing was behind him now. It had possessed him and gone away. He could begin anew. He could fight more mightily this time. And perhaps there would be on the wall, not a record of five days or eight, three or nine, but of weeks, months, years, chalked against his wish for a nobler life.

In this manner he fought through a bitter summer. He might have won if a horrible document had not been placed in his faltering path.

He had just read *The Three Musketeers* and, still under the spell of their magnificent adventures, was hunting for the sequel, when he came upon curious things in an old dresser. There were strange yellow papers, and daguerreotypes of long-dead relatives: some whiskered and dignified, some with cold unreasoning piety in their eyes, some who looked gawky and foolish. These were his mother's people. Here also was a photograph of his mother, taken when she was eighteen or twenty: so tightly bound and corseted that she looked as if she had been melted and poured into satin. There was one of his father with a ridiculous false mustache etched on his lip. Then he dug out a musty moth-eaten pamphlet which asked in huge black words on a yellowing sheet:

WILL YOUR BRAIN ROT?

This, it seemed to him, might afford some curious knowledge. He tucked it under his shirt and left the house and disappeared. Hiding under the fir tree, he read the booklet, and read it again and still again. As he encompassed its sinister meaning, sweat stood on his brow and his heart fell dead.

It offered to his amazed stare the photographs of four hideous men, ripe with ulcer and madness. Had he abused himself? the pamphlet wanted to know. Had he "wallowed in the morass of sin?" If he had, and if he did not seek expert aid at once, sores would burst out on him, his mind would rot and he would be locked up with the idiots. Doctors could not help him. Religion would do him no good. His only road to health lay toward a sanitarium in Delaware.

For an hour he brooded over this warning. Inside the first leaf was the picture of an infuriated man, lips shot out, eyes bulging, arm thrust at the reader; and under it was the question in black words an inch high:

ARE YOU NEXT?

Vridar looked at the angry face and his blood congealed. Was he next? Only God knew. It seemed to him as the minutes passed in the beating of his heart that he was next, that insanity stood not far ahead. A dreadful fear gripped him. He could hear his breath, his heart, and in both sounds was a premonition of doom. He leapt up, utterly terrified, and smote at himself, trying to knock himself out of the deadly torpor that was getting hold of him. He jumped up and down and pinched himself and began to talk aloud. "I'm all right!" he said, and did not recognize his own voice. "I'm all right . . . I'm all right . . . . " The words sank, fell to a hoarse whisper and died. He stood still, expecting something . . .

He read parts of the pamphlet again. He looked at the faces, the leprous skin, the rotting flesh; and while he looked he again heard his breath and his heart. He began to shake. He shook so violently that his teeth clicked and the book fell from his hands. Around him, stealthily moving in, unseen but vividly felt, was a suffocating dread. He fought it. He struck against it. And then with a mad yell he began to run, going blindly through the bushes and trees, leaping in frenzy, trying to escape from the thing that was getting his mind. But it followed him, as remorseless as time. It was everywhere. He felt it in the sky and the earth and in the strange quiet of trees. It filled this prison-home from wall to wall, moaned in the river's going, rang out in the hawk's wild scream. It was in the yellow sun and in the summer-smells of the air.

Finding it with him at every turn, he stopped, panting, and looked round him. There was no friendliness, no aid. He was asylumed here, walled-in, with this dread piled upon him. He was gasping and quivering and feeling the sweat over him in a warm sheet when he thought of God and of Jesus, his Son. Sinking to his knees and raising arms to his wet chest, he prayed for help. He asked God in the name of Jesus to save him from disease and lunacy; to lead him back to the paths of holiness and fill him with strength and courage. In return for this he promised not to err again. The prayer poured out of him, desperate word upon desperate word. Down his face sweat ran, blinding him, dripping its salt on his white mouth. He felt a little better then. He stood up, weak and unnerved, but feeling around him a great and inexplicable goodness and infinite peace on earth. He went quietly to the house and got the New Testament and hid, and read the Gospel of Luke.

But he had not conquered. There was drained out of him the strength which he took from prayer; and the dread closed in like twilight and darkened his life. As his hunger grew, so did the dread, the two rending him with their conflict. The Idea would come, gently insinuating, voluptuous and soft and sweet; it would grow in his being like a lovely fragrant weed until the small garden of his better self was choked and overrun; and then it would flower upward, pushing its alluring foliage into his mind, sinking caressing roots down into his heart and his blood. It twined tendrils round his nerves and filled his breath with its loamy odor. And as it grew and ripened in luxuriant sensuous stealth, until all his hunger accumulated from days of self-denial filled him from head to feet, the Thing obsessed him again and his dread deepened. It made a suffocating solitude of earth and a passionless gray waste of the sky.

Then he would fight. Then he would run aimlessly, seeking a task to distract him or a power to save. He would pounce upon books and try to read. He would think of the pamphlet. But there was something in him, a dark lusting hunger, that would make him forget the pamphlet, its insanity and rot, and think only of the delicious rapture. With tragic earnestness he would try to push his thoughts, as with his palms, to subjects that were holy. But they came back. They melted his will and enfolded him with their promise.

Perhaps he would wake in the dead of night to find himself shaking, gasping and drenched. He would sit up in sudden terror and stare into the darkness and listen. He would lie down, telling himself over and over that he had nothing to fear. Then, hardly aware of what he did, he would slip out of the wet bed and enter the night. He would look at stars, trying to think how far away they were and how many; at the mountains, trying to realize their peace; at shadows where the river roared to the sea. He would go to the corral and speak to the beasts and smell their warm earthy bodies and listen to their untroubled breathing; and all this would comfort him a little. But when he entered the bed again the dread would return and night-long he would tremble and wait.

Or perhaps he would be toiling in the fields. He would be raking hay, using a hand-dump machine that exhausted him with every shift. He would be feeling happy, for larks sang around him and the air was heavy with the odors of new hay. Then in spite of his will he would think of the pamphlet, and out of the whole world the power would gather to choke him. It would grow as he went round and round the field and he would begin to talk aloud. Over and over he would speak the beast's name or verses from the Bible or lines from a poem. "Helen, thy beauty is to me . . . Let him who is without sin among you cast the first stone . . ." The talk seemed to help a little: it fell and echoed like the meaning of a great sane earth into the withdrawing breathing of doom. But after a while the talking was of no use: the words became nothing, nothing at all. "Let him who is without sin . . . ": but the words were empty now. "Out of the night that covers me, black as the Pit from pole to pole . . ." But he was not the master of his fate!

Failing in talk and growing aware of himself as the core of a world becoming steadily more unreal, he would leap down and stare crazily around him. He would clutch hay to feel the life of it, but it was only shadows in his hands. He would smell or count the spokes in a wheel, trying with all his senses to keep the meaning of himself as an individual from being lost. For it was a feeling of being depersonalized that tormented him, of losing even memory of his own name. And at last, when his mind was like a throbbing thing ready to burst in his skull and he was shuddering with the horror of it, he would begin to babble and pinch himself or clutch the earth or run trembling hands over the beast, feeling all the while that he was being

187

withdrawn from reality into the impalpable and the nameless. In the extremity of his terror he would sometimes lose consciousness and fall.

Out of this he would be awakened by a sudden sound, by the snort of the horse or the lark's song, and he would struggle up and furiously smite himself and kick his naked feet against the iron wheel. With all his strength he would fetch himself back to a sense of what he was and where he was, and then sink in prayer and supplication, with sweat pouring out of him.

Time after time when alone he examined himself for signs of rot. He would pinch his flesh and look at the white skin until its color returned; and it would seem to him that the whiteness had a leprous appearance, as if his blood was vile. Upon a small pimple he would pour carbolic acid. Aches in his jaws, rheumatic pains in his knees, tendril-like spots floating in his vision, all sent him desperately in search of cures.

There were a few longer whiles when he lost possession of himself and went insane. The experience he was to remember best occurred out on the Antelope hills. He had gone two miles from his home to harrow land for a neighbor. After three teams were harnessed and hitched to a large harrow he drove them round and round a plowed field, round and round an enormous land. Before noon came he was feeling queer. He watered the beasts at a cistern when noon came and put hay and oats before them and entered the house. He found canned peas and beans and tomatoes, salt bacon, coffee and stale bread and tried to prepare a meal for himself; but the thought of food made him ill and he went outside. Afraid to be alone and aware that the mood was again enfolding him he went over to the horses and sat close to them and began to weep. Save for the distant mountains, all around him he could see only this desolate landscape, and no house but this shack; and he could hear no sound but that of horses eating oats. More than anything else it was the silence that terrified him. As in so many times he was haunted by the sound of his breathing and the beating of his heart. He got up and began to walk and aloud he told himself that he ought to eat, but he did not recognize his own voice. He went to the shack again and looked at the food. Then above a tin wash basin he saw a mirror and he wanted to look at his image but he did not dare. For months now he had been afraid of his eyes. He went outside. When he walked he could hear the sound of his feet and this sound troubled him. He went on tiptoe and again sat near the beasts. But he could not remain sitting. Going to a small stable he peered inside; it was as empty and silent and meaningless as the sky and the earth. Unable longer to endure the silence and the waiting he hitched the teams and went out to the field.

Round and round he went and the dread grew. It was in the noiseless clouds of dust, in the creaking of harness, in the lather between thighs, in the harrow's monotonous drag. If a horse snorted the dreadful imminence seemed for a moment to break and roll back; but then it closed round him again, more remorseless than before. To try to save himself he began to talk aloud. He did not know the names of the beasts, and so he gave them names and spoke the names over and over: "Bess! . . . Jim! . . . Eagle! . . ." Or he would say a name over and over until it so lost its meaning that he could not spell it:"Eagle . . . Eagle . . . Eagle . . ." He no longer knew what an eagle was. All the names became dismayingly meaningless. He uttered his own name and it was meaningless also. He tried to spell it but could not remember how it was spelled. Knowing, then, that he was being buried in the quiet, dissolved into the awful calm, he began to shout at the beasts, to shout their names over and over, to yell at them as the frenzy possessed him.

Then the thing happened. It came suddenly, swiftly, as it had always come; as if his feet had slipped on a brink and he had fallen; as if his breath had been jerked like a quivering tongue out of him; as if his skull had been laid open and the whole gray desert of solitude had fallen like a blanket on his mind. He could no longer speak the names. He tried to scream but he could not scream. Something was in his throat and his lungs and his weak shaking flesh. With only one thought, to get home before he slipped into darkness beyond recall, he swung the teams and headed for the barn. He shook at the reins and smote the beasts with clods to make them gallop but they would not gallop; and then, knowing that he could not wait, that he did not dare to wait, he dropped the reins and ran and did not pause until, shaken and reeling, he stood by the shack. The physical exertion as always cleared his wits a little, and he felt remorse and shame. He looked back at the beasts, knowing that he should bring them in and unharness and feed them, but the power drew him another way and he entered the shack.

Now he suffered a peculiar change. He stopped his babbling and became sly and stealthy, as though another being possessed him, another will. In reality he was now two, the cowering terrified one and the crafty fascinated one. This crafty one wanted to look at the mirror and see his face. It drew him against his will and he went tiptoe and with bated breath. He looked in. He stared for several moments. What he saw was so ghastly in its whiteness, so wild and horrified and insane in its eyes, that he began to shake. Only in asylums in a later time was he ever to see such a face as this. He forced himself to look at it. Drawn to those terrible eyes, so haunted and mad, he put his face close, so close to the mirror that his nose touched it. Then the eyes in the mirror became so horrifying that he could not look at them. He swung and raced homeward, with a gathering world of terror at his flying heels.

Until this day he had hidden his fear from everyone. His mother had been worried by his emaciation and silence or by his sudden screams when he slept but she had never seen him stricken and frantic. She saw him today, for today he was beyond self-help; he entered the house like a wild thing and flung himself at her feet and began to scream, with his breath coming in spasms and choking him, with his hands clutching his face. His father came running. They put cold rags on his brow and chafed his wrists, they poured tea down him and spoke his name. He knew nothing of all this. When he returned to himself, hours later, he was lying in bed with his mother sitting by him; and he felt like one who had been to far dark places and had come home. To all questions now and thereafter he gave the same reply, that he had drunk several cups of black coffee as thick as mud and that it had made him sick and queer. His parents believed this. He never told the truth.

Under his breath as he lay here utterly spent he was murmuring Invictus. Out of the night that covers me, out of the night . . . But why did he drink so much coffee? . . . Out of the night . . . He must not drink coffee again; For some people it was very bad . . . Out of the night . . . Besides, it was contrary to Mormon belief to drink coffee . . . Black as the Pit from pole to pole! "Son, are you listenun to what I say?" Out of the night that covers me, out of the night! . . .

XXV

With their father the boys went to Rigby and there built a grim gray room of concrete, with one door and two small windows. For the better part of the next four years it was to be Vridar's and Marion's home. Their father went home when the labor was done and the boys, tense with excitement, prepared for school. After they had scrubbed themselves and put on their new coarse suits, bought from a mail-order house, they crossed an alfalfa field that lay between them and the town. Vridar was awed. Mountain-bound and nature-tutored, he felt gawky and foolish and very much out of place. They came to a dirt road and stopped and Vridar looked at the high school building, aware that his clothes smelled like a store and that his shoes were ugly and stiff.

There came down the road a young man who was perhaps twenty but who looked to Vridar like an ancient scholar. He was short, brisk, solemn; he had about him an air of importance, as though he had already overturned kingdoms; and he was immaculately dresesd. Vridar looked at the stern and educated visage and decided that this man was the high school principal.

"You going to school?" the man asked, looking at him with black intellectual eyes.

"Yes sir. Are you the Principal, sir?"

"I'm a senior," he said.

Vridar might reasonably have breathed more freely now but he did not. A senior! He walked reverently at the man's side, wondering how full his head was of algebra and Latin. This reverence in Vridar for scholars and educators persisted for years, though now and again it suffered disastrous setbacks. He had the notion that nearly all people in the world were honest, wise, and brave. In educators, especially, it seemed to him, there could be no meanness, no dark guilt of the kind that tortured him, no exploitation of the defenseless or weak.

And so he was at a loss to understand what he saw in his teachers. One of them seemed to be a shameless rogue. Another stared at the legs of girls until, becoming self-conscious, he blushed and looked away. A third seemed to be interested only in the more erotic poetry in the textbook. The Principal's name was John Hannibal Short. His great head was completely bald. His eyes were large and bulging, and had the cold gray opaqueness of thick ice. He taught Latin. As a matter of fact, though, he hardly taught it at all. His time and his gracious charm he gave to an effort to entrench himself with his students. He was not a Mormon in a Mormon town and he had enemies in the Church; and so it was that, instead of teaching Latin, he told stories, embroidered the whimsical and droll and invited his students to be his friends. A teacher's position he said again and again was the most insecure of all positions in life. "After years of devotion he is suddenly kicked out. There is only one way to stop it: some day, some of you will be members of the school board. Well, who wants to translate now?"

The teacher of algebra was Franz Le Bon, a tall handsome consumptive with eyes as deep and haunted as twilight. His interest seemed to be only in girls. He would stare at them with hunger so intent and obvious that they would blush and giggle.

He embarrassed Vridar to the point of suffocation. It was not what the man did or said; it was a part of him, rising visibly against his trousers; and even more than that, it was the way the fool would lean far back and sway and gently twist at an ear, as though wholly unconscious of the reason that made the men snicker and the girls redden.

The teacher of logic was a short and kindly man named Jonathan Bowl. He had a square face and a deep dimple in his chin; and behind very thick lenses his near-sighted eyes seemed to be popping from his head. He blushed and lost his voice whenever the subject alluded even remotely to sex; and syllogism he pronounced with a hard g, because when pronounced with a soft g, the last syllable was a local vulgarity for semen.

The teacher of literature was Sylvanus Stanley Mope, a small slouchy man whose withered neck was fenced with a tall rubber collar. He dwelt at great length on the more scandalous verse, rolling his lips over it, tasting its faint scarlet. He spent three recitations on Goldsmith's When lovely woman stoops to folly . . .

"Mr. Hunter," he said, looking up at the ceiling, with enough room between his throat and collar for a loaf of bread, "when—uh—lovely woman stoops to folly—uh—what does the poet—uh—say then?"

Vridar hesitated. He did not know what manner of answer was expected here. Besides, he was morbidly shy in class and could not speak at all without blushing and choking.

"Why—"

"Yes?" said Mope, gazing at the ceiling. "Go on."

"Why," said Vridar desperately, his face spotched white and red, "he says—he says what art can wash her guilt away!"

"Ah yes, her guilt. Now, Mr. Hunter, what is the guilt?"

Did the fool really expect a reply to that! "The—the guilt, sir?"

"Yes, the guilt. Uh—why, well, then, what is the precise folly which Goldsmith has in mind?"

Vridar had a notion of what it was but the classroom, it seemed to him, was no place to elucidate it. He hedged. He lied. He said stutteringly that he did not know. Mope's gaze came down for a moment and surveyed him. It shot ceilingward again.

"Very well, Mr. Hunter, another question. The poet says, you recall, that the only art which can—uh—bring repentance to her—uh—lover is what?"

"To die!" Vridar gasped, and wished that Goldsmith had never been born.

"Ah yes, to die. That is precisely what he says. To die. Now, Miss Morehead, do you—uh—think the poet meant that?"

This bold yellowhaired girl with many secrets in her vivid green eyes gave a disconcerting answer. "Sure. He meant she dot to kill herself."

"Ought, Miss Morehead. Well, now," he said, looking at her reproachfully, yet with bright interest. "Would you say that was—uh—moral advice?"

"It sounds all right to me."

"But why should she?" asked a voluptuous blackeyed maid. "Just 'cause she stooped, that ain't no reason. Why ain't she got as much right to stoop as a man has?"

"Ah now," said Mope, warming to the possibilities here. He looked at the girl and pursed his mouth, drawing a deep curved furrow into either sunken cheek. "That is an interesting point. Has a woman the right to sin?"

"If not, what right has a man? She ain't made out of ice."

"Now wait a minute," he said, a bit alarmed. "We shall have to get down to fundamental principles . . ."

The teacher Vridar liked best and the one who was to mark a turning in his life was George Albert Turner, a giant of a man with gargantuan laughter. He had brown, silky hair that fell in soft curls round his ears and down his neck, large frank eyes, and a very large and very sensual mouth full of strong perfect teeth. He swept his classroom with tides of enthusiasm and tempests of wrath. Though Turner loved science and despised art, Vridar felt that he was a big man and belonged in a university.

Turner was the only teacher who showed a warm interest in him. He would call Vridar to his office and exhort him to abandon literature and pursue science; warn him against self-preoccupation; advise him to nourish an ethical unrest; and rock him with such stupendous laughter that for a little while Vridar would feel purged. "You're morbid," Turner said to him one day. "Next thing you know you'll be going to Sunday school and talking about sin. Get out of the Middle Ages! Read Huxley and Darwin . . ." Vridar would stare at the man, wishing he could laugh as Turner laughed.

Such were his teachers in those years when his life was drawing to a crisis. Before them he sat in awe, though unhappily feeling that Bowl was afraid of life, that Le Bon should never have left Boston, that Mope was an erotic clown. But his credulity during these years was insatiable. Having fallen on a vagrant copy of *The Appeal to Reason* he became an ardent Socialist, and deliberated with boundless contempt —the outrages of Republicans and Democrats. He practiced small economies in food until he was able to subscribe to this organ of the millennium. He resolved to write books that would scourge the impostors and parasites of society, and the first of them he wrote in his freshman year.

Principal Short allowed him to use the office typewriter. He learned to type quickly, and then set up his poems, embroidering and embellishing with asterisks, hyphens, dashes and colons. When his task was done he had a precious book in manuscript, without erasure or smudge or blot; and he pored over it, admiring its more dreadful platitudes, and decided to write a novel. Every Sunday he went to the schoolhouse, lifted an unlatched window and crawled in. For hours he would dash off the pages, heaping his drama to smashing climaxes; and when June came the book was done. Inarticulate with fury and plot, it was the story of a noble young man, enlisted in the Socialist army and crusading for the common good. This man's enemies were scoundrels of wealth, seducers of virgins, immaculate cads. They all had black waxed mustaches, glittering manners, cold despicable eyes, and they wore spats and carried a cane. The heroine was a sweet and demure

192

blonde. Her prototype was Norma Burke, a lass for whom Vridar was nourishing a consuming passion.

This is the book's title-page, endowed with all his typographic art:

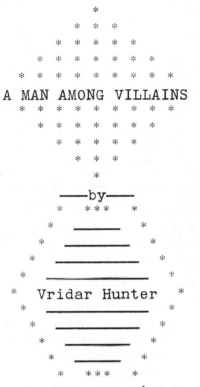

A MAN AMONG VILLAINS

——by——

Vridar Hunter

astra castra, numen lumen
Licht, liebe, leben
gardez la foi

Here is a page from Vridar's novel:

At this moment Reginald Overholt Maximus came running to the scene. His eyes were blazing. He clenched his hands and gritted his teeth. And when Dirk Bugg stepped in his path Reginald hurled him aside and Dirk spun around and fell on his insolent face.

"It's men like you," Reginald cried, "that make life a hell on earth! If you believe in the brotherhood of men and equality and love, then throw away your spats and come humbly and walk with us! If you insist on exploiting the masses and grinding them down, sucking their last ounce of blood, then be a dirty stinking capitalist and we'll smite you hip and thigh! We'll say in the words of Danton, You ask for more profits and we give you a capitalist's head!"

Outside a big mob was growing like that in Paris during the Revolution. Mothers carried starving babies in their arms. Old men covered with filth hobbled on crutches. These were the Hegla Doom miners. They were fighting for a right to live. *Absit invidia!*

Dirk got up shaking like a leaf and slapped Reginald with a glove. "I challenge you to a duel!" he cried, and hissed with villainy. "I'll shoot your ears off!"

"This is the way men fight," said Reginald, and struck Dirk in his mouth.

He yanked the fallen man to his feet, crying, "Jesus fought the money-changers and I'll fight the enemies of a decent social order, with equality for all! *Dieu dayfand le drot!* Now get the hell out of here!"

Here is a scene of love:

Norma was standing in a garden, full of lilac and rose and moonlight. She knew Reginald would come. But what if he had been slain! What if Dirk Bugg had got him at last? She ran down the path, whispering in the beautiful still night, "Reggie, Reggie, my love, come to me!" But she waited a long time and he did not come. Had the capitalist villains outsmarted him at last? She bowed her head to the blossoms and wept, her tears shining like rain, and making the flowers sweeter. Then she heard a gate open and her heart stopped beating. She could not move. Ah, he has come! she thought, and thanked God, who watches over the virtuous and pure. She heard his steps and then, "Norma!" he whispered, and lowered his handsome head. "Norma, my love, my love!" "Beloved, is it you?" she asked, looking at him with misty eyes. "Oh, my darling, my own!" "I love you," he said desperately, trembling before her, "but I am a Socialist and you—you are the daughter of a Republican governor! Between him and me," he hissed, "it is war to the death!" "But Reggie, you're the whole world to me! The stars could fall, the seas dry up—" She humbly kissed the blue denim over his heart, a symbol for her of honesty and toil. "I love you," she said, proud as a queen, "and love knows no barriers, no doors, no parties. Like the wind it goes everywhere and is free." She looked up and put arms to his neck. "My father is wicked," she said, "and I hate him! You have made me understand . . ."

This scene and others Vridar read with mist steaming from his eyes, with his heart almost breaking. What an epic he had written! He had a vision of publishers fighting for the copyright. His book had two hundred and eighty-seven typewritten pages. He thought it perfect and reverently laid it away.

He also wrote bales of verse—odes and sonnets, madrigals and triolets and elegies; but he showed it to no one. One Sunday he was furiously typing when Hannibal Short softly entered and looked over his shoulder and read. "You writing poetry?" he asked.

Startled, Vridar leapt up, and then spread palms over the sheet.

"Tut-tut," said Short. "Let me read it. I didn't know we had a poet in the school."

Vridar distrusted the man's voice. He looked up and distrusted the man's eyes. "It ain't no good," he said charitably.

"Isn't any, Vridar. Don't say ain't and don't use double negatives."

"It isn't any good."

"Let me read it." Reluctantly Vridar withdrew his hands, and Short read the verses: they were a wildly metaphorical apostrophe to the glories of Socialism. "Well, well," said Short. Wretched and quivering, Vridar waited. Short now looked at him with his large cold eyes and said: "What do you expect to be?—a farmer?"

A farmer! If the man only knew how his parents slaved to make something of him besides a tiller of earth! Yet he hesitated, afraid that his reply would sound ridiculous. "A writer," he said.

"A writer?" On Short's mouth, it seemed to Vridar, was a sly ironic smile.

There was cold incredulity in his eyes. Perhaps he was a Republican! "Well, I guess a farmer can be a writer. Or try to be."

Was the man mocking him? Vridar did not know. He trembled with resentment.

"You and your brother are batching, aren't you? You live in that little house out in the lucerne field?"

"Yes sir."

"Have you always batched when you went to school?"

"All but one year."

"Well, well," said Short and the irony seemed to leave his mouth. "Let me see some other things." Reluctant still, Vridar dug out of a pocket two or three other poems and Short read them, his brows drawn, his eyes coldly intent. "Not too bad for your age. Of course you'll burn these in a year or two. But keep writing. You've set your ambition high but no one can tell."

When he was outside, Vridar glowed with contempt. Burn his poems? What a preposterous thought! But he knew that he would. He had already burned what he wrote in earlier years.

A rumor ran from tongue to tongue that a poet was in school. Vridar heard it but pretended not to hear. He pretended not to understand. He made polite inquiries, asking who the poet was. Nevertheless he was all ears. His inflated ego together with his morbid shyness and his sense of guilt and worthlessness impelled him to do shameful things. Choosing from his poems one which, because of lofty sentiment and facile rime, he thought would please the multitudes, he typed it neatly and embroidered it and then hung it on the blackboard when the study room was empty. He rushed outside and impatiently waited until students entered the room. Then he followed them, trying to affect a most casual nonchalance, and took a rear seat to watch. Several students were reading his unsigned verses. They were reading with a loud brawling voice and they were laughing and shrugging and turning away. Watching them like a hawk, Vridar wanted to strike them dead. He thought of them as the lecherous and unconscionable sons and daughters of capitalists.

Then Norma came in. He was so infatuated with her that the sight of her stifled him. She was only sixteen but a full woman, with large firm breasts and alluring curves in her waist and hips. He watched her, hardly breathing at all. Would she see it and read? She seemed to look at the blackboard but then yawned and patted her mouth, and went over to sit by Bill Duncan. Vridar hated Bill. He left his seat and went outside.

But he persisted. Almost every day for weeks he slyly tacked a fresh poem to the board and waited. Day after day he saw students read and heard their scornful laughter. Wait till I'm famous! he thought furiously. Then laugh!

One day Short called him to his office. Vridar went apprehensively, wondering what dire punishment or derisive rebuke awaited him. He met the pale glacial eyes a moment and then stood, fingering his cap.

"Listen, Vridar, don't you think you'd better not put any more of your poems

195

on the blackboard? I know your intentions are good but the school is laughing at you."

"They don't know it's mine."

"Well, that may be. But they're laughing at the author." He came over and for a moment laid hands on the boy's thin shoulders. "You don't want to make a fool of yourself, do you?"

"No sir."

"Then I wouldn't do it, Vridar. You are rather too serious about it, aren't you? You may never be a poet, you know, and if you get too serious, your disappointment . . . Well, you understand me?"

"Yes sir."

Vridar walked home, feeling inexpressibly wretched and defeated. Marion got supper but Vridar did not eat. He sat for hours, his eyes weird with loneliness and fear, and then crawled into bed, with the old sense of loss and guilt and despair closing round him.

XXVI

In an effort to put away his dread he went more and more frequently into the town. It was only a main street, with alleys running back to the country lanes; but it housed two banks, two drugstores, two poolhalls, a small dark theater, a dancing pavilion and a dozen shops; but Vridar found wonder in all these things. At night two feeble street lamps threw weird shadows, and the lighted interiors were alluringly warm. He would look into poolhalls and see the tobacco fog and hear the loud talk. The Wicks, father and son, were two such grotesque men that he was never done with looking at them. Adolphus Wick, the elder, was nearly seven feet tall and seemed to be all bone and hide and ears. His ears were semitransparent and shone as if a light was behind each; and his nose was so huge that Vridar imagined that he could have put an egg into either nostril. Out of the nostrils hair fell like a mustache that had grown upward, seeking shelter; and above the nostrils the bone rose like a huge bunion. Adding to Wick's grotesqueness were his enormous pale eyes, his wide mouth filled with rows of gold teeth, and his braying speech. It was commonly said in Rigby that he was the eighth wonder of the world. His son in height and features and in broad meatless shoulders was exactly like his father, save that he looked younger and had white teeth instead of gold. In the nose, ears, eyes, mannerisms, and voice Vridar could see no difference at all. When either Wick laughed the sound was like that of a mule; and the man would then wipe his mouth with a huge paw gleaming with rings. They owned a drugstore, a poolhall, and the dance-floor above. One night Adolphus Junior booted Vridar out into the street for a reason that he was never able to understand. He conceived a violent dislike for the man and in the Wick drugstore he learned to steal.

In this store during the evenings gathered the school's rowdies. Joe Shannon came; he had small black eyes and bushy brows that ran down his nose. He was Rigby's wildest gallant and most adored athlete. Rumor said he was intimate with Sybil Morehead, with the bold blue eyes and golden hair; and for this Vridar envied him. Quint Peter came, another athlete, tall, rangy and arrogant; he was wooing the bewitchingly rounded and sultry Leorial Lee. There were the Porter brothers, Ben and Hank, superb in physique, frank and gracious in manner; and the Grabber brothers, Bard and Hun and Mart, the first two strong and quarrelsome and cowardly, the third a shy and unobtrusive dwarf. There was Bush O'Brien, Vridar's enemy from afar.

Among these rowdies Vridar liked to move, trying to absorb a part of their bravado and storm. He did not like their obscene jests, their lewd fables about women and their brutal clowning; but he felt that behind these lay a zest and power of life, a raw elemental vigor, which his own body did not have. He envied with bitter heartache their strong faces and their muscled limbs. He envied their way with women and their lusty eagerness in love.

The only clerk during the evenings was a fat jolly youth named Tubby Beal. He was suspicious of his classmates and suspected them of theft, but he was helpless. A group would gather round to imprison him, while others filched candy and gum, pens and cigarettes and cigars. After hungering night after night for some of the loot, Vridar decided to take part. He slipped near a cigar case and when none could see he slid the door back a litle and filled a pocket. Failing to smoke the cigars because they made him ill, he stored them away and hoped next time to steal some candy and a pen.

One night a poolhall burned down. When Vridar reached the scene men were carrying out into the alley cartons of cigarettes and cases of beer. They piled these by a coalshed and returned for more. A crowd gathered. Vridar watched the men and he saw one and another furtively lift box or case and sneak away into darkness. The owner came out, howling with rage, cursing them all for thieves, and turned to a big silent man. "You look honest!" he yelled. "Watch this stuff for me!"

"Sure," the man said. As soon as the owner had vanished, the man looked round him, made a sly face at nobody, and walked off with forty cartons of cigarettes. Sensing the apportunity here and remembering the adage of the early bird and the worm, Vridar laid violently on a case of beer and staggered away. It was like a ton of lead. Gasping and groaning but with no thought of yielding it, he got it over to a hedge and ran back, hoping to seize another. But they had all been carried off. The building was two walls of flame, and of its contents only the owner remained. Disappointed, and chiding himself for not having acted sooner, Vridar went back to the hedge and considered. He reached into darkness and counted the bottles; he smelled of one and held its cool glass to his cheek and tried to read its label. How, he wondered, could he get his treasure home!

Waiting until silence was everywhere, he lifted the case, which now seemed heavier because he was less excited, and staggered off. He made a wide detour, crossing the railroad track, slinking along an embankment and at last entering the lucerne field. Now and then he paused to count his cargo and anticipate its joys. He hugged it to him as though it were a gold mine; and if his conscience reproached him, he dismissed it with a scowl, for he was a Socialist now. Life, he had begun to see, was little save exploitation of the weak; and honesty was largely a myth. Comforting himself with such reflections, he arose and staggered again, drawing out

197

of shaking bones and sinews every ounce of their strength. On arriving home he went to a soft ditch bank and dug a grave and lowered his treasure into it. Every day he slipped over to see if it was still secure but he did not drink of it for some time. He would try to convince himself first that he had done no wrong.

He committed other thefts during these years and each made him feel bolder and a little less afraid. He and his brother had little fuel and during the winter months nearly froze. Great cars of coal came out of the north and from these a few lumps dropped; under cover of darkness Vridar would gather them and slink home. He went to the coal yard and found a small aperture in the high board fence and he would reach through a few lumps. Then he would build a fire and sit by its warmth, meditating on the inequalities in life and the dogmas of Marx.

He also raided a hencoop. One of his neighbors out in this lucerne field was the Kale family. Lorry, the older son, was yellow and freckled and gave himself airs. The Kales stood high in social Rigby because his uncle owned a store. The second son had the strange name of Hinge. One night at the suggestion of Lorry, Vridar went with them to an isolated coop. They listened but no dog barked. They then crawled into the barnyard and put ears to each building, trying to catch the sleep-sound of chickens within. When they found the coop, they sneaked in and seized two drowsy cocks by their throats and raced homeward. By a canal they ripped off the feathered hides, tore out the vicera and sent feathers and guts down the stream.

In Vridar's house they made a great meal. They boiled the roosters for an hour, then smeared them with lard and set them to roast. Slipping outside, Vridar went to his cache of beer and drew out four cool bottles. Lorry bawled with joy. "I'll tell you," he said, "we need some girls." Had Vridar heard about the huge Negro and the white woman they had taken off the train? Yes, Vridar had heard, for the whole town was agog with the story. The story as Vridar heard it said that the Negro had raped her and in the embrace they had got stuck, like dogs. He had never heard of what he was later to read about as vagina dentata. He did not know whether to believe the story or not but Lorry said it was true. In their agony, he said, the man and the woman had bitten and clawed one another until they were bloody corpses, stone dead when found.

They stood by the table and fed like pigs. Using neither knife nor fork, they tore off dripping flesh and shoved it into their starved mouths. Vridar felt quite splendid now. He thought of pirates and laden ships and Samarkand; of Captain Kidd and Jesse James and Jim Bridger; of Satan and Cain.

"You know Maggie Beal?" said Lorry. "I had her out."

Vridar smelled seduction here. He began to feel angry.

"She sure yelped," Lorry said, talking through a mouthful of leg. "I just choked her and done it to her good and hard." He chewed steadily and blinked his small eyes. He was eighteen. He reminded Vridar of Hankie.

Hating the youth, Vridar went outside. Everywhere were maidens, so lovely and fresh that to look at them made him weak; but he was harvesting none of their youth. Scoundrels and lechers like Lorry were taking them off into field and hedge-row. Memory of field and hedgerow was in the girls' eyes. Ah God! Vridar thought, standing in shadow and wondering what to do. He resolved to get drunk. Striding into the house he knocked the top off a bottle and jerked the column of foam to his mouth. He drank the entire quart, coughed a little and wiped at his eyes. If he only had a bottle of rum, he thought, remembering Treasure Island. He scowled at Lorry and wanted to strike his thin arrogant face. What a beast he is! he thought, for in his mind was a picture of a weeping girl, of the ravished and strangled Maggie. He thought of the hero of his novel, a tall pure man. Then he thought of downy fragrant beds with a maid in each—of white flesh and the deep hush in eyes and mouth. He thought of Betty, who had kissed him. He went to his treasure and knocked another top off and poured another bottle down. He stared queerly into darkness, wishing he could see Norma Burke; and the thought of her shook him like springtime and bugles.

He staggered around, drinking a bottle now and then until dawn came. He was drunk. Inside the house Lorry and Hinge were shouting and pounding on the concrete walls. Vridar thought they might break the furniture or burn the shack down, but he was too drunk to care. A great boldness had seized his wits. He wanted to fight now, to mow with one scything reach of his arm a whole battalion of men. He wanted a woman. "If Betty was here!" he groaned, and looked into the northeast where Norma slept. He thought of going to her window and crawling in. Then he thought of the big Negro and the white woman and went reeling through a fog of shame and hunger into the house and slept until late afternoon.

This school had its bullies, too, but Vridar was not troubled by them until his sophomore year. One day Lorry came to him and said that Hun Grabber had called Marion crosseyed. Hun was a big lubber who let everyone know that he had a set of boxing gloves and was training to be a prize-fighter.

"Where is he?"

"Inside by the stove."

Vridar walked around a little while to summon his courage. How long, O Lord, how long would he have to face bullies because of his brother's eyes! When at last he entered the building, he saw Hun standing by the stove, talking to Wanda Lee. He went up to Hun and seized his coat and swung him around.

"Did you call my brother crosseyed?"

Hun was amazed or pretended to be. He looked at Vridar and laughed. "No," he said.

"I'm told you did."

"All right, then, I did."

"You'll have to take it back." Wanda was looking at Vridar's white face. He liked the way she looked at him.

"Take it back! Who in hell says so?"

"I say so."

"Listen, you realize I'm a prize-fighter?"

"No matter what you are you'll have to take it back."

"And what if I don't?"

"Then you'll have to fight. I'll be outside."

Vridar waited an hour and Hun did not come out. He found Marion, and

199

Marion said that Hun had apologized. If I am a coward, Vridar thought, then what are these others who are so much stronger than I?

It was also in this year that the crisis came with Bush O'Brien, which Vridar had expected for so many years. Bush belonged to the McGard clan: his mother was a sister of that Jeb who had chopped off his mangled fingers. He was a husky youth and very dark and ferocious. Vridar had never seen him without a scowl.

Bush's only interest in Vridar had come through Hankie. After Hankie had been threshed for robbing the nest, he had said again and again, "I'll tell Bush about this and he'll knock your daylights out." On entering high school and finding Bush there, Vridar had avoided him, and even in the drugstore if he saw Bush he stole away and went home. He had seen Bush looking at him and he had known what the look meant.

One evening in the store the rowdies were filching from cases and Vridar was trying to enter into their spirit when suddenly before him stood Bush O'Brien. Bush looked at Vridar, his lips snarling, and Vridar went over to the door intending to go home. He went outside but Bush darted ahead and swung to face him. He said nothing but there was no need to; his eyes were speaking for him. Vridar returned to the store and stood by his brother. Bush now came up and took a fighting pose and knocked Marion's cap off. Vridar knew that this was a challenge to him. He leapt in and with all his strength pushed the youth and spilled him over a table. Bush sprang up, his body tense and quivering and his hands clenched.

But now a strange thing happened. Slowly Bush relaxed and then grinned. He was not afraid and Vridar knew that he was not afraid. There was a kind of friendly astonishment in his grin. He went over to Marion's cap, still lying on the floor, and picked it up and brushed it and set it on Marion's head. Then he came over to Vridar.

"I guess you're a relation of mine, ain't you?"

"I guess so," Vridar said.

"Hankie said you're a coward. I wanted to see." He still grinned at Vridar. "Is it true you made Hun take it back?"

Vridar drew a deep breath. "Yes," he said.

"Would you have fought with me now?"

"Yes."

"You're all right. Here, let's shake hands."

Vridar grasped the big strong hand. He knew the meaning now. The McGards despised cowards, especially within their clan. Bush had admitted a cousin to fellowship.

But of the rougher and more violent experiences, one happened two weeks later that he remembered best. On the edge of town was a large indoor roller-skating rink. Its crowds were rough and profane. Chief of its brawlers among the men, when full of whisky and seeing red, were some of Vridar's relatives. They were a turbulent and dangerous lot. There was Beed, short and powerful and bloodshot, with most of his teeth knocked out; and there was Irish, a stuttering moron who would rather battle than eat. These two when fighting asked no mercy and gave no quarter; they used teeth, they gouged at eyes and tore at loins.

It was rumored that there would come from Menan a man who had been warned to stay away. He was known as a remorseless fighter who prowled into strange places in search of trouble. When it became known that this Bardell Jasper was coming to the rink, Irish McGard trod the earth, followed by his henchmen, among whom was Bush. "I—I—I'll dit him!" he cried. "You leave him to muh—muh—me!" Vridar liked to watch Irish talk: he opened his mouth wide, moving his jaws convulsively up and down and choking; and when at last he got the words out he grinned with evil triumph. "I—I—I'll kill the sssson of a bih—bih—bitch!" he said.

It was agreed that Bardell was to be left to Irish. If Irish was vanquished, Beed would leap in. If Beed was no match for the man they would call on the great Burns. Vridar was trembling with excitement. He had never seen a fight to the finish between powerful men. He was to see one this night.

When he entered the rink in company with Irish and Bush and others, reflecting that these terrible warriors were his own kin, Jasper was already there. He was skating gracefully with a tall lovely girl. Vridar sized him up. He was a large man with powerful shoulders and a neck ridged like a bull's. His eyes seemed blue and whimsical, but his mouth, pleated like a bulldog's, revealed the savage heart. Vridar looked next at Irish. Irish was possibly of the same weight, but shorter—so short and thick indeed that he looked like an ape. His eyes were wicked. He was lusting for battle.

"How'll I d—d—dit him outside?" he asked, turning to Beed.

"Put some skates on, then fall down in front of the son of a bitch."

Irish liked this idea. He grinned like a child and ran for skates. Then he came out on the floor and for a little while raced up and down the long hall. Vridar saw next that he was following Jasper. Jasper saw him. Vridar saw Jasper go to a half-dozen men and speak to them. He came back and took the girl's hand and skated. Irish was now circling him. Suddenly he cut in, fell to hands and knees, and both Jasper and the girl pitched over him and sprawled. Vridar was now trembling and softly moaning.

Both men jumped to their feet and ran to the skate-room. A river of men poured down the stairs and into the night. There was no moon and no street lamp near. Keeping close to Bush Vridar went with the eager men and saw them make a circle and saw Irish step into it, grinning like an imbecile. Across the circle stood Jasper, flanked by his own men. One of them spoke. What kind of fight was this to be? he asked. Did they want rough and tumble or stand up and knock down?

"What kind you want?" asked Burns.

"Any kind."

"Irish, what you want?"

"Rough and tuh—tuh—tumble!" said Irish, still grinning.

"That all right with you?" Burns asked Jasper.

"God damn it, yes, but no brass knucks and no knives."

"You search him," said one of Jasper's henchmen to Burns, "and I'll search your man."

The men were searched. Everything including watches and coins was taken from them. Vridar thought he would faint. It was a new world, this in which strong men for the hell of it fought like beasts and tried to kill one another. He looked at the dark quiet face of Bush, at the eager vivid face of Beed. What a coward I am, he thought, yet some of these are my people! Burns was speaking again.

"Everything is fair in this fight, is that it?" A man turned to Jasper. Jasper nodded assent. "All right, let the best man win!"

The two battlers leapt and Vridar heard the dull impact of fists. He felt deathly ill now, yet he was determined to see this violent drama to its end. He stood on the inner circle, with Bush on one side and Burns on the other. Before him in the dusk the two men were struggling cheek to cheek like fiends. Then Irish heaved his foe upward and pitched him over his head and brought him down with bone-crushing power. He was on top of him like a tiger, his mouth open, his teeth seeking a vulnerable spot. His teeth found one. He got the little finger of Jasper's left hand in his mouth and Jasper began to bawl like a calf under a branding iron. Two of his henchmen moved but Burns sprang forward and thundered, "Stay back or I'll bust your skulls!"

Jasper was wildly begging now. His voice was screaming out of what seemed to Vridar to be unbearable agony. His finger, he howled up at them, was being chewed off. But no one interfered, nor would Jasper say that he had had enough. He fought and yelped and implored mercy; and Irish all the while was clawing down upon him, his face and Jasper's left hand pressed against earth. Vridar stepped back, afraid that he would vomit; he had smelled the warm smell of blood. After a few moments he forced himself back to watch. Jasper was howling like a man caught by death. His futile right hand was yanking at Irish's hair and trying to twist his ears off or gouge his eyes out; but all the fight, all the will and lust, were being drained out of him by Irish's strong eager teeth. With a despairing yell he said he had enough.

Irish sprang up, his face bloody from his hair to his throat, his mouth a scarlet grin. Jasper leapt up and ran. Vridar had never seen a man go so fast or desperately. After he was gone Irish gave a horrible savage laugh of triumph and then spit from his mouth a little finger, chewed off at the second joint. Beed picked the finger up and turned it over and over in his palm. Then he tossed it into darkness.

"I'll bet the son of a bitch don't come here no more," he said.

The men moved away, the McGard clan grimly silent and implacable. All but Irish: he snorted and choked and mopped his red face, mixing sweat with blood; he laughed a strange wild laugh. He said there was another finger that he had chewed half-off. Like one who had looked into hell, Vridar slipped away and went home, sick in his whole being, wondering why his mother had never told him the truth about men.

XXVII

But there was a tender side to his high school life. Though he still thought of Neloa, of Helen, he became infatuated with Norma. He had loved Neloa for the dark way of her, Helen for her frank sensuous warmth. Norma he loved for the perfection of her face and form. Her eyes were a misty blue, full of shadow and dream; her hair was a soft fluffy brown; her oval cheek and her red mouth were of springtime and legend. But it was her body that made him reel, that choked his heart: he would have given all his odes and elegies and his novel with them to hold her for a moment against him.

He wrote poems to her endlessly. He would lay one on her desk and watch her roll it into a paper ball and throw it at Bill. Bill Duncan was a tall young man. His most noticeable feature was his lips: they were full and thick like a Negro's, with the raw part of the underlip turning far down. A scar like a welt lay across his nose; his coarse black hair was roached like a horse's mane. Why Norma liked him was a riddle to Vridar. Bill would hover near her, feeding her from his lunch; or take her to the drugstore where he bought for her candy and ice cream and sodas, extravagances that Vridar could only dream of; and when school was out he walked her home.

Vridar's jealously was insane. It raped him of all strength and left him sitting in abject self-loathing. It filled his dreams. She would be with him in a wildrose lane, deep with knotgrass and dandelion yellow and larkspur blue. Golden warblers filled the thickets. Sunlight was golden in the hushed valley of the sky. For miles they would walk hand in hand; she would smile at him in warm-mouthed rapture or lean against his strength. Under a flowering bush she would sit, her back to a wall of fragrance, and push the straps from her white shoulders and draw her silken blouse down. He would then put his cheek to her lovely breasts, with his hands on her thighs; and she would bow her head to his lips as Betty had done, and in the hot hungry rapture of mouth to mouth he would lose his ache and loneliness. But when he tried to embrace her the world broke into ruins, and he would awaken, feeling pain in his loins as though he had been unmanned, and look at chalk marks on a stable wall.

He played the spy. On their way home they crossed the lucerne field and Vridar watched them pass. Sometimes they ate peanuts from a paper sack or peeled oranges and licked their fingers and laughed like children. Or they would walk hand in hand. One afternoon he followed them, slinking a safe distance behind. They walked on the rails, reaching across hand to hand, or picked wild flowers, which Bill set in her hair; and when they kissed Vridar went blind with grief. Then again they walked on the rails. There was a legend in Rigby that anyone who could walk a mile on a rail unaided and without stepping off could marry whom he pleased. Vridar had tried it and succeeded, and dismissed this legend with those about Jonah and the Red Sea. When they came to Norma's gate they kissed again and Bill turned home. The next day Vridar would stare at Norma's red mouth, trying to realize that Bill had kissed those lips. But he could not imagine it. They looked as if no man had ever kissed them.

In his lunacy he wrote an anonymous letter in which he warned her that Bill Duncan was a cad and a scoundrel, who wished only to seduce her and cast her off. He addressed and stamped an envelope and for an hour in the post office stood in wretched indecision. He tore it open and read it again, addressed a fresh envelope and bought a new stamp. He walked the streets, carrying the letter in his hand, wondering if he should send it or feed it to flame. Knowing that it was a cowardly thing to do, he posted the letter and the next day stared at Norma with solemn interest. He could see no change in her. Then unexpectedly she looked at him. Was her glance reproachful or astonished? Blushing furiously he hastened outside.

Night after night while dreaming of love he was haunted by the train. It came thundering out of the north. He could hear it coming like a deluge of water, like tides of wind. For him it was a symbol of the great broad world, of the far away and strange, of all that he hungered for and would never find. Leaving his bed he would go over and look at it; and its rows of brilliant windows were windows upon the unknown. Its wheels, showering violence and flame, had that strength of heart and purpose which he would never have. He would tremble with longing as it rolled out of fableland into the commonplace; panted for a few moments and opened its casements; and sped again into the fabulous acres of life. He wept to see it, to hear it. Only a little more, only a very little more of such wonder as this, and his heart would go out of him, his mind would break.

Night after night, month after month, he listened to it. At its first faint murmuring far in the north, he would come wide awake. His bed was close to its path, and often it seemed to him that the thundering avalanche of destiny would sweep over him, shatter his world and build it again. Sometimes he would steal up its pathway and stand very close to it as it rolled by, catching the breath of wheels and the leaping petals of fire, the power and smell and taste. And when it sped southward like a vanishing crimson beacon he wanted to run after it and catch hold of it and be borne out of this world which he hated.

Night after night, month after month it haunted him and stored its meaning in his blood. He would turn wet cheeks to the pillow and clasp his aching throat, trying to undertsand all the incredible beauty and sweet deep wonder of life that he had never known.

Sometimes out of sensuous darkness there would come faint and far-away music. It was tender, poignant, sad. It was waltz music, drifting through the open windows of the Wick hall. For him it filled the whole night with enchantment and witchery, aroused him to inarticulate gropings and frenzied unrest. Until unable at last to endure his loneliness he would feverishly dress and stumble across alfalfa and dike, to find the town, to feel, however obscurely, that this pulsing melody, this lonely mourning of violins, was a part of the ancient and the eternal in his own soul. So strong was his sense of this that he looked upon the violin with awe. The organ or the wind instruments he understood and scorned: they were so blatant and loud and obtuse: but the violin was subtle, hauntingly timeless and nameless. It had a soul.

Going to the drugstore front, he would stand in shadow and listen. Above him he could hear dancing feet and laughter and talk. Radiant girls were there, hushed in mouth and eyes and eager for embrace; and he felt the old yearning and tenderness, and then the pain in his loins. If curious people looked at him here, standing like a ghost against the wall, he would squeeze himself into the deep dark canyon between the drugstore and the hotel. For an hour he would not stir. Tears would grow in his eyes, break and drop to his cheeks; an inexpressible hunger would fill

204

his heart. He would drink the violins until dizzy, until drunk, until in his whole being there was only the soft allegory of the waltz. Then like a thief he would slink away. He would hide behind a dike in the lucerne field and weep until he could weep no more.

Sometimes he would go to a school dance. He did not dance, he did not know how: no, he would stand on the balcony and look down. Never did he come here to watch for an hour without loathing himself and wishing to die. He loathed his pale timid inefficiency; his sudden heartbeat, his blush, his caught breath when a girl looked at him or smiled his way. He wanted to be one of them, with joy, with courage, instead of the outcast, the wretched quaking thing that he was. More than he wanted food and air he wanted to move in the golden haze of the music, in the full current of being.

But he stood apart, aloof, trying to seem inscrutable, content. There below was Linda Jarrup, a gorgeous creature, floating in the arms of Bill Sykes. Bill had a magnificent physique. He had a red birthmark across one cheek and because of this he always talked to or looked at people in sidewise fashion; but he had the strength and grace of a panther . . . There was Leorial Lee, dusky and alluringly sullen, dancing with Quint. She danced snugly against him, her eyes closed and her hand on his heart. When Quint passed behind a pillar he stooped and, unseen by any save Vridar, kissed her; and her hand patted his back. There was Wanda Lee, her sister, with a body even more perfect than Norma's: she had been interested in Vridar ever since she heard him force Hun to back up. In school she wrote to him, or looked at him and smiled. But he felt only distrust. He could not believe, he dared not believe, that any girl, and certainly none as lovely as Wanda, could see in him anything but the emaciated shadow of what he ought to have been. He looked at her now and strove to imagine himself alone with her; he shut his eyes and dreamed upon the picture—and again had the strange sense of having been unmanned . . .

He came again and again. He forced himself to come, he employed a threat. If you go, he warned himself, his ruthless personality speaking to his timid, and if Norma is there you dance with her! If you do not, you coward, you may never go again! His feverish haste was assent. Yet his manner in this as in so many things was strange and absurd; for he went, assenting, yet praying to escape. One part of him was thinking of excuses and preparing for failure; the other part, stern and unpitying, was driving him to courage. You dance! said this stern part. Yes! said the other, meekly, and hoped there would be no dance.

But Norma was not there. As before he hid, trembled in the timeless longing of violins, stared greedily at the girls whom he would have died for. His hunger became so intense that he left balcony and went below. He wanted to be nearer the heart and youth of the hour.

"Hello, Hunter," said Joe Shannon, mopping his brow with one hand and keeping his other to Sybil's waist. "Why don't you dance?"

"I don't care much about it," Vridar said.

Joe was looking at him. "You'll study yourself to death. Have you brung a girl?"

"No."

205

"You like to dance with Sybil?"

"I—I—" he said. He looked at her. He saw her cold disdain. "No, thanks," he said.

The music struck up and the dancers flowed away. Despising himself, he went into the cool night air. On the steps sat Leorial and Quint. In a buggy close by was another couple, wrapped in a blanket with only their hair showing. Out from the door and open windows came the ancient sadness of violins. He returned and sat in misery and watched. What girl would dance with him! He would be awkward, he would stumble like a cow, he would be thinking of his mail-order clothes and his ugly shoes. Cupping his hands he breathed into them to learn if his breath was sweet. Well, he could turn his head away but who would dance with him? . . . There was Arabella Glover, thin, black-eyed, caustic. One day in school she had touched the points of her thumb and finger together and circled the end of his nose. He had wondered why she did that. There was Wanda who might dance with him, or Iris Dugan: Iris always wore in school a gray sweater that showed to the full her plump ecstatic breasts . . .

He went below again and moved through the crowd, his heart a great pulse under his ribs. Wanda came over to him and asked him if he would dance. "With you?" he said. He dragged forth a handkerchief and then observed that it looked bad, for he had laundered it himself. She moved close to him and touched one of his hands. It was only a brief friendly touch but it went through him like fire.

"Would you dance with me?" she asked, looking up at him. His gaze met her luminous eyes and fell to her mouth. Then he glanced at his hands and perceived that his nails were dirty and thrust his hands into pockets.

"I don't know how," he said.

"I'll show you how."

He shook his dismal head. He glanced round him to see if anyone was amused.

What happened next he hardly remembered at all. He knew that she took his arm; he would never forget the sudden rapture of that. She must have led him outside, because when his wits cleared they were standing in the schoolyard under a white moon. He could feel her arm against him, and knowing this he had power to realize nothing more. He could not remember that they said anything for some time; they just moved back and forth under the moon. She took his arm and he trembled.

"Are you cold?"

Cold in an April night: what kind of man, then, could he be! A weakling with sluggish blood and impoverished bones? "No," he said.

"Vridar?"

He looked at her. Her eyes were lustrous, dusky. Her mouth . . . "What?" he said.

"Put your arm around me."

He did not. He strove to realize how much he wished to. She took his arm and laid it round her waist and with one hand held it there.

"You're very brave," she said.

"I?" he asked, astonished.

206

"You made Hun Grabber apologize. Not many would have done that."

"I don't think I'm brave at all," he said.

"I do and I like you. Do you like me?"

"Yes," he said.

She walked toward the building, up the steps, and turned to face him. "You going to dance with me?"

"I can't dance. God, I told you I can't dance!"

His vehemence startled her. She hesitated, then took his hands. "Vridar, you're very lonely, aren't you?"

"Lonely?"

"Yes. And you will dance with me—some time—won't you?"

"Yes."

She patted his helpless drooping shoulders. With a quick movement she stood tiptoe and kissed him lightly on the mouth and whispered: "Vridar—goodnight."

"Goodnight."

He watched her run gracefully into the hall and after a few minutes he went guiltily in to see what she was doing. She was in Quint's arms now, round and round, her eyes closed as her sister's had been, her head on his heart. Vridar turned away and went home.

His nearest neighbor was Jimmie Jake O'Dowd, a sewing-machine salesman. He tried to be a social aristocrat. Vridar had known that Jimmie regarded him and Marion as queer fellows and their father as an uncouth boor. Mrs. O'Dowd too adorned herself with haughty airs. They had a piano, running water in their house, and a canary; and all these in Vridar's mind set them apart from his own caste. Jimmie always wore white shirts and gay neckties, and he whistled superbly, caroling across the field when he left in the morning or came home at night.

Vridar's sense of social inferiority was so deep and intense that it was with him always. In the manner of people whose work was more of the head than of the hands, or whose work allowed them to wear neat clothes, he had long felt contempt: a condescension in gesture and tone, an incredulous start. It was in most of his classmates. He despised them but he despised himself more.

During the summers of his high school years he sometimes went with his mother to the valley to help her peddle her cheese, chickens, and eggs. He felt ashamed of his mother and loathed himself for feeling shame. Her hands were red and gnarled, her clothes shabby and dust-filled, her stockings torn and her shoes run down. Still, it was not these that made him writhe most, nor the horrible squawking of roosters smelling of dung in their gunnysacks, nor the piles of cheese and the eggs crated in oats. It was his mother's attitude. Her face was proud and unbending, but he saw shame in her eyes and heard it in her voice. When she plugged a cheese so that a doubting woman could taste it or counted the eggs or dragged a rooster out of a sack, he saw in her and felt in her a deep sunken resentment, a sense of disgrace, a wretched unhappiness in the face of those whose pride was less. She had to suffer insolent remarks; she had to be looked upon and spoken to as if her mind never rose above a cheese-press or a hencoop, as if she were only a dust-drudge, a peasant from the back hills. Feeling her humiliation, it became for him intolerable and he sought to escape.

After they had covered the thirty hot gray miles to Rigby and their vulgar howlng wagon was entering town, he would excuse himself and walk in. He did not want classmates to see him drenched with dust and sitting on a plank seat with sacks of roosters piled behind him. He would slink away and meet his mother in an alley behind a store. He felt shame when his mother with dust in her hair and dust streaking her clothes bought only the cheapest merchandise and refused one thing and another because the price was too high. He would go to a far part of the store as though he were not with her; and he would see the white exhaustion of her face and the defiant light of her eyes. He wanted none to know that this was his mother. Nevertheless he despised himself for his shame. He knew that her poverty and degradation and hard labor were for her children, but he remembered the insulting appraisal of his parents which he had heard in Annis, in Poplar, and in Rigby: "Dirty, good God! You think Joe ever takes a bath?"—"His parents are the misers up in the hills . . ." He had seen this appraisal in the eyes of Jimmie Jake O'Dowd.

He hated Jimmie but two of the O'Dowd children he hid not hate; they were frank and generous and full of fun. Larry was fourteen, the girl Anna was twelve. There was an older sister, Jocelyn, who was sixteen; she was haughty and suspicious, and under the blouse on her flat chest she wore padding to make it appear that she had full firm breasts. Despairing of learning to dance, Vridar played hide-and-seek with the O'Dowd children. Jocelyn came now and then, but she always looked bored and she said this was a game for little tots. One night Vridar ran away to hide and jumped behind a dike and found Jo there. He moved at once to leave, but suddenly she was on top of him and trying to kiss him and searching over him with her hands. He then did what he later thought was an unaccountable thing. He rolled her under him and fell upon her, clumsy and feverish, and kissed her mouth. She leapt up then and smote his cheek and began to scream.

"You beast!" she said. "You raper of women!"

"What?" he said, astonished.

"I'll tell papa about this! Ohhh!" She swayed and thinking she would faint he moved over to support her; and then she was all lightning and wildcat. She struck furious blows and screamed again. Then suddenly for a moment was quiet; she was looking at him and thrusting her tongue out. She made a hideous face and spit at him and became hysterical again. He was frightened. What was the meaning of this? What kind of woman was she anyway?

"Jo," he said, "I'm sorry!"

The sound of his voice seemed to silence her. Again she looked at him, with something unfathomable in her eyes; again she made a face at him and spit. She bowed her head and was quiet as if listening. But suddenly, as before, she yelped horribly and began to run. She went screaming to her house like one on hot irons.

"What did you do?" Larry asked.

"I don't know. Nothing much."

"Well," said Larry, "if you're mean to her she bawls and if you're good to her she bawls even worse."

Vridar expected dire consequences to follow. He thought Jimmie would come over and flog him or have him locked in the town's dingy jail for rape. But Jimmie did neither. The next morning he did not whistle. That was all. Jocelyn never came again. Anna came with Larry but only in moonlit nights, and one of her parents always sat at a window to watch. After a while Vridar understood what this meant. The parents looked on him as a bad youth, as one who had tried to rape Jocelyn and might rape Anna. When he fully sensed that this was their view of him, he was dismayed and appalled: he, Vridar, the timid and ineffectual and quaking one rape a girl! What under heaven could be more absurd than that? But he was a little flattered too. He tried to think of himself as a bold and dangerous young fellow who crushed women under him and kissed their breath out; but this notion of himself collapsed in the most memorable of all his experiences in high school.

XXVIII

Marion dashed in one day, panting and trying to speak; and when at last he could get his breath he asked Vridar to guess who was over town.

"Who?"

"Guess!"

"Mater?" Since studying Latin this was his name for his mother.

"No, not Mater."

"Pater?"

"No, not him either. Think of the one you want to see most. A girl."

"A girl?"

"What girl do you love best?"

Vridar's thought went to Helen, to Norma—and then to Annis! He was looking curiously at his brother: what did Marion known about his interest in girls? He thought he had kept these things secret. He did not know his brother. "You mean—?"

"Yes."

"Neloa!" Neloa, whom he had not seen for years! Neloa, with the great mane of Indian hair and the deep inscrutable eyes and the deeper ways! "Where?"

"In the Golden Rule store."

"How long ago?"

"Just now. You'd better hurry."

Vridar rushed to the wash-basin and dug under his fingernails to remove the dough. He plowed through his hair with a big dirty comb. Then he withered. He was afraid to see her.

"I'll bet you don't dare," said Marion. "You'll spy on her and sneak home!"

Again Vridar stared curiously at his brother. This was a Marion he had never seen.

"I guess you wouldn't," Vridar said.

"I certainly wouldn't. I'd take her out and kiss her. I might do more than that."

"You!" Was this the crosseyed boy he had defended all these years? Vridar did not recognize him at all.

"If you don't," said Marion, "I will."

That settled it. Vridar shot arms into coat sleeves, crushed a cap to his skull, and sprang to the door. After him he heard Marion shouting, "Kiss her! I'll bet you don't dare to!" Vridar dashed across a snow-covered field, troubled by this new vision of his brother. He had never paid much attention to Marion; for what had the boy been but a burden, a symbol, a shadow at his side? Was Marion kissing girls? What had he meant by saying that he might do more than that?

Vridar ran until he came to the Golden Rule door; then, because he was witless and shaken, he did not enter at once, and doubted that he would enter at all. He crossed the street and hid in shadows and watched. People came out, people went in, but Neloa was not among them. Perhaps she had gone home. This thought made him bolder, and he ran over to the store and searched among the shoppers. In later years he was to reflect upon the terrible irony of this moment: if he had known she was in the store no doubt he would have deliberated and agonized and gone home; and how different his life might have been then! But convinced that she was not there, he went in and was caught almost before he knew it. He suddenly found himself face to face with Neloa and one of her aunts and he stood gawking at them, unable to speak.

"Don't you know us?" the aunt said. "Neloa, here's Vridar."

Neloa was looking at him as if she did not know him from Adam. The aunt now did a most tactful and gracious thing; she excused herself and went to another part of the store. Vridar knew that she had done this for him. But he was witless and dumb. Neloa now turned her back on him, for after all he was an amazing person, with his eyes burning in adoration and his tongue mute. He moved toward her, knowing that he must speak now or not at all. His hands were trembling at his side. He recalled what Marion had said and forced a question out of his heart: "Neloa, will you go to a show with me?" He waited. She did not turn or look at him or speak. "Will you?"

She glanced at him and said, "Yes."

What should he do now? He did not know. A bewildering happiness had left him utterly senseless. He could think of nothing to say, nothing to do. He waited, quivering, until the aunt returned. She gave him a swift knowing smile. Ah God, how he loved such understanding as hers!

The aunt and her niece gathered bundles and went toward the door, leaving Vridar crestfallen. Where would he see her again? Where was she going? He followed them half a block behind; now hesitating and looking round him like a dog that has been told to go home, now walking again. They went up a street and crossed to a corner. The aunt looked back. Vridar hastened toward her and again she smiled.

"Won't Neloa talk to you?"

"She—she said she'd go to a show with me."

210

The aunt looked at her niece. Neloa was looking away. "When does the show start?"

"Pretty soon, I guess." With a stab of fear he shot a hand to his pocket to count his coins. He tried to tell by feeling whether they were dimes or pennies. They all felt like pennies but he knew that some of them should be dimes.

"We'll have to take our things home," the aunt said. "Will you wait here?"

"Yes!" Vridar said.

While they were gone he strode about, trying to quiet his heart. What an incredible and contemptible jackass he was! God help him, he would now be poised and at ease! He would talk of impersonal subjects, eloquently and well. "The war now, it's terrible to think of all those European countries fighting again. War is such a senseless thing. It grows out of the capitalistic system and until we have a Socialist State . . ." But no: that would not do. "Have you heard that our Principal has been kicked out? Fancy such a thing!" He was now imitating the hero in a novel. "No good reason, you know, none at all. Not a Mormon, you say? But are we to have freedom of speech and thought no more? Tell me, if you will: is our Bill of Rights dead? Must a man be crucified if he dares to think? . . . Well, I rather fancy, yes. Hasn't it always been so? . . . I beg your pardon?" He was murmuring in his breath: "My work in school? I've done rather well, I suppose. Mathematics I don't care for, but in English and history and Latin . . ." Round and round he walked, trimming his phrases. "Ah, you have heard that I have written books? Yes, two, in fact, and am busy on another . . . Fame? Yes, I suppose that some day I shall be famous . . ." Over and over, building himself on the heights, putting warmth and significance into his famished soul.

But when he saw them coming, all his fine fancies and his rhetoric fled. He began to tremble again. When they came up, the aunt smiling, Neloa looking downcast, he walked at the aunt's side and was silent. The aunt talked to him but he had nothing to say. She spoke about harvests and the weather and the last show she had seen, but he had no phrases about these. At the theatre he saw the aunt buying tickets, and suffocatingly aware of his ineptness and stupidity he was too bewildered to protest. He tried to dig money from his pocket and spilled it in the snow. When he had recovered it they were gone. Here, great God, was a chance to flee! But he did not. He jerked his cap off and went into the dark inside. He saw a dim sheet with figures racing across it, and for a few moments he looked with amazement, for he had never seen a motion-picture before. Near him was a huge stove, redhot, and he went over to stand by it. The aunt and Neloa were nowhere in sight. He would look at the picture a few moments, and then scan the huddled forms, row on row. He told himself that he might as well stand here, for was he not cold, indeed, almost freezing? To convince himself of this he chafed his hands and lifted a foot to the heat.

Then he saw a dim shadow looking round at him. It beckoned to him with a sweep of its arm. He knew it was the aunt, sitting on the aisle, with Neloa on the next seat inside. Whether there was a vacant seat by Neloa he could not tell. He rubbed his hands again and told himself that for such fools as he the only place was home. Melted snow was dripping from his trousers. He bent over to feel his wet

211

garments and wondered again what Marion had meant. The shadow again looked round and beckoned but he pretended not to see. In the gloom he looked at a coat button which he had sewed on with white thread, reflecting that he should have used black. The shadow now rose and came up the aisle. The shadow whispered that there was a seat by Neloa and it took his arm and led him to her.

The next hour he sat in a trance. He tried to look at the picture but he saw only galloping ghosts and changes of light. All the eyes of his being were for this quiet girl at his side. If a villain was shot he was unaware, save in a vague way; but if Neloa moved a hand, changed the tilt of her head or even drew a deeper breath, he knew it vividly. He dared not look at her and she did not look at him. But what an hour of glory this was! He could have sat here until all life was done.

When the show ended, Neloa and her aunt put on wraps and turned away. He followed them up the aisle. They went up the street and he trailed them, despising himself as he had never despised himself in all his life. Should he slip behind a wall and disappear?—or should he go up and walk with them? Not once did they look back. Were they offended because he had not bought the tickets? Had they perceived in him the fool that he was? They came to a house among trees and the aunt took Neloa aside and seemed to be whispering to her. Then she waved goodnight to Vridar and went inside, and Neloa waited by the gate. Vridar now advanced until he stood before her, knowing that he must speak if he would keep her here, yet unable to think of anything to say. He was never to know how much time passed before he spoke. At last with a desperate effort he said: "I guess you'll be in high school soon."

She now looked at him. She tossed her hair scornfully and looked away. "I don't like school," she said.

That was a blow indeed! If she was to be his wife she would have to like school. But he offered no reproof. On the contrary, he told a lie so contemptible that he was never to forget it. "I don't like it so much either," he said.

And again they were silent. He looked up for a moon and then for a moment examined the gate. "I was surprised to see you in the Golden Rule," he said.

"Oh," said Neloa, "I go there a lot. I guess your brother told you."

"A lot? You mean you live here?"

"I been here a month," she said, again giving him that swift curious appraisal, as though to determine what sort of creature he was.

"A month!"

"I'm leaving for Annis tomorrow."

That dashed him. He was wondering if she would see him tomorrow when she said: "I must go in now."

He wanted to throw himself at her feet, to say, "Stay in Rigby a while longer!" He wanted to say, "Neloa, don't leave me yet! I love you, Neloa, I love you!" But he said nothing. Wretchedly unhappy he waited, hoping she would change her mind.

"Goodnight," she said, and before he could speak or move she was gone.

For perhaps an hour he stood here in the gray night, thinking that she might come out again. But she did not come. The house was dark and silent and everything was asleep. He went home like one in a dream and lay awake until morning, thinking of her. Almost two years were to pass before he would see her again. But he did not forget her. It was one of the strange and tragic things in his life that he could not forget her. This meeting with her awoke in him again the passion that had burned in Annis, that had been smouldering all these years in his heart. Many years later he was to smile when he read Stendhal: "In those days I was in love with love." Had he only been in love with love when he felt himself so allured by her, as by midnight and dark flowing water, by shadowed lonely coves and by the fixed horror in a dead thing's eyes? Had it been only a spell, both sinister and holy? Whatever it was, it had seized him when he first met her and had been filling him since, in the way that twilight filled his homeland. From this hour, this night he saw that his destiny lay with hers. Or he felt it, rather, but did not see. If he had seen, if he had been able to look beyond—but this belongs to his later story and another time.

XXIX

Neither the brutal nor the holy experiences were the most dramatic of his high school years nor more than interludes when the sun was shining. A sense of guilt and of doom was always with him and his desperate struggle endured. The high school and his four years within its walls were something on the margin of his life; a tavern of light to which he went, a haven that sheltered but could not heal. His world was himself and his shack and the pencil marks on the window sill. These marks grew in number until they encompassed weeks, even months, but he still felt a remorseless disintegration of body and soul. He became so morbidly shy that he was forever miserable, even in sleep. His dreams were of humiliating hours in which others taunted him for his white face or looked into his soul at its burden of sin. He could not speak in the classroom. If he saw persons grinning and whispering he felt sure that they were talking about him.

He was a very emaciated youth. Naked before a mirror he would look at himself; and without expanding his chest he could count every rib, see the sunken flesh round his collar bone, and the blue veins. His Adam's apple thrust out like a fist under the skin of his throat. And his face at all times save when embarrassed was almost as white as death. For him at least he looked more like a specter than a human being, and he was appalled. He fell into insane rages and smote himself; despised himself for his want of flesh and the color of health; loathed his haunted eyes and his solemn mouth on which there was never laughter. So great was his shame at last and his desperation that he got a bottle of red ink; and before going to school he would tinge his lips and cheeks. So that Marion would not know, he did this in the privy outside, taking a mirror with him and a piece of rag. He had studied healthy faces—ah God, how he had studied them!—to observe where the color lay, how large the areas and how deeply dyed; and with extreme care he tried to give the glow of health to his face. One day Joe Shannon said, "For Christ sake, what you got on you?"

"On me?" asked Vridar, and the ink was lost in a wave of blood.

"It looks like red ink," Joe said.

213

Vridar did even more in a bitter effort to seem to be what he was not. From an old cotton blanket he cut strips and bound these on his chest and around his thighs, to make himself appear well-fleshed. When thus padded he walked with care. He looked at himself in the panes of windows along the street. It was also Joe who one day took Vridar's arm and felt of it. "How much you weigh?" he asked.

"About one-fifty," said Vridar, lying by twenty pounds.

Joe felt again. "Where do you carry it?"

It was, one of Vridar's habits to stare enviously at the well-muscled young men in the school. He watched them on the basketball floor and on the athletic field. He doubted that he ever would be or could be such a man as these but he would not admit defeat. When thrown into deep madness, he would think of suicide and he would look at the acids in his chemistry class, wondering which to choose. But he was not ready to die. Within him was a love of life and a resolve to fight his way clear. He would win. Even when drugged by despair or frenzied with dread, he felt that eventually he would win. He cast round him for an open door to health and peace.

It was this seeking that led him to Sunday school. He had never been baptized; he had never been inside a church. His parents were orthodox, they believed in all the terrible things which God did in the Bible; but they cared little about church-going and public prayer. The earth, Joe said, was his church, and the things of nature were his choir. But Vridar observed that most Rigby folk went to church. Even the town toughs went and sang and prayed and talked about the holy ones. Supposing there must be good in this, he went one Sunday morning to the cold waters of a canal and was shoved under, and on his way home he wondered if all his sins had been washed away. It did not seem reasonable to him: this was too simple a way to get to heaven. In Sunday School he found that the service was almost barren, with little ritual and no mysticism. The meeting opened with a hymn, and with the words of it Vridar was so preoccupied that he forgot to sing. All the hymns seemed to him to be pompous and arrogant and childish; they spoke of chosen people, of a new Zion in the the Rocky Mountains, of the saints of God in the lovely Deseret. After the hymn came a sermon. As likely as not it exhorted the people to raise more sugar beets, to have more babies, to stop eating pepper and drinking tea, or to go as missionaries to heathen lands. Sometimes a returned missionary would bear his testimonial: he would tell how in a savage and sinful wilderness he was starved and foot-weary and how he knelt in prayer; and how by a bush he found a loaf or a cake, left there for him by an angel. After this came the sacrament, water in tall glasses, broken bread on plates. Vridar partook of both and wondered how people could believe that these were the flesh and blood of Jesus. He doubted that partaking of them did him any good. They had been blessed but the bishop who blessed them seemed to Vridar to be a scoundrel.

The congregation was then divided into classes. The teacher of Vridar's group was a young man, smug and self-complacent and ignorant. That Jonah slept in a whale or that the Red Sea rolled back or that the sun was stopped he accepted as a literal fact. Parable and allegory meant nothing to him. Having been in France, he expatiated at length on that nation's degeneracy and want of favor with God.

Vridar wanted to say, "What about Judas now? Are you fair to him? If Jesus were to come again would *you* leave wife and home to become a disciple and an outcast?" He wanted to say: "The New Testament contradicts itself in a thousand instances. How can you believe *all* of it?" He wanted to say: "I think the whole story of Jesus is a parable, an allegory. If you insist on making it literal you destroy it." But he was too shy to to speak and he said nothing at all.

When the classes were done, the people again sang and prayed. Vridar did neither. He looked around him, noting the presence of one and another, comparing their faces now with what they were on business days. There was Arthur Beal, of whom opinion would have said that he was the holiest of the lot. But Vridar had gathered potatoes for him and he knew that the man was a slave-driver with a miserly soul. There was Jim Crudder, song-leader who had married one of Vridar's cousins: his face was rapt now with Sunday holiness but on the other days he was a social snob. His wife gave afternoon teas and denied that Vridar was a relative. None of her daughters would speak to him, but in church they lifted sweetly pious voices in hallelujahs to God.

With all his eyes and ears Vridar noted the difference between what people were on Sunday and on the other six days. There grew in him distrust of church-going and church people and of public prayer. The more he thought of the matter, the more he doubted; the more he listened to racial intolerance and the bigotry of chosen people, the more he turned away. He left the church after a few weeks and never returned. Learning of this, the bishop called him to a mission, and for days Vridar spent feverish hours in self-searching and prayer. No young man of his faith, no young woman, ever refused this summons when it came. He had seen youths leave high school, beardless and ignorant, to carry the gospel to far places. He had seen some of them return chastened and some of them debauched.

His struggle to come to a decision robbed him of appetite and sleep. It exhausted him until he felt spent and crazed. And one day while sitting in the shack with his head bowed, he leapt to his feet and like a wild man bolted across the field. As in that hour on the Antelope hills, he half felt himself being drawn into that danger-zone from which there could be no return. He was off to seek Dr. Gunn, a queer shabby man with crossed eyes like Marion's, who was said to be a brilliant surgeon when drunk. Vridar came to the building and sprang up dark unclean stairs and knocked on a door.

"Well!" said the doctor, astonished by this sweat-drenched youth. "Come in."

Trembling to his bone, Vridar went in. He sat in a gloomy unswept office. He met the doctor's gaze.

"What can I do for you?" asked a kind voice. A short unclean hand reached for a cigar.

What could he say, how could he tell! He said nothing for a little while. He would shake violently for a minute and then be as still as death; and then something would snap in his body and he would shake again.

"Just take your time," the doctor said. "There's no hurry."

Then—of all humiliations the worst!—Vridar began to weep. If there had not been such kindness in the voice, such understanding in the eyes, he might have withstood this emotional flood. But there was no restraining it now. The intense almost cataleptic state of his being melted and left him limp, choked, undone. He threw his arms out, trying to push the boiling surge down.

"Don't struggle," said the doctor kindly. "Just relax and then you can talk."

But Vridar's shame was too galling. He fled to the hallway and stood there, until, spent and shaken, he returned to the dark office and spoke.

"Maybe," he said, his eyes aglow with shame, his voice shattered and gasping, "maybe there's nothing to tell! But I—I feel crazy! I can't go on this way! O God, I can't go on this way!" He looked up, his face white and wet. "Day and night, night and day, it's with me! This—this—O my God!" He choked and bowed his head.

"It's not that serious," said the doctor quietly.

Vridar sat up in a great shudder and then recoiled. He rose to his feet and swayed in the bitter blackness of his world and then collapsed to the chair. The doctor stood up and laid hands on Vridar's head. Then he talked and his voice was kind and old and patient. Vridar shook under the hands and clutched his bloodless face and wished himself dead. He could hear the words, but at first he did not understand. Again and again he would start up in sudden desolate fear, but the doctor would push him back and pat him and talk in the same strong untroubled voice.

At last Vridar raised his head and tried to smile. "I—I feel better," he said.

"That's fine. That's very good."

"I—I'd better go now."

"No, not yet. I want to talk to you."

Vridar wanted to escape and go off and rebuke himself for his weakness and shame. He was wondering how he could get away when the doctor's words amazed him. Quietly, the doctor was saying:

"Most boys, nearly all boys, do what you have done. Did you get the idea you were the only person in the world doing that? How silly, if you did. Most people do these things sometime in their lives. Haven't you known that?"

Vridar stared at him. He knew that denial was useless. "You mean—? Oh, but it can't be true!"

"It is true. But most of them don't get so upset about it. They don't think they're going crazy and all that tommyrot. You've been listening to silly stories or reading quack books. . . . Haven't you?"

Had he? Ah, great God! "Yes sir," he said.

"Now I'm going to tell you what to do. Your metabolism may be low, but I don't think there is anything seriously wrong with you. You must get rid of this silly notion that you are going insane. Then work. It doesn't matter what you do —but work. If you have nothing better, dig holes and fill them up. Get your mind off yourself. Work and work until you're so tired you'll sleep. Get an appetite. Live out in the sunshine. Try to be cheerful. Work and eat all you can and be cheerful." There was a pause. "In a few days come and see me again."

Vridar stood up. He felt as if he had been long underground and had come into the enormous clean air of life. But his eyes were wet again, with gratitude now and

216

with hope. He wanted to kiss this doctor's hand, to express his humility and his thanks. But he could only falter and dig for his coins. The doctor placed a hand on his shoulder.

"You owe me nothing," he said. "You owe a lot to yourself. Aren't you Joe Hunter's son?"

"Yes sir."

"Are you going to college some day?"

"I hope to."

"That's fine. Now don't forget: work and eat and sleep like a log. And come see me again."

Vridar let himself out and found the street. He hastened home and got an old shovel and began to dig, and for hours he worked like one driven. When he could no longer see anything but the sky, he climbed out of the hole and entered the shack and slept.

But not for long did he dig holes and fill them up. In an old junkpile he found a discarded set of boxing-gloves and turned to athletics in his home yard; he sparred for hours with Marion, or alone he hopped about and smote concrete walls. At last he invited Hun Grabber to come over, the husky youth who dreamed of being a great fighter. Hun had read about fighters and he copied their ways.

"That nose of yourn," he said with an evil grin. "How the name of God did you ever come out of your mother with a nose like that? I aim to make a pancake of it."

He feinted and then struck a hard blow in Vridar's relaxed stomach. Vridar fell to the earth, his diaphragm paralyzed, and writhed in agony. When he got to his feet, he was weeping with rage. He came in blindly and Hun smote him a crushing blow on his mouth and laid him senseless by the wall.

But he persisted. He would go with Hun to an empty boxcar and practice there. His face was so grimly earnest that his opponent would retreat and stare at him. "Get that crazy look off of your mug!"

"Never mind how I look."

When Hun advanced, eyes lit and mouth cruelly intent, Vridar's face would take on remorseless purpose and he would stiffen from head to feet. After a few weeks of punishment and instruction, he felt more at ease. He had grown in strength and skill. One afternoon he caught Hun off guard and struck with all his power, and knocked the astonished youth through the car door and into a pile of cinders. Hun sat there, licking blood from his mouth. He never came again.

Vridar exercised in other ways. He practiced jumping and shot-putting, using for the latter a stone. He cleared a height of more than five feet, and a distance of twenty feet. Of both these feats he was inordinately proud. On the ranch during his vacation he rode wild horses, because his sister, now a girl of twelve, was an expert and fearless rider. Her horsemanship put Vridar to shame. He resolved to ride every dangerous beast he could find. "I will," he told Diana, "or break my neck." He almost broke his neck. When he came to, the world was spinning in mammoth vistas of green, and by him was Diana, mopping his brow with a wet rag.

217

XXX

Though he stuck with desperate tenacity to his effort to make himself rugged and dauntless and though the words of Dr. Gunn were always with him, he could not throw off the feeling of guilt. He needed catharsis, and pursuit of dangerous exploits was not catharsis. When engaged in strenuous physical activity, he would forget himself for a little while; but out of the exhaustion and quiet would come the old dread. Prayer was of no use now. He was past all grief and tears. There was something else that he needed, but he could not divine what it was.

During his senior year he would sometimes hide out in the woodshed. While sitting there he would feel something snap in the awful power that held him, as if a knife had cut through his nerves; and he would leap up, released again to frenzy and hurl himself headlong against the wall. Stunned, then, he would lie in a heap, and his hands would reach out to find sharp things with which to gouge at his flesh. For it seemed to be only through pain that he recovered touch with life. He would smite his head against the wall, trying to knock out of his skull its years of accumulated unreason; he would crawl on hands and knees, feeling within him the jungle and its ancient terrors, thinking obscurely of himself as a jungle beast. Some day, he thought, I will return to the simple level of the apes, and start out from there to build my life, with uncomplex meanings that I can understand. . . .

In his more lucid moments he knew that he was mad. It was like living in a dark room and coming out for a moment and going back into the dark. He had lost most of his sense of himself as a human being in a world with his fellows, and he was afraid that he would lose it completely, and be sealed away in a small world of his own. Then he would no longer return, like a wanderer visiting home shores. Then he would sink into the delusions and the quivering heartache of his own self-created vault. Against all this he seemed to have no defense, no power to find his way out. When he recalled the doctor's words or meditated on the precepts of Jesus, he got only shadows of what once had meaning. Worst of all, it seemed to him, was that this mood which possessed him was coming to be intimate and friendly; to seem to be what he was, his breath and life and atmosphere, as though from early childhood he had belonged to it by right of birth. It seemed to him that he had learned to understand only horror and pain. So strongly did he sense this now and then that he would feel relief, as if struggle were futile, as if all struggle were done; as if he had been fighting against the only meaning that was possible for him, and at last was coming home. Then it was that he wished to be taken away to an asylum and locked up, to be at peace with this terror and go with it to his death.

Late one spring morning he was trotting down a country lane just outside the town. He had been thinking of killing himself—of throwing himself into a canal, of drinking poison, of putting a noose round his neck and jumping from a tree. He had stood on a canal bank and looked at the soft depths of the water's peace and sleep; and the lure of it had become so strong that he had run away, lest he plunge in. He was fleeing from his compulsion when coming down the lane toward him he saw a man, and recognized George Albert Turner, the only teacher in high school whom he had loved. Turner was walking on long strides, his shirt open and his head bare. Vridar turned to flee, but the man yelled to him and he stopped. Turner came up and for a long moment looked at him.

"Well!" he said, and his voice was astonished. "What are you doing out here?" Vridar tried to smile. He tried to speak. Turner came up close and looked into his eyes and said: "What's the trouble?" And still Vridar was unable to speak.

Turner sank to a grassy mound and looked up, studying Vridar, his strong fingers stroking his chin. After a few moments he began to laugh. The laughter at first was a kind of rumbling and gurgling sound, as though the man's vocal apparatus were tuning up; but presently the laughter spilled out of him in rushing tides, gargantuan, pagan, uncontrollable. It dyed his face and throat and ears; it shook tears from his eyes; it rang in the earth and the sky and went away on the wind. Still hoping to escape, Vridar looked at the wide mouth and the strong perfect teeth.

"My God!" Turner roared. "So—so—it's true, then!" The words came out in a choked blast of incredulity, of amazement, of scorn. He doubled over, convulsed; he sat up, his face a violent agony of red; and he collapsed again.

Vridar did not know what to make of this. He stared at the man and waited.

Turner was bellowing again. He was like some kind of sardonic beast, bending over, as if gathering his body full of sound, and then rising a little, as if to let the flood out. Such laughter as this Vridar had never heard. It was immense and clean like a thunderstorm. Somehow it seemed to make a shadow of his horror, an obscene memory of his fear. His eyes lost a little of their desolation, and his white face relaxed into a feeble grin.

Turner had stopped laughing. He looked grave now, but again and again a great hiccough of joy leapt out of him, like the last outriders of a storm.

"Gunn told me," he said. "Yes, but I couldn't believe it. Is it true?" Vridar felt silly and he looked silly. This man had laughed God out of his heaven and sin off the earth. Missionaries had taken to their heels and vanished down the sky. "Come here and sit down," Turner said; and when Vridar had sat, Turner asked: "Did you ever read Darwin and Huxley as I told you to?"

"Some," Vridar said.

"What have you read most in your life?"

Vridar considered. "The Bible," he said.

"Good God, that explains it. Is it true that you almost went on a mission?"

"I—I guess so."

With the suddenness of a bird taking to flight, Turner roared again. His huge hands threshed the air. His blood shot his ears full of scarlet and seemed ready to burst from his cheeks. Wholly unaware of what he did, Vridar began to laugh. His laughter at first was thin and tortured but it caught depth and tone, it rocked him, it fetched burning tears to his eyes. His face became red too and his breath hissed and gasped and his hands clutched his aching throat. Not in all his life had he ever laughed like this. Coming out of a violent spasm, Turner would point a reproachful finger at Vridar and then break over his knees, howling like a madman, all his energy pouring from his mouth. Vridar lost his breath and fought for it, beating at nothing with his arms while his eyes bulged and his face ran white; and then caught his breath in a sucking howl and fell over backward, shaking in the grass. When he sat up and glanced at Turner, there was the thrusting scornful finger again and Turner's face choked and strangled; and again Vridar was off, convulsed with laughter as he had never imagined he could ever be. After a few minutes they looked at each other, exhausted, wet and limp.

"I—I feel better!" Vridar gasped.

"Don't any of your people have a sense of humor?" Turner asked. And there he went again, his scornful finger pointing Vridar out for all the world to see, his large handsome face again drenched with blood, his blue eyes almost popping from his head. Vridar barked suddenly and then exploded and fell over and rolled. Ah God, what was this that had happened to him! All the shame and terror seemed to be gone, to have been blown out in gusts of joy. What was the meaning here?

"Why did you consider wasting two years of your life on a mission?"

"Why—" The dread was coming back. He got to his feet, but Turner seized his hand and jerked him down.

"Tell me!"

"I—I've sinned," Vridar said.

"O my God!" cried Turner, and he was off again into mammoth laughter. He stood up, shaking like one tortured. He walked round and round, bellowing at the sky. Vridar tried to laugh with him, but he seemed unable to laugh now. He made only a queer sound. "You—you believe in—in sin?" Turner roared, looking down at him, mist streaming from his eyes. "Really, you do?"

"I—" said Vridar. "I mean in the moral and immoral."

"Indeed!" Turner sat again. "Vridar, tell me something that's immoral."

"Well—— You say something immoral?"

"Are animals immoral?"

"N—no."

"Then why is a human being?"

"Because—because we know better."

"You mean an animal can't be immoral until it's intelligent? Then you would exempt fools?" Again Turner's thunder filled the sky. Tears on his cheeks, he moved over toward Vridar and thrust at him with a finger. "It's time you got out of the Middle Ages. Now where in hell did you get this idea of sin? From Paul? From your mother? . . . Answer me."

"From both," Vridar said.

"Are they sufficiently civilized to instruct you? And what do you mean by sin? Vridar, look round you." Turner's gesture embraced the trees and flowers, earth and sky. "Do you see any sin in these things? Are they not beautiful and clean? Vridar, you've got a bad medieval odor about you. Before you accept Christian dogmas, why don't you read the great scholars and find out where the dogmas came from?"

"I will,"

"Fine. Now what is sin? Another name for prejudice. Is murder a sin? Millions in Europe are murdering one another right now—and they're all Christians. Is masturbation a sin? Only for those who think that all pleasure must be evil. Is copulation a sin? Only for those who want more of it and don't know how to get it. Prejudice, damn it, prejudice!" He reached over and plucked a wild flower. "Smell it," he said.

Vridar took the flower and smelled it.

"After this," said Turner, "when you get to thinking of sin go smell a flower. Hug a tree. Get out and watch the sun come up. And in the name of your own future, read—read—read. Not the Bible, not that, but Darwin, Huxley, Russell, Wells, Paine, Ingersoll—and the great scholars, the really great ones, Vridar, not the impostors with their brains full of ancient superstition. Will you?"

"Yes."

"Well, we'd better go now."

They walked up the lane. Turner drew the morning deep into his lungs. He pointed his nose to each breeze, catching its fragrant journeying; he reached out to the color of life, to its touch. There was no death, he said; there was only life, and the only sin was in turning one's back on it. The only religion was to be found in standing up to it and loving it instead of ducking into a church pew to pray. Vridar listened to these heresies. He looked up at the sky and round him at the earth; he heard the song of larks. It was his habit, Turner said, to come out and smell the morning and watch the sun rise, for it was then that he knew God.

When they came close to town, Turner stopped and faced Vridar. "Remember, go smell a flower, lie in the grass, watch a frog sing; and read—read the right things, the things written by free men, free minds, the things that God himself is glad to see men write. Do you promise me this?"

"Yes," Vridar said.

"And when you go to college, write to me once in a while. Let me know how you're doing—and above all, what you're reading. Have you ever read Frazer?"

"No."

"I'll send you something he wrote. Read it. Think about it. Do you have a motto to guide you?"

"No."

"I'll tell you mine. When Huxley's son died, a writer named Kingsley sent him a letter; and in his reply Huxley said, Follow humbly and to whatever abyss Nature leads, or you shall learn nothing. Say it for me."

"Follow humbly and to whatever abyss Nature leads, or you shall learn nothing."

"Remember it, Vridar. Remember it. Keep it in your soul."

Turner left him and Vridar walked alone, murmuring over and over the words that Huxley wrote to Kingsley. He felt better. There had been something deep and clean in Turner's laughter. In Turner himself there was something deep and clean. Vridar felt this all the more firmly after there came to him in the mail a paragraph that Frazer had written, after he had read it over and over until he knew it by heart. These are Frazer's words that Turner sent him:

It is indeed a melancholy and in some respects thankless task to strike at the foundations of belief in which, as in a strong tower, the hopes and aspira-

221

tions of humanity through long ages have sought refuge from the storm and stress of life. Yet sooner or later it is inevitable that the battery of the comparative method should breach these venerable walls, mantled over with the ivy and moss and wild flowers of a thousand tender and sacred associations. At present we are only dragging the guns into position; they have hardly yet begun to speak. The task of building up into fairer and more enduring forms the old structures so rudely shattered is reserved for other hands, perhaps for other and happier ages. We cannot foresee, we can hardly even guess, the new forms into which thought and society will run in the future. Yet this uncertainty ought not to induce us, from any consideration of expediency or regard for antiquity, to spare the ancient moulds, however beautiful, when these are proven to be outworn. Whatever comes of it, wherever it leads, we must follow the truth alone. It is our guiding star.

He did not know who Frazer was but he felt the nobility and courage in his words; and he said to himself, I will be a great scholar some day; I will be one' of those other hands to whom the task of rebuilding is reserved. This would be his way, a clean way, neither haunted nor lonely, neither abject nor dark. He felt the intimations of it and he knew that he was a Mormon no more. And when school was ended and he had his diploma he did not wait for a parent to come with the wagon, but set out to walk.

It was early morning and ahead of him he saw a faint flowering in the east. From far horizons and out of sunlit seas it spread its golden acres. Turner said this was God. Follow humbly, Turner said, to whatever abyss Nature leads, or you shall learn nothing. He would follow. The old dread was still with him, it might be with him all his life, but he would not let it conquer him. Breathing into his lungs the fragrance off dew-wet clover he made a vow to himself: he vowed that he would conquer fear, he would learn to laugh and be glad. "I will, I will," he said, "so help me, God!" He would keep close to him this vow and Turner's words and he would be all right. He touched flowers along the way and looked up at the round blue sky. In the east now there was a great light; he looked at it and walked toward it. He broke a golden flower from its stem and smelled it, remembering that Turner had said that he had a medieval odor about him. He did not quite know what this was but it was bad and he would get rid of it. "I will," he said, "I will! I'll laugh and be glad some day!"

Morning had come. Bareheaded, smelling the flower, looking at the light filling the east, he went up the long road to the hills of his home.

PART TWO

NINA

"Nina, another form of Ishtar, was a goddess of creation typi-
fied in the teeming life of the ocean, and her name is written
with a character standing for a house or receptacle with the
sign for 'fish' within"—Pinches

I

He pressed his face to a pane, trying to look back, but his parents were now far behind. They would be going homeward in a lumber wagon, turning from lane to lane; and he was journeying above roar and shriek and the singing of rails to a far strange place. Houses sped past, barns and coops, gardens and ditches and poles; and in the east was the backbone of a mountain, hauntingly blue and remote, yet very close to his heart, like the mountains of his childhood. He remembered now that he had often been homesick. He wiped guiltily at his eyes and tried to blow his nose without making a sound, for at his side was Stanley Trout, a high school classmate who would be college mate and roommate now. Stanley was very tall and slender, with dark curly hair.

By looking between fingers he saw that Stanley seemed very quiet and at ease, as though riding trains had been part of his life; but when Vridar again looked through the window and saw houses like the shacks in which he had lived, or patches of brush, or marshland and creek that reminded him of childhood scenes, nausea swarmed up from his vitals and all his blood seemed to wait in his heart. He was homesick and desolate, but Stanley was now looking at the college catalog, chewing a pencil and meditating on the curricula, or writing notes on a sheet of paper. Stanley was intellectual and serene and some day would be a famous man. But what in God's name, Vridar asked himself, will I ever be! The first of his clan in Idaho to graduate from high school, he would be the first to enter college; and in that, it seemed to him, he should find some reason for strength and pride. But with the miles rolling endlessly under him and the world outside looking feverish with haste he would in this moment have sacrificed all his ambitions to be back in the mountain-walled and river-girt bowl of his home. He peered again at Stan. What kind of thing am I? he thought; for he was twenty, he was almost a man, if he ever would be—older than many who were married, than many who were fathers. . . .

Rising, he went down the aisle, having observed that other passengers did so; and at the far end he turned clumsily, looking for a drink. Unable to release the water and feeling that people were watching him, amused and derisive, he sank to a half-hidden bench and tried to draw back out of sight. For an hour he did not move. Feeling that he was again being drawn into the dark, he called to mind Huxley's words and Frazer's and Turner's and struggled to keep a grip on himself. His being was full of train-rhythm, and of the great void under it and the quiet. Knowing that he must do something, he stirred, and fetched his thoughts out of their depth. He looked himself over and noted that his mail-order suit smelled of wool; and from a lapel he drew a long black hair that looked like one from a horse's mane. This suit had been guaranteed all-wool: he would have to write his mother about the horse-hair in it. His shoes were pug-toed and ugly compared with those the other passengers were wearing. His shirt cuffs, showing pompously below his coat sleeves, were fastened with huge cheap studs; with dark misgiving he pushed them up and out of sight. Then with a gasp of alarm he thought of his money and dug into a pocket, as alarm closed upon him like a sheath of frost. But the money was there. His fingers closed round it and drew it forth, and within the shelter of his coat he counted it, ten notes, fifty dollars in all, a part of his parents' meager savings in twenty years. He counted the notes again and still again and pushed the wad down into a deep pocket, withdrawing his hand carefully, lest a part of the money follow it. He stuffed his handkerchief into the pocket to keep the money down there, deep and secure. Two hundred dollars, his father had said, should be enough. It would take eight hundred dollars to put Vridar through college, eight hundred for Marion and a like sum for Diana. Twenty-four hundred dollars! Vridar deliberted such a staggering fortune, trying to see its limits: it would buy a herd of cattle, or enough Antelope land to graze ten thousand sheep, or half the empty lots in Rigby.

He was passing now through barren country, unrolled in a plateau of gray to the Utah line. There was a girl back in the car at whom he had wanted to look. She had reminded him of Neloa. From a coat pocket he drew forth a letter, so frayed and worn out that it was little more than a palmful of flakes. As in so many times he put the flakes together and read:

> Dear —————, I was sure surprised to get your card. I am up in Paradise now. I guess you know about Amos Hufford being married. I was to his wedding dance and had a swell time. We have a dance up here every Friday night and have lots of fun but I guess you don't care about anything up here. Don't be so long writing next time. Well, I guess you will be tired reading this nonsense so will ring off. Goodnight and sweet dreams from

Neloa
xxoo
all for you

The reading of this letter had always filled him with a vague sense of grief and shame. He had observed that the number of kisses was intended to be generous but no doubt she wrote that way to all men. She was going to dances and she was very young. He had not seen her for two years, not since that night when, stupid and worshipful, he had followed her like a dog into the theater. But he had written to her, trying to suggest that some day she would be his wife and that she should keep herself unsullied for him. He touched his lips to the fragments and put them away. Then he straightened his tie and wiped some dust from his shoes and with a match dug at some spots under his nails. How, he wondered, did the back of his head look to those who observed him when he passed? Did they know that his mother had cut his hair? Did they know that he was a wretchedly self-conscious youth who was trying to seem at ease? Did they know that he was a mountain-lad, a hill-country plowboy, who had never been on a train before?

He had seen men leave this car and enter the car ahead. He did not know that they went to the smoking-room. They were worldly folk, he supposed, determined

225

to get the worth of their fare; they wore their courage jauntily and did things that would have made him sick to think of doing. They blew their noses in great snorts of thunder or put their feet upon the cushions ahead or turned to stare with superb gall at a woman. While thinking about such browbeating of life, Vridar saw a man in overalls and rundown shoes enter the car ahead, and reflected that where such a man went he might go also. He stood up and prepared for adventure, but when he came to the first door and tried in vain to open it he felt panic. It it had been possible he would have jumped off the train. While feeling desperate the thought came to him that he could pretend; and so he looked through the glass of the door as if searching for someone, and he shrugged, as though weary and impatient, and with his most worldly air he returned to his seat. Thereafter he watched men open the door, hoping to discover its secret; and when sure that he could open it without fumbling he again went forth. He came to a car with many empty seats and chose one and sat, feeling that he had acquitted himself well.

Only men were in this car and they were all smoking. Vridar had never smoked, save a few disastrous attempts with filched cigars, but he wished now that he had a cigarette. There was magnificent arrogance in the gestures of a young snob who sat ahead: he knocked ashes off with an imperious finger, he gazed with obvious and withering disdain at the country around him, or he rolled over a little and farted as unselfconsciously as a man of stone. While studying this prig and enviously noting every detail of his dress Vridar came to himself with a start: across from him a big-bellied man was appraising him with cold blue eyes. Fetching himself together Vridar acted a part: he reached into pockets as if for cigarettes and finding none patted himself as though annoyed. Then the man reached across and offered cigarettes. Vridar took one and flushed and mumbled some nonsense about having left his in the other coach. He searched vainly for a match and the man struck and held a light. Then Vridar inhaled and exploded with a violent snort. A swift desperate glance told him that the man was smiling.

"Where you off to?"

"College," Vridar said, and choked again.

"What college?"

"Wasatch, in Salt Lake City."

For a little while the man looked at him and was silent. Vridar puffed at the cigarette and tried to make it appear that he was inhaling: he would hold the smoke in his mouth and breathe down through his nose, and then in a long thin stream he would let the smoke out.

"What you intend to be?" asked the man.

"Uh—a teacher and a writer."

"That don't pay much. Corporation lawyer, that's the stuff."

Stanley Trout now pushed the door open and came in, and when he saw that Vridar was smoking he was too amazed to speak. He pursed his small mouth until it looked like the mouth of a fish and his small eyes darkened. Because Stan was a fanatic on diet and exercise and health, and a very devout Mormon, Vridar enjoyed his consternation.

226

"I'm talking with this gentleman," said Vridar, waving his cigarette at Stan, "about becoming a corporation lawyer."

Stan looked at the gentleman and swung and disappeared. "Your friend?" asked the man.

"He's going to college with me. He's very religious and doesn't believe in smoking, or even in eating pepper."

"The hell he don't. What religion he belong to?"

"Mormon."

The man grimaced and stretched out lazily to the seat ahead. "He'll go to heaven, I suppose, and it will serve him right."

When the train stopped in the lovely little town of Brigham most of the passengers got off and stretched themselves in sunlight, and Vridar returned to his seat with Stan. Stan was bent low over the college catalog. Without looking up he asked: "Do your parents know you smoke?"

"Oh, of course."

"You'll always be a scrawny runt," said Stan. "Your soul—"

"Never mind my soul, you tall shitepoke!"

"You'll die of consumption," Stan said.

Vridar felt very unhappy. After all, Stan was to be his roommate, his only friend in a big friendless city. He did not want to quarrel with him. He bowed to his arms to consider what had been said, and he wondered what Stan would think of him if he had known how sick and frightened he was inside. When he looked up, dusk was falling and he saw so many things—groves of trees, areas of gray earth, far mountains in blue and mist—that recalled to him the hills of home and piled up in memory all the stricken hours of his life. But he must be strong now. He had embarked on a great journey, taking with him the faith of his parents, slaving to set him on a high clean place. He would have to be a man now. But as lights spread over the valley, as so much sped by that was strange and no part of him, he was so horribly afraid that he wanted to leap out and roll in the black night to his death, and be forever done with the pitiable play of trying to be what he was not. When the train poured with a sound of rolling boulders into the station of light, Vridar seized his bags and stood up, trying to quiet his trembling limbs. He went out with Stan and they came to a broad brilliant street, and Vridar stood on the shore of a new world.

Close by the college the next day, after a miserable night in which Vridar slept hardly at all and Stan was scornful and impatient, they found themselves in a vile den in the dark basement in the home of Professor Jeremiah Yupp. Their room was about sixteen feet by six and its only window was one small pane so begrimed with coal dust that it gave almost no light. The south wall was the furnace itself and a darkness that led to a pile of coal. Their furniture was an old shabby bed, two broken chairs, a table, one gas-plate, and a few dishes in a cupboard. The cupboard was a packing-box spiked to a wall. For this dismal room, the dirtiest that Vridar was ever to live in, they were to fire the furnace, take the cinders out, and sweep leaves from the lawn. Though unaccustomed to a modern house or to luxuries of any kind, Vridar was sickened and outraged by the underground cell.

It would not have been so bad if the furnace had been shut away, but standing as it did in the room itself it filled the whole basement with intolerable heat and covered everything with ashes and smoke.

In Yupp's big house, Vridar afterward learned, there were thirty-two rooms, most of them large enough for only a bed, a chair or two, and a gas-plate. The professor and his family occupied the first floor: it smelled of old furniture and dust-filled clothing and age. Above that were three floors, with once-spacious chambers partitioned off into stuffy little dens; and above the fourth was the garret, itself containing four rooms, each with a wan little sky-window, each with a ceiling that would not allow a man to stand up. In the rear of each of the four main floors was a porch; and Yupp, in overalls and unaided, had made four rooms on each porch, building the three additional walls of rough lumber and battening this with strips from grocers' boxes; and all these overgrown bird-cages he rented to students. His house when seen from the rear looked as if a drunken carpenter had spiked to it from bottom to top an outlandish assortment of hencoops.

So this, Vridar thought, is a college professor!

Yupp was a lean, quick, and nervous man with furtive eyes that never directly met the gaze of another. His chin and mouth were weak, his forehead narrow, as if a part of his skull had melted and run down to form his big nose. He had handsome gray hair, but this, Vridar learned, was a wig; for in his classroom one day an impudent wind found the sash open and leapt in and took Yupp's hair off. His head was then as bright and bare as a skull. But Yupp was a very devout Mormon and Churchman, who looked with dismay even on those who ate pepper. They would be saving of coal, he told Vridar and Stan, gesturing alertly like a bird. In overalls and canvas gloves he showed them how to stoke, how to remove clinkers, to regulate the water and heat. His eyes darted thither and yon, as if spying out enemies or sinners, or as if afraid of what they might see.

In contrast with his new home, Vridar thought the campus a glorious thing. It had spruce and fir, magnificent buildings, and a library that took his breath away. As he turned cards in the catalog and read titles, he trembled with excitement. He wrote down the books which he must soon read, and in a few weeks had hundreds of titles. Like Coleridge, he would read the library from end to end. He would open a book and hungrily scan a page and be astonished by what he read. It was Plutarch, who said that superstition was an insult to God. It was Lecy, who said: "A candid examination will show that the Christian civilisations have been as inferior to the Pagan ones in civic and intellectual virtues as they have been superior to them in the virtues of humanity and chastity." But was chastity more important than mind? It was Cicero: "My own conscience is of more importance to me than what men say." It was Thoreau: "The cost of a thing is the amount of what I will call life which is required to be exchanged for it." Good Lord, what windows these authors opened! He knelt to the library and dedicated himself to the world of books.

His professor of sociology was as queer a man as he had ever seen. His more impudent students called him the monkey and the name was apt. Prof. Bogan was an old man and very lean and very small. His face was almost entirely hidden by a stubble of beard, and out of this stubble spread a curious nose, flattened in the arch and gaping in the nostrils. His eyes were grotesquely small and close together, and full of simian alertness; and above them were bushy brows and under them was the beard. When Bogan walked he moved like an ape, as if unaccustomed to going on two legs; with his small shoulders hunched up and his head thrust forward, and his eyes, all pupil and darkness, constantly shifting as those of a monkey do. Vridar studied photographs of apes in the library and now developed a habit that was always to be with him, that of seeing the simian in the human face.

In Bogan's class some students slept and snored, some made love; and Vridar, who sat well toward the front, saw that Bogan's eyes missed nothing. Now and then his stubble would crack in a faint smile and his eyes would fill with bright malice. "Mr. Young," he would say, "would Sumner think a classroom the proper place to woo a maid?" Or to a young athlete shuddering under his snores: "Mr. Homney. . . . Will someone kindly wake Mr. Homney up?" After Mr. Homney had risen, looking wild and sleepy: "Mr. Homney, is it true as our author says that women are more desultory and volatile than men?"

"More what?" asked Mr. Homney, rubbing at his eyes.

None of the students ever guffawed when Bogan turned on them his dry and malicious wit. Vridar liked this strange shabby little man. He was awed by the wealth of his learning. And for his professor of history, too, he had only respect. The man had a handsome kingly head, bronzed over: of all members of the faculty he looked most like a thoroughbred—dignified but gracious, an animal in whom Vridar could see traces of the ape, but also a human being at the human level. By temperament, training, and tastes he belonged to the academic world.

Professor Yupp was another kind: he digressed again and again into furious tirades on cats. He hated cats because they killed birds. When he spoke about cats, his sallow cheeks would burn like pink fire, and his eyes would look strangled and wild. His voice would choke and then expire in a wail of anguished reproach. Vridar would listen to the man and think, Yes, cats eat birds but birds eat worms and you eat pigs and steers and all sorts of living things! Worse than that, you pretend to have great compassion, yet even while you rave about cats students are freezing to death in the hencoops you have built on your house to enrich yourself!

The one course to which he gave his enthusiasm and his soul was that in writing. Most students thought the writing of themes a detestable chore, but Vridar wrote and revised, tore up and wrote again, and dreamed of the time when he would own a typewriter. His professor of English was his favorite: this dark man, whose ways hinted of violence, had a twisted sardonic mouth, eyes in which his thoughts burned like black fire, and a way with words and idioms that filled Vridar with joy. Prof. Arnold always paced back and forth when lecturing, his hands behind him, his mind reaching out into many fields of knowledge, his sentences dropping, trimmed and burning, like aphorisms out of the masters.

But before all his teachers he sat in humble awe, marveling at their knowledge, their self-assurance, their poise. He dared not believe that he would ever be their equal: they were princes of learning, and he was only an uncouth fellow from the back hills. He was awed, but years of loneliness and self-searching had given to

229

him even at this early age an almost preternatural power to read human motives, to look behind the mask, under the subterfuge. He sensed the deviousness and insincerity in all people. Just the same, when he saw in his professors the small tricks of dodging, the evasions, the pompous philandering with honesty and truth, his heart discredited what his mind perceived. He did not want to believe that they could be guilty of any malice and meanness. It was to take many years to force upon him the truth of university life, the venom and cowardice of its household.

One day he was sitting on the campus with Stanley, his being overflowing with what he had learned. He had just read in a book by Eward Carpenter a statement by a Catholic priest about the people of Tartary: "This only do I affirm, that the devil so mimics the Catholic church there, that although no European or Christian has ever been there, still in all essential things they agree so completely with the Roman Church, as even to celebrate the Host with bread and wine: *with my own eyes I have seen it.*" That statement had set Vridar to thinking; and after telling Stanley about it he said: "Doesn't it seem to you that religion may be about the same everywhere?"

"No," Stanley said.

"You mean you still believe only Mormons have the truth?"

"I know it," Stanley said.

"And if most of our professors don't agree with you, are they wrong?"

Stanley turned to look at Vridar, and then said: "If you lose your religion when you go to school you'll be wasting your parents' money."

"Oh, the hell I will! My parents expect me to use my mind, don't they?"

"They expect you to live in the one true faith."

Vridar arose and went away, wishing that he had a friend to whom he could open his soul. He had been losing himself and his fear in books. The realm of knowledge was so broad and various, the beauty so sweet and infinite—and he was such a nobody, such an ignorant and ill-clothed and frightened nobody, that it made him sick to think of it all! It filled him with ache to realize how little he knew, how much there was to be known. If only he had someone to talk to, someone to sense with him in its tremulous wide immensity the incredible wonder of life! But he had no one—no one but books. He went to the library and sat alone in a dim corner and buried himself in *Jude the Obscure.*

II

Stanley Trout was for Vridar a strange young man: opinionated, violent of temper, scornful, contemptuous. He had read everything he could find on dieting and health and exercise; his god among mortals was Bernarr McFadden; his bible was the physical culture magazines. Every night at ten he went to bed and every morning at six he got up. If he found his sleep disturbed, he would rise and take soda or massage himself or take a walk. His chief desire during these weeks was to increase the size and strength of his neck. Promptly at nine-thirty he would erect himself on his head, with his long legs thrust to the ceiling; and he would move his shoulders back and forth from side to side, until his eyes bulged and his face was dark with blood. For ten minutes he would grunt and distort himself. Then he would lie on the bed with his body bridged from skull to heels, and give his long slender neck further punishment; and his veins would swell as if to burst. He took abdominal exercises too, or he would rest on his heels and alternately rise and sit, or he would bridge himself on his palms and toes and move his body up and down.

At first Vridar approved these things and became a willing student. He also wished to have a thick neck, arms and legs like those of old gladiators, muscle on his belly like steel plate. He stood on his head so long that he ruptured a blood vessel in his neck; but he persisted, and after a while he could hold the position for half an hour, and his neck go so large that he could hardly button his shirts. Stanley watched him and gave advice. He told Vridar to eat no meat, but only raw fruits and vegetables. Stanley ate all his food uncooked. He would fetch to the basement cell carrots and turnips, radishes and lettuce and apples and raisins; and these he would eat, skin and all. For breakfast he ate a cereal called grape nuts; for lunch, a glass of buttermilk, a handful of raisins and an apple; and for supper, vegetables and milk.

For many days Vridar ate as Stanley ate. He ate grape nuts until the stuff made him ill to look at; and uncooked vegetables and fruits until he hungered for a chunk of meat and a slice of bread. Stanley's diet was inexpensive, but it was calculated, so far as Vridar could tell, to starve a person to death. Still, Stanley looked healthy, and he never took laxatives or caught colds.

One day Vridar bought a small piece of steak and alone in their room fried it. Its odors made him ravenous, made him feel as if his blood and bone were alloyed with carrots and apples. While he was eating it in desperate haste, Stanley came in, sniffing the air like a vice-sleuth.

"You eating meat?" he asked, horrified.

"Yes," said Vridar through a mouthful.

Stanley seized the uneaten portion and threw it into the furnace. Vridar turned on him, shaking with fury and choking on meat that had lodged in his throat.

"Listen," he said. "You eat what you please, don't you? Is it any of your damned business what I eat?"

Stanley's eyes shone with crusading zeal. "All right," he said, "kill yourself. Eat meat and get yourself constipated. Do you know constipation is what's wrong with people?"

"Well, by God, I'd as soon die of that as of carrots! And it's my business how I die, isn't it?"

"All right," said Stanley with a shrug, "go on and kill yourself."

For six days—Vridar counted them—neither spoke to the other. Stanley took his exercises and ate his raw food; stoked the furnace on alternate days; read his journals and then hid them; and kept his peace. Vridar became more and more annoyed. He was not vengeful, and he hated this slow patient measurement of vengeance. Knowing that Stanley disliked him and really had no wish to talk to him, Vridar was thrown back into the old desolation. He resolved to force the matter to some kind of crisis. Stanley's gymnastics, he decided, largely in self-defense,

231

were silly and effeminate; and at last he said so. He said he was tired of going to bed always at ten and getting up at six; tired of a tall gawky Mormon who usurped the bed for a headstand; tired of all the munching on raw carrots and celery.

"You may some day be another Sandow or Strongfort but you're only a carrot-eater to me! I'm sick of having you turn the light off while I'm reading! . . . Do you hear me?" He waited for a reply but Stanley ignored him. Stanley was reading his latest copy of *Physical Culture*. "I'm talking to you!" Vridar cried. "Has raw food made you deaf?"

"I heard you," said Stanley quietly. "As usual you are not worth listening to."

"So! You gandershank of a turnip-eater! What in hell have you ever said to astound the world. You reader of love-crap in the *Saturday Evening Post!* A fine college student you are, devoting your life to weight-lifters and circus-freaks!"

"You'll be sick again," said Stanley. "Anger fills your blood with poisons."

This cool rebuke made Vridar sputter. He glared for a moment at Stanley's journal and then smote it and knocked it fluttering to a wall. "If you're looking for trouble," he said, trying to restrain his rage, "stand up and I'll give you a real massaging!"

Stanley walked over and picked up the journal. He glanced at Vridar, his eyes black with spite.

"This room," said Vridar, mixing his words with gurgles of fury, "isn't big enough for both of us. You can stay or get out, take your choice."

"I've been intending to get out," said Stanley quietly. "I can't live with a person as constipated as you."

"Constipated!"

"All people who fart are constipated. You do it in your sleep."

Deeply ashamed now and feeling that he had been mean, Vridar did not know what to say or do. He wanted to forgive and be forgiven and be friends again, for there was in him little power to hold a grudge or nurse a grievance. But he knew that Stanley disliked him and that there was nothing to be said. Stanley now lay down and massaged himself and grunted. He looked at his tongue and his teeth and with a thermometer he took his temperature. The next day he moved, without saying goodbye, and soon thereafter he left the college. Vridar heard many years later that Stanley was an osteopath in a small town.

Alone with himself, Vridar was both frightened and pleased. He was now his own boss. He could eat what he wanted to and read all night if he wanted to. He could wander and stare at lovely girls, and when he returned, no one would ask him where he had been. But on the other hand he felt a terrible loneliness in this small dirty place. There remained in it the personality of another, as if a dear friend had died. In all its homely details he could see a curly-haired youth and hear the munching of celery. He spent little time in the room, save to tend the furnace and eat his meals and sleep.

It was the fear and loneliness in him that led him to seek a friend. He wanted a woman to talk to but he was afraid of women. In November he spoke to a young man who was to be a vital influence in certain years of his life. A. M. McClintock —he swore by all the angels that he had no first name—was twenty-one, an orphan and a sophomore. He was a handsome man in a cynical and evil way. His eyes were of a strange metallic color, and all that the man was, it seemed to Vridar, was recorded in the eyes. All his features were strong and well-formed. He was about five feet and eleven inches in height and was well-muscled, quick and powerful.

Day after day Vriday had sat by him in a classroom. He had asked for Vridar's paper during an examination and Vridar had slipped it to him, and with unblushing gall McClintock had copied it word for word. This had brought upon both of them the suspicion of Professor Yupp. He had looked at them with enraged eyes and he had tapped the two papers and had said that there were students in the class who were cheating. "The son of a bitch won't do anything," McClintock had said. "We're his tenants and all he wants is the rent."

McClintock lived in an attic room on the top floor. After the two in a way became friends McClintock would come down to the basement cell to show off his new clothes or to talk about his latest girl. Vridar distrusted him but liked him. He liked the man's arrogant swagger and his brash way with women and his unabashed boasting. He called McClintock Forenoon and the name stuck.

"You should screw a girl," Forenoon said one day. "I got an old one you can have."

Vridar was insulted but he toyed with the notion. He asked what she was like.

"Dark, this one. She loves with her arms and legs all at the same time. She'll chew your tongue if you give her a chance. Did you know some women like to bite a man's thing?"

Vridar did not know it. He stared at Forenoon and hated him for his intimacies with women.

"Or I got a redhead. I got anything you want. White, yellow, short, fat, tall, hot or cold, just name your preference."

About once a week Forenoon came down to tell of another conquest. He spoke of so many that Vridar thought the man lied and he told him that he lied.

"Well, by God, I'll prove it. Just walk down the street with me."

After hours of envious brooding, after nights of wild fancies and dreams, Vridar consented to go with Forenoon. They went along State Street and entered a drugstore.

"It's the blonde," Forenoon said. "The purple skirt."

Vridar looked at the girl. She was lovely, though he told himself that she was not; she obviously was infatuated with Forenoon, but this also Vridar tried not to see. She came up smiling and dimpling and round the end of the counter gave Forenoon her hand. She did not look at Vridar at all.

In other shops other lovely girls had eyes only for Forenoon. Then by a window he stopped and said, "I can't go in there. I got her in trouble." He withdrew beyond the window. "The dark one at this end."

Vridar looked at the dark girl inside. She too was lovely, and while staring at her Vridar told himself that men who betrayed innocent women ought to be caponized or jailed. "A hell of a man you are," he said, turning away. "Isn't there any principle in you?"

"What are you saying?" asked Forenoon.

"Seducing innocent girls!"

Forenoon shrugged. "If I didn't," he said, "some other guy would. I'd rather it would be me than the other guy."

"That would be his sin, not yours."

"Sin? Listen, you idiot, the girls want it. I give them what they want, don't I?"

"You take advantage of them. They don't really know what they're doing."

"Like hell they don't. When I get done with them they know. And they like it."

"What a citizen you are!" said Vridar.

"They chase me to death," said Forenoon.

Vridar dwelt for a moment on this horrible picture of a scoundrel pursued by innocence. He groaned and blew his nose.

"Don't be a fool," Forenoon said. "Get your share of the girls. Ten to one you'll marry a girl some other man has screwed."

"Me?"

"Yes, you. And it would serve you right. You men of principle rant around and get left; and then you marry some jane we've all had."

"You're stupid," said Vridar, and he thought of Neloa, who was sweet and innocent.

Forenoon said he would help Vridar to find some girls but Vridar would have to spend a little money. He himself allotted five dollars to each prospect; if she did not surrender when he had spent that much he gave her up. Five dollars would buy theater tickets, candy, flowers, and with most of them was enough, though now and then there was a stubborn one. He had wasted money on only two.

The next Saturday evening Forenoon came down attired in his smartest outfit. He brought some garments for Vridar. To tell the truth, he said, no man could get a girl with such outlandish clothes as Vridar wore. A girl looked at clothes before she looked at the man. If a man had barnyard shoes and a necktie like a piece of old ribbon and a self-laundered collar he might as well stay home and read a book. Vridar knew well that his ties were cheap silly things, his mail-order suit smelled like a saddle blanket, his cap (he had no hat) was a shapeless rag that had cost only a few cents; and his shirts and collars he laundered himself. But Forenoon had expensive clothes and he looked like a dandy when he got himself ready for the chase. His hair was oiled, his nails neatly trimmed and polished, his face carefully shaved and creamed and powdered. He wore his hat at a cocky angle.

"Put these on," he said, "and we'll step out."

Vridar protested. He said he was not feeling well. He said he did not care much about girls and would be wearied by their chatter. But he yielded. He put on silk socks, a pair of expensive shoes, a silk shirt, a broad flowing tie, and a suit that looked as if it had been tailored for him. He submitted to having his nails trimmed, his beard shaved, his hair slicked and oiled and scented. When he entered the street he felt as fastidious and curried as an earl. Tonight, Forenoon said, they would pick up two girls, for he wanted a new one. This proposal made

Vridar shiver, and to change the subject he said they should both enlist and go to war. To hell with war, Forenoon said, as long as there were girls to seduce.

"How the shoes fit? . . . Say, good God, you got your hat on backwards!" He seized the hat and turned it around. Vridar had not known that the bow ought to be on the left side. "And your collar!" cried Forenoon, appraising him. "Didn't you ever wear clothes before?" He adjusted the collar and picked two hairs from the lapels. "Little things like that," he said, showing the hairs to Vridar, "have fouled up a lot of seductions. It's clothes that make the man. Haven't you ever heard that?"

"I've never thought much about clothes," Vridar said.

"Well, good God, start thinking about something besides all the damn books you read. Just a hat on backwards or dandruff on your collar or a broken shoe-lace or a little dirt under a fingernail will spoil a seduction. Girls don't mind going to bed with a man if he looks right and smells right."

Forenoon saw two girls coming toward them and he looked them over with critical interest. He said they would do. He told Vridar to have some nice things ready to say. Vridar strove desperately to think of a few polite phrases, pleasant flattering phrases, but all he could think of was hello and how do you do. As the girls drew near he fell into panic, his heart shaking him like blows.

"Ge up here!" Forenoon hissed, looking back at Vridar.

Vridar made a tremendous effort but still lagged behind. He heard Forenoon talking to the girls: "Hello, sweethearts, you going my way?...Lord, what gorgeous dresses! Did you know that they exactly match your hair and eyes?...Great Scott, what faces and what figures! See those feet. . . ." One of the girls was twittering in a choked way; the other, more dignified, was smiling. It was clear to Vridar that they liked Forenoon and his words.

With a lordly gesture Forenoon swung to Vridar and said, "Meet my friend Mr. Keith Foxhall." (The Foxhalls were one of the city's most elite families.) "The most brilliant student in college," Forenoon was saying. "Me, I flunk everything but love. Ah, love! But look into Keith and you'll see the complete works of Shakespeare. . . . Keith, I want you to meet two darned swell girls."

Vridar's face was as red as the red in his tie. Forenoon took the lovelier girl by an arm and turned down the street. Vridar stumbled along with the other girl, feeling unspeakably awkward and silly. The girl ahead looked round at her friend and winked. The girl with Vridar made a droll face. Vridar knew that both girls preferred McClintock and he wondered how he could excuse himself and slip away. Forenoon was talking to his girl and fingering her scarf and gently caressing her arm. Glancing at the girl who walked with him, Vridar thought she looked stiff and annoyed. He ought to talk to her and make little amorous gestures but he did not know how.

"You live in Salt Lake?"

The girl's shrill laugh was almost a whinny. "Madge, you hear that? He wants know do I live in Salt Lake."

Madge looked round. "No, she lives on the moon. She's just visitun."

Blood dyed Vridar from his collar to his hair.

"They both live on the moon," Forenoon said. "Can't you feel how cold they are?" Both girls laughed at this. The one with Vridar kicked playfully at Forenoon and he yelped and capered.

Vridar made another heroic effort. "You a college student?"

The girl clapped a hand to her mouth and shrieked. "Madge, listen! Now he says am I a college student!"

"Sure," said Madge. "The college hard knocks and big bumps. Two more kicks and she'll graduate."

Well, Vridar decided, there was no use talking to this creature. He thought her dull and stupid, but a sidewise glance told him that she had a full bosom. He trudged along, self-conscious, wretched, aware of all that was said and of every little thing that was done. When they came to Main Street, the girl boldly left him and walked with her friend. After a few moments Vridar dodged into the foyer of a hotel and passed through a barber shop and emerged and headed home. What, he asked furiously,did he care about girls?—and he said over in his breath an ode by Keats which he had got by heart. He thought of Neloa Doole, the dark inscrutable lass whom he had idolized for years: she was a different sort: there were in her no amorous twitterings, no childish infatuation with such hellhounds as Forenoon. She was as chaste as his own sister, and as unapproachable as the philosophy of Kant. He would write to her.

He came to his room, still thinking of Neloa, and feeling a little faithless and guilty, for he had been walking with another lass. He wrote a burning letter, pouring into it all his indignities and heartache; telling her that he was living only for books and a great future; promising that when the Antelope hills were again green or golden he would come to her. He asked her to wait for him. He said he would send her a poem. He was reading the letter and feeling very put upon and tearful, when he remembered that she went to the Antelope dances, and waltzed no doubt with such lechers as Dave Wolf and Alvin Kress. Hating her, hating himself more, he tore the letter into shreds, carefully mutilating every term of endearment, and banked the furnace and went to bed.

But he could not put girls out of his mind and he was thinking of them the next day when Forenoon came in. "Where in hell did you sneak off to?"

"That girl didn't like me."

Forenoon dropped to a chair and gave him a leering appraisal. "You fool, you can't expect a girl to like you all at once. Girls are fussy. You have to work on them."

"To hell with girls," Vridar said.

"I tell you again that you'll marry some jane a lot of men have had. But not me. I'll be in bed with Madge in a week and then her future husband can have her."

"I don't care what you do. There are your clothes, take them away."

"Get yourself some decent clothes, you idiot. Steal them."

"I don't steal."

"All right, but you'd be better dressed if you did." Forenoon stared at him a long moment and said: "You help me in exams so I want to help you. I'll bring a girl right here to your room."

"Oh no you won't!" Vridar said.

Forenoon picked up his clothes and said he would fetch a girl and Vridar could spend the night with her. "If you don't sow your wild oats you'll be a hell of a husband when you get married. That's what a man told me."

"I don't care what he told you."

"I'll fetch you an easy one. You won't have any trouble at all."

"Oh, God damn you," Vridar howled, "get out!"

Vridar tried not to think about girls, but he wanted more than he wanted food and air to be with them and share their youth and love. His hunger was like an intense burning pleasure that fed on pain. On his right in his sociology class sat a lovely maid named Delia Farns. She was attracted to Vridar and Vridar knew it: in one glance from a girl he could unerringly read her favor or her scorn. Delia was small and fair, with hazel eyes and an aloof manner. He had never spoken to her, though now and then he swept her face with a quick appraisal, or peered between fingers at her shapely legs. His senses swam in rapture when her arm touched him.

In his English class was a girl named Lottie Ulster. She also was interested in Vridar: more boldly than Delia she looked at him and smiled, or sometimes spoke. She was small and dark and quite pretty, but for a mustache. Vridar thought with a sinking heart of the black hair on her lip but was invited by her glances and driven by his own self-contempt to take an interest in her. When the class was done, he would slip out and wait in the hall, hoping that she would come out alone; but she always came out with friends and he would then go away, feeling very inept and absurd.

One day he saw her alone on a campus bench. There was snow and the weather was cold but there she was. He hid behind a snow-covered bush and looked at her a few moments; he withdrew to examine his emotions and his courage and returned; and again he spied on her. From time to time she would look up as though expecting someone; and at last, when she seemed about to leave, he prodded himself and moved toward her, pretending not to see her at all. He resolved to walk past her but like a man in deep thought, with his gaze on the earth. If she called to him he would show surprise, and if she did not, he would pass on and forget her.

She called. He gave a violent start, much too violent, he realized with dismay, and turned to look at her. "Is the scholar deep in meditation?" she asked saucily.

"Scholar?" he said.

"I wish you'd tell me what a gerund is."

"A gerund?" He went over and stood before her. Well, at least he could speak of gerunds. "It's a verbal noun," he said. "It's derived from a verb but used as a noun."

"Oh?" she said, and he knew then that she was not interested in gerunds at all. She was one of the brighest students and she knew all about gerunds.

"Running is good exercise," he went on blunderingly. "The word running is a gerund."

"Really?" she said, her black eyes studying him. "I've heard that Professor Arnold regards you as his best student."

237

"Me?" he said, blushing a little. He glanced at a spruce laden with snow; he stepped to one side and glanced down the walk, as if he had heard sounds of murder there. He felt dreadfully silly. "I've been wondering," he said, "if you—I mean—" She was smiling at him and waiting. He forced himself to say it: "Would you go to a show with me?"

"I'd love it. When?"

"When?" he said, his mind running empty. "Oh, any time!"

"Tonight?" She wrote on a slip of paper and handed it to him and he saw an address and a telephone number. "If anything turns up that you can't come, you call me."

He liked that. It gave him a way out if his courage failed him.

But at eight o'clock he stood trembling at her door and rang the bell. The bell sounded very loud in the house and he wondered if he had given it too much of a yank. A moment later he was ushered into an enormous room that overwhelmed him with the height and ornateness of its ceiling. Lottie came out draped in folds of red and gave him her hand and said she was very glad he had come.

Of this evening Vridar could afterward remember only a little. They went to a show and they walked up and down a street and they rode on a car. While riding on the trolley with her there was only one thought in his mind, a tremendous dilemma: should he be the first to leave the car or should she precede him? He did not know. He agonized over this awful problem; and all the while Lottie talked to him, gay and vivacious, and now and then pressed his arm. Perhaps, he reasoned, he could tell by her manner what he was expected to do; and when they came to her stop he went down the aisle ahead of her and stepped aside, as if waiting for her. Women, he was telling himself, always went ahead of men, and if this was an exception it was a horribly stupid one. But when she glanced up at his face and then went ahead and stepped down he knew that he had blundered. Her manner was different now. Save for a cool goodnight, she did not speak again, and he turned away from her door, sweating with shame. For two days he ducked his English class, not daring to face her scorn. She never spoke to him again.

This unhappy experience with women convinced Vridar that he ought to leave them alone. He buried himself in books. Women, he assured himself, were not worth the time of any above-average man; and love— What in hell, he asked himself, was love?—and searched in books for an answer. And for the gracious amenities of human intercourse, which had always troubled and annoyed him, he now cultivated a stupendous scorn.

But Forenoon for some obscure reason was determined to have Vridar share his amorous adventures. He often came in; he told with leering relish the details of his own affairs; he urged Vridar to go to a party or a dance. When he told how his girls kissed and moaned and cried with rapture, Vridar hated him. He tried to look weary and sleepy, but his mind was alive with the pictures and his blood was on fire.

One evening Forenoon told about Ardith Young whom he had seduced right on the sofa in her own living-room; but he was tired of her now. The idiot wanted to marry him. She wept and entreated and threatened to jump off a high building or tell her father. She threatened to tell the president of the college. "You got to take her off of my hands," Forenoon said. "You go to make her forget me."

"You have your lousy nerve! You think I want your castoff mistresses?"

"Do it as a friend," Forenoon said. "I'd do that much for you."

"To hell with it. If you get in trouble you can get out."

"I'll pay your expenses," Forenoon said. "Take her to shows and buy her some flowers and stuff. When you get her mind off of me you can put her to bed. She's damned good-looking and she knows her stuff."

"Thanks!" said Vridar.

"I'd do it for you. If you get in trouble I'll help you."

Vridar stared bitterly at Forenoon and said: "This city will be full of your kids. You'll be seeing them on every corner."

"Like Brigham Young," said Forenoon, grinning. "Well, every man worth his salt has a lot of kids he has never seen." He mused a while and added: "I guess you don't know Bertha Owen. She's married now. Married the guy she was engaged to when I met her. She has a kid and it's my kid but the bastard she married thinks it's his kid. Vridar, God damn it, none of us can be sure about our own dad. You'd be surprised how many girls pan kids off on the other guy."

"I'm not interested in such girls," said Vridar. "There is another kind." He was thinking of Neloa Doole.

"No, there isn't any other kind. If you were engaged to one right now I'd bet you I could seduce her."

"You lie!" said Vridar. "The woman I intend to marry would have only contempt for you."

Forenoon grinned, a sly evil grin. "Introduce me to her," he said.

A week later he dashed into the room, agog with excitement, and found Vridar in bed. He said he had good news. "Listen, I got a girl for you and she's right here, almost under your nose!"

"Stop shouting."

"Listen," said Forenoon, glancing round him like a conspirator. "She's up in my room."

"In your room!"

"In my room," he said, whispering. "I locked her in. Listen. I'll sleep with her tonight and you can have her tomorrow night." Still whispering, Forenoon said he had found her on the streets, starved and penniless; he had fed her and brought her to his room. And there she was, undressed and put to bed. "I'll keep her locked in. I'll give you the key tomorrow. I'll sleep here."

Vridar was too amazed to speak. Taking his silence as consent Forenoon slipped out, and Vridar heard him climbing the uncarpeted stairs. He lay in bed, thinking of the matter: now Forenoon was with her, in bed with her, drawing her to him in close embrace. Vridar sat up. He was thinking of this girl as a poor forlorn waif, abducted, ravished, imprisoned; and he deliberated rescuing her, as men used to do in old books. Here was life indeed, dark and melodramatic; here was the old triangle, the villain and the hero and the maiden who implored help. In a number of roles he saw himself as a hero. He saw himself pitching Forenoon like a sack of barley through a window and carrying a weeping and beautiful girl in his arms. He saw himself enshrined in glory, his name on the front pages and his heroism burning in the editorials. . . . But he sank back, knowing that he would do nothing at all.

As a matter of fact he wanted to see this girl and be alone with her—not to be intimate with her, Lord, no, though he liked to play with the thought and to luxuriate in his fancies. Luxuriating he turned over to sleep and was tormented all night in his dreams. On his way to the campus the next morning he looked up at Forenoon's window, trying to realize that a girl was there. As the day waned and evening came on he began to feel afraid, not knowing what he would do or what he wished to do.

Forenoon came in, not excited now but jaded and spent. He looked as if he had not slept at all. He said he had not. It had been a wild night of rapture and love. The girl was a little scrawny but very ardent and very insatiable. "Tomorrow," he said, "you'll feel the way I feel now."

Vridar said nothing. He would pretend that he was going to sleep with the girl.

"Here's the key," Forenoon said. "Don't make a racket going up the stairs." He lay on the bed and stretched out and yawned, showing his strong perfect teeth. "Run along," he said. "I want to sleep."

Vridar stood up, his knees shaking, and went to the door.

"In the morning," said Forenoon, "leave the door unlocked so she can sneak out."

Vridar passed into the hall and found the street. His thoughts and emotions were running wild races while he wondered what he should do. He crossed the street and looked up at the window but the window told no tale. Still, there seemed to be light behind the shade. While he stood in wretched indecision, girls passed him, twittering, like adolescents in springtime. Vridar stared after them until they passed from sight. Then he went to the porch and softly climbed the stairs.

Halfway up he paused and considered again. It was while he was standing here, undecided, that he thought of Neloa. Memory of her was like a burst of light. He would keep himself pure for Neloa because she was pure: she was not another Tess and he would not be another Angel, vulgarizing the bridal night with confessions of old wrong. He climbed again. He came to a small unclean stairway that wound upward in a corkscrew like those in a tower. He followed it and came to a low-ceilinged room that was used as a kitchen by the attic tenants; and ahead of him was McClintock's door. He went over to it and listened. There was no sound within but a tiny spray of light came through a crack. For a few minutes he stood here, trying to control his shaking legs and his wild heart. Then softly he inserted the key and turned the lock, stepped quickly inside and closed the door.

The girl was sitting on the bed and she was looking at him with large dark eyes. He saw at once that she was very thin and pale, a tiny thing with a pinched face, and big eyes wide open, looking at him. She had her shoes and stockings off, her dress loose at her breast, her hair down. Vridar went over and looked down at her and she looked up but she did not speak. He thought there was something cruel and

240

flickering in her eyes. He was feeling great pity for her, a virgin only two days ago, now a forlorn thing ravished and undone.

"Why are you here?" he asked, and was startled when her response was a hysterical giggle.

"Why am I here? Where in hell should I be?"

"This," said Vridar sternly, "is no place for a woman. Where is your home?"

"My home! The streets."

"You mean you have no home? Where is your mother?"

"Christ, how should I know!"

Vridar sat on the bed and studied her. There was something hard in her tone and her face, as if she had been kicked about, homeless and unloved. Perhaps her parents had deserted her. Perhaps she had fought the fight Paul spoke of, keeping her virtue and her pride until hunger drove her to this. While he was wondering about her, she moved close and fell into his arms. He thought she was sick and faint, and he held her, looking at her white pitiful face, and feeling great compassion and strength.

"Why don't you go back home?" he asked gently.

"Listen, kid, the world is my home. It's big and I like it."

"How old are you?"

"Old enough to know my way around." She reached up and caressed his cheek. "Kid, where's your beard?"

This insult to his thin beard annoyed Vridar. "Never mind about beards. I came here to talk to you about serious things."

"Yes, darling, like a whore's dream. I know what you come for."

"You don't. I'm not that kind of a man."

"Then what kind are you?"

"I'm not like the one who stayed with you last night."

"Darling, he was nice. He give me nice things to eat. He give me new stockings. And if you can love like he can it'll put hair on your face."

Vridar was baffled. Her casual use of endearments and her profane tongue and her hand on his thigh: what did these mean? Was she actually a harlot—or was she only sick and abandoned and desperate? "Listen," he said, "you stay here tonight and in the morning you go back home." Her hand still stroked his cheek. Her other hand had moved between his thighs. He took it away.

"Honey," she said, purring. All her movements were feline.

Vridar shook her a little. "Promise that you'll go home."

"Don't!" she cried, and her voice was so cold and hard that he could not miss it. "I hate cavemen."

"Promise that—"

"You mean to go to church?"

"I mean—"

"Darling boy, I want some ice cream."

"Please be serious. If you will promise—"

"Are you up here to sleep with me?"

"No," said Vridar, looking at the guile in her eyes. "I came—"

"Boy, I know what you came for. Your friend said you would. And do you want it for nothing or will you get me some ice cream?"

Vridar pushed her away and stood up. He was troubled by the feeling that he was being incredibly stupid. "I came up to help you," he said, looking at her.

"Like a bishop's bells you did! You got a cigarette!"

"No."

The girl was now looking at him curiously. Had he really come to help her? she asked, and suddenly she began to weep. She threw herself on the bed and sobbed like one overwhelmed by remorse, and Vridar stared at her, unable to tell whether her grief was real or feigned. Were there tears in her eyes or was she only making the sounds of grief? His thought went back to Agnes, who had wept to have her way with Borg, and to his mother who had told him—O Lord, how many times!— that all women would be chaste and pure but for the lusts of men. He was still wondering what to say, what to do, when the girl sat up, her eyes running water, her hair in a ragged tangle. She reached for one of his hands and she seemed then to be so pathetic and lost that he sat on the bed by her; and at once she moved over to lie in his arms.

"What shall I do?" she whispered, looking up at him.

"Go home."

"But how can I? I'm flat on my rump."

"Where is your home?"

"Butte."

Vridar considered. "How much is the fare to Butte?"

"I don't know. Fifteen dollars."

"I can't give you that much."

"Darling, then how can I get home?"

He looked at her mouth, wondering if she had ever brushed her teeth; at her thin pinched nose; at her large tearful eyes which were gazing up at him. He thought of Neloa and felt a pang of guilt: great heavens, what would she think of him if she could see him now!

"Give me the fifteen dollars, kid, and I'll go home."

"I can't give you fifteen."

From one of his eyes to the other, back and forth, here own eyes were looking, searching. "How much can you give?"

"Five, maybe."

She sat up and tossed her hair back. "All right, kid, let's have the five."

"I don't have it with me," he said. Perceiving that she doubted him he dug into his pockets, turning them inside out.

Her eyes narrowed. "You're like all men," she said. "I thought you was different but you ain't."

"I don't have the money with me," he said, a little angrily, "but I'll give it to you."

"Where?"

"At the drugstore corner, just below here."

"When?"

"Oh, about eight in the morning."

"You mean five dollars?"

"Yes."

"Well, kid, you just as well stay with me tonight. I'll try to give you your money's worth."

Vridar stood up. "No, thanks." He went to the dor and turned. She was sitting on the bed, wide-eyed, her mouth open, two sagging breasts half out of her blouse. Softly he opened the door and stepped into the hall and closed it; and when he was again on the street he looked up at the window, wondering how much of the experience had been true, how much of it false. This woman, he supposed, was a harlot—but Jesus had lifted up the harlot. Jesus had said— Yes, yes, he thought, I know what Jesus said, but I'm a fool for all that. His mother had made a fool of him. This girl had made a fool of him. Bonnie had made a fool of him, and Betty, and Wanda: what had he ever been but a fool for women? But I won't be a fool all my life, he said, walking round and round the block, waiting for the dawn. I won't let Neloa make a fool of me. I'll never let any woman make a fool of me again. . . .

But he doubted this, and he felt miserable and shamed and stupid when at last he went into the basement cell and aroused Forenoon. Forenoon sat up and rubbed at his eyes and said: "Well, how was she?—all right?"

"All right, I guess."

"How many times did you do it to her?"

"That's my business."

Forenoon reached for his socks and began to dress but he was looking at Vridar. Then he grinned, that sly evil grin. "You feel all right?"

"Of course I feel all right."

"Maybe you won't in a day or two. I think she gave me a dose of clap."

A few days later Forenoon came into the room, fuming and cursing. He said the lousy slut up in his room had given him a pretty one. By God, it would take all the money he had for a cure.

"Did she give you a dose?"

"No."

"You lucky bastard! This is the third time I've been caught!" He stormed outside, cursing women, swearing by all the angels that they would pay for this. They would pay and pay. . . . Vridar sat on the bed, thinking of the five dollars he had given to a whore, thinking of himself as one of the most incredible fools on earth, yet feeling that somehow he had done right, for Jesus himself had lifted the harlot up and blessed her.

III

With five dollars he could have bought a pair of shoes and a hat; he could have had a decayed tooth crowned; or he could have had a dictionary and a thesaurus. Shamed by his stupidity, he counted over and over the things that five dollars would have bought. To make up for the loss he became during the holidays a clerk

243

in the grocery department of a large store. He tried to learn quickly by observing the ways of the older clerks and he tried to be cheerful and courteous, but the patrons exhausted his patience and he wanted to boot them into the street. . . .

"Here, boy," said an enormous woman with a sour face.

He was annoyed because she called him boy. "Yes, madam. Can I be of service to you?"

"You'n take my money, I guess. That's what you're here for, ain't it?"

"I'm here to serve you."

"Serve me!" she snorted, and barged from place to place, with Vridar following her. "Boy, where's your lettuce?"

"This way, madam."

She went to a crate of lettuce and pawed with big dirty hands. "Where's your potatoes?"

"This way, please."

"You don't have to say please. If I want to buy I'll buy. You can't coax me. How much are they?"

"Three cents a pound or a dollar a bushel."

"Who said I wanted a bushel? Where's Maggie?"

Vridar looked around him. "I guess she's out to lunch."

The woman went over and stared into a barrel of coffee. She took a handful and smelled of it. "Give me a pound and don't weigh the sack."

Vridar scooped coffee into a paper sack and set the sack on the scales.

"That ain't a pound," she said.

He added little by little until the hand on the dial stood at sixteen ounces.

"More. You're weighun the sack."

He added a little more. He knew that the manager of the department was watching him.

"More," said the woman.

"It's a pound, madam. In fact it's more than a pound."

"Boy, don't you think I'n see? I didn't come here to buy your paper sacks." The woman became abusive and the manager came over and spoke to her. "He's tryun to cheat me," she said. "When I pay for a pound I want a pound."

The manager took the bag and weighed it. "It's more than a pound," he said, and he opened the sack and poured some out.

"I won't pay for your paper!" the woman cried. "Where's Maggie Simms?"

The manager said she was out to lunch but would return soon. The woman said she would wait, and she went to a bench and sat.

Vridar knew what the trouble was. He had learned that several of the clerks were cheats and Maggie was one of them. When Maggie's friends came in, they bought a few bulky things like vegetables and breakfast foods, and into the bags Maggie slipped small expensive things—canned chicken, olives, vanilla, jams.

The clerks were on a competitive basis. If Vridar's sales averaged fifty dollars a day, the manger had told him, he would be kept as a Saturday clerk throughout the year. Vridar had thought it fair enough. But he soon learned that women came here expecting more than they paid for, and that some of the clerks gave

244

them more, and so kept them as steady customers. Vridar gave to each buyer what she paid for and some of them never came to him a second time. But by working swiftly and being alert he kept his sales up and got the dislike of clerks who had been with the store a long time. When after a few days the manager dismissed him he said it was to keep harmony in the department, and Vridar wanted to say, "Your clerks are cheaters and you must be dumb or you'd know it." But he said nothing. For telling tales Jed Bridwell had half-killed him. He had resolved never to tell again.

To find another job he went to Annie G. Foote, the dean of women. Aunt Annie, she was called; and the more impudent students when speaking of her said Aunt Annie gee! She was a huge woman with a face to match her well-padded frame. She was elderly and a spinster and a tradition.

When Vridar entered her office, she was busy giving loud advice to a professor. She said the man was not eating the right food and he was not exercising enough. While she talked, Vridar sized her up. She had a tight mouth, hair twisted into a knot, large powerful hands. She would weigh, he imagined, more than two hundred pounds: never had he seen so much woman in one dress. But it was her eyes that held his interest. They were small and gray and full of light, and it was the light in them that baffled him. It was a ravenous light, alert, greedy, flickering, morbidly curious. They were the eyes of a full passionate woman, removed from life and impounded in a deanship. After the abashed professor had got his hat and slunk out, Annie swung in her chair and looked at Vridar.

"Well, young man, what can I do for you?"

"Why, I—I wondered if maybe you could help me find some work."

"Supporting yourself?" Her manner of speaking, hard and clipped and deep-bosomed, was almost offensive. Her questions came like blows. "A freshman?"—"Living alone?"—"Sit down."

He sat and she looked at him.

"Where you from?"

"Idaho. Antelope."

"Never heard of it. Parents living?"

"Yes maam."

"Farmers?"

"Yes maam."

"Poor?"

"Quite poor."

For a few moments her strange eyes studied him. "Where you living?"

"At Professor Yupp's."

"In one of those drygoods boxes?"

"In the basement. I tend the furnace."

Under her breathing her bosom moved up and down like a great pillow. One big hand on her desk toyed with an inkstand. "Cook your own food?"

"Yes maam."

"What you eat?"

"Well," he said, blushing a little, "cereals and fruits and vegetables."

245

"You don't eat enough. You're pale and skinny. Sleep with your window open?"

"It won't open."

Her grunt was a grunt of scorn. Professor Yupp's basement, she said, wasn't fit for hogs. "Eat more. Get fresh air when you sleep. Drink lots of water?"

"Well, yes, I think I do."

"Drink more. Eat more. Exercise more. As soon as spring opens, I'll want my yard dug up. That will be good for you. Meanwhile I'll see what I can find." Vridar stood up, thinking the interview was over. "Sit down," she said. He sat. "Remember, eat more, drink more, get fresh air, exercise. You're too puny and pale for anything."

"Yes maam."

"Smoke?"

"No maam."

"Come tomorrow." She turned to the next student and Vridar almost tiptoed outside.

When spring came, he spaded in her back yard. Birds sang round him and the earth was rich and sweet. He felt nostalgia for the wild flowers and fir trees and blue mists and loneliness of his homeplace. One afternoon Annie came out to watch him toil. She said he was working too fast. She said he looked just as pale and scrawny as ever. Had he been drinking plenty of water and sleeping in fresh air and eating more food?

"Yes maam," he said.

It was while she was here that he got his first and only full vision of the woman's soul. She had some chickens in the yard, and a rooster started in pursuit of a hen. The rooster overtook the hen and mounted her. Vridar, feeling acute embarrassment, glanced at Miss Foote. What he saw in her face and eyes he could never have found words for; but its meaning was plain to him, as plain as if he had seen it in print. Never had he seen and rarely was he again to see such morbid fixed interest, such girlish adolescent wondering, such hunger and loss and loneliness in a person's eyes. His heart went out to her in great compassion. He understood her now and all her abrupt imperious ways; and he loved her.

He was still looking at her, astonished by what he saw, when she noted his stare. A wave of blood went up her throat. "Is that any way to gawk at a person?" she asked, and turned and entered the house.

Vridar earned four dollars spading her yard. He now had nineteen dollars of his own, but he bought nothing for himself. On the contrary, his wish to be faithful to his parents and to spare their savings impelled him to extremes of labor and self-denial. He still laundered his clothes and cooked his own bread. From where he lived it was two miles to the shopping center but he always walked. He bought groceries only on Saturday night, so that he could return after dark and not be seen; and if he saw students coming or anyone who looked like a student, he would pull his cap down to hide his face.

One of these journeys he was never to forget. He had his arms full. He had a small bag of flour and another of sugar, and some canned goods and vegetables and fruits. He had thought he could carry all these, but after climbing the mountain

246

for a mile or more he felt exhausted and spent. Sitting on a curb with no house close by, he wondered what he should do. At one side was a billboard on a vacant lot and he went behind it and dug a hole and buried a part of his groceries. The remainder he carried uphill to his room; and early the next morning when almost nobody was astir, he returned for what he had left. It was in this way that he saved a nickel, only a nickel, not for himself but for his parents, for whom a nickel meant more than an hour of toil.

It was in this way and in other ways that he saved sixty-five dollars of the two hundred which his parents had given him. In later years when he heard young men say that they would have gone to college if they had had a chance, if they had had the money, he would look at them and feel pity. Yes, they would have gone, but only if their meals were cooked, their room cared for; and if they had money for fraternity dues and girls and clothes. They would not have trudged two miles up a mountain to save a nickel. They would not have worn ugly shoes and a rag of a cap and one cheap shapeless suit. They would not have lived in a smoky cell and stoked a dirty furnace and lived with the sense of being a social outcast. . . .

Vridar had not expected to find snobs in college, even though he had known them in high school. He had thought that college students would be humble and studious and lovers of books. He strove for months to believe that college was all that he had dreamed it would be. He resisted the truth and fought stubbornly against it. But the evidence of his folly, of his stupid credulous childlike faith, was so overwhelming that he was filled with dismay. Week after week and month after month he saw more and more clearly that Wasatch College was largely posturing and farce. Its disregard of truth appalled him. Its fawning obeisance to wealth and politics made him deeply and unhappily aware of the simian in the human face.

Its students, save a handful, were not interested in books at all. They were interested in its social world: its fraternities and sororities, ranging in snobbery down through three nationals to a score of locals; in its clubs, which established the prominence of the choicest aristocrats; in its Junior Prom, a stiffly formal extravagance afforded only by a few; and in dances and athletics and erotic pastime. They were interested in making monkeys of their professors and a casual compulsion of their studies.

The social leaders he could tell at a glance. He knew them by their smart clothes, but most of all by their yawning boredom in the classroom and their undisguised contempt for their instructors. They were brawling adolescence in the halls. They gathered near the bookstore in the main building and the men cut capers and guffawed, and the girls in one moment looked haughty and in the next giggled and squeaked. So many obscene things were said, especially about the dean of women, that he wondered again if mankind was as vulgar as it seemed to be.

And always, no matter where he went, he was conscious of derisive eyes. He would look about, curious to know if he was the shabbiest person in the College, and decided that he was. Others were out of style; others wore cheap garments. Others went timidly about, as he did, overcome by the splendor and the scorn. But he saw no one who seemed to launder his own collars and to look so homespun and out of place. In a classroom while intent on what the instructor was saying,

247

he would become aware of searching eyes. He would turn to meet them, and he would find one of the aristocrats looking him over. Then he would sweat with shame, and his mind would be a void. Perhaps it was his long hair which needed trimming, or his self-laundered collar stained from the iron, or his ridiculous tie. Sometimes on the campus students would turn to look at him and speak to one another. He would then burn with fury, with dark awful hatred. He would recall with but little comfort what a critic had said of Dickens, "He disliked a certain look on the face of a man when he looks down on another man. And that look on that face is the only thing in this world that we have really to fight between here and the fires of hell." Why was it that in a college, of all places, human understanding and fellowship were not the shining lights! Why was it that so many of the lowliest ones, the bookworms, the sons and daughters of the soil, aspired to social distinction? Forenoon said they did. When he spoke of fraternities and the other social life denied him, he got into a furious sweat. He cursed the school and his own humble birth. He became a practiced thief. "If you have money you belong! If you don't your brains aren't worth a God damn!"

"You know what Ruskin said?"

"Ruskin who?"

"He said self-complacency is the mark of a secondrate intellect."

"Balls! Who was he?—a professor of education or something? If you have money you don't have to worry about brains."

"I'd rather have the brains."

"Take mine and give me your money. We'll see who is happiest."

"I haven't much money," said Vridar drily, "but it's enough, I imagine, to buy all the brains you have."

"Listen! Next year I'll be in the Poison Skull. Watch me."

The Poison Skull was the College's most exclusive male club. Only juniors were eligible, and they were chosen by the Albatross and Padlock, senior members of the Poison Skull. Each year the initiates clowned about the campus and then in the auditorium. This spring Vridar watched them.

They appeared in garb chosen by the Albatross and Padlock; one of them as an Indian with feathers in his hair and red paint on his naked arms, legs, and torso; another as an old woman with a broom; a third as a Bushman, carrying a half-dozen cowbells. A fourth was dressed as a young girl and was said to be a very amorous virgin. A fifth was an escaped jailbird, attired in outlandish pajamas. The sixth was an idiot who went babbling and jibbering while pursuing girls or thieving from the bookstore. The seventh, a huge fellow, was grotesquely padded, with two pillows on his chest. He represented the dean of women.

Into the history class one morning came the Bushman, his bells in terrific uproar. The class shouted approval, but Professor Johns had only contempt for such antics. He flew into a rage and ordered the Bushman outside; and with indignant sympathy the amorous virgin and the dean of women followed him. Most of the students whooped with glee.

During this whole week the campus was turned into an orgy of nonsense. Classes were deserted while students followed the clowns. During the noon hour they gathered in the main corridor, and taking turns standing on a large box they told jests so vile that Vridar's ears burned. Upon spinsters and particularly the dean of women they turned obscene anecdotes. If now and then a professor ventured close to listen, he soon slunk away. But these indecencies were nothing compared with the show in the auditorium. After the Bushman had given a vulgar dance, after the amorous virgin had performed so lewdly that the assembled students dared not applaud, the idiot made preposterous attempts to rape the dean of women. The few instructors who had come and many of the students left the hall.

So this, Vridar reflected, was higher education when it relaxed! For this his parents had slaved and hoarded, for this he had fought his way through school. He had expected to find a scholarly atmosphere and he found a circus; he had expected to find quiet halls of learning, but often professors had to pause and wait because of honking horns and racing engines in the driveway outside. And in the library study was almost impossible: it was the rendezvous of social groups and lovers and clowns.

Cheating, Vridar learned, chiefly from Forenoon, was as common as vulgarity. One fraternity house had a room devoted exclusively to old compositions, term papers, and solutions of problems in the sciences. In Vridar's own class, he heard, Arnold had read aloud and praised themes that were ten years old. Yes, this was college in his own land. For this he had cooked his own meals and lived in shacks and suffered outrage and shame. Nevertheless, he might have reconciled himself to all this but for another matter. It was the faculty, after all, and not the students, on which he had set his faith. If he had found them noble and generous, without envy and malice and with devotion to truth, he would have found an anchor. He would have cared less what his clothes were like; he would have braved the derision. But little by little he came to see his teachers for what they were. He respected Arnold and Bogan, but most of them were not guides, not philosophers and friends.

This was college, and when spring came Vridar was sick of it. He thought of an old Jewish proverb which he had read: men are like trees, and though some grow taller, down in the earth where they are rooted they are all alike. Was there nothing more? He was wondering if there was nothing more when there came to the campus a famous novelist, Mr. Harold Bell Wright. Mr. Wright spoke to Arnold's class in English composition; and Vridar, sitting on a front seat, leaned forward, his ears open, his eyes fixed on the great man. He thought the novelist gave a noble and impassioned address; and when the class was dismissed, Vridar hastened to the library, convinced that here was a great man whom all men could esteem. In former times he had searched in vain for the works of Turgenev and Meredith and Flaubert, but Mr. Wright's novels were there. He thought with pride of the library, his library in his school, that stacked its shelves with the thoughts of great men. He chose a novel and began to read.

For a few moments he thought the book was all right. Then doubt came and the doubt grew and he closed the book and tried to think about it. There was something wrong here. There was something terribly empty and silly about these pages—for they were no better than the stuff he had written when a high school freshman. He opened the book and read again and came to this:

> He was really a fine looking young man with the appearance of being exceptionally well-bred and well-kept. Indeed the most casual of observers would not have hesitated to pronounce him a thoroughbred and a good individual of the best type that the race has produced.
> "—Barbara," he cried, "don't you *know* that I love you? . . . Your desert has taught me many things, dear, but nothing so great as this—that I want you and that nothing else matters. I want you for my wife!"

Good God! He had written that kind of stuff when only a child, and later had read it and with shame had burned it. Had the desert, so vast and terrible in its beauty, taught a novelist no more than that? The book was stupid and false because it had taken a common experience, a sweet and lovely experience, and had made it indecent and silly. The man was a sawdust creature, a shop-window dummy, and words came out of him as out of a phonograph and there was no meaning in the words. He returned the book and went to his room, thinking of the novelist's earnest face and impassioned words; remembering: "Some write of the ugly things at their feet but I write of the beautiful things up there in the stars." What an impostor, what a fraud! And why in heaven's name had Professor Bogan invited into his class a man who had nothing to say?

In this spring, after the city and the mountains had flowered, Vridar took long walks alone, striving to understand his place in life. He still dreamed of becoming an author but doubt in him was chronic, doubt of his capacity and powers. The sweetness and light of surfaces he had no interest in; the dark depths under the surface he did not understand. His mother had wanted him to become a doctor, and so one day he went to a big room in a building that smelled of acids and ether. A student of anatomy spread a rubberized cloth over a dead Negro and sat on the corpse and ate his lunch. In a big vat Vridar saw a dead man afloat. This room was called the Chamber of Stiffs and it reeked of death and alcohol.

While the students ate their lunch, Vridar listened to their jesting about this Negro, and about another man, a murderer who had been convicted and shot. "Hear the guy," said the student perched on the Negro. "The bastard is squawking."

"Maybe he isn't dead," said another. "Whack him on his casa innominata."

"He's rumbling," said the perched student, "in his Haversian canals. The bloke is full of air."

Another student came over and pulled the cloth back from the head. "He was sure a big son of a bitch. What knocked him over?"

"Diabetes melitus, and boy, he had it plenty."

"I wouldn't mind cutting him up. I've always wanted to carve a Negro—but me, I have only a dame that died of ovarian tumor."

"You're lucky," said a fourth, sitting on a vat and munching a sandwich. "You would get a woman."

"What in hell can a guy do with a dead woman?"

"Some do plenty. Ever heard of necrophilia?"

"Not me, I'm dumb. I've just heard of liver fluke. . . . Well, what in hell is it?"

"It would be dangerous to tell a guy like you."

Vridar meanwhile was moving about the room, affecting to be only mildly curious. He envied these men who could jest about the horrible. He was looking at a jar when one said to him, "That's what you looked like twenty years ago. It has a tail."

"We all had tails," said another.

"You looked like a rabbit."

"Like a fish first. Then like a rabbit. Then like a monkey."

"Say, this God damned nigger keeps letting off big sighs!"

"Get off him, you fool. You're sitting right in his stomach and you're hurting him."

The one sitting on the Negro pulled an apple from his pocket and wiped it on his shirt sleeve and began to eat.

Vridar went out into clean air, knowing that he could never be a doctor. His father had suggested law, but the students of law on this campus were so aggressive and self-assured that he gave up all notions of law. He might be a teacher in some great school, though he had begun to wonder if truth had many friends in American colleges and universities. His deepest wish was to be a writer, but he remembered with distaste his earlier poems and his novel and doubted that he had the talent.

Taking his problem with him, he climbed to a northern peak and looked across mountains and valleys toward his home. The flowers were out now. Bluebirds and finches, warblers and meadowlarks were in every bush and tree. The hills of Antelope were green again, and upon these hills in a two-room shack by the dusty highway was Ncloa Doole. She was about fifteen now. He had not seen her for two years, but he knew that she was tall and queenly, with a great mane of hair that fell down her back and almost to her knees. He had written many letters to her but had posted none of them. He knew she was not going to school, for no high school was on those hills; yet if she became his wife she would have to be, like himself, a lover of books. . . .

A few days later there came from his sister a short letter. It said:

Dear Brother,

Everything is about the same up here. It looks like an early spring. Father is getting out wood and mother is cleaning her coops. There isn't any news.

I do sometimes wonder if you are still interested in Neloa. I don't like to be a tattletale but I think you ought to know some things. She's running around with Dave Wolf. You know what he is. He'll have her in trouble if she doesn't look out. I've heard that she is pretty wild. I only know what I hear and I just write this in case you'd like to know.

Your loving sister

Diana

Vridar read the letter a dozen times, and its implications became more horrible with each reading. Yes, he knew Dave, a sandy lecherous fellow whose wife had

251

left him. He could not believe that Neloa was going with him. Yet here was Diana's letter and Diana would not lie. Perhaps Neloa was only having a little fun. Still. . . . He decided to write to her and he wrote one letter after another, each becoming, it seemed to him, more feeble and childish than the one before it. He spread them out and read them over and over and at last chose one:

Dear Neloa:
I have been told that you are going with Dave Wolf. That is your business, of course, and not mine, but I think you should know that his wife left him because of his lecheries, and that his interest in you is not honorable. You are very young or I would not presume to speak to you in this way.

Love, as always,

Vridar

After he had posted the letter he again walked, trying to put down his jealousy and suspicions. If Wolf seduced her, ought he to kill the man? Should he toss a gun to him in the way of strong men everywhere? He knew that the thought was silly. He believed that Neloa was still sweet and pure and that some day she would be his wife. His faith in colleges had been shaken, and his faith in people; but Neloa had been the loveliest thing in his dreams ever since that morning many years ago when he first saw her in the road. He told himself that he was being very foolish and unreasonable, for she had a mother to admonish, a father to protect his own. But back in his room the doubts would not be put away. Feeling more and more wretched, at last he wrote to Diana, asking her to be very explicit, to say in plain words exactly what she knew. Was it not merely an idle rumor? A few days later her reply came:

Dear Brother,
your letter sounds like you don't think I told the truth. Have I ever lied to you? Neloa has been teaching the Nevel children this winter and Dave was up there for three days, just him and Neloa with the children. I know this because father was out there and saw them. I do not say that she has done wrong and I don't think she has. I just wrote to tell you what we all know because I thought you would like to know. But if you do not care about her I will not mention it again.

Diana

Upon the words, I do not say that she has done wrong, Vridar fixed his burning gaze. He stared at the words until he could see only a black line in a mist. Would Neloa be all right until he saw her again? He wanted to believe that she would, but Forenoon had said: "I can seduce ninety-five girls out of a hundred, including that stupid Antelope peasant you are breaking your heart for." Was Forenoon right?—or had Vridar's mother looked to the deeper truth when she had said that all girls preferred to be chaste, if men would only leave them alone?

Two weeks passed and no letter came from Neloa. Vridar sent another warning and waited again. With no interest in school now, or in anything save this tremendous dilemma, he moved about like a dazed person occupied by one emotion.

He thought of leaving school and going home. He searched in books to learn what great men had said about women, and in Michelet he found these words:

> Woman, busied during the later centuries with men's affairs, has in requital lost her own true role,—that of *healing,* and *consoling,* that of the fairy that restores to health and happiness. This is her true priesteshood,—hers by divine right, no matter what the Church may have said

to the contrary.

He read the words over and over, trying to reach with all his senses into their full meaning. What *had* the Church said? What did Michelet mean?—that women had lost their true role, that of healing and consoling: had men done this to them? He read further:

> With her delicate organs, her love of the finest detail, her tender appreciation of life, she is called to be its quick-eyed confidante in every science of observation. With her gentle heart and sweet pity, her instinctive kindness, she is a heaven-sent healer. Sick folk and children are very much alike; both need a woman to tend them.

He wrote the words down and slipped the paper into his inside coat pocket and walked again; and he read them over and over as he walked, until he knew them by heart. He felt that there was a deep truth in what the great historian had said, a truth that was somehow related to what his mother had said, to what she had suffered from her husband. Healing! he thought. Healing is what I need—and consoling. But would Neloa be the one to console and heal him? Would she understand that he belonged to the sick folk and the children?

He waited for a letter and abandoned hope; and then one day the letter came. In all his years afterward it was to stand in memory as sharply etched as flying geese in a gray sky. This is what it said:

Antelope, Idaho
May 14, 1916

Dear Friend—if you don't like my gait (gate) don't swing on it.

Neloa Doole

IV

Summer was warm and full on Antelope now. The lower hills flanking the fields of Poplar were a desolate gray, but they were always so. Above them in the east was a rolling prairie of green, draped with shimmering haze; and beyond was the great arc of mountain, sculptured in purple and black. In the northeast where the bowl of his home lay, with the river flung like an arm around it, Vridar could see clouds like white floating islands. Down under the clouds was the awful quiet.

When he came to Antelope Creek he paid the mail carrier with whom he had ridden and set his bags by the roadside. Across the six miles between him and his home he would have to walk. He was in no hurry; he went over to a cove with his bags and sat in thought. He was curious to know how he felt, now that he was so close to that spot where he had spent so many bitter hours of his childhood

253

and youth. Would the power seize him as formerly and shake him with the old dread, or had the last nine months set him free?

For another reason, too, he sat here. Not far away he could see the log shack where Neloa lived. He looked at the place, thinking of her as walking in that yard, down that road; sleeping under that dirt roof or sitting in that swing; striving with each picture to make it seem real that she lived there. He thought of her a moment as one who had been seduced and now walked with the memory of it in her thighs and on her lips; and certainty that this was so became such madness in him that he went over the hill and to a glen quite close to her house. Her father was in the yard, the lean and furtive and Indian-looking Tim Doole; and her mother also, a tall gaunt Danish woman with a sad face and tragic eyes. For an hour he stared but there was no sign of Neloa. He then arose, hating her and himself, and picked up his bags and turned homeward; and as he trudged through sagebrush and across wheat fields he became sure of one thing: if she was to be his wife—he could imagine himself with no other girl—he should go to her at once and declare his love and ask her to return to school.

But where to meet her, how and when, was the problem. He could not meet her at a dance because he did not know how to dance and he could not take her for a drive with team and buggy, for his father had no buggy. He was afraid to go to her home. He devised a plan, and though it seemed to him to be very childish and unmanly it was all that he could think of: he would give a party at the home of his parents, and if Neloa came among the guests he would go into the woods with her and tell his love. Having settled this matter, he walked swiftly, eager to see if the old nightmare endured. As the upper benchland came in sight, and Black and Burns canyons, the river and the Bridwell place, he knew that it did, for the old suffocation enfolded his heart. If he had spent all his life in a hospital and had then gone into fresh air and returned, the smell of ether and medicines and sickness could not have been more vivid than this power, impalpable and odorless, that claimed him. Out of yellow sunlight, out of song and foliage and out of the river's thunder it came to him and built its prison; until he walked at last as a man entering the solitary, as one weary with hiding, returning to his cell. This power, this nightmare, would have to be broken or he would never be free; but with what force or goodness or prayer he was to break it he did not know. Would a woman's love do it?

As he walked he felt more and more oppressed, borne down, defeated. He fought against the power but knew that his struggle was useless: drawing a quick breath he would shrug, trying to shake it off; and for a moment, indeed, he would. He sang songs, he thought of his college books, he made a map of far countries, strange shores, striving to grasp and hold the detachment which he felt must be his strength. But this force was like a body of water: he could strike out and so, for an instant, achieve a vision of freedom; but the water would close in, patient and inescapable. On the brink he sat for a while to look. The old house was abandoned now, for a new house of lodgepole pines stood among the trees. He saw his mother enter a dugout coop and emerge and go to the barn; he saw his father down in the marshland, digging cress out of a slough. He gazed at the old dooryard where, crazed with fear and loneliness, he had awaited his mother's return; at the fir tree under which he had played at husband and wife with his sister and Hankie and Jewel; at the field where Jed had thrown him down and stuffed his mouth and throat with earth. And again he felt that sudden sharp pain in his loins.

Did he love this place at all, where he had suffered almost beyond human endurance? He had memories of wild flower-smell and bird-song, the taste of rose petals and gilia and of serviceberry, blue mist and golden dawns, and the touch of strong earth, all these lying in gentle beauty beyond the pain. The smell of fir and fields of clover and strawberry bloom in the meadowland; but superimposed upon these like one photographic negative upon another was the weird pattern of delirium, blood, death. The silence was terrible but within it in memory was the fluting of larks. There was the yellow intense insanity of the sun but under him was the deep strong peace of earth. And so the picture shaped itself, coming out of memory, with a kind of friendliness smiling out of all the brooding desolation.

He took his bags and started down; and as in former descents it seemed to him that his journey fell into a prison, down from the hills and the sky. A moment ago he had looked a hundred miles into the west, but the picture had closed like a shutter, until nothing was visible but his home, its river and walls. By the time he came to the house he was pale with exhaustion and drenched with sweat. He saw Marion first, who during the past year had been a senior in the high school. In his brother's letters he had sensed a change: Marion had been president of his class and had taken a leading role in the school's drama. The brothers looked at one another, strangers still, to be strangers always.

Vridar went outside and saw his father and grasped the man's powerful hand. "Hello," he said.

"Hello," his father said.

His mother Vridar found sitting by a bush. She came to him swiftly, and he folded her in his arms, and was conscious of shame when for a moment he felt her thighs against him. "How's mater?" he asked, backing away.

"Oh, I'm all right. How's my son?"

What a strange family it is! he thought a little later. There had been little love here, little kindliness—for there had been too much toil, too much poverty, too much loneliness. Vridar knew that they were watching him, waiting for him to talk.

"Glad to be home?" his mother asked.

"I guess so."

"You guess so! Ain't you sure?"

"Well, yes, I am glad."

"How did you like college?" Diana asked.

"It's all right."

He looked at his parents and saw there what he had seen so many times: pride in education and knowledge, pride in their daughter and sons. But he had always returned from school disappointed in what he had found; it had been so in Annis, in Rigby, and it was so now. But knowing how proud they were and how they had slaved to send him away, he had never told the truth but had always pretended

255

that schooling was a glorious thing. Oppressed now by their doubts he said: "Sure, college is a fine thing. Everyone should go." That was better. The doubt left their eyes.

"What you learnun?" asked his father.

Vridar hesitated, knowing that his father hoped that his son had learned a great deal about Mormon doctrines. "English—economics—sociology—such things."

Joe glanced at his wife. Prudence said: "Marion has been a leader this year." And she looked at Marion, who always stood in his brother's shadow.

"Yes, I know. He wrote me about it."

There was a long silence, the silence of strangers who were growing more strange. For the homecoming of her sons Vridar saw that his mother had cleaned and repapered the house; and of a photograph of him and Marion taken a year ago she had had an enlargement made. It showed two youths, lean and pale, solemn, staring. They looked as though they had never smiled in all the years of their life.

"You like it?" Prudence asked. They were all looking at the photograph.

"No," Vridar said. "They're too serious."

"They *are* serious. They have big serious thoughts."

Good Lord! In his face and in the face of his brother Vridar saw childlike credulity, a kind of weird zeal, that annoyed him. He was not quite what he had been a year ago. To get away from the earnest faces of his parents Vridar said he would go out to see how things looked and he left the house. Towser, his companion in so many hours of terror, was an old dog now, with a lot of gray in his hair. Prince, second in favor of all beasts here, was graying also and looked shaggy and forlorn. He was the most intelligent horse Vridar was ever to know. Formerly, when at the sawmill, he would escape and come to the river; but he never plunged in blindly as other horses did. He would look across and choose his landing and then go up the river, looking across from time to time, as if to judge the speed of the water and the distance to the far side. Other horses got lodged under high banks or drowned in whirlpools, but Prince always landed where he expected to. He was a grotesque fellow, handsome in his head and neck but very ugly elsewhere; and he was cynical because he was clever. While Vridar stroked him, Prince looked round him for a halter, for he was suspicious of such kindness.

In the house an hour later Vridar looked curiously at his sister. She was fifteen now and plump with womanhood—too plump, he thought, and her legs were too short for her torso; but under her blouse he could tell that she had full breasts. He was thinking of her breasts and of those hours under the fir tree long ago, when she met his gaze. She colored and said sharply: "What are you looking at?"

"You," he said, wondering about her.

"Or Neloa," she said.

Prudence was listening. "Son, are you really in love with Neloa?"

"How do I know?" he said. He flushed and went to the door.

"If you are you should go see her. I don't like to say it but she's quite wild."

"Gossip!" he said. "Why do you listen to gossip?"

"Where there's smoke there's usually fire. I been thinkun I'd ask her up here and let you find out how you feel about her."

And so the stage was set, the plot laid. His mother and sister were determined that he and Neloa should come face to face. If he did not love her, his mother said, he should find it out and if he did, he should watch over her, for she was becoming a wild girl. Feeling wretched, feeling like an utter fool caught by a childish infatuation, Vridar would go off alone to examine his emotions, to try to understand what he should do. If he was to become a college teacher or a writer, was Neloa the kind of wife he should have?—the kind who would heal and console? He doubted it but he was unable to put her away. Diana rode out to ask Neloa to come, and Vridar waited, consumed by an old passion and new doubts; and when he heard Diana coming, he ran out to meet her.

"Will she come?"

"No."

He drooped. He felt as if all life had been knocked out of him. His face was so foolish and woebegone and his body so limp and ridiculous that Diana laughed. "Cheer up," said Diana. "She'll come."

"She will? Tell me, how did she act?"

"Oh—she just smiled and said she'd come."

"Who—who did you say asked her?"

"You."

If you don't like my gait don't swing on it. "You shouldn't have said that."

"But you're the one who wants her, aren't you?"

He thought he heard bitterness in her words. She was leaning back to draw the horse in and her breasts were beautifully outlined under her blouse. "What else did you tell her?"

"I said you were dying to see her."

"Why did you tell such lies?"

"Because you are. It's a riddle."

"What's a riddle?"

"Why you're so crazy about her."

"I'm not crazy about her."

"Oh yes you are," said Diana, and galloped away.

Vridar went off alone with the delirious joy of his heart, the doubts of his mind. Everything around him seemed tender and sweet and good. Neloa!—the Neloa he had loved for so many years: he felt as if he would bubble and purl like a brook, or rise from the earth full of music and light. Rapture was in him with the burn and fragrance of wine; love was a suffocating glory around his heart. He went over the hills, frisking and capering and spending his joy in wild fierce nonsense; and anyone seeing his transports would have thought him mad. He embraced trees, and felt a moment of shame when he realized that he had pretended that the trunk was a woman's thigh. He leapt over bushes and fell and rolled, and then gurgled with pure delight. He stood on his head and turned somersaults; he ran on hands and knees and barked and growled. He exhausted himself and suddenly his mood changed as though a light had been turned off, and he walked like an old man.

There had come to him in a flash of divination, as if for a moment the future had opened, the wish that she would not come! He examined his emotions and was certain that the wish had been there: why, then, had he been behaving like such a fool? Feeling intolerably wretched, he went in to supper, and he looked so haggard and absurd that his mother was alarmed.

"Son, what is the trouble?"

"Nothing."

"Why do you look so unhappy? Neloa said she will come."

"I don't care."

"Son, you don't care?"

"I just want you to leave me alone."

"It's a riddle," said Diana.

Vridar did not eat but went to the bedroom and crawled into bed. He could hear the family talking about him, and Diana's rather shrill laugh; and a little later his mother came in and sat on the bed and tried to stroke his hair.

"Son, why do you act so strange? Tell mother."

"I want to be alone."

"Do you really love Neloa?"

"Good God, why do you ask such questions?"

"You love her a lot, don't you?"

"No."

"Do you think she'll be the right wife for you?"

"No. And who in hell said she'd marry me anyway?"

"Oh, I think she would. Girls try to marry well, and how many on Antelope can marry college students?"

"How many would want to?"

"All of them. Son, she could stay up here several days, if you want her to. Then you could be sure if you love her."

"Why do you suppose she loves me?"

"Girls don't have to have love to marry."

She kissed his forehead and patted his hands and left the room. He lay a long time thinking of her words: girls don't have to have love to marry. He had not known that. He wondered if his mother was right, or if she had said it only because she had not loved.

He spent three days and nights of heartache and doubt and waiting. He slept little and ate little and felt very silly and futile. Diana teased him, and he sensed something in her teasing that he did not understand. Marion was cynical. Prudence and Joe were silent. Though common peasants of earth, they were proud, and they had hoped that their sons would marry college women. They liked Neloa and her family, but the Doole clan was a rather thriftless and nomadic lot, strongly marked with Indian, and with no more interest in books and education than they had in the Baffin Islands. Prudence said she thought Neloa was all right; but would he be happy in marriage with a girl who had been only through the eighth grade?

"If she becomes my wife she will go to school."

"But I don't know if she likes school."

258

The talk of marriage bewildered Vridar: he was interested not in marriage but in love. "I don't intend to marry," he said, scowling at his mother. "Good God, I may be a man in years but I'm really only a child. What would I do with a wife?"

"We would help you through school," his mother said.

And now Vridar sensed what he had sensed before: his mother wanted him to marry. He did not know why. He resented her wish to have him marry at so young an age; he despised all Mormons who believed in early marriage; and he resolved that he would not marry for ten or twenty years, if ever. He tried to resolve not to see Neloa, but his yearning to see her left him helpless, without mind or will.

Diana saddled two horses and said she was going to get her woman, that she would fetch her if she had to rope and hogtie her. Vridar hated her words: how absurd for his family to act as if Neloa must be brought to him, dead or alive. For three days Diana had been tormenting him. "I'll herd her over just like she was a wild cow and the rest will be up to you." Why was Diana so determined to bring him and Neloa together? He did not know. He sat on his heels, a preposterous shivering gallant, watching his sister prepare to fetch the bride. Good Lord, he was the one to go! How stupid and silly to send his sister, as though he was afraid, or as though he were an Asiatic lord summoning brides to his harem! He went off alone, detesting himself. He heard Diana galloping up the road, up into the mountains and the sky. If Neloa came, what would he say to her, what would she say to him? What *was* there to say? What was there between them, save an infatuation on his side, which had refused to die when his childhood died?

He climbed the mountain, thinking that he would go far away and not see her; but he knew that he would not go far away. He thought with scorn of his limp and irresolute manhood, of the birdlike fluttering within his breast. What a magnificent man he was! If she did not like him, would he care? Will when looking well won't move her looking ill prevail? The more he reasoned with himself, striving for poise, the more he shook and gurgled, as if full of deadly ills. Talking to himself did no good and walking did no good.

He stood at the top of the dugway and looked west. As punishment for his want of manhood and will, he hoped she would not come, that he would never see her again. Why should any woman ever look at him, save to laugh, or speak to him, save to ask why he trembled? He was torturing himself with ridicule, he was formulating phrases to express his loathing, when his heart leapt to his throat and was held there. Down the road the two riders were coming, Diana and Neloa. With a gasp he fled. He went down the mountain pellmell, leaping over bushes and rolling and trying to get lost. Under a bank he came to a stop, wheezing and blowing like a foundered nag; he mopped his brow and fanned himself. She was coming! She would look at him. She would say, "You asked me to come, now what do you want with me?" And he would writhe and hesitate.

Going quietly through trees he went to a grove east of the house and stopped, wondering what he should do. He thought of getting a spade and going off to build fence, as though he had forgotten that she was coming—though the coming of all the suns in all the years of life was not as bright as her coming! He thought of taking a pole and going to the river to fish. He remembered Bonnie, his thought

259

fiashed to Neloa, and there was again the pain in his lions. Round the trees he went, softly, stealthily, and came to a woodpile and stood behind a bush. In a few moments the girls came to a halt within forty feet of him. Diana was talking, but Vridar's eyes, his whole being, was fixed on the tall lovely girl whose hair fell in splendor to her waist, who had the light of a thousand mornings in her eyes. She was such a vision that he held his breath, and the moment became one of the supreme and wordless moments of his life. He saw her dark voluptuous beauty, heard her rich throaty laugh, felt her warm deep-bosomed womanhood, and in fancy touched her and trembled at the touch.

Then the girls went to the house. Vridar grasped a shovel and began to dig postholes, as if he had acres of labor to do; but his body was drunk and his senses swam in memory. He saw her again on that day when she first entered his life; and that evening when she stood at his side in the school's contest, with her hair spilling round her; and that winter night in Rigby when, after the theater, she stood by the gate and looked at him. His whole life, it seemed, had been full of her, as indeed it had.

"Vridar!"

For how many years had he loved her? He had loved others too, but not with such hopeless unreason, not clear to the bottom of his soul. Helen he had loved, Norma he had loved. Neloa he had worshiped.....

"Vridar, where are you?"

He turned. He realized that someone had been calling his name. He could hear the word in memory as though it had been called a dozen times. "What do you want?"

Diana came through the trees. She came up and looked at him, and again he was troubled by what he saw in her eyes. "Why don't you come in."

"I'm working."

"Listen, you silly numbskull. Neloa is here."

"Oh, is she?"

"She howled all the way up but I made her come."

"Did she want to come?"

"That's for you to find out."

"I'll come in a minute," he said.

Diana left him and went to the house. Virdar thought he would stay here until in possession of himself, but the more he fought for control the more he shook. In despair he seized a barbed wire and jerked it, and the barbs cut a thin furrow down one palm. He looked at the blood and felt quieter. He had an excuse now: he would enter the house for iodine and a bandage. At the door he lingered, looking round him for a place to hide if he heard footsteps; but when he heard footsteps, he pushed the door open and stepped inside. Prudence saw his bleeding hand.

"What have you done?"

"Cut myself a little. Where's the iodine?"

She searched for iodine and he searched too; and from the parlor Diana taunted him. Prudence found iodine and poured it into the wound, and Vridar liked the pain. He wished he had cut his hand off. To postpone his entrance into the parlor, he found fault with the bandage, asked his mother to use stouter cord, in one way and another delayed the meeting. But at last, with his mother impatient and Diana taunting, he could pretend no longer. He had to enter now. But first he got a drink and brushed his hair a little. Crossing the room he got his hat from the floor and hung it on a spike, and then stepped outside to knock dust from his clothes. With the amused eyes of his mother and the mocking eyes of his sister upon him, he came back in, went to the pail to drink again, feeling more and more absurd all the while; and then desperately swung to face them and walked into the parlor.

V

Without looking at Neloa he crossed the room and sat in a corner at the end of a chiffonier hidden from her sight. His mother and the girls talked. The sound of Neloa's voice, bringing to him memories of other times and of a few priceless moments with her, made him tremble, and to try to hide his emotion he kept trying to adjust himself to his chair. His mother's eyes were still amused, Diana's still mocking. Had the cat got his tongue? Diana wanted to know; or was he trying to act worldly?

"He's talked about you for days," she said, with that dreadful want of tact common to sisters. "For three nights he hasn't slept and now he's as dumb as an egg."

Vridar glared at her and said nothing. Then suddenly he started and almost left his chair. Across the room from him was a large wall mirror, and when he glanced at it for the first time since coming in he saw Neloa looking at him. Good Lord! he thought. He had imagined himself securely hidden and she had been watching him all the while! What queer distortions of face and what ridiculous postures of body had she seen? He thought it was very mean and silly of her to spy on him. He glanced again at the mirrored face and saw that she was smiling. Her smile was a little curious, a little amused, but it was friendly. He looked at the image and their eyes met, and he blushed and turned away. Thereafter when he glanced at her, he found her gaze fixed on him, searching but not critical.

"Move out," his mother said. "Mebbe Neloa would like to see what you look like."

As if she had not already seen! He seized his chair and moved out into full view, feeling horribly exposed, as though his trousers were unbuttoned. Well, she could not see him in the mirror now. He glanced at her again and saw that she was still smiling, that her gaze was very intent. He sat in utter wretchedness for a few minutes and then excused himself and bolted outside.

He did chores until long after dark, and when he came in he was thankful for pale lamplight. Sitting back by a wall and listening with all his being, he glanced at Neloa from time to time, giving her swift furtive appraisals; or stared boldly when she turned her back. She was taller than he had thought she would be. She was more than five feet and seven inches and he was an inch under six feet: her height made him feel dwarfed. Her body, his mother had said, was quite perfect; and he fed on her loveliness, wondering if this was so. She had very beautiful arms and hands but her ankles were too thick. Once when she sat her skirt was drawn

261

above her knees and for an instant he saw white flesh; and once when she stooped he saw the womanly fullness of her breasts. He would have to teach her to keep her dress down and her blouse tighter. His own sister had been taught to stand with her heels together and never to sit with her legs crossed; to wear her clothes firmly so that they would reveal nothing; and not to bend over like a man but to sit gracefully when she recovered anything from the floor. He supposed that Neloa was not wanton but only careless.

He went to bed and the girls slept in the parlor. While they undressed he could hear them gurgling with nonsense, and once he heard Diana shriek, her voice running high and wild. He sensed in their gurgles and laughter an erotic emotion and was disturbed: how silly it was that they should be feeling, even if only subconsciously, that a man and a woman had come together and might eventually mate. This was the thing he had felt in all of his father's people. His own love was so pure that it was impotent; and when at last he fell asleep the most that his dreams dared, and all that they wished, was to be alone with her.....

When he awoke the next morning, he heard Neloa talking, and there came to him again the incredible wonder of her being here. He dressed and crawled through the window and went to chores. He came awkwardly and speechless to breakfast. Then Prudence took Vridar aside and asked if he did not want to take Neloa for a walk, to be alone with her for a while. She even suggested that they might cross the river and walk up Black Canyon to an old millsite. He left the house, his heart pounding like mad: what a miracle it would be to walk with Neloa through the leafy corridors and under the firs! But first, of course, he would have to ask her to go. This he could not do with his family present: there would be Diana's giggles, Marion's scorn, his mother's compassionate amusement. After a few minutes Diana and Neloa came out and went to the barn and lingered there; and Vridar knew that they were out there for him to speak. But his heart was almost out of him and his thoughts were away like leaves in a wind. He forced himself to approach them, and he maneuvered until he stood by Diana and then jabbed her ribs with an elbow. She shrieked and looked amazed.

"What's wrong with you?" she said.

Lord God, what a dumb sister he had! She might know as much about horses as any woman could know, but she knew nothing about love. He looked at Neloa and saw that she was smiling at him, that she was looking at him with bright glowing eyes, as though she thought him a fascinating riddle.

"Speak up!" said Diana. "What's wrong with you?"

"I wonder," he said, looking at Neloa, "if you'd like to take a walk."

"I guess so," she said. "Where?"

"Oh," he said, looking round him at all the canyons and peaks. "Anywhere. We might take a boatride."

"Let's all take a boatride," Diana said.

A worse idiot than his sister, it seemed to Vridar, he would never know. But the matter was settled; Diana said they would all go boating, and she ran off to find Marion, leaving Vridar and Neloa alone. He looked away at mountains and heard the ridiculous pounding of his heart. Neloa's gaze was steady.

"You like college?" she asked.

"I guess so." He knew that she was smiling and that her eyes were amused.

"When does college start this fall?"

"Oh—September, I suppose."

"Will you go this year?"

"Oh, of course."

Then they were silent and Neloa still watched him. He was thinking of her curt note about a gate and his not swinging on it, and he could hear his own breathing and was annoyed. Thinking of her note gave him a little ease, a little anger and boldness and scorn; and he turned suddenly and faced her, and his stare was so searching that she was startled. Then Diana came up with Marion and they all went up the lane. Neloa moved up to walk with Diana, but Diana in her blunt way took care of that.

"Get back there!" she cried, and pushed Neloa toward Vridar. "Marion, you're my beau today."

Marion walked ahead with his sister, and Vridar and Neloa walked behind. Diana overflowed with gay nonsense and tactless quips, but the others rarely spoke. Vridar glanced up at the sky, wondering if it might rain; fields, to note the depth of hay; saw a bird running and stared at it with exaggerated interest, as though he had never before seen a bird like it; and all the while struggled to seem casual and at ease, as if walking with a girl bored him a little. They came to the boat and Vridar bailed water out, glad for this chance to turn away and be with himself. Diana said they would all cross the river and go up the canyon to the old millsite; and when Vridar looked at her and winked mysteriously she cried: "What are you winking at me for?" When the boat was ready, Vridar sat and took the oars. Neloa stepped down to the boat, with her skirt drawn up, showing a part of one thigh. Then Diana moved to enter but Marion grasped her arm.

"We're staying here," he said.

"Oh no," said Diana, looking at him. "What do you mean?"

Holding Diana's arm, Marion said to Vridar: "Get going."

Vridar grasped the oars and shot the boat into deep water. Neloa sat facing him. Her smile was inscrutable, a dimpling warmth on the surface of her thoughts; and her eyes were inscrutable too. Vridar bent to the oars. An expert with a boat in dangerous waters, he was determined to amaze her with his deftness and strength; but he realized after a few moments that she was not at all interested in his rowing. He abandoned his titantic efforts to pull the boat in two and luxuriated in self-pity. When they reached the far bank, he anchored the boat and looked back across the two hundred yards of water. Diana and Marion were sitting like Indians on a huge stone. Neloa left the boat and he turned with her into a forest and in a few moments they were lost.

Of all times in Vridar's life none was ever to surpass in pure romantic glory the next two hours. They were cloudless and infinite and perfect. He and Neloa walked up the old mill road and they said little, but no happiness before, none that came after, was so deep as this. It was enough, it was almost too much, to be so near to her and alone. Now and then when a branch hung across their path, he would lift it aside; now and then he would glance at her lovely face; but in all else he moved in a dream, marveling at the wonder of this hour. He never took her arm, never touched her, save by chance; and when her arm did touch him, or when, as once, she slipped and put a hand to his shoulder, such rapture flooded him that his gaze was darkened. It surged through him in tides of emotion and rolled in a surf of glory over his heart. He was not conscious of the slightest wish to kiss her. Out of the hunger of flesh he distilled a spiritual ecstasy, and this, for the present at least, was enough.

When they came to the old mill he knelt at the stream and drank, and then washed his hands and she drank from his cupped palms. When her lips touched his hands something went through him that was like flame. They sat on a grassy bank and heard the low murmuring of the stream, and they breathed the air of bearberry and wild currant and fir; or they looked up at the dark and blanketed mountain; or they looked at each other and smiled as children do. Vridar was feeling more at ease now. His joy, so intense in his held breath, broke on a great sigh and he laughed. Neloa laughed too, and he glanced at her and laughed again. Their laugh, he knew well, was a mutual recognition of his shyness, of his desperate wooing in Annis, of so much that he had done that was too silly for words. He felt as if a part of his darkness had been lifted away.

"I wonder if we should go back," he said.

"I guess so," she said.

"I don't want to," he said. He faltered and forced himself to say it: "I want to stay here, just to be with you."

Her only answer was a smile, and the smile, for such love as his, was not enough. He had offered his heart and he thought she must have known that.

"We can stay a little longer," she said.

He looked at her with such devotion that he blushed, and then seized a stick and whipped it across his legs. "Someone ought to kick me," he said, and laughed again.

"Why?"

"Because I'm such a fool." He glanced up at the penstock of the old mill and said: "I dreamed the other night that I was drowned when I was born." He had not intended to say those words and he wondered why he had said them. "I suppose you think I'm queer, don't you?"

"A little," she said.

He looked up at the mountain and told her of an adventure he had had the previous summer. He had killed a bear without hitting it, but had never understood how. Perhaps he shot just over its skull and stunned it. Anyway, it rolled off a ledge and broke its neck. He glanced at her and saw that she was not interested in the bear; and he felt again, if for a moment only, that he was a fool to love this girl.

"What makes you think I'm funny?"

"Oh, I don't know. You just are."

"Do you like queer people?"

Her smile was faint and baffling. "I like you," she said.

264

He glanced at the penstock and said: "I once almost drowned in one of those. It seems to me that I have been almost drowned ever since birth."

"You *are* funny," she said.

They turned down the canyon, walking slowly; and the half-mile for Vridar was only a hundred yards. Not a word was spoken. He thought she was shy, that she was not used to being alone with men; and he liked her shyness and silence. Still, there was something in her eyes. . . .

When they came to the river Marion bawled across at them: "Hurry up! You've been gone hours!"

They entered the boat and crossed, and when they came to the far bank Marion rebuked again. It had been no fun waiting for them. Diana seemed to be sullen. Why, Vridar wondered, had his brother and sister not gone home?

Going down the lane, none of them spoke. Marion scowled, and Diana sulked, as if her day had been spoilt. Prudence came out of the house and took Vridar aside. How, she asked, was Neloa going home? Would he like to hike out and borrow his uncle's buggy and drive her? At such a prospect of heaven, he did not hesitate; he told his mother to see that Diana did not run off with Neloa, and he hastened to the barn to harness a team, and then went up the mountain and over the hills.

"For why you want it?" his uncle Dock asked. "You takun a girl out?"

"Yes."

"That Doole girl?"

"What if I am?"

Dock's grin was big and round and lewd. "You ever seen her dance? You ever seen how her tits jump up and down?"

"What are you saying?"

"Mebe I know more about her than you do." Dock's eyes were large and cunning. "Yes," he said, "you'n take the buggy. But no monkeyshines. Lots of girls has learnt things in buggies."

Vridar dashed home with the ramshackle buggy lurching from side to side. Neloa was at the woodpile. He came up at a gallop, with the wheels squealing and the boards of the seat clattering; and when he swung the team the buggy spun round on two wheels. Then, remembering what his uncle had said, he walked round the team, pretending that collars needed adjusting, that the neckyoke was broken, that a bridle was too large. He was trying to convince himself that he should not drive Neloa home, for if he drove her home there were things which he would say. He would tell her that he loved her and he had a deep unhappy feeling that he should not tell her that. But Neloa had climbed to the buggy seat, and Prudence was telling her that she must come again soon.

Then they were off. The buggy rattled and shook, and the wheels, turning on axles worn thin, reeled drunkenly like things about to collapse. Vridar was so shamed by the vulgar squealing and the wired doubletree and the patched tongue, the rickety seat and the lopsided dashboard, that he looked straight ahead of him for a while and said nothing. They went up the dugway and to the benchland; they went down a dusty gray road, the horses trotting now; and he looked to the north

265

or the south, wondering about himself and her, wondering what he would say. Dusk had fallen and stars were coming out; the night was fragrant and warm. Once when the wheels on Neloa's side fell into a deep rut she threw an arm to his neck, and again rapture was in him like hot wine. An impulse came up from his wild heart and found words, bold incredible words, which he had never dreamed he could utter.

"It's all right to keep your arm there," he said.

Her laugh was low and pleased. "All right," she said, and laid her arm across his shoulders, her hand almost to his cheek.

Rapture filled him and shook him, and mist gathered to his eyes. For a mile or so they journeyed, neither saying a word. When the buggy lurched, her hand touched his cheek; and after a while, yielding to another impulse stronger than his will, he pressed his cheek to her hand. Then he looked at her and saw that her eyes were full of bright tenderness. Feeling a little bolder, and wishing to stop time and hold it close to his heart, he drew the horses to a walk. That they might ride all night, forever and ever, with her arm against him! This was heaven, deeper and fuller than his dreams of it.

Seeing ahead of him the Doole farm, he was driven to do something to fix this hour and make it eternal. If he let her go now he might never see her again. He could not let her go now. He loved her with all the love unspent from his childhood and youth. It was, he told himself, no spontaneous passion of an hour: no, it reached far back and had its roots far back; it had grown into him in the way that branches reach to a tree's heartwood, and it had been most of the foliage and flowering that he had known. But he doubted that she loved him and pride would not let him confess his own love. Yet he must speak. This that time and loneliness had built into his being, this that now surged through him like his own blood, must be confessed. He stared out into the night and tried to quiet his emotions. The world around him was a mist of softness and his eyes were full of mist. And when at last he spoke, his voice was so strange, so unlike the voice familiar to him, that he did not recognize it at all. He forced himself to say: "Neloa, if you loved a man you would let him kiss you, wouldn't you?"

"Yes."

He looked ahead of him, blinking his eyes to shed their mist. He moved under her circling arm and half-turned. "May I kiss you?"

Her reply as before was a low vibrant yes. But he did not kiss her at once. He thought of his questions, her replies, doubting that either had been spoken, wondering if he dreamed. He pulled on the reins and drew the team to a halt. He turned to her, trembling, and gently drew her to his arms. She came willingly with a little sigh, her hair falling in glory round his face. He pressed a little kiss on her mouth and then put his cheek to her cheek.

After a few moments, he released her and spoke to the team. A full moon had risen and everything was very clear and he could see far down the road. He clasped one of her hands and they rode to a corner and made a turn. Then he spoke again.

"Neloa, do you love me?"

"Yes."

Oh, but he could not believe it! Turning to her, he looked into her eyes, trying to read there the deeper truth of her being. They were dark luminous eyes with something in their depths that made him tremble. He looked away, his heart caught in his throat.

"Will you marry me?"

"Yes."

This could not be! So much of heaven was never meant for him! Did he dream? Did he dream that he was here with her arm around him: this girl whom he had idolized, for whom he would have died? It was all a trance and he would awaken soon. He would find himself in bed and life would be what it had always been. To try to determine whether he was here or far away he pressed her hand, and was conscious of a sinking in his emotions when she did not return the pressure.

"Are you sure? . . . Neloa, be sure."

"Am I sure of what?"

"That you love me."

"I am sure."

"But it can't be!" he cried. "How could it be? You've seen me only a few times and you've never thought of me."

"Oh, haven't I? How do you know that?"

"But have you?"

"Yes."

"Neloa, Neloa, be serious with me! If you don't love me, send me away now. Tell me to go and I'll go."

"I don't want you to go."

He struggled with his doubts a moment and said: "How much do you love me?"

"Lots."

"As much as I love you?"

"Yes."

"Oh, but you don't, you can't, you never will!"

"But I do."

"How long have you loved me?"

"A long time."

"In Annis?"

"I guess so."

"When we went to the show in Rigby, did you love me then?"

"Yes."

Her replies troubled him. He could not put away the feeling that she was saying what she thought he wanted her to say. "When will you marry me?"

"When do you want me to?"

"Tonight. Will you marry me tonight?"

"Yes."

O God, how preposterous! Yet in a frenzy of joy, he drew her to him and again kissed her lips, softly, purely. They had come to her home gate, and Vridar now helped her down and hitched the team to the fence. He drew her to him, but not

267

firmly, not with her legs or breasts touching him; and for a moment he searched her face, her eyes, doubting that she understood.

"Neloa, if you love me, say it again."

"I love you."

It could not be! It was so with him but it could not be with her! He tried again to drive under her strange calm. "But you, Neloa, you're not impulsive like me. You don't——" He finished with a sigh. Again he studied her face. She was a lovely girl, he thought: her eyes were like dark and luminous velvet; her very dark brown hair was burnished with the sun's light and hung in a great mane to her waist; and her teeth were the most perfect he had ever seen. But her smile even more than her eyes was the glory of her face. "I wish——" he said, and broke off, feeling stupid. "Neloa, I wish I could tell you how I have loved you all these years, ever since that first day on the butte. But you wouldn't believe it. No one would believe it, for it doesn't make sense. And how much I love you now." Again his eyes had filled with mist, but through the mist he could see her looking at him in that strange baffled way. "I—I worship you, Neloa. O my God!"

He turned away and tried to shake his grief off, but it surged up out of his dark years and he was overcome. He went to a post and sat and bowed to his knees. After a few moments Neloa went over and sat by him and put an arm to his neck. But almost at once she withdrew her arm.

"I'm an idiot." he muttered. "I am, and I hate myself for it! But you don't understand, Neloa. I have loved you so much."

When his grief was spent, he arose and she came to him and they stood as before. He saw that there had been no tears in her eyes. In her eyes he saw the same quiet bewilderment that seemed to be suffused with soft gentle amusement.

"We'll be married some day," he said.

She squeezed his hand. He drew her closer then and softly, purely kissed her lips, her eyes, her hair. The time was past midnight, and she said she would have to go in.

"Not yet!" he implored her. He drew her hair around until it filled his arms and was soft beauty between them. "When'll I see you again?"

"When you want to."

"I want to see you all the time. I'd rather die than leave you now." He thought of the work at home to be done, of his duties. "Next Sunday," he said. "I don't want to come to the house. Meet me on the road."

"All right," she said.

"Neloa, at one o'clock. You won't be late?"

"No, I won't be late."

"Just above the bridge."

She turned away, smiling her strange smile, and went toward the house. He felt sudden awful despair. It was if she had gone and he would never see her again. He ran after her, crying, "Neloa!"

"Yes?" she said, turning. He went up to her, so shaken that he could barely stand. He looked at her, again searching her face and her eyes.

"Neloa, I can't let you go!"

268

He saw that she wanted to go. Instead of being resentful, as was his proud suspicious way, he thought her very sensible, himself very silly, and he said goodnight and went back to the team. He watched her and when she came to the house she turned and waved to him. Then she entered and the door was closed and he was alone. He waited for an hour, hoping she would come out; and if she had come, eager to see him, he would have been delirious with joy. But she did not come. He stood in plain sight in the moonlight, so that she might see him if she looked through the window; but she did not come. He climbed to the buggy and drove away through a wide gleaming night, his heart bursting. The ache in all his being so choked him that now and then he had to stand up to get a full breath. It felt as if a hand had reached into his breast and now lay within.

While he rode home there came to him in sudden flashes, like lightning from emotions and perceptions that had waited out on the margin, premonitions of things to come. These could have been no more sharp and real if tongues had spoken. But he did not want to understand them. In an instant they were gone, and there was only the deep fragrant night that was full of her, and the buggy that was full of her. He turned to that part where her hair had spilled and pressed his lips to the hard board. He reached out and could almost feel again the clasp of her hand. He listened, and could hear soft assents. And then the flashes came again.

VI

From this July day until September 6, Vridar's life, save for two small incidents, was perfect. It was a cloudless idyl of the kind he had never known and was never to know again. When he looked back upon it from a later time, he saw it as a cloud, bright and tender and nebulous, floating between a darkness out of which it rose, and another darkness into which it passed.

On reaching home, he lay awake until morning, reliving with all his senses the wonder of his hours with her. A little after dawn he heard his father speaking.

"Time to get up!" Fellers who go to dances have to pay the fiddler."

Marion awoke and looked at him. In his father's words as well as in Marion's dubious stare, Vridar thought he perceived a touch of malice. Why did people so resent the wooing of a man and a maid! His mother, too, after he had dressed and entered the kitchen, regarded him with eyes that were a little caustic. They wanted to know why he had got home so late and what he had done. At the breakfast table they thrust at him with veiled hints and he grinned at them and tried to seem at ease.

"He's in love," said Diana. "It sure didn't take him long."

"In love?" said Prudence. "How long, son, have you been in love with her?"

Vridar looked sheepish. "A long time," he said.

When, trying to speak quietly, he told them that he was bethrothed to Neloa, they all looked at him with amazement. This, his father said, was faster than young men worked in his time. Ordinarily they went with a girl several times before popping the question; and he stared hard at his son, as if wondering what kind of son he had.

Diana was looking at him with sisterly misgivings. "You mean she said yes? And you have said you'd never marry young!"

"I'm not married. I won't be for a long while."

"He's just trying her out," said Marion, and this was his only comment.

When alone with Vridar, Prudence gravely studied his face. She said she wanted him to be happy. She thought Neloa was a nice girl. "But when you're married, my son, you're married a long time."

"I'm not married," he said.

Prudence seemed not to hear; she was listening to her own inner voice. "She's a nice girl, but I'm not sure she's the wife for you."

While pitching hay he thought of his mother's words, for she had said what the lightning had said. What kind of girl, he asked of the sky and the earth, did they want him to marry anyhow? But he knew. Why were mothers so suspicious of their daughter-in-law and why did they imagine that they knew what was best for their sons? But he knew. His parents had slaved for him, they were proud of him, they wanted him to go out into the world and achieve. They felt that an uneducated girl from the Antelope hills was not for him. Down under his romantic ardor and the glow that lit up his whole being was the unhappy feeling that they were right. They felt that this was only an infatuation, but when he asked himself, Do I love Neloa? all his blood surged upward in a great affirmative. It was the one hot and tremendous certainty of his life.

During these days while waiting for Sunday he could think only of the tall beautiful girl who was his. His inner life was so turned to her and his absent-mindedness was so absurd that they laughed at him and jibed and made fun of him; but he merely grinned and said nothing, for out of passion so overwhelming there was nothing that they could understand. Neloa had become his consciousness, his emotions, his dreams, He dwelt on the touch of her arm and the smell of her hair and the sound of her voice. He relived his hours with her, telling them over and over, until she was life and the only meaning, and all else was dark. Sometimes he doubted that she had been here; and he decided to fetch some token home, a lock of her hair or a confession of love in her own handwriting, to convince himself that his happiness was real.

When Sunday morning came he arose at daybreak. He went out and saddled his sister's pony and was ready to go, when he remembered that their meeting was for one o'clock; and he groaned at his stupidity and hated himself for a fool. If he had said eight o'clock they could have spent the whole day together and part of the night, too: seventeen hours in all, for he counted them, one by one. And now their hours together would be only twelve. Should he go at once and dash up to the house and summon her? No, he could never do that. He went to the house and looked at the clock and hated it. He was infuriated by its round face and by the smug preciseness of everything it did. For fifteen years he had hated clocks.

His mother came out, brushing her hair that was as long as Neloa's, She looked at his doleful face and laughed. "Why, son, what's the matter? Why you up at daylight?"

270

He gave her a feeble grin and blew his nose, savagely twisting it as if to tear it off. "I don't know," he said.

"When are you to meet her?"

"One o'clock."

"And you get up at daylight!" She smiled, a bit archly, as was her way with him. "Love is an awful thing. I don't know, son, if it brings more sorrow or joy."

He went over to the river and sat on its bank, and watched its tumbling and heaving acres rolling to the sea. His mood was strange: intense in its longing and very bright in its core, but with a need to weep or pray, somewhere far down inside him: a mist of pain, within which was a stark searching loneliness of soul. In a little while he would see her and walk with her through the golden hours; and yet his need, the ache of his being, went beyond her and far away. There was terrible hunger in him that made him reach to what he had never heard of, to aspire to what he dared not hope to find, as though Neloa were only a door that might open into a larger world. When he returned the family was eating, but he did not eat.

"You better eat," his father said. "I never got so stuck on a womern I couldn't eat."

"If you don't eat," said Marion, "you'll have rumblings in your stomach. You can't make love if you rumble."

"You can't make love," said Joe, "on an empty stummick."

"A few hours from now," said Marion, "a steak will taste better than a kiss." This statement so amused Diana that she choked on a biscuit and left the room. She came in, coughing and giggling and stared at Vridar; and suddenly her laugh pitched into a shrill wail and died.

"Better eat a bowl of mush," said Joe. "Oatmeal is what you need to make love."

All this jesting Vridar thought in poor taste. But it was the way of his people, at least of the Hunters and O'Rourkes and McGards, to make a lewd thing of love. It was only something that led to babies and deep-hipped women and sagging breasts. He went outside and walked, thinking that love for him would be strained of all impurity and enfold him like intense light. Such wooing as he had seen— prancing like a stud and biting, or climbing naked to a stump to roar and slap the genitals—would never be his way. At the mill one morning his uncle Dock had found Vridar in bed and had thrown himself upon him, saying, "Let me show you how to do with a woman." Dock had got between Vridar's thighs and hugged him up and almost suffocated him. Love for man and woman, it seemed to Vridar, ought to be what song was for a bird, sunrise for the morning, moonlight for the night.

It was still early but he went to the pony and mounted, intending to linger on the way. When he came to the top of the dugway, he did not linger, but gave rein to the horse and went like the wind. The sky was a glorious blue pasture, with mountains banked high against it in purple mist. Larks sang from post and sagebush, and fields of wheat sank in broad dimpling caresses under the breeze. On reaching Antelope Creek he looked at the sun, but it was still low in its leisurely journey across a mellow forenoon. Riding to the top of a hill, he looked down at the Doole buildings, hoping that Neloa would appear; and when she did

271

not, he returned to the highway and took a road south. He climbed for two miles to a wilderness of aspen and looked across at Black Canyon, a great secret of forest and haze, and northern peaks upon which clouds were piled like hills of wool, with warm pink fireplaces in their lower banks. Around him were many wild flowers; he plucked a few scarlet gilias and stuck them in his lapel. He thought the sun had passed its zenith, and he rode back to the highway and galloped west.

After rounding a curve he dismounted and led the horse, and presently he saw Neloa far down the road, coming slowly toward him. His heart now shook him so that he could see the flowers tremble. He walked down the road, leading the pony, and she came forward to meet him, looking very tall and queenly, yet very girlish, too. He saw that she wore a simple pink dress, with the dark wealth of her hair falling down over her breasts. Then he saw that she was smiling and that her eyes were full of light. That much he saw, that much he would never forget, though everything around him was phantom land. As into a mist, as through a dream, they came together, with the earth and the sky moving in to frame the moment. Nothing in his life had ever been more unreal than this meeting: it was impalpable blue wonder, and in this wonder he said hello and she replied, but he could never remember that either spoke. She came into his trembling arms and he kissed her and they both laughed.

Then they turned and walked down the road. They left the road after a while and followed a dirt road over a hill to the brink of the river's gorge; and they looked down through blue mist at a river of light. They had walked a mile and a half and neither had spoken. It seemed to him that there was nothing to be said. The silence was perfect and the day was shimmering glory and they were alone. Now and then he had glanced at her, doubting that she was with him; he had seen the luster of her eyes, the heart of springtime in her cheeks. Her mood was his mood, deep and wordless; her thoughts, he imagined, were his.

Leading down was a dugway, and they took its path down to bottomland and crossed to the river. Vridar tethered the pony and they sat on the bank. For a few minutes they looked down into a swirling eddy under their feet, and then Vridar looked at her and reached out and touched her hand.

"I thought the days would never go," he said. "They seemed like years."

"Yes," she said.

Into her dark eyes now, as before and in times still to come, there was something that baffled him. As nearly as he could ever put it into words it was this: a brightness of love, of hunger, and beyond these, a single question fixed in anxiety and loneliness: one dark solitary fear, against which, as against a backdrop, her soul stood in silhouette. She looked at him and he saw this strangeness written in her eyes; and then her lashes fell. He was troubled by what he saw but he refused to think about it.

"You love me still?"

"Yes."

"Neloa, come here." He drew her to him across his lap, with her hair falling over him and to the earth around him. She looked up at him a moment and then closed her eyes. There was something in the swift brief glance that shocked him, as though the female had called to the male. He looked down at her mouth. It was not as lovely as her smile, her eyes, her hair. Her mouth was really lovely only when she smiled. Her nose was rather long and fell downward a little in an even curve from its point to her brow.

"You happy now?"

"Yes."

"I could sit like this forever."

She smiled and glanced up at him and her lashes fell again. In that moment he saw the strange thing in her eyes that troubled him. She talked very little, he reflected; most of her answers were only yes. Born to silence and always afraid of it, he yet loved its worth, imagining in it the deeper things where the eternal held its forces. He looked down at her; and because her eyes were closed he looked over her body, at her beautiful arms, at the fullness of her breasts, at her slender waist; but there was nothing amorous in his gaze. Her lying against him stirred no passion: tenderness only, a wish to cherish and protect, a prayer for so much that was his. Her breathing was slow and deep but he could tell by her face that she was not so tranquil as she seemed to be. Lifting her a little he bowed his face to her hair.

"Neloa, remember the first time I saw you?—on the butte in Annis?"

"Yes."

"That was long ago. How long?"

"Eight years mebe."

"Nine years and ninety-eight days today."

"You have counted all the days?"

"How many times! And I followed you to school. Did you know that?"

"Yes."

"I watched you all day long. Did you know that?"

"No."

"Remember when I walked home with you? I tried to, I mean."

"Yes, I remember."

"What a silly thing I was! But I loved you so much, even then."

She stirred in his arms and clasped one of his hands. This response shook him; it was the first of its kind today.

"And the school contest? We stood in the front of the room and you had your hair down like this."

"Yes. I missed erysipelas. I can spell it now."

"Then you went outside and wept."

"I was silly too."

"And the show in Rigby, do you remember?"

"Yes."

"You were awful," he said. "You ran off and left me."

"I was just a girl."

"You're only a girl still, barely sixteen."

"Fifteen," she said. "But I'm a pretty big girl. I'm as big as a house."

"Would you like to be smaller?"

"I don't want to be a mountain. I get bigger and bigger."

"You're just right," he said and he thought he meant it.

They were silent a while. Stealthily Vridar drew from a pocket a pair of small scissors and severed a lock of her hair. He stored the lock away and returned the scissors and drew a sudden breath. He watched the surge and foam below him or he worshipped her face, and each bewildered glance at her fetched another sigh. It was ridiculous to think that Neloa loved him; and yet—and yet, what? He had kissed her only once today. He wanted to kiss her again and again, not with passion, but with tenderness, with the infinite tenderness that filled him. Drawing a handful of hair to his lips he kissed it, and then he took her free hand and kissed it and pressed it to his cheek.

"You know what?" he said, with a strange laugh.

"What?"

"I want to kiss you."

She looked up, her eyes wide and bright and wondering. "Then why don't you?"

"I—I'm afraid to. I'm a fool." He hoped she would draw him down and kiss him, acting on a wild impulse; but spontaneity was not her way. She only smiled a little and for a moment studied his face. He flushed and turned from her.

"Don't look at me!" he said.

"You'n kiss me if you want to."

He looked at her, blood hot in his cheeks. "If you want to! But I don't want to unless—" He broke off, feeling very mean and wretched.

One of her most charming mannerisms was a scowl full of humor and light. She scowled at him now and tried to shake him; she rebuked him with eyes mocking and intent.

"But I don't," he said stubbornly and knew that he was being very stupid. He wanted to tell her again that he was a fool, that he had always been a fool; but out of desperation vanity rose in a moment of triumph. "I judge by the way you act."

"How do I act?"

"As if you don't care," he said dismally. He turned a little from her and looked down at the eddy of foam. She moved over to shake him.

"Kiss me."

"I don't want to." That was a horrible lie, but it made him feel better. He had so completely revealed his soul to her, and her soul was so completely hidden.

Neloa now tossed her long hair back and studied his face; then, like one who despairs of winning, she tried to draw him to her. He resisted, knowing all the while that he was mean and contemptible. He was not always going to ask for a kiss—but did he have to ask? He was not going to open all the windows of his being, while she kept her own soul shuttered! But had he asked her to show it?

"Vridar," she said, and it was the first time she had ever spoken his name.

"What?" he said, looking at her. She was staring at him as if he were an utter riddle.

"Why won't you kiss me?"

"Why should I? I make a fool of myself to you, but you are concealed and tranquil. I—I let you see me—"

"But you see me."

"No I don't."

Again for a moment there was that something in her eyes. It was so plain that he could not doubt. He felt that his world was about to be shattered and he burst forth with bitter words. "You don't love me as I love you! I'm an idiot, a plain God damned idiot—and I know it! All these years I have worshiped you because I've had nothing else! I wish I had some sense!" He was so vehement now that his words, his bitter confession, poured out of him in a great breath. He got to his feet and looked down at her and spoke again. "You've been loved, I suppose— by your parents at least; so what can you know of what I am saying? What will you ever know? I would die for you, I would fight the world for you! Everything about you, your clothes, the dust on your shoes, the things you have touched mean more to me than life! But can you understand that? I oughtn't to love you, Neloa! I ought to go away from you! But I can't, I can't!"

He stopped, white and shaken; and Neloa now arose, a little pale herself, and looked at him. With the right word, the quick warm impulse, she could have broken him to penitent devotion; but she did not understand him—his passionate idealism, his loneliness, his violence, and his need of love. She could only stand bewildered, looking at his tortured face, feeling the destroying power of his self- scorn. He moved toward the river, thinking to throw himself in; and then swung and faced her.

"Neloa, I mean this: I don't think I'll be good for you, or you for me; but I am helpless. You are not. You have the strength to break this off and tell me to go."

"But I don't want to."

Then he was amazed, for he saw that her eyes were wet. He saw mist in them first and then tears that gathered to her lashes and fell. She looked at him through tears and said, "I do love you."

"Neloa! O Neloa!" Unable longer to dam the flood, he dropped to earth and let his desolate grief find its peace. For several minutes the anguish poured out of him, unendurable, blind. It was the grief of one still enfolded by terrors, of one who had lived exiled from love and tenderness almost from birth.

"Vridar," she said, but she did not try to quiet his grief. She did not touch him. She waited until he was spent. Then she sank to his side in quiet humility, and he sat up, loathing himself, yet knowing that what he had said should have been said. After a few moments he looked at her. If he had seen in her face the smallest hint of scorn, of pity or amusement, he would have left her and walked out of her life. But he saw none of those. Her eyes were deep and sad and question- ing. With a cry he threw himself to her lap and put his arms round her and pressed his lips to the cloth over her thigh.

VII

And so the weeks passed, each with six days as long as centuries, with a short Sunday at its end. Had it not been for his father Vridar would have gone oftener, possibly every evening, but Joe said once a week was enough: he had courted only on Sundays, spending his other days in the fields. A lot of men wasted themselves in love.

When Sunday came Vridar was up at daylight and without breakfast he was off, meeting Neloa a little after sunrise. Always they went over the hills to the river and spent their precious hours there. All these Sundays—there were nine of them—were for Vridar almost perfect, save one. While night still lingered in cove and dell, they were following the lane that climbed the hill, when, looking back, they saw a farmer filling his water-tank at the creek. Who he was Vridar did not know and he did not care. But when he looked at Neloa he saw that her eyes were strangely bright: with that intuitive insight, born from years of loneliness and self-searching, he read in her eyes and in her whole face a warm interest in this man. His world darkened, as if its sun had passed into a cloud. He grasped her shoulders and looked into her eyes but what he had seen there was gone. She amazed him by saying simply: "I know who he is."

"Who?" asked Vridar. He turned and saw that the man was looking at them.

"Francis Henderson."

"Oh? And who is Francis Henderson?"

"He lives over there," she said, indicating a distant farm.

The man now waved to Neloa and she returned his greeting, and jealousy rose in Vridar in a vomit of rage. Sick with doubt, he looked at her. Perceiving that he was furious she changed suddenly, in the manner of a playing child that is rebuked. Something strange entered her eyes and the smile left her mouth.

"Let's go on," she said.

"No," he said, convinced that there was more than he had seen. "How long have you known him?"

"Oh, about a year."

"Have you been out with him?" His face was so morbidly earnest that she shrank from him and looked scared.

"Once."

"Only once? When?"

"Oh—" she said. "Oh, about two months ago."

"How long before—before you came up to our place?"

"Oh—about two weeks." She was annoyed. Her voice trembled a little and there was dark resentment in her eyes.

"Do you love him?"

"Don't be silly!" she said, and her eyes for a moment were afire.

Vridar had never seen this Neloa before. He was touching depths that he had suspected but had never found. He drew a sharp breath, feeling that she was right, that he was silly. She had gone with him once, she had waved to him a greeting: this surely was no matter to get furious about. He took her arm and they walked again. She was pensive now, sullen even: if he pressed her arm she gave no response, and by the way she moved her feet he could tell that she was very angry.

"I'm sorry," he said, and he looked around, trying to meet her eyes. There was the dying flush of anger in her cheeks. There was something hard and evil in her stare. "Neloa, I'm sorry. It was only because I love you so."

"You were mean," she said.

"All right, anything. But let's not spoil our Sunday. Please."

She did not sigh or in any way betray her thoughts. Her face was still brooding and dark. He stopped and drew her resisting to his arms, and she put her hands up to push him away.

"Neloa, please! I'm awfully sorry. Please, let's not spoil our day." She looked at him and he did not like what he saw in her eyes. He had seen it in her father's eyes, a look that was sly and evil and calculating. "Neloa?" he said, becoming frantic.

"What?" asked Neloa, looking far away.

"Don't you love me any more?" She did not reply at once. She was looking far away at mountains or sky. "Neloa, don't you?"

"I guess so," she said.

"Then please don't act like this! Darling, please! . . . Neloa, smile."

"No."

"Please smile."

"No."

He drew her to him again and she did not resist. He kissed her lips and eyes. "Smile!" he said. "I'll kiss you until you smile." She looked at him and very slowly she smiled. The darkness left her eyes, the anger faded from her cheeks, and in their stead came a sort of whimsical humor that he loved. "Now we're all right," he said. "Neloa, aren't we?"

But not for hours did he recover the lyric sweetness of their former days. Something troubled her. Her gayness, never bright or spontaneous, touched her but lightly now; and her eyes again and again were shadowed and still. But because his need was so great, he reposed in her an implicit trust that was the heart of his being.

Another incident which, on looking back, he thought was also trifling, occurred a few days later. With one exception during these weeks he saw her only on Sunday but on the Mormon holiday, the 24th of July, he mounted the pony and rode forth, telling himself with great glee that he would surprise her. When he came within sight of her home he stopped. He saw her in the yard and she saw him, too, it seemed, because at once she dodged round a building and entered the house. He rode down the lane and through the gate. After greeting her parents, who looked at him as they always did rather curiously, he threw the reins over a post and went to the door.

"Is Neloa inside?" he asked.

"Yes," her father said.

He pushed the door open and went in and saw Neloa lying on a bed. She seemed to be asleep but he knew that she was not. Nevertheless, when he spoke to her she did not answer and when he went over and sat on the bed she did not move.

"Neloa," he said, "you're not asleep."

277

She feigned the confusion of one coming out of sleep who had been startled. She stared at him and blinked her eyes; and her acting was so silly and artless that he did not know whether to be furious or to laugh.

"When did you come?" she asked, rubbing at her wide-awake eyes.

"When did I come! You saw me come, so why do you act this way?"

"I guess I was asleep," she said.

"You weren't asleep. You were out in the yard and you ran in here to pretend. Why did you do it?"

"Do what?"

"Pretend this way."

Now she dissembled anger. She arose and went to a mirror and brushed her hair. He followed her.

"Neloa, why?" She tried to look at him with scorn but her eyes were guilty.

"What makes you think I wasn't asleep?"

"I know you weren't. So why do you lie about it?"

"I don't lie."

"Have you ever lied to me before?"

"No."

"Only today?"

"Not today. I *was* asleep."

"That's a lie. If you're going to lie to me—well—" He got his hat and moved toward the door. She came to him, swift and wild. She grasped his arm and tried to drag him away from the door and he allowed her to. But when he faced her she did not speak. She only looked at him, her eyes guilty and anxious. "I don't want you if you lie. I don't lie to you."

She laughed, and her laugh was strange and low, its meaning concealed in its own dark. She tried to draw him to the bed but he would not budge.

"Did you lie or didn't you?"

Her lips trembled now and she went over and sat. He stood in wretched doubt and indecision, looking at her. If she would only talk instead of sinking into these awful silences!

"Neloa, were you only playing? Was it something a woman does?" He waited but she did not speak. He knew as well as he knew his own name that there had been something deeper in it than playfulness. He turned to the door again, and she was after him, frantic in her haste. He cupped her chin and forced her eyes to meet his. "Neloa, why?"

"Oh—oh, I just wanted to see what you would do!" Her voice was full of vexation and grief.

And Vridar felt, as he had felt in former times, that it was he who had been silly. She had only been playing, she had wanted to see what he would do; and again he had tried to make a mountain out of a molehill. Or had he?

Save those two incidents their first days together were as flawless as light. Time and again, it is true, he would rebuke her, when overcome by doubt or loneliness; and he would get himself into such a panic of despair that he would want to die. But these explosions only heaped sweetness upon the hours that

278

came after. Then he would lie in her lap or take her to his arms and his happiness would be unutterable. Not always did he maneuver the day into a tantrum. They would gather wild flowers and breathe of gentian and gilia and fireweed, aster and goldenrod, mimulus and cinquefoil and rose. He would put roses in her hair or press rose petals to her lips and then to his. Or they would sit by the river, laying their hands in its coolness and watching the trout. Or they would climb up to the fir trees and gather gum and chew it, and breathe the odor of ripe chokecherries and juniper. There was so much tenderness, so much peace, that he would marvel at life, having found it so clean and good.

Not once during these days with her was he conscious of a wish to embrace her. The purity of his love was so extreme that it came to be, when he looked back on it in a later time, one of the incredible circumstances of his life. Not even when he kissed her did he have a conscious wish to do more. For him she was like the flowers and the sky, the evenings and the mornings, and he could no more have proposed intimacy, or have consciously wished it, than he could have taken his own life. She was his god, and his hours with her were his testaments and his prayer.

The flavor of his love is to be found most amazingly in an experience that fell in August. She had to go to Idaho Falls to nurse a relative, and told Vridar that if he saw her the following Sunday he would have to see her there. He told her he would. He rode down with the mail carrier, and met her in the railway station just after dark. She smiled and came toward him, but he did not take her in his arms there. Too many persons stood around and there was too much light. Without speaking, save as his trembling body spoke and his eyes, he led her to the street and they walked into town. He was troubled by the thought that she would leave him in an hour or two and he would have to spend the night alone; and as they turned from street to street he wondered how he could keep her with him. He was willing to sit on a park bench all night, but he could not ask her to do that. The night was warm; he wanted to go to the edge of town and sit under trees, but this too, he imagined, she would think a foolish thing. Besides the bench or the country there was nothing but a hotel.

"Neloa, when do you have to leave me?"

"By midnight, I guess."

They pased a drugstore and they peered in. "It's after ten now. Less than two hours!"

"Mebbe I can stay till one."

"Less than three hours! Neloa, couldn't you stay with me all night?" She looked at him with astonishment. He pressed her arm. "We could go to a hotel. It wouldn't be wrong, would it?"

She gave no reply. He thought she was horrified, but he urged on her his proposal, telling her that it was entirely their own business, for they were betrothed. He had enough money for two rooms, in some cheap place, and they would get two rooms, if she wished. They could sleep alone but he would be near her, even with a wall between.

"Darling, I can't let you go in three hours. Will you?"

"I don't know."

279

"Why don't you know?"

"I shouldn't, I guess. My aunt is quite sick."

"But if you go to her you will go to bed. Won't you? What difference would it make?"

"I don't know." She drew away from him and went to a window. She looked at dresses, spread in piles of color under a light. Vridar was annoyed. How could she look at these things when another matter, so vast and important, weighed on their souls!

"That's a pretty dress," she said. "Isn't it?"

"I suppose," he said, scowling at an overflowing mass of pink taffeta. They went down the street and Neloa stopped at other windows. Feeling resentful, Vridar wished he had not come. "Will you?"

"What?" she asked, staring at a velvet skirt.

"Stay with me tonight. Will you?"

"I don't know."

"Neloa, please!"

They walked again. He saw in her eyes a bright hunger for lovely things. At a jeweler's window she stared earnestly at brooches and rings, bracelets and necklaces and watches, lavallieres and beads. She said she wanted a lavalliere and he said he would buy her one when he could. He took her arm to lead her away but she turned, as a child does, to look at all the shining things. He took her into a drugstore and to a booth and gave her the menu, and he saw her eyes brighten as she read.

"What do you want?"

She chose ice cream dressed with marshmallow and pecans, a dish, it seemed to him, that must be terribly expensive; and he chose a plain soda, having noted its low price. Whether he would now have money for two rooms and his journey home he did not know; and his worries multiplied as he watched her eat. She was excited, not by him, he realized, but by the city life around her. She looked very lovely, with her eyes shining and so much color in her cheeks.

"You haven't told me. Will you?"

"Mebbe," she said. She looked at him, her eyes dark and wide.

"Neloa, say yes."

"Yes."

He forgave everything now: her window-shopping, her interest in jewels, which he thought barbaric and detestable, and her misuse of their hours. That she would spend a night with him in spite of her shyness and innocence was overwhelming proof of her love. She trusted him and put herself in his care.

On their way out he fell behind to glance at the bill, having until this moment loftily ignored it; and when he saw that it was only thirty cents he felt more at ease. He smiled at the cashier and said good evening, as though he were a worldly fellow who knew his way about. The time was now eleven and he walked up and down the streets, seeking an unpretentious hotel. Most of them had magnificent lobbies. He would have to find a small hotel and he pretended to her that it would be best to do so: in the larger hotels they might be recognized.

"I know one," she said, "I stayed in it once."

She led him to a street and he looked up at a building that was gloomy and still. He took her arm and opened a door and they climbed a dark stairway and came to a small desk, feebly lighted, above which he read a sign which asked him to push the button to his right. His heart was racing, and his hand trembled when he pressed the button. From a dark corridor came a huge woman with a coarse lewd face and a sharp voice.

"Well?" she said, looking at Vridar.

"Do you—uh—have rooms?—vacant . . . I want two."

"Two?" she said, and looked at Neloa.

"You see," he went on, hastening to explain, "we're not—well, not married. We're engaged, I mean." Her stare was so incredulous that he quickly added: "You see, she's down here nursing and I—well, I mean I came down to see her. We live at Antelope. . . . We—I mean we just want to be close together." That, he thought sounded pretty silly. "If you have two rooms—" He broke off. The woman's shrewd cold eyes were looking through him.

"I got one room," she said.

"Only one?" His heart sank. "You sure you have only one? If you had two together—"

The woman was staring at Neloa. "You'n have it," she said, turning to Vridar.

"But we're not married," said Vridar.

Her smile was faint and cynical. "It will be a dollar and a half for two."

"But we're not married," he said, bewildered. He turned to Neloa to see what she thought of this. Her eyes were bright and her face was a little flushed. Then it occurred to him that they could take the room and Neloa could sleep and he could sit up.

"Do you want it?" the woman asked sharply.

"Yes," he said.

"Sign here."

Vridar wrote his name and Neloa's and his mind shook so that his writing looked strange to him. The woman took a key and led the way down a black corridor. She unlocked a door and ushered them into a room that smelled of old bedding and dust. She turned a feeble light on and looked at Vridar a moment and went over and drew the shade. Then she went out and softly closed the door.

It was the way she closed the door that made him feel guilty. He did not turn to Neloa at once. He was astounded by his boldness and too afraid that he was being very uncircumspect. He walked round the room, pretending to be inspecting one thing and another but really fighting against a sense of shame. What did she think of him, fetching her to a room as though they were man and wife? When at last he looked at her, he was surprised by the happiness in her face, and he was glad that he had brought her here. They would spend the night together, and if anywhere on earth there was greater joy for anyone he could not imagine what it was like.

"Neloa, you're not angry?"

"No."

281

He took her in his arms and kissed her and they sat on the bed. She laid her head on his shoulder and he put an arm round her waist. For a little while they sat this way.

"I guess she thought we were up to mischief," he whispered. Neloa gave no reply. Vridar wished she would talk more and not keep so much of herself deeply hidden. He went over to the one dirty window and peered behind the shade and into the street. He was thinking of the way the woman had looked at him after she had drawn the shade. What a fool he was! Did she imagaine that if a man took a woman to a room he must inevitably have dishonorable intentions? Then he felt dismay, for there came to him the horrible thought that possibly he had taken Neloa into a whorehouse.

He returned to the bed. She looked flushed and excited but he could not blame her for that, so incredible was the thing he had done. He would be very gentle with her and she would feel all right.

"Neloa, you don't love me any less, do you?"

"No," she said, and gave him that strange dark look.

He framed her face and forced her gaze to meet his, but he could not read the meanings in her eyes. Only rarely, if at all, had he ever read them. So much was there, so much had always been there, in the soft and inscrutable depths.

"Are you sleepy?"

"A little."

"Would you like a drink?"

"Yes."

He went over to the dirty washbowl and found a dirty glass. He scoured it and filled it with water. He took the glass to her and she thanked him and swallowed a little; and he realized that she was not thirsty at all. What else could he do to make her feel at ease? Turning the cover back he examined the bed: the mattress was old and unclean and rotten, the springs sagged. The covering was unclean too. He hoped there were no bedbugs or lice. Neloa, now very quiet, seemed to be looking at the wall. He sat by her and took her hand. What should he say?

"Do you want to lie down?"

She gave him that strange look that so troubled and disturbed him. He folded pillows and propped them up and lay against them, and drew her to his arms. She could sleep like this, he said. She could sleep and he would lie awake and look at her and be sure that she was warm; and he laughed a little, thinking how absurdly happy he was.

Neloa gave no reply. She was deeply silent and he could not imagine what she was thinking about. By the way she looked he knew she was thinking. Out in the hall he could hear a woman's protests and a man's angry voice, and he went over to lock the door. But there was no key, no latch. He stood a chair on its heels and propped the door and came back. The man was loud and abusive and the woman was crying as if in pain; and then steps went down the hall and the building was silent. Vridar looked at Neloa to see what she made of this.

"Sounds like a quarrel, doesn't it?"

"Yes."

He turned the light off and the room was very dark. Telling Neloa she ought to sleep now, he drew the covers back, and she kicked her shoes off. She lay on the bed and he put a quilt over her; when, after taking only his shoes off, he lay at her side and put an arm round her. But he lay without cover, feeling that it would be indecent, even with clothes on, to enter the bed with her. He asked if she was warm and she said she was. After a little while he became aware that his arm was against her breasts and he moved it down to her waist.

She lay on her back and he lay on his side, with his arm round her over the quilt, with his face in her hair. Her hair was clean and fragrant and he loved the smell of it. He kissed her hair, softly, so that she would not be aware of it.

"Are you all right?" he asked.

"Yes."

"Happy."

"Yes."

He felt very tender and protective, as though they were lost in an alien land and she was his to defend. She would sleep but he would not. All night he would lie awake, trying to understand that the Neloa whom he knew in Annis was here at his side. When they were married he would lie with her every night and smell of her hair and feel the pressure of her lovely hand. He thought she had the most beautiful hands he had ever seen. Her arms were beautiful too, but loveliest of all were her eyes and hair and smile. It seemed very strange that a beautiful girl should care for him at all.

After a little while she slept and he was pleased to learn that she did not snore. Her breathing was only slower and deeper. She was lying on her side away from him and he moved his face close to her, but not his body, and he thought of how innocent she was and how she trusted him. It would always be that way. Their life together would be like a poem that you had to read many times before you understood the full wonder of it. He sighed, for his heart was very full. Again and again he pressed his lips to her hair or softly to the cloth of her dress. Kissing her, more than anything else he could do, seemed to heal and restore him and obliterate the memories of childhood.

He became sleepy after a while but he did not sleep. His hours with her, so few each week, must all be given to realization and thought. If he were to sleep he might as well be in China or at home in his own bed: no, he would lie here and listen to her breathing and tell himself over and over how much he loved her and how happy they would be. This he did, shaping his dreams until morning came. All night he kissed her hair, piled round his cheeks; he gathered it and covered his face with it; or he patted her arm or her shoulder and kissed it, as in years long ago he had kissed the Bible. . . .

When morning came Neloa still slept, and Vridar lay by her worshipful and wide awake.

VIII

But this interlude of happiness came suddenly to an end. At midafternoon three days later everything was still perfect; by ten o'clock that night he had suffered the most terrible disillusionment of his life. As strange as lightning in a clear sky came its first intimations, and then flash by flash it heaped its blinding ruins upon his world.

Unable to wait for Sunday, he had ridden out and gone with her over the hill and to the river. Vridar then did what he was always to think of in memory as an unworthy and contemptible thing. Credulous, yet suspicious, and with a sleeping jealousy that could easily become insane, he had never been able to convince himself of Neloa's love. He told himself again and again that he had no reason to doubt. She went with no other man and she always seemed happy to see him and she yielded to the shaping power of his will. It was something which he felt in her: in her eyes at all times, often in her voice, sometimes in her way. Love made him blind but not stupid: he knew that there was a deep slyness in her of some sort, and hidden things, things that if she had her way she would never tell. Because he was abnormally proud and lonely of temper and because he gave to chastity a value which it could never possess, he resolved to put her to some kind of test. He never for a moment suspected what his words would lead to.

"Neloa," he said, "I have something to tell you, a shameful confession to make. You may not love me after I have told. But we shouldn't marry with secrets between us, should we?"

She hesitated a long moment before in a low voice she said no.

"It happened last winter," said Vridar, staring at his hands. "I was pretty wild, I guess." Good Lord, how wild! "I went with a girl and she fell in love with me, or said she did. She wanted to marry me. We went to shows and dances and that sort of thing." She glanced at him, and in the moment when he met her eyes he saw that she was anticipating what he would say. This confused him a little. He toyed with a stick, both because he wished to seem ill at ease and because he was; and then, during the remainder of his tale, he watched her steadily, trying to read the effect of his words.

"Well, there isn't much to say. We—I—well, the truth is I was intimate with her." He saw Neloa catch her breath. He saw that strangeness in her eyes, like pain but not pain at all, no, but her own hidden things. "Well," he said, "she —this girl, I mean—she's going to have child. It's my child." He was looking at her eyes. He saw them darken and then become bright and wet; he saw tears gather to her lashes and fall. Her lips trembled. But she did not speak. She only turned to look at him, as if hurt beyond the power of cure. He wanted to cry out that he had lied, had lied, that he loved her and her only, and so take the pain out of her eyes; but he must be very sure. "Neloa, will you marry me?"

She still looked at him, her tears falling, and then slowly she sank to the earth and wept. With all his being Vridar wanted to comfort her, to tell her that he had lied, to enfold her and kiss the pain and hurt away; but he must be sure. He sat and listened to her grief and waited; and after a little while she raised her head and looked at him again.

"Neloa, will you?" She gave no reply. She looked away from him and tears rolled down her cheeks. "I love you, Neloa, I love you. I did not love this other girl. I did not want to marry her. I know it was a shameful thing I did. If you tell me to go I will go. . . . Neloa, shall I go?"

Again she looked at him, her eyes filled and lustrous and very beautiful. He got to his feet and started away; and as he did so she made a choked sound and bowed to the earth. He went a little way up the mountain and looked back at her, and then stood there and waited but she did not look up. "Neloa, shall I go?" She did not look up. He could see that she was shaking with grief. He went a little farther and turned again and said: "Neloa, I am going now." He went up the path, glancing back from time to time, but she did not raise her head. He was out of sight and he was convinced that she would let him go, when he heard her voice crying his name. She came frantically toward him but the moment she saw him she stopped. He went down the mountain and faced her. "Shall I go?" She looked at him and again he saw those strange secret things in her eyes. She was trembling, and never, he reflected, had he seen her so deeply moved. "Neloa, shall I?" He moved closer and touched her arms. He forced her head up so that her eyes would meet his, and for several moments he looked into their strange wet darkness. They told him nothing that he wanted to know. "Neloa, shall I?"

She looked away and drew a sudden sharp breath. "No," she said.

With a cry Vridar took her to his arms and kissed the tears from her eyes and cheeks. He led her to the bank and they sat, with Neloa lying against him; and he said: "I have another confession."

With a gasp she fought away from him and sat up. He struggled with her and drew her to him.

"It was all a lie," he said. "There was no truth in what I told you, none, so help me God. You're the only girl I ever went with, except once to a show."

He thought she would be overwhelmed by relief but she was not. On the contrary her behavior now completely baffled him. She moved away from him as if his touch annoyed her and she sat, staring out into distance. Vridar studied her face, trying to sense the quality of her emotion and divine her thoughts.

At last she said: "Mebe I should confess too."

"You?" he said. He looked around, trying to meet her eyes. "What in the world would you have to confess? That you danced with men like Dave Wolf? But I know that. You confess!" he cried, and the idea was so preposterous that he laughed. "Neloa, you don't have to test me. I love you. You don't have to be silly because I was."

She made no reply. She was still looking out into distance and he thought there was something sad and wistful in her gaze. He helped her to her feet and kissed her and they went down a path by the river. He did not know that she had deliberately chosen this path. He was telling her that he was sorry, that he had been mean and stupid; and he hugged her to him and kissed her with such rapturous devotion that color drenched her cheeks.

285

In a few minutes they came to a large aspen tree and Neloa glanced up at it and turned to him and said: "Look up there."

He looked up and saw carved on the tree above his head these letters:

N D

H K

"Whose are those?" he asked, looking at her. "N. D., that is you." He saw that she was smiling up at the letters as though glad to see them there. He stared at her face and a horrible doubt seized him. "H K, who is that?"

"Harvey Kress."

His heart sank. His thoughts went back to school days in Poplar and to Alvin Kress, the sallow insolent lad who had wooed Helen and whom he had threshed by the barn. "Is he Alvin's brother?"

"No, his cousin."

Knowing by Neloa's face that she had things to tell, he went to a fallen tree and sat. What was the meaning of this? Why had she smiled so happily when she looked up at the initials? Great God! he thought and looked over at her, while doubt and jealousy and rage filled him. Then she came to him and looked at him and the smile left her face.

"You mean," he said, "you were down here with him?" She did not reply. He met her eyes and saw in them that baffling strangeness that had always been there. "Were you?"

"Yes."

He was silent a moment, trying to get a grasp on his emotions. Softly he asked: "When?"

"Oh, last spring a year ago. Last summer it was."

"A year ago. Did you spend a whole day here?"

"Yes."

"When you—were only fourteen?"

He strove to think about it. She had been here with Harvey Kress and had spent a day with him, and they had wandered here like lovers, and he had climbed that tree and linked her name with his. What did it mean? What had they said, what had they done? Vridar stood up, his senses darkening, his world full of a strange humming sound. He laid hands on her arms and swung her to face him. He searched her eyes but their lustrous velvet told him nothing at all. When he spoke again his voice was hoarse, and his hands trembled on her arms. "Did—did he kiss you?" Now there came into her eyes something which he understood. It was cold annoyance, a kind of sly contempt, mixed with bewilderment and fright. His fingers sank into her flesh until she cried with pain. "Did he?"

"You're hurting me!"

"Did he?"

"Yes."

As if she had struck him, he released her and sat. He was trying to under-stand this simple fact, that she had been kissed, kissed by another man; but the meaning eluded him and went off into darkness and became an inexplicable thing. For how could it be so! She was so guileless and so young: how could it be? She

286

had been down here, he told himself; she had wandered here with another, even as she had done with him; and they had kissed and laughed. He shut his eyes tight and breathed through his mouth; he shuddered and was still. How could it be? It was so silly of her to tell him that! . . . And then he knew . . . yes, he knew. . . .

He stood up, looking haggard, and went stumbling through brush to a path and found the road. Neloa followed him, many yards behind at first, but little by little she narrowed the distance until she walked at his side. He did not look at her. He stared ahead of him up the mountain, and in the anguished darkness of his mind he recalled things that had baffled him: the light in her eyes when she waved to Francis Henderson; the deep guiltiness that he had so often seen in her eyes; her curt note about not swinging on her gate—these and other things. Yes, he knew! For as he walked the doubt within him grew, the whole matter became certain, so certain that there was only intolerable waste in his whole being. He was feeling rather weak and sick. He was feeling that terrible strangeness of his earlier years, the nightmares and lunacies, the exile and loneliness. . . . But all the while he tried to find a way out. A kiss itself meant nothing, or very little: he told himself this but it did no good. It would take more than a kiss to explain all that was leaping into meaning now. Of what she could tell him the certainty became so appalling that he sank by the road and bowed his head and tried to steel himself for what must come. He sat there, and Neloa stood in the road and waited. Not once during possibly an hour did he speak. Not once did she speak. Darkness came and he rose again and walked, and very silently she walked at his side. He stumbled as though unable to see the road, as indeed he was; and once he fell and lay a few moments without realizing that he had fallen. For his body now moved as if it had been severed from his mind; and his mind, intense and isolated and dark, had only one meaning in it.

During the whole distance home they walked and neither spoke. God give me strength! he prayed; God give me strength! He opened her gate and she followed him and he went up the road and entered the barn. He became aware now that he was sweating, and with a shaking hand he wiped his brow. He went to the manger and leaned into it, thinking he would vomit, but he only retched and felt deathly sick. It was sickness not in his stomach but in his soul. He went to the pony and bowed his head to it and tried to weep, feeling that he must somehow throw off the desolation and pain or go mad. But there were no tears in him now. His anguish was too deep; his heart seemed to have been dropped into it out of reach, his mind seemed to be fading away. He knew vaguely that Neloa was standing by the door. He tried to understand why she was there and to think of her, but thinking of her was like probing into a wound and he drew farther away from her into the dark.

For perhaps half an hour he stood by the pony and did not move. He told himself that he should lead the horse out and mount it and ride away. While striving to do this there came to him suddenly a bright hope: perhaps she had been innocent, perhaps the kissing was all she had to tell. He could forgive that, he could take her to his heart and let his grief out; for his need of her was greater than his pride.

He went over and put hands on her arms and turned her, so that moonlight fell on her face; and he looked into her eyes and at her mouth, and what he saw there left him no hope. If her guilt had been written in black and white it could not have been plainer.

"Neloa, have you ever lied to me?"

"No."

"But you never told me these things."

"You never asked."

"I never asked?" No, great God, his trust had been absolute! "All right, tell me now."

"What?"

"All that you have to tell."

She looked away and he saw the secrets in her eyes. Her eyes indeed seemed to be only a black record of untold things. Again his heart sank, drawing most of his breath with it.

"Tell me."

"What?"

"Do you have to keep saying what? You know very well what I mean." In her eyes he saw fright.

"I don't know what you want me to tell."

"You're a liar. Do you tell, or shall I go?"

"You mean about Harvey?"

"Let's begin," he said bitterly, "with Harvey."

But still she would not speak. When his grasp tightened on her arms, she looked annoyed and said he was hurting her. She tried to throw his hands off. This infuriated him and he shook her so savagely that she gasped.

"Stop it!" she cried.

"You will suit yourself," he said. "If I turn to the pony I shall be gone and I shall not come back. I have been a fool. In all the world there is no fool like me. All these weeks you have been deceiving me and no doubt feeling contempt for me, because I have so idolized you. Now you will talk or not, as you please, but I'll not wait long."

Her gaze was far away. In her faint smile he saw contempt for him. Or was it contempt? He shook her again.

"Don't."

"It might be best if you say nothing. I will go. You can marry a man here. But if you marry me there will be no secrets between us."

She drew a sharp breath. "It happened last summer."

"What happened last summer."

"This you want me to tell."

"Oh, of course you don't want to tell it!"

"I went to the valley with daddy, and Harvey, he went too. We went to Idaho Falls."

"Go on."

"Well, daddy got two rooms, one for me and one for him and Harvey."

288

"Yes?" Vridar said, looking at the strange things in her eyes.

"You'n guess the rest."

"Oh, the hell I will! I'm not guessing!"

"Don't! You're hurting me."

"Go on."

She shrugged. "Well, when daddy got the rooms Harvey took the key to my room. He said he would give it to me later. . . . You'n guess what happened."

"Oh no I won't!"

She glanced at him and her glance was scornful. She shrugged again. "Well, Harvey came to my room. . . . I don't see," she cried, with sudden fire in her voice, "why I have to tell you any more! You'n use your imagination."

"My imagination? Yes, I suppose I could." His lips curled. "I hadn't in mind that you would tell all the little erotic details. Did he stay all night with you?"

"No."

"How long?"

"Oh, an hour or so."

"And what was your idiot of a father doing?" She did not speak. "Jesus Christ, some father you have! He takes his fourteen-year-old daughter to the Falls —Is this the Kress who went on a mission?"

"Yes."

"—and turns her over to a Mormon missionary son of a bitch!" Vridar could feel the blood surging in his throat. He went over and leaned against the pony, and within him everything was a horrible confusion of hatred and pain. He was afraid that he would break soon, that he could not endure this without some awful violence; but not until he was through with her, not until he had heard it all. Above his desolation now there was a bright ruthless cunning, and a thought of murder and suicide: he went back to face her. He grasped her and swung her to the light, and she cried with pain and struck him. He turned on her a diabolic grin.

"How many times with this missionary?"

"Let me go!" she said, her eyes like black venom.

"Oh no! A man doesn't lose God so easily!" He broke her to her knees and then lifted her to her feet. He saw terror in her eyes. "How many?"

"Two."

"Where was the other?"

"By the river."

"Where we were today?"

"Yes."

He looked at her and was jolted by a thought. "And in Idaho Falls did you stay in the hotel where we stayed?"

"Yes."

Staggered, he released her. She had been intimate with this man, perhaps in a spot where he had sat with her, worshiping her; and she had led him to the very hotel in which she had been seduced. In this hotel he had been with her only a few days ago, possibly in the same room, on the same bed; and he—God, what a fool he was!—had never thought of intimacy, had wished only to cherish her and

289

be with her alone. He stood by the pony, shaking with humiliation and self-loathing. What sort of woman was it who could lead her betrothed to *that* hotel?—who could sit with him Sunday after Sunday in the spot where she had lain with another man? He went back to her, his face white and dreadful, with no pity for himself now, no pity, but only contempt.

"Is that all?"

"All what?"

"Neloa," he said softly, "don't fool with me. Do you understand?" His words were so gentle but so terribly ominous in their gentleness that she shrank away, horrified. She moved as if to flee but he seized her and dragged her back. He broke her to her knees and lifted her and slammed her to the wall. Then he held her with a clutch on her wrist.

"Please don't!"

"Neloa, let's understand one another. If you don't want to tell, I will go. If you don't want me to go, then you will tell. Who else?"

"Please, you're hurting me!"

"Who else?"

"No one."

"You lie!"

"I don't lie!"

"You lie. Shall I go?"

"Only don't hurt me."

"Which of us is being hurt? I tell you a man doesn't lose God so easily." He studied her face. "Do you believe in God?"

"Yes."

"All right, go bring a Bible."

"I won't."

He turned to the pony and saddled it. He was making ready to lead it out when he heard her say that she would go; and she ran away and he waited, feeling strangely calm now. He thought he would kill her and then kill himself and he looked round him for weapons. He saw a rope and decided that he could hang himself with it, and he looked up at the rafters of the barn. Yes, he was calm, but under his calm was a mad strangled violence, a wild unreason that waited and beat in him but would wait only a little while. He could feel the power of it, lying against his will like floods against a dam. Then he heard her coming. She entered the barn and gave a book to him, and he held it in moonlight to be sure what it was. He told her to place both hands on the Bible, and she did. He told her to repeat these words:

"I swear to tell the whole truth and nothing but the truth, so help me God." She hesitated. "Say them."

"I—I swear to tell the truth—"

"—the whole truth—"

"—the whole truth and nothing but the truth—"

"—so help me, God."

"—so help me, God."

"Now," said Vidar, "keep your hands there and remember that it is a terrible thing to tell a lie on the Bible. What other man have you been intimate with?"

She looked away and caught her breath.

"Answer."

"Dave Wolf."

He would have been no more amazed if she had thrust a knife into his heart. With blackness storming his mind, he turned away for a moment; and then he went to the pony and leaned against him, feeling that he would faint. A violent retching shook him and came up his throat and he wiped bitter froth from his lips. He was remembering Diana's letter the previous winter. He stumbled back and looked at her, and with the voice of a man past all hope he said:

"All right, go on."

She was holding the Bible and looking at him. "You mean—tell about him?"

"Yes, Neloa."

"It was up at Nevel's. I was teaching their children."

"When?"

"Last winter."

"Go on."

"I was alone with him and the Nevel children. Mr. and Mrs. Nevel, they went to the valley."

"How long were they gone?"

"Two days."

"How many times with him?"

"Two."

"If they had been gone four days," said Vridar, with dry hard bitterness, "I suppose your answer would be four—or if ten, ten." He was studying her face, trying to understand this thing. It was so much to understand, to believe. "Any more?"

"Yes."

He started as if struck. Great God, did she mean she had had more than two lovers? "More than two?" he asked incredulously.

"Yes."

He put a hand to his brow, unable to see and barely able to stand. "Who?"

"Francis Henderson."

It was another blow but the blows were not so hard now. "The man you waved to down on the creek?"

"Yes."

"When? . . . Neloa, when was this?"

"Oh—about a week—or two weeks before I went to your place."

This was another blow but he was past all feeling now. The meaning came to him obscurely, like something out of an old nightmare: a week or two weeks before she walked with him in Black Canyon, before she promised to be his wife, she had lain with this man. And when he drove her home he had hardly dared to ask her for a kiss! That was what she said. It was impossible to understand it or see any meaning in it but that is what she said.

"Where?" he asked dully.

"On the bed."

"Your bed? What bed?"

"Just outside our house."

He thought of this bed against the north wall. He felt a strange impulse to go over and look at it. "How many times with him?"

"One."

"How many times did you go with him?"

"Once."

Again he stared at her, incredulous. Did she mean that she surrendered to a man the first time? Good God, not even Forenoon's girls did that! Did she mean that this girl whom he had idolized so many years— "Who else?"

"That's all."

"Oh, that's all. Not yet fifteen and that's all. It—it would seem that you have done all right."

He moved away from the barn but without its support he reeled and had to grasp a log. He passed a hand over his brow, his mind groping, his thoughts trying to plot her death and his. A little while ago, it seemed to him, he had thought of a way; but he could not remember it now. Unaware of what he was doing, he sank, for his legs were nerveless and would not support him. He sat with his legs spread out, and bent over, his arms to his knees. "Sit down," he said.

She sat and laid the Bible in her lap. He studied her face a few moments but his eyes were full of anguish and mist and he could not see. "Do you love any of these men?"

"No."

"Did you?"

"No," He tried to understand that. What kind of woman was it who gave herself to men without love?

"Did they want to marry you?"

"Only Dave."

"Didn't that missionary bastard want to?"

"He never asked me."

"Would you have married him?"

"Mebe then but not now."

He sat with elbows to his knees, hands to his hair, still trying to understand. The deep quiet within him was more terrible now: for several minutes he neither moved nor spoke, nor did Neloa, and he could hear only his breathing in the profound silence. He was fighting against the power that held him but he knew it was useless to fight. He would have to break to some kind of frenzy and let it out. And suddenly he felt an impulse to laugh. The first sound he made was strange and choked; it startled him and he leapt to his feet and roared. It was violent laughter, empty, empty and desolate. He walked round the barn, letting the frenzy pour out of him; and when he stopped, the emotion surged up and was damned in his throat and held there. He threw his arms out like a man strangling; and then turned and came back and with a terrible cry threw himself to her lap. On his knees he rocked back and forth, trying to release his torture, to purge himself with an overwhelming flood of grief or rage. It was grief that saved him. He bowed to her lap and let it out of him in sound and tears. It beat within him and rose in gasping sobs and shook him until he was blind.

Out of his grief, as though it had been there all the while, came a wan hope. It became a prayer that she had lied to him, as only a few hours ago he had lied to her. He prayed to God to make it all a lie. Then he sat up and looked at her, but he could not see her, and he reached and found her hands and kissed them. He pressed her hands to his cheeks, to his mouth. "Neloa," he whispered, "tell me it's not the truth! Say it's not the truth!"

"But it is," she said.

"Oh no." He moved up toward her face, trying to see into her eyes. "It can't be true!" he said. "Neloa, it can't be!"

"But it is."

Struggling free of him, she stood up. He rose, trembling, and faced her, trying to see what her eyes said. "Please, Neloa! Please tell me it is not true!"

"I can't" she said, backing away from him.

He struck an arm to his brow and looked wildly round him and saw the Bible in her hands. He told her to place her hands on it. "Do you swear that what you said is true?"

"I swear everything I told you is true."

He looked at her. The furious hope died within him and again there was only the desolation. He led the pony out and sprang to its back, and the pony leapt ahead at full speed. Neloa ran after him, calling his name. He turned the horse free and went swiftly through the night, seeing only the shadows, hearing only the galloping feet. For six miles the horse did not break a gallop, uphill or downhill, and when Vridar came to the dugway the beast was white with lather and foam. In the yard he jerked the saddle and bridle off and went running to the house. There was a light in the kitchen, and when he burst in he found his parents there, as if awaiting him. Prudence gave a cry, and Joe, usually so imperturable, got to his feet; and they both stared at their son. What in the world had happened? his mother asked; and Vridar paced the room or fell to a chair, only to rise in a moment and pace again. His mother was talking to him but he did not understand what she said. After a while he sank again to a chair and shook and moaned, or struck out, fighting the air around him, trying to calm himself. And at last he blurted out the bitter story of the night. He poured it out of him in wild inarticulate words, flung it out with frenzied gestures, trying to purge himself of it and all memory of it. Then his mother tried to comfort him but he thrust her away, for he was now deeply ashamed and wished he had not told.

Refusing breakfast, he went outside and all day he prowled, trying to tell himself that he had only dreamed. He climbed the mountain and walked aimlessly among trees; he went to the river, obsessed with a wish to kill himself, to be forever done with humiliation and shame and his blundering efforts to take his place as a man among men. Over and over pride told him to renounce the girl and forget her; but within him there was a force stronger than pride, a love—or was it love?

he asked himself—stronger than death; and the more he agonized over the matter the more deeply he knew he could never spurn her.

But pride was a fierce and inexorable thing in him, and all day long pride and love fought in him, until he was goaded beyond endurance, until he cursed himself and the hour of his birth. He could not forget how calmly she had made the confessions, how unconcerned she had seemed to be, how abject he had been in his beseeching, how stupid and blind he had been during all these weeks. It was not so much that she had been intimate with men; he had learned from Forenoon that many girls lay with men before marriage. It was the ease with which she had surrendered: it seemed that she had need only to be alone with a man, any ardent man, any man with whom she found herself alone. He knew now that she would have surrendered to him in Black Canyon or on the drive to her home, or any Sunday during these weeks. What sort of woman was it who gave herself so easily?

He climbed the mountain and came down and climbed again, trying to wear himself out. He wanted to see her and talk to her; to learn if she had been suffering his anguish, if she had felt any shame. To hell with her! he thought. To hell with her! She's only a little better than a whore! But his contempt was so traitorous to his heart and his need that at last he went to his sister. Diana looked at him with amazement.

"You were right in the letter you wrote me last winter," he said. "But never mind that now. I want you to go out and take a letter to her. Will you?"

"I guess so," she said.

"I'll write it while you saddle the horse."

He entered the house, refusing to meet his mother's gaze, for he was deeply humiliated and wished he had not told. He went to the bedroom and sat at a desk and wrote this letter to Neloa.

> Dear Neloa:
> I suppose it would be best to call it quits, for you and I do not see some things in the same light at all. Do you understand, for instance, how deeply I am hurt?—or do you think that this in me is only self-pity?
> I need to know how you feel. Last night I did not sense any shame in you for what you had done: fear I saw; anger, scorn I saw, but not shame. It would be silly to think I could love you or marry you if you have not been shocked into some realization of your wantonness. You would have to change some of your values and go to school and try to be the kind of wife I need. You would have to understand that faith as utter as mine cannot be suddenly rooted out, that a man does not give up God so easily. You would have to restore that faith in you which I have now lost. I do not know if you wish to do these things. If you do not, then farewell. If you do, Diana will fetch your letter.
>
> Vridar

Diana took the letter and rode away, and Vridar went up to the benchland to wait there. Three months ago he had filed a homestead claim and built a shack on it, and he now went to the shack. Standing in the doorway he looked out at the western hills. It would take Diana almost an hour to go, an hour to return, and possibly she would be there an hour: three hours to wait, three eternities, with only his thoughts. He tried to remember what he had said in the letter; he wondered if he had said too much or too little, had been too scornful or not scornful enough. He tried to walk into the east but he kept looking back to the west, kept listening for the sound of a pony's feet. Going a few hundred yards away he returned, went again and returned, completing this aimless journey a score of times. He had not eaten for almost forty-eight hours and he felt faint and sick. Within the shack he sat on a pile of straw but at once came out, feeling stifled with a roof over his head. Then he went down the road where Diana had gone; returned, and tried to think, to understand what he should do. But it was impossible to think. His whole being was fixed on the homeward gallop of Diana. If he imagined hoof beats, he would start westward, running down the road; then, seeing nothing, hearing nothing, and despising his weakness, he would stare at the sun, trying to tell the hour. What would Neloa write to him? What would she write to him! This was the one, the only question in his mind. Would Diana find her weeping her heart out, and would Neloa write to him out of loneliness and grief?

Going again on the hills he circled and came back; and went again. In this manner he spent the bitter and unforgettable hours. The sun was only an hour high now. He took the road westward, breaking from time to time into a trot; and almost unaware of what he did, he covered two miles of the distance to Neloa's home. He stared down a long lane but there was no moving thing in sight. He sat by the road and waited and the sun sank and the hills were blue with dusk. Then, despising himself for being here, he started home, but again and again he sat by the road to wait. Stars were out when he came to the shack. He waited perhaps a minute, though it seemed an hour, and took the westward road again; and presently on a far hill he saw the streak of white in the pony's face. He ran to meet Diana with his heart intense and smothered in every breath. Looking up at her face, his eyes asked a question; and Diana with grave pity looked down at him.

"The letter!" he said. "Great God, give me the letter!"

"She sent no letter."

"She— You mean that—that she sent no letter?"

"She sent no letter."

"Diana, please don't tease me! Give me the letter!"

"But she sent none. I asked if she was going to write and she said no."

He turned away for a moment and looked at the stars. He began to count them, as long ago he had spoken over and over the names of beasts, to keep his grasp on reality. Diana got down from the horse and sat on the high bank of the road.

"Sit down," she said, "and I'll tell you what happened."

Vridar turned and sat, reaching under him for the bank, because his gaze was on his sister's face.

"Well, first I gave your letter to her. She took it and read it and tucked it in her dress. I watched her face and it didn't seem like she cared much what you wrote."

Vridar was looking at Diana's eyes. "What—what did she say?"

"Oh, not much. Not anything then. We went to the house and she helped get dinner. I wouldn't say she seemed very bothered or upset or ashamed or anything. Then Dave Wolf came in—"

"What!" cried Vridar. "Dave Wolf?"

"What is the matter with you?"

"Dave Wolf? Did you say Dave Wolf?"

"Why do you look at me that way?"

"Go on," he said.

"Well, he stayed for dinner and talked some and that's about all. I had to wait until he went until I could see her alone."

Vridar was still staring at Diana's eyes. "How—did she act with him?"

"Oh, about like a woman would with a man. They talked and she smiled at him and he smiled at her. Then they sat together when we had dinner."

Vridar was now looking into a black world, his amazement complete. Only last night she had sent him home crazed; and today she sat at dinner and smiled at the man with whom she had lain six or eight months ago. Is that what Diana had said? It was impossible to understand a thing like that. He was trying to understand it when pride came up, and scorn, and he felt a little stronger.

"What else?" he asked softly.

"Well, after Dave left I got Neloa alone and said you wanted her to stay with me in Rigby and go to high school. She said she would. I said we'd go down day after tomorrow and to be ready and she said she would. I guess that's all."

"And—and she sent no letter?"

"I asked did she want to and she said no."

"Did she—did she say anything about last night?"

"No."

"And—and you say she acted happy?"

"Well, she didn't act like her heart was breaking or anything. She smiled and talked. She acted like she always does." Diana was thoughtful a moment and said: "She et a big dinner."

"Oh?" Vridar turned away. He took the road and Diana followed, leading the horse; and on their way to the house nothing was said. Without eating supper, he went to his bed and lay in silence, and again love and pride fought. Marion came in and Vridar saw him undressing in the gloom. He wanted to talk to his brother and ask his advice, but toward Neloa and toward Vridar's love for her Marion had shown a strange hostility. The gulf between the brothers had become wider and darker.

Marion turned to the wall and was soon asleep. Tortured, enraged, bitter, sick, Vridar lay in the night-silence, turning over and over in his mind pictures of Neloa with Harvey, with Dave, with Francis; seeing the man's mouth on her mouth, the man's body above her; seeing her today sitting by Dave and smiling and eating a big dinner; until at last, feeling murderous, he dressed and went outside. He walked, plotting the murder of the four of them and of himself, thinking with savage pleasure of their cries for mercy, wondering where he could find the Mormon missionary bastard Harvey Kress. After midnight he went to the kitchen and wrote a scathing letter out of the ruins of his worship:

Dear Miss Doole:

It must seem to you as it seems to me that I have been an awful fool. What things you must have thought of me, when your contempt was veiled and hidden; but you have taught me much, you have taught me never to be the fool again.

I don't like your gate and I will no longer swing on it. When you are older you may realize that the things you did are the sort that women are usually paid for. You must see how stupid it would be for me to marry a girl like you. Women, I perceive now, I don't understand very well; but I am sure there are some who are not the common property of every man. I suggest that you marry Dave Wolf, or some moron like him, and live with him in an Antelope shack and have a bunch of kids and grow old and tragic like your mother. I shall go on. I shall if I can find God again.

I give you in farewell something to flatter your vanity. For two days and two nights and until past midnight of the third night I have not slept or eaten; and to you who ate with such appetite a few hours ago, with an old lover at your side, I must seem to be the last word in stupidity. I am. But years ago I fought a worse fight than this one and kept my feet; and I will keep them again.

Let Dave swing on your gate, lady!

Vridar Hunter

He read the letter over and over and then fed it to the flame of the lamp. He could no more have sent it than he could have cut off his hands. And he knew it. It was this bitter knowledge that sent him to bed loathing himself, heaping scorn upon himself, until he sank abject under the bright derision of his mind and the contempt of his pride. The next day he resumed the struggle, never suspecting that this decision, so heartbreaking to make, would be the most decisive of his life. It seemed to be only a choice between love and pride. It was infinitely more than that. If pride had won. . . . But love won. He told his mother that Neloa was going to Rigby, there to live with Diana and go to school. The decision was made. He thought another crisis in his life had passed.

But it had not passed. He went again to college, and he was not quite the simple and credulous youth who had gone the year before. He hated credulity now, hated it above all in himself; and he resolved to cut free of his old anchors, his old faiths. Betrayed by his home-training, made a fool of by devotion to mother and Neloa and God, he plotted his life toward moral disintegration and the ways of the social outcast. Only phenomonal luck saved him from utter ruin.

IX

Again he lived in the basement cell and stoked the furnace, and again Forenoon lived in the attic above. As in the previous year Vridar cooked his own meals, laundered his own clothes, and lived in all respects as frugally as he could; and Marion lived with him. Marion lived with him but he was almost never aware of Marion. During the first weeks he devoted himself to his studies and planned for himself a quiet and meditative life. But the plot of his life was now beyond his control.

If Neloa too had devoted herself to study and had written to him of love and penitence, urging him to forgive and forget, he might have been sober and industrious this year. He would have forgiven, even though he could never forget; he would have sunk himself in love of books and scholarship. But Neloa's letters were not penitent, save now and then when he rebuked her; and books for her were not and could never be the golden sun in the heavens that they were for him.

This year Vridar kept a journal in which he set down all his bravado, bewilderment, doubt, and heartache. It recorded also the unwise role of Diana, for it was she who spied on Neloa and wrote to her brother admonitions and advice. At the train before leaving Vridar spent a few minutes with Neloa, feeling the old tenderness, the old faith; and Neloa promised to write at least once a week, even if he did not write to her. Soon after the brothers arrived in Salt Lake City Marion had his eyes operated on—and then again—and again; and Vridar *was* aware of Marion's courage and patience, as day after day he sat blindfolded and waited. But a week passed and no letter came from Neloa; and another week; and remembering the fool that he had been, Vridar looked around at other girls. "Am I," he asked in his journal, "to be mortgaged all my life, body and soul, to an adolescent love-affair?" Then after two weeks a letter came:

> Sweetheart:
>
> Well, I'm in school and I guess I like it all right. The weather here is awful today. It is cold and windy and I'm shivering while I write this. Diana and I get along fine. We both cook and keep the house clean and we usually walk to school together. I've been looking for a letter from you.
>
> Well, I don't want to bore you so will ring off for this time.
>
> As ever
> Neloa

The letter annoyed Vridar. For one thing, he thought it wanted dignity and taste. For another, it did not breathe of penitence or love. He thought of the letters Elizabeth wrote to Robert Browning and decided to burn Neloa's but did not. He kissed it and put it away. He practiced boxing with anybody he could find to spar with him; he went to watch young people dance, and felt, because he was so intuitive, all the erotic emotions of which most of them were unaware. He perceived that a girl now and then was interested in him; but he could not believe it, and he would stare at himself in a mirror, at his dark and haunted eyes, his pale skin, almost as soft as a babe's, his thin mouth. Then there came another letter from Neloa:

> Dear Boy:
>
> I don't know why you haven't written. I guess you don't care any more and I should worry. We have some snow today and the weather is very cold. I think my English teacher is a cross old hen. She makes me write themes and I hate themes. Well, I will ring off for this time.
>
> As ever
> Neloa

What a hell of a letter it was! Vridar told himself. Was this the way a woman wrote to a man whom she loved? He sent off this reply:

> Dear Girl:
> If you feel the way your letter suggests you are wasting your stamps. When I left you in Rigby you said to put your love to any test I could think of; and now, because you haven't heard from me, you write as if you don't give a damn. Is this your idea of love? Does it all mean to you no more than that? If so, address your letters to another name.
>
> Vridar

Did strong men, he wondered, ever fall in love?—or was this passion found only in fools like him? Her letters, he said in his journal, were like Wilson's Mexican negotiations that left him no wiser. He was thinking of enlisting in the war when a huge man named Gudler came furiously to him and accused Vridar of trying to sneak into bed with his wife. It was Forenoon, who in his treacherous way had called out that he was Vridar, while running for cover. Then came a sweet and earnest letter from Neloa and he thought he should buy her a ring; but instead he rented a typewriter and began to write a novel and found himself for a few days in heaven. Then two weeks passed and no letter came and he made a date with a girl and she failed him; and in his journal he wrote: "It begins to dawn on me that man's a worm and woman is a robin. I'll have to be a scholar, and some lovely thing in fiction will be my wife: Elizabeth Bennett—Portia—The Wife of Bath!" A letter came from Diana, telling him that Neloa was flirting with other men; and he resolved at once to take dancing lessons. "I am learning the Canter Hesitation Waltz, the most sidesplitting arrangement of advance and retreat and St. Vitus ever contrived to bring lust to the surface, out of those pious Christian depths where St. Paul buried it. Most people are deceived in their reasons for dancing—or in their reasons for marrying, as I was not so long ago."

But he did not take dancing lessons at once. He waited, and another letter came from Diana, which told him that Neloa was writing to several men. On their way to and from school if a strange man waved to Neloa, she always returned the greeting; and sometimes a man would come over and walk at her side and ask if he could take her out. Vridar considered the matter a few days and then wrote:

> Dear Neloa:
> When we parted you said I could trust you henceforth in all things. We agreed to have no secrets, tell no lies. I now learn that you are writing to other men and seem to be approachable. Is it always to be this way? Will you never be honest with me? I should like to have a reply at once.
>
> Vridar

The reply came at once. It said:

> Dear Vridar:
> You seem willing to believe your sister instead of me. It's true I've answered some letters from old friends. They're just friendly letters and I didn't bother you with them. You may see them if you wish.

It's true that men seem attracted to me. You ask if I'll ever be honest with you? I can't love a man who believes his sister instead of me.

Neloa

Vridar was still undecided what to do when unexpected events shaped his life. The first of these was the dastardly and shameful way in which he changed his lodgings. Forenoon was a sly and sadistic fellow who thieved and whored with equal zest and had a most wicked sense of fun. He was sick of his cold dark room in the attic. He despised the avarice of his landlord. One day he told Vridar he had found two well-furnished and well-heated rooms where the three of them could live together, but Vridar demurred. He knew that it would be unwise to live with Forenoon but at last he overrode his best judgment. Forenoon engaged a truck and said they would leave at midnight. "I owe a month's rent," he said. "I have to sneak out."

Vridar owed no rent because he stoked a furnace for the underground cell. He went to Professor Yupp and said he was leaving; but he did not say that Forenoon was going, for this, it seemed to him, was none of his business. He and Marion packed their things and waited for the truck, which was to come at midnight.

An hour before midnight Forenoon came stealthily down with his bags and whispered that Yupp was asleep. Vridar took his things to the sidewalk and for a little while the three waited there. Then Forenoon said he had to piss and went back into the building. He returned in a few minutes and was unable to restrain his monstrous glee; he clapped hands to his mouth and sputtered and choked and then reeled down the walk, bellowing. Vridar became suspicious but dissembled a most obtuse unconcern. He confided in Marion, and Marion decoyed Forenoon to the corner drugstore. Vridar dashed to his room and what he found there amazed him. Forenoon had utterly demolished the chair, the table, the dishes and the light. He had jumped on the iron bed and kicked holes in the springs; and with a knife he had gutted the mattress, which was now only a pile of cotton and rags. He had torn the curtain in two and riddled the window shade.

Filled with wonder and rage, Vridar stared at the ruins, and then, with only vengeance in his mind, went quietly up the stairway and entered Forenoon's room. Working swiftly he destroyed the dishes; knocked apart the rickety chair and table; jumped on the bed and so wrenched its frame that it looked as if it had come through a fire. He demolished the shade and the curtain, and with a knife gashed the ugly faded paper on the walls. What else could he do? He saw a piece of shabby linoleum and tore it in shreds. Then he went down the stairway and to the sidewalk.

Presently Forenoon and Marion came up from the drugstore, and when Forenoon saw Vridar, he began to snort and choke with infernal mirth. Vridar looked at him as though amazed. Forenoon walked round and round Vridar, howling with glee, his eyes bright with malice. Hearing a noise he sobered, but after a moment exploded again, and then went off into the night, howling. "He broke everything in our room," Vridar told his brother. "But his room now looks worse than ours."

The truck came and they rode to Second East and entered their new quarters. The two rooms were small and shabby but clean. The man who owned them was a Jew who had a grocery store out front: Forenoon said he would steal all their food

300

from this store. "Jews aren't human," he said. Forenoon took his choice of the beds and sat and began to unlace his shoes, but almost at once toppled over, roaring like a madman. Vridar also began to laugh and they made such a din that there was a knocking on the door. "Come in!" Forenoon cried, and a Jew wearing pyjamas thrust his head around. He asked them to be quiet.

"Take your mug away," said Forenoon, "or I'll throw a shoe at it!"

The face vanished and the door was closed. In a few minutes there was another rap and the Jew entered with a policeman. "What's the trouble here?" the policeman asked.

"We were laughing," Vridar said.

"No more racket or I'll run you in."

After the two men had gone, Forenoon said he would steal the Jew blind and seduce his daughter. He undressed and crawled into bed, chuckling, and during the night from time to time he awoke and snorted. When morning came he was bursting with the secret.

"You must be an awful fool," he said, grinning at Vridar. "Are all the people in Antelope as simple as you?"

Vridar thought of Neloa. "Some people in Antelope know more than they tell."

"Listen, you halfwit, you know why I've been laughing? You'll blow a slat out when I tell you."

"You're the one who'll blow a slat."

Forenoon ruminated a moment and became suspicious. "Why?"

"Because, you thickheaded moron from Cedar City, your room looked twice as bad as mine."

Forenoon stood up. "You mean you busted my room?"

"It looked as if a Texas cyclone had been playing in it for a week."

Forenoon scowled and clenched his fists. "You dirty—"

"I wouldn't start anything—unless you're damned sure you can finish it."

Forenoon sat and began to roar again. Good God, he said, what would Yupp do? The greedy old son of a bitch would have a convulsion and bite himself. He rolled down to the floor and howled until he was spent; and then he staggered up and said he was going down to have another look at the Jew's daughter or to steal a pound of butter. He came back and said the Jew's daughter was a darling. He would have her in bed in a week.

The next day on the campus they came face to face with Professor Yupp. He looked at them, his small eyes full of pain, his lips twitching. Never had he known that there were such young men in the world! "What would your parents say?"

"I haven't any," said Forenoon.

Yupp's eyes had filled with tears and Vridar felt horribly ashamed. It would have been bad enough, Yupp said, if common street hoodlums had done it; but that college students should do a thing like that! "To hell with him!" Forenoon said, after Yupp had gone. "He freezes students to death with all those God damned hen coops. We ought to burn his house down."

Though Vridar despised Yupp's sanctimonious greed, he felt only shame for what he had done; and the next day he went to Yupp's home and knocked and

301

Yupp came to the door and looked at him. "I want to explain," Vridar said. "What I did was dastardly, but McClintock smashed my room and I was so furious I smashed his. I want to apologize and to pay for what I destroyed."

Yupp looked at him for several moments. "Very well," he said, "I'll send you a statement." And coldly he bowed to Vridar and closed the door.

The next event reached deeper. Saturdays he again clerked in the store of the previous winter. Some of the clerks were thieves and Vridar knew they were thieves: one of them, a man, slipped small expensive articles into his pockets before he went to lunch and again when he left at night; and some of the women put such things into the bags of their friends. Vridar wondered why the manager of the department was so stupid that he did not see these things.

One Saturday Vridar's sales broke a record that had stood for years. Some of the clerks became openly hostile. The next Saturday the manager came to him and drew him aside and asked to see his sales-book. He then went over and talked to the cashier and Vridar knew that he was being watched. The next Saturday he was more closely watched; several times he saw the manager standing by the cashier's window, studying sales-slips. Just before closing time, Vridar was summoned to the office of Archibald Drake, president of the store. He sat, and for several moments Drake studied him; and said at last: "You needn't come next Saturday. We won't need you."

"You mean—I'm fired?"

"I mean we'll not need you."

"May I ask why?"

"I do not care to discuss the matter. You may go."

Feeling insulted and furious Vridar stood up, and when he spoke again his voice shook. "I have a right to know why. Hasn't my work been all right?"

Again Drake studied him, his eyes searching and without pity. "I don't care to discuss it. You may go."

"If you don't tell me why I'm fired, you'll have to throw me out!"

"All right, if you insist. We have reason to believe that you are dishonest. Is that clear?"

"That I—I'm dishonest! My God, who told you that?"

"I have no more to say." Drake took a paper and began to read.

Mad enough to kill, Vridar looked at the paper and said: "Anyone who says I've been dishonest lies! In fairness you should let me face that person!" There was no reply from behind the paper. The paper was turned and the man read on another page. "You do have clerks who are cheats," Vridar went on furiously, "and I can name them! Why don't you fire them?"

The paper fell and the man looked at him. "Will you go now?" he asked quietly.

"Yes, I'll go, but not before I tell you that anyone who says I cheated is a dirty stinking liar! And that goes for all of you!" He swung and left the room, so blind with fury that he could barely find his way down stairs. He went to the cloakroom, his thoughts busy with vengeance; and while he stood there, taking off his apron and jacket, his glance fell on a stack of sales-books. Hardly aware of what he was doing, he thrust one deep into a pocket and put his cap on and found the street.

He went home convulsed with rage and wondering how he could avenge this insult. How could he outwit this arrogant millionaire whose only evidence had been the hostility and spiteful gossip of other clerks? When Forenoon and Marion came in, he told them what had happened. "I'll get even!" he said. "I'll get even if it costs me my life!"

Forenoon was delighted. A chronic thief himself, he laid hands on everything he could take. All his clothes he had stolen, from stores or from the college's gymnasium. "Make him feed us," he said. "That's the way to deal with millionaires, especially if they are Republicans."

Vridar hadn't thought of that. Now plans leapt to his mind, and each he examined, probing to the possibilities and the dangers. At last he said, "All right, he'll feed us." He walked the streets and at last hit on a stratagem that was as crafty as it was dangerous. He called me a thief! he thought. All right, I'll be a thief!

For several days he deliberated, weighing the risks, trying to anticipate the unforeseen, exulting as he wrought the pattern. "You should realize," he said to Forenoon, "that if we are caught it's ten years for us. That's all right for you, you don't have any parents."

"Thank God. They're a hell of a nuisance."

"If you lose your head—"

"Who in Christ are you talking to?"

"You, you damned coward. If you swipe a can of peas you shake around for an hour. So understand that if you bungle things I'll probably kill you."

"Are you trying to bluff me?"

"I'm saying if you haven't guts, stay out of this." Step by step, then, Vridar outlined the plan. He looked at Forenoon and said: "You'll go buy a half-dozen oranges and fetch me the sales-slip. I'll write the order and you'll get the oranges with the sales-slip into the box. Is that much clear?"

Forenoon shivered. "But how'll I get it in the box?"

"I explained that, you blockhead. Cut a hole in one overcoat pocket. Reach a finger through the hole and carry the oranges under your coat. You'll be standing by the box and someone will push you and you'll drop the oranges."

"Who'll push me?" asked Forenoon. "And what if I get caught?"

"Keep a cool head."

"Is that all I have to do?"

"That's all." Vridar looked at him pityingly. He was a thief, but he had the courage only of a petty slinking thief, and sometimes he hadn't that.

Forenoon got up, trembling, and went out, but in a few moments he was back, crying: "Your plan sounds fishy! I won't do it unless you do it first."

"You coward."

"I tell you it's fishy."

Vridar knew that he would have to be a forger also. In imitation of handwriting he possessed considerable skill, having in his high school years spent many hours copying the signatures of poets. He had copied their names because he envied them and wanted to be like them.

"Forgery too?" Forenoon cried, aghast. "You can't do it!"

Vridar asked Forenoon to write his name; and after practicing a few minutes he laid two signatures before him and that bewildered and astonished young man couldn't tell which was his own. "Neither is," said Vridar drily. In great excitement Forenoon went to the store and got the oranges; and then Vridar sat by a window and studied the sales-slip. It was a woman's writing, small and precise, and difficult to copy.

"You idiot! Why didn't you get a man clerk?"

"God, I never thought about it."

"I'm no wizard. Go back and get a man clerk."

While Forenoon was gone, Vridar went to a telephone and called the grocery and asked the prices of various items. He waited a few minutes and called again and another voice answered him; and again he asked the prices. Then he checked the two sets of figures against one another. Forenoon brought him another slip and for an hour or so he copied the writing, with Forenoon standing by, protesting, advising, ready to flee.

"That's a hell of a bunch of food to go to jail for! Get some fancy stuff."

"No. We're playing it safe. They never deliver fancy stuff to a place like this."

Forenoon said the order looked fishy. He held it to light and turned it over and over. "It won't work," he said. "If we have to go to jail let's rob a bank."

Vridar was trembling a little. The crucial moment had come. "I'll put it in the box," he said, grinning at Forenoon. "Get yourself ready for jail."

"I'm going to beat it!" said Forenoon, shaking. "Good God, this is fishy!"

In a pocket of Forenoon's overcoat Vridar cut a hole and then put on the coat and reached down through the hole to crook a forefinger under the string of the orange bag. He felt a little unnerved until he looked at Forenoon's white face. "A hell of a crook you are!" he said. He went to the store when he knew it would be dense with shoppers and pushed through the crowd to the box. As he passed the box, which was on the floor, he moved close and a part of the coat was dragged over the box. In this moment he dropped the sack. He felt an impulse to run but he went out casually and stood on a corner and casually looked at passing faces. On his return he heard a bird sing and he stopped to identify the bird, as though in no hurry at all. Back in their room he found Forenoon groaning and mopping his brow.

"We're goners!" he said, staring at Vridar. His face was as white as chalk. "Good God, let's beat it! What do we wait around for?"

Vridar crossed the room to get a drink. He looked at his hands and thought they were trembling a little. He shrugged.

"In God's name!" Forenoon howled. "Let's go! In an hour we'll all be in jail!"

"That's all right," Vridar said. "A lot of good men are in jail."

Forenoon mopped his brow again. Sweat was running down his face and his greedy eyes were bright with terror. At every unexpected sound he leapt up as if kicked. He went to a window and peered out and then stood by a door and listened. He lowered his voice to a whisper. "They can't arrest me," he said. "I had nothing to do with it."

Vridar took a book and tried to read but he was fascinated by Forenoon. He had not known that there were such cowards in the world. "Get hold of yourself," he said.

"I'm going!" Forenoon gasped, and feverishly he began to pack his things. He jerked a bag open and was piling clothes into when there was a knock on the door. For a moment no one spoke. In a last desperate effort to escape Forenoon vanished under a bed.

"Come in!" Vridar called.

The door was opened and a man entered carrying a box. "Groceries for McClintock," he said.

"Set them on the floor," Vridar said quietly. He went over and checked the groceries against the slip and said everything was all right. The man went out with the box, and when he heard the door close Forenoon thrust out a white face.

"Is he gone?"

Vridar burned the sales-slip and destroyed the ashes. Forenoon came over and looked at the groceries on the floor. "Jesus Christ," he said, "we just as well have had a lot more stuff!"

From December until spring Vridar maneuvered with care and cunning, and their groceries cost them only a few cents a week. Yielding little by little to McClintock's greed, he ordered toward the last only the best of everything: the choicest fruits and pickles and jams, crab and boneless chicken, imported cheese, nuts and stuffed olives, and the finest of sifted peas. Forenoon said they needed better lodgings. He said they might as well order ten times as much stuff and sell most of it. They could buy in case lots and sell at a discount.

"As a fool," said Vridar, "you have no competitors."

"Did you call me a fool? Listen, I'll lay your eyes right out on your cheeks!"

"Why don't you try it?"

McClintock was a powerful man and he was quick; but twice before Vridar had called his bluff and he had cursed and gone out like a match. Now he said, "Christ, I'm hungry. Let's eat."

Vridar sometimes thought of the risk he was taking, and of his parents, and then his shame was deep. But he was a Socialist! There were the exploiters and the exploited, the overprivileged and the underprivileged; the reactionary and venal Republican party, and those odious creatures called capitalists, among whom Archibald Drake was one. And there was Neloa, who had not written in weeks. Had she left school and gone back to Antelope and her old lovers? Or was she studious and faithful while waiting for him? He did not know, for Diana did not write any more.

For months he fought the bitter struggle with his conscience and late in April his conscience won. He told Forenoon that he would be a thief no longer. He was sick of it. Forenoon begged him not to be a fool, urged him to write at least one more order, and threatened him with ruin if he did not. The threat stirred Vridar to fury.

"You'll do what? Listen, Forenoon, if you ever say a word about this I'll kill you as dead as a doorknob!"

305

"Oh, yeah? You're going to heaven, I guess! You'll be a Mormon angel and wear wings!"

"Just remember to keep your mouth shut. I'm through, do you understand? And understand this, that it would be a public service to kill a man like you."

Forenoon looked at him and then crossed the room to get a drink.

Vridar thieved no more but this was late in April. Before April came, he had been guilty of another theft and of other kinds of devilment. The story now reverts to these.

X

McClintock was a malicious and destructive person. Undisciplined and unmoral and with fierce resentment of his humble origins, he vented his spite in nihilism. His glee in smashing furniture and enraging landlords was fiendish; and he seemed never so happy as when pursued by one whom he had outwitted. Before a week had passed in their new lodgings he had broken the hall lights and demolished the mirror in the bathroom and twisted several keys off in doors. Then one day he tricked Vridar.

He locked him in the bathroom and left him there, impotent and furious, for hours; and a week later when the rascal was asleep, Vridar bound Forenoon's hands with cord and roped him to the bed. When Forenoon awoke he cursed and made such a racket that the Jew came and told them they would have to move. They went to a cheap hotel and engaged a large corner room. Now, said Forenoon, a maid would clean their room, and that, he said, winking at Marion, was not all she would do.

Under their corner was a drugstore; the druggist had upon a long case a huge assortment of lotions and perfumes, precariously balanced. Forenoon liked this store: while buying a pencil or a package of gum, he would steal dyes and laxative tablets and garden seed and a lot of other thangs for which he had no use. One day he came sneaking in with a big syringe under his coat.

Now and then he and Vridar would go to the school's gymnasium to wrestle, or sometimes they wrestled in their room, or boxed, using a set of gloves that Forenoon had stolen. Because Vridar usually triumphed, Forenoon became spiteful and vindictive.

"Are you a maphrodyte?" he asked one day. "Or a capon? . . . Have you ever screwed a girl? Honest to God, have you?" Vridar was reading a book. "If you have she must have been a homely bitch. Something on Antelope." He waited but Vridar did not look up. "You know how many girls I've slept with? I have a record." He rummaged among his things and found the record. "Listen, you steer, and I'll tell you. There's Mary Smith. That sounds like a phoney but there's lots of Mary Smiths in the world. She was a relative of the great and fornicating Joseph. It says here she cost me three dollars and ten cents. But God damn, she wasn't the first one. The first one was Susan Dalton. I was fourteen and she was fourteen." Fourteen! Vridar though, trying to read. "I didn't spend any money on her and I can't remember what she looked like. Or smelled like. Did you know

306

every girl has her own special kind of stink? . . . Well, the next was Kate Olson; I took her to two shows and bought her one ice-cream cone. I don't remember what she looked like either. I should ought to publish my record. Don Juan? He was a bum compared to me. Well, the next, it says, was Mabel Turner, a fat blonde. I did it to her on her back porch and once was enough. God, she was fat and you can't do it to a fat girl very well. . . . Next was Ophelia Summers here in Salt Lake. She cost me four dollars and sixty cents. It says here I bought her some sweet peas and two boxes cherry-covered chocolates. I got them on sale. Christ no, I think I swiped them. . . . Well, next was Janice Hunter. You got any relatives here? Hey, you capon, you got a sister?"

"Go to hell," said Vridar.

"I'll bet I could do it to your sister in a week."

Vridar laid the book aside and looked at McClintock. "Leave my sister out of it."

"To hell with you. I'd even sleep with your mother."

Vridar stood up, feeling hot. "Leave my mother and sister out of it."

"Draw in your wattles, capon, draw in your wattles. I'd even screw that girl from the sticks, that Neloa thing. I'll go up some day and give her the works."

With a cry of fury Vridar leapt and seized Forenoon's throat and they struggled and rolled to the floor. The room shook. They were on their feet and went reeling to the bed, with Vridar trying to choke Forenoon and with Forenoon trying desperately to escape from the mad hands. Then Vridar whipped Forenoon up and pitched him over his head and the two of them came down like bags of sand. There was a terrific crash in the store below. Sobered, they dived into a closet. In a few moments a knock sounded and Vridar heard two men come in. He heard them talking excitedly, and then was conscious of Forenoon, doubled over, hands clapped to his mouth, trying to restrain his glee. The two men left and Vridar and Forenoon went down to the drugstore. It looked as if a bull had been loose there. Broken glass was scattered over floors and counters, and into the street poured the heavy odor of perfumes and lotions. Two men and a girl were busy with brooms.

That evening the hotel-keeper handed them a bill for $217.20. They would have to pay it, he said, or go to jail. As soon as he had gone, Forenoon took the bill and touched a match to it. "We have to move again," he said. "I'll find a place and get a sleigh." Two hours past midnight they slipped with their things down a back stairway, leaving no clues behind, and hauled them to rooms on Seventh East Street. Their landlady was a tall bleak spinster who never smiled, but she was patient, and for several weeks they played the devil here without drawing from her more than a gentle rebuke. Once they wrestled and shook the ceiling below, and she came to tell them that pieces had fallen from her chandelier. And once when Vridar shoved Forenoon through a window and that astonished young man crashed to a porch roof and then bounded off, demolishing some lattice-work, Vridar was reproved so politely that he went at once and repaired all the damage. But they became more violent. . . .

There was talk of war and talk of prohibiting alcoholic drinks. Vridar's interest was aroused; he had never drunk anything but beer, save the few drops in the whisky bottles which Charley Bridwell had tossed away. He read in a local paper a sermon on alcohol, which charged it with various catastrophes, from idiocy to pauperism. Vridar resolved to get a bottle of whisky. When he entered a saloon he was spellbound; for there seemed to be thousands of bottles, each with its own lovely color, its regal stamps and seal. He watched men at the bar; on the whiskers of one, beer foam was like milk-froth. The man drew hair into his mouth and licked the foam off, and then drank with such gusto that Vridar felt enormous thirst. With a quart of bourbon he went home.

He opened the bottle and breathed of it and then let Forenoon breathe. They began to drink and an hour later both Vridar and Forenoon were drunk. Vridar did not know that he was drunk. He knew only that he was set upon by all sorts of weird and ridiculous impulses. He thought of Neloa with a vast and yearning tenderness—and the next moment wanted to fight or sing or weep or stand on his head. It was strange, he reflected, that he should be in such a predicament: feeling by turns so elated or so wretched; now lusting for battle, now overwhelmed by Socialistic compassion for all the underprivileged. The room was dancing and Forenoon sat in a blur or moved around like a phantom. The whisky was burning through and through him with rapturous flame. His thoughts came and went in flashes of chaos, in tenuous wraiths of fire, or in sudden black bewilderment that blotted out the light. He stood up and the whole world spun in darkness, and from far away he heard faint and melodious song. He sat again and shook his head and tried to see. He smote himself, trying to clear his senses; and after a while he began to talk.

"What's wrong with me?" he asked, and heard himself cackle. This astonished him and for a few moments he thought about himself. "God, I feel queer!"

"You look queer," someone said. It was Forenoon but he could not see Forenoon. . . . Yes, he could see Forenoon. The idiot was over by a window and he was doing something there.

"Forenoon, you fool. You dreadful unmitigated fool."

"Fool yourself. Big dumb Antelope fool yourself."

Hanging from the eve were enormous icicles and Forenoon leaned out and grasped one, a tapering cylinder of ice weighing a hundred pounds. He broke it off and dragged it inside. He clutched it as he might have a bag of grain and staggered round the room with it. "What'll I do with this?" he asked, going round and round. Marion told him to throw it out but Forenoon said he wanted to do something with it. Water was running down him and filling his clothes. "What'll I do with it?" he asked, still staggering round and round.

"Kill yourself with it," Vridar said. He liked the notion. He rose and staggered around with Forenoon and he said again: "Kill yourself with it."

"I can't carry this thing around here all day," said Forenoon. He went to the door and staggered out into the hall. For a moment he stood by the rail and looked down and then with all his might he heaved the great cylinder of ice to the floor below. It fell with the sound of crashing glass. Forenoon was giggling now and Vridar went over and giggled with him and they both looked down at the pile of ice. The landlady came out. She gasped with amazement and stared up at them and Vridar thought her face looked very silly.

"What does this mean?" she asked.

Forenoon leaned against Vridar and choked with happiness; and Vridar, pushed off balance, almost went headlong after the ice. The woman came up the stairs. Vridar sensed that she was very angry but he did not seem to care.

"Who done that?" she asked.

"He did," Forenoon said, and he shoved Vridar and Vridar sprawled in a heap. He looked up and saw the woman staring at him.

"He did," said Vridar. "That fool did."

"If you were only a young girl," said Forenoon, giving her a drunken leer. "I'll bet you were some ladybug."

"You clean that mess up!" the woman cried. "I'd be ashamed! I'd go off and hide my face!"

"A face like mine?" asked Forenoon.

"Hide your face," said Vridar, still piled up by the wall. "Where are your manners, you big stupid lubber? Shame on you!"

The woman was growing hysterical. "You clean that up!" she wailed. "I'll have you arrested!"

"He'll clean it up," Vridar assured her. "He's a gentleman and he'll clean it up. Forenoon, clean up that mess."

"I'm going to puke," said Forenoon. He leaned over the rail and the woman seized him and dragged him back.

"You nasty drunkard!" she shouted. "Get out of my house!"

"I have to puke first," he said.

"You let him be," said Vridar, staring at her through fog.

"I'm sick as a dog," said Forenoon.

"He's sick," Vridar told the woman. "He's sick as a dog. Go on and die, you miserable nasty drunken dog. . . . Forenoon?"

"What?"

"Go on and die. You drop ice in nice ladies' houses. You should die."

The landlady had entered their room and was talking to Marion. Forenoon doubled over and groaned and swore that he was dying. In a minute, he said, he would vomit all over the city. He would blow whisky clear over the Mormon temple. Vridar crawled over to him.

"Get to the bathroom," he said, yanking at Forenoon's legs. "For God sake, don't puke here. Haven't you any manners?" Vridar drew himself up and put an arm round Forenoon and tried to lead him away. He broke Forenoon's clutch on the railing and they both reeled and pitched headlong. The woman came out like a hornet. She was crying wildly and threatening police and arrest and disgrace, and all these threats came with vague gentle insistence into Vridar's mind. He rose to his hands and knees and looked up at her. "I'll clean it up," he said. "Please don't talk that way. We're gentlemen. We're gentlemen and we'll clean it up." He moved on all fours to the head of the stairway. He tried to go down the stairs on hands and knees but his arms folded under him and he rolled, fetching up at the bottom with a yell and a crash. For a few moments he was stunned and unable to tell where he was. Then, on hands and knees, he stared up, and saw as if far away the face of the woman looking down at him.

"I'll clean it up," he said. "Just give me a little time." Moving about like an animal with four legs he got a chunk of ice and crawled over to the door with it. "See," he said, "I'm cleaning it up. I'm a gentleman and I'll clean it up." While laboring he poured a stream of assurances and apologies and confessions at the floor above. "You look down and you'll see I'm cleaning it up. You watch me. I'm a gentleman and I always do what I say. . . . I drank some whisky, that's what's wrong. Well, I'll pay the damages. You just give me a bill and I'll pay. . . .If you want your lawn cleaned I'll do that. I'll cut your wood and milk your cow. Anything. Just don't be angry. . . . I shouldn't live with a man like Forenoon. That's the trouble. . . ."

He sat and looked up, trying to see the woman. He saw a face but he could not tell if it was her face. Laying an arm across his chest and gathering ice and banking it against him along the arm he spoke up to the face. "A girl betrayed me, that's all. That," he said, staring at the face, "is really what's wrong with me. I loved a girl. She lied to me and I don't care much now but my mother told me always to be a gentleman. . . . You send me to jail and I don't care. Shoot me and I don't care." Moving to the door on his rump he tossed the ice out. He came back and piled other fragments against his arm. "Have me arrested if you want to," he said to the face above. "Do what you want to. I'm headed for the dogs anyway. A lot of men go to the dogs on account of women. Did you know that?" he asked, trying to see her. He moved over again and threw out another armful. He came back. "Bazarov says—he says a man who stakes his whole life on one card, a woman's love, and when that turns sour, he—he lets himself go till he's fit for nothing, he's not a man but a male." He reached out for pieces of ice and stacked them against him, up to his chin. "I'm only a male," he said, glancing up. "I'm not a man. I staked all my life on a woman's love and now she doesn't even write to me. . . . So I should enlist and get shot, I guess. That's about all I'm good for. But you look down and you'll see that I'm a gentleman. I'm cleaning it up. . . ."

He shuffled over and threw out another armful. When he could see no more ice around him he dragged his handkerchief out and mopped the floor. He would crawl to the porch and wring his handkerchief dry and return to saturate it again. Everything was so blurred that he could not tell water from shadow, and so felt over the floor and then put his palm to his face to see if it was wet. After he had wiped the floor dry, he crawled up the stairway and into his room. The woman was sitting on the bed, weeping and blowing her nose. Vridar sat on the floor and looked at her.

"Don't cry," he said. "I cleaned it all up. I'll pay the damage. But have me arrested if that will make you happy. Just do what you like." He looked at her with sober interest. He wondered why she was weeping now and he wished to comfort her. His eyes filled with mist and he felt great tenderness and pity for everything. He loved the whole big sad world and this woman and he wanted to comfort her. He dragged himself over to the bed and patted her arm. "I staked everything on a woman's love," he said, "and she fooled me. But please don't cry. Everything is all right now. . . ."

After the woman left the room, Vridar felt very depressed and sick, and Forenoon lay on the bed and groaned. He said he was dying and Vridar said he hoped he died. "I'm drunk," he said, "and I'm sick and all because of a woman. I've disgraced my parents and myself and I'm sick and the world would be better off if I were dead."

Suddenly Forenoon rolled off to the floor and sat up. He whinnied with glee. "So a girl broke your poor little heart. Was it that Antelope hick?"

"Shut up."

"She fooled you, did she? You mean she'd been screwing other men?"

"I said shut up."

"And you won't love no more, oh nevermore." Forenoon snorted. He loped over to the window and leaned out as if to vomit; he heaved and moaned and came back and lay on the floor. "Once," he said, "I puked out a window right on a baldheaded guy. He humped straight up and yelled. . . . Well, so you're through with women."

"Hell no, I've just started."

"Let's step some out tonight, some wild ones that kiss like tannic acid. And let's get some more drink."

"Sure. I'll be a drunkard. Some of my mother's people drank themselves to death. So did a lot of poets. James Thompson B.V."

"B.V.D." said Forenoon and snickered. "Well, comb your hair. Why in Christ don't you ever comb your hair?"

Forenoon went to a closet and laid out two suits. He said Vridar could wear one of them as well as a pair of his shoes and one of his hats. He brought forth lotions and powders and rouge and told Vridar to put on some dog. "No wonder girls lie to you," he said. "It would be awful to tell you the truth." Forenoon poured tonic on Vridar's hair and saturated the hair with perfumed oil. He got his razor and scraped the down off Vridar's face and massaged his face with lotions and powders. "I'm one of God's blessings to women," he said, "but I wouldn't exactly say that you are."

Vridar put on one of Forenoon's suits and a pair of his shoes; manicured his nails and rubbed on his hands something that smelled of heliotrope; and then pulled on one of Forenoon's silk shirts. Forenoon chose a gay necktie for Vridar and put a knot in it two inches long. Girls loved long slender knots, he said.

"They're phallic," said Vridar. "Like earrings."

"You have to give girls what they want or you can't seduce them."

Vridar stared in a mirror at his scented and gleaming head.

"Slick up the shoes," Forenoon said. "A girl always looks first at a man's feet." He poured shaving lotion into a peanut butter jar and filled the bottle with whisky. They both drank and entered the street. "What kind of girl do you want?"

"Any kind."

"What does this Antelope hick look like?"

"Leave her out of it!" Vridar cried, and pushed Forenoon off the sidewalk.

311

"Don't get rough," said Forenoon. "I'm a tough son of a bitch when I'm half-cocked."

"Just leave her out of it."

"A sagebrush hick," said Forenoon. "They're all whores."

"God damn!" said Vridar. He clenched his hands and squared off.

"Stop it," said Forenoon. "When I lick you it won't be over an Antelope chippy."

The words stung Vridar. He howled with rage and stripped his coat off. "You take that back!"

"Listen," said Forenoon, "we have to be friends. I could send you to jail for life. Here, shake hands." They shook hands. "We're two crooks and we're friends."

They returned to the sidewalk. How many men in this moment, Vridar wondered, were embracing women. Thousands, perhaps millions. In his addled wits he tried to figure it out: if there were a billion men and women and they embraced an average of twice a week, then in any hour of the day or night it was about twenty-four into two hundred million, or more than eight million. Good Lord! Eight or ten million copulating every hour around the clock! That was something to sober a deacon. And right now, over the world, ten thousand or a hundred thousand virgins were being seduced and most of the seducers were Forenoons. . . .

Forenoon said they would visit the Bateman sisters, Molly and Joan. He had seduced Joan but he hadn't seduced Molly yet. He said Molly would make Vridar boil like a Stanley steamer. They were twins. They were twenty-two. "Never fool around with girls under eighteen. If you do the law will take your pants off. It's rape."

Oh! Vridar thought; so Neloa had been raped. He asked for the bottle and they went into shadows and drank. Molly was so hot, Forenoon said, that if buried in ice she would drown in ten minutes. They went down State Street and from time to time slipped into an alley to drink; and when they came to Ninth South Forenoon indicated a huge building and said he danced there. He was champion one-stepper in Zion. He picked up Gertrude Grant there and slept with her on their third night out. Vridar glanced at him and thought of Lorry, that lewd sallow youth in Rigby, who had said that all his girls wept. He was trying to realize that this rake at his side had been intimate with dozens of girls and that seduction was his major interest. He had a vision of all the young lovely things, as clean as flowers and as eager as morning. He choked with resentment and fury.

They went up Ninth and stopped before a house, a shabby illbred huddle of old masonry. Forenoon pushed a button and they heard feet approaching from within. Vridar was trembling. Forenoon admonished him to show good manners and breeding; for girls, he said, loved above all things to be seduced by well-bred men. The door was opened and in the dim light Vridar saw a girl, alluringly half-dressed, as if awaiting a lover. Her hair fell in clusters of ringlets.

"Hello, Molly. How's my sweetheart?"

"Fine," said Molly. "Come in."

Forenoon strode in and Vridar followed, quaking and abashed. He found himself in a large vulgar room with sofas and cushions everywhere and with calendars and magazine covers on the walls. With a lordly gesture Forenoon drew his gloves off and gave them and his hat to Molly. "Miss Bateman," he said, bowing, "may I present Mr. James. Mr. Vancouver James."

"Hello," said Molly, and gave Vridar a small soft hand.

"Where's Joan?"

Joan was dressing. She would be out in a minute; and if they would excuse her, Molly said, she would dress too. After she had vanished, Forenoon turned to Vridar and leered.

"Your name is Vancouver—what did I say?"

"You said James."

"James. And mine is Jack Welland. Don't forget." The Wellands were a socially prominent and wealthy Salt Lake City family.

"You mean—?"

"Listen, you idiot. Have you lived all your life in Antelope? You have to be an actor. You don't just walk out and tell a girl all about you, so she can have you arrested and slap you into jail. What if you knock one up? You don't want her to know your right name."

"I need a drink," Vridar said.

"Listen," said Forenoon, whispering. "Act bored. Always act bored around women. They love it. Seem like women are no mystery to you. A woman doesn't care how many women you've screwed if you tell her she's the nicest one you ever met." He was looking at Vridar. "Yawn once in a while, like you been up late. Act well-bred like you've been to Europe. And call me Jack."

Forenoon now walked about the room, looking at magazines and books and softly humming a love-song. He was enviably at ease, Vridar thought; a worldly chap in his way, a Don Juan in Mormondom, waiting for his mistress. Vridar tried to look bored; he too walked around and opened books and glanced at pages, or stared vacantly as if his thoughts were in Nice or San Isidro. But he was volcanic ash within. His emotions were like glowing cinders under the reproachful scrutiny of his mind; he felt white and washed-out. There was something horribly anemic in his surging blood, as though it had been filtered through fear and had lost its color and heat.

From a room came girlish warblings and giggles, and the sound of water boiling round a bowl. Then Joan came out. Forenoon, Vridar perceived, affected not to see her; he whistled softly and thumbed a book. Then he turned and said, "Oh, hello," and wearily he took her hand and led her across the room. "Miss Bateman, allow me to present Mr. Vancouver James, a great grandson of Jesse James the famous outlaw."

Vridar staggered to his feet, sweating under this new indignity. He bowed as if pushed from behind; he came up, his face red, and drew a handkerchief out and erupted in a violent sneeze. He could hear Forenoon talking but he did not understand. Desperately struggling to seem at ease, he could think only that he had burned like fire when introduced to a girl and then had wildly snorted. He tried to cough gently, reflecting that he might somehow excuse the sneeze, or at least make it seem reasonable, if he could lead her to suppose that it had been only a

313

sort of cough too long restrained. He felt utterly preposterous; and when at last he glanced at Forenoon, he saw that young man observing him with cynical eyes.

"It's all right. I told her I put pepper in your handkerchief. She's gone to fetch you a drink."

"Thanks," said Vridar drily.

"I told her you're a dead shot with a gun. Women like dead shots."

Vridar needed the fire and courage of whisky. He glanced at the door wishing that he could sneak out. "I have to have a drink," he said.

"By God, I thought you were a good actor. You can forge signatures but a girl scares your ass off."

Vridar shrugged and went to a couch and sat. Above all else he wanted to be a good actor, an inscrutable person affronting the world. He stretched his legs and yawned. "Listen, Welland, when do I get a drink?"

"That's better," Forenoon said.

The girls entered the room. Joan bore glasses on a tray and came first to Vridar. Then she went to Forenoon and he rose and bowed and accepted a glass. "I thank you," he said. "You become sweeter every day."

Vridar, closely observing, was appalled. He had sat as if roped to the couch; but Forenoon, with his manners glittering, had accepted the favor with a smile, two bows, and a pretty speech. In social decorum, Vridar told himself, seething within, he smelled the superficial and the insincere: manners were fraud, perjury and humbug.

"How is it?" Forenoon asked.

"Fine."

"Is it strong enough?" asked Joan, smiling.

"It probably isn't," said Forenoon. "He can drink two quarts and walk a tightrope and shoot a cigarette out at a hundred yards."

"My!" said Joan, looking at Vridar.

Holding his glass and hand to conceal his face, with a finger against his nose, Vridar stared at Molly. Half-buried in a fluffy dress, she looked very soft and womanly. His gaze moved down to her breasts, her hips, her ankles: yes, she was very alluring He tried to imagine how it would feel to have her in his arms with her warm flesh against him and his mouth on her lips. She had softer lips than Neloa's. . . . He sighed and looked up; and when he saw Molly gazing at him, he started and almost dropped his glass. He gulped his drink and again glanced at the door.

Molly came over, her whole face smiling. "Will you have another?"

Vridar looked up at her and her eyes held him speechless. His heart was pounding so madly that he could feel the pulse in his throat.

"Give him another," Forenoon said.

Now, still holding Molly's gaze, Vridar saw the smile leave her face. He saw something like fear shadow the gray of her eyes, and he saw her catch and hold her breath. Then quickly she took the glass and left the room. Again and again Vridar's gaze was to meet a woman's as only now it had met Molly's, and he was to be delivered helpless into an indefinable power. He was to feel the depths and

314

heights of being; in such moments he was to touch, it seemed to him, the one universal truth. It shook him like a bugle; it circumferenced his homelessness and gave it a home; it reached deeper than anything he had found in books. But what was it?—this thing so certain and so ancient, that for a moment he felt as if unexpectedly he had touched the earth's heart, and then lost it.

When Molly came with another drink, he looked into her eyes but there was nothing in her eyes now. In her eyes now there were surfaces without depth, notions wthout intensity or outline or form. What was it that he had seen?

Sipping his drink, he felt more at ease now, and he watched Forenoon and Joan. Joan was sitting on Forenoon's lap and she was kissing him with huge amorous kisses, deep and wet. They were using their tongues: Vridar had not known that people used their tongues in kissing. Clearly enough the girl was Forenoon's to do with as he pleased. What was there in this fellow that made him so attractive to women? He was handsome but there was about him so much craft and stealth, so much insincerity in his mouth, so much greed in his eyes. Were most girls so stupid that they could not sense the nature of a man? Well, had he not been stupid? Had he read Neloa? . . . He now studied Joan. Like her sister, she had brown hair and gray eyes and a clear healthy skin. Her body was shapely enough. But Vridar found her wholly unalluring; her emotions like summer days were too much alike: she was a summery girl and Molly was a summery girl: June girls with no hint of March, August girls with no hint of November. They would both be midsummer wives: growing calm and murmurous, placid, dull, and plump for death.

But Neloa? She had the tragic in her, and passion that could be dark and wild. She might be a nun or a pimp's moll. With whisky homesickness he thought of her —and of the hills of his home and the aspen with the initials carved on it and the bed by the north wall; until he sank into his old shy loneliness, with memories walling him in. His glass was filled again and he drank. He no longer looked at Joan and Forenoon or at Molly; there was nothing here for him. Suddenly he rose without speaking and got his hat and went out.

XI

He walked under a clear night-sky thinking of Pascal's words: "When I consider the short duration of my life, swallowed up in the eternity before and after, the little space which I fill, and even see, engulfed in the infinite immensity of spaces of which I am ignorant, and which know me not, I am frightened, and am astonished at being here rather than there; for there is no reason why here rather than there, why now rather than then." He looked up at the sky and thought, Yes, I am frightened and there seems to be no reason: no reason why I should love Neloa, no reason to get drunk or not get drunk; for in all these broad immensities what am I? So I returned, and considered all the oppressions that are done under the sun: and behold the tears of such as were oppressed, and they had no comforter; and on the side of their oppressors there was power. . . . Would it always be so or would Socialism build a better world?

He was walking down a dark street when accosted by a negress, a foul hag

315

toothless and old. She took his arm and tried to lead him into an alley and in a whining voice said to him, "Only two bits, kid. Just a quarter, just two bits. It won't take long. . . ." Knowing her purpose to be vile, Vridar jerked away from her and ran. What had she proposed? His thoughts went to the Bible with its record of sexual evils; and he thought of words he had found in books—sodomy and lesbianism and necrophila, nymphomania and pedophilla erotica and zoo-erasty and satyriasis—terrible words which tried to define the thing man had made of his sexual passion. He thought of gonorrhea: Forenoon a few weeks back had yelped in the bathroom when urinating. That and syphilis and these others things were common to human beings, it seemed, but not to the other animals; and Vridar thought with wonder of mankind, who for no reason was here rather than there, now rather than then. "I spent five bucks on the bitch," Forenoon howled, "and she gave me this! Did you know that some sorority girls are plain whores?" There was ancient Sybaris and its women; Francastoro's Syphilus: what things shone like lights in the dead acres of history! Life had touched Villon and Salome and Proserpine and Psyche and Sappho and they had burst into flame; but had they left any meaning?

This, he concluded, was whisky meditation. His mind had cleared a little. Under the stars there was good, there was evil; but why should he dedicate himself to the good? When he passed a girl and she gave him a quick glance of inquiry his heart leapt. He turned to look at her and saw that she was looking back. Was she a whore? He followed her discreetly and when he saw that she was loitering he stopped by a window and looked in. She was smiling at him. Even the best of women seemed to wear their virtue lightly: it was only a diaphanous gown, and gracefully without shame they could lay it aside. Forenoon would take a virgin to church on Sunday and seduce her Sunday eve. He had told Vridar that some girls could be erotically excited if you read to them certain passages from the Bible, such as the 23rd Psalm. Vridar was thinking of this as he stared unseeing at forty pairs of shoes. The girl had gone. He went up the street and another girl smiled, a thick stupid wench: Vridar glanced back and saw that across her rump she was as broad as a doorway. He ought to go home but he stopped on a corner and watched girls pass and he lusted after them.

"You're a hell of a man," Forenoon said the next day. "Joan wanted to know were you impotent or bashful. I said impotent." He walked round and round Vridar as if to see what sort of animal he was. He snickered and clapped a hand to his mouth. "Why don't you take a Bible and go out to a desert? You'd be a swell monk."

Vridar went into the closet to hang clothes up and Forenoon slipped over and shut and locked the door.

"Let me out!" Vridar howled.

"You're in a monastery now and women won't scare you. You want a Bible?"

"I'll kill you when I get out."

"I'll bring you a rosary. You want some beads?"

Vridar seethed and listened. After a few minutes he heard Forenoon take his books and leave. Vridar smote the door but it was sturdy and well-secured; he was trapped, locked in like a wayward child. In blind rage he seized one of Forenoon's coats and tried to tear a sleeve off; and then grasped a silk shirt and tore it in ribbons. For three hours he remained in the closet, plotting vengeance: he would bring upon Forenoon a public scandal: from the housetops he would denounce him as a liar and a thief. But no, he would punish him with clean hard blows. He would tell Forenoon to stand up and he would knock his teeth into his throat. Why had dueling gone out of fashion? If it were legal he would get a brace of pistols and a ton of ammunition and retire to six months of practice; and then like Plummer of Alder Gulch he would be a dead shot and a dangerous man. He would challenge a score of men to duels, including Forenoon and Drake and Neloa's three lovers; in a gray dawn under a ceiling of oaks he would shoot all of them and sheathe his pistol and walk away.

Oh, but he would do nothing of the sort! His blood was whey, his will was soft, he was only a woman with a man's parts. If he could only go forth as history's conquerors had gone, slaughtering the helpless as Caesar had done, razing kingdoms as Napoleon had done, destroying cities in the name of God as Simon de Montfort had done. To his lusts and ambitions the Corsican runt had sacrificed whole armies—and for this historians wrote books about him and called him a great man. But here he sat in a closet, a witless zany who recoiled from murder; who was a Socialist because he hated war; who fretted and fumed and then turned his other cheek. . . .

"You still in there?" Forenoon was asking. "I told your professors that you're a monk now. I said you'd gone to the desert to flog yourself a while." He was silent; and then: "There are big opportunities in this country for monks. The more monks, the more women for men like me. The Catholic system of celibacy would be ideal for me if nine-tenths of the men were priests. . . . Are you listening?" He unlocked the door and Vridar stepped out, grinning, but the muscles of his face twitched.

This evening, Forenoon said, he was taking a girl out. He bathed and shaved and oiled his hair. He had a new flame, he said: her name was Alice Hanson and she was a slick babe; she did not wear corsets or garters, and when she kissed she gave all she had to it. "My God," he said, "I forgot to bring you a Bible!" He leered at Vridar and showed him his new studs, which he had stolen, and looked at his handsome face in a mirror. "I also stole an opera glass," he said. "When you see it your eyes will stand out like the breasts on a woman." He then went to the closet and his amazement was vented first in a grunt and then in a howl. He was holding up the shirt that Vridar had torn into ribbons. He plowed deeper into the closet seeking Vridar's garments, and with one bound Vridar sprang to the door and locked it.

"Let me out!" Forenoon roared. "You Mormon son of a bitch, I'll beat your brains out!" He raised a great storm in the closet. He smote and howled and jumped on the floor till the building shook. "I'll beat you until your tongue hangs down like a steer's dewlap! You lousy stinking Antelope hick!"

"Stop it or you'll break the door."

317

"You impotent steer, let me out!" He was bellowing horribly now. "You Mormon pig-feeder! I swear to Christ I'll beat your brains out! You capon!"

The door was opened and the landlady came in, her eyes weird with fright and rage. The closet was shaking and Forenoon behind it was cursing and kicking. She went and tried to turn the key, and Forenoon all the while was pouring at her his insulting abuse.

"You son of a bitch, you'd better turn the key! You beardless halfwitted Mormon! You steer without balls! In the name of God—"

Then the key was turned, and Forenoon, bounding furiously out, struck the woman and hurled her to a window; and glass fell in a shower and the woman screamed. She struggled to her feet and screamed again, pointing at Forenoon and wailing like a squaw.

"Let's beat it!" said Forenoon to Vridar.

Still looking at McClintock as if he were the Devil himself, the woman left the room and peered in. Her teeth chattered so that she could barely speak. Her mouth opened and shut like that of a dying fish. "You—get—out!" She thrust a shaking finger at Forenoon. "You get out!"

"I will," Forenoon said.

The woman looked at the broken window and began to sob. She was hysterical. She said she would call the police.

"I'll pay for the window," Vridar said. "We'll move right now."

Forenoon went out to find another place, and Vridar worked swiftly, rolling clothing into bundles and tying strings around books. Forenoon came back and they carried their stuff to the sidewalk and entered the kitchen, to look at their groceries banked against a wall.

"Let's leave it," Vridar said.

"Hell no." He gathered an armful and went downstairs. Shrinking to a wall, the woman watched him, her eyes bright with fear and loathing. Forenoon told her he was leaving more than enough groceries to pay for the window.

"Get out!" she said.

They went down and stood on a sidewalk and in a few minutes a truck came and they rode to Fourth Street. They entered an enormous room. It was forty feet long and almost as wide and had a very high ceiling.

While they were eating, Forenoon said their hysterical landlady was crazy. Did Vridar know she had the habit of talking to herself while prowling? Yes, Vridar said, he had known that. "That's what happens to old virgins. I do a hell of a lot of good for women. Did you ever think of that?"

The door was opened softly and a face looked in, the face of a very curious and quite lovely girl. "Hello," Forenoon said. The face did not speak. Its child-like eyes were grave and searching. "Who are you?"

"I'm Anna Mullen."

"Well, Miss Mullen, come on in."

"No."

Forenoon chewed tinned beef and looked at her. "How old are you?"

"Nineteen."

"Come on in so I can see your shape."

"No." She was holding the door against her cheek and peering round it.

"Who are you?"

"My father owns this place."

"Then you're an heiress. What else does he own?"

"I don't know," she said, her face as changeless as still water.

"Come on in. I'm nice to good-looking girls."

"I'll bet."

"Where's your room? Where do you sleep?"

"Just across the hall."

"Fine. I'll be over tonight."

"Oh no you won't."

"What would you do?"

"I'd call my father."

"Your father! I'd run him through a meat-grinder and feed him to the cats."

"I'll bet."

"What color are your eyes?"

"Blue, I guess."

"I'll find out," Forenoon said. But when he started toward her the face vanished and the door was closed. He opened it and looked out but nobody was there. He returned and said: "What's wrong with her? Is she a halfwit?"

Vridar was annoyed. He had a sentimental picture of the girl as a sweet and innocent thing, and of Forenoon as an utterly contemptible cad. If there were many men in the world like him no man would ever marry a virgin and most children would be bastards.

"Within a week," said Forenoon, "I'll be sleeping with her."

The next morning he went up and down the hallways looking for the girl. He stood on a chair and peered through transoms; he tried one door after another and found them all unlocked. Hours later Forenoon was pressing his trousers and Vridar was reading a book when the door was opened and the girl looked in.

"I'll be damned!" said Forenoon. "You back again?"

"Yes."

"Let's go to a show," Forenoon said.

"When?"

"This evening."

"All right."

Forenoon lathered his face and began to shave, and Anna, peering round the door, watched him. Vridar, self-appointed guardian of innocence, looked at the girl across the top of his book and wondered if most girls were as simple as they seemed to be. Even a moron would be aware of the only purpose that Forenoon ever had in mind. Anna was watching Forenoon with rapt interest.

"Run along and get ready," he said. She went away. "She's pretty dumb," said Forenoon, grinning at Vridar. "She'll be easy. When I'm done with her she'll wear a surprised look for life."

"A fine son of a bitch you are," Vridar said.

319

"There speaks the monk. Some of us do what women want, and the rest of you just sit around and envy us."

Vridar went out to the long front porch. He went ouside, he imagined, because he was sick of Forenoon and his evil ways, and sick of women; but his real reason, unperceived by himself, was to waylay Anna and admonish her. He wanted to say, "Take my advice and leave that man alone. He's had gonorrhea three times and he'll ruin you." Still deeper lay the thought: "I'm the kind of man you should go with. I'm the kind who cherish women." He paced back and forth, his emotions savage, his mind seeing this poor simple girl being ravished. What a stupid thing, what an intolerable blockhead she was! He was still pacing when Forenoon came out with Anna.

"Aufwedderseen!" Forenoon called. "Odiose and bone joor!"

Vridar scowled at him. Forenoon turned. "Eine der Taguszeit beeten!" he called, for he had studied German. "Moot fassen!"

"Das dumme Geschwatz!" Vridar said.

"We both speak a dozen languages," Forenoon said to Anna. He was holding her arm.

"Yes I'll bet."

They went down the street and Vridar watched them go. When he could no longer see them from the porch, he went to the sidewalk but they had disappeared. He returned to the porch and went into the huge emptiness of the room. Marion was reading. What kind of person was Marion, he wondered: he would sit for hours poring over logarithms and equations and formulae as senseless as runes; but did he have any sense of the wonder of life, its passions and hungers, its loneliness and madness and heartbreak? Vridar took a book and tried to study, but he was furious. Books, he reflected, were only the epidermis of experience: lovely sometimes, as hair was lovely, or skin, but as superficial as skin or hair. He went outside and walked in the dusk, thinking of Neloa, who had not written in a long while. Perhaps she was kissing another man now. He was unhappily aware that Neloa and Anna were alike in some ways; they both surrendered easily to a man's fingers on their arm. He wished he had the strength or the courage or the wickedness to debauch himself—to get drunk and find a woman and go to bed. But he knew that he would be impotent with a woman in bed.

He was sitting on the porch despising himself when Forenoon and Anna came out of the night. They came in silence and entered the house and Vridar followed them in. Anna went away and Forenoon sat on a bed, looking cynical and evil.

"It must have been a quick show," Vridar said.

Forenoon's sneer spread to his eyes. He looked at Vridar with infinite contempt. "You can have her," he said.

"Who?" asked Vridar, pretending.

"That stinking filthy trull."

"I don't want her."

"Sure you do. You can be a missionary with her. You can clean her up and teach her to bathe." He wrinkled his nose as if smelling a stench. "God, did you smell her?"

"I don't go around smelling girls."

"You wouldn't have to go far to smell her. At first I thought it was the house. When we got out on the street, I thought it was the street. It might be the Mormon temple, I said. But it was her all the time. She stinks like fury." He groaned and clutched his face. "I don't mind clean dirt, country dirt; but hers is city dirt. Mary Smith, she was never clean, but God damn it she didn't stink." He stood up and made a face. He sniffed.

"Didn't you take her to a show?"

"Listen, capon, don't be funny with me. When I spend money on a woman I invest it. Like in a bank. I expect interest. If I spent any money on her it would be for soap and lye and Dutch cleanser." He got his book of telephone numbers and turned the pages. "I can tell you a lot," he said, looking at Vridar. Vridar observed that Marion was listening. "You're only a damn greenhorn. One thing you should learn is that some girls smell all right and some smell like fried cabbage. The first thing to do with any girl is to smell her."

"Thanks," Vridar said.

"The smelly crotch," said Forenoon and made a dreadful face. "By nature women are a lot dirtier than men." He went out to telephone and came back and bathed and rubbed himself with scented oil. "Let's go to a dance," he said.

"Where?"

"The Bonneville. A lot of girls are there and they dance like the wind. And most of them don't stink." Forenoon laid out a suit, shirt, tie and shoes. "Here, get some of my clothes on and let's be off. You'll never learn any younger."

The Bonneville was the largest and most vulgar hall in the city; Vridar had heard that it was a rendezvous for harlots, drug peddlers, sharpers, and pimps. He went with misgivings but with something like a song in his heart. A lot of young men went to the dogs. The road to hell was broad and odorous, with lighted taverns along the way: he might become a libertine, a worse hellbound than Forenoon, a disgrace for his parents and a shame for himself. For so many years he had been his mother's manly little man, the guardian, the brother's keeper, the reader of the Bible, and the embryonic prophet. . . .

Forenoon was telling him that he knew many swell dancers, but he could not introduce them to Vridar. Vridar would have to pick up the drones and wall-flowers until he learned how to dance. "Or the older whores," said Forenoon. "They don't care what they dance with. Or the younger whores, they don't care either."

"How do you tell a whore?"

Forenoon turned to look at him. "Any woman who'll dance with you is probably a whore."

They entered an enormous hall, alive with music and dancing and lovely girls. Almost at once Vridar tried to slink away, wishing to hide for a while and examine his emotions; but Forenoon grasped his arm and led him, red and expostulating, into the flood of light. They stood by a huge rope—the dancing floor was fenced off—and watched the crowd; and Vridar's heart sank. He had seen dancing in Rigby but nothing like this—nothing like this gleaming grace and variety of movement, this superb gliding and skimming and whirling. He saw no one who seemed not to dance well. And besides, the men were so polished and insolent and self-assured, the girls so elegant and splendidly haughty, that compared to them he thought of himself as the gawkiest oaf anywhere. If he tried to dance no doubt he would be hissed at and booed and driven out.

"Well," said Forenoon, "let's dance."

"You dance. I—I'll watch."

"Oh, God damn it, come on!"

"You dance and I'll watch how you do."

Forenoon was flattered. He went to a group of girls, and a few moments later he was superbly perfect in the one-step. The involved one-step glide and long graceful spinning, attempted, Vridar observed, by only a few, but accomplished with complete mastery by Forenoon, was for him an amazing feat. He could never do it. If he practiced a thousand years, he could never do anything like that.

He sighed and glanced round him. Standing in groups, each apart, were young men and young women. A few of the men seemed to be much like himself: they had starved and hopeless faces, as though they had tried to dance and had been jerked off the floor. The idle girls tongued gum and giggled and looked as unapproachable as the summit of Everest. Vridar watched the men dancing and in his bitterness summarized all of them as fops and carpet knights.

Forenoon danced over, nimble and leering, and cried: "Come on, get you a jane!"

Vridar stared at Forenoon's girl: she was tall, queenly, scornful; she looked at Vridar half in wonder, half in astonishment, and floated away. Vridar went outside. He stood in cold air and looked up at the stars, trying to imagine that his destiny lay up there. Had history's great men been dancers? Had Dante, Shakespeare, Milton, Wordsworth, Darwin? It was unthinkable. Imagine such men shimmying around in a big vulgar hall! . . . No, he ought to be sitting by a fireside under a golden lamp, with the *Odyssey* on his knees. He ought to be writing a sonnet or listening to the Ninth Symphony or reading Kant. . . .

But the music poured out upon him, the mad lonely music full of the jungle. It was Belial's orchestra, playing to the fallen angels. Vridar tried to move away from it, bent on going home, but his feet were heavy: should he return to that big cold room and a dead book? Here was life, delirious with hungers rising from the unconscious; and here were beautiful women, ready for the male. In his room were the ashes of Rydal Mount. Here was the raw spermy stuff of life. Here hunger beat in the tom-toms, barked in the cornets, and blared in the trombones. It was life. Its furious vitality called to him and he paced in the darkness, racked, goaded, undone; until he knew that he would have to dance, he would have to get inside life and feel it and smell it and enfold it or go mad.

He went back in with a purpose so fixed that it gave to his face a desperate soberness and to his eyes a morbid stare. He saw a group of girls and one of them, he thought, looked rather dowdy and forgotten. Perhaps she would dance with him. She hesitated; and then with a brusque "All right" she went with him to the floor. He circled the girl's waist, hardly aware of what he was doing, and moved off, with his emotions rocking him like a wind. Never daring to look at her, he plodded and stumbled, his face burning, all his flesh burning, under the stares which he imagined were upon him. It was a fox-trot, but it might as well have been an Elizabethan jig for all he knew. He kept his gaze down and fumbled with sightless courage round and round.

Then the girl stopped. "I want a-quit," she said.

"What?" asked Vridar.

"You heard me! I wanna quit."

She walked away and left him, and all around Vridar the hall was like sheets of pale fire. In the glowing mist he saw dancers moving round him and knew that they were looking at him; and he stumbled among them like a man going to his death and found the night. Bursting with sweat, he hid in shadow and tried to remember just what had happened: the girl had spurned him, that was all, perhaps because he had been walking on her feet. With his emotions and nerves in violent mutiny, he smote himself and called himself a fool, a dolt, a blockhead, a lummox, a halfwit: one personality in him unpitying and calm, speaking to the other with scathing derision. . . . Well, by God, he would go back and try again, with his eyes blind until he learned and his pride under his heels! To reassure himself he reflected—in how many times had he done this and with what fruitless results!—that the people inside were not worth his shoestring. Pimps and whores, a part of them were; and the others would be housewives and clerks and salesmen. What difference, he asked despairingly, should their opinions make to him?

He jumped around like a crazy fellow, abusing himself and trying to reason. He was not vanquished yet. Once he set his heart on a thing, not all the derisions in hell could turn him back. He could be outraged until his grief was too bitter to be borne, until his self-esteem was a handful of chaff; but he would return and fight again. Using what cunning he had to restore his confidence and clear his wits, he would return like a man driven by his own lash to the scene of his humiliation. And so it was, white with desperation, that he entered the hall again; and because he loathed his timidity, he forced himself as with a hot pike to the severer ordeals —to refuse to count one girl more approachable than another—to go to the first one he saw. . . .

"Will you dance with me?"

She looked at him with slow painstaking care. Her glance went down to his feet and came back to his eyes: he could see no disdain in her face, only a well-disciplined curiousness, patient, unamazed. She did not speak. While Vridar waited a man came up and led her away.

"Will you dance with me?"

She turned as if mildly astonished. She was chewing gum, and flakes of rouge patched the flesh of her lips. "You speakun to me?"

"I asked if you'd care to dance."

She looked at the other girls and then at Vridar and grinned. The other girls pretended not to see him. Then suddenly her face hardened, and she said no and turned away.

"Will you dance with me?"

The girl twittered and fell against her companions. The four of them looked at him as though amazed and laughed outright. The twittering girl looked down at his shoes; and in this moment two thoughts came to him: Forenoon's statement that a girl always looked first at a man's feet; and Dock's statement that when Neloa danced her breasts bounced up and down. Vridar was hoping that these girls would all marry blackguards, when Forenoon came up.

"Why in hell don't you dance?"

"They don't want to dance with me," Vridar said.

"It's because you don't know how to talk to them. Come, I'll show you." As they moved through the crowd Forenoon advised him. "Don't ever let girls see you looking at them. They don't want to be sized up. They might have a crooked seam or be in their menses. If some won't dance you can drag them on; some women like to be knocked around. Some like to be flattered. You have to size them up."

Forenoon accosted three girls. "Hello," he said. "Darned if I don't think I know you. You go to the College?"

The girl addressed was nonplused and a little astonished, but also, Vridar could tell, a little pleased.

"These are college girls," Forenoon went on, speaking to Vridar. "You can tell by the way they stand. They have poise."

The girls were looking at one another. They were flattered.

"I know where I saw them," said Forenoon suddenly. "At the Junior Prom." One of the girl's giggled, another's face broke into a smile. "How about a dance? But I'll bet a girl as lovely as you hasn't a single dance left." The girls looked wonderingly at each other and then at Forenoon.

"You go to the College?"

"Oh yes. I'm a Sigma Chi. I think I've seen you on the campus."

"You musta seen a ghost."

"Honest now, haven't I? Aren't you a Chi Omega?"

"Heck no. I wisht I was."

"You're the Chi Omega type," said Forenoon gallantly. "Let's dance." He took her arm and led her away and Vridar was left to face the other two.

"Would you care to dance?"

"You go to the College?"

"Yes."

"You know Ann Morris?"

"No, I guess not."

"She goes. She's a Delta."

Then the girls ignored him, and he didn't know whether to stand his ground or walk away. Should he ask again for a dance? That would be stupid. He glanced at his shoes; he drew forth a letter and tried to look at it with sober interest; he rocked on his heels a little and shrugged and felt unspeakably silly. Some persons roundabout were staring at him. He felt drenched with sweat and heat and weakness. He moved away, looking over heads as if there was someone whom he must see; he even stood tiptoe and peered. As he moved from place to place like one searching, his acting was thorough: instead of retiring and becoming lost he kept himself in view; he went from group to group, his gaze sweeping the hall; and after a while walked back and unconcernedly past those who had been staring at him. He scowled and looked annoyed and now and then glanced at the clock at the building's end. This dramatizing of his shame and fear became so real that he almost believed that he was searching: he would lift his brows and show sudden interest, as though he had recognized the one he sought; he would go rapidly, looking over heads, as if to keep his quest in sight; and he would shrug to show his disappointment. He was still acting when Forenoon grasped his arm. Instead of being himself, Vridar clung to his pretense; he tiptoed and stared and said, "I was sure I saw a College girl here." Forenoon became interested, as Vridar had hoped he would, and they went from group to group, looking, Vridar said, for a slender brunette.

Then he was satisfied. Those staring at him curiously must have been convinced, if they had taken the trouble to watch him.

"Come on," Forenoon said, "let's pick up a couple. That one I had didn't smell very good. . . . There, the one in red, the one in blue." They made a turn and came back. "Hello," said Forenoon. "Where you been hiding?"

"Me hidun?"

"Don't you remember me? I danced with you at the Odeon." He turned to Vridar and shrugged. "I told her she was one of the swellest dancers I ever had and now she doesn't know me! If I had been the Prince of Wales and the Sultan of Whamtam!" The girl was obviously trying to remember. "I danced with you twice," Forenoon said, speaking to the lovelier girl. "I asked if you ever went to Bonneville. You said yes. I said I'd see you there and you said all right. And now you pretend you don't remember!" His tone was aggrieved. He shrugged again and glanced over at other girls.

"Sure," said the one in blue. "I remember. You asked would I give you my phone number and I wouldn't."

"That's right, and I've been looking for you ever since. I've been here a dozen times. That's why I asked where you've been hiding."

"Wouldn't you like to know!"

"They lead you on," said Forenoon to Vridar, "and then laugh at you. No wonder I'm getting bald."

The girl in blue twittered. The other girl was smiling. The girl in blue said: "We don't usually dance without a interduction."

"That's easy," said Forenoon, sweeping an arm across his chest and bowing. "Miss Beautiful, may I present Mr. Vancouver James? Miss Lovely," he said, bowing to the other girl. "I am Jack Welland of Wasatch College."

The girls looked startled but they were pleased. "You say things in a nice way," the one in blue told him. "You're sure original."

"Jack Welland?" the other said. "I've heard that name. You play football?"

"I'm the left halfwit—I mean halfback. James here is the middle—I mean center."

"I knowed I'd heard your names," the girl said. She was warming. Her smile had lost its ice.

"And now for the dance you promised me."

"You care to dance?" Vridar asked the girl in red.

"No, thanks."

Vridar looked at her and what he saw in her face filled him with sudden rage. He went to a bench and sat. So this was what girls were like! He saw Forenoon drag an unwilling maid to the floor. He heard him force another's consent by telling her that she looked like Norma Talmadge. Then he withdrew to a corner, bitterly reflecting on women and thinking of Neloa. They capitulated to the most stupid flattery. They showed no more acumen than a chicken with its head under its wing. Men they judged by their clothes and their tongues: like birds they chose as mate the one most gaily attired, employing in an age of reason a biology that was ancient and silly. Like frost on a pane their emotions lay on the surface, icy and rather opaque, but melting under the most ordinary flummery; and showing then like the pane emptiness beyond.

He walked home, feeling a vast friendliness for hermits and monks and all the other weird celibates of history. Caught up by passion not of their own choosing and shaken like a rat in a dog's mouth, they went off to scourge themselves and abash their lusts. How many men—great men, that is—had been faltering toward their kingdoms when overhauled by a woman's arms? The law, it seemed to him, gave a woman a deed to a man, as to any other piece of property; and she then staked him in her domain, to use as whim prompted, for breeding and toil. And if a man escaped, he was thrown into jail like a bull into a paddock. If he fled another woman would seize him and the luckless zany would find himself mortgaged again; until at last, fleeing in and out of marriage, he would have only one privilege left, that of dying.

Why should he bother with girls? Why was he drawn to them like a dog after a bitch? What was life but a cockeyed blunder from the hand of God that He was now ashamed of—asylums, jails, hospitals, whorehouses! What was the language of love in the books he had been reading?—fornication, wenching, impudicity, incest, rape, prostitution, adultery, cuckoldom, stews, harems, seraglios, aphrodisiacs, pornography, Lesbianism, sodomy, satyriasis—if it was not all these things and more, where had the words come from? He got a volume of Pope and sat to read but soon laid it aside. He got a volume of Pater and presently he came to these words: *For the way to perfection is through a series of disgusts.* Good Lord! he thought, I must be on the right road! He rose and took his cap and entered the night. He was not through with women. He could no more have lived without women than without air. Morbidly sensitive and to be for a long while incurably erotic, he saw women as the core of life, with all things swimming in cetripetal convolutions to their center. They drew him irresistibly. They were the gravity of being and he was water seeking its level. No more could he remain on the heights in the polar air of his negations than water could resist seeking the sea. This which he felt, that laid hold of him with its awful power, was more than women: it was the enormous pulse of creation, with women as its lovely and alluring symbols. It was the huge body of all-that-is and women were the fertile life in its depths, its sensuous color and warmth. If all women were dead this uterine pulse would still live, would still pour like fire through the waste of the uncreated. For in some form it was to be seen in every tree and flower, in every field; and where it was not, there stood the unbeautiful dead. Was this not what Emerson had in mind when he wrote:

> 'Tis not in the high stars alone,
> Nor in the redbreast's mellow tone,
> But in the mud and scum of things,
> There always, always something sings!

And it was in the mud and scum that he was trying to find the beautiful meaning.

Even when in classroom or walking the streets, Vridar felt this power, this impalpable yearning out of the insensate, this reaching up out of midnight to the sun. In countless things, infinitely small but jeweled with meaning, he saw its gesture: in the way a girl turned her head, in a man's sudden lift of his eyes, in his instructors when pausing in their shifting and feeble patterns of thought they reached down for a moment to a depth that lay asleep. He found it in the poets. He found it in the coming of spring.

When golden days again stood from valley to sky and lay dreaming on the city's hills, the thing that possessed him was like an open hunger, like a fire feeding on itself. It rose in gardens of color on the lawns; it sang in girls like music in violins; it was new life like the sea's own in the hearts of men. Books were forgotten while all of life moved to the heart of April. On the blackboards were the pathetic symbols of the meaningless, and in the classrooms were the dead empty chairs. Outside was the sorcerous lyricism of shrub and tree. Had Vridar been living where all things were half-asleep, surfeited with breathing and effort, where in every new day fragrant morning did not drench his senses, where a thousand things did not awaken the memories of childhood, he might have sat with books and been content. During the white half-death of winter he had held his emotions like things on leashes; but now, with earth pushing out of sleep its incredible rebirth of beauty and with odorous horns calling, he was drawn into the mighty current of being and all his paths led to its irresistible power.

No, he was not done with women. He had searched books to learn what great men had thought of them and for a little while he had reposed within the ironic worldliness of Gibbon. When Gibbon broke off with Mlle Susan Curchod and then discovered that in Lausanne she was surrounded by wooers and was gay and heartfree, he had written: "The episode has been of great use to me; it has opened my eyes to the character of women, and will serve me long as a preservative against the seductions of love." It had served him to the end of his life. Susan in Lausanne and Neloa in Rigby—it was all the same, but he did not have the great historian's urbane scorn. His intelligence and his will were overridden and his hunger rose like waters to a dam, only to fall back and rise again; until he was caught in the whirlpools and spun like seadrift. Carylye had been convulsed by negations; Swift had gone mad under the extravagant blundering of passion; Swinburne had fled naked before the winds.

He would read, and, reading, would feel upon books the shadow of life and would then lay the books aside. Within him beat by beat would rise the ancient and

327

solitary hunger. He would go to the street and return; he would go to the city and look at persons and wonder how they could be so quiet. He would go to the Bonneville hall. And one night, trembling in the music, he forced himself to enter and try again. He forced himself to ask a woman to dance, and to his amazement she smiled and took his arm. She led him to the floor; and while he slipped and stumbled and burned with shame, she talked to him, instructing him in the steps. Rebuking his clumsiness, he would say, "I can't dance," and she would say softly, "You will learn." She was not young and she was not beautiful, but she was very patient and kind. Dance after dance during a long evening she spent with him on the floor, teaching him simple movements in the one-step, the fox-trot, the waltz. After a while he became aware of her as a woman in his arms; she was plump and uncorseted and the flesh of her back was warm and alive and her full bosom pressed against his heart. When the last dance was done, he looked at her and saw something in her smile and her eyes that frightened him.

"You'll learn," she said and her eyelids drooped. "Will you be coming here again?"

"Why—why yes," he said.

"I'll be your teacher. And now, Mr. _____?"

"Hunter."

"—if you'd like to take your teacher home?"

He didn't know what to make of that. He hoped she was not a bad woman.

She took his arm and led him outside and they crossed the street to wait for a trolley. "You going to the College?"

"Yes." He did not like her mouth. It was not a lovely mouth and he had no wish to kiss it. His gaze lingered for a moment at her breast, and he knew when she smiled and touched his arm that she had read his thought. Sitting with her on the trolley, he tried to seem at ease. Once or twice she let her head touch his shoulder, lightly; and when she bent to fasten a shoe, she rested an arm on his knee. How Forenoon would snort if he could see him taking a middle-aged woman home! When they passed the statue of Brigham Young, Vridar thought of two lines that were popular on the campus:

> Oh, I think Brigham Young is a funny old crank
> with his ass to the temple and his hand to the bank!

It was true. He did have his rump toward the Mormon temple, and his arm stretched out to the biggest bank in Zion. There was a man who had got what he wanted! He had had so many wives that he couldn't remember all their names; so many children that he couldn't tell his own from the neighbors'; and so much money that he couldn't calculate its sum. When Brigham's wives began to look used up, he simply went out and found a fresh bride. The scoundrel! Vridar thought. And some of the old codgers in the Bible took women as their right. If the old custom were in vogue now a weakling like himself would perhaps have no woman at all. Polygamy, another institution of privilege! Polygamy . . . .

"This is my stop," the woman said.

Vridar preceded her down the aisle. Well, thank God, he knew what a man was expected to do—to hop off and assist the woman as though her legs were weak. They walked up a hill and came to the woman's house and stopped. She looked at him and Vridar looked at her; he couldn't tell if she expected to be kissed, and he felt very silly to be wondering about it. Then she spoke and her words amazed him.

"You just as well come in. My husband isn't here tonight."

"Your husband!" he gasped. "Good God, do you have a husband?"

"Women usually do get a husband, don't they? But they don't always get rid of the louse."

"The louse!" said Vridar, dismayed. "You mean you don't love him?"

"Don't be silly. I've lived with him twelve years."

"I suppose I should go home and study," he said.

The woman was tactful and wise. She did not urge him. "Some other night," she said. "We could talk a while."

As he went down the street, Vridar wondered if he should have gone in. This deeply-breathing woman made him think of Betty Mill—voluptuous Betty who had baked loaves for him and pressed his face into her bosom and kissed his mouth. On his way home he counted his steps, not knowing why, hardly aware that he did. He thought of the number as he got into bed and was still thinking of it when he fell asleep.

The next day his country declared war, and Vridar felt as if he had been walking in a noisome place and had come upon a dead thing. War for him was not glamorous adventure. Though a lad still in his emotions, he was man and in some respects an old man in a few of his thoughts. He had read about wars and he hated their brutality and slaughter and waste. He felt that war fed on jungle instincts, on primordial violence; that it turned the brute out of its civilized prison and gave to primitive hands the tools of death. No, there was not in him, as in most of his classmates and professors, a patriotic fervor that made apes of men. He did not believe with Forenoon and others that the Germans were raping Belgian women and cutting the hands off children. When in the classroom he heard his teacher of history furiously denounce the Germans as subhuman and uncivilized, he stared at the man and wondered if he had spent all his years in a cloister. If an educator, a man past sixty, who had been president of two universities, could be so prodigiously stupid, then what was the world coming to? If his professor of English could say that the Germans at heart were still wild and savage Norsemen, and his professor of French could say that until Germany was destroyed there could be no peace on earth; and if his professor of economics could say that the German purpose was the subjugation and serfdom of the world, then what was a professor anyway but a head-hunter lost to his tribe?

His country had gone to war and the campus was wild with approval. Among the students there was only one question: When are you going to enlist? In the girls there was a new vitality, a strange eagerness: the old dark spirit of the war-dance was in their gestures and speech. It was as if they heard the tom-toms; as if they saw the male, armed with noose and war-club, painting their bodies for the chase. This was stronger and deeper in them than fashions and sororities and teas. And in this atmosphere, electric with the jungle, Vridar felt lost; and he thought:

Some day I'll go into the past and discover out of what we have come. He might have fought to slay regilious bigots or economic exploiters or pimps; but not to slay a German whom he had never seen, not for a cause that would be as all wars had been a colossal butchery in the name of God. Perhaps the French Revolution was a decent struggle. The American war for independence had been so in its beginnings. But the Spanish-American war had been so appallingly selfish and so bullying and so greedy that it made him sick to think of.

Forenoon shared the hysteria. "You're a hell of an American!" he said. "By God, we have to defend our country!"

"Against what?"

"The Huns! The Barbarians! The rapers of women and the butchers of babes!"

"That's propaganda."

"You ought to be jailed. You ought to be deported." Forenoon was in a fine patriotic rage. He was swearing by God and the flag and the mothers of men. "Watch me when I get over there. I'll shove bayonets in their guts and twist it off."

"What will you be fighting for?"

"Why, God damn it, for justice. For the honor of women."

"You're a hell of a man to be talking about the honor of women."

"I honor women!" Forenoon cried. "Women are our fairest jewel. They're the cornerstone of our civilization." Forenoon was pacing the floor. "I'm going to report you," he said. "You must be a German spy."

No matter where Vridar went, he saw patriotic zealots lusting for blood-feuds, felt their dark atmosphere of murder and vengeance, heard their demands for armies and weapons, until at last the whole frenzied orgy seemed to be insane. It recalled his early years when he had hunted through pitch-night looking for the dawn. He had been trying to keep close to reality like a man hugging the shore; and an ocean of terror like a rolling void had been receding, had been withdrawing to the black immensities of the dead. But now the whole tide had turned. Now as formerly he felt that life was an enormous seething bedlam, with civilization's outposts drifting in shipwreck. Under the silence he could feel, and, feeling, could almost hear, the great unrest, the sightless questing, the vast mad heartache. On the surface now and then a wave broke into meaning, into light, an eddy fell into calm; and in the wave for a moment stood the wraiths of the civilized, in the lap of the eddy philosophy caught its breath and meditated; when, far out in chaos, out in the sunless waste of distance and time, a fresh tide, nameless, chartless, gathered its strength and rolled in, and life shook under its coming and had wreaked upon itself another beginning and another void. In all this movement, stupendous and blind, he and those around him were insigificant parts, controlled by a destiny too dark for their lanterns, shaped by a power that had violence but no will. They were adrift in a limitless body of change that was changeless, on an ocean of doing that had no purpose, on a universe of darkness that set faint lights and washed them out and set them again. In all this, it seemed to him, madness was the moving, the creative spirit; for it wrought its strange figures and destroyed, heaped its aimless tides to their meaningless summits; and life was its spindrift, seeking its way to consciousness and beauty; but in an unexpected hour when purpose began to glimmer and hands to reach to towers, the great emotion shook in its depths and drew its enervated surface back into its body to endow it with its original force. The process of enfeeblement men called culture; the restoration to the primordial they called war.

So it seemed to Vridar who had gone into the depths and had known their darkness and terror. He had felt intimations of abysses and heights, of the formless wonders beyond consciousness, the blind mightiness of the all-in-all that can never be felt by a sane man. In this lusting for battle he felt what he had felt years ago, but with a difference: these persons around him caught only the glow, only a vitalizing warmth, from those awful deeps. He had felt their heat. He had known how their power, ravening and sightless, could build only to destroy, could suck into the black womb of the unconscious all the long pilgrimage toward zeniths and suns. These people felt it as a thing to exalt and ennoble; he had known it as a force that debased and disintegrated.

No, war for him was not an adventure into glory; it was a path to that darkness where he had lived. But he might have gone his way in peace, looking with amused eyes at the turmoil of his fellows, had he been able to get away from it. But the newspapers were full of it. Professors were full of it. Men began to appear in uniforms and to march with guns, the sabers agleam; and girls turned their thoughts to the flow of blood and the healing of wounds. Peace overnight had fled the city, and war waved its flags from the housetops. And then there came a letter from Neloa. She said she was thrilled to death, for Vridar would now be her soldier boy. She said she wanted to be a Red Cross nurse. Furiously he wrote his reply:

> Dear Neloa:
> Your attitude toward war is too stupid and silly for words. War is madness and I have been in and out of madness and have had enough. Go on and be a nurse. Be an idiot if you want to. But don't call me your soldier boy. Wilson is a fool and a double-crosser and this war is being fought for no good reason. I'll have no part of it. So find yourself a soldier boy, some dumb egg who wants to give his blood for Morgan. And luck to you!
>
> Vridar

The coming of war wrought in Vridar more than a handful of similitudes. It affected him in a strange way. Afraid of life hitherto and longing for a refuge, he now threw his fear overboard. He did not conquer it. He temporarily renounced it. If the world was headed for ruin, it would be stupid of him to falter and hang back. In a few months he might be fighting in France. In a year or two he might be dead. Neloa could become a nurse and kneel to the wounds of her head-hunting manikins; he would make love to every girl he met. While time was left, in the year or two between him and dust, he would ravish girls and break hearts and go to the devil in his own way. Perhaps Gibbon was right: women were cheats and frauds: the strong man spurned them, the weak man broke their hearts. But to break hearts he needed clothes. A girl measured a man by the crease in his trousers and the polish on his shoes. Her interest was not amorous but economic. What they were really after, Forenoon said, was a husband; and a husband meant a man who would buy a nest for babies and furnish it. "If you want to knock them cold say you have money.

331

Say you'll take your bride on a honeymoon to Italy. A girl would rather go to Venice with a hunchback than settle down with Romeo in a one-room flat . . . " Vridar was wondering how to get clothes when Forenoon suggested a thieving exploit: they would pay down a small sum and give references and buy suits on credit.

His name, he said, would be Earl Tavish; Vridar's would be Richard Jones. Their addresses would be 468 K Street. "I've done it before," he said. "They might ask us the same questions. We have to have the same answers. We're both twenty-two and we're cousins."

"All right, we're cousins."

"We don't have a telephone. If you have a telephone they call up. If you don't have one, they send a messenger out."

"Your name is Earl Tavish. You're a college student."

"And your name is Henry Jones."

"Damn it, you said Richard."

"Did I? Well, we have to give the same answers."

They rehearsed the matter over and over and then chose a store and entered. They looked at the suits. Forenoon, Vridar observed, was nervous; he kept glancing guiltily at people like a thief out of jail. They chose suits and went to a window and the clerk said: "These gentlemen want these on credit."

The man behind the window was a lean cunning fox. A man came to another window and called Vridar over. The other man was questioning Forenoon and Vridar saw that Forenoon was trembling. The jig's up! he thought, and he saw himself in solitary confinement, eating stale bread.

"Your name?"

"Richard Jones."

"Where do you live, Mr. Jones?"

"468 K Street."

"Your parents live there?"

"No."

"Where?"

"Jackson, Wyoming."

"Where is that?"

"On Snake River south of Yellowstone Park." Vridar glanced over and saw sweat on Forenoon's brow.

"Is the other gentleman a relative?"

"Yes, we're cousins."

"What is his name?"

"Earl Tavish."

"What is your occupation?"

"We are both college students." Vridar's answers were glib, but he knew that he was being trapped. When the questioning was done they were asked to change places; Vridar looked into the eyes of the lean cunning man and saw cynical amusement.

"What is your name?"

"Richard Jones."

"Is this man with you a relative?"

"We are cousins."

"What is his name?"

"Earl Tavish."

"Do his parents live here?"

"Yes."

For a moment the man looked straight into Vridar's eyes. "This is rather strange," he said. "Mr. Tavish says his parents are dead, that your first name is Henry and that you are brothers."

At this moment Forenoon turned with the cry of a stricken beast and dashed wildly to the street; and after a moment's hesitation, Vridar followed him. He expected to be seized by hands and to hear furious yells: *Stop thief!* and *Catch that thief!* But there were no shouts. He rounded a corner and with flying heels the two of them sped away and disappeared. They ran for a mile and were winded and drenched before they stopped.

"You!" Vridar said. "You unspeakable and unmitigated and unprecedented idiot!"

"Are we safe?" asked Forenoon, peering round him.

"If men like you can steal and stay out of jail, I can't imagine what the intelligence is of those who get caught!"

"Don't insult me," said Forenoon. "I thought we were brothers. Then I remembered that we had different names and I said we were half-brothers. That showed presence of mind."

Vridar was staring at him and Forenoon was looking anxiously down the street. "Without question you're the biggest blockhead I've ever known—and the biggest coward!"

"I just got mixed up a little," Forenoon said. "Let's try another store."

"Not unless I manage the whole thing."

"All right, let's go off and figure it out and memorize it."

They went to their room and Vridar wrote on paper all the questions he could think of and their answers, including such things as their jobs and where they had labored and for whom; their common acquaintances among folk of the city; the courses they were taking in college; the names and ages of parents, brothers and sisters; the diseases they had had, the places where they had lived, their high school, their hobbies . . . .

"The important thing," he said, scowling at Forenoon, "is to keep cool. The man could tell you were guilty by the way you acted, you preposterous idiot. You were sweating."

"It was hot in there," Forenoon said.

"But not for honest men."

They went to another store and chose suits, and as before they were called to windows and questioned. Vridar watched himself, careful lest he be too glib or too hesitant, striving for a nice balance between the two. And he watched McClintock. Then they were called to the same window and their answers were verified.

333

"You want to take the suits now?"

Forenoon was about to say yes when Vridar kicked him. "Well," he said quietly, "it doesn't really matter. We're going out this evening and we wanted to wear them; but if you'd rather send them out—"

The man was looking at him searchingly. "We usually deliver, but I guess you can take them now."

Vridar was careful to show no eagerness. He turned to Forenoon. "We could wear our last summer suits. Is yours cleaned?" He knew that both men were sharply watching him.

"Why—uh," said Forenoon, "mine's pretty dirty."

"It's no worse than mine. You can wear it this evening."

One of the men spoke up. He said it was all right, they could take the suits now.

When they had the parcels in their arms, Vridar walked calmly, Forenoon with haste, to the street. Outside, Vridar turned and looked at the window display of this store: he suspected that the men were still watching him. Forenoon stood ready to flee. Vridar called him over and talked to him matter of factly about ties and shirts and shoes, pointing to one thing and another.

"Let's go!" Forenoon gasped.

"I like that tie," Vridar said. He went inside and bought the tie and saw that the men were no longer suspicious.

In their room Forenoon put his suit on and swaggered, full of bluff and brag. Vridar was quiet. He had outwitted two cunning men, and that, he thought, was nothing to be ashamed of; but he had deceived his own kind, he had betrayed that trust which people had to have in one another to make a society possible; and this, it seemed to him now and was to seem to the day of his death, was the blackest and most unpardonable of all crimes. He told Forenoon he would order no more groceries, that he was done with stealing, and he folded the suit up and wrapped it and laid it away.

XII

A few days later he went to the store and paid for the suit but he was still unwilling to wear it. He might never have worn it if he had not been enraged by what he thought was a piece of unspeakable cowardice. He was fond of his professor of German, a quiet, learned and cultured man, and for some time he had known that this teacher was very unhappy. He was unhappy because he was a German and his colleagues were whispering about him, saying that no one who was German could be trusted, no one who was German could be any good. One day the man quietly resigned and disappeared. "My God!" Vridar wrote in his journal. "*These* are supposed to be educators, *these* are supposed to be civilized men! What cowards they are!"

He put the suit on and went to dances six evenings a week, becoming so nimble a dancer that he won a prize. He made love to girls. Before June came he was bethrothed to three, besides Neloa, for he had the childish notion that he could avenge himself on her by deceiving other women. He knew that he was being a cad; but when conscience rebuked him he would think of that sad frightened man who, without fellowship among his colleagues, had quietly slipped away. Then he would explode with rage and despair and write in his journal: "If this is the best mankind has to show for all the centuries of blood and persecution and terror it matters little what I do. Lecky says, In looking back, with our present experience, we are driven to the melancholy conclusion that not only has ecclesiastical influence had no appreciable effect in diminishing the number of wars, but that it has actually and very seriously increased it. We may look in vain for any period since Constantine, in which the clergy, as a body, exerted themselves to repress the military spirit . . . . These men whose cowardly whisperings drove Professor Muller from their company call themselves Christians!"

It was at the Odeon that he met Laura Cunningham, a lovely sylphlike girl with dusky eyes and a sweet mouth. She was earnest, humorless, pious; her mission in life, she said, was to make some good man happy by being not only wife but mother and sister as well. She said Vridar looked very unhappy and she asked what deep and bitter woe was housed in his heart. Had he ever been in love? He admitted that he had. Laura enfolded him with compassion. "Were you—? Did she—? Vridar, tell me!"

"She deceived me. I don't want to talk about it."

Laura looked deep into his eyes and squeezed his hand. She called him a poor dear. So many women, she said, were cold and heartless and full of guile. Lots of men were womanhaters, and with good reason; but Vridar would learn that not all women were bad, and some day he would love again and be happy. Her pieties wearied him because they made him so conscious of his own.

They were following a heavily-wooded street in a dark night, and obeying an impulse Vridar slipped an arm to her waist. He thought she would protest but she did not; she yielded to his pressure and brushed his shoulder with a cheek. He wanted to kiss her lips but she was talking in her solemn and monotonous way about heartbroken men she had known, their grief, their hurt, their loneliness. They were like brothers to her, she said; they loved one another in a pure way. In her mission of sisterhood on earth he smelled something unwholesome, unclean. He pressed her supple uncorseted flesh and even slipped a hand up until he could sense her breast, but she kept on talking about the evil in women and the good in men. At her front door she smiled like one who bore great burdens and bore them nobly, and said she was sorry that she could not ask him in. But she did take him into a dark hallway and they stood there and she still talked. Then:

"I guess you'd better go now," she said.

Vridar did not budge. He was determined to kiss that lovely mouth. "You might kiss me goodnight," he said.

Laura rebuked him with a frown, a patient sisterly frown. "No, Vridar. A good girl doesn't kiss every man she meets."

"But I'm not just any man. We understand one another." Ah, what a hypocrite he was!

"Yes," she admitted, and sighed. She tiptoed and offered her lips and he touched them. "Now you must go."

Instead of going he yielded to an impulse that astonished him. He jerked her to him and folded her in his arms, and though she fought against him with tiny hammering blows he found her mouth and pressed into it deep.

"Don't!" she gasped. "Vridar, don't be like other men!"

That sobered him. He turned to go, but she came quickly to him and grasped his arm. "Are you mad at me? . . . . Vridar," she said reproachfully, almost pouting, "you expect too much. If you must act like other men you should go with another kind of woman."

"I will," he said.

"Vridar, dear, you don't mean that! Look at me." He looked into her eyes. "Aren't you going to see me again?"

"Why should I? You think I'm a lecher."

"A what?"

"A woman-chaser."

"Oh, darling, I don't! I like you. I might learn to love you. But deep love doesn't come all at once, you know."

Vridar looked at her, wondering if she was as stupid as she seemed to be. She stepped close and put hands on his shoulders and looked into his eyes. "You may kiss me again if you want to."

"I don't want to."

"Then I'll kiss you," she said, trying to be coy. She tried to pull his stubborn head down. "All right," she cried, "I'll kiss you here!" and quickly she kissed one of his hands. Then she ran inside and looked out, smiling. In a low seductive voice she whispered, "Vridar dear, good night!"

It was also at the Odeon that he met Kitty Murdock, who allured because she baffled him. Her moods changed like the mountain sunsets of his homeland; now burning with clear golden intensity, now fading into great shadowed pools of lilac: in one hour autumn brown and loneliness, in another, a dissolving mist of gray. He felt in her something tragic and bitter but he could not define it. He felt in her lyric raptures, a melody of emotion, that fed on nothing real, nothing earthly, but drew its fires from celestial nothingness.

When he asked her to dance, she assented with a grimace of weariness. Wearily she danced twice round the hall and suddenly changed; hugging closer to him she looked up and smiled and began to sing. It was a kind of wordless idyl of song, hinting of pastoral acres and running brooks and mating birds. After the dance he sat and looked at her and she did not seem to mind. She was not beautiful but he liked her face—the soft irresolute mouth and flushed cheeks and strange intentness of her dark gray eyes. Unexpectedly she met his gaze and gave him a droll wink. "Well," she said, "do I pass inspection? Am I a stranger to you?"

"A stranger?"

"I've known you for years."

"Where?" he asked startled.

"In Utah, Shanghai, Paris, Boston."

"I don't understand you."

"Let's dance. Then maybe you will."

They danced again and all the while Kitty looked up at him, her eyes searching. Vridar became embarrassed. What sort of person did he have here? She was a little mad, he supposed, but her madness was indefinable, like that of the eagle and the hawk.

"Do you understand yet?"

"No."

She snuggled close to him, her hair in his face. Her next words astounded him. "I like to dance with you," she said, "because your sex doesn't rise." When the dance was finished, she walked away from him; and though he searched in the throng he could not find her and he went home feeling wretched. He went the next evening but could not find her. He was sitting alone when suddenly out of nowhere she appeared and sat by him.

"You know me yet?" she asked. "It's queer that I have known you so long, while for you I'm a stranger."

"I still don't know what you mean."

"You're not stupid, are you?"

"I suppose I am."

"Do you know people by their names and faces or by what they have suffered?"

He looked at her more sharply.

"Let's not dance," she said. "Let's walk." They left the hall and went over to Liberty Park. Vridar was uneasy and perplexed. This girl was a riddle; he had no idea of what she intended or why she was walking with him. He put an arm round her, experimentally. She put his arm away. "Be yourself," she said.

"I'm a man," he said. "Biology will be biology."

Her response amazed him. She went down the walk like a banshee, chanting a weird dirge; running her naked arms through foliage, pirouetting to a lawn and falling there in languishing abandon, her arms spread to the grass, and then rising and coming to him, her steps heavy and dead.

"Biology? That was a little allegory all for you."

"You're mad," he said, lost in bewildered admiration.

She tiptoed and put arms to his neck. "Kiss me and get it off your mind. Then we can be friends."

Something broke within him. All his inhibitions fell like a dam under dynamite and he was helpless in the flood. He stooped to kiss her and then the dam arose and the flood rolled back.

"What is the name of the woman you love?"

"What makes you think I love one?"

"I know it by the way you acted then. Vridar, do you ever look at the stars?"

"Why, yes," he said and looked at the stars.

"You know Milton's words?—the dark, unbottomed, infinite Abyss—a dark illimitable ocean without bound. You know what Byron's Cain said?—O thou beautiful and unimaginable ether! You know what Pascal said?—when I consider the short duration of my life, swallowed up in the eternity before and after, the little space which I fill engulfed in the infinite immensity of spaces, I am frightened, am astonished. Aren't you?"

"Yes," he said, looking at her.

"But think! Human beings imagine that they are standing on a great immovable thing. They aren't. If the time ever comes when they understand—understand how fast they are journeying on this little thing of rock and water in the immensities, then will they all go mad? Then will they all be too frightened to live?"

"They might be," he said, still looking at her.

"Vridar, doesn't it hurt you here?" She pressed a hand to her heart. "Doesn't it hurt when you think about it?"

"Yes," he said.

"Doesn't it—can you—O my God!" With a cry she threw herself down and began to weep. Yes, he undertood now: all that Kitty had said, all that she had done, was now clear.

When she had wept her grief out, he walked her home. She was weary now and a little sardonic. She would not ask him in, she said. All houses were jails, in which people hid from understanding. She took his lapels. "Do you know me now?"

"Yes."

"How long?"

"Years."

"You think we should see one another again?"

"I don't know."

"We shouldn't. You love a woman and she probably isn't worth you. I love a man and he is no good. We'll marry, I guess, but we'll always live alone."

"And some day we'll kill ourselves."

"The world will say we were mad but the world is stupid. It builds asylums and jails . . . . Well, kiss me goodbye."

"It isn't goodbye."

"Don't kiss me then. Kisses do things to us. Goodnight."

It was at a Mormon dance that he met Martha Grant. She was a little stout, but indolent, voluptuous, full-bodied, womanly, warm. Her gestures were sensuous and lazy. Her full bosom and her ripe mouth, everything about her was hungry female, natural and unashamed. She was, Vridar supposed, the kind of girl he should be with. Laura was sunk in scruples, Kitty was morbid and volatile. Martha was as sane and placid as a cow. After dancing a number of times with her, Vridar took her home. On her porch was a swinging seat and they sat there and she asked Vridar to talk.

"You're a college man. Tell me something interesting."

He turned over in his mind the subjects he had been studying: English literature, French, German, history, psychology . . . . "The French Revolution, would that interest you?"

"Gosh no. I think I studied that in high school."

"Poetry? . . . . Wordsworth?"

"You mean Henry Wordsworth Longfellow?"

"No, William Wordsworth."

"Did he write love poems?"

"Not exactly."

338

"I wouldn't like him then."

"Well, there's psychology. My professor of psychology hates Freud. He says Freud is an erotic fool."

"What does erotic mean?"

"Oh, too much interest in sex."

"I'm erotic," she said, and with a warm amorous laugh she fell to his shoulder. She sat up and tried to look dignified and curious. "What does this Freud believe?"

"He thinks most babies are sexually stimulated—that many men have incestuous yearnings toward their mothers, many girls toward their fathers. In such instances, the sons hate their fathers, the daughters their mothers."

"Do you hate your father?"

Vridar was about to say no when an inner voice spoke and he hesitated. Troubled by the strange and sudden emotion in him, he turned away but Martha seized his arm and drew him toward her. She said she had been in love a lot of times. She laughed happily, flattered by her thoughts. "Is a woman erotic if she likes to be kissed? I mean kissed a lot, hours at a time."

Vridar's heart leapt. He looked at her mouth.

"I'm a case," she said, and sighed, as if annoyed by her folly, as if pleased by it too.

Vridar was confused. Forenoon had told him of soul-kissing: of the sucking of tongues, of mouth-to-mouth caresses that endured in passionate exploration for a long while. He wanted to kiss Martha, but he knew that he could not kiss her the way she wanted to be kissed. Good Lord, he would kiss her as he had kissed Neloa, chastely, guiltily! He stared at his hands and said: "Freud might say you have a compulsion."

"Good heavens, what's that?"

"An unreasonable wish to do something."

"But it isn't unreasonable. This Freud must be a fool." She was looking gravely at Vridar. "Where does he live? Have they locked him up?"

"In Vienna."

"That explains it. They don't have any beautiful women over there."

But Vridar was not listening. His attention was absorbed by the struggle going on within. He prayed that something would snap and set him free, so that he could take this girl, so that he could rise to manhood and claim his own. But he was only a fool. A girl offered herself and he quaked and ran cold, as though his veins were filled with embalming fluid . . . . He made excuses about having to study and early morning work. Would he come again? Martha asked. Yes, he said, but he did not intend to come again. When she stood up, he did not kiss her, he did not look at her eyes; he said goodnight and she said goodnight and he turned away.

Never in his life, not even in high school, had his self-loathing been more furious than now. Hatred of himself, bitterness and contempt, so blinded him that he stumbled, wishing that some power would strike him dead.

The more he sensed that June was approaching and the hour when he must go home, the more desperate Vridar felt. He did not want to see Neloa again. To save himself from further humiliation with her, which he knew must inevitably come, he thought he should marry one of the girls here. But which one? Not Martha: she would have children and grow fat and thick and dull. Not Kitty: they were too much alike and would drive one another deeper into lunacy. Not Anna Mullen, whom he had persuaded to bathe and keep herself fragrant: she was a sweet simple girl but she was stupid and she had the soul of a prostitute. He made love to these and to others; in his shameless way he asked them if they would marry him and they said they would. In his desperate way he kissed them and tried to force himself to intimacy with them and failed. He knew that he was a fool, that he was contemptible, that he was adrift; and one day he went with the psychology class to the institution for the insane in Provo. He felt almost at home there. He talked to a few of the patients and decided that some of them were no more insane than he was. Those in one ward his professor called schizoids; Vridar liked them best, he felt that he understood them—their ambivalence and their indrawn and withdrawn natures, their egocentric loneliness, their fear. He wondered if he was the schizoid type.

He wondered if he should enlist and go to war; or if he should become a wanderer and spend his years in vagabondage, joining the human driftwood and floating from eddy to eddy, unsocial and homeless and lost. He wondered if he should marry, and over and over he thought of the girls but none seemed to be the wife for him. When only a week remained before he must decide, he was feverish with inner conflict and on the brink of collapse. He slept little and ate little. He withdrew as much as possible from the College, despising its shallows and hysterias and the obscene thing it made of the human mind. He tried to debauch himself with whisky but the fortress of scruples which his mother had built around him was too invincible. It is impossible to say what he might have done if his pride had not suffered stinging humiliation.

He went one Sunday evening to see Laura. After a day of doubt and struggle he had resolved to marry her, thinking that she might be the tower beyond tragedy for him, in which he could recover health, sanity and peace. These thoughts were in his mind when he greeted her at the door and when he sat with her in the parlor. If this was to be his wife he ought to look at her with critical detachment; and this he tried to do, thinking meanwhile that he might live with her forty or fifty years. That was a long time to live with one woman. She was lovely—there could be no doubt of that—but how long would she remain lovely? Her eyes were of a most unusual color; her mouth was as sweet as a girl's mouth could be; her body was slender and well-formed, she had good teeth, a sweet breath, and lustrous brown hair. She was a senior in high school and after they were married they would pursue their studies together. They might both teach, or perhaps she would teach and he would write; and after he became famous and pests were after him for his autograph, they would tour the earth, passing in serene fulfillment from shore to shore, as two might who had lived wisely and well.

Yes, he thought, she would do, though she aroused in him no furious hungers, nor even much tenderness. Unlike Neloa .... The intrusion of Neloa stiffened him. He asked Laura if she would fetch him a drink of water. For a moment she looked at him and then went to another room and returned with a drink. She gave it to him without speaking.

"I've been thinking," he said, sipping the water and looking at her across the glass.

"So have I," she said.

"Oh?" He set the glass down. He did not like her tone. "I've been thinking about us." He went over, intending to kiss her but she waved him aside.

"Don't," she said. "I don't want you to."

"You don't?" He was dashed. "Why not?"

Her gaze was level and searching. "Because I don't."

"We're betrothed, aren't we?"

"Not exactly. You've never given me a ring."

Her words incensed him. He did not like jewelry, chiefly because he had no money for such things. "What difference does a ring make?"

"Maybe none to you."

"A ring! Is it a ring you've been in love with?"

"Vridar, sit down. I want to talk to you."

He sat. "What is it?"

"I still like you a lot. You know that."

"You said you loved me."

"I don't."

"You don't? Then did you lie."

"I do love you in a way—like a brother."

"A brother! Are you jesting?"

"Tell me," said Laura, "why you came tonight."

"What a hell of a question. To see you of course." He thought a moment and said: "I came to see when we'll be married."

Laura smiled. Her smile was tired, pitying. "Never. I'm not going to marry you."

Vridar stood up. He looked down at her and something in his eyes alarmed her. "Don't look at me that way."

"How shall I look at you?"

"Sit down and I'll tell you why."

Vridar still stared at her. That this girl should not love him he found plausible enough; that she had the effrontery to tell him so to his face outraged him. But he sank to a chair, still looking at her. "Go on," he said.

"Vridar, you know you're a very thoughtless person. You're not like other men."

"Thank God for that," he said.

"See how vain you are." Her lips had curled. "No woman can ever be happy with you."

"No woman?" he said, astonished. "None?"

"None."

"Why not?" he asked, looking at her.

"Because you're too selfish."

"I am selfish?"

"Don't shout that way . . . . Yes, Vridar, the most selfish man I've ever known."

"Thanks," he said.

"Shall I tell you how?"

"If you wish." He loathed himself now. He wished he had the pride to rise and go.

"How long have we been going together?"

"I don't know. Does it matter?"

"Two months," she said.

"Two months," he said, trying to remember in what ways he had been selfish.

"In all that time, Vridar, you've never given me a single thing. Not a box of candy, not a single bunch of flowers." She was speaking with some vehemence. She was speaking as one deeply aggrieved.

Vridar sat in amazement under her charge. Not for the world could he have spoken, so deep and complete was his astonishment.

"Other men," Laura was saying, "give me things. When it's my birthday they give me a present. You never even asked when my birthday is. When they call on me they bring candy or flowers or something . . . . But you—you've been here fourteen times and you never brought me a single thing. Nothing but yourself."

"I thought," he said with wry bittterness, "that was enough."

"See how selfish you are? And so," she went on quietly, "I don't want you to come any more. If you want to we can be good friends. I like you but not in the way I did. We can be brother and sister," she said. She added with a strange little smile: "But even brothers, they give to their sisters sometimes."

Vridar's wits had cleared. Dark scorn had been gathering in him, and now up through it came his thoughts, colored by it. He rose and looked at her. "It's all clear now."

"Vridar, don't look at me that way."

Trying to speak calmly he went on: "You like men who bring flowers, who sweeten their kisses with candy. You think such things mean love." He paused, feeling that his words lacked edge and vigor. He grinned at her. "All right," he said, holding her startled and anxious gaze. "Flowers and candy do have their meaning. I have a friend who uses them. Each seduction costs him maybe a box of chocolates, a bunch of roses, a few violets or sweet peas. He keeps a record of all these things. He has seduced dozens of girls and he knows exactly what every one has cost him in flowers and candy. I'll give him your name and address." He went over and picked up his hat and turned, feeling that into this superficial creature he had not driven the rapier home.

"Miss Cunningham, you have done me a favor. I have known that candy and flowers mean a great deal to most girls—but as things from the hands of men I doubt that they meant much to Jane Carlyle or Elizabeth Barrett." He looked at her, wondering what else to say, feeling that he had said too much, but still not the right thing. He spoke again out of bitterness but never suspected how truly he spoke. "You will marry one of these carpet knights with his hands full of violets. You will have a dull husband and six dull kids; and some day when I'm famous you will write to me, for you will be curious about my books. And when you are thick and untidy and unlovely candy and flowers won't mean as much to you as they mean now." He went to the door and turned and bowed and said: "Goodbye."

He walked home in a cold sweat, his humiliation so bitter that he did not look at anyone who passed him. He knew that he had been mean, that he had been cruel. He despised himself for that. He had not acted like a man with character, dignity, pride. Had he loved her? Yes, in a way he had. He had been very fond of her and had pleasant memories of many hours with her. He told himself, sitting on a chair in his room, his head sunk, that he owed her a debt, for he would have been fool enough to marry her. He would be fool enough to marry another who probably was no better. He got a photograph of Neloa and sat alone with it, and midnight came and the night passed, and it was morning. He packed his few things into a bag and took the next train home.

XIV

He had copied a paragraph from Black's *Green Pastures and Piccadilly:* "But I will tell you my belief, that all the battles and wars that ever were in this world have not caused the fifteenth part of the misery and tragic suffering that have been caused by this very thing you are laughing at—those false ideals formed before marriage." Ah Lord, had he only the power to laugh at it! He was going home to a girl who might not be waiting, and he felt with intolerable certainty that he should not go. He had tried to be wicked and had failed. He had kissed a number of girls, he had danced with many, but he had not been able to surrender in the normal, easy, animallike way of Neloa. He had tried; great God, how hard he had tried! And now, with a solemn conviction of his own stupidity and folly, he was going back home, to face the scene and the person of his deepest humiliations. He wished he might have been held in Salt Lake City in chains, instead of going now like a vanquished weakling, to pick up the threads of his life. His reason, with its handful of portents, each marking a reef ahead, was like a full moon in the sky when the sun shines. The sun and the moon as he journeyed became a kind of parable of his conflict, the moon becoming more spectral like a nimbus of fog as the sun stood out in golden flush, lighting up his hunger for a girl whom he had tried to put away. In later years he was to wonder why he did not turn back. It was to seem very strange to him. But his love for Neloa was so wildly unreasoning and so much a part of his loneliness that he had no power to renounce it. When far from her he could mark the danger-zones. He could feel, however obscurely, that her interests were not his, that his were not hers, and could never be; that his hunger to achieve was no part of her hunger; that they would live as strangers in the same house. He would try to think of her as the girl who surrendered the first night out to a lover; but standing beyond the wanton was the shy lass on the Annis butte, the girl who stood with him in the school contest—the symbol and the ideal that had been the soul of his worship and the beat of his heart. To see her for what she was he would have to sever her from all those early years, and this he could not do.

When he sat with the mail carrier he moved in dark bewilderment, his whole being set on one end. She was up at her Antelope home now. Around him now were the hills of Antelope with their sage and great open spaces, that he hated so, yet loved more. While journeying through Poplar he had stared at the landmarks of his years there: against that ramshackle schoolhouse he had been driven to frenzy by Ollie Bitt; on that canal he had skated in delirious joy with Helen; and there by the barn he had knocked the daylights out of Alvin Kress. Over in the field was the cold shack where he and Marion had lived . . . . Poplar had fallen behind and he was now only a few miles from Neloa; he would meet her with everything that he was ringing in her name. She would come to him and they would meet in the inevitable way of rivers and fire and of all things that belonged to each other in meeting . . . . Only two miles to go! There was no moon now. There was still the night, somewhere far under, throwing its shadow over his senses; but most of what he could feel was golden day and blue sky and larks singing on fence posts. Dressed in a simple gown she would be standing in the dooryard, looking into the west and waiting for him; and she would run down the road to meet him, her hair flowing behind her on the wind. He would hold her very close, whispering, "Neloa, darling Neloa!" He would then step back and perceive that her eyes were wet.

When he left the truck, he was so shaken he could hardly stand. He paid the carrier and gathered his bag; when, with shimmering fields and mountains banked in purple fog all around him, he went up the road to Neloa's house. He rubbed at his eyes and then knew that his hands were trembling. It was all so unreal, so heartbreaking, so terrible, this coming to her again. Neloa . . . Neloa! He would break at her touch or the sound of her voice and he would cry like a child . . . . He was at the gate now. He could see nobody nor any sign of life. She was not in the yard, waiting for him: he went slowly up the road, pausing, walking again. Should he turn back now? Or should he go off alone to examine his emotions, before seeing her? He was trying to determine the matter when the door opened and Neloa appeared.

For a long moment they looked at one another. He could not cry her name, he could not move. He could only look at her; and while he looked at her all the strangeness of life filled and overflowed the moment . . . . Then Neloa left the door and came toward him. She came uncertainly, as though not sure what he would do, as if a little afraid; and Vridar, no longer trembling, stood like a man of stone. The passionate cry was dead in his throat; his intolerable heartache had moved back and now waited. She came up and faced him and their eyes met. His stare was searching, hers questioning and afraid. If she had come running to him, if she had shown half the eagerness that had shaken him mile after mile, he would have been frenzied with love and forgiveness; but her body was stiff and her tongue was mute.

"I guess I shouldn't have come," he said. He saw again the familiar things: the troubled darkenings in her eyes; a way of lifting her brows to show incredulity; a quick faint smile which for an instant left her face cold. He moved to pick up his bag and turn away.

"Vridar!" She sprang toward him but she did not touch him. She was interrogating him with her whole face, her whole body, for she did not understand: his wish to dramatize the moments and lift every experience to its highest emotional pitch was alien to her. He had wanted their meeting to be intense and deep and wordless, but it was being spoiled with questions, doubts, fumblings. Rather than love helpless before such stupid sterility he preferred the lone integrity of pain. He wondered what he should do. She waited, her face puckered with questions; and he thought again that love for her and her people was not moonstruck and headlong and unutterable, but only the casual surrender, the birth, the chores . . . .

"Let's walk," he said.

They turned down the road and for a mile or more they did not speak. What did people think who saw them along the way?—that the lover had been gone for months and at once took his girl to a secret place to be intimate! How else could they think of it? When they came to the brink and looked down, he wanted her to clasp his hand and say, "Down there we spent so many hours together alone and every hour was a lovely and perfect thing. Down there—how many Sundays?—we were shut away, only the two of us, and the eighteen hours were only so many minutes. And then came confession and bitterness; but darling, we shall put all that away and forget it and go on . . . ." But these were not her thoughts. They went down the dugway and to a fir tree; and he looked round him as a man might who has been away a long time and has come home.

He turned to her and said, "Look at me." She met his gaze for only an instant. She flushed, for she was annoyed. She turned and looked away at the mountains and he looked at her. He wanted to make her weep, and in later years he was to understand his reasons. For one thing her tears always stirred his erotic longings and gave to them softness and glamor: in legend the woman at the grave of her husband surrendered easily to the passing soldier because of her grief. The strange relationship between grief and erotic intensity he had dimly understood for a long time. Another reason was his notion that tears purged her: her eyes then lost their stealth and memories and became luminous with love. The third reason, both now and later the most important of all, was the artist in him: his childhood and youth had been so tortured and empty, so insignificant and futile, that he wished to dramatize all things relating to himself. He wanted each lovely experience to move through a soft prelude; to deepen then in power and intensity as it came to its crisis; to be stamped on completion with the inevitable finality of the perfect. But making Neloa weep, as he had learned, was not easy. There was no hysteria in her. Her emotions had no need of catharsis . . . .

"You don't really love me," he said, "so I don't understand why you pretend that you do. Is it because most women are content with the best marriage they can make?" She glanced at him, alarmed. "Marriage often lasts a long time; we should know what we are doing. I think I am not the kind of man you feel most at home with. Those with a normal, eager, animallike interest in sex—aren't they your kind? I have a sense of right and wrong that may be silly but it is not yours. I question whether you are moral at all—not immoral, I think, but just unmoral. For I have sensed in you no shame, no regret. A friend in Salt Lake says that no woman has ever lived who has regretted intimacy with a man that was pleasurable. Is that the great difference between us? Yet the men with whom you feel most at home are exactly the men, after your confessions, who would have kicked you out. But I— fool that I am, idiot that I am—send you to school. I try to forget and forgive, but you think these things like gastric juice are secreted by a gland. I mean that you take it all for granted."

They sat now and she looked at the mountains and he looked at her and considered. If he could only force her to pour out in a flood of words all that she felt, then he might know what to do. But this girl before him sat like a Buddha.

"Neloa, I have been going through hell for you. That is no exaggeration. I suffered and struggled this past year; and it seems to me that if you had been conscious of it you would have been in Rigby like Caesar's wife above reproach. But Diana wrote that you quickly responded to every eligible man who showed an erotic interest in you."

She turned and looked at him, her eyes cold. "I have told you that if you believe your sister instead of me I won't marry you."

"But did she lie? I know that you do respond that way. If you did not, then after the night of your confession you could never have sat at the table with Dave Wolf and smiled at him as though you had not sent me away crazed a few hours before."

"What would you have me do?"

"What you must. I can tell you only what I would have done. If I had sent you away in such desperation, and if I had really loved you, I would have gone to find you. I certainly would not have spent part of a day in the company of an old mistress. Not if I loved you. But that I suppose is a basic difference between us. That is what worries me. If the thing had been reversed and you had gone away to Salt Lake, red with humiliation and shame that you had been such a fool, I imagine you could have surrendered easily to one man and another to even the score. But I could not. Only God knows how hard I tried but I could not. I went with girls who would have been mine for the taking; but I couldn't take them, I could be only a simple God damned fool. I could not put you away. I could not forget that grotesque and fantastic idolatry of you that had crowned you for nine years. Month after month I tried to put you out of my heart and soul, out of my consciousness, out of my dreams . . . . "

He glanced at her and saw that her eyes were wet. He could feel the mist in his own.

"I have—I have an absurd idealism, I suppose; yet I read a lot in the lives of great poets and they seem to have had it—too much of it, I mean—or is it too much? I have had an ideal of marriage, of love, of women. Those ideals, William Black says, have caused more tragedy than war. They might do that for us, and certainly will do that for us if you fail to understand how I feel in these things. I'm not asking you to be extreme as I am. Let me put it this way. Michelet, a great French historian, says that women in a man-made society have lost their true rôle—that of healing and consoling. That, he says, is her true priesthood by divine right. That healing and consoling is, I suppose, what I need. For in all my life I have not had love—devotion, yes, but not love, not from anyone. More than most people I probably need it."

He bowed his head, and after a few moments he felt a hand on his arm. A hand gently cupped his chin and tried to turn him.

"Don't," he said, for now he was weeping.

"Vridar."

He flung away from her and staggered to his feet. He turned up the mountain and she ran after him and grasped his arm and tried to hold him.

"Don't" he said.

"Vridar!" she was aroused now. She was weeping too but her grief was deep and soundless. "Vridar!"

He tried to break away from her but she clung desperately. With both arms round his neck she dragged him to the earth and drew him to her and held his head to her breast; and her tears fell to his cheeks but she made no sound of grief. She held him and like a mother she rocked him, but what she might have said she had no power to say. Vridar was aware that he lay in her arms against her heart. Memories and bitterness fell away and he could be conscious only of his overwhelming need of her, of his blind and unreasoning devotion to her.

"Neloa, I—I worship you still."

"Yes," she said, without knowing what he meant.

"I can't give you up."

"I can't give you up."

"Can you be what I need? Can you keep me from going mad?"

"I will try," she said.

"The healing I need because of my childhood, can you do that?"

"I will try," she said.

"And when I am wild and abusive will you understand? Will you understand that you have to be so much for me and of me until I am stronger?"

"I will try."

He sat up and then threw himself to her lap with his arms around her. "Neloa, don't leave me, ever. No matter what I do don't leave me ever . . . . Speak!"

She drew him close to her and laid her wet cheek to his cheek. She clasped one of his hands and he could feel her tears falling.

The next day he told her all that he had to tell about girls and about thieving in Salt Lake City. He told her a few things about his childhood, and his awful hatred of his homeplace and the Antelope country. He told her that he hated the men with whom she had lain, yet knew that he should not, and some day would not, if she could only console and heal. And a week later he told her—had she known this? —that in the country roundabout people were talking about what she had done and calling him a simpleton and a fool. What was he to do about it?

"My pride," he said, "won't let me endure it. What shall I do? It seems that some of these men have told that they were intimate with you. My uncle Dock says they put it this way, that I can marry you but they were first. What can I do about it?"

"I don't know."

"If you were in my place what would you do?"

"I don't know."

They were sitting on the river bank. He asked her if she would die with him, now,

347

and she said yes. Doubting that she meant it he led her to the bank and said they would clasp hands and both jump in and drown. "Are you ready?"

She clasped his hand. "Yes."

He knew then that she would have jumped. "You must love me if you would die with me."

"You big silly, of course I love you."

"But not enough to die for me."

"Enough for anything."

"Then help me decide what to do, for this is your problem as well as mine. We can't marry and go away, for I have no money. I must go to school. Since we can't go away we must stay here—all summer, while the gossip gets deeper and thicker. What shall I do about it?"

"I don't know."

"Will you help me?"

"Yes," she said, without knowing what she said.

He understood that she did not know what she said when he rode out unexpectedly the next day and found her alone in the Doole house with Dave Wolf. She had not heard him coming, and when Vridar appeared at the door the two of them were sitting in the kitchen, talking and smiling much like man and wife. Yet this man had told far and wide that he had lain with her. Vridar forced himself to go in and to sit and look at them and listen; and his wonder grew as he listened, for they went right on smiling and talking as though the three of them were casual friends and no more. In the way Wolf looked at him now and then Vridar saw triumph, not sly triumph but a triumph that was bold and open and unabashed. Vridar might have burst with rage and killed the man, and her and himself also; but he only sat, studying his emotions and wondering about this girl to whom he was betrothed. She might have said, "You will please go now because Vridar has come." She might have taken Vridar's hand and gone with him to the river. But she did none of these things, and when Vridar arose to leave she made no move to stop him; and when he mounted and turned to ride away she did not come.

After he had ridden a little distance he began to laugh. Was it all plain enough now, even for his thick head? Yes! he said, and roared at the sky. But after he had exhausted himself with terrible insane bellowing he knew that it was not plain at all. He knew that she would have leapt into the river with him and drowned. In God's name, what kind of person was she?—that one day she would walk to death with him, and in the next sit with an old lover and not even move to stop him when he turned away! May God forgive me, he thought, what a fool I am! Was she so artful and cunning that he missed her entirely?—or so incredibly insensitive and obtuse that she was less than human? Was she being intimate with Dave now? He did not believe it. No, it was simply that he did not understand her, and the effort to understand this person so unlike himself almost unseated his mind and will.

He was still bowed under the shame of it when one day he met his uncle Dock on the hills. Dock had large bulging pale blue eyes and a lewd grin. He now grinned at Vridar and his eyes rolled when he said: "That-air Dave Wolf, he says you'n marry her but he beat you to it."

"He's a lying son of a bitch!"

"Well, if he lies," said Dock, "why don't you make him eat his words?"

"I will."

In such manner the die was cast and picked up and cast again; for Dock went on to say: "And Shard Higgins, he says he beat you to it."

"Who is he?"

"You don't know?" asked Dock, opening his eyes wide. "Why, my God, he's the prizefighter down in Ririe."

"He's another lying son of a bitch."

"I don't kallate you would darst tell him that."

"I will tell him."

"If you do, he will beat you up something awful."

"Then he will beat me something awful."

"He's a big bastard," said Dock. "He's a heavyweight."

Under the strain of this Vridar had turned pale. "I don't care how big he is," he said.

Dock picked up the die and cast it again. "And Alvin Kress, he says he done it."

"He's a liar."

"Well, I don't know," said Dock, thoughtfully tonguing his quid and spitting. "The way I see it, if these is lies you shouldn't stand for it. A man don't let no one talk that way about his wife."

<h2 style="text-align:center">XV</h2>

It was a grimly determined young man who rode next day to the Doole farm. He was not thinking of himself as a gallant, lifting his lance for a woman; nor even as one who was brave where courage was called for. As when bully boys had taunted him about his brother's eyes, so now he felt that he had to do what a man must do to keep his honor. What sort of person, folk were asking, could this Vridar be, that he should love and intend to marry a girl about whom men were telling these things? He would show them what sort of person he was. He recalled Seneca's words, "He who injured you was either stronger or weaker. If he was weaker, spare him; if he was stronger, spare yourself." But this was a counsel of perfection! He recalled the words of George Savile: "Everybody has not wit enough to act out of interest but everybody has little enough to do it out of vanity." But this was a counsel of retreat! "Men always want to be a woman's first love," Oscar Wilde had said. Vridar did not miss the sting in that. He did not miss the sting in Helvetius: "To be loved we must merit but little esteem; all superiority attracts awe and aversion." He did not miss the sting in La Rochefoucauld, that it is less painful to be deceived than undeceived by those we love, or that in jealousy there is more self-love than love. The words of these men and of others came to his mind as he rode and he was not unaware of his folly and of himself as a fool. Execute every act of your life, said Marcus Aurelius, as though it were your last. He would do that. Weakness, not vice, said La Rochefoucauld, is the antithesis of virtue. He would not be weak.

When he walked into the Doole house, Neloa's mother looked at him with her bleak eyes, her father with his dark stealthy ones.

"Where's Neloa?"

She was up at a sheepcamp, said Mrs. Doole, cooking for the sheepmen.

"Sheepcamp! Where?"

"At the head of Birch Creek."

Vridar looked at the mother, at the father: were they as stupid as they seemed to be? He went outside and rode again, telling himself with growing amazement that Neloa was far away in the hills with only lewd men around her. Her sister Connie was with her, but Connie was only a child. Why had Neloa gone far back in the hills to cook for men?

On the Antelope flats he met Curt Obbing. Curt in the tales about him had seduced more women than any other man in this area. He was a Mormon and he had served a two-year mission; and he got up on Sunday and sang hymns and prayed and talked about virtue. At least three bastard children in Antelope could have called him father . . . .

Curt hailed him and Vridar stopped and looked at the man. Curt came over, his manner fawning, his eyes mirthfully insincere.

"Where you off to? But hell, I know. You're off to Birch Creek to see your girl."

"How did you know she's on Birch Creek?"

"I know a lot of things." He tapped Vridar's leg with a patronizing hand. "I'm oldern you. I should ought to advise you, I think."

"About what?"

"Well now, don't put your ass up. I mean well. Like a Christian. Like one Mormon to another in the brotherhood of men."

"To hell with your pieties. What's your advice?"

"This," said Curt. He rolled a cigarette and studied Vridar's face. "You aim to marry Neloa, don't you?"

"That's my business."

"There you go! This-here I want a-say is for your own good."

"All right, let's have it."

"Neloa's a nice girl. I like her fine. But there's lots of stories about her."

"What?" said Vridar, as though he didn't know.

"They ain't nice stories. Now if I was to marry a girl, I wouldn't want people tellun such things."

"Who?"

"Well now, that's a horse of another color. I don't tattle out of school."

Vridar reached down suddenly and seized the man by his hair and shook him. "By God, I suppose you've been lying about her too!"

"Me?" said Curt, backing away. "I never talk about women. Now you and Neloa . . . . "

Vridar smote his pony and galloped away. He climbed a long mountain to its top and all around him could see small lovely valleys and rounded peaks. Then he came to a ewe. She was standing alone in a glen and in her side was a panful of maggots, swarming in nasty white sickliness like things boiling in their own grease. This ewe

350

like many others had been cut in shearing and had come off here to die. Her eyes were already dead. She would stand here until she dropped. The maggots would breed in the wounds and slowly push into her, and her guts would become a rolling mass of worms. He looked into the sky and saw three vultures sailing round and round. He rode on, thinking as he had thought so many times of man's ruthless ways with all the things brought under his hands. He saw another ewe, also dying, and he was sickened and enraged when he rode into the camp. Around a long table in the sun nine men were eating. Neloa stood close by, serving from a hot stove. Vridar's swift glance told him three things: the men resented his intrusion, they were bantering Neloa, and she was pleased by the banter. He leapt down and went over to her. He took her arm and told her in a savage whisper to come with him; and when she resisted, he clutched her arm with murderous fingers and jerked her toward him. He led her beyond hearing of the men and swung her to face him.

"What in hell are you doing here?"

She tried to jerk free. She glanced over at the men who were eating and watching her. "Don't!" she said.

"You idiot! You incredible unspeakable idiot! What did you come here for?"

"Let me go."

"You're leaving this place. Do you hear me?"

"I won't. I'm the cook."

"If you need work couldn't you get respectable employment? Do you have to come off into the mountains with a bunch of men? . . . . Are you coming?"

"No."

"All right, then, we're through."

"Vridar."

"I said we're through. Go to hell in your own way." He started off but now she clung to him; and Vridar, knowing that nine men were watching, was humiliated. He told her to act with dignity and sense.

"You can't go," she said, her face now as desperate as his. "When the meal's over we can talk."

He considered this. "I'll be down there in the trees," he said. He went back to his horse and mounted and rode away.

He had not been in the trees long when he heard her coming. He knew by the distress and anxiety in her face that she had not expected to find him here; but almost at once her face lost its anxiety, and Vridar, watching her like a hawk, saw her shrug, saw in her eyes the old look of scorn.

"Tell me why you're here," he said. "I've no time to waste."

"You know why. I'm here to cook."

"But why come away out into the mountains to cook for a gang of vulgar men?"

"They're not vulgar."

"Oh no?" he said softly. "You mean they're your kind of men? You mean—"

"Vridar!"

He grasped her arms, his fingers closing like steel. "You fool," he said. He searched her eyes, her face. "What have you been doing here?"

"You can't insult me that way!"

351

"Insult you? Is that possible?"

"I'll go!" she cried, shaking his hands off. "I didn't come here to be insulted."

He seized her and crushed her to the earth, shaking her as she fell. "I ought to kill you! Honest to God I ought to kill you!"

"I wish you would," she said.

"I will."

"Do it. I'd rather die than live this way."

"Live this way?" he said, sitting by her. "Is it my fault if everybody is talking about you? Is it my fault if you run off into the mountains to cook for men, with no other woman within miles? Is it my fault if your father is a sly no-good and your mother is too damned stupid to know how to raise a daughter? I don't know why in hell I keep coming to see you."

"I don't know either."

"One of these days I'll come no more."

"And one of these days I'll kill myself."

He looked at her. "What a cheap threat! Only cowards kill themselves."

"I can't do anything to please you."

"Good God, did you think this would please me? Did you think___"

Suddenly she was on her feet looking down at him. "I've no clothes to be married in. I thought you'd be pleased."

He stood up and looked at her. "You mean that's why you are here?"

"Yes."

"And you don't realize that I'd rather you were married in what you stand in than have you here?"

"I'm sick of life," she said. "I can't stand much more."

"All right, Neloa, you don't have to stand me. I will go any time. But if I am not to go, then you must play the game straight."

"I do."

"Neloa, you're not stupid. So what am I to make of you? I come unexpectedly to see you and find you alone with Dave Wolf."

"I was just friendly."

For a moment Vridar was too overcome to speak. At last he said, his voice soft and menacing: "Just friendly? But how can you be friendly with a man who has told that he lay with you? Are you still fond of the skunk?"

"He's not a skunk."

"If a man is intimate with a woman and then boasts about it, isn't he a skunk?"

"I don't know."

"Oh, in God's name, you don't know! Is it that you like to have him around? Is it that you care nothing about my feelings? Is it that you can't tell him to stay away? And if you can't, is it because you don't want to?" He dropped to the earth and said: "Sit down." After Neloa had sat he squared around to face her. "Neloa, in the name of heaven let me understand you once and for all. You know what stories are being told about you. If it was being said that I had had a lot of lovers and that you were a fool to marry a man like that, how would you feel? . . . You do not tell me. You know what Alvin Kress says?"

352

"Alvin Kress?"

"That freckled dog. Do you know?"

"What?"

"That he has been intimate with you."

"He lies."

"Oh, he lies?" said Vridar, searching her eyes for guilt. "Did you ever go with him? . . . . Answer me!"

"Yes."

His thoughts went like a storm of fire into the past—to Helen's birthday party, Alvin's insults and the fight by the barn. "You mean—you went with *him?*"

"Yes."

"When was that?"

"Oh, a year ago last spring, I guess."

"How many times?"

"I don't know. Not many."

"And you were not intimate with him?"

"No."

"Then why should he say it?"

"You'd better ask him."

"What did you do with him?"

"Just went to dances."

"And he kissed you, I suppose."

"I don't remember."

"You lie. Did he?"

"I suppose."

"What else?" he asked, for he knew that there was something else. Her gaze had fallen and color had deepened in her cheeks. "Why can't you look at me?"

"I can."

"Then do it."

"I don't want to."

"Oh, you don't want to. What else did you do with that son of a bitch?"

"Nothing."

He seized her and shook her; but then, ashamed of this, he stood up and said: "All right, I'll go. If you must lie I won't stay with you." He moved off.

"Don't go!" she cried. She bowed her head and moaned.

"I'll give you five seconds to answer," Vridar said.

She looked up at him. "And if I don't, will you—kill me?"

"All right," he said. "One—two—three—four—"

"Wait! He put his hand down here." She indicated her breasts.

"Oh?" said Vridar, with a strange laugh. "And what did his hand do?"

"Tickled my nipples."

Vridar walked out into the sun and looked up. A little while he fought for control and then came back and said: "What else did he do?"

"Let me think."

"You don't have to. This is the sort of thing any person remembers."

"Well, he—he tickled my hand." She opened a palm and with a finger indicated what she meant.

Again Vridar's thoughts leapt to his dark past. In Annis, in Popular, in Rigby the tickling of a girl's palm had meant a wish to embrace. School children had snickered about it, knowing that it was terribly shameful.

"Anything else?"

"No, so help me God."

Vridar sat again. "And what did Shard Higgins do?"

"I don't even know him."

For a little while he looked at her and considered. "Neloa, it is important for us to understand one another if we can. You say you love me—"

"I do."

"Then why do you do these things that make my life more wretched? It is known all over that you are up here. People everywhere are talking, saying I'm a fool, that you are wanton, that—"

"I had to come. Daddy told me to."

"A hell of a father you have. Come here," he said. He drew her to his arms and looked down at her face and talked to her. "Is it impossible for you to see my side of the thing? Impossible for you to understand how certain men look at me? Impossible to understand my hurt and humiliation when I came the other day and found you with Wolf? Impossible to know my grief because when I turned away you did not try to keep me?"

"I didn't think I could."

"Neloa, if you were in my place I'd move heaven and earth to make things easier for you. I'd be very careful not to do anything or say anything to bring back bitter memories. I'd no more allow my old lovers to think that I might still be receptive than I'd sell my own mother into a brothel."

"They don't think I am."

"Don't try to fool me. I look into a man's eyes and see what is there. If you don't want these men to have the notion, the best thing is to make it plain to them that you don't want to see them again. Since they talk about you, I'd think you'd have contempt for them. Above all, I'd think you'd have some consideration for me."

"I want to."

"If it were turned around and you had found me with one of my women, would you have liked it?"

"No."

"Do you think I like it? . . . . There's another thing. I can't live here and let these stories be told. I may be a fool, and I suppose I am, but I'm going to make these men eat their words. The question is, will you stand by me?"

"Yes."

Vridar looked at her and the words that he had intended to say died in his throat. He wanted more than these simple affirmations, so easy to give. He wanted something to convince him past all doubt that she did care, that she also was humiliated by the gossip, that she wished above all to go with him to another life and forget. But nothing in her spoke deeply of these things, or even spoke at all, so far as he

354

could tell. He arose and left her and went off and hid; and when he came back it was dark and Neloa had gone. He went quietly through the trees and looked at the camp; and he saw the men talking; and he saw Neloa in firelight, smiling at their words. He slipped away and mounted his pony and rode home.

XVI

Neloa left the Birch Creek camp and came home and a few days later went as cook to a ranch in Swan Valley, twenty miles away. Again Vridar was astonished when he rode to her house and learned she was gone. "To Swan Valley!" he cried, and looked into the east. She must have known that Swan Valley was too distant for him to go see her. She must have known that he would wish to be consulted in these matters. But without a word to him she had gone. He spent a few wretched days of indecision and then followed her and sought work as a farmhand. He labored a-cross the road from her and every evening when his work was done he went over to be with her till midnight. They would walk down a fragrant canal bank or out into a field smelling of newmown hay; or they would sit in the dark entrance of a large barn.   All these evenings—there were six of them—were the same: he would try in one way or another to touch that sleeping or buried part of her which he had never reached. He wanted to strike into the depths of her and bring her candor to the surface; but the most he could do was to make her weep, and to realize then that her grief was superficial, that the woman in her lay beyond his scorn.

When Saturday night came, they went to a dance. Vridar had never been to a dance with her. His uncle Dock had said, "By God, you should see her! She hugs a man up like she was growed to him. She presses them big bubbies agin him so tight she nigh shuts his wind off . . . ." Vridar had another reason. He had heard that Harvey Kress, a gay dog with the women, sometimes came down from Afton, Wyoming, to the dances here. This man it was who had taken the key to Neloa's room and slipped in to seduce her, in that very hotel where he had lain with her all night.

"Let's go to the dance," he said to Neloa, cunningly watching her.

She was pleased. "Goody," she said.

"We've never danced together, you know. Had you ever thought of it?"

"Yes."

"We won't dance with anyone else but only with one another. Is that the way you would like it to be?"

"Yes."

"You won't dance with any man but me? You mean that?"

"Yes."

"Even if other men ask you—and of course they will—you'll not dance with them?"

"No."

"All right then, that's how it will be. I'm going in overalls. You run along and get ready."

She ran to the house and with cynical eyes Vridar watched her go. Thought of a dance, he was thinking, seemed to give her more joy than he had ever given her.

Was she nothing but a child? He had with him a small book of La Rochefoucauld's aphorisms and he now called to mind one that he had dwelt on while mowing round a field: Enforced fidelity to one's beloved is no better than infidelity. Was he *forcing* her to *fidelity*? Had she really meant it when she said she preferred to dance only with him? He sighed, for she was more of a riddle with each passing week.

They rode to the dance with Vridar's cousin, a big hardfisted and illiterate man; they came to the small place called Irwin, with its store, poolhall, dancehall, and schoolhouse; and when they drew up at the hall, Vridar could hear music and dancing feet. They entered the hall and he saw a scene typical of American settlements still close to the frontier: big rough men in overalls and denim shirts; old women by the walls with small children playing over their laps; bashful youths cluttering the entrance and looking on with starved eyes; and a floor alive with the vigorous jigging and hugging of the dance. He clasped Neloa's hand and led her to a bench. He told her that before dancing he wanted to learn if a certain man was here. "I'll be back in a moment. Remember, we're going to dance only with one another. Isn't that so?"

"Yes," she said, but she was looking at the people.

He sought his cousin and said, "Tell me if you see Harvey Kress here. I have some business with him." Then he returned to dance with Neloa but she was gone. He stared round him, searching for her in the idle crowd, never dreaming that she would dance first with another man; and his amazement was simply beyond words when he saw her in the arms of a stranger. For a few moments he could not believe his senses. He brushed at his eyes and looked away and again at Neloa. Then he swung and went outside into night air, trying to realize the meaning of what she had done. "Good God!" he muttered. "Good God!" His cousin Luke came up and Vridar took him aside. Now was the time to leave her, now was the time to go! Now was the time if there was ever to be a time; for after promising that she would dance only with him and that she would wait, what could he believe, but that she was very stupid or very wanton? He was about to ask Luke to take him home when Luke said:

"You want some whisky?"

"Yes, sure I want whisky." He gave Luke five dollars. "Bring me all that will buy."

Luke grinned and went out of sight into the dark. Vridar listened and could hear no music. Knowing that the dance had stopped, he entered the hall, shouldering his way through the throng, looking for Neloa, and telling himself all the while, Now is the time to go! Before he saw her the music struck again. And when he saw her he would have been no more startled if a man had knifed him: there she was, in the arms of Mike Andern, one of Vridar's boyhood enemies. Mike looked over at him and grinned.

She was dancing very close to Mike, with her head on his heart, for he was a very tall man; and Mike's arm was far around her, his hand under her left breast. After a few moments Mike danced close to Vridar and looked down at him and grinned again; and he patted Neloa's shoulder and Neloa looked at Vridar and smiled. They were dancing close together in the manner of sweethearts, and Vridar saw that her face was radiant, her eyes shining, her whole body electric with music and a man's arm. But how was he to believe it? How could any man believe this!

356

He swung and left the hall. He found Luke waiting for him with a quart of whisky. They went into shadows and Vridar drank four or five ounces without taking the bottle from his lips. The stuff went into him like a stream of fire, made a pool of flame of his stomach and burning filaments of his nerves.

"You seen Kress?"

"No."

Luke drank and Vridar drank again. He was surprised by the change that seemed to be going on within him. He felt very queer and stupid and insignificant and he wanted to laugh. He walked twice around the hall, when, burning with whisky and rage, he strode in. He saw Neloa dancing with a third man. He went toward them and pushed the man away and jerked Neloa to him. "I thought we were to dance together!" he whispered. "I thought you promised that!" She gave no reply. She seemed to be struggling to get away from him.

In this valley there was a dangerous fighter named Brig Flammer. Vridar had heard about him. Even the Antelope country had heard that Brig trounced every stranger who came to the Irwin dances, beating some of them so brutally that they were sent to a hospital to meditate on their folly. While Vridar was dancing with Neloa and whispering questions and reproaches, Brig dramatically entered his life. Suddenly a man struck him a blow that spun him like a top. Staggering, he released Neloa and glared round him at the faces; and when he saw a man grinning he leapt forward and struck him, sending both him and his partner to the floor. He then heard a voice speak. Desperate and ready, with hands clenched, he saw the one who had spoken and he saw that his grin was evil.

"I hit you!" the man said. "I'm the one who done it!"

With murder in his heart Vridar looked at the man. "All right, come outside!"

"Oh no, we'll fight here!"

"To hell with you. Come outside."

Vridar started for the door and most of the men in the hall followed him. When he went through the door, he missed a high step and fell and rolled. A hundred men had come out and two of them now seized his arms and dragged him behind the hall, with the other men following; and the two men held him and a third man faced him and squared off and struck. Vridar called to his cousin and then understood that men were holding Luke. The man struck him hard blows on his mouth, on his eyes, on his skull, until all his senses rang and his mind swam in darkness. He could taste blood and feel blood running from his nose and he fought with all his desperate strength to be free. Then he heard a man's voice saying, "Here, let me hit him, the son of a bitch!" The blows fell again. He would have been knocked down with every blow if two powerful men had not held him on his feet. He understood dimly, in this nightmare of horror, that men were taking turns smiting him. Of what happened after that he knew only what he was told. An officer stopped the brawl and Vridar was dumped into his cousin's Ford and driven home and put to bed in a haymow.

Some time before noon he came painfully and horribly to his senses. It took him a little while to remember what had happened. Remembering, he felt anxious, and he sat up and carefully felt over his face and head, trying to tell if he had been serious-

357

ly injured. He examined his teeth first; a corner was missing from one and a few of them seemed to have been loosened but none had been knocked out. Next he examined his eyes and realized that he could see only dimly, for both his eyes had been struck and were swollen. It seemed to him that his nose was broken but he could not be sure. He could feel dried blood in a rim round his mouth and in patches over his face; and he could feel bumps on his cheek and skull. He crawled down from the loft and went to the canal and washed himself; and in a clear pool he looked at his face. The flesh round his eyes was black and swollen, one cheek was torn, his nose looked like pulp. He became aware now that he was not able to breathe through his nose. After staring at himself with grim amusement, he went to a pasture and saddled his pony and turned home.

His parents looked at him with amazement. What in the world had happened to him?

Vridar's distorted face grinned. "I been in a fight," he said.

"He looks," said Diana, "like the German army had run over him."

"Like he been hit with a axe," said Joe. "That's how he looks."

"Son," said his mother, "are you only a hoodlum? Who you been fightun with?"

"Just fighting," he said. "I'm the way a famous man put it, as soon as you know a man is blind you imagine you can see it from his back." He grinned again. "I'm blind and I guess the man saw it."

Prudence applied poultices to his eyes and liniment to his bruises; and later, when looking at his face, Vridar hoped that the beating had done him some good. His wits seemed to be cleared, as though a lot of nonsense had been knocked out of him. While riding home he had said over and over, Now is the time to go! Neloa had not gone to the haymow with him. She had not come out the next day to see how he was. So far as he knew, she had remained at the dance and another man had brought her home. So far as he knew . . . . . Well, he was done with her now: there was a limit to the humiliation any man could take.

But he was a drunkard and Neloa was his whisky. He renounced her and for days he shrugged contemptuously when he thought of her; but the old hunger and loneliness again rose within him and drew him to the road. He went until he could see the Doole house and then sat on the pony and looked. "To hell with her!" he said. He went down the road and out of sight of her house; and he would stop now and then and try to think, and ride again. He kept riding until his journey became a symbol. He came to Poplar and still rode into the west; he came to Ririe. I'll never go back, he thought; I'll never go back! He stood by his horse in Ririe, thinking, I should be riding on and on! One hand rested on the pony, his gaze was on the ground. Now and then he would draw a deep breath and look up but he never looked back. The sun had set now. Bewildered, fixed in deep and quiet indecision, with no power to return or to go on, he still stood by the horse; and then a voice spoke. It was Jim Terris, a highschool classmate. It was Jim who had told him about Shard Higgins.

"Why you old son of a gun!" said Jim. "What you here for?"

"Hello," Vridar said.

Jim shook hands. "You want a job?"

"What job?"

"Pitching hay . . . .What in hell's the matter with you? You look funny. And you have black spots all over your face."

"I feel funny," Vridar said.

"Here, shake my hand again. I'm married."

"I'm sorry. I thought you had more sense."

"Come with me. You remember my sister Arlee? She's dying to see you."

"Where does this Shard Higgins live?"

"Miles from here. Why?"

"You know why."

"Well, he's still telling the story. But no woman, Vridar, is worth a fight. Come with me."

"Where does he live?"

"I'll tell you: we'll go to the dance Saturday night. Then you can see him. But don't get in a fight or he'll kill you. He's licked every man around here."

They mounted their horses and rode to the Terris farm and ate supper. Across from Vridar sat Arlee and she looked at him with such solemn interest that he was annoyed. She was not unlovely, but she was short and plump and as serene as death. He was annoyed by the whole family because they talked to him and he did not wish to talk. It was impossible to understand what they were saying.

"He must be in love," Arlee said.

"What?" said Vridar, looking at her.

"I said you must be in love."

"If a man is blind," said Vridar, "you think you can tell it by looking at his back. I am that way."

He slept outside. The sky above him gleamed like a jeweler's trinkets and the night was deep and still. He looked at the stars and thought of his pony, feeding below; and he said, I should be going. I should be riding on and on . . . .

For almost a week he pitched hay and ate his meals and said little. He was like a man who had become a stranger to himself. While at work or eating he listened to Jim's banter and he knew that Jim was trying to arouse him; but all that was said, all that was done, seemed meaningless now. When he crawled into bed he sank at once into deep slumber; and when he awoke he could remember no dreams. He did not know that Jim had written to tell Neloa where he was. On his fifth day here he received a note from her. It said:

> Dear Boy, why didn't you come to see me last Sunday? I waited
> all day for you. I waited Monday and Tuesday and Wednesday.
> I don't know if this letter will reach you but if it does, write to
> me. I'm so lonesome and I watch the road all day long.
> > your sweetheart
> > Neloa

Vridar read the letter again and again and the old passion awoke; but he shook it off and sank again into quiet. He tore the letter into strips and walked to a canal and saw it drift away in the current. He took his pitchfork and set to work. In God's name, what kind of person was she anyhow! Did she only wish to keep him on a leash? When he was eager for her, when he was her captive, did she turn

359

away?—and when he turned away, did she come running? Were women like that? Did she think she could outrage and humiliate him, yet he would always come back? Or had she simply no sense of these things?

"Tonight's the dance," Jim said. "We'll quit early and slick ourselves up."

"What dance?"

"The dance at Ririe. Tonight Shard Higgins will peel your hide off."

Vridar looked at Jim. He wondered why most men liked to see men fight. They went to the house and Arlee said that if Vridar wanted his head washed she would wash it. Jim said he had a suit Vridar could wear.

"No thanks. I'll go this way."

While shaving with Jim's razor Vridar saw that Jim's wife was digging wax out of his ears. Jim said that Arlee would be glad to dig wax out of Vridar's ears.

"Women don't like dirt in men's ears. Why is that?"

Something flashed in Vridar. "Because for women the ear is a gential symbol. They are very sensitive to uncleanness in *that* part of them."

"Oh?" said Jim, looking at his wife. "I never heard that before. Arlee, get him some wine."

Looking in the mirror, Vridar could see Arlee watching him. He saw that her ankles were thick, her breasts very large. She had lovely eyes and a lovely throat. She now went into another room and returned with a pitcher of wine. She poured wine into a glass and set it near Vridar. After shaving and bathing he took the wine and went outside to sit on a wooden tub. Jim came from time to time to look at him. Arlee framed herself in the doorway and stared at Vridar, as though by looking at him intently and long enough she might force him to an avowal of love. She annoyed him terribly.

But when they came to the hall, he danced with her and with Jim's wife, both of whom were very awkward and murmured apologies. Vridar then went to Jim.

"Is he here?"

"Yes."

"Point him out." When Vridar knew which man was Shard Higgins, he looked at him. Higgins was a big rawboned fellow with yellow brows and reddish hair. Vridar took a deep breath and said, "All right, are you coming with me?" He crossed the hall with Jim at his side. He faced Shard Higgins and looked him up and down. "Is your name Shard Higgins?"

"That's what folks call me."

"My name is Vridar Hunter."

"The hell it is." Shard glanced round at other faces and grinned. "What's on your mind?"

Vridar had closed his hands. He had put his left foot a little forward, his right a little back, so that if he struck he could roll with the blow. "You know Neloa Doole?"

"I wouldn't reckon that's any business of yourn."

"She's the girl I intend to marry."

Other men were listening. Other men had closed in.

"The hell you say. Well, you want me to congratulate you or something?"

360

"I've been told," said Vridar, trying to speak quietly, "that you've been telling stories about her. I mean dirty stories that are lies."

Shard lifted yellow brows in astonishment. "Me?" he said. He tried to laugh. "What if I did?"

"Did you or didn't you?"

"That's my business. Mebbe I did, mebbe I didn't."

"If you did," said Vridar, "you're a God damned liar!"

There was no mistake about Shard's astonishment now. He drew himself up and the evil grin left his face. "Listen," he said, narrowing his eyes, "you know who you're talkun to?"

"I'm going to marry Neloa and no son of a bitch can talk about her. If I hear any more stories out of you I'll knock your brains out, and if I can't knock them out I'll shoot them out. Do you understand me?"

Shard's laugh was a whinny of derision. He looked at the men standing round him. Vridar, sensing his advantage, knowing that the bully had faltered, was quick with his next words. "I don't know if you told the stories or not. If you did I'll be waiting for you outside." He turned and left the hall.

Stuttering with amazement Jim came to him. "God blast me!" he said. "Man, you've got him bluffed!"

"I'm not bluffing. Go and see if he's coming."

Jim went to the door and looked in. He came back. "He's still there. I don't think he'll come."

"I'll wait a few minutes," Vridar said.

He waited half an hour and then mounted his pony and rode south to the cross-road. Should he go east or west? If he went west there would be no coming back. If he went east . . . . For perhaps an hour he considered, knowing well that this was one of the major decisions of his life. East or west? He turned and galloped into the east.

It was a beautiful night. From fields to the north of him came the smell of hay and orchards; from fields to the south came the smell of ripening grain. The sky was a low-hanging realm of clouds and the clouds moved like shutters in confusion, and lights appeared and vanished above the swimming dusk. After riding eleven miles he stopped on a hill and looked at the Doole farm. The buildings were only shadows, deeper than the shadows they cast. In daylight they were shabby things without secrets, but now they were strange with the meaning of darkness. Even the ramshackle barn, made of poles and straw, took witchery from the clouds and stars; its straw sides were like glimmering veils, and its poles, thrusting up from the roof, were faintly luminous spires.

Vridar rode again and dismounted at the gate. He took his pony to the barn and then walked across the yard to the door. The lower panes of the window were bright but the upper panes were almost black. He stood by the door and listened. Neloa would be asleep in this room with Connie. He tried the door and found it unlocked, as he knew it would be, and gently he opened it and looked in. The smell of breath and sleep came to him but no sound. He closed the door and sat on the step.

361

He wanted to write a letter to Neloa but he had nothing to write with. Searching the yard for paper, he went at last to the privy, but only a mail-order catalog was there; and then he took his shoes off and opened the door and stepped inside. He found paper and a pencil. He looked over at Neloa's bed but could not see her face. Stepping outside and softly closing the door he sat in starglow to write.

> Now is the moment when, if we could take
> Enchantment by the arm and find the trails
> Leading to temples and the holy grails,
> Our love could flee the wrong and fear and ache
> And loss of one irrevocable mistake;
>
> And kept too long within its petty jails,
> Nighthawking in the dark, could set its sails
> Daringly like pilgrims, and come wide awake!
>
> Victorious we could be, could be!—but you,
> Retired to dreams, have missed the road ahead.
> In future years, tonight may always be
> Declaring what might have been for you and me;
> And what we could have done but did not do,
> Restoring to silence what was never said!

Opening the door he dropped the paper inside and went to the barn. He had intended to ride home, but now, changing his mind, he decided to sleep here. After watering and feeding the pony, he spread straw by a wall and lay down but he did not sleep. He was too happy to be here, close to her, and he tried to realize that she was a mere hundred yards away and that he would see her in a little while. The sky was clear now and by the position of the stars he could guess the time. He sat in the barn door looking at the house, wishing that Neloa would find the sonnet and come to him. A little later he walked up the road, leading the pony, and waited until smoke rose from the chimney. Then he mounted and galloped up to the door.

He knocked and entered and found Tim filling a kettle and Mrs. Doole combing her hair. The room smelled of sleep and smoke.

"Is Neloa up?"

"Why, I don't know," said Mrs. Doole. "Neloa, Vridar is here." She looked at Vridar and gave him a tired wrinkled smile. "I guess she'll be out in a minute."

Vridar left the house and walked in the yard. When after a few minutes Neloa did not come, he went to the door of her room. "You up?"

"Yes," said a sleepy voice.

He went in. He saw his poem on the floor. Neloa, brushing her long hair, turned to smile at him. "You're sure early," she said.

Vridar looked at the sisters, Connie and Blanche, and wished they would leave the room. Connie looked at him with mocking eyes as though she knew all about love and its tyrannies. She said: "You must be in an awful hurry to see someone." Then Connie swept the room and Vridar's romantic verses were gathered to a pile of dust. With annoyance waxing to rage, he went over and picked them up and left the house: no matter how he tried he could not raise his love above chores and brooms and cooking and the brushing of hair! Its parable was swept like a dead cockroach into a pile of dust and would have been thrown into the stove. Its moments of beauty were lost in the smell of frying pig and a babble of nonsense about breakfast and in all the dull prose of filling stomachs and scouring dishes and making beds.

In such moments of humiliation, he was unable to hide his scornful dismay. It was in his eyes, his scowl, even in the way he moved. He had gone to the valley and flung a challenge in the teeth of Shard Higgins, he had ridden through the night to see her again, and for two hours he had written a sonnet. But what had he got for it? . . . .

"Breakfast!"

Why in God's name did he persist in being such a fool? She had been watching the road all day, she said; yet when he came to her, she sat brushing her hair and did not even rise to meet him! Love in the great and fragrant legends had been more than that. It had been more than that for Daphnis and Chloe, for Aucassin and Nicolette, for Heloise and Abelard . . . .

"Vridar, breakfast!"

He turned and looked at Connie. "All right," he said. Should he go in? Should he go in to see the look in her eyes, the look which would say, Well, you came back but I knew you would. Should he . . . .

"Vridar, are you in a trance?" It was Connie again. She came up to him, her eyes amused. "I been calling breakfast an hour. Why don't you come?"

"I'm not hungry," he said.

"Are you mad at Neloa?"

"Hell no. Why should I be?"

"Well, come and eat and you'll feel better."

"I feel all right."

"You don't look all right. You look mad."

Connie took his arm and led him to the house; and when he entered, Vridar tried to look calm and dignified. He went to a basin and washed and he kept his face out of sight. But he could not dissemble. He could feel the sullen wrath in his being and its shadow in his face. He ate a little breakfast without once looking at Neloa and then sat on a bench by a window. Tim talked to him about dull things and Vridar gave replies, feeling mean all the while, contemptible, stupid; for her knew that Neloa was working swiftly and that when her chores were done she would go anywhere with him to spend the day. He was fertilizing an emotion of tenderness toward her when Dave Wolf entered the room.

The man came in, grinning and jovial, as though he belonged here. He spoke to the parents, to Neloa, to the other children, but he did not speak to Vridar. After a moment he turned his back on Vridar, and Vridar looked up at the man's back and knew that the insolence was deliberate. With rage possessing him, he got to his feet and looked at Neloa; and when after long moments of waiting she did not meet his gaze, he left the house. He went to the barn and led the pony out, intending to ride away; but to give her a little time he tinkered with the bridle, examining the throatlatch and bit and reins, and all the while watching the house. After a few minutes Neloa came to the door and looked across at him. He now pretended to be unaware of her. He gathered the reins and mounted, and at once Neloa came running to him. She grasped the reins. "Look out," he said, and tried to unclasp her fingers.

"Vridar!"

"Let me go," he said, but he hoped of course that she would not. He glanced at the house and saw the Dooles watching him from a window. No doubt they thought he was absurd and he *was* absurd; but what did they know of the philandering hypocrite in their house! "Go on back to your Dave boy," he said.

"Vridar!"

He tried to release her fingers but they were like steel. He looked down at her with a bitter cynical grin. "I think I've seen you somewhere. Aren't you the girl who said she would dance only with me?"

"Vridar, please."

"Aren't you the girl who said she would tell that son of a bitch to stay away?"

"Vridar, please get off."

"Aren't you the girl who has been spending the past week with him?"

"That's a lie."

"You mean he hasn't been coming over?"

"Not to see me."

"Oh no!" Vridar snorted. "I suppose he comes to see your mother."

"I don't know why he comes."

"You don't? Really!"

"Please don't go."

"You're engaged to me," said Vridar, "and he knows it. Still he comes. Why?"

"I don't know."

"Of course you know. It's because you encourage him. Do you think he'd come if you told him to get out? Are you an idiot?"

"He means nothing to me."

"He flatters you. Women like to think that old lovers can't forget them. You like to play with him as a cat with a mouse, except you want to sleep with him instead of eat him."

"You lie!" Her eyes blazed with hurt and fury.

"Well, it's queer—isn't it?—that this man can tell what he did with you, yet you still smile at him, as people may at one another who have been intimate?"

"Stop saying that."

"What shall I say?—that he's making a damned silly feebleminded knothead out of you and out of me? And you think I'm going on taking it? Take your hands off."

"I won't. If you go I'll go with you."

He looked down at her. He saw that her hands on the bridle were so rigid with purpose that the knuckles were white. Vridar spoke again and his voice was quiet.

"Will you tell me once and for all just what you expect? Am I to go on forever being humiliated? Am I to shove the lie down the throat of Shard Higgins and ride all night, only to find one of your lovers showing up at dawn? Do you think I have no heart and no pride?" She did not speak. "Does it mean nothing to you, Neloa,

364

if a man grins at me as if to say, Take her, brother, but I beat you to it? I suppose it doesn't mean anything to you."

"It does."

"What in hell do you do about it?"

"What can I do?"

"God damn it, tell him to get out of your sight and stay out! . . . . Listen—but never mind. I'm going now."

"No!"

"What shall I do?"

"Stay with me."

"Go in the house and let that homely bastard grin at me?"

"We'll go off somewhere."

"Run away from him? No, thank you. I'll tell you what I'm going to do. I'm going to make him eat his words." Vridar dismounted and led the horse to the barn. He came back and looked at her. "Well, what do you say? Are you with me or with him?"

"With you."

He started for the house but stopped and turned. "Go to the barn and wait. I'll call him out." Neloa went to the barn, and to one of her brothers Vridar said: "Go in the house and tell Dave Wolf I want to see him." Then he joined Neloa at the barn and searched his pockets for things that might be destroyed in a fight. A cheap watch which his mother had given him he told her to hold. A door was slammed shut but he did not look up. Feet sounded in the yard and drew nearer. Vridar glanced at Neloa; her face was white. He turned, and the two men looked at one another: in Dave's eyes was cunning derision, in Vridar's remorseless hate.

"I've been told," said Vridar, "that you've been talking about Neloa. I suppose you know I'm to marry her."

"I heard something the sort," Dave said.

"Is it true you've been talking about her?"

"How you mean?"

"You know how I mean!" Vridar closed his hands and advanced, his eyes paralyzing in their wild wrath. "You've said you were intimate with her! I know all about that, you dirty son of a bitch, and for a cent I'd cut your heart out! Any man who tells that sort of thing about a woman is a skunk and a dog and a coward!" He still advanced, and Dave retreated. He shot a clenched fist at Neloa. "Go over there and apologize before I break your neck."

The grinning derision had left Dave's face. He turned to Neloa. "I apologize," he said.

"And now," said Vridar, "get out of here and don't ever come around her again!"

Dave went away. Vridar was shaking so uncontrollably that he went into the barn and dropped to a pile of straw. Rage had poured such heat into his brain that he was now sick. Neloa meanwhile stood by the door and stared blankly at the watch in her hand.

XVII

When gossip had been hushed and every tale laid to its grave, Vridar felt so shamed that he wanted to leave this country and never return. He had been a crusader on the field of honor and like all crusaders he had been a clown. He had forced men to perjure themselves but had achieved nothing beautiful or good. He had tried to make Neloa seem virtuous in the eyes of those who knew her and had been forced to the bitter realization that he was the only one who cared. He unhappily sensed that the lewd bandying of her name had been pleasing to her, and he remembered again the statement about which he had thought so many times, that no woman ever regretted a pleasurable sexual experience. Did any man? If not, what a thin veneer morality was! Neloa told him one day that he had too many ideals and that he would lose a lot of them before life was done with him. That, he admitted to himself, might be so: where was the golden mean?—somewhere between her extremity and his?

The next day after his violent scene with Wolf he entered the Doole house and Neloa did not come to his arms. He looked at her a moment and said, "Let's go," and she came at once, as she always did. They went to the river and sat on its bank. Whether he should marry her Vridar still did not know; he was still determined, if this were possible, to strike into her depths and reveal her soul. He took one of her hands and upon it printed in pencil the letters H K. When she saw what he had done she sprang to her feet, quivering with pain. She looked down at him, her eyes wide with astonishment, and cried:

"O sweetheart, how could you do it!"

Was that what he wanted? Had he found the depth?

Neloa went down the bank and washed the letters from her arm. She returned and sat by him, and her eyes like the eyes of a bewildered child studied his face.

Had he found the depth? He had brought a small kodak with him and he now helped Neloa to her feet and led her to a background of dead briars and thorns. "I want to take your picture," he said. He placed her half in shadow, half in light, and told her to look steadily at the lens. "In this picture," he said, talking to her in an impersonal way, "I want the evil part of you—the woman who might have been a whore. So think of your past and its pleasures and let your eyes be full of them." She started toward him, her face dark with protest. "No, stay there. Back a little. You say you didn't love these men and wouldn't have wanted to marry any of them. That's rather peculiar. In the case of most girls they are fond of a man if they surrender, aren't they? But you weren't. I want that part of you." He considered a moment, wondering how to persuade her. "You're a fine actor," he said. "You can look like a devil or an angel. I've seen both. Now I want the devil . . . ."

Annoyed by his persistence, she yielded to his wish; and into her face came such cunning and slyness as he had never seen there before. Astonished by this vision of Neloa, he stared at her. Was this the depth?

"Well, hurry!" she said, and her voice was like her eyes.

This at least was a part of the depth. "More," he said quietly. "Can't you look more evil? Let's see all the cruelty and wantonness that women are supposed to have. You can do it. You could be a marvelous actress. You might even be a Lady Macbeth . . . . There. Now hold it." He closed the shutter. Neloa came over and looked at him, and again he was lost in wonder at what he saw in her face. "Now," he said, looking at her curiously, "I want the other side of you." He took her to a lovely spot and unfastened her hair and spread it in a mantle down her back and over her shoulders and across her breast. "Now I want the part of you that said, O sweetheart, how could you do it!—the mother, the angel, the girl who stood with me in the Annis contest—the girl who watched the road all day for my coming . . . ." He talked to her, reproaching, chiding, drawing to the surface the other Neloa; and in a little while her eyes filled with tears and she looked at him through the mist. There was no cunning, no slyness in her face now. "You're looking into the future," Vridar said. "Soon we'll be husband and wife and we may live together thirty, forty years. We'll trust each other, building my life in yours, yours in mine. We'll have children—and you'll love your children, won't you? So look down the years to what you can see . . . ."

With her head raised and her body tense as if for flight, she looked at him with wet eyes; and Vridar closed the shutter again. He led her to the bank and they sat there and he talked. Of both sides of her, he said, he had a picture now, and names for both: he had read a Russian story in which the heroine was named Mifanwy: she was simple and sweet and childlike like the Neloa he loved. The other part of her he would call Moll. "Moll and Mifanwy; but you can't go on being two persons. Do you understand that one of them must die?"

"Yes," she said.

He looked at her, his gaze still curious. Did she, then, admit the whore in her?—or did she have no notion of what he was saying? "I think two persons about to marry should be very frank with one another. I doubt that we are mated. It would be hypocrisy to pretend that I have no doubts. I cannot be sure whether I respect you or trust you. I cannot be sure how much of this in me is love, how much is childhood infatuation. Knowing these things are you still willing to marry me?"

"Yes."

"You're not being very wise, are you?"

"I think so."

"But don't you realize what a time you'll have living with me? I'm a sentimental, ignorant, idealistic, ambitious, violent, and—I suppose—half-mad person. I'm certainly not husband material for any woman. Don't you honestly think—haven't you sometimes wondered—if it would be better for you to marry someone else?"

"No." She was not looking at him. She was looking far away.

"Neloa, I'll never make you happy. That I think is certain. Or don't you think so?"

"No."

"Are you willing to be unhappy with me?"

"I'll not be unhappy."

"You don't know what you are saying. It would be foolish of you to expect what you won't get."

For a few moments she was silent while he studied her face. When at last she spoke her words startled him. "I'd rather be unhappy with you," she said, "than happy with anyone else."

He drew her to him and kissed her and put his cheek to her cheek. "Darling, you don't know what you're saying. Or do you love me that much?"

"Yes."

"And you're willing to suffer with me?"

"Yes."

Did she mean it? "And you won't ever regret it?"

"Never."

"No matter how I treat you, no matter what I do?"

"Never."

"And you'll be the kind of wife I need?"

"I'll try."

"And you know what kind I need?"

"I'll try to learn."

"Then tell me, why have you acted as you have the past two weeks? You used to come and kiss me but you don't any more."

"I didn't know you wanted me to."

"But you know I love you more than life."

"Just sometimes."

"All the time, even when I'm abusing you. I suppose it will always be that way." Her fingers tightened on his arm. "Even if you abuse me, I'll still love you."

"And nothing will ever change that?"

"Nothing."

"You would leave all your people for me?"

"All."

"You would go away with me and never see them again?"

"Yes."

"Soon we'll be married," he said. "I doubt that we should, but when I think of life without you everything goes crazy and dark . . . ."

A few days later they were married. Yielding to her wish, he sent invitations to relatives and sixty persons came to the wedding. The house overflowed with his people and her people. There was a great feast. There was lewd talk from his people, not hers, about brides and bridegrooms, and vulgar excited interest touched with malice in nuptial nights. There was absurd clowning in the front yard. So far as Vridar could tell, his father's people had only one thought in mind, that a man and a woman had been licensed to copulate. The thought was in their eyes and their words and their clowning. His father, who all these years had had so little to say to his sons, took Vridar aside and told him that Vridar and Neloa this night would occupy the bed of his parents. "It's a good place to make a baby," Joe said gravely, and Vridar was astonished and shocked. O father, my father, he thought, what a thing to say to your son!

After the guests had left, Prudence took Vridar for a walk and told him of a dream she had had. It troubled her; she could not get it off her mind. How did he interpret it? He tried to shrug the matter away. He had read Freud on dreams but he did not understand what this dream meant. If he had understood . . . .

"She looked so pale and homeless," Prudence said. "I can't forget how she looked. It haunts me."

"It doesn't mean anything," he said.

"Oh my son, it does!" She began to weep. She said she wanted Vridar to be happy, that she would give her life to make him happy; but she was afraid. "I'm afraid for you!" she gasped, weeping. "My son, my darling son!"

If he had understood!

He went off alone and thought of the dream, telling himself that it was only a mother's delirium; but he could not shake it off. He went to Neloa and asked her to walk with him, but he did not mention the dream at once. "You're my wife now," he said. "How strange it is! For years I've wanted you to be my wife—and now you are. Does it seem real to you?"

"Yes," she said and pressed his arm.

"It doesn't seem funny to think of me as your husband?"

"No."

"My mother had a dream," he said. "I suppose I should tell you about it, but you must not let it bother you. It is very silly. The time was five or ten years in the future and the place was a big city. She saw you as a harlot, going from street to street. She says you were very thin and lonely and seemed to be looking for someone. Then you came to a big house of stone with a fence around it and an iron gate. I lived in the house. You knocked timidly on the door and I opened it. You went down on your knees and begged me for forgiveness. I spurned you. I kicked you from the door. Then you went away.

"A little later she saw you again. You went off alone and you looked all around you. She says she knew you were thinking of death. Well, it's very silly. It doesn't bother you, does it?"

"No."

He stopped and faced her. He looked into her eyes and saw something there so strange that it made him tremble. "Neloa, why do you look at me that way?"

"What way?" she said, smiling, and her smile too was strange.

"What are you thinking of?"

"Nothing."

"Neloa, please tell me."

"Nothing." She was looking beyond him at the mountains. He studied her face, trying to understand what it was in her eyes and smile. "Nothing," she said again.

"You're not going to let a silly dream bother you, are you?"

"I wasn't thinking of the dream."

He looked at her eyes and smile and felt the blood leaving his cheeks. He felt something awful, an emotion that was almost pure dread, as though the whole world had darkened and death had become a palpable presence. He moved to draw her to him, but she put his hands away. She glanced at him and shrugged. She gave a low laugh; and in her laugh, her shrug, her smile there was something that chilled him. There it was, the terrible depth of this girl, the sleeping part of her, looking at him now.

They went back to the house. Prudence came out to say she needed water. Then Marion came out with a pail and went to Neloa and put an arm around her; and together, with his arm around her, they walked down to the spring, a hundred yards away. Deeply troubled, Vridar stood in the yard and looked at them, and suddenly turned to see something strange in his mother's eyes.

PART THREE

NARCISSUS

"This my self within my heart is tinier than a rice-corn, or a barley-corn, or a mustard-seed, or a canary-seed, or the pulp of a canary-seed. This my self within my heart is greater than sky, greater than heaven . . . . This my self within my heart, this is Brahma."

I

"Have you any idea," he asked, "why my father loved to bite his daughter's ear?"

She looked at him with the strange expression on her face and in her eyes that she always had when he baffled her, and though he was not aware of this, he baffled and confused her most of the time. Books for him had long been the soul and mind of the world. Books for Neloa were only books. He arose early in his third year of college, and studied and read all day and half the night. He felt with despair that was utter misery that because he had been born on a frontier and had come late to school from an uncultured background he would have to read much more and study longer and struggle harder than other students. As he had said to his wife, he would have to catch up, even if it killed him. Every day he brought books home and read only as a goaded man could read, impatiently scanning pages, searching the indexes, making notes, with Neloa now and then watching him, her look baffled and uneasy, or fascinated. She had married a man whose nature was a riddle to her.

Among the authors he had been reading was Freud. "Have you any idea?" he asked, still looking at her, still unreasonably pressing her to speak. "How many times in my childhood did I see this thing? My father would say to Diana, Come over here, I wanna bite your ear. She was always frightened because usually he bit too hard and she would cry. Then my mother would angrily rebuke him and his face would redden and he would be angry, too, sullen and resentful, like one denied his rights. But when he wanted to bite his daughter he would insist. There was something in his face, his eyes, that embarrassed and shamed me—a light like that of a stud waking. I saw the shame in my mother too. I suppose she sensed that there was something unclean in a father who wanted to bite his daughter's ear."

Vridar was silent, looking into his wife's black baffled eyes. What he saw there annoyed him, for he saw the look of a woman—of a girl really, for she was still a child—who wished that her husband could be more like other men. In such moments the scorn in her face and eyes drove him to say things to shock her. He now said, with toneless contempt for himself, "For many years I wondered if my mother defecated, and was forced to the unhappy conclusion that all women did: female animals, you know, are usually not so tidy in that part of them as the males: a ewe or a cow can be a hideous sight." He wondered if Neloa understood the word. "I mean if she had bowel movements. It reminds me of Stendhal. He said that through being in love he acquired a very comic virtue, that of chastity. I acquired that early in life through being in love with you." When, remembering the kind of girl she had been, for whom chastity was not even a reality, and the kind of fool he had been, for whom chastity had been the greatest virtue, he smiled his bitter ironic smile and looking into the velvet depths of her eyes, he saw there resentment of him that was almost weird in its intensity. He now went on, still trying to shock her: "Lady Mary Montagu says of the Duke of Bedford—but wait till I find the note." He searched through a pile of notes. "The Duke, she says, who by the care of a pious mother certainly preserved his virginity to his marriage-bed. Then?" said Vridar, looking over at her. "Then he was so shocked that he puked at the very name of his bride. And all that, says Lady Mary, comes of bringing boys up to think that women are composed of nothing but lilies and roses. That was me, except I wasn't a duke."

Again he was silent, thinking about her; and Neloa looked at him, never taking her gaze from his face. His own gaze left her eyes and fell to her lips, and for a moment he wondered about her lips: when Neloa smiled, she had the loveliest mouth he had ever seen, because in part of her perfect teeth; but her lips were not the kind a man liked to kiss: they were too firm and unyielding, they did not surrender and melt under pressure, as other lips had which he had kissed. His gaze rose again to her eyes.

"It may be," he said, "that you think it was a nice fatherly gesture, his biting his daughter's ear. Most people would think that, wouldn't they? Most people are ignorant. Diana would shrink back in fright but my father would persist, with that stud-light in his eyes. At last she would have to go over, and while she shrank from him he would clasp her head with his big hands; and he would draw the lobe of her ear between his lips and seem to taste it, and then between his teeth; and he would bite too hard and she would scream and run away from him. The more reluctant she was the harder he bit. After she had screamed there would be in his face a dark scowling resentment with the stud-light glowing in it; and it was then that I hated him most—even more than when I saw him yanking the testicles out of yearling bulls. A hundred times I saw him bite my sister. Why did he?"

Neloa looked at him steadily, without understanding or love.

"As far back as I can remember he bit her ears; and he continued to bite them until she was almost a grown woman. He sometimes bit the ears of other girls, if they would let him—even of baby girls. I must admit in fairness to him that it is the only erotic gesture toward the other sex I ever saw him make. He liked female ears. I say erotic gesture. Do you understand what my father really wanted to bite?"

Neloa's eyes wavered a little. He thought she drew a deeper breath.

"I won't tell you," Vridar said. "You wouldn't believe it. Like most people you will believe nothing that shocks you. As for me I've taken to heart what Huxley wrote to Kingsley: Follow humbly, and to whatever abyss Nature leads, or you shall learn nothing. I have taken to heart what a high school teacher told me, one morning when I was out of my mind: Read the greatest books and follow them. Until we learn to accept the truths that outrage us, we may as well stand in barn stanchions with the cows and bulls."

He searched through his notes a few moments and suddenly looked up with the smile that always startled her: she did not know and was never to know that it was only a smile for his own ignorance and follies. "A strange thing about people like you," he said, "is that the truth shocks you, but you like privy legends in which vulgar minds try to hide it. Can you imagine which of all the things you ever said shocked me most?"

373

"No," she said at last.

"You once said to me, with pride, that you didn't think any person in the world knew more dirty stories than you knew. That was a hell of a thing for lilies and roses to say. Can you see how funny it is? You'd think me quite a guy if I'd swap dirty stories with you and laugh over them, but the first time I put a hand on your genitals you were shocked. You said the other men never did that. Have you any idea what I thought the first time I embraced you?"

"No," she said.

"I thought of the remark by a woman in a Stendhal novel. What, she asked herself with astonishment, is love no more than this? Why, then, do they condemn it! She looked at her lover and burst with laughter and said, What!—this famous love, is it no more than that? You think that a rather indecent remark, don't you?" He waited. "Tell me, do you?"

"Yes," she said.

Vridar's laugh was low and mirthless. "You see nothing funny in it?"

"No."

"How strange that we should have married, whose minds are so far apart! I'll try again. Macaulay said that the Puritans suppressed bull-baiting not because it gave pain to the bull but pleasure to the Christians. You see anything amusing in that?"

After a few moments she said, "No."

"I think it delightful. Well, I'll try again, for there must be something in the world that we'll both think amusing. Montaigne tells of a fastidious criminal on the scaffold who refused to share a cup with the hangman lest he get the pox. In Antelope they call it the clap. Does that amuse you at all?" There was no reply, only the strange unwavering stare. "Neloa?"

"Yes?" she said softly.

"Damn it, I'll try once more. There is a story told of Saint Perpetua, who was gored by a bull. It says that even when dying she instinctively drew her dress together to cover her nakedness. Does that amuse you at all?"

"No."

"It doesn't amuse you at all that for twenty years my father insisted on biting his daughter's ear?"

"No."

"Have you any idea what the ear was a symbol of for him?"

She gave no reply. He expected none. Her eyes held that wariness of him which had become a part of her. For the past hour there had been no movement in her, save in her lips when she spoke, in her eyes when she blinked. Her hands were together in her lap, her beautiful tapering hands, the most beautiful hands he had ever seen. Her knees and her feet were together. They were living in an attic with only a skylight, and she was sitting so that the light fell on her face. Vridar was at a rickety table, with piles of notes and books before him.

"How strange that we married," he said again. "It was my doing. How strange that we know so little about one another—for we lie in one another's arms in man-woman intimacy, we share the same two dismal dirty rooms, we intend to have children. You think we'll ever really be husband and wife?"

"We are now," she said.

"Only legally. No, we haven't a marriage yet. Anatole France says that knowledge of oneself is a source of worry, unrest and torture: since I'm determined on it, I don't suppose I'll ever be much of a husband. I have been such a fool, such a blind ignorant incredible fool, that I must find knowledge of self, or I'll always be a fool." He turned over some note cards and said, "Chesterfield has made what seems to me to be a profound observation. I'd like to know what you think of it. He says search every person for that ruling passion to which all other passions are subordinate. Use that ruling passion, he says, to enforce your will over other people, but never trust them where that passion is concerned. The ruling passion with some, it is said, is greed; with some, fame; with some, social position or power." He met her eyes. "What is your ruling passion?"

"I don't know," she said.

"A wish to have many men interested in you? The other evening we went to a dance and I left you a moment, asking you to wait; and when I returned you were dancing with a tall stranger. We had a bitter quarrel and again I made a fool of myself. In Swan Valley I left you a few moments, after you had promised to dance only with me, and returned to find you dancing. Is men your ruling passion?"

With a trace of anger she said, "No."

"An English novelist has said that the most exquisite torture is doubt of those we love. Must I always doubt you?"

"Of course not."

"Then why, when I leave you a moment, do you so quickly turn to another man?"

"I don't."

"Like hell you don't. You always have and I'm beginning to think you always will." He looked into her eyes and asked: "Has my brother approached you yet?"

"No."

"No?" he said, wondering about it. "You'd not tell me if he had. Well, as nearly as I can figure you out, your ruling passion is men. What is mine? It isn't women. A wish to be famous? To rise above my uncouth ignorant background? . . . . Or is ·
it you?"

"It's not me," she said. "You love books more than me."

"I love you and books in a different way—one with my heart, one with my head. If your passion is to be men and mine books—well, I'm telling you, Neloa, a man and a woman can't build a marriage on that."

Her eyes flashed. "Men aren't my passion."

"Books aren't," he said.

"I read books."

"Yes, darling, you're going to high school and you do read a little, the way a child takes castor oil. You—" He broke off. He had seen her stiffen. He saw the look in her eyes that warned him of explosive passions just under the surface.

"You forget," she said, her voice cold with hate of him, "that you're way ahead of me. You're a junior in college and I'm only a sophomore in high school. But you expect me to know as much as you do."

"Not that," he said, gently, feeling it a waste of time to talk to her about books; feeling pain that she should try to read, without deep hunger for learning to guide her; feeling above all that he was mean and unworthy to press upon her matters in which her interest was superficial. "It's not what a person knows but what knowledge means to him. In my notes here someone says that very few people will accept knowledge that outrages their self-esteem. It's that kind I seek most.

"I'll give you an instance," he said, looking with compassion at the uneasiness in her eyes. "Balzac said that he had never had a mother. In the sense in which he meant it, I never had one either. I never had a mother's tenderness in my early years. Not once," he said with passion, "not once! Lack of a mother's tenderness did something to me. But this is the thing I want to tell you. Goethe, it is said, could not be intimate with any woman he respected: I don't know if I could have been with you, before you made your confession. I've seen in your eyes the contempt you feel for me. I seem to be," he said, with a twisted smile of self-loathing, "what psychologists call a psychic impotent. What a confession for a man to make to a wife! But let me tell you this, that I'll not always be what I am now, and if you are content to be what you are now, we'd better not have children, for our marriage won't endure.

"To go on with the confession. Psychologists say that frustrated sexual desires can lead to sadism—that is, to cruelty—toward the one loved. That may be why at times I have been brutal with you." He studied her a few moments. "Do you get any sense out of what I am saying? Do you," he asked with sudden passion, "know what shameful things I'm confessing to you? Does it do anything to explain to you why I must hate you, if when I leave you for a moment you must turn to the first man who approaches? Do you understand why I must have knowledge of myself or go mad?—and that I must be able to trust you or I shall have to leave you?"

She was looking at him steadily. He did not miss the triumph in her voice when she said, "I'm not abnormal like you."

"Good God no! You're not! I suppose it's normal to be proud of knowing a lot of filthy stories."

"All girls know such stories. Men too."

"You must except one," he said, "the miserable no-good fool who married you."

"You'd know them if you wasn't abnormal."

Her words astonished him. He stared at her, wondering if there was truth in what she said. "You mean it's normal to smear with filth what should not be filthy?"

"Most people do."

"Yes," he said, fenced in by her logic, "most people do. Most Christians. I'm abnormal because I don't like the odor of a cormorant's vomit. I'm abnormal because I can't get my thing up the moment a woman offers herself. I'm the guy who thought you were lilies and roses. I'm the guy," he said, his bitterness growing, "who would have bet my life that you were my dream of you. I'm that in-

376

credible blockhead. But I'm also the one who will understand a lot of things before I die, including the reason people smear love with filth."

She had had her moment of passion and now looked a little abashed. Whatever her faults, he knew that she had fire and spirit, and courage in a crisis. He admired her for that. She would fight back, but she would never know how to fight one with his cunning and adroitness. Or would she? He was looking into her eyes, studying her mood. He forced a smile and said, "Sir John Harrington has left it on record that it is better to love two too many than one too few. I may have to agree with Sir John some day. Tell me this, how many men of the kind who attract you would you like to go to bed with before you are old?"

"Just you."

"You lie. Montaigne said that nobody who hasn't a good memory should ever take on the trade of lying. The terrible thing about you, Neloa, is that you don't know when you're lying."

"You mean you want a lot of women?"

"All bulls and studs want a lot of females, but being abnormal I'll be content with one. When I become normal—"

"You never will."

"You mean I'll never be able to take a woman who offers herself?"

"No."

"What do you mean by no?—that I won't? But can you live with that kind of man?"

"Yes."

"Is it because I force you to an orgasm and the other men didn't? But to hell with saying bitter things. Let us understand one another, before children come. Let us talk to one another out of our hearts and souls—as when I say, you were brought up on a farm, you saw it, you saw men tear the testicles out of animals. I had a lot of terrible experiences in my childhood but none, I think, that went into me deeper than that one. What did *you* see? You saw your father and brothers out in the corral throwing the bulls down. You heard the agony of the beasts under the branding iron and the saw. And you thought, They're branding and dehorning and castrating today. I thought, My father has that look in his face again; he likes to do this, for some dark ugly reason. Did you suffer because it was done? I suffered horribly. I had nightmares about it. I would slip out after the bloody brutal butchery was over and look at the poor wretched things. Castration isn't such an ordeal for a small calf, but for some reason my father, like so many farmers, let the bull calves get big before he took them, and those big castrated bulls, some of them two years old, are with me yet—the terrible sadness of their eyes, the pools of blood under their belly where they stood, the empty bloody dripping pouches—and their ghastly heads from which the big horns had been sawed off—and the huge black brands burned almost through their hides. The sight of it, the smell of it! It made me sick and furious and it made me hate brutality as I hate nothing else in this world.

"All that," he said, looking all the while into her eyes, "is not the worst of it, with me. I felt that I'd been castrated. For days I felt the pain in my loins and for

377

days I moved in their slow stiff tortured way; for I felt dehorned and branded and unmanned, yes, and sick, sick! This must sound pretty silly to you: I can see by the look in your eyes that it does. You're thinking again that I'm abnormal—and if hatred of brutality is abnormal I certainly am."

He was silent a few moments, feeling again the sickness of childhood. Then: "But all that only leads up to what I wanted to say. Freud seems to think that psychic impotence in the male is fear of the father because of incestuous interest in the mother. That's not always the case. How could I have had any incestuous interest in a mother who never once gave me a tender moment? In my sister but not my mother.

"Here's another shameful part of it. When I was a small boy, the school bullies often threw me down and threatened to castrate me. And Jed Bridwell. I went mad and blind with fear. I sometimes was so sure I'd been castrated that for days I didn't dare look at myself. I thought I'd see blood and an empty pouch. I felt the pain I had felt when looking at the bulls."

He saw now in her eyes the strange and wordless wondering about him.

"I don't pretend to understand these things, not yet. I'm no Freud. I'm only an absurd ass from the Antelope hills. But I'll understand some day. I'll read my eyes out, I'll work my brain into powder. I suppose you'll wish all the while that I was more like other men, who know what to do with a woman when they get one in their arms, and what a woman wants done with her. Not," he said, with a dry smile, "that I don't like it. My mother tried to make a monk of me, and if she had, I'd have been a Rasputin. I like it—I like it more than you like it, and you liked it well enough. I intend to like it as long as the passion is in me. Have you ever felt I'm not a man that way?"

She hesitated. She made a strange movement, and then said something that astonished him. "You're not like the other men," she said.

He stared at her. "How do you mean?" It took him many minutes to drag the confessions from her—that he put his hand on her *there,* and the other men had not; that he had kissed her in her pubic hair and down her thighs and up her spine— and the other men had not. He could tell that she felt these were shameful things to do: never would he fully understand the peasant's nature in this matter until he read the Kinsey reports.

He was flabbergasted. A little humiliated and angered, he said bitterly, "How strange that a woman can foul her mouth with filthy stories, yet think a man's hand on her vulva is an abnormal thing! How much I have to learn!—about you and about me." He forced a laugh and stood up, and looked down at his notes and the books—a Stendhal novel, Freud on dreams, Chesterfield's letters, a volume of the Cambridge history of English literature, Keats, a book on anthropology. Trying to speak like a reasonable and self-disciplined man, which he knew he was not, he said, "We must persevere in our efforts to understand one another. If you see the sexual act at the simple level of beasts I must learn to live with it: I'll try to be more normal if you'll try to be more abnormal. I'll even go out for football. I mean I'll look at you with a bedroom look if you try to understand Radcliffe's statement that it is the first proof of a superior mind to liberate itself from the prejudices of country and education." He broke off, feeling that he might as well talk to a woman under hypnosis. While he was looking at her she said,

"I don't have a superior mind."

"I may have none either." He shrugged. He smiled at her and said, "In one of his novels Hardy says that a woman who arouses a young man's passions just when he is trying to shine intellectually is a criminal. Are you a criminal?"

He had driven her too far. She drew a sharp breath and looked at him hard, her eyes narrowing; and with an obvious effort she said, "All right, why don't you play football?"

He sank to a chair. "Football? You mean I should go out with the muscled morons?"

"They're not morons. They're good-looking."

He wanted to laugh at her absurd non sequitur but he was stung. "Why should I play football?"

"Other men do."

"A few of them. You mean I should do what other men do. Thoreau said that the head monkey in Paris puts on a traveler's cap and every monkey in the United States follows suit. Why should I play football?"

"Just because."

"Because dull women throw themselves at football players? You mean I should be a hero? Or what do you mean?"

"That you should be more like other men."

Looking at her he was silent. The implication in her words stung him but he tried to hide from her his hurt. He tried to speak quietly when he said, "More like other men. More muscle, you mean, and less brains. Would you rather have a football player than a writer?"

"No."

"All right," he said, ominously quiet, "I'll play football. I don't think I've ever had hold of a football, but I'll make the team or break my neck. Then you'll admire me. You'll say, My husband hates books but he can kick a punt sixty yards. As though I ever could! You'll say—"

"I won't."

"Then why do you want me to play?"

"I didn't say I did."

"You asked why I don't play football."

"I just asked."

"And I know why. You don't think I have the muscles or the grit."

"You do have."

"I don't have the killer instinct. I don't have—"

"I didn't say it."

"All right, by God, I'll play football. Do you believe it?" He stood again. He saw her look at the clock. He looked at the clock and then laid out a sheet of paper, and taking up a pencil said, "Let's make up the all-time football team. We'll put Newton at center because he knew a lot about gravity. For guards—let's take Keats and Beethoven, big husky brutal titans, almost five feet tall. For the tackles, the bone-crushers and killers, we'll take Shelley and Swinburne. God, what a pair of assassins! Shelley was built like a stork, and Swinburne weighed a hundred pounds with his overcoat on. For the ends, those fleet ball-snatchers, we'll take Byron with his club foot, and Alexander Pope with his hunchback. There's our line," he said, looking at the names. "Imagine how that line would run over the Army!"

He turned to her, smiling. "Now for the backfield. Shakespeare had a nimble mind, so let's stick him in at quarterback. The halves? How about Socrates and Dante? They were big muscled blowhards — almost as big as Swinburne and as fast as Byron. For fullback? Do you have any suggestions? The fullback must be the bone-crusher of the outfit—as big as Keats anyway—a monstrous fellow only nine inches shorter than you. Musset? He was such a gargantua that he sat on George Sand's lap. Or Balzac, who could run a hundred yards in four minutes. I tell you the man! Bernard Shaw, with his thighs like oak beams and a chest of boiler plate. What a fullback! Lord God, can you see that team running over Harvard? Do you like it?"

"No."

"Too much muscle for you?" He went to a small mirror under a dim light. He did not like his face and had never liked it and would never like it. He now stared at it, trying to imagine it as the face of a football player. It was a long narrow face; it had a big strong nose and a strong chin, the chin of his mother and her people. "If I were a half-back," he said, "my nose alone could open a hole in the line for Shaw." He had the Branton mouth and he did not like his mouth: it was too small, and so earnest and dedicated that it wearied him to look at it. He looked into his eyes and saw amusement and cunning in the depths of mellow brown credulity. He did not like his eyes, though Neloa's mother said he had the most beautiful eyes she had ever seen.

"I look like a football player," he said. "I have a strong brutal face, a low forehead, wide unbreakable jaws. I'm the guy for line-bucks." He looked down at his hands. They were small, with short fingers: he detested them. "I've the hands for passing," he said, "for I can reach halfway around the ball. Have you ever noticed my shoulders?—as deeply muscled as a bull's, with bands across my chest like Swedish steel. I've the mighty arms of a Shelley, the thighs of Bernard Shaw—and twice his mind. I've the muscular belly of a Balzac. I'll be the all-conference choice," he said, glancing round at her. "I'll be invited into a fraternity, and the sorority girls will swarm around me, begging to be seduced. Newspaper headlines will say, Vreed Hunter, the greatest halfback since Lars Ongin of Chicago minced the army line, plunging for a total of nine thousand six hundred yards, and completing eight hundred and twenty passes of eight hundred and sixteen tries!"

With a last contemptuous look at his image, he went to the table and sat before his notes. Neloa had not moved. She was still looking at him with wordless things in her eyes, like one both horrified and fascinated. He picked up a card and read it and turned to her. "Schopenhauer said that innocence is in its very nature stupid. Cain, who acquired a knowledge of guilt, and through guilt a knowledge of virtue, and so came to understand the meaning of life, is a tragic figure more significant and more respectable than all the innocent fools in the world put together. What a tackle he would have made! Not Cain, Schopenhauer."

Suddenly he went over and knelt at his wife's feet, and drawing her dress up and her stockings down kissed her thighs. After a few moments he felt her trembling under his hands. He looked up and saw a light coming into her eyes that thrilled him like violins, and he wondered if it also shone for other men. "My heart aches and a drowsy numbness pains . . . . Neloa darling, try to understand me . . . to indulge me a little .. . to be compassionate while I grow up; and I'll try to understand you, I'll love and cherish you, I'll be husband, lover, and guide; and some day perhaps what is best in both of us will rise under the ministering of gentle hands, and the understanding in gentle eyes. For I love you, I love you! . . . ."

He arose and kissed the tears away from her eyes and drew her to the bed.

II

Vridar decided that he had not been bluffing. The next afternoon he went to the coach and asked for a football suit. Where had he played football? Ongin asked; and when Vridar said that he had never played, had never even had hold of a football, Ongin looked at him with open astonishment. "How much do you weigh?" "One fifty-six stripped." "You're pretty light," Lars Ongin said. Vridar knew what a preposterous figure he made, but when he set out to do a thing he gave to it all his heart and mind, all his will and courage. He did not think for a moment that he would make the first team, or even be a sub in a waiting squad; but Neloa had challenged him and he would do his best. He felt gawky and stupid as he struggled into the uniform, fumbling with pads and laces and buckles. He felt even more ridiculous out on the field.

Football players were muscular giants but what was he?—weighing a little over a hundred and fifty pounds stripped! The other men, it seemed to him, were fleet, powerful, and self-assured: he was awkward, self-effacing, and self-conscious. Lars Ongin, the coach, an all-American halfback at Chicago, was big, profane, aggressive; he could punt seventy yards, he could run a hundred yards in ten seconds, and for Vridar he was superb and overwhelming. My God, Vridar thought, watching the other men kick, pass, and run, what am I doing out here! He fumbled the ball when it was thrown to him and was unable to throw it back because his hand was too small to clasp it firmly. In scrimmage he tried to tackle a man and missed by five yards. In the line, bent over, one hand on the earth, he felt gawky and absurd, and he wondered why in heaven's name he had been fool enough to forsake scholarship and books.

In the dressing-room and showers he suffered the worst anguish. His underwear was ragged, his other clothes were shabby; he went into hiding to undress and he undressed with furious haste and he tried to take his shower where nobody could see him. Here, as on the field, other players stared at him with open astonishment, as though wondering where he had come from and where he had got the gall to fancy himself as an athlete. The all-conference end slammed a hand against his belly and said, "Pull your gut in." The coach said, "What in hell do you think a football is? Are you afraid of it?"

But contempt only made him fight all the harder. He was out to win or die and most of the time he wished he might die—as when Ongin roared at him, "God damn it, when you tackle a man make his ribs stick out like a picket fence!" He made a line on the earth. "Get back there and when you leave that line leave the earth and when you come down be sure I'm under you." Vridar went thirty yards down the field and turned and ran. He leapt when he struck the line and came down on his head. "Suffering Christ!" said Ongin. "I could jump farther than that before they took my diapers off! Get back there and this time bring me down. Kill me." Going back down the field Vridar thought, I hope to God I can! He gathered all his strength and fury. He ran and leapt from the line and brought Ongin down, trying at the same moment to drive a knee into the man's ribs.

Ongin got up and grinned. "That's better. When you tackle a man put him out. There will be somebody to carry him off the field."

A week later Ongin called all the men before him and walked back and forth, his cruel brown eyes studying their faces. He glanced at Vridar a time or two and at last fixed his gaze on him. "Hunter," he said, "you look like a fighter even if you play like an old woman. Take the ball." Vridar took the ball. That he made the first team and during the whole season was never assigned to the benches or taken out of a game he was always to look back on as one of the riddles of his life.

He grieved over so many afternoons spent away from books, but he learned much from his weeks in football. He learned the spirit of give and take, of which he had so little; he learned to keep his furious temper in check; and he learned that this game, so dear to the American heart, had little of the sportsmanship which it was supposed to have. He was astonished to learn that it employed all kinds of mean and stealthy tricks.

Early in the season his team opposed a squad from a near-by fort. The man who faced Vridar at center was a huge raw-boned army sergeant with yellow eyebrows, stained teeth, and an evil grin. The man chewed tobacco and squirted the juice over Vridar. He said, "Does your mother know where you are?" He said, "Kid, if you go over me again I'll jerk your cock down and stand on it." Ongin had told Vridar to drop and block on defensive, and on offensive to go over his opponent if he could. When he fell to his knee to block, the army center in going over him would kick at his face; and when Vridar tried to go over his opponent he could feel the man's hands clutching at his genitals. "The son of a bitch," Vridar said to his captain, "is trying to castrate me!" Dick Hortell, all-conference end, said quietly, "Keep your temper. We'll take care of him soon."

Then it came. Bob Glauber, all-conference fullback, struck the army center in his teeth and laid him out cold. Down from the stands came hundreds of soldiers, howling for vengeance. Vridar and his teammates were mobbed and one of the men was taken to a hospital. Later, tweaking his bloodied nose, Vridar said to Neloa: "That's football for you. Only the coach and the players know what it is like."

His team went to Colorado to play against teams there. Again Vridar was faced by a giant who tried to frighten him with ridcule, and though he was not frightened he was confused. At a critical moment he fumbled the ball on a long lateral pass and it was recovered by an opponent and carried to a touchdown, with Vridar in wild and futile pursuit. Between the halves Ongin addressed himself to Vridar. "God damn it, Hunter, did someone have his finger in your eye? Or were you playing with yourself?"

"He bothers me," said Vridar stupidly.

"If he bothers you, kill him! Break his neck!" Ongin swung to his quarterback. "Hotchkiss, what in hell were you doing? You handle the ball like a girl with her first penis." He looked Hotchkiss up and down and at last said with crushing scorn: "You have been breaking training rules. Your pubic hair is wet." Then he spoke to the eleven men. "You all run around today like a bunch of old women. Jim, take that end out. Kill him. You, Noral, stop tackling as if you had your arms around a woman. Mawry, they open a hole through you big enough for the Chicago fair. God damn it, if you're not football players turn in your suits! Go back and tear their guts out! . . . ." The men stood up, looking very resolute, and trotted back to the field. They smashed the line and boxed up the flanks and made two touchdowns on a faked reverse. Vridar, plotting to put the big center on the benches, drove into him on interference and stretched him prone on a foul play. His captain came over and patted him on the back.

It was in the final game of the season that he learned how stealthy and ruthless football could be. They played their traditional enemy, another Utah team. The tripple-threat man on this team was a Jew, an all-conference quarterback, and a superb open-field runner. Ongin said, "Put Cohen out. Put him out quick." To Glauber, their big fullback, was given the task of putting Cohen out.

During the first quarter Glauber tackled Cohen again and again, but that elusive Jew was like rubber. The coach was alarmed. He called the captain over and the captain then went to Glauber and said, "What in hell is the matter?" Glauber said, "I don't know. I give him all I have." Then it happened. Cohen tackled Glauber and Glauber lay like a dead man. The game was lost, thirty-one to seven. In the dressing-room Vridar wept. All the men wept but Dick Hortell. The coach went outside and smoked a cigarette. He said later that Glauber was knocked out because he had broken training rules: he had been smoking and he had been wenching.

But football was not all stealthy treacheries, unobserved by the spectators. There was heroism in it; there was the stern discipline of emotions and mind; there was drama and glory. Though it seemed to Vridar that he was the weakest man on the team, he walked with new pride. Without experience, without anything but grit and perseverance, he had made the first team and played the season through. "You wanted me to play football," he said to Neloa. "Are you proud of me now?" She was not. She had never lived in a city, where men are often sallow and weak; she did not have the city woman's interest in big men with mighty hands. She did not understand women who adored fullbacks and bull-fighters. Only once did she go to watch him play, but she eagerly accepted him as a lover, though aware that the coach had ordered his men not to touch a woman during the season.

For Vridar each game was a bursting glory. When he and his mates trotted to the field and the spectators stood in a vast cheering multitude and the fighting music

383

of a band rolled over the stadium, his heart almost went out of him. He would look at a hillside of faces to the west, to the east, and feel that to be all-conference would be almost as good as to be Shakespeare. He tried to think of himself as a mighty one, but all his playing, save in one game, was feeble and obscure and no oceans of humanity shouted his name. In this exception he faced a timid opponent and floored him, and again and again threw the ball-carrier for a loss. Again the captain patted his shoulder. The coach shook his hand.

But he knew that all his teammates save one held him in contempt. On a journey to Colorado an arrogant halfback looked at Vridar's silly cap and said, "Where did you get it?" and threw it out the window. Sweating with shame, Vridar looked at the men more closely to see what they wore. He had not known that they all wore hats but him. If given five dollars he would have bought a book instead of a hat. The contempt made him conscious not only of his shabby garments but also of himself as a social outcast. Because he was a football man, he was stared at in the classrooms and on the campus, and scorn made him for a little while a social coward. He left his proud and wretched isolation and became a fraternity man.

In this college most of the fraternities and sororities were locals and the difference between them and the few nationals was that between the sun and the moon. The nationals admitted only the choicest aristocrats. The Sigma Chis were the athletic monarchs; the Pi Kaps were the princes of scholarship and scribbling; and the Phi Delts were lords of the gardenia and dress suit. Among the sororities there was only one national: its members were chiefly daughters of prominent and wealthy Mormons.

When he was invited to a fraternity house, he went and he was pledged and he felt pretty silly about it, not because he had to run petty errands and polish shoes and do stupid things, no, but because of the undisguised malice and sadism in those who ordered him around. "Shine them shoes, Hunter! You gotta learn spirit." The initiation amazed him. He entered a sepulchral chamber hung with crepe and wanly lighted by candles. The assembled brothers were so solemn that Vridar, looking at them, wanted to laugh. Mawry, the president, usually so friendly and whimsical, now stood by a sputtering candle and looked as grave as an owl. Vridar looked at two other pledges and saw that they were deeply affected, as though they had entered Rosicrucian corridors or the catacombs of the dead. Vridar wanted with one infernal laugh to shatter the monkey business but he only grinned.

In this gloomy crypt the secret rites were performed. Like one talking for God Mawry imparted to Vridar the dreadful and holy secrets, his tone sounding spectral as if his lungs were a vault. Vridar thought he seemed to be peering at his nostrils, like one who saw live things crawling there; and while the farce was solemnized Vridar was convulsed within, never having known before that men could dwell on childish ritual with such preposterous earnestness. When he was asked to repeat the oath of allegiance and brotherhood, the mirth within made him shake. "I do solemnly vow and promise that I will hold sacred . . . ." The oath was given and pledged and Vridar was then taught the handclasp, an intricate piece of nonsense of interlocking fingers and thumbs. Masking his mirth, Vridar asked gravely, "If a brother lost his right hand how would he recognize another brother?"

"In our secret archives," said Mawry, "it will tell."

"How often are we supposed to shake hands this way?"

"When a brother meets a brother."

"If I meet a stranger am I to shake to learn if he's a brother?"

"No. If he says he is you shake hands to find out. Then you speak a word. If he answers with the right word—"

"What word?"

Mawry looked round him as if for spies. "The word," he wispered, like one imparting the profoundest secret of life, "is ylang-karma-ylang."

"What does it mean?"

"It means the inseparable bonds of brotherhood."

Vridar was then ushered from the ritual chamber into a spacious room. The master of ceremonies there was Bill Oaks, a sturdily dull fellow with malicious eyes. "Get them duds off," said Bill. Vridar and his brothers-in-the-making undressed. At one end of the room was a table and on the table were twenty beans. Across the room the brothers formed a double line, each one grasping a stout slat.

"See them beans?" said Bill to Vridar. "Each time you carry a bean we get a swat at you. We're going to learn you some spirit."

Vridar drew a deep breath and, remembering the admonition of the teammate, drew his gut in. Naked, he ran between the lines to the table and every man on either side struck him with a board. The men howled and fought for advantage, and in his eagerness one brother struck another on his chin. Before Vridar was done with this weird flogging, his breath was like flame in his throat and there was blood on his back and rump. My God! he thought, wondering how men could talk brotherhood in one moment and flog you in the next.

He went to another room and could hear the slap of boards and the shouts of glee. Then suddenly there was silence. Looking back into the room, he saw that one of the pledges, a frail youth, had fainted. What was it in men that impelled them to such devilish cruelty? This, it seemed to Vridar, was the spirit of the Crusades, when armies raped and mutilated and murdered in the name of Jesus. This was related to witch-baiting, lynching, and third-degrees. In a dark and awful way there was something sexual at its source. If he could have found his clothes and dressed, he would have sneaked out and gone home.

He was now initiated into the third act. Oaks placed a chair by a wall and told Vridar to stand on the chair. "Stick your hands straight up and turn your mug to the wall. You're gonna sing. And when I say change, change your tune."

"And what if I don't?" asked Vridar, looking round at Oaks.

"Then you get a pop with this club."

"All right . . . . ready . . . . GO!"

"Ohh my darr-ling Nellie Gray
 they have tak-en you awaaay—"

"Change!"

"Be it evv-ver so hummm-bull
 there's noohh-oh place like hohmmm—"

"Change!"

"The sunn shines bright on my ohhhld Ken-tuck—"

"Change!"

Vridar looked round. "I don't know any more songs."

"Sing!"

"Twen-tee frog-gees went to school
  um-tum tum-tum tum-tum pool!
  Twen-tee—"

"Hey, for Christ sake, cut out that um-tumming! Sing!"

"I don't know any more!" said Vridar angrily.

Oaks clubbed him with the slat. "Sing!"

"I tell you I don't know any more!"

"Sing," bellowed Oaks, "or I'll knock your ass off!"

"That'll do," said Mawry quietly.

"He don't have the right spirit," said Oaks. "We gotta learn him spirit."

In the fourth act of this fraternal drama Vridar was hobbled to the frail youth. Boxing gloves were laced on their hands. The one who got knocked down, Oaks said, would be shoved into a tub of water and ice. "And let's have no damn girlish slapping and clawing. Drive from the shoulder and hit to kill."

Vridar looked at the pale and frightened young man facing him. What a pity, he thought, to knock him down! In a whisper he said, "Go on, knock me over."

"Here, you!" Oaks roared. Aggrieved, he turned to Mawry. "I tell you he ain't got no spirit!"

"Go on and fight," said Mawry. "It won't kill you."

Vridar studied his opponent. The youth's legs were shaking. His eyes were frightened and beseeching. Thrusting a glove at the youth's face, Vridar pushed him over, and he went down willingly, as if preferring ice to blows. A huge bathtub was half-filled with water in which floated snow and chunks of ice. Into this the youth was thrown headfirst and shoved under, and when the snow closed over him he screamed. Gurgling and blowing snow, he came up and was shoved under and held under, and frantic breath spouted from the water and made dancing eddies of the snow. Then he was dragged out like a hog from a barrel and set on his shaking legs. "Gosh!" he gasped, pawing snow from his hair and face.

An hour later in his clothes Vridar walked from room to room, his flesh burning, and Oaks followed him. "Why don't you set down?" asked Oaks, grinning.

When alone with Neloa Vridar dug into his piles of notes and said, "It reminds me of the curse laid on Spinoza. Listen. By the sentence of the angels, by the decree of the saints, we anathematize, cut off, curse, and execrate Baruch Spinoza, in the presence of these sacred books with the six hundred and thirteen precepts written therein, with the anathema wherewith Joshua anathematized Jericho; with the cursing wherewith Elisha—or was it Elijah?—I think I have an error there—cursed the children and with all the cursings that are written in the Book of Law: cursed be he by day, and cursed by night; cursed when he lieth down, and cursed when he riseth up; cursed when he goeth out, and cursed when he cometh in; the Lord pardon him never; the wrath and fury of the Lord burn upon this man, and bring upon him all the curses which are written in the Book of the Law. The Lord blot out his name under heaven. The Lord set him apart for destruction from all the tribes of Israel, with all the curses of the firmament which are written in the Book of this Law. There will be no man speak to him, no man write to him, no man show him any kindness, no man stay under the same roof with him, no man come nigh him." He looked over at Neloa. "That is the way the Jews of the Portuguese synagogue at Amsterdam in 1656 took leave of great and kind and wise Spinoza." In her eyes he saw that strange uncertainty, that baffled bewilderment, which was always there when he spoke with anger and bitterness. He turned through his notes and read again: "Whenever we read the obscure stories, the voluptuous debaucheries, the crime and tortuous executions, the unrelenting vindictiveness, with which more than half the Bible is filled, it would be more consistent that we called it the work of a demon, than the word of God. It is a history of wickedness that has served to corrupt and brutalize mankind; and for my part I sincerely detest it, as I detest everything that is cruel. Thus spoke that great man Tom Paine. Shall I read more?"

"No," she said.

"The initiation reminded me of such things. I want to know why men delight in being brutal to one another. It is not so with other animals except when they fight for females. Is it because men are no longer allowed to fight for females?"

"I don't know," she said, the strangeness in her eyes deepening.

Vridar remained in the fraternity less than a month. To the parties he was told to wear formal clothes and to bring a sorority girl. "That's for prestige," Bill Oaks said. "If you bring a non-sorority girl it will look like hell. It will look like we got no prestige." And Vridar was asked to investigate a prospective pledge.

"If Lincoln were a student here, would you pledge him?"

Bill grinned. "You can't figger every guy with sawdust in his hair is gonna be president. Hunter, you don't have the frat spirit."

"I never will have."

"Then get out."

"I intend to."

But first he talked with his friend Dave Roth, a brilliant and cynical Jew. Dave was a fraternal brother.

"Why," Vridar asked, "did you join a frat?"

"In American colleges and universities," said Dave, "Jews are social outcasts. Socially we are hyperconscious. For centuries we've been kicked around as if we were a football and the world was a stadium. Had you heard?"

"Yes," said Vridar, looking at the bitterness in Dave's face.

"In the Christian world every Jew has to be a Machiavelli. No doubt if the western world were less Christian we'd be less persecuted." Dave's smile was sardonic. "So my philosophy, Vridar, is this: I take what I can and give as little as I can. Being in a frat makes it easier for me to get along. I can go to social parties. Now and then a Christian smiles at me. And that," he said, flicking ash from his cigarette, "is manna to a Jew. Of course we gave you the Bible and Jesus—but not the Inquisition or Mormons. You'll have to settle with God on those."

"I'm not a Christian," Vridar said.

"Oh yes you are. Religion is like smallpox, you wear scars."

"Well, I'm going to leave the frat."

"All right, you don't need it; but for me it's like a pessary, it has its uses. I can have some fun without having to marry the damned thing."

The next day Vridar went to Mawry. "I want to be kicked out," he said.

"No," said Mawry, shaking his head sadly. "Listen, we're about to make a national."

"So you can be national prigs instead of local prigs."

"Vridar, it's like Bill says, you don't have the right spirit."

"I never will have. And, Mawry, I'm really as sorry as hell. I just didn't know what I was getting into. I was a fool to join and I'm sorry to embarrass you."

"Be honest," said Mawry. "What's your real reason?"

"I've told you. I simply don't believe in what fraternities and sororities stand for. And you couldn't give me the right spirit, as you call it, if you worked on me a thousand years. My people are common people. They work hard and are fairly honest and that's about all. I don't want to stand socially above anyone. I don't feel right about it. I feel silly and stupid. You know Austen's Mrs. Hale? She was captivated by some old lace a Mrs. Thorton wore because it showed she had ancestors. Tiberius said a great man is his own ancestors. I shall try to be mine."

"My God!" said Mawry, appalled. "You're really stuck up."

"No, just so close to the bottom that I must climb."

"All right," said Mawry, "we'll kick you out."

III

"That's it," Vridar said to Neloa. "I'm so close to the bottom that the only way for me is up. And what a damned fool I've been to neglect my studies for a stadium and a fraternity's social posturings! I'm going to the library to get an armful of the best that has been said and thought."

While crossing the campus he felt wretchedly self-conscious. Only Dave of his former fraternal brothers now spoke to him. And other students, having heard of his expulsion, looked at him with contempt, as though he had been a traitor to country or God. He had indeed become a social outcast and he suffered under the scorn. One personality of the two that possessed him was like a bewildered child: it saw and heard and recoiled, not knowing what the crime had been. The other, the ruthless and vengeful part of him, looked at scorn with scorn and said to Neloa, "I will climb, for there is no way but up." And Neloa looked at him as she always did, as though he were perverse and impetuous and childish. His cyclonic furies left her confused and frightened. He cursed so many things now. He cursed the exploiters who, he said, sat at home stuffing their purses while young men went to France to die. He was bitter toward his teachers; they talked of loyalty and progress and truth but their words seemed to him as empty as teacups turned bottomside up. Sometimes when bitterness overwhelmed him he would clown.

"Brown got stuck in sentiment today. I'll show you what he did." Vridar stood behind a chair and said the chair was his desk. "You're the students," he said to her. "I'll tell you what he said. Listen. If any one of you is to be married in June I'll give

388

you an A. There's nothing I'd rather give an A for. Let me tell you the story of a young man. He was a simple honest fellow, ambitious and humble and proud. There came into his life a blackeyed lass. They had been childhood sweethearts. She became his inspiration, his philosopher and friend. At this point," Vridar observed, "he lifted a few metaphors from Wordsworth. This girl inspired him to noble endeavor. She stood behind him, a simple girlish creature, yet a pillar of strength. In his senior year he led her to the altar. In June she became his bride. That meant more in this young man's life than books and philosophies and the eternal verities. That is what education meant to him: a blackeyed girl in gingham who looked at the stars and charted his course. And then? This proud and humble genius who married the blackeyed lass is now the dull humorless hack who pretends to teach and who gives A's to the brides and bridegrooms. And can you guess why he does it?"

"He believes in marriage," said Neloa.

"No. That's what down deep in him he doesn't believe in. He's sick of his blackeyed lass. He has eleven kids. And he wants other men to suffer as he suffers. He wants to take them out of circulation so they won't seduce the virgins. Can't you see it? He wants to seduce them himself. Ah, good Lord, I have seen him for weeks slyly looking at the legs. I've been reading his lecherous heart. It is told of him on the campus that when he hikes to a conference he does his damndest to pull off a seduction. And if the sweet young things in his class will only step up to the altar they will get an A!"

Vridar knew the reason for his tirade against Brown. He also wished to seduce the sweet young things and with a deep inner grin for the irony of it he thought of Stendhal's nobleman who said to an aged marquis that he had long adored her in vain; to which she replied, "Ah, my God, why didn't you tell me before? You would have had me like all the others!" The conflicts within him gave him no peace. He did not suspect that his personality had almost been split by the strange ambivalence of parenthood and the ordeals of his early years; he knew only that he was struggling toward an unimpeachable integrity of mind and heart and that he must find some great light or be drawn under into the dark. In search of that light he read books by the scores, all day and far into the night, and he made thousands of notes of the best that had been said and thought but the light was not there; and while he was seized and held in suspension by the compulsions within him, Neloa staggered him one day with a simple statement. She said she was pregnant.

Vridar sank to a chair and looked at her. "Are you sure?"

"Yes."

"Have you been vomiting?"

"Yes."

"My God!" he said. "Here we live in an attic and we wear rags and I've no degree and no job and we have a child coming?"

When Vridar married he knew almost nothing of contraceptives. He had planned that they would not have a child until they could care for it and he had Neloa use a warm water douche with a pinch of salt in it. He had gone to doctors to learn a better method but with scared and anxious eyes they had dismissed him. He had told Neloa that they would have children when they had the means to support them. "I don't have much pride in parenthood," he had said. "I want no Vridar Junior. Most men have a silly pride in fatherhood, but this power, which they regard as miraculous, is shared, I observed, by bulls and boars—and even flies."

Now he was trapped. "Are you dead sure?"

"Yes."

He saw that Neloa was pleased. "It's a hell of a mess. I have nothing to support a child with. Besides I'm going to war."

"Vridar!"

"Don't Vridar me. Tell me what we're going to do about it. I'm not through school yet. Must I go back to Antelope and be a farmer? No, I'll go to war."

"You won't."

"I'll take out a big insurance policy for you and then go die for the Morgans."

"Don't talk like a fool."

"Why not? I am a fool, a fool of incredible proportions and persistence. I don't believe in the spawning of children by parents who give no thought to their health and education. This halfwitted notion that souls are waiting to be born! It's better, say these Christians, to be born hunchbacked or idiotic than not to be born at all. Isn't that a lovely doctrine?"

"Ours won't be an idiot."

"How can we know? Half the morons in eastern Idaho are my relatives. My father has a hundred cousins who can't talk plain or count change. Have you heard of Mendel's Law?"

"No."

"You should. Then you wouldn't want a child by me. But like women you want children, enough to cover an acre; and when we have twenty I'll shake hands with the President. On the contrary I should be hung up by my ears with weights on my feet. Darling, if a big family is an honorable thing, why don't we erect a monument to rabbits?"

"We'n have an abortion," Neloa said.

"No. They cost money. They're dangerous. They're hard on women. No, good God, we'll have to go through with it. But where has all this stuff about glorious Mother Nature come from? She's nothing but a big fecund womb that is unhappy when empty. The world will have three billion people, then four billion, and famine and war, pestilence and plague will still try to keep a balance between human stupidity and the earth's resources. Had you ever thought of that?"

While Vridar was agonizing over the matter, there came to him a letter from Washington, D. C. It invited him to join the air corps. A letter like his own, he learned, had been sent to every athlete in the school. He was flattered. He hated war, but he liked to be thought of as a candidate to its most difficult and dangerous service. It offered a dramatic way to die. Better to be set aflame in the air than to be rammed with a bayonet while stuck in the mud. He went at once to be examined. Twelve athletes went with him and he was one of five pronounced fit. After being spun in a chair, he lay by a wall, sick through and through and as white as death. He thought he had failed but the captain said he was all right.

"But won't flying make me sick?"

"You'll get over it."

He rushed home to Neloa, crying, "Your football hero is now a flying cadet!"

She came to him, looking frightened. "Please don't go!"

"Would you have me be a coward?"

"But you don't believe in war."

"Imagine me," he said, "ten thousand feet up. A German blows up my gas tank and I come down in flame, cremated and ready for the funeral sermons."

"Darling, please don't go."

"Would you have me be a slacker?"

"But you don't believe in war."

"I'm not a Christian so how could I?"

"If you go what'll I do?"

"Be a war widow. The country will be full of war widows. You'll get a big wad of insurance money."

"I don't want it!" Her eyes flashed and then her eyes were wet. She looked at him and great tears fell down her cheeks. Vridar was deeply moved. He let her hair down and felt her tremble under his touch.

"Don't worry about it," he said gently and kissed her. "If I don't go they'll draft me. That would be worse."

"You can go to jail. You said you would."

"You'd hate me then. You wouldn't respect me then." And to hush her grief he lied. He said he would be careful, that he would not be killed, that he would return to her when the war was over.

"If you don't," said Neloa, "I'll kill myself."

"Don't be silly. What about our child?"

"I'll kill it, too."

"Don't worry," he said. "I'll come back."

But he did not intend to come back: he saw in the road to France the road out. He never suspected all the vanity and self-pity in him, nor, above all, the terrible over-submissiveness in him against which he struggled so desperately, of which he was so sick and tired. Without perceiving his motives at all, he thought it would be best to die.

In March he was called and Neloa went to the station with him. He thought she looked very lonely and lost. When she kissed him goodbye, she did not break and weep but she shook in his arms. In Vridar's mind was only one thought: he was leaving this girl whom he loved, he was riding out of her life, he would never see again, never again look into those lustrous eyes or feel the touch of those beautiful hands. "Goodbye," he said, patting her. "It's goodbye now."

"Not goodbye," she said, looking at him through tears. "Just—just till we meet again!"

"Yes," he said, holding her close, whispering, "I'll come back . . . But Neloa darling, if I do not come back, remember that I loved you. Never doubt that."

"I won't," she whispered.

"Neloa dear, I've been mean to you sometimes, I've said contemptible things, but

all the while I have loved you as I love nothing else on earth. And—our child—"
He broke off. He could feel her tears against his face and her hands trembling on his back.

"Write often!" she whispered.

"I will."

He broke free a little and met her gaze; and then, "O sweetheart!" he cried, and she came swiftly into his arms, shaking terribly. He glanced at the clock and knew that he must go soon. He tried to put her away but she clung to him. "I have to go now."

"I know!"

"Darling Neloa, I must go now."

"I know!"

With an effort she hushed her grief, but when she looked at him her eyes were wet and blind. He picked up a shabby bag and turned away but after a moment looked back and saw her standing alone. She looked so desolate and forsaken that he had no power to go. He could only look from the clock to her eyes, from her eyes to the clock. Then he dropped the bag and ran to her and folded her in his arms, kissing her hair and her wet eyes and her wet mouth. Then with all his strength he swung and seized the bag and ran and he did not pause or look back until he found the train.

Sitting alone in one end of the coach, he bowed his head. Never in life had grief been in him in such deep and dark bitterness, in such utter desolation of soul: he heard the rails singing under him and he knew that the miles were spreading away like a carpet of landscape behind. He knew that back in the city, alone, was this girl, this child, whom he loved more deeply than he loved himself. Then he tried to think of life, its loveliness and pain, its ancient loneliness and its strange haunted dark; and he thought his heart would break. For it was all so impalpable and elusive, it was like smoke in a closing hand, it was like the pain under a wound that had healed. Life was around him, life was everywhere, and everywhere through it moved the troubled wonder, the searching, the heartache, the fears and hopes of mankind. You could look at a photograph, as he now looked at one of Neloa, and you could say, This is a living thing, it feels and breathes, it loves and it will die; and the philosophers had learned no more. You could try to think about it, to remember that only an hour ago you had touched it and kissed it; but you could not understand what it meant. He came to doubt that he was on a train or that Neloa was somewhere climbing a hill to an attic room; for the old sense of being depersonalized, the old nighmare, was closing in. He began to whisper words, as so many times as a child he had done; he began to pinch himself and massage his flesh, trying to keep a grasp on reality; but only intimations of it were brought forth to his senses, as the lights of a rainbow are brought out of the darkness of storm. He wanted to yield to the power, feeling that there was death in it and peace, or at least a stronger will that would possess and nourish his will; but he fought to keep a realization of himself and of where he was, and got only momentary flickers, as rockets burst and go out. Then when the light failed there was only the great and dreadful void, flanked by darkness, with shadows above and below, and strange intimations, as of faint far lights in the boundless and the infinite. The night closed in on the inexplicable wonder of himself who was no longer himself, until he felt borne down and pinched and snuffed out; and he tried to cradle himself in bewilderment and sleep, as he had done as a child. . . .

After a few hours he forced himself to look out the window. He saw an ocean of stars and the misty backdrop of mountains and the ghostly nothingness of trees; and once in a while he saw a far and lonely light, as though of a sheepherder's wagon. Could it be true that there, under canvas gloomy and hushed, a man lay in sleep and breathed? Each star, he had read, was a vast white sun, immensely larger than the earth's own; each was a gigantic sphere of heat and leaping coronas, hurled through space in its awful journey. But what did it mean? How was it related to Spinoza and the odes of Keats and Meredith's love in a valley and a lonely pregnant woman in an attic room? It was all like kissing an image in a mirror. Once he had moved to kiss Neloa's image and suddenly with astonishment had found his own instead; and it was this imprisonment in self that he wanted to break out of, to the enveloping goodness and the larger will. But he, a pilgrim, as all human beings were pilgrims, seeking the invisible canterburies of their dreams, would live within his own heartache and span a few years and die. Somewhere he would find his gethsemane and his cross, death would offer the vinegar and the book would shut. Staring into the black night, with a lonely light here and another there, he wiped at his eyes and shrugged; and the shrug meant that he wanted to be done with life, with its tempests and turmoils and inexorable tides and dooms, its bitterness in having to hate and its heartbreak in having to love. He stared again at the likeness of Neloa and kissed it and bowed over it, offering to her, as he had offered only to her, all his devotion and his soul. All night he was awake and then morning came and then evening, and he found himself in a different world.

Berkeley and the campus of the university were lovely in March. Used to naked winters and the blizzards and slush of northern springs, Vridar looked with wonder at fragrant gardens and flowering trees. Afraid to report, he spent hours on the winding trails, smelling the loveliness or climbing to a hill for his first view of a great ocean; and thinking all the while of Neloa. When at last he forced himself to report for duty, he was given common army equipment: a cotton uniform and a pair of infantry shoes. The cadets here, he had already observed, shone like officers: they had tailored serge uniforms and polished boots. When Vridar meekly protested he was told briefly and sharply that he could buy a better outfit if he wished to. Filled with misgivings and shame he fingered the few coins in his pocket and went to the barracks. On the way he met Lars Ongin, his football coach.

"Hello," said Lars cordially. "When did you blow in?"

"This morning," said Vridar, observing that Ongin was as immaculate as a general.

"Can I help you in any way?"

Vridar looked down at his clothes. "Do I have to wear these things?"

"Christ no," said Ongin. "Go buy you a couple of uniforms."

Go buy you a couple of uniforms! He had only a little money and had given nearly all of it to Neloa. Here, among these splendid cadets, he would be as he had been in college, a shabby oaf in cotton and cowhide. He had imagined that a democratic spirit prevailed throughout the military forces! In the barracks he was assigned to a cot, on all sides of which were cadets with their expensive uniforms and boots and luggage; and he sank to the cot, appalled. He knew that the cadets were looking at him, some with astonishment and some with amazement. After a while one came over and asked if he could help.

"I don't know," said Vridar, sweating with shame. "I guess—I guess I need a decent uniform. How much does it cost?" A smartly tailored outfit, the cadet said, could be had for about seventy dollars, including the boots. He said Vridar would need two. A man could get along with two.

"Thanks," Vridar said. A hundred and forty dollars! Of course he would be paid a salary, but he would have to give that to Neloa, or most of it. Even if he were to buy from his salary, he would have to slink around here for a month in cotton—or was it wool? He felt of the stuff, reflecting that he had got himself into a hell of a mess this time. Aviation, like fraternities, belonged to the sons of wealth: for him and the common fellows like him there was the infantry, the bayonets and dugouts and mud. What could he do? How could he honorably escape to a branch of the service where he belonged?

When evening came he observed that the men around him were preparing to shave. Every one of them had a princely outfit. What did he have? A cheap tarnished razor, a shabby little brush that had lost most of its hair, and a chunk of handsoap—these and a comb with several teeth broken out of it. He wanted to laugh. He wanted to stand up and say to the cadets, Look at me! I thought war was murder and that nothing mattered but guns that shoot straight and men with guts to shoot them. But even in war, I now preceive, fashion declares the mode and wealth is at the top . . . . He wanted to say: This preposterous outfit is all I have and all I can afford. But it wouldn't do, I can see, for one of Uncle Sam's aviators to be shot out of the air in duds like these! He must come down, tailored in the finest wool and leather, with his boots polished and his frat pin on.

He followed the men to the washroom where they shaved. Now and then one glanced at him, brows lifting in gentle amazement, as brows had lifted in the football shower. The eyes would go down Vridar to his shoes and return to his face. As usual when desperate Vridar resorted to clowning: affecting astonishment he looked down at his baggy trousers and ugly shoes and then gave the cadet a solemn wink. But under his clowning he was shamed and angry. He hung about the washroom, waiting for a chance to be alone, but no chance came. Once when for a moment it was empty he dashed in and was furiously lathering his face when a cadet entered; and now, instead of shaving, as he had meant to, he pretended to be washing only; he scrubbed his ears and neck, making a big racket, as if cleanliness and godliness in his mind were one. And slyly he watched to see what the cadet did. The cadet opened an expensive leather case and drew forth expensive tools and powders and creams and lotions. The man's slow leisurely way suggested that he had spent most of his life in tiled bathrooms in a Hillcrest mansion. Returning to the barracks, Vridar hid his absurd bag under the cot and headed for Berkeley to get a shave. On his way back he was hailed by a guard. The guard came up and stared at him.

"Where in hell have you been?"

"Over town getting shaved."

"Who gave you permission?"

"I didn't know I needed permission."

"What's your name?"

"Vridar Hunter."

"All right, Hunter, you'll be reported. Get to your barracks."

Around him in the barracks Vridar saw naked men inspecting themselves. Some were manicuring their toenails, some were brushing their hair with costly-looking brushes, and some from big leather bags were laying clothes out. They all had pajamas. He had none. They all were superbly equipped, untroubled, at ease, even though naked before one another. He shrank from them. He wanted a small dark room and books and solitude. Again sweating with humiliation, he crawled into bed with his underwear on and pulled the covers over his head.

The next morning he was awakened early, and when he saw men around him he sprang from his cot and dressed with frantic haste, trying to conceal the fact that he had no pajamas. He saw that other cadets were making their beds and he tried to make his own. The other beds looked neat and orderly, but his own, in spite of all he could do, bulged and spread and showed clearly that it had been slept in. He watched the deft movements of others. He yanked his bedding into its several pieces and tried again. While he was on his knees, wholly engrossed by his efforts, he heard a man speak. At first he paid no heed, but when the voice spoke again it was sharp and furious and he looked round at the man. He saw a glittering officer. He saw the other cadets standing like dummies of leather and serge.

"What's your name?" the officer asked.

"Vridar Hunter."

"When did you get in?"

"Yesterday."

"Say *sir* to me!" Vridar looked up at the small angry fellow but he did not move. "Get on your feet!" Vridar rose to his feet. "Attention!" Vridar looked round him, wondering how to stand at attention. "Get those heels together!" the officer roared. Vridar clicked his heels. "Salute!" Vridar made an awkward gesture. Then for a long moment the officer looked at Vridar's uniform. His gaze was unpitying and hard. It traveled from Vridar's throat down to his shoes and lingered there; and came back to his throat. Then the man's eyes met Vridar's, and Vridar hated with all his strength what he saw in the man's eyes.

He attended classes but for him they were riddles. Drawings of engines, magnetos, carburetors: he might as well have been looking at Sanskrit. He listened to instructors with only faint notions of what they were talking about. The Eiseman G-4 magneto had secondary windings of the armature and primary circuits and distribution brushes, but for Vridar such things were as incomprehensible as Norse runes. There was talk of a thermal principle and of a Bosch-Rushmore system and of an Entz system; of the Atwater-Kent polarity switch; of primary intakes and auxiliary air valves; of ballast resistors and field poles; and for all that he got out of it Vridar might as well have been listening to a Moslem's prayers. The cadets around him, he observed, looked as if they understood. They made notes and drawings and they asked questions. Vridar made notes, too, a caricature of the instructor and a sonnet for Neloa:

> I listen while these solemn asses name
> The p's and q's of war and death and hate.
> I smell the ardor of their tongue and breath
> But over in France I hear the blind and lame
> Or see the rotting carcasses piled high
> To make the Morgan bonfire; and I know
> That God somewhere now hides his face in woe
> Against the smell of murder in the sky.
>
> Dear Neloa, I can no longer see
> The face of Jesus in the human dream.
> His bones, I think, still hang in Galilee;
> His heart is still there, spiked upon the beam.
> And now instead of aconite we set
> Against his lips the bomb and bayonet!

He drilled with the cadets and he was the only one in a cheap uniform. He looked like the gawkiest recruit in the world and he felt like it. Sweating with shame he fumbled and stumbled, acting more like a wooden soldier than a man of flesh and bone. Now and then an officer would stare at him. For ten days he endured this spiritual anguish. He drove himself from task to task, trying not to see the amusement or contempt in the eyes of his fellows. War was murder, he reasoned, and it made no difference whether a man was slain in cheap wool or in serge: death would level the derisions and give to every soldier the same quality of dust. "It's a living hell," he wrote Neloa, "but I'll try to stick it out. The man who shaves with handsoap makes as good a target as the man who is pomaded . . . ." But at the end of ten days he could stand no more. He resolved to leave. If he could not get an honorable discharge he would desert: anything to be done with this stupid aristocracy within the shadow of death. Early one morning he presented himself to the Commandant.

He clicked his heels sharply and saluted, but for several minutes he was ignored. The room was full of officers: they were all glittering, plump, immaculate, and to him they all seemed to be arrogant. He knew that they had seen him and that they did not want to see him. At last a colonel, sitting like an overstuffed Napoleon behind a desk, turned to Vridar and spoke. "Well, what do you want?"

"I'd like, sir, to speak to you."

"Well, you have a tongue, haven't you?"

Vridar advanced to the desk and stood at attention. A dozen officers roundabout were looking at him. He looked into the Colonel's cold blue eyes. "I want to leave this place."

"Say *sir* when you address an officer . . . .What do you mean?"

"I mean, sir, that I don't like this place. I want to be discharged."

A silence fell. Not a man stirred and for what seemed to Vridar a long time not a man spoke. The Colonel looked bloated with amazement.

"You don't like this place? What do you mean by that?"

"I mean, sir, that I don't like its spirit."

The officers looked at one another. The Colonel looked at his staff as if to say, Did you ever see such insolence? Then for a hard bitter moment he looked at Vridar. "Explain yourself!" he cried. His face had turned red.

"Do you mean, sir, I'm to say what I think?"

"Exactly! And be brief."

"I think, sir, that these cadets are a bunch of prigs. I don't like their spirit. It's bad enough to have social arrogance in civilian life. It's ridiculous to find it in men who are going out to face death. I believe—"

"Enough!" the Colonel roared. "I don't care what you believe."

"Sir, you told me to be frank."

"You've said enough. You've insulted every officer in this room." The Colonel rose from his chair, his face mottled with rage. He stared round him as if baffled and then with dreadful eyes looked at Vridar. But Vridar was not to be intimidated. He was a little shaken, but he enjoyed the consternation and rage in the men here.

"Pardon me, sir, but you did not allow me to finish."

"Allow you to—to finish!" the Colonel thundered. "You upstart! I'll have you thrown into the guardhouse!"

"Sir, that is all right with me. Do with me as you please but let me finish." The Colonel looked at him, speechless with amazement. Other officers began to murmur. Vridar seized his chance and went boldly ahead. "You see me, sir, in a cheap uniform. It's all I have and all I can afford. My people are poor. They haven't yet learned how to make other people work for them. I—"

"That'll do!" the Colonel shouted. He banged a clenched fist on the desk. Then in a sudden blaze of passion, fury came to life in Vridar. Stepping closer he met the Colonel's outraged gaze and spoke straight into the man's face, his voice ringing.

"I enlisted to fight! I didn't come here to put on the dog! I didn't come here to strut around in serge while men like the men of my people get gutted in the trenches! And I won't do it!" He paused a moment and went furiously ahead. "There ought to be a democratic spirit here but there is only arrogance and pomp! And I hate it! Do with me as you please! Throw me into your damned guardhouse! Take me out and shoot me for insubordination! A hell of a lot I care what you do! But you can't scare me with your damned glittering discipline and you may as well stop trying! Say if you want to that I don't have the right spirit but the spirit here and my spirit are not the same!" He was now shaking from head to feet. His face had turned white.

The Colonel as if stricken sank to the chair. He looked round at his staff. "What," he asked, "shall we do with him?"

"Discharge him," said one. "We don't want such men here."

"An honorable discharge—" Vridar began.

"Shut up!" the Colonel thundered. "You'll take what we give you and it will be more than you are worth."

"All right, sir, make it as dishonorable as you can."

"Harriman," said the Colonel, turning to an aide, "fix him up." Then like an old man he rose and left the room.

An hour later Vridar rode a ferry to San Francisco and walked down Market

397

Street. He entered a building and presented papers and was given an honorable discharge and his fare home. Never before in his life had he felt, never in all the years to come would he feel, such tremendous relief as filled him now. He went into a saloon and drank whisky and bought a quart and found the railway station and took a train home.

IV

Neloa meanwhile had gone to the Antelope hills and it was to these hills that Vridar was now going; and he drank from the bottle and brooded and hated himself for a fool. Was there in him some fatal weakness, some sickness of the soul, some disease of the mind or will? Why could he not be like other men? Was it he who did not have the right spirit? Was he to live all his life outside the fellowship of his own kind, a misfit, an outcast, an object of amusement and contempt and pity? If he had more character, less false pride, less stupid shame and tortured self-consciousness, would he have gone ahead with his training, indifferent to the opinions of others?—and in time would they have learned to respect him if with quiet dignity he had borne their derision? He suspected that this might be true and his shame was even deeper now, as his mind forced his heart to ask the questions. Was he a coward? What in God's name was wrong with him that everywhere he should find the contempt of men!

He tried to comfort himself with the thought that he was not going back to the dreadful places where he spent his childhood. His father a year ago had stepped into conference with a fortune-teller; and this woman, arrayed and adorned like an Oriental sage, had foretold great things for him. The stars, she said, had marked him for leadership. Looking at his hands and smelling the barnyard in his clothes, she said he had been wasting his genius with binders and plows. He had the stuff in him of a mechanical wizard and the stars were calling him to school. He would own a chain of garages from Canada to the Utah line. Joe Hunter, a deeply superstitious man, believed every word she said.

He leased his ranch and with his brother Ike, to whom had also been granted a larger destiny, went to Portland to school. With raw and unflagging enthusiasm Joe studied everything known about automobiles; and with his brother and one of the instructors he went to Idaho Falls and bought a garage there . . . . No, Vridar was not going back to the scene of his humiliations; he sipped from the bottle and told himself that it did not matter a good God damn where he went. He was no good and he would never be any good. Men like him were war fodder and in some gray morning he would be a scattered armful of viscera and legs in France. That was all he deserved: as the Colonel had said, anything he got would be more than he was worth. When he arrived in Idaho Falls, he bought another bottle of whisky and caught a ride to the Antelope hills. On the Antelope flat he sat under the creek bank and drank and the whisky made everything unimportant and senseless. Over there in the Doole stable Neloa had told of her lovers; but what did that matter now? In a mad world, with bayonets in the guts of men and blood fertilizing the poppies, what difference did anything make?

398

He hid the bottle and staggered up the road, despising himself for being so eager to see the wife of a stupid marriage, yet with no power to turn away. When he came to the Doole yard, he saw Neloa in the doorway and she came running to him. Vridar tried to stop her, crying, "See the great American aviator!" and feeling, though drunk, that self-contempt was somehow his worst vice. But Neloa did not stop. She came and flung arms round him, trembling with joy; and Vridar buried his face in her fragrant hair, whispering, "I'm drunk!"

"O darling, you big silly goose!"

"I'm drunk," he said, "and I'm no good. I'm a coward of some sort and I'm no good."

"You big silly thing! Shame on you!"

"I'm no good, Neloa, I'm no good."

"Stop saying that!" Neloa was laughing and weeping and hugging him to her. "O darling, darling!"

"You're my darling," he said, kissing her hair, "but you married a no-good. I disgraced myself."

"No!" she whispered fiercely.

"But I did, I did . . . ."

He went as hired man and Neloa went as cook to the Con Wote ranch, the most manorial of all the places in the Antelope hills. Its manager, short, fat and cold, gave himself feudal airs, as did his wife, a huge woman with a heavy dead face. Lizzie Boe now and then would ask to have her breakfast served at her bedside; and she affected a yawning luxurious weariness, as befitted one who had been president of a bridge club. John Boe would dress up like a steeplechase lord and ride over the fields. Both of them assumed a vast and hungry interest in culture and in far strange things like the French Riviera and Mardi Gras festivals and Venetian glass. Their big words, invariably mispronounced, and their allusions and dinner-table talk they gathered from advertisements in magazines.

At first they amused Vridar but after a while they annoyed him. Their patronizing gestures made him furious. When at table they addressed their remarks to each other and took it for granted, it seemed to him, that he was a dusty ignorant fellow who had never been to school. They spoke to one another as Mr. and Mrs. Boe. They murmured with small apologies. They often alluded to the time when, living in a town somewhere, they gave afternoon teas and played bridge.

"Anne writes she's visitun Yoorup this summer." It was Lizzie speaking. She yawned behind her napkin and turned to Neloa. "Uh — another cup of coffee, please." She looked across at Mr. Boe. "And Mr. Boe would like some eggs, I think."

"Yoorup," said Mr. Boe. "The Rivarah, I suppose."

"Oh yes, to the Rivarah. But also to Buden-Buden. Then the Awlps." Mrs. Boe loved the broad a.

"The Alps?" murmured Mr. Boe, who was not so cultured as his wife.

"Neloa," said Mrs. Boe sharply, "Mr. Boe would like some coffee." Neloa rose and served the coffee. "After Boden-Boden," said Mrs. Boe, who apparently had decided that she had mispronounced the word, "she will go to Frenzy."

"Ah," murmured Mr. Boe, catching up. "That's the Eyetalian word for Venice."

"Yes. Neloa, I think Mr. Boe would like some bacon." Neloa rose and served the bacon.

"And of course she'll see the Reems cathedral and Shartur and Klogn."

"It will be a nice trip," said Mr. Boe, and politely dabbed at his mouth with a napkin.

While riding a plow or bunching hay or milking cows, Vridar thought about the Boes. "They're hard," he said to Neloa, "on a Socialist." He had cherished the notion that country people were unaffected and genuine, and that city folk were evasive, dishonest, and a little degenerate. These ideas he had gathered from his reading. Poets, and novelists, too, were forever extolling the rustic and excoriating the urban. Country lasses in gingham smiled innocently from magazine covers; scoundrels of the city sneered and smirked on the inside pages. The pastoral, tradition said, was close to the heart of the beautiful and the true. There was the verse of Whittier and Bryant, Shelley and Tennyson; the novels of Cooper and Hardy and a hundred others; and the countless books which made glamorous the doings of frontiersman and cowboy. Was human nature much the same in every land and clime, or did a man's abode make either an angel or a rogue of him? . . . . Later he was to fall upon the early novels of Willa Cather and to read them with amazement and contempt.

To Neloa he said: "It won't take much more observation of people to knock all the Socialism out of me. Look at these God damned humbugs! Is there a man on earth who would not be a tyrant if he had a chance? Is there a man who would not exploit in a position of power and with specious argument make it seem all right to his conscience? If so, Socialism as a system would be utter fraud." He thought a few moments and added: "If I ever write novels I'll tell the truth about people. I won't simper over them like a Dickens or a Hardy."

Neloa looked at him with unhappy eyes. "You won't be popular," she said.

"As a philosopher said about the skeptic, he doesn't want to be popular, he wants only to be honest."

Vridar's wretchedness of spirit these weeks was caused by more than the priggish airs of this household. When toiling in the fields he could see the blue backdrop of his home and he never looked at it without bitterness. He thought of Neloa's amazing loyalty to this country and to her people. The Doole clan had the blood integrity of an Indian tribe. They banded together in their thriftless nomadic ways and every one of them, no matter how stupid or unworthy, dwelt in the clan's bosom. "It's ridiculous," Vridar said. "Some of your people, like some of mine, aren't worth shooting. Why stick to every single one of them?"

"You stick to yours."

"Like hell I do. You Dooles have great clan gatherings. The Hunters don't, or if they do I'm not there."

"Blood is thicker than water," she said.

And he was distressed by Neloa's pregnancy. As the summer passed, he saw this stately girl grow shapeless and stout. She looked, he reflected, as if she had swallowed a bag of wheat. Why had an all-powerful God—if there was a God—contrived

400

procreation with such unaesthetic distortions of the female form! In flowers, in trees, the way was beautiful and clean. But the more civilized the animal the more ghastly was its way of aborting its kind. A cow or a mare looked stuffed but only as if over-fed, and their delivery, though hideously unclean, took only a little while. The calf or colt after an hour or two was spry and alert and good to look at. But a woman swelled up as though bloated with some horrible disease; she went to bed and some-times screamed all night; she sometimes lay close to death before the ordeal was over; and the infant when it came was incredibly raw and ugly and helpless. In the previous year he had read a book by a doctor, addressed to married folk; and this author, to Vridar's amazement, had in two rapturous pages eulogized the roundness of a woman's belly. He had written: "A husband looks at this full rounded cradle and reflects that is is the noble and miraculous repository of sons and daughters that will soon shout in angelic innocence around the nursery . . . ." What kind of man could write such nonsense? Never again would Neloa have the alluring body of girlhood. She would spread in her hips; and her breasts, which had always hung too low, would fall down like two empty bags after she had given suck. Yet women, roped and tied to an inexorable biology, expected a man to be the same kind of lov-er after a child had come . . . .

But the matter that distressed him most of all was his struggle to keep his Socialist-ic principles while feeling more and more that they were stupid. On the football field, in the classroom, in the fraternity and with the cadets he had been forced to look at human beings for what they are, and he felt with increasing certainty that entrust-ing the welfare of the many to the management of the few could only lead to exploit-ation and tyranny. Where were the men so civilized, so disciplined and compassion-ate and disinterested, that they could govern the less intelligent and less privileged, without enhancing their own power and prestige and fattening their own purses? Where in history among the rulers had there been such men? Aurelius? But he had turned the people over to a vicious and degenerate son. This struggle in Vridar be-tween his ideals and the realities was to be long and desperate. Now, with war up-on the world and his own future in the balance, he could stay no longer on these hills which he hated; and he went one morning to Boe and said, "Give me my time, I have to go."

He went with Neloa to Idaho Falls and lived with his sister and parents in a dark and ugly apartment. He wanted to enlist but Neloa wept and begged him to stay with her. "You should think of our child," she said. "You should wait till our child is born." Yes, Vridar thought, he owed a duty to the child. He decided to wait.

"I'll be drafted," he said. "That'll be another disgrace."

"Maybe the war will stop."

"Not as long as there are fools like me to die for the profits of the Morgans."

Early in August Neloa went to the home of her parents. Vridar worked in his fa-ther's garage and walked the streets at night and one day there came to him an Ante-lope farmer so agitated that he could barely speak. He made Vridar understand that he was a father now! A father! Vridar thought. I've about as much right to be a fa-ther as I have to be a saint! Deeply lost to himself he entered the man's car and was driven to the Doole home, thinking all the while that he ought to be punished for having become a father, when he had no job, no future: here he was, a man bewildered and driven, with a child on his hands—a son born of his own haunted flesh and blood. He would be killed soon and his son would grow up and go to another war and there was no meaning in it.

He entered the house and looked at Neloa on the bed. She was very white and weak but her eyes were radiant.

"O sweetheart!" she cried, her voice ringing. "Darling, see!" He looked at the hideous infant. "It's a boy! Aren't you glad?"

"What difference does it make?"

Neloa reached out and grasped his hand. "Aren't you going to kiss me?" He stooped and kissed her. "Now kiss *him!*"

"What an ugly brat," said Vridar.

"O darling, how can you say that? He looks just like you. Mama says he does."

"Like me?" he said, looking at the child. "I know I'm an ugly bastard but I never knew I was that ugly."

"He has your nose and your mouth."

"Nonsense."

"He has eyes just like yours. Look!"

"All babies are said to look like their parents. That's vanity."

"Sweetheart, kiss him, please!"

"No." Then Vridar saw tears in her eyes and compassion overwhelmed him. He sank to his knees and put arms around mother and child and he kissed the babe; and he could feel Neloa's hand gently patting him and moving softly over his hair. "Darling wife!" he whispered. "My dear sweet Neloa! . . . ."

Two weeks later he was called in the draft and he wrote to Marion in Salt Lake City to ask if he could go with him. Marion came on the next train and went with Vridar to the Board. "My brother and I," Vridar said, speaking to the sheriff, "want to go together. Is that all right?"

The sheriff looked perplexed and pulled at his drooping mustache. He turned to other members of the Board. "How about it?"

The other members looked very grave, as though there had been put upon them the fate of nations. They asked a lot of questions. Why did the brother want to go?

"We want to be killed together," Vridar said.

The sheriff stared at him like one wondering if he plotted treacheries. He became suspicious. "Are your parents—well, what nationality are you?"

"American."

"I know that." He was looking into Vridar's eyes. "Are they German?"

"What difference does that make?"

"Answer me!" barked the sheriff.

"Some German, some Dutch, some English, Scotch, Irish. My forbears fought in the War for Independence, in the War of 1812, and my father's father fought in the Civil War."

"Which side?"

"The North but what's the difference?"

"We'll think about it," the sheriff said, "and let you know." An hour later he called Vridar. It would be all right, he said: Marion would take the place of Arthur Hammond, who had been summoned.

That evening Hammond came to Vridar. He was a big flabby man full of self-pity, and he broke and wept. Blubbering like a child, he said he was married, he had a little baby . . . .

"I've a child too," Vridar said. "Two weeks old."

"You—you have! Oh, that's too darn bad!"

"Besides, it's my brother who is taking your place. If you want to thank anyone thank him."

Hammond wrung Vridar's hand and went to find Marion. He shook with gratitude and grief. To celebrate his good fortune, he borrowed a shotgun and went duck-hunting. He fell into a bog and then caught influenza and two weeks later he was dead.

Vridar went to Antelope to say goodbye to Neloa. She was up but she was very thin and white; it tortured him to see how pathetic and lonely she was. She wept in his arms while he spoke jestingly of war and said he would be back soon; but again he was thinking, I'll never see her again, in life or after death! He went to the bed and kissed the child. He again held Neloa and kissed her hair and cheeks and throat and lips, and again he turned away with his heart breaking. On his return to the city, he drove his father's Ford with such reckless speed that he ran over a hog and some chickens and lost the cushion from the rear seat. He and his fellow-recruits bought whisky and prowled through the streets, looking for a fight; and to one man and another Vridar said, "Do you believe a just God approves war?" Seeing that Vridar was drunk, they said they did not, but at last he met a man who rebuked him.

"Go on home before I knock your ears off!"

"But do you—you believe—uh—"

"Yes, God damn it, I do!"

"Then you're a cockeyed imbecile."

The man sprang to the fight, but other recruits, also dizzy with whisky, led the warriors to the back of a garage. They went to the part where pails of oil stood about and grease was deep on the floor. There they fought. Of this fight Vridar was able to remember nothing clearly. When he came to he was in bed; and his garments, piled on a chair beside him, looked as if they had mopped up a barrel of grease. He left the bed, calling to Marion, "Our train leaves in an hour!"

An hour later they stood on the platform and watched the train roll in from the north. Their parents were with them. Joe showed no sign of grief, but when he tried to say goodbye the words stuck in his throat. Prudence smiled through her tears.

"Goodbye!"

"Goodbye!"

And they swung up to the coach and were gone.

V

Besides Vridar and Marion there were nine recruits, bound for Fort Rosecrans at San Diego. Vridar had been put in charge, and now, with the men sitting round him, he studied their faces. They were the sons of farmers, simple, earnest, and illiterate. In their own small worlds they had been hardfisted and tough, but now they were off to war and their bravado was hushed. When noon came he led them to the dining car. While he stood at the entrance, looking for tables where they could all sit together, the head steward came up and spoke sharply. They were blocking the passage, he said. Vridar flushed with anger. He had observed the deference paid to well-dressed diners: the eleven men were only greenhorns in shabby clothes who were going away to die for their country. "Come on!" Vridar said to the men. The diners stared at them, and Vridar hated what he saw in their eyes. Their eyes did not say, Here are men, offering their lives: steward, make room! Their eyes said, Why do they allow such hayseeds to come in here!

Vridar and Marion sat at a table for two. He told the men to sit where they could and they fell into seats. One of them, a hulking youth, sunbaked and unwashed, sat across from a haughty woman who looked at him with unconcealed scorn. Abashed, the man looked at Vridar. "It's all right," Vridar said, speaking so the woman could hear. "If she doesn't like us, she can get out." The woman rose and left the car. Well-dressed diners, Vridar observed, were bowed to seats and served at once. He and his men waited. "We don't matter," he said to Marion. "We're only men headed for the trenches."

Marion was furious. "Tell the steward that if we're not served like the others, we'll throw him off the train . . . . Go on, you're in charge of this bunch."

Vridar rose and went to the steward. "Why aren't we served?" he asked. "We've been here longer than some now eating."

"You'll be served," said the steward coldly.

After Vridar and Marion had eaten, they slyly placed twenty-five cents under a plate. When the men came in to their next meal, he was amazed to learn how potent a tip could be. The waiter smiled at him and Marion and served them at once. The other men had not tipped and they were ignored. Vridar looked at his food and waited. "We made a mistake," he said. "By tipping, I mean."

Twenty minutes passed before food was brought to the other nine, and when it came he saw that their portions were less generous than his own. He knew the meaning of that: these men had not tipped and they were being rebuked. This unspeakable insolence aroused him to murderous fury and he arose and went to the head steward. "Listen," he said, his voice shaking as it had when he faced the Commandant, "I'm in charge of these recruits. They're nobodies: they're only going to France to die while you stay home. They didn't tip at noon because they've never heard of tipping. Now they're served less than I, who tipped." He was looking into the steward's cold incredulous eyes. "The Government is paying for their food and they're going to get it. We've been drafted to fight and we don't care when the fighting starts. You know what I mean?"

404

Vridar thought the man's eyes showed fear. "Don't they have enough?"

"See for yourself." Vridar went back to his seat, and the men looked at him, their eyes questioning. "Don't worry," Vridar said. "They'll bring you what they're supposed to or we'll throw them off the train." Two waiters came and took the food away. They returned with heaped plates and the nine men grinned like schoolboys and ate. "The more I see of people," Vridar said to his brother, "the more I suspect that Socialism is a fraud."

"I've always known it," Marion said.

In San Diego barracks Vridar lay on his narrow cot and said: "Well, we're in it now. I can smell the saltpeter."

"God yes, the saltpeter."

"We'd better learn to smoke. We'll be hellish soldiers if we don't smoke."

"And drink and chase women. God help any women who come around here."

Vridar fell asleep while thinking of his brother. He did not know him or understand him. Marion, the crosseyed lad, with his eyes now straight, seemed to have made women his major interest in life . . . .

The next morning the recruits were called into line, and Lieutenant Jacks, commanding officer of the battery, looked at the men. Vridar looked at the men, too. Some of them were from Idaho and Montana and California, but most of them were from New Mexico and these men looked sullen and evil. Some of them looked like Indians or halfbreeds. Jacks wanted to know if any of the men could use a typewriter. Vridar put his hand up and then saw that he was the only man with his hand up. "Come with me," Jacks said, and Vridar went with him to a tent. "Sergeant Strumm, this man is a typist. Find out if he is any good." Strumm was paunched and bowlegged and had a round florid face. His blue eyes were whimsical. Vridar sat at a typewriter and pounded the keys and the two men watched.

"You'll do," Strumm said. "You'll be company clerk." After Jacks left, Strumm talked to Vridar as man to man. Vridar was a lucky dog, he said; the clerk had a job that was soft and safe. In a few days Vridar would be a corporal, and he would be a sergeant when the battery landed in France. Vridar was flattered. He typed reports and letters and began to feel like a corporal. Two days later stripes were sewed on his shirt sleeves and his coat and he wrote to Neloa that he was Corporal Hunter now. But his joy was short-lived. In an awful moment the appalling truth of what he had done came to him when he looked at Marion's eyes. Generously, without having been called, Marion had come with him, assuming that they would be in the ranks, side by side. In Marion's eyes when he came in from drill Vridar saw the contempt and pain, and he thought, What a son of a bitch I am! He went to Strumm. "I don't want this job," he said. "Please get another clerk and reduce me to the ranks."

"What in hell's the matter?"

"I want to be a common private with a gun."

"Gonococcus! You're the clerk and you'll stay here."

"Sergeant, please do this for me. Listen. My brother came with me. He was not drafted but came in the place of another man, so we could be together. Honest to God I never thought of that when I put my hand up and I don't want this job."

"Don't be a fool. You're the only typist we have."

"But I tell you I don't want it!"

"Well, go see Jacks, but he'll laugh at you."

Vridar went to Jacks and saluted and stood at attention and waited.

"Well, Corporal?" said Jacks at last.

"Sir, I don't want to be company clerk. I want to be in the ranks with my brother."

Jacks looked at him. He was a huge man who had been an all-American guard. He was brutal and arrogant. "Coporal Hunter, go back to your work."

"But, sir, you don't understand. My brother took the place of another man—"

"Corporal, did you hear me?"

"Yes sir. But we were to be together in the ranks. Please, sir—"

Jacks rose suddenly from his chair, his face dark with anger. "Corporal, there's no place for sentimentality in war. Go back to your work."

Vridar went to the company tent, but he hated his work now and he hated himself. He would have given anything, even his life, to have taken that look out of Marion's eyes. "All right," he said to Strumm, "but don't think I'll sit in a tent when we get to France. I didn't come here to pound a typewriter."

"You're a strange bird," Strumm said, looking into Vridar's eyes. "Most men would jump at your job."

"But I'm a traitor to my brother."

Strumm began to whistle. "I like you," he said after a few moments. "I think I can trust you. I want to tell you something . . . ."

Alonzo Strumm, top-sergeant of the battery, had been a soldier for nine years but he was not a soldier. He loved books. He read Dante and Hindu philosophy, Hegel and Kant. All the men in the battery liked him. "Obey orders, you jackass," Strumm would say. "Life is a battlefield and you may as well fight in the army as anywhere else. Don't take it too seriously and death may miss you somewhere . . . ." And Strumm would smile.

"I want to tell you something," he said to Vridar. "I'm in love. You ever been in love?"

"All my life," Vridar said.

"Then you'll understand." He gave Vridar a cigarette and studied his face. "There's no place in the army for love. Here a man eats saltpeter with his beans. Can you taste it in your chow?"

"I've tasted something."

"That's it. The army buys it by the ton." Again he studied Vridar. "I'm in love with a married woman," he went on. "She's a doctor's wife over in San Diego, the swellest woman God ever made." He was silent a moment. He inhaled deeply and said: "Her name is Dorothy but I call her Dolly and she's a peach. I've been seeing her twice a week. Now what I want to tell you is this: it's against orders but I have to see her. Out on the hill. Out in the bushes just like a damned schoolboy . . . . I want you to help me."

"Sure, if I can."

"When I'm gone, if Jacks comes blustering around, wanting to know where I

406

am, you make some excuse. I'll do something for you sometime. When we're in France. You married?"

"Yes."

"So am I. My wife's in Seattle, but what good is a wife when she's in Seattle and I'm in San Diego? That sounds pretty bad, I guess. But this is decent between Dolly and me. Don't get the idea that she lives out there under a bush."

Vridar grinned.

"Army life is hell," Strumm went on. "It's beans and pomp but a man can get used to it. Well, when we get to France I'll do something for you." Strumm rose from his chair. His manner changed. "Corporal, is that report ready?"

"Yes sir."

"Corporal, you may go now."

But there was none of the book-lover in Lieutenant Frederick Jacks. He was a scowling tyrant and all the men despised him. He seemed to dislike Vridar from the start, and he chastened him again and again, until their scorn of one another became frank and open. One afternoon a sergeant entered the tent and spoke to Jacks and left.

"Corporal Hunter, go tell Sergeant Adkins to come back."

Vridar left the tent and hailed Adkins. He delivered the message and returned and saluted. "Sir, the fellow says he'll be back in a minute."

Jacks turned slowly in his chair and looked at Vridar. "Hunter, you're in the army. Did you know that?"

"Yes sir."

"Then what do you mean by calling Sergeant Adkins a fellow?"

"Why," said Vridar, "he is a fellow, isn't he, sir?"

Jacks rose to his feet and gave Vridar a hard and unpitying appraisal. "Corporal Hunter, there are no *fellows* in this army. They're all in college. In this army there are soldiers and officers. Can you understand that?"

"Yes sir."

"Go tell Sergeant Adkins I want to see him at once."

Vridar left the tent, hot with shame and rage. But a few days later his attitude was changed, not only toward Jacks but toward army life. He sat at his typewriter to work and saw in the machine a paper. It was a letter and Vridar read the salutation and the first line. It was a letter from Jacks to his mother. After hesitating a moment Vridar read swiftly and his amazement grew as he read.

> Dear Mumsy:
>   The longer I stick around in this cockeyed army the madder I get. I hate the whole mess. All my superior officers are over-bearing fools. When Colonel White comes around he bawls me out and tries to make me look cheap. It's the same with the others. Nothing that I do is right. Nothing pleases them. To hear them tell it my battery is the worst in the army and I'm the most inefficient officer between here and Verdun. White and all the other stuckup asses come parading around to show off and it gets under my hide. I won't stand it much longer. One

of these days I'll draw my good right arm back and smash White
in his mouthful of gold . . . .

The letter was unfinished. Vridar went to the entrance to look out. He read
the letter again and then copied it; and all afternoon he could think of nothing but
the implications in what Jacks had said. For several days he pondered them. Then
he wrote to Neloa.

> Dearest Girl:
> The other day I got the surprise of my life. I've been trying
> to figure out why Christians who profess peace tax themselves
> to death to support armies and navies. I thought it was because
> men aren't civilized—and of course they aren't. They don't love
> peace. They love feuds and danger and battle. That's why ships
> aren't sunk and soldiers aren't sent home to mind their business.
> Another reason no doubt is profits: munitions-makers are
> war-makers, though they probably go to church and pray and
> donate to peace foundations. A third reason is women: they
> love to see men march away to fight. As long as women admire
> uniforms more than poets we'll have bigger and better wars.
> But the most important reason of all I've just stumbled on to.
> Being a man I blush to name it; for men, my dear, are indescrib-
> ably vain and petty and love nothing so much as power over
> their fellows. They love to give orders and make men jump
> through loops. They love to swagger and put on the dog. Ob-
> serve the outlandish uniforms of kings, the plush and padding
> and glitter of religious dignitaries, and apes starched to a fine
> stupidity at formal dinners. War serves male vanity and love of
> power on a huge scale. And I see now that the only soldier
> who doesn't sweat under the discipline is the knothead at the
> top: Pershing probably writhes in his polished boots under Foch,
> and Foch is the only murderer in the whole outfit who doesn't
> have someone knifing his self-esteem. I've been detesting Lt.
> Jacks for an overbearing fool. But no more. I see now that his
> superior officers make him jump like a circus monkey; and so
> he makes us jump; and no doubt I'd be making someone jump if
> I could. I remember with shame how I felt my oats when I be-
> came a corporal; how it pleased me to reflect that I outranked
> most of the army and had privileges not given to a private. Now
> I want to get back to the ranks where a man it a target and God,
> poor fellow, is on both sides.
> Does it amuse you? Is there some relationship between war
> and sex? Did Napoleon ever have a good orgasm? Did Alex-
> ander copulate with his mother? Before Caesar marched on
> Gaul was he frustrated in his efforts to seduce the wife of some
> friend? Smile, my dear, but truth of all things is strangest be-
> cause we see so little of it . . . .

Vridar was seeing human nature in the raw, without its mask of Christian myth.
The spirit of the men became steadily more reckless and fatalistic as they yielded
their wills to the army's will. And all of them put on weight. Vridar gained twenty
pounds, now weighing a hundred and seventy-six; and Marion weighed a hundred

and ninety. The two brothers ate together notwithstanding the stripes on Vridar's arms, and they were always first to offer their tins for a second helping . . . .

> O—ver there!—o—ver there!
> Send the word, send the word over there
> that the Yanks are coming, the Yanks are coming,
> the drums rum-tum-ming everywhere! . . .

In a spirit of fellowship new to him, he looked at the men. He liked them and he felt something deep and good in the common purpose that united them in devotion to a common goal:

> And we won't come back till it's o-ver o-ver there!

He heard them singing when he went to the canteen for tobacco or sweets or when during the evening he prowled with them up and down the tent-aisles:

> Goodbye sweetheart, wives and mothers,
> it won't take us long!
> Don't you wor-ry while we're there,
> it's for you we're fighting too!
> So goodbye Broadway, hel-lo France!
> We're going to square our debt to you!

Men sang who had never sung before. Vridar sang, and then marveled at this new spirit which possessed him. There was more in war, he reflected, than he had imagined: something beyond definition, as in religion there was something beyond the empty rituals, as in poetry there was an untouched wonder beyond the reach of the poet. After a few weeks Vridar fought against this possession of himself by a power that he did not understand: he had not come here to be a uniformed robot: he wanted to keep a sense of detachment, to see and study this enormous process of annihilation. He wanted to study the change in the men. He saw obscurely at first but more sharply as the days passed that the training of a soldier was very devious and cunning: these men were being stripped of their scruples and filled with the primitive and elemental emotions of the brute. They wanted to fight. They were eager to get to France. In one event and another Vridar looked into their savage minds and hearts.

He saw, for instance, the malicious cruelty of the company surgeon. When the men passed in single file round a room to be inoculated against typhoid, Vridar while moving slowly in the line studied the doctor's face. It was a large coarse face covered with a devilish grin. When a soldier flinched under the needle, the surgeon's joy was as unmistakable as the epaulets on his shoulders. He thrust more deeply, it seemed to Vridar, into the arms of those who were scared. Three men fainted while Vridar was in the room, the first sprawling as if shot. "Take him away!" the surgeon roared, and two corporals dragged the man out and hurled a pailful of water into his face. The man came to, gasping and white, and was yanked up and set on his feet; and when he staggered from the room, there was something in his eyes that went into Vridar like the needle.

"If you men topple over at a needle prick," said the doctor, looking round him, "what in hell will you do when you get a bayonet in your guts? . . . . Next!"

It was not, Vridar perceived, the thrust of the needle that unnerved the men; it was the cruel cynical face of the man with the needle. It was his gloating sadism in a world that had become unfriendly and strange.

The inoculation made Vridar sick, so sick that he thought he would die. He had hot violent nausea and a raging fever. "I'm sick as a dog," he said to Marion. "Tell Strumm I'm going to stay in bed." Then Strumm came to the tent and put a sympathetic hand on Vridar's brow. "What's the matter, Corp? It's inspection this morning. Can you get up?"

"I wouldn't get up for Pershing himself."

"Well, all right. The Major will bawl hell out of you."

A little before ten o'clock Vridar heard the Major and his retinue coming down the aisle between the tents. Vridar lifted a flap and peered out. Men on both sides of the aisle were standing at attention, with everything about them scrubbed and polished. The flaps of every tent were thrown back to show the soldierly discipline within.

"What's the trouble here? Lieutenant Jacks, why isn't this tent in order?"

"The man in there, sir, is ill." It was Strumm speaking.

"What's wrong with him?"

"A little typhoid, sir."

The Major came to Vridar's tent and raised a flap. "You there!" he barked. "Are you sick?" Vridar pretended to be asleep. He breathed deeply so that the Major would see the blanket rise and fall. The Major entered the tent and roughly seized Vridar's shoulder and turned him to the light. "Why aren't you up?"

"Sir, I'm sick."

"You don't look sick to me." He laid a palm on Vridar's brow. "Do you think you're sick every time you get a little fever?"

"No sir."

"Sergeant, give this man three pills."

Vridar shuddered. Three of the little black pills were enough to physic an elephant.

And in his own brother Vridar saw the brute rising. Now a powerful broadshouldered man, Marion, sensing his new power, carried himself defiantly, neither seeking trouble nor avoiding it. One evening at mess he was in line, with Vridar just behind him, when a huge halfbreed with messtin in his hand pushed into the line ahead of Marion. Marion turned to Vridar and said, "Did you ever see such God damned gall! Here, hold my tin." Marion stepped out of the line and with all his might smashed into the halfbreed and floored him. The man leapt up, ready to fight.

"Go to the end of the line," Vridar said. "You've no right to push in here."

The man shrugged and went; but later, when Vridar and Marion were sitting in their tent, the flap was raised and a dark Indian face looked in. "Come on out," the face said. Then another face appeared, that of the big halfbreed. "Come out," he said, "and we'll finish this thing."

Marion rose to go, but Vridar took his arm. "Just a minute," he said to the halfbreeds, "and we'll be out." The faces disappeared. "They'll knife you," he said to Marion.

"Well, let's go out."

They went out. The big halfbreed was waiting with a half-dozen men around him. "This way," he said.

"Where?" asked Marion.

"Over the hill."

"Oh no you don't," Vridar said. He took Marion aside. "They'll knife you."

"You're an officer. Search them."

"No, they'll gang up. I'll report it to Jacks." He sent Marion into the tent and turned to the men. "I'm an officer," he said. "I suppose you know that." The halfbreed shrugged and the contempt made Vridar furious. "You'll obey orders or you'll be thrown into the guardhouse! Stay here." He went to Strumm and told him what had happened. Jacks swung in his chair.

"Where are they?"

"Near my tent, sir. They are waiting."

"Bring them here."

Vridar went to the tent and told Marion and the seven men to come with him. Jacks meanwhile had put men to work, and under a hanging light they roped off a ring. Jacks came over to Vridar and said, "Which ones are they?"

"Here, sir. My brother and this man."

"All right," said Jacks, "strip to your waist." The two men stripped and six-ounce gloves were laced on their hands. "There'll be no rounds in this fight," Jacks said. "You'll fight until one of you has enough. All right, Sergeant, let them go."

Vridar stood among soldiers by the rope and looked at his brother. Marion was a little pale but seemed grim and determined. The big halfbreed, muscled like a gladiator, looked at no one but Marion, his face dark and murderous. In the fight that followed there was no feinting, no guarding of belly or face; they drove their blows with all their power. The soldiers roundabout howled like mad men and urged the warriors to mightier efforts. Vridar shook as he watched the fight and looked inward to his emotions: more than anything else he wanted to leap into the ring and take Marion's part, as he had done so many times in childhood. When he saw the halfbreed strike Marion in his teeth, spilling blood, or saw Marion writhe from a driving smash in his belly, Vridar babbled with fury, as though his own son were being slain before his eyes. Once he moved to go under the rope but was seized and thrown back.

The men fought until they were bloody and exhausted and staggered like drunkards or fell under their own blows.

"Shall I stop them?" Strumm asked Jacks.

"They wanted to fight. Let them fight."

Then the end came. Men entered the ring with pails of water and drenched the two fighters and Jacks said, "Get back to your tents." Vridar rushed in and took the gloves from Marion's hands and led him to the tent, wiping blood from Marion as they went.

"I'm all right!" cried Marion impatiently. "The son of a bitch didn't hurt me."

411

In the tent Vridar stared at Marion's bruised face and wondered if this was the timid lad who had gone to school in Annis, in Poplar, in Rigby. It was hard to believe what army training could do to a man. Then suddenly Rollie Pitkin slipped in, a slender youth who always looked frightened. "Listen!" Rollie said, whispering.

"What is it?"

"I just heard them halfbreeds talkun. They plan to kill you both. I heard them say it. When we get in France—"

"Oh, when we get to France!"

"I heard them say it!"

"Thanks, Rollie. We'll keep our eyes open."

Rollie left the tent and the brothers looked at one another. "They'll do it," Vridar said, "if they can."

"That," said Marion, "is a game we can both play."

"But not at their level. They'll do it behind your back."

Marion shrugged. "They're morons," he said. "I'll be able to read their plans in their faces and I won't be the first one to die . . . ."

VI

When with Neloa Vridar could not duck the feeling that his marriage had been a mistake, but when away from her he felt only tenderness and a wish to cherish. One day early in November when the battery's departure for France was imminent he took her letters over the hill and sat to look at the ocean and read them again.

> Dear Heart:
> Well, another lonesome old Sunday has about dragged itself to a close and I am still able to smile. Agnes has been singing Somewhere in France is Daddy and Keep the Home Fires Burning and I have been so lonesome I have cried . . . . Dearie, when you write again tell me how you spend your Sundays. Are they the same as every other day? Your father has been preaching to Agnes trying to make a Mormon of her but I'm afraid he didn't accomplish very much. Sweetheart, haven't you taken any photos since you got down there? I wish you would take some and send them to me. If you only knew how much I love you and how I love your letters you would steal time to write to me every day. I love you, love you. O sweetheart . . .

He read:

> Darling Boy:
> I don't know what is wrong with your mother and Diana but they are so cross they make life a misery for themselves and every one around them. But there, I don't want you to think I am complaining. I'm just telling you how things really are here. Babe and I are well and happy so don't you think we aren't. Do you know yet when you will leave? I got a basket and baby is sleeping alone now. Your father said to tell you you can just expect to sleep alone when you come home. I'm afraid he would have an awful time stopping you, wouldn't he? Darling, when you come home I'm going to stick to you like glue.

Dearie, you're in for an awful lot of loving when you get home. And will you be glad?

I have our future all pictured and it hasn't a single disturbance in it. I'll be terribly surprised if we ever have the least bit of trouble again. I am suffering tonight, too, dearie. I suffer when you suffer and I always shall. I thank God for your love and pray the time will come when you can forget the old Neloa, who is dead now, and live with and love your own. It was your love, dear, that made me what I am now. Sweetheart, I will swear to you that if I were to be hanged and could save my life by telling a dirty story, I could not do it . . . .

Vridar looked away at morning on the sea. After she had boasted that she probably knew more dirty stories than anyone else, he had cunningly led her to confession; and never for a moment suspecting his motive, she had emptied her memory of more filth than he had imagined any woman's mind could hold. Her stories had not been witty, not ironic, not even humorous; they were simply foul privy-legends that made stupid and feeble jest of the body's functions. He had stared at her with amazement, remembering his mother's teaching that all women were good and pure. Was it true that she no longer had interest in this gutter-stuff of Christian repression and shame? He believed it was true and he sighed and read again.

Dearest Heart:

You know what my dream is now? To go somewhere far away where there will be no memories of the past to haunt us. I want a little home with just you and the baby, a small world of our own. I don't want ever to see the Antelope country again and when I die I don't want to be buried there. I don't want to be buried in Idaho for I hate the place. And I have learned, dear, that we can never live around your folks or mine.

I am getting fat, really. I now weigh 138 with my suit and hat on. Don't you think that is pretty good? I am weak and my nerves are bad but don't you worry about me. If I got sick I don't think they'd let you come. I wonder if I'll see you before you see France. I must, darling, because I love you with the truest strongest love a woman can have for a man. And don't feel so sorry because you have been what you call mean to me. No matter what you have said or done I'll always love you. Just think of our future, for we shall be happy, dear. Oh, so very happy when you come home! And I know you will come! Love, darling, with all my heart!

Did she mean these things? He believed that she meant them for the reason that he had to believe. He kissed her letters and sat in thought, feeling a great loneliness, not only for himself and Neloa but for the men in camp. They were dying now like hogs with cholera. Influenza had struck here. Half the soldiers were stretched out on cots and some had died. Rollie Pitkin was in a box now and on his way home. The big halfbreed was close to death. He lay on his belly and wrote to Neloa:

I know, dearest, that you forgive, because forgiveness is one of your golden virtues; but just the same I am sick to death of the

413

shameless way I abuse you when we are together and of my awful dark worship of you when we are apart. God knows I've tried to fight out of it and see my way clear but there is something in my blood or training that is more terrible than nightmare and I can't see what it is. And I'm so damned weary of trying. I believe it would be better for you, yes, and for me, if I were dead; and I might easily die here, for the flu is everywhere. A stronger will than all other wills keeps me in life because I love you and want to see you again . . . .

As company clerk I take care of the mail. Some of the letters don't have return addresses on the envelopes and I have to open them to get the address. I don't have to read them but I do. Listen to this one:

Dear husband mine, you don't know how me and baby miss you. Every day is just like a awful dream. I try and keep busy but I just think about you all the time and it seems like I couldn't stand it. I try and keep busy making things for you. Honey, did you get the cake I sent and was it nice and fresh? Tell me what you'd like. I dreamed about you last night, honey. We was in the woods where we used to walk on Sunday and you was in a uniform but it seemed like you had come back to stay. And oh I was so happy I just cried and cried and when I woke up my pillow was all wet . . . .

He has gone back to stay, Neloa—in a box. And now listen to this one to Private Harry Johnson:

My own dearest, I'm just so excited I can hardly write. Daddy says the war won't last much longer and that you'll be home for Christmas! Imagine, dear! He says he knows it's true and I can't believe him but something deeper than reason tells me it is so. And, Harry, do you know what I'm doing? Oh, you wouldn't! You men! I'm making my wedding gown. *Harry, dear, I'm making my wedding gown* and mama is helping me. Dearest, let's be married on Christmas day! You'll be my wedding gift. And the gown, it's just too darling for words! And won't we be happy? Please write and say I'm not foolish and my father is a good prophet and you'll soon be home! Love, dearest, worlds and worlds without end!

Again Vridar sat in thought. He looked away to the Pacific, his eyes wet; and barely able to see the paper he again wrote to Neloa.

Over such letters I have wept like a fool, as one must weep over the heartbreaking when it is meaningless. Harry *is* going home. He died last night. And what, Neloa dear, is the sense in it all? Because of the blunders and follies of old men young men are called to die for their country; but they don't get to die a clean honorable death. They die of some stinking undiagnosed disease, with not a soul around who loves them, almost with no one to care; so many men are sick that we haven't doctors and nurses for them, and those thought to be hopeless are carried away to the death-ward and there they die, alone, save for the few minutes when I go in to take down their last gasping words to their loved ones. My God how I hate it!

Perhaps the father was not a bad prophet. There is rumor of an armistice . . . .

Is it true? the men asked, and nobody could tell them. Many men were gone from the mess-line now, many cots were empty. A hundred lay in the gloomy hospital down the hill. One would come to Vridar and ask, "Is—is Latrielle dead yet?" "I don't know, I'll see." Another: "Corporal, can you tell me?—is Huff—?" "Yes." Sometimes the question was only a whisper. Sometimes a man turned away choked by grief.

"How do you feel?" Vridar would ask his brother.

"All right. And you?"

"All right. I have a secret, we're to leave for France in two days."

"Thank God for that."

But they did not leave for France. "Well," Strumm said a day later, "the damned thing is all over. An armistice has been signed."

"You mean we're not going to France?"

Strumm swung in fury. "God damn it, you heard me! You heard me! I tell you the God damned thing is all over!" And like a man who had lost all interest in life, Strumm left the tent and disappeared.

"It's all over," Vridar said to Marion.

"For Christ sake!" said Marion and sank to his cot.

Vridar went over a hill and sat under a bank. For the soldiers in France he was glad peace had come, but what would he do now? Must he go back to Neloa, back to his passion and nightmare? If he had been killed, she would have had ten thousand dollars and she would have lived through her grief and forgotten him and married a man closer to her heart. Now he had to go back, back to his violence and shame, back to his fight . . . . He wanted to go—to go to Neloa; to kneel to her as to an altar; to beg her to help him see his way out of the darkness. But he felt that she would destroy rather than free him. In her quiet way, in her undeliberate childlike way, she had conquered him at every turn: in Annis, on the Antelope hills, and in every bitter hour since; until she had become not a woman but a force, not a wife to soothe and heal but an elemental power that engulfed his will. He felt that in her ways was wisdom, in his ways the frenzies that were symptomatic of his time. He felt it but was unable to see why. He could no more chasten himself to the simple unquesting way of her life than he could sit happily with her among dull people in a dull house. And now, from a world of war he had to turn back to a world of peace, in chaos. Three weeks later he was on the road home.

He and Marion and forty others entrained at San Diego. On the way to Los Angeles a fierce rivalry developed. Most of these men had wanted to go to France, they had wanted to fight. Now they turned on one another. Those from northern California, led by an ex-pugilist, challenged those from Idaho and Montana to combat. "You hog-gelders!" he sneered, standing on a seat in full view of them. "You stable cleaners and cow bums!" Hearing him, the Idahoans and Montanans rose from their seats. The San Franciscan addressed himself to Vridar: "You got stripes on your arm, you been pretty high and mighty: now I'm gonna knock that Goddamn big nose offen your face. Your men ready?"

"Just a minute!" Vridar said. He turned to the men around him. "We're about even," he said, counting the men at either end of the coach. "What are the rules for this fight?"

"They ain't no rules, you long-nosed steer. When you bastards is all smacked to the sawdust the fight will be over."

"Oh yeah?" said a giant from Montana.

"You cow-milkers ready?"

A few moments later Vridar was lost in a terrific brawl of curses and fists. The coach shook and glass was smashed from windows, as the men fought like pirates. Vridar had leapt to a seat; as the enemy rushed forward in a tide of fists and blasphemy, he hurled himself on a man and clutched and went down. He had a man by his throat and with all his power he broke the man under him and shoved him to his knees and struck him a dreadful blow in his teeth. He then struck him in his soft throat; the man went down, limp and unconscious; and when Vridar came up, something smote him like a sledge of iron. It spun him and he fell backward into the aisle, and the men leapt upon him or over him as they fought. He protected his face and shook his head, trying to clear his wits. When the dizziness left him, he crawled to one side between seats; and after a moment he came up again, ready to strike. In this instant, glancing round him, he saw Marion bring a man up over his head and break him across the hard arm of a seat; saw Marion's savage and bloody face; saw the giant from Montana measuring blows; saw a welter of men sprawled or standing. Then there came upon Vridar that madness that used to seize him in Annis, in Poplar, when driven to the wall by school bullies; and he began to babble with fury. He saw a man kick another, prone and helpless, in his face, and he sprang forward and got the man by his throat and choked him until his tongue fell out. He was lost now to everything but murder, and he might have killed the man if a terrific blow had not laid him out senseless. He rolled over on his belly and was still . . . .

When he came to, the fight was over. In one end of the coach the Californians were nursing their wounds; and in the other end were his own comrades, some of them bloody and undone. Dizzy and sick, Vridar allowed Marion to help him to a seat.

"You hurt?" Vridar asked. Marion said no but his nose looked broken. Vridar stretched arms and legs to learn if he had broken bones and then rubbed a hand over his skull. On the back of it he had a lump the size of a small egg. The giant from Montana was standing in the aisle, looking at the enemy. His blood was still up.

"Come on, you yellow son of a bitch!" he called to the pugilist. "Let's finish this!"

"Go to hell," said the pugilist.

"When we get off the train in Los Angeles, we'll finish this." When they left the train at Los Angeles, the man from Montana like a hound to a scent was after his foe. But the pugilist ducked and vanished. "The yellow dog!" said the Montanan. "I wanted to yank his heart out and stick my arm through it."

"You done enough," someone said. "You knocked most of his teeth out."

"I wanted to knock his jawbones out. The son of a bitch, calling me a cow-milker! I never milked a cow in my life."

The men prowled in underground places and found whisky, and when they entrained for their homes every one of them had a quart or more. The Montanan had a gallon jug. Hour after hour he drank from his jug and cursed the pugilist. In a voice of utter disgust he would roar, "Calling me a cow-milker!" and would drink again. One of the men had a broken finger which he had bandaged; another had teeth missing and teeth loosened, and thoughtfully he fingered them, trying to fix them solidly in place. After a while they all sang through shattered windows into the night. Vridar and Marion sat together and drank.

"Well," Vridar said, "it's all over now."

"Yes. France got licked and now Germany is licked. They will fight again."

"Remember what pious little lads we were? Look at us now!"

"We were fools," Marion said.

"What will become of us?"

"What does it mater?" He looked at Vridar with pain and disgust. "You had to be an idiot and get married. We could have taken to the road."

"Yes, I suppose I was an idiot."

After a while Marion slept; and Vridar, full of whisky and woe, studied his brother's face. It was a large strong face but there was something weak, something very loose and sensual, in the mouth. There was something bitter in the eyes. Our childhood years have licked him, he thought; they have licked both of us. The man from Montana had fallen forward over his jug and was snoring into his lap. After a little while he awoke and looked round him and cursed. He saw Vridar looking at him and came over, bringing his jug.

"You been to college. Tell me why that son of a bitch called me a cow-milker."

"He called us all that," said Vridar, grinning. "He didn't mean just you."

"You married?"

"Yes."

"I was," the man said, looking at Vridar strangely. "But my wife—I guess your wife didn't get the flu." The man raised the jug to his lips but he did not drink. He set it down and left it in the aisle and went to a seat. He bowed his head to his arms. In a few moments he was weeping like a child.

VII

It was morning when the two brothers stepped down in Idaho Falls. They went to a small dark house, and Prudence came running and was gathered to their arms. Vridar asked where Neloa was and his mother said she was out in the yard, hanging clothes. When he saw Neloa, he stopped for a moment and looked at her. She was very white and very thin. Among his memories of her this was to be one of the most vivid: a tall girl, a white and lonely girl, hanging diapers from a line. He moved again and she turned and looked at him with amazement. Then "O sweetheart!" she cried, and he never forgot the wild tone of her voice. She came running

417

to him and was in his arms and his face was lost in her hair. "Sweetheart!" she cried, her voice choked with wonder and grief.

"Sweetheart yourself," he said and kissed her white lips.

She stepped back to look at him. "Darling, is it you? I can't believe it!" She hugged him, her hands locked behind his back as though she would never let him go. "I've been so lonesome!" she said, coming again to his arms. "Darling, you don't know how I've missed you!"

Vridar's eyes were wet. He was looking far away at the Antelope hills and trying to push his grief down but it was hot and overwhelming. "I love you!" he said, trembling to her touch. "Neloa, Neloa, I love you!"

"And I love you! Are you really glad to see me?"

"You know I am."

She yielded now to one of her rare impulses: with palms to his cheeks she drew his head down and kissed his wet eyes. "Now," she said, trying to be gay, "you must come and see baby." She led him to the house and Vridar entered a bedroom and looked at their son. "Isn't he sweet?"

"Yes, I suppose." Now, as formerly when with him, she became ill at ease. He saw her distress and drew her to him. "Sure, he's a fine son."

"Darling, aren't you going to kiss him?"

"Oh, of course." Vridar bowed to his son and kissed a soft red cheek. For a moment he looked into the wondering blueness of the child's eyes.

Neloa took the child in her arms. "See, baby, this is daddy! This is your daddy, back from the war!"

Vridar thought he had never seen her so deeply moved. She was shaking all over and there was something almost hysterical about her. Filled with great tenderness and pity, he took the child from her and laid it in the bed and drew her to him. "Neloa, dear, you've changed."

"Uh-huh," she said, smiling at him. There was something terrible in her smile.

"Haven't they been good to you?" Ah, what a blind man he was, to have imagined that his mother and sister would be good to her!

"I don't care, because you're with me now. Sweetheart, you won't ever leave me again? Ever, *ever?*"

"Not if I can help it." He drew her to him and she shook in his arms, but she did not weep.

An hour later he went to the garage. Tires and tubes, wrenches and empty bottles, old cans and papers and odds and ends were scattered everywhere. He smiled, thinking of his father and uncle as business men: how little they knew of the fine and subtle hypocrisy of trade! In the repair room he found his father under a car, soaked to his skin with grease and gasoline, and Ike under another car, cursing Henry Ford. "Hello under there!" Vridar said to his father.

Joe paused in his efforts and grunted. "Is that you?"

Vridar went over and peered at Ike. "Are you trying to ruin that Ford?"

"The God damn thing!" said Ike. "A Ford is a bunch of tin with four holes for spark plugs and a crank. Hand me that-there crowbar." Vridar picked up a crowbar sheathed with oil and pushed it to Ike. "I'll move this nut," Ike said, "or I'll split this son of a bitchun Ford wide open." Vridar grinned, remembering that for years Ike had been a blacksmith.

"If you got nothun to do," said Joe, "you might set in the office. Some feller might want gas."

"Do you leave your office open like that?"

"It's just to set in," said Ike.

"Don't people steal things?"

"Let the sons of bitches steal. They ain't enough to make anybody rich."

Vridar went to the office and after a little while Joe and Ike came. They looked as if they had been rolled in grease and sawdust: it was in their beards and hair and it sheathed their naked arms. A motorist drove up outside and honked and looked in.

"He wants something," Vridar said.

"To hell with him," said Ike. "Let him come in. He ain't no bettern I am."

Vridar went out to serve the motorist, but the outraged man slammed his door and drove off. "You're fine business men," Vridar said, returning to Ike. "You lose trade that way."

"We ain't lackeys," said Ike. "They even want us to pump up their God damn tires."

"You need a manager," Vridar said, "and I'm looking for a job."

Ike grunted and rolled a cigarette. His cigarette paper was black with grease. "What for do we need a manager?"

"To build your trade up. You'll go broke."

And so Vridar became manager of the garage. It was he who, prudent and tactful, pumped air into tires, filled radiators, wiped dust and grime from windshields; who studied the methods of competitors to learn wherein they succeeded or failed; who soothed the anger of customers when they felt they had been overcharged; and who added to the dignity of the place by having stationery printed, a new pump installed and a sign hung above the door. He persuaded Ike and Joe to have taxi service, too, and his family to live in the city, so that his mother or Neloa could step into the office while he made a call. Within two months he had doubled the firm's business and redoubled it, but he was not happy in this work. The odors of gasoline and oil sickened him. He was sickened too by the sly dishonesty of methods which in competition with others he was forced to employ: selling cheap oil in trademarked containers or pretending that a car needed repairing when it did not.

There lay ahead of Vridar the decade of the lost generation, with its bootleggers, gangsters, corrupt politicians, and self-pitying authors. He felt the mood of it, the reckless emptiness, the crumbling of moral values. Nations were wrangling over the spoils. Soldiers, stripped of their ideals, had come home to find their jobs gone. Bootleggers were laying the groundwork of their vast industry, and women were lifting their skirts and painting their cheeks and bobbing their hair. Henry Ford was crusading against the Jews. The old ideals which had led nations into blood and fire were now ghastly silhouettes in the world's mind; and a new generation, cynical, desperate, pleasure-mad had taken the stage.

Vridar, with his old anchors gone, cared little if witch-hunters nailed freedom in its coffin or the Russian delirium engulfed the world. He strove to renounce all ambition and despise all doctrines and creeds. Human nature, stripped of its civilized veneer, had again shown itself to be the brutal and primitive thing that it had always been. He was weary with trying to understand what had betrayed the world: those who had stayed home, greedy for profits, now followed like buzzards after the crippled, the shellshocked, and the insane who came back. What was there for a man to love and cherish? Nothing—at least nothing that a mankind full of self-betrayal could point to.

When his mother rebuked him for smoking and drinking, he swung to her with scorn. "I'd talk, Mater, damned if I wouldn't! What did your generation do with all its pious cant? What have you to show for it? A mad world! I should think your words would gag you and the millions like you. And your generation with all this blood and betrayal on its hands would tell me what to do! I'm done with it and all that it stands for and I hate it clear to the bottom of my soul! Your phoney ideals have driven us to ruin but still you talk and talk and talk. Millions have just died for these stinking ideals you talk about; and yet in your smug and halfwitted Christian piety you tell me what to do! Mater, please understand that I hate your pompous little religion and am done with it . . . ."

He did not know that his self-pitying tirade was already one of the voices of the self-pitying lost generation. It seemed to him that the world was good save where humanity touched it and wreaked upon it the ironic and obscene flummery of its ideals. Everywhere this Sunday, he reflected, men and women were murmuring their trite phrases of love and peace; and yet at this moment when so many prayed and sang hymns there lay upon Christian Europe the awful waste and smell of death. Human legs and arms and heads were scattered there in thousands; graveyards with their white crosses covered acres; and it had all been done in the name of a symbol of peace on a cross. Hiding behind its pious humbug, the Christian world had released a vast and primordial passion as ancient as the sea, left kingdoms devastated by its destroying power, and put a new and terrible nightmare into the Russian heart. But why did mankind convert its ideologies into monstrous self-betrayal? He went to Neloa, who was sewing by a dark window, and knelt to her as he had knelt so many times. "Help me," he said, "not to be engulfed by this fresh insanity in the world, for I grow weary with trying and I am sick . . . ."

In spite of himself his journey again turned downward and for months he was lost in desperate cynicism. He became a bootlegger; he moved in this city's underworld with the thieves and pimps and whores; and for days at a time he was never sober. Late each night he came to Neloa but he never abused her now or taunted her about the past. He was done with all that. Intellectually he wanted to be done with everything that he had been. Emotionally he was still chained. With remorseless earnestness he tried to root out of himself every ideal, every precept, and every dogma that he had been taught as a child. He turned to the underworld to learn what its people dreamed and what they did and whether their ideals betrayed them. He found the way to them easy and he went.

Looking back in a later time he wondered how he escaped death; for as a taxi-driver, he was sometimes drunk and always reckless. He drove a big Auburn that had no brakes, and he ran over beasts and once swept like a war-tank over a herd of sheep. Twice he thought he had killed a man.

He was driving without lights in a black night. Now and then he stopped and struck a match or on hands and knees felt over the earth to find the road. Suddenly without warning there was a terrific crash. Then he heard a horse galloping furiously down the road, and while he sat in the car, wondering if he had killed the other horse of a team, a match flared and he saw the face of a man. Then the light went out and the man gave a blood-curdling yell. "I'm killed!" he roared. "Someone has killed me!"

Vridar left the car and groped through darkness and found a buggy. He saw the dim form of a man. Then there came another chilling scream. "Someone has killed me!" the man yelled.

"You sound very much alive to me," Vridar said. He struck a match and saw a husky young swain with blood running from his nose. The man had blood on his hands and he was staring at it, speechless with terror. Vridar got the man into the car and drove him to a doctor, who, after a brief examination, said he was not hurt at all. Vridar then bought salves and bandages for the man and took him to a hotel and paid for his room. He forgot the matter until a week later when the man entered the garage, scowling and looking suspiciously round him. "You owe me big damages," he said to Vridar. "If you don't pay me I'll sue."

"For what?"

"Listen, I been to a lawyer. He says I suffered—well, shock, he says. He says you owe me big damages."

"How big?" asked Vridar, amused.

"Ten thousand. But if you settle out of court, well, my lawyer says—"

Vridar had fallen to a chair and was roaring with laughter. "Go away," he gasped, "you're killing me!" He arose and bent over a counter, with tears bursting from his eyes. "I'm—I'm going to—sue you! I'm going to sue you for a million dollars."

"A million dollars!" cried the astonished young man.

"Yes! I suffered traumatic shock, and that's the worst kind! Doctors say your screams have made a nervous wreck of me! You understand? I'm going to see a lawyer now . . . ."

But it was not his many accidents that deeply concerned him. It was the meaning of this new lawlessness in young people, this open contempt for the old. He wondered about it but only once, it seemed to him, did he look close to its truth. Once a week he went to a small outlying hamlet to fetch the teachers to their homes. They were young women, amorous, starved, and twittering. Three of them sat in the front seat with him and wanted to learn to drive and at last he surrendered the wheel to a plump girl named Bertha. She seemed to know what she was doing and she drove all right until she rounded a corner and saw before her an enormous truck. Thrust out from the truck was a wooden beam. Missing the brake she stepped on the gas and shot ahead, and like a mighty arm the beam swept windshield and glass and top from the car and the car careened off the road and crashed into a fence.

Vridar stood up, spilling glass, and thinking ruefully that this was not the Auburn but a car in storage which without permission he had taken. He looked at the stricken faces of the girls. Then he leapt out and went over to a bank and looked into the sky and began to laugh; and one by one the women left the car and came over and laughed with him. The men from the truck stood in the road and looked at them. "It was fun!" one said. "I liked it!" Another said it was the only exciting thing that had ever happened to her. A third said it was better than teaching school. Sobered, Vridar stared at them with astonishment: their faces were strangely radiant and excited, as if for the first time in their dull years they had touched life. They went singing down the road like a group of children . . . .

> Hail! Hail! The gang's all here!
> What the hell do we care?
> Oh, what the hell do we care . . . .

He had become a bootlegger. After a week of wrestling with his conscience, Ike became his partner, but the uncle drank more than he sold. Together they had a jug in a secret place and they drank from the jug. Often they went together on taxi calls, taking with them a quart of whisky; and they drove madly through the country, singing folk-ballads, or now and then they sat on a hilltop and waited for the dawn. Vridar had genuine admiration for this uncle, the mightiest of Joe's brothers. Ike was a handsome devil, though one eye was brown and one was blue. He had unspeakable contempt for order and routine and the fixed purpose. As a young man he had loved only three things, women and whisky and fighting; and now in middle age he only reversed the order, loving whisky best and women least. After becoming a mechanic, he had picked up a fondness for what he called do-dads.

One evening there came in for storage a huge new Packard, and the moment its owner was out of sight Ike entered it and with a child's curiosity examined the instruments on the panel. He said he would drive it just outside and return. Straight across the street was a cafe. Ike started the car and maneuvered it into position and headed for the street. Then something went wrong. Ike said afterward that the clutch stuck, but Vridar thought it more likely that Ike lost his head. With a sudden burst of speed he shot across the street and up over the curb and sidewalk, struck with a terrific crash a hundred square feet of plate glass window, and plowed into the cafe among tables and diners and went clear to the kitchen. Diners fled as though pursued by war-tanks, the owner of the cafe danced up and down in rage, and the police and fire departments rushed to the scene. When Vridar reached the car, his imperturbable uncle was sitting quietly in the front seat, fingering the gadgets and trying to tell what they were for. After he returned from the police station, he said: "I couldn't figger out what all them God damn do-dads is for."

This, then, was Vridar's partner in bootlegging, this man who cared no more about policemen and jails than he cared about the grease in his beard. They prospered in their trade, for nearly everyone, it seemed to Vridar, was drinking whisky now. Girls bought the stuff, and ranchers, flushed with war-profits, and

422

respectable men and women of the town. Saturday evening the people would come to Vridar and he would slip into the basement and dig bottles out of a cinder pile. He would take the bottles into a dark alley and set them by a wall. By all of this, the prevalence of drinking, and the kind of people who drank, he was astonished. He had thought that only the wastrels, only the sotted and bedeviled part of mankind, debauched themselves with strong drink. He learned on the contrary that it was chiefly the good folk who seemed most bent on finding hell. The harlots drank very little and some of them did not drink at all. Most of the other taxi-drivers were sober and earnest. There was Roy Shell, a cab-driver and a bootlegger. He never profaned and he never drank and there was about him a quiet professional dignity and a pitying smile. In all his dealings he was a man of integrity; his home life was charming and quiet; and when the day's work was done he took his children to his knee and recited pious legends. He went to church and he sang hymns and prayed. Or there was Bill Rummon, the pimp, who spent much time in the garage office. An orphan since birth, Bill had been jerked up by the hair of his head and turned loose into the world at the age of ten. Like Roy he was an earnest-minded fellow who saw no meanness or shame in what he did.

"I don't understand it," Vridar would say to Neloa. "I was taught that there are good people and bad people. In books they're that way—they're villains or heroes. People here remind me of the Italian girl Anatole France tells about. O Blessed Mother, she said, you who have conceived without sinning, give me the grace to sin without conceiving. Confucius said that the man of honor thinks of his character, the inferior man of his position. All these people think of their position.

"Or look, in God's name, at me. I was a good boy. By the holy angels, what a good boy I was! Now I drink Rummon was a bad boy and now he is as sober as an owl. What does it all mean?"

Or to his mother he would say: "The world isn't what you said it is. A man who preached in church last Sunday was stretched out last night with a quart of whisky in his belly."

"I don't believe it," she said.

"Then go look at the Packard. He hung over it all night and puked it full."

"Son, I'd be ashamed!"

"And what about Jim Brown, the undertaker? He's a swell Mormon, isn't he? You come in and choose a swell casket and you all stand around and say what a beautiful corpse. You mean of course what a beautiful casket. After you leave, Jim yanks the dead guy out and nails him up in a wooden box. I mean," he said, looking at his mother's outraged face, "that he has sold the same casket a hundred times. No wonder he has two Packards and his son has a Buick. Mater, why in hell didn't you tell me the truth when I was a kid? Where are all the honest people you told me about? Where are the virtuous women whom men must protect? Yes, and where are the men?"

The world, Prudence said, was going to the dogs. In her day young people were all right. It was these automobiles.

"In your time it was the bobsled. When you went to a dance to the jingle of sleighbells, you all crawled under blankets. What did you call it then?—bundling?"

423

"I never did."

"Maybe you drove. What were the others doing under the blankets?"

"Nothing bad. I know that."

"A great lot you know. A lot of people now alive got their start under those blankets and some of them have never known their own fathers."

"Be foolish, son, but I know better."

"Answer me: why didn't you tell me the truth when I was a kid? Nothing that you said seems to be true. And now, because I'm learning the truth, you say I'm going to the dogs."

"You've forgot all your training," Prudence said. "I trained you right."

"Forgotten my training? Mater, that is exactly what I am trying to forget. Mark Twain said that Byron despised the race because he despised himself. I feel as Byron did, said Mark, and for the same reason. And so do I. I despise the thing your training made of me, but I'll not always be that kind of thing."

He turned away, thinking of Stendhal, feeling a strong kinship with that man. He had been shocked by Stendhal's frank confession that as a child he and his mother had ardently kissed one another and that he had wanted to copulate with her. He had been shocked by Stendhal's confession that all his life he had hated his father and had called him the bastard and the murderer. Stendhal had said, "I am going to be turned into a barbarian—a barbarian lost to the arts." That is the way Vridar felt about himself during these months.

VIII

Idaho Falls was a thriving city of twelve thousand people; it had wide clean streets and Snake River rolled under its west end. Far to the west were white or blue mountains, and to the east was the misty blue backdrop of Vridar's home. In the northern part of the city lived the socially elite; just beyond the railroad tracks lived the middle class; and in the south flanked by warehouses were the slums and the dark retreats. Out in an acreage of sand with weeds overtopping it and with gophers heaping their mounds, was the golf course; and there on Sunday afternoons the industrial and professional baronage waded in sand and drove golf balls into jungles of thistle and redroot. Those with less prestige went to the hills to fish, and the earthborn sat on the river bank or the bridge.

It astonished Vridar to learn that this city had an underworld. On the surface it looked respectable and commonplace, with doors made to open, sidewalks to tread, and gutters to spit in. The countryside on weekends poured into it in a flood of gingham and overalls. On holidays there were noise and scattered bottles, dust and swarming children and exhaustion. There were hotels, drugstores, poolhalls, garages, shops . . . .

"And what else?" Vridar asked Neloa. "You'd be surprised. Bootleggers, pimps, harlots, and scoundrels of a dozen other breeds. What a fool I've been! I had never dreamed that human nature is what it is. I've always despised myself, believing that I was much worse than the average of mankind. With you I've been the way Strindberg was with Lily von Essen. He had the same headful of illusions and he quarreled with her bitterly and he brooded over the world's suffering; and when she left him, he wrote his terribly bitter A Fool's Defense. That's the sort of book I may write some day. But first I must find out what life is like. Do you care?"

"Not if you want to."

"I have to. There's no other way."

He was finding out, and to this young man with his heritage of absurd ideals there was offered one amazement after another. Save once, memory of which still galled him, he had never talked with a whore, though he had been accosted by them and had seen their hard faces and eyes. He had thought about them, wondering why they sold their love; and how many men at one time or another slept with them; and why. He was eager to study them and discover their meaning.

In his taxi he met the trains. One midnight a woman came down the steps and paused and looked at the cabmen. She came to Vridar and he drove her to an ugly old building. "I don't have no money with me," she said. "Come up to my room."

He followed her up a dark stinking stairway, and she entered a room and turned on a light. He waited by the door.

"Come in," she said.

He entered the room. The woman ignored him and took off her shoes. "Set down," she said. Vridar went to a chair and sat. Now the woman took off her stockings and Vridar began to wish he was out of here. If she would pay him, he said—and she looked at him, her eyes flickering with amused pity. "I don't have no money," she said, and by her tone he realized that she had said more than that. He rose to his feet.

"Well, then, I guess you can't pay me."

"Set down," she said.

Feeling like an oaf at a fair, Vridar twirled his hat. "If you haven't any money—"

"Money, kid, ain't the only thing." She looked at her legs, now bare to the knees; and Vridar looked at them too and thought them good to look at. The woman was now taking off her clothes.

"I have to go," he said. "I have other calls to make."

"But honey, I haven's paid you yet." She rose and came to him, soft-footed and evil. She tried to put arms to his neck. "Kid, I like you," she said, smiling up at him. "You're young and nice. Have you ever kissed a woman?"

"I must go," he said.

"Hey, for Christ sake, don't push me like that! . . . . Listen, boy, don't you want it?"

"No."

She seemed to be surprised. "Look me over, kid. Ain't I all right? Here, look at this leg." She drew her dress up and exposed a lovely thigh. "Feel my breasts. They ain't soft yet, kid. I don't let every son of a bitch play with them." She took Vridar's hand and he allowed her to lay his hand on her breasts. "Squeeze," she said.

"No. I'm going now."

"Listen, kid, what the hell's the matter? Ain't I all right?"

"Sure, you're all right."

"Then love me, honey." She began to strip her clothes off. Vridar moved to the door, but she sprang ahead of him and turned the key. She hurled the key and it clattered in a dark corner and was lost. While Vridar looked at her, wondering how far it was from the window to the street, she took her clothes off and stook naked before him. "Look at me, honey: do I suit you or don't I?"

"Please let me out," he said. He started for the corner, thinking to find the key, but the woman faced him at every turn, dimpling, smiling; and at last he roared: "God damn it, let me out of here!"

"Are you afraid, kid? I'll treat you nice. It'll be nicer than it's ever been for you. I know all the ways . . . . . "

Convinced that she was determined to make him surrender, Vridar shouted at her. His words, imprudently chosen, ringing with anger and contempt, brought a crisis. She leapt at him as if stung; and then, like a white flash of fury, she hurled things at him—clothes, cigarette trays, anything she could seize and lift. The air was full of things, and Vridar, lost in amazement, ran to the door. With all his strength he wrenched the door open and flung it back and leapt to the stairway; and behind him in furious assault came odds and ends, curses and shrieks. When he reached his car a naked woman leaned from a window and poured down at him such hysterical profanity as he had never heard. Driving to a dark street, he stopped and sat for a while in thought.

"I don't know," he told Neloa later, "what it means. You're a woman: do you?"

She gave him a strange smile in which there was pity. "I could guess," she said.

This was in March and he knew little about whores then. Six months later he knew about them, he imagined, all that was to be known. Though never their lover, he talked with them and studied them, determined to understand their point of view. He discovered of course that most of them were very vain and stupid and unspeakably foul. But he liked them nevertheless. They did not, like most persons, pretend to be more than they were. Love was not for them, as it was for him, as it was for most of the people he knew, passion that was sequestered in a vague and unhappy sense of guilt and shame. Everything about whores was as bold and frank as sunlight.

"And did you know," he said to Neloa, "that a lot of the most respectable and devout married men in this city spend a night now and then with these women? There's John Curtin, civic leader, prominent churchman; but I've seen him stretched out in bed with a whore. And the funny thing is that John is a pretty good man as men go. And Mrs. Oldham, she's the wife of another prominent man, yet she slips out now and then to be a whore. She says her husband is stingy and she gets her pin money that way . . . . "

He came to know most of the harlots of the city; and because he drove a cab, men came to him—out-of-town men looking sheepish—to ask where they "could find a woman." With a cynical smile Vridar would ask what kind of woman they wanted. One would say, "Oh, any, just so she ain't too skinny"; or another would say, "Not too danged expensive. Two bucks is all I got." One day there came to him two of his former comrades in the San Diego battery. They asked for whisky first, and when a little drunk they asked for women. Vridar took them to a shabby building, dark and smelling of age. They climbed a dark stairway and were met by a har-

426

lot. Three whores lived in this place. One was a big surly creature with a birthmark across her mouth; another was tall and thin and sullen; but the third was a very lovely woman. It was the third one who met them, wearing a flesh-colored gown of silk, her hair falling in a lustrous darkness over her breasts. The four of them went into a room.

There the big harlot had a knout in one hand. A man, naked, drunk, and grinning with rapture, was lying on the floor and the big harlot was flogging him. She was striking with savage blows and the man was exploding great groans and guffaws of joy. When she smote the man's genitals, she softened her blows, but after he had rolled over she flailed his buttocks with all her strength. The two ex-soldiers were staring, pop-eyed. They seemed unaware of the harlot in the silk gown who was rubbing against them and reaching down to them with a soft lovely hand . . . . .

Vridar had seen erotic floggings and things more shameful; and from week to week he revised his opinion of human nature, observing how the same impulses and the same hungers were in all men. As for the harlots, now and then he met one who had womanly warmth and a generous heart and a sense of humor. There was Betty McCoy, a Sctoch-Irish lass, petite and lovely and alluring, who traveled up and down this line. She went as far south as Ogden, as far north as Butte, stopping off in Idaho Falls once every fortnight. She did not get a room, as most whores did, and throw her door open to every diseased or sotted wretch who appeared with three dollars in his hand. Her clientele—she called it that—was, she told Vridar, only the very best people: business and professional men, bankers, lawyers, and merchants, and now and then a minister. "I treat them decent," she said. "I never rush them. They take their time . . . . ."

Vridar liked Betty and she liked him. She was not lewd. There was about her, in fact, a quiet dignity, a simple earnestness, beyond the girlish vivacity of her charm. Her profession for her was no less worthy than that of housewife or social worker. She was in her way a therapist and she was a dedicated woman. Vridar always met her at the train, knowing when she would come. The first time he saw her, she seemed to take a fancy to him, for she asked him into her room and inquired with quiet dignity if he would take his fare in money or trade. In money, he said, and she never asked that question again. But always he went into her room and sat for a while and talked; and he thought it very strange that he should like this girl, that he should respect her even, for she was a whore after all. He liked her because there was no shame in her, no sense of guilt, no pious pretense: in so many ways she was what he was not and despaired of ever being. While looking at her lovely face and small exquisite body, it was hard to believe that so many men embraced her, that so many lips sought her own.

One evening she talked about her clients. She did not give names; a whore, she said, could be as moral as anyone else. She had a sense of honor, of what was right. She spoke of her mission in life and what she did to make the world a happier place. Vridar was impelled to ask a question that had been in his mind for weeks.

"Betty, tell me why married men go to—to harlots. I can understand it in single men but not in the married ones."

Betty laughed. Most married men, she said, were unhappy. They did not love their wives. Did he not know that those women whom the Christians called good were invariably poor lovers? "When their husbands come to me they take all their clothes off and they don't feel any shame at all." She looked at him a moment and said: "Do you love your wife without shame?"

"Me?" he said stupidly. "Well, I think so. How can I be sure?"

Most men, said Betty, idealized their wives and they thought it sort of terrible to make physical love to them. God made wives to have babies. But there was no sin in sleeping with a bad woman. "God made us—" She laughed merrily and took a cigarette.

One evening when Betty came to the city, she told Vridar she wanted to talk to him and he entered her room and she closed the door. Then she sat on the bed and told Vridar to sit by her and he went to the bed, feeling bewildered and foolish. She laid a hand on one of his hands.

"Vridar, I like you an awful lot and I've been thinking."

"About what?" he said, looking at her.

"Us. But first I want to tell you about me. I'm twenty. I was married at sixteen when I was a freshman in college. I married a big football mug and I couldn't get along with him. He wanted a lot of mistresses. He was brutal when he embraced a woman. I'm pretty small," she said, "and some men, well, are pretty big." She was silent a few moments. "I've a child back home, a boy of three. Now tell me, how much do you make on your job?"

"A hundred a month," he said. He concealed his profits in bootlegging.

"That's no money," she said. "That's my fee for one night."

"One night!" he said. He was used to one-and three-dollar whores.

"Vridar, why don't you come with me?"

"What do you mean?"

"I mean travel with me. Don't think I'm going this way all my life. Some day I'm going to marry and settle down and have a home."

"But why should I go with you?"

"To help me. In three or four more years I will have enough for us. Then—"

"You mean," he asked, horrified, "that I would be your—" She clasped a hand to his mouth.

"Don't say it."

"But that's what you mean."

"It would be business. Then we could marry. We could travel in Europe."

He stared at her, incredulous. "But I'm married," he said, not knowing what else to say.

"But you don't love your wife."

"Oh, but I do."

"You just think you do. Like a lot of men you think you do because you think you should."

He stood up, gesturing helplessly. "But I do love my wife. I've loved her ever since I was a child."

Betty rose and faced him. "Well, think it over, you may change your mind." She wrote her address on a card. Vridar took the card and looked at it and turned to the door. If Betty had swung on him in furious contempt, he would have felt all right.

"I'm sorry," he said. He went over to the door and fumbled with the knob. He turned and said again, "I'm sorry," and let himself out.

He told Neloa about the matter and she looked at him, her smile strange and inscrutable.

"It's funny," Vridar said. "She's a whore but I like her. And she has taught me things. She says a lot of married men have never seen their wives naked. Did you know that? Do you know what the chief thing is that I am learning?"

"What?" asked Neloa, still smiling strangely.

"That there's no such thing as good people and bad people. Betty is a whore but I respect her. Some of the most respectable people in this city I despise. Our vices and virtues are assorted differently and that's about all. And that," he said, "is a hell of a lot to have learned."

The garage office was the lounging-place for a number of men, and Vridar studied them day after day, wondering if they were an average of mankind. Larry McInnes was a crafty scoundrel whose smile hid from all but the most discerning the treacheries that occupied his mind. Short and lean, he wore roomy trousers that hung from suspenders like a sack. Avaricious, alert, restless, he was always on the go, profaning, chewing tobacco, and looking for credulous farmers, to whom he sold his worthless used cars. Everyone liked him, even those whom he duped; for in this nervous and unconscionable shyster there was boyish fellowship with his kind. He gave money as though his pockets were full of it, as indeed they were. He bought a home and furnished it for his favorite whore.

Rollie James was a different sort. A more cold and ruthless rogue Vridar was never to see. His mind was a reservoir of plots for preying on his fellowmen; but Rollie was a gentleman and he dressed like one: his hands, his clothes were immaculate, his voice was soft and wellbred. Though he had about him the stealthy look of a coyote searching for a hencoop, he was held in respect by the city, and he delivered funeral sermons over the dead. After the sermon he would sell a useless car to any fool who would buy it, for he was in business with Larry and they prospered.

There was Shorty, the hunchbacked dwarf. Shorty was an armful of deformity with an ancient and sardonic face. He was young but he looked old and evil. With no neck, with his shoulders bunched up to his ears, he would come into the office, a cigarette hanging from his white mouth, his eyes shifty and spiteful; and he would sit on a chair with the hump on his back pushing him forward, and laugh in a queer strangled way at Larry's jests. Vridar liked this strange little grotesque for whom there could never be love or children, or anything at all but the contempt of his fellows. But Vridar did not like Shorty's brother. Jimmie Duff had everything that Shorty did not have: a strong body, a handsome face, and a winning smile. This man, like Forenoon McClintock, made seduction his chief enterprise. "I'm a passionate bugger," he would say, and so he seemed to be, for he ran with harlots, too. Vridar's chief memory of Jimmie was to be of a man in the toilet yelping with pain. "A lemon's supposed to be a good test," he said, "but the damned thing never works for me."

There was George Pitman, partner with Joe and Ike in the business, a small man

429

with abnormally long arms and a long thin nose. His marriage, like Vridar's, had grown from a childhood romance; but now he hated his dowdy little wife with her huge torso. Mrs. Pittman's big belly became a legend and jests were made about it. For months George thought he had a child coming but when a doctor examined Mrs. Pitman he said she had a cyst. "He says I'm to blame," said George and his smile was both sheepish and proud. His grin was proud because of what he could do with ten half-dollars. He would take men into the rear of the garage and lay wagers with them; and on a table he would arrange ten half-dollars in a row, from the edge inward; and after working up an erection he would stand against the table and with his penis sweep the ten half-dollars off. Men's eyes bulged with wonder. They would measure a half-dollar and solemnly declare that it was an inch in diameter. "Ten inches!" they cried, staring at George. Much of what Vridar remembered from childhood now became clear to him: legends of Jake Barg in Annis who had to wear a rubber collar—how his father's people used to howl when they told about it!—and of folktales about the size of a man's nose and its sexual significance: George Pitman's nose was half the length of his face. "I think," Vridar said to Neloa, "that it's the men raised on farms who feel that they have been cheated. As boys they looked at the stud and bull, the boar and ram, observing the extraordinary length of their organs. And they looked at their own. I admit," he said, grinning foolishly, "that at times I felt cheated, though my big nose would suggest, in folklore at least, that I had no reason to. I doubt that men raised in cities feel that way. But it is a common matter of jest with men who grew up on farms. Had you known it?"

"Yes," she said, but what her eyes were saying he could not tell.

There was Bill Rummon, the lean and lecherous pimp. His pale green eyes were as fixed and changeless in expression as the eyes of a hawk. Their only meaning was of craftiness no longer alert, of passionless amusement that had worn thin. But his mouth was full and alive with a sensual fruity ripeness, and when he talked he would pause to suck his lower lip in, nursing it as if it were a teat. After studying the eyes, Vridar was astonished by the mouth; after studying the mouth he was astonished by the eyes: they seemed to have been taken from different faces. Bill had a whore in the rooms above the garage, a huge and terrible creature who cursed and drank whisky. Now and then she would thrust her head from a window and shout down at Rummon and he would leap up as if kicked. "Men don't like her any more," he would say. Vridar despised the man but he talked with him often, determined to understand what had made him. "It's my profession," Bill would say with comical dignity. "If ladies (he always spoke of harlots as ladies) sell their love they have to have gentlemen to help them. I take a commission just like a banker. I mean I handle the business end of it . . . . ."

Bill had his eye on a wild lovely madcap who was the talk of the countryside. Her name was Madge Eppert. Vridar hardly knew what to make of Madge or of others much like her in their reckless abandonment. Now and then he was tempted, when one made it plain to him that her favors might be had; but he was Neloa's slave. If he had been bound and trussed, if he had been roped to her bed with his arms and legs in stocks, he could not have been more completely faithful. He hungered for a

great clean freedom, but he was a man in jail, pouring whisky upon his curse. Only once during almost a year in this city did he try to break free. He drove with Bill
and Madge and another girl into the country. Bill and Madge left the car and went
down the road and Vridar saw them leave the road and enter a grove of trees. Then
he turned to Maxine Allen, a girl with red hair, and put an arm round her; but she
was like a thing of lead. When he touched her breast, she swung on him in horrible
fury and smote his face. He was too astonished to move.

"What in hell's wrong with you?" he asked.

"Don't touch me!" she shrieked.

He seized her throat and shook her and in that moment he wanted to destroy her.
"You God damned idiot!" he said, breaking her across his lap and then roughly
setting her up and choking her again.

"I'm not that kind of girl!" she gasped.

"You infernal liar!" He shook her again and she began to wail. With violent hands
he shuttled her back and forth and from side to side until he felt her will run limp.
He realized then that she liked to be roughly handled. He broke away, feeling disgust
and shame; and at once she smote him a terrible blow across his nose and kicked
wildly at him and with both hands yanked his hair. He seized her again and crushed
her to the bottom of the car; dragged her up, his hands like steel on her naked arms;
and again she was limp against him and her mouth kissed his throat. But the moment he paused in his violence, in his efforts to rend her flesh and break her limbs,
she was at him again, her hands like talons in his face. This was too much for Vridar. He left the car and looked at her. Her mouth was wet and open, her eyes were
savage. He turned away, leaving her there, and walked back to the town.

The more he learned during these months, the more bewildered he became. The
riddle of life become darker. Moving among the outcasts, studying them, eager to
know what lay in their hearts, he saw them as animals, feeding their appetites and
exploiting one another. This city, he reflected, must be like other cities; these people, the respectable and the outcast, were like people everywhere. But where was
the grandeur, the idealism like acid upon the dross, the chastity that was not cowardice, the pride that was not arrogant and mean? Between the respectable and the
outcast he could see little difference. He had seen harlots give to beggars. He had
seen Bill Rummon, moist of eye and quavering of tongue, rebuke a lout who had
taunted Shorty Duff. He had seen lawyers perjure themselves and their clients and
he had seen a churchman steal and he had seen a bootlegger help an old woman a-
cross a street. In himself at times he felt a dark murderous lusting or hatred of the
male for the male; or a strange sense of kinship with the lewd and the unclean; or
a deep and self-pitying wish to give his life to make the world better. In books human beings were not as he found them now. In books right was right and wrong was
wrong; the hero was a splendid fellow with his emotions always in the upper half of
his torso; and the villan was a monster without a single redeeming trait. He was sick
of life here but there was no power to lift him out of it and send him back to his
ambitions and his books. He told Neloa he needed such a power and asked her
where he could find it . . . .

In an August night and a terrible day that followed that power came.

431

IX

Bill Rummon came to him one midnight. He wanted to go to Pocatello, he said, and when Vridar went to his cab he saw that Madge Eppert was already there. He got in with Bill and roared out to the highway; and this midnight ride in a blinding downpour was the most reckless of all his journeys in a car. Bill had brought two quarts of whisky and every few minutes he and Bill drank. Vridar could barely see through the windshield; the road was only a faintly luminous streak but he pushed the gas-lever clear to the floor and the car under him was a mad thing rushing through the storm. After a while he saw the wan lights of Blackfoot like matches in a fog; and then in a moment of terror he saw that the highway turned in a right angle but he had no time to stop and his speed was too great for the turn. He went straight ahead with terrific power and there was a sound of flying stones and of sand in a whirlwind. He and Bill got out in the drenching rain. The car had driven into a huge pile of sand and gravel and had buried itself to the frame and every wheel was spinning. After they spent two hours digging out of this mound and were completely drenched with rain and mud, Vridar drove again and lost the highway. In the mud of a country lane he came to a stop on a high bank, and though he was pretty drunk he knew that the car was rocking under him. He opened the door and stepped out and plunged headlong twenty feet downward into a great open pit filled with water. Threshing about and trying to find something to clutch, he looked up and saw the car, swaying gently. For what seemed to him an hour he struggled to get out of the pit, and when at last he crawled up a muddy bank to the car, furious at Rummon for not coming to his aid, Rummon and Madge were gone. He routed farmers out of bed and they put long poles across the top of the car and chained them to it; and while they hung from the end of the poles to keep the car from falling into the pit Vridar carefully drove it out. It was after daybreak when he reached Pocatello. He went to cafes and hotel registers and taxi offices. Yes, a cab-driver said, he had fetched a man and woman in and they had taken an eastbound train. Vridar turned away, thinking of Madge Eppert, headed for whoredom; and then, sheathed with mud from head to feet, he entered his car and drove home. His life years ago had been a meaningless delirium of terror, and now it was a senseless nightmare of whisky and whores and pimps. Marion had come home with a scar in his scalp. It had been like fiction, he said; if the bullet had been even half an inch lower . . . .

"What are you now, just a woman-chaser?"

"That's enough," said Marion. "I listened to your pious lectures for fifteen years."

While driving home Vridar was thinking of the way Marion sold photographs. There was nothing to it, Marion said. First, you saw a child in the yard. Then you found the mother and said, "I'm a professional photographer and just happened to be passing. You have a very beautiful child. Do you have a photograph of him?" She had one, of course. Then you told her that it would enlarge remarkably well. The whole thing with frame cost you two dollars and you sold it for ten and all you had to do was to exploit a mother's vanity. "Flatter people," Marion said, "and they'll give you their shirt."

When Vridar reached Idaho Falls, he went to the basement and sat with a jug of whisky, telling himself that he was nothing but a worthless sot. He had wanted to be a writer and here he was, a fool with his jug. For an hour he sat there drinking, telling over and over his pitiable absurdities, hating himself, loathing himself. He wished some power would shake him out of this paralyzing apathy, this emotional rot; some force that would wreak upon him a new courage; some light that would break through the dark. But he could think of none. Tomorrow he would drink again, as thousands did; and the next week, the next year; and what could save a man from that? What could save a man from himself? Nothing had saved Thompson . . . Villon . . . Swift . . . Collins . . . Marlowe . . . Poe . . . Bierce . . . Leopardi . . . Coleridge . . . Nietzsche . . . and thousands. Nothing was saving thousands today. In one way or another they burned out in awful fire, in lust, madness, drugs, or drink: and among them the great in both mind and heart. They were spurts of fire in a wilderness of dark, matches flaring in cupped hands in a wind: that was all, and he would be less, infinitely; and it did not matter. Mankind was only candles in a wasteland: most of them trimmed wicks with a round immaculate poise; and some caught a strange brightness that burned and went out; and some never burned at all. He went at last up the stairs, praying that some power would deliver him to a vision, or at least to a catharsis of fire. He climbed to the room where he lived with Neloa and out of his own self-loathing he built the crisis.

When he entered the room his son was squawling hideously. "What's the matter with him?"

"I don't know. He cries most of the time lately."

Vridar went over and looked at the child. Ah, blind father with no eyes to see! "What's wrong with you?" he asked. "Shut up!" He looked at the furious red face and the wide bawling mouth. He picked the child up. "Stop it, you damned little tyrant!" He turned to Neloa. "What in God's name is wrong with him? Don't you know?"

"Of course I don't know. He just howls."

Vridar shook his son. "Shut up, you idiot." The child redoubled in anguish and volume. It was sixteen pounds of red flesh and wrath and open mouth. "It's temper! Where in hell did he get all this temper?"

"I'd ask that!" she said.

Vridar shook the child, crying, "Shut up, damn it, you monster of bad heritage!" Then, suddenly, he saw that the child was still. Into its face, red with fury a moment ago, had come the whiteness of death; and it closed its eyes like a mechanical doll and was limp. "My God!" Vridar said.

Neloa screamed and rushed to him. "O Vridar, what have you done!"

"I've killed him," Vridar whispered. He looked at her, his face as white as the child's. Neloa screamed again. She tried to snatch the child but Vridar pushed her away. "Be still," he said. The whole world was quiet now; he could feel a great and terrible silence everywhere. Putting an ear to the child's chest he listened, but he could hear nothing. "I've killed him," he said again. "I've killed our son." He looked at Neloa. She was shaking uncontrollably and twisting her hands and moaning. "Go call the police," said Vridar quietly. But then: "Wait, where is Marion's gun?"

433

"O Vridar!"

"Go get it."

"Vridar, get a doctor, please!"

He had not thought of a doctor. "You think he isn't—dead?"

"Maybe not! And for God sake, *hurry!*"

Vridar seized a blanket and wrapped it round the child and was out of the room, taking the stairway six steps at a time. Like a wild man he was down the street with Neloa after him and up another stairway and into a doctor's office. "Quick," he cried, "see if I've killed my child!"

The amazed doctor looked at him and then took the bundle. He laid the limp child on a couch and bent over it, and Vridar saw his hands moving up and down the spine. He turned to Neloa, who was wailing, and said gently, "Please be still."

"Oh—I can't—help it." Her voice was strangled. It frightened him a little to look at her.

"He's not dead," the doctor announced.

"He's not? Thank God, thank God!"

Neloa now went to pieces. She fell to the floor screaming and Vridar bent over her. "Neloa, please, please!"

"Ohhh!" she cried, moaning horribly.

"Neloa!" he had never heard such agony in the human voice. "Is he hurt?" Vridar asked, turning to the doctor.

"He'll be all right. What did you do?"

"I shook him." Vridar wanted someone to flog him, to take a club and knock his brains out. But he was very quiet. He was always quiet when faced by grave danger or sudden terror. Going to Neloa, he lifted her and she shook in his arms and fainted against him, and he sank to a chair and held her and looked at her ghastly face. He kissed her white lips. "He is all right," he whispered.

It had been a close call, the doctor said. A vertebra had been dislocated in the neck. But the child would be all right. "Just keep him very quiet for a while."

They returned to their room. Neloa was still white and trembling and she lay on the bed and very gently Vridar laid the child at her side. Then he sat and stared blankly at a wall. He could see nothing, he could think of nothing but his terrible childhood—the deep prison of his home and the mad river and the empty sky, and a boy there fighting through nighmares . . . .

"Neloa, are you all right?"

It was all of one pattern, that and his drunkenness and his blind rage an hour ago: without relief, without change, the dark and terrible pattern of it, the desperate meaninglessness. Through all his years death like a shadow had walked at his side.

"Vridar?"

He went over and knelt by the bed and put his arms round her and the child. He kissed them, and when he saw that she was weeping he wept too. She reached to him and he put his lips to her hand and wept out of bitterness worse than death. After a little while he went to the garage basement and took the jug of whiskey and hurled it crashing against stone. It was a flash of amber and glass and then it was only wet fragments and a sudden smell. He returned |to the room and bathed and

434

put on fresh garments; and then he knelt by the bed and put his lips to Neloa's palm. He was sunk in desolation that was deeper than grief. . . .

"Well," he said to her next day. "I can see it all now, the fool I have been. All my life. This past year I've been a bootlegger but I feel no regrets about that. I've saved enough money to go back to school . . . . Neloa, let there be no suspicions in your mind. I've done nothing I haven't told you. I have not been intimate with any other woman. I have not even kissed one. Few persons perhaps would believe that, knowing the kind of life I have led, but you must believe it. Do you?" He thought he saw doubt in her eyes. "Do you?"

"Yes."

"Be honest with me. We cannot go on together if you doubt me. So be very sure and do not lie to me."

She was looking at him. She was not smiling but there was a strange smile in her eyes and in her thoughts. "I believe you," she said.

"Do you want me to swear to it?"

"No."

"All right, we'll call that settled. I needed something to shock me out of myself. I got it. I'm through with whisky and cigarettes, pimps and whores. I'm going back to school. My deepest regret is that I have wasted another year—wasted it when I was already so far behind. Now I'll have to work twice as hard. I'll have to read my eyes out. You may feel neglected, you may feel, as you have before, that I love books more than I love you. But you must be patient. Achievement is less genius than more intensive effort. I may have no genius but I can work hard. I think often of what Walton said of Donne, that his mind was liberal and unwearied in the search of knowledge. I think of what Milton called the changes from that which is called fortune from without, or the wily subtleties and refluxes of man's thoughts from within. I must find if I can in the vast unintelligible some meaning more permanent than candle-flame.

"We have enough money saved for this year. What we'll do after that only God knows. Possibly I can get a fellowship or something. You must realize, my dear, that it is poverty for us, perhaps for a long time. And I want you to go to school. I want you to like books."

"I do," she said.

"Not really but you may learn to. I'll wash our clothes and I'll scrub the floors if you will spend a part of your time reading." He looked at the dark solemn wonder in her eyes, the resentment, too, the fear, and something hopeless, as though she were weary with trying to understand him. "Neloa, dear, the time to understand the sort of future you'll have with me is now. I expect to work myself half to death. There'll not be much time for shows and dances and those things which you enjoy so much and I so little. But if you don't like the prospect you may have a divorce and find the kind of life that would please you more. You have only to be honest about it.

"I don't imagine I'll ever be a very good husband. I brood too much. Right now I cannot forget that the Treaty of Versailles is a big stink or that Wilson's head has more nonsense in it than mine. The light streams upon the path ahead and nowhere

435

else, he says. He's a bigger fool than I am. The light streams—and cities now are rioting, aliens are being shipped out as if they were spuds and the world is getting ready for some kind of horrible madness. Lead, kindly light, we are following you all right! Well, I know that you don't have my interest in these things. I'm a rebel and you are not. So now is the time to decide whether you'd be happier with someone else."

"You're silly," she said.

"Neloa, be sure."

"I am sure."

"And you'll never regret it?"

"Never."

"No matter what happens?"

"No matter what happens."

"Come here." Smiling, she came to him and he kissed her. "And you really love me?"

"No," she said, frowning with one of her most charming mannerisms, "I hate you."

"That's right, hate me." He kissed her and she trembled in his arms. "Neloa, why do you love me? Do you know?"

"You're so crazy. You're different from other men."

"Don't you think it would be better if we had never met?"

"No."

"But we're not happy together."

"We have our moments," she said.

"When you speak like that," he said, kissing her again, "you're a poet and I love you."

And so, after eight months of reckless despair, Vridar found that his path again lay in the sun. Since September 6, three years before, when Neloa wreaked confusion within him, he had been spending himself in blind gestures toward ruin and death. He had been trying to purge himself of his ideals and dreams but something all the while had been like a full sun on his back. He had forsaken books and now returned to them and he would never forsake them again. Like Spinoza he would dwell in the kingdom of the mind and his talent would come forth and ripen, and he would sit at last in the firelight of old age and fame. Or he would be a Socrates . . . .

But Spinoza was laid under an awful curse, and the journey of Socrates led to hemlock. Vridar thought he was done with furies and heartache, that he would be happy among books and that Neloa would be happy with him. He thought all the past had been shut away. He looked forward to years of study, with a doctor's degree magna cum laude at the end; and to the books he would write and the clean strong life that he would build. He set about earnestly to sow the seed and gather the harvest, never suspecting for a moment what terrible things he had buried that must some day be lifted out of darkness and faced.

X

In Salt Lake City they lived in a dark ugly room with a gas-plate in a closet. On weekends Vridar helped launder the clothes, even washing the diapers; and usually he scrubbed the floor. On Sunday if the weather was fine he would carry the child and they would walk to Liberty Park to breathe the Indian summer of the golden trees. Once or twice during the year they went to a show. Most of the time Vridar was busy with his writing and his books. "Good God," he would say, "but I am an ignorant fool!" He would come home with a stack of books and read until midnight; now laying a book aside and opening another; now trying to read two books at once, as he felt upon him the swift passing of time. "I'm so far behind," he would say. "I'll never catch up!" He ranged out into philosophy and comparative religions, and into still other fields, searching, trying to see the boundaries of knowledge and the limits of what men had explored. Sometimes for hours he would be so absorbed by books that he would be unaware of his wife and child and the room in which he sat. When a thought touched him deeply, like a sudden hand on his shoulder, he would look at Neloa, with the thought building a light in his mind.

"Listen," he would say, and he would read to her: " 'Knowledge is only the impression of one's mind and *not the fact itself,* which may present itself to many minds in many different aspects.' Sensory impressions may be much the same to all people, but when people interpret them they take on the color of motive, prejudice, hope, all past experience. So knowledge cannot be the same thing for any two persons!" And he would rise and pace and talk, trying to formulate the meanings.

"Listen," he would say. "J. E. Boodin tells us that the nature and test of truth are not to be confused with the practical motive that leads to the seeking of it. How true!" Neloa would pucker her brows, as she always did when bewildered by what he read. He would stare at her and repeat the words and ask if she knew what they meant. "It means that people test truth by the motives that compel them. That explains this silly feud between Darwinism and the Church . . . . Do you see?"

"I guess so."

"Listen," he would say, touching a big book on his lap. " 'Mr. Marett has shown that a prayer which relies on the use of a name of power'—like God," Vridar said, glancing at her, " 'is not far removed from a spell or magical incantation.' You must read this book."

"What is it?" she asked unhappily.

"Conybeare, *Myth, Magic and Morals.* It shows what a silly thing Christianity is." He rose, excited, and walked the room. "Do you know why Jesus never married? Do you know the real meaning of the crucifixion? Do you know where the idea of virgin birth came from? Read it. It will knock the silly Mormonism out of you."

"If," said Neloa, "I read all the books you want me to read I'd have to live a thousand years."

"I don't bring you many," he said, glancing at a great pile in a corner which he had brought for Neloa to read. "Well, read this one next.

"My God!" he would cry. "Listen! 'When to a man who understands, the Self

437

has become all things, what sorrow, what trouble, can there be to him who once beheld that unity?' This is by Carpenter, *The Art of Creation*. But how can the self become all things? That would be hypnosis, wouldn't it?"

Neloa was confused and distressed. She was trying so hard to grasp this notion of the creative life.

One evening he burst forth: "I shouldn't be writing plays! This man—it's *Literature and Insurgency*—says the novel is the expression of modern life. Damn it!" he cried, and Neloa jumped. "I should be writing novels. Who in hell ever got me off on plays? It was Donnaugh . . . ."

Not only did Vridar quest among books, searching their pages for meanings that were sharp and clear; he wrote also, with emotions surging up and pouring like driven winds around an idea; with the idea getting lost, like the core of quiet in a cyclone; with the idea typed to a page in a jungle of metaphor and simile, until, upon reading what he had typed, he could find no meaning in the sensuous eloquence. He wrote allegories so saturated with color that he could find no coherence in the voluptuous masses of his effort; could feel only intoxication and chaos, as when he stared at the formless tumbled glories of a sunset. For his one-act plays were purple parables draped like velvet around the crater of an idea. They were great involuted rhythms, their long cadenced periods rolling in tumult, with the puppets buried under headlong and sensuous nothingness. His poems, he was to perceive later, were only voiceless intensities; his epigrams were choked red in the face by bombast. It was as if, he said to Neloa, he had set a child to play, and returned to find it dead.

But Professor Donnaugh did not share his feeling. Vridar was, he said, the most promising student he had ever had. One day Donnaugh strode from office to office, waving a play by Vridar and crying, "If Dunsany had written this they'd be shouting his name around the world!" Then, feeling that he had stepped out of his dignity, like a naked man out of a bathroom, he called Vridar in and gave him a sober round-faced lecture. " Your play can be improved. Don't ever get the idea that your work is perfect . . . Look, you must revise this"—and Donnough thrust a short fat finger at a hysterical rhapsody.

Vridar would wonder about this man. Donnaugh was short and plump and round, with a round fat face. His colleagues detested him but his students adored him; and Vridar liked him with a steady affection, a warm vigorous esteem, that was to stand invincible against the years. But he was not blind to the man's immense vanity, and in the classroom he studied him, observing his dynamic energy and his unaffected enthusiasm, his rather pompous and oracular manner, his morbid hunger to be distinguished and have the esteem of his fellows, and his deliberate and cunning pretense to more knowledge than he had. Like some of the other instructors Donnaugh strove, with tags of Latin and Greek and allusions to the obscure and remote, to hold his students in awe. "He rolls his tongue in his fat mouth," Vridar said to Neloa, "as if tasting the vowels, and he has some mannerisms that are calculated to knock you off your legs; but he stands head and shoulders above everyone in his department. He's no Bush, with his grand manners of a gentleman and his palsied trying to hold

438

the hands of his girl students. He's no Ackworth, with his two-by-four belief in Mormonism and Milton."

"Does he like your last play?"

"He says he does." Vridar dug out the play and read parts of it. "No, it's all wind and wheezes. It limps and finally sits down. My stuff is no good. God help me, I don't think I'll ever be a writer but maybe I can be a scholar."

One day Donnaugh called Vridar into his office. His manner was round and apple-cheeked and humorously sly. "Sit down," he said, and for a little while was busy with stacks of paper on his desk. Vridar knew that he was merely sitting there, plump and efficient, sensing his power and his tremendous duties, happily feeling their weight in the scales of his life. Then he swung. "You'll be graduated in June?"

"I hope so."

"Then what?"

"I don't know."

Donnaugh laughed. He laughed often but his laughter was mirthless. "How would you like to teach in a university?"

"I—Why, sure. But—"

Donnaugh exploded another mirthless volley. His fair skin was dyed red and his blue eyes twinkled with jolly mischief. He pursed his mouth and chuckled. "How would you like to teach in my department?"

"In your department! Here?"

Donnaugh shook again, his eyes full of dancing twinkles. Then, casting off all nonsense, he stiffened until he looked like a Harvard man. "Hunter, I'm about to offer you a position here, but on one condition, that you go East to school this summer. Will you?"

"Why—I'll try."

"That means you'll go. Go to Midwestern. Of course," Donnaugh said with charming egoism, "Harvard is the one school in our field. My old friend Kittredge is still there. My old friend Robinson. . . ."

Vridar's smile was not visible. This man in the classroom and out, spoke of famous scholars, writers, and educators as his old friends.

Vridar ran home and burst into the room. "Look at your husband!" he cried. "He has just been offered a tremendous job."

"You have? O darling!"

"Dean of Education." He winked at her. "Will I make a good dean?"

"Vridar, tell me!"

"Head janitor."

"Vridar, I'll shake you!"

"Shake me. It arouses my ardor."

"Vridar!"

"Donnaugh has offered me a job."

"O sweetheart!"

"I feel pretty damned important, so come sit on your lord's lap." Neloa came over. She framed his face and kissed his mouth. "I have to go to Chicago," he said.

"No!"

439

"Yes. I have to go to Midwestern this summer."

"And I—what will I do?"

"Live with my folks, I guess."

"But I don't want to."

"I know it. But this is a big thing for us. I'm the only student Donnaugh has ever offered a job to."

"But I don't want to live with your folks."

"Neloa dear, we must do what we must do. We haven't enough money for you to go with me."

"But I won't live with your folks."

"Why not?"

"I hate that Antelope country!" Her vehemence startled him.

"Well, what can we do?"

"Maybe I can get work here," she said. She did not look at him.

"You mean stay alone here?"

"Yes." She did not look at him.

"Oh no you won't. You'll go to my folks or your folks."

"I tell you I won't go to my folks!"

"All right, then, you'll have to live with mine in Idaho Falls."

Then she looked at him, and there was something in her eyes that he was never to forget.

XI

Only a violin could fill Vridar with such loneliness as the journey of a train. Now, smelling the dusty seats and the roadbed and the smoke and listening to the furious music of the wheels, he went back in memory to those years when, haunted and desperate, he had in Rigby stood at midnight by the track to watch the monster thunder in. A train in the night with its yellow windows and its searching headlight was for him a symbol of something—of life maybe, with its far shores and distant lands. Or perhaps it was a kind of lighthouse for a lonely people. As he sat by a window, looking out, his memory was a backdrop and pictures came and went. There was Neloa's face as he had seen it a few hours ago, her dark eyes blind with tears; and Neloa in Antelope moonlight; and Betty McCoy with her hand on his hand; and Kitty Murdock weeping under the timeless quiet of stars and sky; and Donnaugh saying, "I want you to make a record back there. You're the first of our graduates to go to Midwestern. Make us proud of you . . . ."; and Neloa saying, "Darling, please write every day. Oh, I'll be so lonesome! . . . ."; and the wheels talking under him of distance, with night flowing past in a strange world of cloud and trees. It all filled him until he was choked with it, until he wanted to cry out of its beauty and pain, until he wanted to be lost to consciousness and sucked down under the wheels and destroyed.

This mood grew until it completely possessed him. When he reached into a bag for a sandwich or lay in a seat to sleep; or when, looking at the endless distance of

Wyoming, with its blurred desert and its few lonely lights; or when he looked at strange faces, strange pilgrims, going only God knew where; or when, staring at a photograph of Neloa, he saw it as a memory of something that had come and gone, like the trees and mountains and barren wastes, then it filled him, this intense and baffling darkness, this terror, and he shook in the power of it and struggled to be free. It grew with him like time and distance, for it was all the sagas of hope and despair that men had made, and all that history had written down. During the past winter he had thought he had found peace. But books now and all memories of books were scattered into nightmare. Life was not in books any more than the sea was in a cistern or sunlight in a lamp. Every faith, every ideal and hope that had been gathered from months of reading, were now rolled under with the miles. He wanted only to be drawn out into the loneliness and dark of the night and be obliterated.

If he rose to walk from coach to coach or looked out a window at the flowing world, a fresh fire burned in his heart and a new frenzy seized his mind and he would sink to a seat, sink back into his own fear and emptiness, feeling rent and sick. For his mind was like a small camera: when he turned it upon the boundless, he found that he had only a picture of his small and pitiable self. And so, like river-drift, drawn from its eddy into the flood, he journeyed into a great city; and past him on either side swept an endless acreage of roofs and windows, fog and smoke. Mountains of smoke rose and lay backward and through it came the smell of Lake Michigan and the breath and living of millions; and all about him was a vast confusion of lights. He was afraid of this mammoth city, built upon streets of stone: it was so full of canyons and darkness and terrors. Driving headlong into it went the train, as if to split it apart and roll the two halves back; and smoke in clouds entered the train and he could see nothing—could only taste and smell the smoke and feel the grinding of brakes under him. He grasped his bag and in a tide of humanity moved through the station and to the street. He went through a horde of shouting cabmen and porters and to a bridge, and looked down at sluggish black water filmed with green. It smelled of sewage and rotting piers. Looking round him he saw that this river flowed through the city's heart and gathered the city's stink to its journey. He crossed the bridge and walked down a canyon of towers. There was nothing to see save buildings in the image of one another and the tides of humanity moving in their shadows; nothing to hear but the din of shriek and whistle and human voice with a great muffled roaring above it; but for one from the Rocky Mountains there was much to smell. The city came to him most vividly in odors. There was the smell of human breath and of sweat; of buildings with their old paint and their slow decay; of gasoline and oil and fog, dank and heavy. The odors sickened him, and when now and then a breeze came down the canyon he fed on it, though it too stank, with the depths of Lake Michigan.

This was Chicago. He paused by a towering building and set his bag down. All the faces around him seemed friendless and hurrying, as if their bodies were wound up in the city's clamor. They were not faces that he liked. They were too fixed, as though in an old and inexorable routine. When Vridar accosted a man and asked to be directed, the man's voice like his face was stony with indifference.

441

Then Vridar took his bag and walked again until he came to a trolley line. He wanted to enter a cafe for a sandwich, and he looked into one and another but they frightened him. When he moved to enter a trolley, it suddenly dashed off and he was struck and almost thrown down. Red with shame he withdrew to the curb and stood there to observe the manner of a tram's coming and going; and he saw that all of them, like the folk they carried, were feverish with haste. An hour later he was riding, with his bag under his feet. Glancing out now and then, he saw the same unvarying pattern of ugly buildings and unclean streets and he would close his eyes, hating it, refusing to look. After riding for miles, he saw trees and grass and on his right a beautiful park. On leaving the trolley he saw that the park was close by, and he stood for a few moments to consider his problem. Then he took his bag and entered it and followed paths, seeking one that would come to a lost end of its own. He found one that was overgrown and wayward and followed it and came to a grove of trees and dense underbrush, and he stood and listened, wondering if he would be safe here. He lay down in old leaf-depth and stretched out, with his hands clutching the leaves and soil, and in a few minutes he was asleep.

He awoke with his senses full of bird music and looked anxiously round him, thinking at first that he was in the land of his youth. His dreams had been full of rivers and winds. Getting to his feet, he looked at warblers and wrens and knew that he was homesick and afraid; but he had a job to do—"Make us proud of you back there"—and he picked up his bag and walked and an hour later was in a tiny room on Woodlawn Avenue. His small window looked upon a street like the streets he had known, and he thought, It will be quiet here, I will have books, that is enough.

After a bath and a shave he sat on the bed and tried to press his trousers by running the cloth between a thumb and finger. Having no brush or broom, he dusted his garments by threshing them against a chair. He hoped he would be able to do his own washing and ironing. From his big bag he removed a small portable typewriter and sat to write to Neloa: "I don't know why strange places make me feel like a small child in a dark room. But I'll be all right and I pray that you will be all right with my people. Please try not to worry about it. It is only three months, then we'll be together again . . . ." He did not tell her that, hoarding his small funds, he had not eaten for thirty-six hours and had slept in a park.

He walked to the campus and was amazed. Wasatch College, with all its buildings and lawns and trees, was only an academic roadside inn compared with this. The buildings here, mantled with ivy, topped with spires, were somewhat like gothic cathedrals. They had magnificent strength, a stern and awful beauty; and he felt pitiably weak, for in nothing around him save the grass and trees did he feel kinship. For an hour he walked, trying to learn how big this university was: it covered blocks from east to west, from north to south; and all the buildings had the forbidding strength of granite. He entered one, timidly, and smelled its classrooms and offices; read bulletins in the halls; glanced anxiously at passing teachers and students. The whole building seemed to be sensitively alive, as though learning had become a vibrant thing in its masonry and stone.

He then went to the library. Almost holding his breath he went from floor to floor, trying to grasp the size and splendor of this great home of books. The reading-room alone seemed as large as a pasture, and when he looked into it, remembering the giggle and clamor at Wasatch, he was awed by its silence. Even the desk attendant whispered. Then he could stand no more, not now, and he fled to his room and wrote again to Neloa, with emotion shaking him and pouring down to his fingers as he typed: ". . . The silence of these buildings is so deep and awful, their dignity so aloof yet somehow so gentle; and all the lordly wealth of wisdom, all the glory of generations, housed within those library walls! It is what I've been seeking. Professors here will be great men, I know they will; and O darling, I am so shaken and overwhelmed! . . . ."

He registered for a course in Wordsworth, another in Pope, a third in Anglo-Saxon; and he went to these with an awed humility, an aching wonder in his heart, that few students surely had ever brought to this school. Forgotten now was the disillusionment with his high school and undergraduate years: here was a noble school, and noble teachers, and he offered his soul. But his professor of Anglo-Saxon talked so far above Vridar's head that he understood almost nothing. He looked at other students and saw that they understood; then, feeling again like an oaf from the far hills, he studied the professor. He did not like him. He could not deny what was so plainly written in the man's mouth—a loose and cynical dishonesty, a want of firmness and character. Were there charlatans here? He fled this class and enrolled in advanced composition under Harold Denham, a nationally known novelist and critic.

But of his three classes only one touched his heart. Miss Herrold, his instructor in Wordsworth, was an old woman who could barely move in her great burden of flesh. Her face, when unawakened, as most of the time it was, seemed unpitying and hard; but when it came to life, as it did now and then in a picture of warmth almost girlish, Vridar understood and loved her. She was old, he wrote Neloa, and the old were tragic. Her enthusiasms now lay dead like an armful of roses in a burning sun. But now and then the pile was stirred and scattered and you smelled the personality of one who must have been wonderful when young.

He hardly knew what to make of his other instructors. Wilson Albert Holley, professor of Pope, astonished Vridar with his knowledge: the man spouted names and dates and obiter dicta as though he had swallowed a library and could not breathe without delivering a part of his gorge. Beyond the knowledge stood a personality that Vridar did not trust. He had a thin face that had suffered, hands that gestured out of spiritual emptiness, eyes that flickered with spite. He seemed unsure of himself, like one who had found all books meaningless and all knowledge unclean; and his twisted deprecating smile and his frequent shrug spoke from a fixed and deadly cynicism. Maybe, Vridar wrote Neloa, it was because Holley taught Pope; for Pope had been a hunchbacked armful of hatred and malice, though the core of his heart, seldom used and never allowed to speak, was a part of God. And then one day Vridar heard a student whisper to another that Holley had never married because he was a homosexual . . . .

Nor did Vridar feel at ease with Harold Denham. This man had a great forehead and a grotesquely wide upper lip; drooping eyelids that gave to his intellectual

443

face something sinister and chilling; and an aloofness of manner, of thought, that stood like a wall between him and his students. "The last of the Puritans," Vridar heard a woman say. "If he had lived in the 17th century he and Milton would have been chums." Vridar wrote Neloa that Denham looked like the father of Minerva; "but it is whispered among the students that off the campus seduction is his chief interest. In any case, when he gets through with one of my plays that Donnaugh praised there is nothing but a small whimpering wind around your husband's heart."

He recognized that these teachers in their learning and humanity and grasp stood among his former teachers like firs among aspens. Their knowledge was a great and splendid thing. Spurred by that knowledge, he read books by the armful, carrying them to his room and typing summaries of them, until he had great piles of notes. Wordsworth swept him off his feet. He read Harper, Legouis, Dorothy's Journal, and "Tintern Abbey" over and over again: And I have felt a presence that disturbs me . . . . Whose dwelling is the light of setting suns and the round ocean and the living air . . . . A motion and a spirit that impels all thinking things, all objects of all thought, and rolls through all things. From other poems he harvested and typed hundreds of lines: Upon the pressure of a painful thing, the lion's sinews, or the eagle's wing . . . . Some seemed to summarize his own tortured life: No single volume paramount, no code; no master spirit, no determined road. Some came into him like the thrust of a knife: The sleep that is among the lonely hills. He memorized many of them and asked Neloa to memorize also, "Because poetry memorized is an annuity against despair." He wrote to her long letters, pouring into them his furious love, his dreams; telling her that he read until he fell asleep and awoke and read again, and thought until his brain and his senses were aflame; exhorting her to get books from the Idaho Falls library and read; asking her to keep faith in him, his talent and his future . . . .

And so he lived with his frenzied enthusiasms for seven weeks. He kept a book by him when he ate, a half-dozen under his pillow when he slept. If he specially admired one, he would pat it and hold it to his breast and put it on his lap when he typed. Not until his fifth week was he shaken out of himself and then only for a few startled moments. He was sitting on the lawn reading Wordsworth when there came to him a woman, who stood before him and smiled. She saw what he was reading, and she said that Wordsworth was an awful fraud. Vridar looked at her more curiously. She was about thirty, he thought, and a furtive glance told him that she had shapely legs. Her face was attractive but there was something hard and starved in her eyes.

"An awful fraud?"

"He bores me utterly. His Peter Bells, his Michaels, his excursions and daisies and daffodils and forsaken Indian women. How can you read such a silly old Puritan?"

"I like him," said Vridar, wondering if he had erred in his judgment of Wordsworth.

"I think he had water in his veins. You know, I positively hated him until I learned that he seduced a girl in France. What was her name?"

"Vallon. Annette Vallon." Vridar blushed a little for his French.

444

"Do you think he really seduced her, or is that a literary fable?"

Vridar looked at the woman. She met his stare with frank bold eyes and smiled. "I suppose he did."

"My God, I hope he did. If I ever learn he didn't, I'll detest the man. But I can't imagine his seducing *anyone,* can you?"

"Perhaps," said Vridar drily, "she seduced him."

The woman now sat on the grass. Her skirt was pulled to her knees and to free its tightness she pulled it a little above her knees. She looked at the smooth silk of her legs and said: "I can't imagine a poet being faithful to any woman. He wouldn't be a poet, would he? He'd be a monster."

Vridar read the thought in her eyes and looked away. "You think," he asked slyly, "that Dante and Milton seduced women?"

"I hope they did." Her red mouth was charmingly petulant. "After all, no one knew about Wordsworth's fling for a hundred years. The sly old fox! Fancy how his ears burned after he got back to England! And to square himself he wrote odes to duty! . . . . How can you stand the man?"

"He also wrote Tintern Abbey."

"Yes, while out hiking with his sister. How long will it take the world to realize that that's an incestuous poem? Bill and Dorothy, holding hands and sublimating their incestuous yearnings into something that moves through all things! Do you like him because you—?—have you a sister?"

Vridar turned red. He got to his feet and with amused eyes the woman watched him go. He listened to Professor Herrold but understood only a little; the woman out on the grass and her question troubled him. He became very annoyed with himself. When again in his room he felt empty, lonely, lost, as though he drank water while other men drank wine. He wanted to lay hungry hands on a woman's flesh, on the wonder of her breasts and thighs, and to drink from a woman's mouth. And he felt a strange and nameless guilt. That night he dreamed: he was with Diana somewhere in the hills and he threw her down and tried to embrace her. Memory of the dream left him upset and furious and again he threw himself into books, trying to forget the woman with the lovely knees, and Diana, and to remember only Neloa . . . .

At the end of his seventh week the world of books fell round him and again he was lost. From Diana came a letter:

Idaho Falls
Aug. 1, 1920

Dear Brother,

I must write to you about something and I don't like to but I know I should. It's about Neloa. She got a job in a cafe here as a waitress and it's one of the toughest places in town. Every night some man walks home with her and they stand on the sidewalk and talk. Sometimes they bring her home in a car and I saw her riding around the streets with a fellow. And she paints her lips and face and adds stuff to her eyebrows and lashes until she looks like a common street walker. I don't like to write this but you ought to know . . . .

The letter so stunned Vridar that for an hour or more he did not move. Nothing out of life or death could have astonished him more; and so he sat, white and still, trying to understand. There rose before him, not books and the world he had lived in here, but the terrible desolation of his past years, until the old frenzy, the old bitterness and hatred, choked him and he bowed his head. When darkness came he walked the streets, going he knew not where, or why, and wishing himself dead. For it was too much, this agony of indecision and doubt, this gutting of his world when he was working day and night to prepare himself for a position. Returning to his room his typed:

> Dear Neloa:
> I have just learned that you are working in Hank's Cafe. I know that place. When I was driving a taxi it was a rendezvous of whores and pimps. You will leave it at once. You will understand, if you can, that I'll not have my wife working in a den of harlots. I don't understand why you're doing this but I've never been able to understand why you have done many things you have done. You've always refused to consider my feelings: it was so in Antelope, it is so now. I've offered you freedom and you won't take it. If you are to be my wife you'll get out of that cafe and get out quick.
>
> Vridar

He sent the letter by special delivery and he waited, tortured, sleepless, for a reply. His books were forgotten now. He drove himself to his notes and wrote his term papers but he could do no more. Five days passed—six—a week and no letter came from Neloa. He wrote again and his words were violent. And still no letter came.

While walking one night, lost to everything but his grief, he heard the music of violins. It came from a university building, and he knew that persons were dancing there. For a little while he stood undecided. Then he entered the building and watched the dancers. When he saw a girl looking at him and read the meaning in her eyes, he went to her and without a word led her to the dance. She hugged close to him and he knew that she was deeply stirred by his arm and the music; and when the dance was done, they went to a balcony and stood in moonlight. She said her name was Blanche Olson, that she was from Iowa, that she was doing postgraduate work; and he told her his name and that he was married.

Blanche said: "You love your wife?"

"I suppose. How old are you?"

"Twenty-three."

"You should know your way around."

"You mean—?"

"Perhaps. Shall we dance again?"

While dancing he looked at her. She had blue eyes, and she opened them wide when she met his stare as if to show him their innocence. But they were not innocent: there was in them if not craftiness then a desperate hunger that was much like it. Her nose was snubbed. She had gold in her teeth. She hugged so close to him that his leg moved between hers and he pushed her back a little.

446

"Do I embarrass you?"

"No," he said, lying.

An hour later they walked in Jackson Park. Vridar felt her gaze searching him but he did not meet it.

"Why are you so unhappy?" she asked.

"I'm not—am I?"

"Do you really love your wife?"

"Of course."

"Does she love you?"

"I don't know."

Blanche squeezed his arm. They went on a dark pathway and she stopped, with her clutch on his arm. Vridar met her gaze and held it; and at last she said: "What do you want to do?"

"I don't care."

She snuggled close and put her arms to his neck. "Kiss me, then."

"No." He put her arms away.

"Then you *do* care."

"But why should I kiss you?"

"Because it's better than term papers." She took his arm and led him to a bench and sat and she looked at him, studying his face. "I have a problem," she said. "I wonder if you could advise me . . . . It's about my sister Rosamond."

"Oh, your sister Rosamond."

"She's twenty-eight. She—shall I tell you?"

"If you want to."

"Well, she has attacks. Dizzy spells. We went to a doctor last week . . . . Do you know much about life?"

"Not a hell of a lot," he said.

"Have you read Havelock Ellis?"

"Some."

"Well," said Blanche, ill at ease, "we went to a doctor. What do you suppose he told her?"

"I can't imagine."

"Then you *don't* know much about life. He told her—I know you're going to think this is silly. Are you?"

"No."

"Well, you see Rosamond is—well, a virgin. The doctor said she needs a lover. He said she will go on until she has a nervous breakdown . . . . Is that silly?"

"It's funny."

"Funny! It isn't funny for high school teachers in small towns. You have the man's point of view," she said bitterly. "What are high school teachers to do? They can't marry men in small towns. There aren't any they'd marry . . . . Well, are they never to have love? Are they to be nothing but phonographs? What can they do?"

"God knows."

"You don't have any sympathy!"

447

"I have," he said, giving her a faint smile, "but I can't visit all the small towns."

"You don't think it's right for them to have lovers?"

"It's all right if they want them."

"Well, in God's name why shouldn't they want them? They are human beings."

He turned and met her blue eyes and asked: "Can't you find a lover? I mean where you teach?"

"Lord no! Have you a cigarette?"

"I'm sorry but I don't smoke . . . . Well, you mean you've never had a lover?"

"Never," she said, with such tragic earnestness that he wanted to laugh.

"You're lying," he said.

"I'm not!"

"It's all right if you want to lie. The world is full of liars."

"But I've never, really. Do you want the truth? Would you understand it?"

"I can try."

She drew a deep breath and said: "Well, I—I was raped once."

"Raped!" he cried. He turned to look at her. "Raped? Tell me about it." Blanche protested but he knew that she wanted to tell about it. He knew that she would.

"Well, when I was twenty I knew a man—"

"Don't describe him. Just call him a man."

"But I have to. He was big and strong . . . . Well, he asked me to go riding in his car and we went in the country."

"You thought you were going to church?"

"I knew you wouldn't understand. You men never do."

"Go on with the story."

"Well, we were out in the country. Suddenly he stopped the car, said it wouldn't run. I forget why."

"A flat, I suppose."

"No, it was the motor. I remember that. He got out and tinkered with it and after a while I got out to see what he was doing. Then he swung round and took me in his arms. He just lifted me and carried me away. I beat at his face—"

"I can see you," Vridar said. "I can hear the blows."

"Why do you say such things? You don't know how strong he was. I struggled with all my might. After all, what can a woman do against a strong man?"

"Lie down, I suppose. Most of them do."

"But I tell you he was strong! He weighed two hundred pounds. What could I do? What *could* I do?"

"What you wanted to do, and apparently did."

"You're unfair!" she cried. She rose, trembling, outraged. "I was helpless, I tell you! He just—he just crushed me! And you laugh about it!"

Vridar rose to his feet, laughing, and his laughter, bitter and full of pain, frightened her. She drew away, staring at him. "You women!" he cried. "My God, you women!" And he went away into darkness, with bitter laughter marking his course through the night.

XII

This truth, implicit in Blanche's story and in so much that he had read—this stark fact that some women liked to be raped and that some men liked to rape them was like corroding acid upon his ideals. It was opposed to everything that his mother had taught him about women. His contempt for it was mighty and futile; and in the next two days he wore himself out, fighting this deep dark certainty and denying it with all his strength. And because he was spent and sick, he had the most humiliating experience he was ever to have in a classroom.

Professor Herrold had asked him to read his paper on Wordsworth. This, he knew, was an honor and he felt elated; but when he was called to face the class, his face was yellow with anguish and the paper shook in his hands. While he read there were not the words, telling of the poet's intimations, but the desolate hills of his childhood, the river and winds and empty sky. There were the loneliness within which he had lived as a boy and the face of Neloa in the loneliness; and as he read page after page, with a hundred eyes studying his white face, he felt something dark and terrible possessing his senses. All his past was with him, heaped around him in this room. His voice became a strange thing that he no longer understood and could barely hear; and horrible sick dizziness was shimmering mist before his eyes and a rotten warmth in his blood . . . .

Suddenly without warning he broke and pitched forward. When he came to he heard voices murmuring, and it seemed to him that he was back in his home-land, with his mother talking to him after one of his nightmares. Then his mind was clear and he knew that he was lying on a table and that persons were chafing his wrists. Leaping to his feet, his face crimson with shame, he saw the anxious gaze of Professor Herrold, and students around him, some curious and some amused. Then he bolted outside and fled to his room. He locked his door and sat with his face clutched in his hands, trying to realize the awful shame of it. There was blood on his face. Loathing himself he went over and looked in a mirror. His face was ghastly. His eyes—the eyes of his haunted childhood, so terrible in their bleak sickness and disgust and horror! If I could die! he thought. Great God, if I could only die! He went to the lake, wondering if he should drown himself and for hours he sat there, thinking of the peace of dead things in water. But all the while there was thought of his parents who had slaved to put him in school, and of Donnaugh saying, "Make us proud of you back there . . . ."

The next morning there was a knock on his door and his landlady said he had two letters. One was from Neloa. He tore it open and read:

> Darling Boy, my heart is simply breaking tonight and I have got
> to pour out my feeling to you. I want you to write me at once,
> dearest, and tell me just how you feel and what you think of
> everything [good God, as though he had not told her!], then
> I will know what to do. Your mother has been scolding me and
> telling me people have been talking about me. I don't know
> why. She says it is because I work in the cafe and have been

seen walking home with men. I realized when I went to work in the cafe that people have a bad opinion of waitresses. But sweetheart I want to swear to you that I have never said or done anything that I would be ashamed to have you see and hear. Do you believe me, darling? Two or three times I have been coming home and have met acquaintances and they have walked to the door with me and said good night and gone on. Now frankly, is there anything wrong in that? I didn't think so but I feel tonight I don't know right from wrong. I am sorry I am alive tonight because people think as they do. O sweetheart, my heart is breaking! I have thought of you every minute and I always ask myself if you will approve of a thing before I do it. I feel that is the surest way of doing right. And now people are talking. And I have been so careful and have worked so hard and done everything I could that I thought was for the best. I don't know how you will feel [as though he had not written her!] but I wish you could know the truth and believe me, dearest. If you don't write at once telling me so I am *done,* that is all. If you believe anything bad I will not live to see you again. I had planned school and our future and oh, the dreams I had; and now I feel as if the world has fallen on me and I wish I could be in your arms and hear you say you know I have done my best and that you believe in me and love me!

Your broken-hearted Neloa

Vridar read the letter twice. The last pages were barely legible, as if Neloa had written out of deep agony; the writing was wild, the ink seemed to be blotted with tears. With all his soul he believed her and hugged the letter to him. But in the other letter Diana said:

Dear Brother,
　　Neloa is still working in the cafe and everyone here is talking about her. I thought you'd like to know.

Then Vridar did not believe at all. For what could it mean, this ghastly riddle, this tangle of Neloa's life and his own! If she loved him and if folk were talking about her why did she not leave the cafe? She asked him what to do and he had told her what to do! It was all nightmare and he was deeply, utterly sick of it. Here he had been, studying day and night, his whole being fixed on scholarship, on achievement; and Neloa— It was too much!

He sat for an hour or two and then conceived a desperate and shameful plan. He wrote a letter and asked his landlady to copy it and sign it, telling her that it was only a little joke on his wife. This is the letter:

Dear Mrs. Hunter:
　　I don't like to snoop into another person's business but I think I ought to tell you what your husband is doing back here. I know if my husband was away from me and misbehaving I'd think it an act of friendship if a woman wrote and told me. So I'm writing you as a friend. The truth is your husband is in love with a woman back here and I know he intends to run away with her. I heard them talking in his room and they plan to go to Toledo. I think you should ought to know about that.

450

I don't want to see you made a fool of and he's told me you
trust him and so I'm writing you the truth.

Minette Burgess

Vridar posted the letter and for seven days he waited. If Neloa believed it, he told himself, her belief would declare her own guilt; if she dismissed it, he had nothing to worry about. During this week he hardly ate or slept. He felt as he used to feel when, as a boy, he desperately searched for cows on the hills or waited under a dead yellow sky for his mother's return or fled into hiding to pour out his grief to God. He read Neloa's letter over and over, saying, I asked her to leave the cafe and for almost three weeks she did not reply; and then she writes to tell me that her only wish has been to do what I want her to do! Where is the sense in that? He waited for a letter, and when none came, feeling himself close to the void, he bolted like a crazed man across the campus and into the office of Professor Herrold. He did not pause to knock but flung the door open and rushed in, his eyes wild with unreason. Too astonished to speak, Miss Herrold rose and looked at him.

"I—!" Vridar gasped. "Oh, I'm sorry!" He sank to a chair. "I—I need help!"

Miss Herrold moved a chair over and sat, with a hand on his arm. "Tell me your trouble."

"It's—it's— O my God, I can't understand! My whole life has been a mess! All my life I've fought against madness, alone, and I'm tired of fighting!"

"Vridar, tell me."

He got to his feet, his wild eyes looking at her. "I—I'd better go!" he said. "I'm sorry I bothered you!" He sank to the chair and she clasped one of his hands.

"Vridar, please tell me."

His woes seemed pitiably silly now. But it was more, it was infinitely more, than his despair with Neloa: it was his whole dark past, rising to engulf him . . . . And then he told his story, flinging it from him, hating its mean and wretched details. And then: "I'm a fool, Miss Herrold! It's what my childhood did to me! I can't see my way out of it and I've tried and I've tried! I don't know what to do!"

"I wouldn't take it so terribly to heart. You're young and you have your life to live." Then she talked of other matters—of rare books and rare prints and old china, showing him one thing and another but he saw nothing at all. He was turned inward in bitter shame, wishing he had not come to her with his soul naked. And she talked of persons here, of a woman who had twice tried to kill herself; of a young poet who had shot himself through the heart; and of her own unhappy life, empty of everything but books. "Vridar, you go home now. I'll arrange matters here for you. And don't give way to despair. You're a very promising young man and you must have courage and go on."

"I want to be fair to my wife," he said, his passion spent. "Am I unreasonable in asking her to behave with dignity and taste? I can't tell what to do."

"Be patient. Possibly she is only thoughtless."

"But we can't go on like this. I'll give her freedom, anything, but this making a fool of me."

"You are too sensitive and she is young. Your problem will work itself out in time." She reached for a book. "Take this and read it. Try to understand it." It

451

was Cabell's *Beyond Life*. "And promise me, Vridar, that you will do nothing rash."

"I promise," he said, and clasped her hand. He thanked her and let himself out. He fled across the campus to his room and a few hours later he was speeding across Illinois on his way home.

He rode for two days and nights into the west and during this journey he did not eat or sleep. On entering Idaho the morning of the third day he was feverish with weariness and he paced from coach to coach. He left the train in Idaho Falls and went to the building where his parents and Neloa lived; and as he stood there, looking round him, she came up the street. This picture of her he was never to forget. Her cheeks and mouth were scarlet and the mascara on her lashes almost hid her eyes. Then she saw him and stopped and their gaze met.

"Where you going?" he asked. He saw the scorn in her eyes and the sudden proud freedom of her head.

"To work, of course."

"You still in that cafe?"

"Sure I am."

Vridar was silent while his eyes studied her. She took his searching with queenly disdain. "Go down and say you are quitting."

"And if I say no?"

"I'll leave you now. The choice is yours."

"I don't see," she cried angrily, "why I should! Why should I quit because *you* say to?"

"Because I'm your husband. Hurry, I'll not wait long."

He took his bag and climbed a stairway and went quietly to Neloa's room. He sat on a bed and watched the clock. In a few minutes Neloa opened the door and entered, with hatred bright and terrible in her eyes. "Sit down," Vridar said. She shrugged and sat. She looked at him and her mouth drew into a faint ironic smile.

"Well?" she said.

"Neloa, I asked you to give up that job."

"Oh, did you! And who are you to ask me to do anything?"

He knew what she meant. "So you believed that stupid letter!"

The change in her was swift and amazing. All the scorn left her eyes.

"So you believed it," he said.

"Why shouldn't I?"

"Why should you? Neloa, listen. Two years ago I said I'd be honest with you. I have been. I've not lied to you or tried to deceive you. And you said you would trust me. Remember?"

"I do."

My God, was this guile or naivete? "You don't. I had that letter sent to learn how small your faith is. I'm ashamed I did it but you force me to these things. I can't live with you this way, so there's nothing to do but leave you."

"No!" Her cry startled him. She came from her chair, trembling, and knelt at his feet.

"Pease go back and sit."

452

"Vridar!"

"Please. This is no time for hysterics." She returned to the chair and he saw her hands trembling in her lap. He wanted to take her in his arms now. He wanted to comfort and forgive her and ask her to love him. "Neloa, why have you no faith in me? What have I done to destroy it? In what way haven't I been straight with you?"

"I do have faith in you."

"Then why did you believe that silly letter?"

"Oh, I don't know!"

"Have I ever given you reason to doubt me?"

"No."

"Then why?"

"I didn't believe it."

"Don't lie. Of course you did." In her eyes now he saw both stealth and desolation. "Neloa, why did you?"

"Your own brother believed it."

Vridar came to his feet. "Marion? So he did, did he? I suppose he has been a big brother to you."

"He has been very nice to me."

"I dare say." Vridar looked at her, remembering times when Marion had kissed her and put his arm round her. There had been more in it than a brotherly gesture. "Neloa, go wash that junk off your face."

She looked at him and shrugged. She left the room. While she was gone he wondered about his wife and his brother but thought the suspicion unworthy and put it down. Then his mind turned to what Dostoievsky, while still a youth, wrote to his brother Michael: "There is no way out of my difficulties. I am going to become insane." He turned to a mirror and was looking at his eyes when Neloa came in, with that in her manner which said, Well, you've had you way and I hope you like it! There was no color in her cheeks now and none in her mouth.

"Before I hear your confessions," Vridar said, "I'll give you mine. I had supposed that we were done with confessions. I went to Chicago and lived with books and I worked hard, with no interest in women. But after you refused to leave the cafe, I went to a dance and danced twice with a woman and walked with her in a park. I did not make love to her and I had no wish to. That is all. Now we'll have your story."

"What story?"

"You've been working in a den. You've been running around with fellows—"

"I have not!"

"You've been riding in cars with them. What else?"

"I have nothing to tell."

Vridar rose, impatient and weary, and faced her. "Neloa, in God's name will you ever be done with dodging? You mean you haven't been with men this summer?"

"I don't know what you mean."

453

He saw in her eyes the old fear of him, the old scorn. "If you don't want to tell me, don't. But I can't live with you this way. It's not my idea of marriage."

"Oh!" she cried, goaded. "Say what you mean!"

"Have you been with men this summer?"

"I don't know what you mean."

"You've walked home with men, you've ridden in cars with men."

"I told about that in my letter."

"Not riding. Have you been with men in cars?"

"No. Just home."

"You mean only from the cafe here?"

"Yes."

"Two short blocks. And never around the city?"

"Well—only once or twice."

"Why were you riding around with men?"

"I was just riding."

"Who were the men?"

"Just men who eat in the cafe."

"Tell me, why did you go riding with them?"

"I don't know. Because they asked me to, I guess."

"You mean you ride with men if they ask you to?"

"No."

"Then what in hell do you mean and why did they ask you to?"

"Just friendly, I guess."

"Really! Neloa, are you a complete fool?"

"You think I am."

"Do you think men go riding with attractive women to see the sun set or to talk about Plato? Why don't they go riding with their wives?"

"You'll have to ask them."

"They wanted to seduce you and you knew it."

"I did not."

"No?" said Vridar, staring at her, trying to undertand the depth of her innocence or the depth of her guile. "Did any of these men kiss you?"

"No."

"Ask to sleep with you?"

"N—no."

"Oh, so they did."

"They did not."

"Neloa, don't lie. We can't build a marriage on lies. You lied to me before and I forgave you but there's a limit to forgiveness. I ask you for the last time, did any of these men ask to sleep with you?"

She moved suddenly as if to flee. "Yes."

"Did you?"

"No!" The word was furious.

"Did you want to?"

"No!"

"And were you with the man after that?"

"Yes."

"You must like him."

"I do not."

"Then why did you keep hanging around him?"

"I didn't. He hung around me."

He looked at her, trying to understand the kind of woman he had married. "Well, you told him not to bother you. You told him you were married and loved your husband. You told him—"

"No, I didn't."

"Good God, of course you didn't! You were flattered. You're the eternal Eve and men for you are Adams. I go back to work and build a future for us and you paint up like a whore and go riding with lewd men—and why in God's name I love you I don't know. But this I know, I'll not go on this way. If I can't trust you, your dignity, your taste, your good sense, I can't live with you. I have to trust you if I live with you. I don't mean I want you to live your life according to my pattern. You may have your freedom. You may live as you wish. But if you live with me you'll have to be a wife I can trust when you are away from me . . . . What else have you to tell?"

"Nothing."

"Do you swear to that?"

"I do."

"Be sure. I can endure your confessions. I've done so before. I won't endure your lies. You might drive me to the point where I would kill you."

"I wish you would."

"You've said that before. Neloa, you're a wife and mother. You're not a harlot. Is it so hard—"

"If you keep on you'll make me one."

Her words amazed him. He drew his chair close and looked at her eyes. "I'll make you one? Listen. I ask you to remember that you're a mother and a wife and that when you chase around with men you make a fool of me and a cheap thing of yourself. If I object to that you say I'll make a harlot of you. My God, you should burn with shame!" He rose and paced the room, looking at her. There was scorn in her mouth, and in her eyes there was an ominous glitter. "Am I then to let you do what you please? Am I to be ashamed of my wife? . . . . Am I?"

"No."

"Neloa, exactly what do you want?"

"To live with you."

"Well, we get nowhere with talk. We never did. You must understand, if you can, that you must be a sensible wife or I will take our child and go. I mean that, so help me God." He swung and left the room.

He walked the streets, wondering if he should leave her now but he no more had the power to leave Neloa than he had to take his own life. The latter indeed would have been easier to do. His love for this girl was his life and breath and the heaven of his earth; it poured upon his senses and rolled in delirium over his heart. He wanted to take her in his arms and kiss all the loneliness and hurt from her eyes; to feel her lips on him and her arms around him; to have faith in her beyond all doubt, pride beyond all bitterness and pain. He wanted to say, I love her, and when I think of her my thoughts do lie too deep for tears. But all this, he felt deeply, could never be. If she would speak instead of withdrawing into silence; if she would deliver the storm and heartache of her being; if she would abuse him, reproach him, curse him even, making plain what her emotions were; if she would let fury purge her, let hatred and love fight a clean and open battle, then with thunder and lightning they might clear the sky and find the sun. But she never had and he knew that she never would. Through rage and pain and blasphemy he stripped to his soul and stood naked before her; but when he implored her to speak, she only looked at him and her soul was as dark as her eyes. He had tried other ways too: with tenderness, whimsical nonsense, patience, and tact. He had drawn her to him and tried to win her to a full frank moment. But she was a child of the ancient and inscrutable night.

If only I did not love her! he thought, pacing the streets. He wished—as he had wished how many times!—to shake her to the last dark depth of her being, to force her to pour out to him all that she thought and felt. With this wish in mind he left the street and returned to the room. She still sat as he had left her.

"Darling, let's take a walk."

She rose without looking at him and went to the street and there he took her arm. They walked to the river and across the bridge and came to a thicket of trees. He spread his coat and she sat on it and he dropped at her feet.

"Neloa, let us try to talk it out. I love you. I love you with all my heart and I don't want us to be quarreling all the time. I want us to be more than the usual husband and wife, tolerating one another and growing old. I want us to share the same hungers and dreams. But darling, that can never be until we trust one another. Love does not live in doubt. Love is not back-door stealth and after-midnight deceit. I abuse you, I say mean things, but I have not deceived you. I want you to live your life as you want to live it, for it is your life. If you can be happier without me I'll let you go . . . . This, Neloa, is the way I feel. When I'm away from you I want you to know that I'm not trying to deceive you, that I'm trying to be a husband with dignity and taste. I owe that to my wife. And I want to trust you so completely that if a person were to say, Neloa is deceiving you, I could retort, Don't be silly! Is that the way you feel?"

"Yes."

"Then, darling, why are you so thoughtless?"

"I don't know."

"Do you love me less than you used to?"

"More."

"Do you trust me?"

"Yes."

"But you didn't. Listen, Neloa: did you mean that last letter you wrote?"

"Every word of it."

"Then I don't understand. The person who wrote that letter is not the one I met today. How do you explain it?"

"I can't," she said. "I've thought about it, too. Vridar," she said, looking at him, "it's what you do to me."

"What I do? I don't want to do anything but love and trust you." He drew her to him and studied her eyes. "Neloa, you know the one moment of all our lives I love best? It was the night, the last night we were together, before I left for San Diego. Remember? I wanted to but our child had been born only three weeks and I thought I shouldn't. And you looked at me—not as you often look, my dear— and said, Sweetheart, please, I want you to. Remember?"

"Yes."

"You loved me then and I knew it."

"I love you all the time."

"No. Sometimes you hate me. Neloa dear, why are you afraid of me?"

"I'm not."

"You seem to be two different persons."

"So are you."

"But I always love you. Nothing will ever change that. I want to cherish you and believe in you as I used to believe in God." He kissed her lips and her hair. "You're so pale now. You were so rosy when we met."

"That was rouge," she said.

"I know. Well, I'll put some rouge on you now." He reached for her pocketbook and opened it. He saw a letter in it and he took the letter and looked at it; and Neloa, seeing what he did, moved swiftly and tried to snatch the letter away. Vridar got to his feet. He looked at the letter and then at Neloa and saw that she was flushed and guilty.

"No! Vridar, please give it to me."

She came up to him, fighting for the letter. He thrust her away. She sank to the earth and looked up at him, her eyes dark and wild. Vridar took the letter from the envelope and opened it and read.

> Burley, Idaho
> August 11, 1920
>
> Dear Neloa, well here I am, just bumming around. I guess I'll be here until October but I'll see you in Salt Lake. You still intend to be in Salt Lake, don't you?
>
> Love as ever,
> Bob

Vridar read the letter twice and went softly to his knees and looked into the terror of Neloa's eyes. "Bob who?"

"Vridar, please!"

"Bob who?"

"Bob Watkins." Her hands shook. Her lips shook when she spoke.

Still looking into her eyes he said, "So you lied to me again—and swore to it."

"Vridar, please!"

"You told him you'd be in Salt Lake." He read the letter again. "Love as ever. So you and Bob are in love."

457

"No!"

"And he'll see you in Salt Lake. The same old marriage racket—"

"Vridar, please don't!"

"Can't you say anything but Vridar please?" He stood up. "Can't you be decent with me or leave me?" He seized her arm and drew her up and twisted her arm until her gaze met his. He looked at her a moment and then out of his awful bitterness he said: "You whore."

Her response astonished him. She broke his clutch on her arm and stood before him, trembling with dreadful fury. She was like a tigress, terrible in her wild and beautiful wrath; and then, with scorn like flame in her eyes, she drew to her full height.

"You!" she cried, and the word rang with hatred. "You call me—that! Ohh!" Then she swung, superb in her fury, and left him, and Vridar, overcome with amazement, watched her go.

After she had vanished, he looked at the letter in his hands. He tore it into shreds and tossed the handful of paper into the river. Then he went up the street and came to Neloa's door. It was locked. "Neloa?" he said. There was no answer. "Neloa!" he cried, becoming alarmed. He put an ear to the door and listened but there was no sound. "Neloa, open or I'll break the door open!" He kicked the door and Neloa came and opened it and faced him; and her manner, he saw at once, was very strange. It was so strange that he looked round him, wondering what she had been doing; and on a table he saw a bottle and a sheet of paper. He went to the table and Neloa stepped back and watched. He picked the bottle up and saw that it was carbolic acid; he looked at the paper and saw that she had been writing a farewell. Too astonished to speak, he took the paper and read.

> Dear Vridar,
>   I am sick of it all and I'm going. No matter what I do, no matter how hard I try, you find fault with me. You abuse me and call me names and I won't stand for what you called me today. Please be good to our baby and never tell him what

With the letter in his hand Vridar went over and faced her. "You mean—?"

"Yes."

"Neloa, my God!" He sank to a chair, trembling, and Neloa, as imperturbable as stone, sat on another chair and looked at him. Her face was very calm. "But you didn't mean it! Tell me you didn't!"

"But I did."

"Sweetheart!" He went over to her and knelt and bowed his head to her lap.

A few days later he wrote in his journal:

> I don't know what it means. I know only that we seem to be mismated, wretched, hopeless, and only God knows what our future will be. Should I leave her? What is the truth between her and Bob? I'll never ask her. I'll never know. But this I do know, that I can never trust her again.

And Vridar never did.

XIII

He went with her and their son to Salt Lake City and threw himself heart and soul into his work. Love for him, he told himself, had been a cheap and shameful thing. He would try to be done with it. He would live with her and be kind to her because in spite of his violence kindness was his way. And besides, her threat of suicide had terrified him. He thought possibly she had been theatrical and had staged an act to astonish and chasten him; but he could not be sure. There was in this girl something dark and terrible that had no power, as with him, to purge itself in fury and tears.

"Your talk of suicide," he said to her, "was contemptible. I want to make that plain. I suppose that after this if you don't like what I do or say you will threaten to kill yourself. I won't live under a threat like that. Some day I'll tell you to go ahead and do it. Then what?"

"I suppose I'll do it," she said.

"How shameful!" he said, looking at her.

He was in a trap, it seemed to him, and there was nothing to do but work. He could teach. This was an honorable profession and within it he could build a refuge; he could live some sort of life with the best that had been thought and said. Love, after all, was a young man's folly; after it came ambition and achievement, wisdom and calm.

In his second week he was called by President Peter Matwick to his office. Matwick was a humorless man with a round belly, a cropped hedge of whiskers, and bulging eyes that looked strangled. He had once struck a student and knocked him down; and then to the students assembled on the campus around him he had shouted: "I'm running this school! When I say no hazing I mean no hazing! . . ."

Vridar was admitted to the office and stood by the door, waiting. For several minutes he was ignored. This, he surmised, was Matwick's way of calling another's attention to his own preeminence and power.

"You wish to see me?" His tone was sharp and aggressive.

"You asked me to come."

"Oh yes, I remember. You're Vridar Hunter, the new instructor in English. Come over and sit." Vridar went over and sat. Matwick looked at him, his weak chin hiding in his beard. "I wanted to tell you not to get stuck up because you're teaching in college. You're young. Don't let it go to your head." Vridar was overwhelmed by pity. "It's a great honor," Matwick went on, "to teach here. Our college is an old one. We have some big men. But don't get puffed up and imagine you're a great man." The telephone rang and Matwick swung to it as if annoyed but he was not annoyed at all. He spoke sharply into the mouthpiece. He rose to his feet in huge and blustering dignity. "What?' . . . No! If you want to see me come here! I'm a busy man!" He slammed the receiver to the hook. "These small men!" he said. "If they had to do my job . . . . Well, that's all I had to say. Keep a humble heart. You may go now."

Vridar went to a quiet spot to think. So this was a college president, this pompous

Mormon, this humorless prig! This was the man who summoned the faculty and stood, short and hostile, thumping a table with clenched hands. "Are all college presidents like that?" Vridar asked Neloa.

Then he was amused, for a more quaking and scared person never faced a group of students. When he, who had been admonished not to fancy himself a great man, entered a classroom, he would sit at his desk and look at thirty faces, a few of them eager and innocent, a few of them honestly stupid, but many of them dubious and cynical. It was the cynical faces that made him mi.,rably self-conscious: faces of sorority girls and fraternity men, well-groomed, supercilious, bored. If he had been less sensitive to the meaning in eyes and around mouths; if he had been less unerring in reading the casual gesture; if he had not been so wretchedly unsure of himself, teaching would not have been such an ordeal. But while he talked he read responses as clearly as he read his notes, and a sudden vulgar yawn or a faint sneer would fetch him up and scatter his thoughts. Now and then he would break into sweat and his face would burn and then run white, with drops cool and terrible on his brow; and he would fight desperately for control. He would try to shake off the sudden paralysis of mind. His students, aware of his strange manner, would stare at him, some sympathetic and ill at ease, some with leering relish; and the awful silence of the room for Vridar was like that of childhood nightmares.

When the hour drew near to meet a class, he would walk aimlessly, trying to forget himself; or he would go to a lavatory and cool his wrists in water and comb his hair or try to urinate when there was no need. He would return to the office and look at a clock, fighting with desperate sunken effort to get possession of himself. But nothing that he did, nothing that he forced his mind to dwell on, gave him the poise he sought. For he was not in this year the bitter and scathing teacher of a later time. He wished to be honest and forthright, with none of the clowning, none of the evasions and buffing and histrionics of some of the teachers he had known. But week by week he looked upon himself as an abysmal failure.

Donnaugh said he was not. "You're doing fine, Hunter. Your students like you. I'm proud of you. When you get your doctor's degree, I want you here." Donnaugh had written to Vridar's instructors at Midwestern to inquire how he had done and he showed Vridar the letters. "He is very immature," Holly wrote. "He overworked terribly but that is a fault of youth. Of his ability to do graduate work I think you need have no doubt, and this goes for Harvard or any other school . . . ." And Miss Herrold said: "His paper for me, though it offered no measure of what he can achieve in scholarship, was nevertheless the best paper I received. It showed in abundance those rarest of all qualities, sensitivity and imagination; and convinced me that Mr. Hunter can do anything that he chooses to undertake . . . ." Vridar was deeply pleased, but he told himself that he was only a preposterous idiot who ought to be given a good drubbing about twice a week.

Night after night he read, adding to his knowledge, adding to his journal the sayings of great men, until he felt, as he said to Neloa, that he could vomit a barrel of aphorisms. "Reading is like overeating. After a while you need a physic. I need someone to talk to." But he had no one. When his mind was full, he talked to Neloa and she listened; but she rarely said anything and he wondered how much she understood. "I feel as Gibbon felt when he went up to Oxford, 'with a stock of erudition that might have puzzled a doctor, and a degree of ignorance of which a schoolboy would have been ashamed.' Or I remind myself of Byron, who thought himself a philosopher and talked nonsense with great decorum." Neola would look at him with a strange smile. He would say, "I feel as dumb as the dwarf who dances attendance upon Norna in one of Scott's novels," and her expression would not change at all. Or he would say, "If Freud's wife met his domineering demands tactfully, he was enraged, for he said that sparing each other could lead only to estrangement. He was a man who could not express his love until after he had exploded with mistrust. Do you understand that?" And Neloa would say nothing.

There were only two colleagues with whom he felt any kinship. John Agnew was tall, slender, blond, with a mustache, deep blue eyes, and delicate hands. The girls in his classes adored him. They trooped into his office—which Vridar shared—and stared at him and giggled, while Agnew with princely aloofness talked to them about love.

Vridar had learned that sex was the only thing in which Agnew was interested. It was the north star of his being, and all his emotions were a compass fixed unchangeably upon that star. Never had Vridar seen a man so patiently and deeply set upon the erotic. Vridar would talk with the man, and Agnew would reveal himself hour by hour.

"Are you strongly sexed?" Agnew asked.

"How the devil should I know!"

"How often do you love your wife?"

"Oh," Vridar said, coloring, "when I am working hard—"

"I love my wife three or four times a day," said Agnew, speaking as he always did in his calm unemotional way. "And I take her when I want her, even if she's washing dishes or frying a steak."

"You damned liar," said Vridar.

"She likes it as well as I do," said Agnew. "It took me a long time to find a mate."

"I should imagine!"

"Remember the Irishman in Havelock Ellis? I've known such men." Agnew lifted a delicate hand to his wavy blond hair. "Do I look all right?"

"Yes, you look all right."

"I feel all right."

"Is this the reason the girls flock around you?"

"Women can feel virility in a man. It's intuitive with them. As for some of these professors around here, a real copulation would put them in a hospital." He lit a cigarette and quietly smoked. He was warming to his subject. "You know why so many married women are unhappy?"

"No," said Vridar, thinking of Rasputin's belief that in seducing women he purified them.

"Because their husbands are once-a-week boys. And I mean boys. They have the intensity of a pile of cotton." He inhaled and said: "Mrs. Agnew has no interest in other men."

"I can believe that," said Vridar.

461

"Well, that's my point. Show me a married woman interested in other men and I'll show you a husband who is a disgrace to his penis." Vridar was thinking of Neloa when Agnew asked: "Are you normal?"

"Now what do you mean?"

"Don't answer if I embarrass you. I mean do you make an art of love? Do you kiss your wife's genitals?"

"No."

"Most women love it if you don't allow them to think it is shameful. Hunter, the trouble with marriage today is that most men are still striving with their fathers for their mother's favors. Ashamed to be decent with their wives, they sneak off and tell dirty stories. Most women would be fine lovers if men would let them be. They're not ashamed of nakedness. My wife has a beautiful body and I have her strip so that I can look at her. I get the same aesthetic pleasure from that that I get from a Holbein or Beethoven. All civilized life is art and all art is sexual at its source. Am I right?"

"I don't know."

"A man, Hunter, who tells dirty stories is a man with a dirty conscience. Well," he said, abruptly turning away, "I have to read themes now."

Vridar told Neloa what Agnew had said and asked: "Am I a big puritanical stink? Am I striving with my father? Is it because of my inadequacy that you have interest in other men? Have I failed you?"

And Neloa looked at him and said nothing.

Vridar did not like Agnew, but he liked Jacob Arlow. Arlow was a Jew. He was quick and nervous and he walked like one with springs in his heels. When unamused his face was cynical and suspicious; but in moments of mirth he was an irrepressible lad, with the most infectious laugh Vridar had ever heard. They were much together. Vridar liked this Jew's searching mind and his warm impulsive heart. He liked his spontaneous enthusiasms and his simple joy in living, his whimsical irony, his wit. For several years he was to be Vridar's closest friend.

"You like Donnaugh?" Jake asked one day.

"Well, yes."

"How do you stand his damned Beowulfian laughter?"

"It's insincere, but only because he doesn't know how to laugh. Neither do I."

Jake thought himself in love with a Mormon girl. He told Vridar of his doings with her, and how, when weather permitted, they slipped into a glen on the northern hillsides and lay among the leaves. Jake wanted to marry her but thought that Jews should marry Jews.

"Did I ever tell you how I met her?" Jake got to his feet, giggling, convulsed. When he laughed he hunched his shoulders up and almost closed his eyes and he seemed to be bubbling with mirth from his head to his feet. "It was at a party," Jake said, the words gurgling out of him. "I guess—I guess I was the only one really drunk. I saw this girl. I wanted her. I plotted for hours wondering how I could get her." He rose and walked around, his shoulders bunched up, his face red, his eyes strangled with joy. "Then—then I got the notion she lived in this house—and if I could hide there—I could—" Vridar was now howling with glee;

462

and Jake, his face red and choked, was unable to go on. He walked around, giggling and tortured. "Well, I decided—I decided to hide. But where? Where? I looked all around me. I saw a piano stool. I went over—and sat—behind that stool! And oh I was quiet, hoping that no one would see me! I must have sat there for two hours. I wanted everyone to go home . . . . And when at last they all rose to go I was so happy I could hardly wait!" Again his voice died away and he walked about in giggling anguish. "I—I watched them get their coats and hats—and there I sat as drunk as a fiddler, peering at them over that stool!" Vridar burst into violent howls and Jake sucked in his breath, gasping, breathing hard. "Then—then one of them asked—where—where is Jake? I saw them look all around and I was so quiet, thinking I was hidden. Then—"

"Shut up!" Vridar cried. "You're killing me!"

"—then a man came over and—and kicked the stool away! What are you squatting there for? he asked. And God I was furious. I grabbed the stool and—and put it in front of me and—and—"

"Shut up!"

Vridar loved this man but with conflicts storming within him there was little in Jake's paganism that he could use. What he sought was a sharp and tremendous awakening, but there was no awakening in the academic quiet of this school. He decided to join an advanced group in psychology and go through the asylum again. He did not know why he wished to see lunatics. He knew only that the sanity of persons around him seemed monastic and sterile. Donnaugh was forever saying, "Don't say you want to *take* a course in English; say you want to *pursue* a course. Don't say not *as* great as but not *so* great as. Aggravate does not mean to vex, it means to add to . . . ." Agnew could talk only of sex and virility. Jake, in spite of his zest and humor and spontaneity, did not know what he wanted or why. Vridar's other colleagues wearied him.

And so he turned, as he had two years ago, to the lunatics behind their gray walls. With a group of students and the professor of psychology and the superintendent of the institution, he went from floor to floor and from ward to ward; and with madness all around him, he felt at home. He thought he understood most of the lunatics; they belonged to the wild darkness of his world. Idiots he did not like: the big lout who had tried for months to tie a simple knot in a string; the heavy-jawed youth with the death of memory in his vacant stare; the shapeless girl who grinned and slobbered. Here was a hydrocephalic head, there one shaped like a bullet; there a mouthful of grin and black teeth; there a silent hulk laboring with patience to solve the workmanship of a scrubbing-brush. These were the dull or grinning footnotes to the human record of syphilis and cretinism.

Vridar observed now, as formerly, that most of the students were amused. They grinned at one another and exchanged winks; they were patronizing, they asked dishonest questions. As he watched them, Vridar's thought went back to the time when lunatics were baited and tormented or burned as witches at the stake, They went to other wards and around them now were men and women lost to themselves and life. There sat a small sickly woman who wept day and night over imaginary guilt; there one who folded and unfolded a handkerchief in her lap, her gaze forever on the floor; and there one who stared with terrible earnestness at the ceiling. Up and down a corridor walked a man, talking to himself, dramatizing some old wrong or some old failure, his ear cocked to a vast dim audience, his gestures embracing peopled spaces. Standing by a door was a man who took Vridar's arm. "I'd like to speak to you," he said. "All right." "I want you to get me out of here. I'm as sane as you are. They've stolen my money and locked me up . . . ." On and on the man talked, his story earnest and plausible, but when Vridar looked into the man's eyes he saw there what in times gone he had seen in his own. As he passed down a hall, a woman threw her arms to his neck and clung desperately, her wet unclean lips trying to kiss him. A doctor and two attendants broke her clasp and dragged her away.

For Vridar it was all heartbreaking, for he had walked on dim shores and been lost to this world. He felt that he could understand most of the persons here. These tumultuous cycles of elation and depression, he knew them to their core; and these frenzied hallucinations,. these hysterias, or this sunken and eternal grief. He knew this ambition, denied, and now fixed in feverish dramatizing of itself; this changeless meditation on wrong; this deadly inner conflict between two forces. He knew them all. He was wearied by the cool professional commentaries of the doctor and the psychologist, who talked about madness as men might about the stock market; and he wanted to say, "You dull cab horses of the academic world! You sane people! Your knowledge of all this is the mole's knowledge of the hawk!" For here human personalities rioted in their wild fancies, and the sane stared at them and uttered platitudes. How could the doctor live year after year in a place like this and have no record of it in his face? How could the psychologist grin and be so sure of himself? Did he not know that genius itself was on the borderland of madness?

A lunatic came up to Vridar and said he was writing a book. It was about Polyphemus. Did he know Polyphemus?

"Yes, I know Polyphemus."

"He ate the whole earth. He ate his parents and he ate God. Then he married Leda. They peopled the earth and every person had a part of God in him. Do you see?"

"Yes," Vridar said.

It would be a great book, the man said. It would encompass all the bibles and gods and holy men. "Do you know who I am?"

"You are Polyphemus."

The psychologist was talking about the OEdipus complex.

In a small room the students crowded round a vat and the doctor explained that this was a new method of treatment. There was a patient in a tub of warm water. When Vridar elbowed through and saw the patient, he was shocked. She was a young woman. She was bound and she was lying there in warm water, with only her face out. She was Kitty Murdock. He left the room and went outside. He went to the railway station and took a train home. Kitty Murdock, that volatile person with whom he had danced at the Odeon and walked in Liberty Park. What had she said? Vridar, look at the stars. Can you get any meaning out of all that? Doesn't it hurt when you think about it? . . .

When he opened the door of their attic apartment, he thought he heard a sound of footsteps retreating in haste. He turned to Neloa and he thought she looked confused and guilty. But he could not be sure, for he was too confused himself, too deeply upset to care about it.

"Was someone here?" he said, glancing over at the window.

"No."

"I'm back early," he said. "I didn't wait for the group." A little later he talked to her about what he had seen. Isaiah and Jesus, he said, Nietzsche and Beethoven and Ibsen and Dostoievsky were all insane. Howells and Trollope, Brahms and Polk were sane. Wordsworth was mad in his young years and after he became sane he wrote "The Excursion." "I suppose I'm insane," he said, "and I suppose I may as well stop pretending that I am anything else. I'll never leave a calling card or give a commencement address or name a son after me or be a Mason. You'll never find any peace with me. You ought to think about it and decide what is best for you."

"I know what is best."

"What?"

"To go with you."

"But you'll never be happy with me."

"I don't want to be happy. I just want to be with you," she said.

A month later she said she was pregnant. Vridar sank to a chair and looked at her.

"I don't see how you could be," he said. They were intimate only once in a while. Every day he pursued his studies from early morning until midnight and at midnight he was exhausted. And when they were intimate, he used the best contraceptive he knew of and he used it with extreme care. How could she be pregnant? "Are you sure?"

"Yes. Vridar, I want an abortion."

"No. That's hard on a woman's health." He was looking at her and wondering about it. His thoughts turned to his brother, a student here, and he felt shameless and unworthy. "I'll just have to work harder," he said. "Donnaugh says I must go to Midwestern again this summer."

"And what will I do?"

"Stay with my folks a little while until I find a place for us."

"No!"

"Neloa dear, listen. My salary is two thousand dollars. By eating the cheapest food and wearing the cheapest clothes, we will have saved half of that. Donnough says I must not come back until I have my Doctor's. That means three or four years. And we have a thousand dollars! God knows how we'll make it but we must make it somehow." Her eyes had filled with tears. He went and knelt and clasped her hands. "You and our son will come just as soon as I can find a place. Be patient. We must make it somehow. . . . . "

XIV

He had been in Chicago only a few days when he met Blanche Olson. She was eager to see him, and she seized his arm and asked him to walk with her. They went over to Jackson Park.

"Vridar, why don't you like me?"

"I'm married," he said.

"Marriage doesn't mean anything to most men."

"It means a lot to me."

"You remember what I told you about my sister? She's worse. The doctor says she simply must get a lover."

"You expect me to volunteer?"

"Sometimes," said Blanche, "you can be very stupid. Do you know I teach in a small town?"

"You told me that."

"And I'm twenty-four. You know why I came to Chicago again?"

"To take some more dull courses in education."

"No. Vridar, are you really so stupid?"

"Blanche, is it impossible to find words for what you want to say?"

"All right, I *will* say it. I came to find a lover."

"Having any luck?"

She stopped and drew her breath sharply. "Do you find me so unattractive?"

"I hadn't thought about it."

"I have lovely legs," she said. "Men adore legs."

"Really?"

"I won a prize with my legs. You ever watch men when a trolley comes up? They all look at the legs of the women who get on and off."

"These short skirts show plenty to look at. If ugly legs were a capital crime nine-tenths of the women would be shot."

"Not me." She drew her skirt up and thrust a leg out. "How's it look?"

"All right."

"Make you want to see more?"

"Not particularly." When they had returned to the campus he said: "I wish you luck. You should have no trouble."

"I won't. Don't think I will." Coloring a little she stepped up to look into his eyes. "Vridar, every night I walk in Jackson Park."

"Every night I study."

"If some evening you are unable to study . . . ."

"I'm stupid," he said, "but I think I understand you."

Every evening he sat with his books, but he could not forget that out in Jackson Park Blanche was waiting for him. He could not forget, Love as ever, Bob, and Neloa's lies to him. Now and then he would enter the night and walk, trying to forget his wretchedness and his doubts; and he would go to the library and strive to lose himself there. He would think of Neloa but what did it matter now? Perhaps most women deceived their husbands, perhaps most men betrayed their wives. Perhaps marriage was what Thackeray and Meredith had said it was. Now and then he would start for Jackson Park and turn back. He would spread Neloa's letters out and read:

> You know, I sometimes wonder if Dr. Snade is not right when she says emotions and passions cannot be governed by intelligence. When I think what a hard old time we are having to get along and how selfish, cross, little and mean the people we meet every day really are, and what a hell of a world it really is, I find it takes more than intelligence to keep me sane. I have a hard time reasoning myself out of crying . . . . Dr. Snade admires you very much, dearie, and thinks you will be a great man. Now don't get all puffed up . . . . Marion says he is going to get drunk . . . .
>
> I am almost afraid you will become so interested in your work you will not miss me. I am glad you find comfort in your books, but I am selfish enough to want you to miss me sometimes. Now and then I feel that my being born was a big mistake. I have never had a place in the world and have always been where I was not wanted. Perhaps if I had never come into your life you would now have a woman you could love and admire, a woman equal to yourself. It is terrible to feel that I stand in the way of the person I love most and would do anything for. But, dearest, I still have hope of becoming the one thing in life for you. Make a companion of me, dear. You never have. It has been my fault, I guess, but God knows I have tried. I feel like a big volcano all the time, just ready to erupt. You make me afraid to ask you things; and I am interested, dear, so just go ahead and tell me things or I'll always be ignorant. Dr. Snade says I must keep up with you. I want to be educated to keep your respect and be able to entertain your friends and hold a conversation with them you will not be ashamed to listen to. That, darling, is my dream. Good night and try to think kindly of your
>
> Neloa

What a pathetic letter! Or was it? Its sincerity, it seemed to him, rang like a bell from end to end; but what about her deceptions, her stealth, her lies? He would think of the matter until his head ached. If he could have believed in her, he would have dismissed Blanche and given all this time to his books. But he was baffled. When with Neloa he often saw the cunning in her eyes, the faint contempt around her mouth; but when away from her, he turned to her with overwhelming need, forgetting most of the time all the bitterness and remembering only the love.

And so it was that, tortured, he struggled day and night. Rather than be a simple fellow, deceived and mocked by a woman, he preferred death. He preferred death rather than be shamefully unfair to her. But he also believed that if she were not now pregnant almost any handsome man could seduce her. This was the thing that maddened him. Night after night he sat in his room, desperately loathing himself, trying to determine what he ought to do. Between him and Blanche stood these letters; if he were to go to her he would have to trample them under, sheet by sheet. He could not go. He tried to but he could not go.

467

To Neloa he wrote:

The only facts I can get hold of are these: you deceived me, you lied to me, you almost drove me out of my wits. That and one other: I love you. But I cannot for the life of me understand how you expect me to trust you when you so thoughtlessly destroy trust. If we ever come to that companionship you speak of you will have to speak from your heart. You will have to be honest in what you want. You have no more interest in books than I have in President Harding. How can we get anywhere until you distinguish what you feel from what you pretend? I want to cut my way out of this emotional nightmare in which I have been all these years. But I can't do it as long as you are as silent as a wooden Indian. Sit down, my dear, and write out of you all that you think and feel and believe. Be honest and to hell with the cost . . . .

Forgetting Blanche, Vridar waited for the reply. When the letter came, he thought it a remarkable document. She said:

Dearest:

You have set me a rather difficult task. I can't imagine why you have asked me to write as you have, I only know you have asked it and that is enough. I shall try to tell you just how I feel. And will you understand me or will you think again that I am trying to deceive you?

I frankly admit that I often wonder if you love me at all. Didn't you have a fancy for me and don't you regret now? You have told me so many times that I have disappointed you, that you could learn to forget me or even to hate me, that your marriage was a mistake. In view of all this is it strange if I sometimes doubt? You often think, dear, that it would have been better if you had married a girl with an education equal to your own. I realize I am not your equal in that respect. But I believe that I can become your equal if I have the chance. It is hard for a woman to try to make a home, raise a family, and at the same time keep up with a very studious man; but that is my one wish now. I want to do all three and do them equally well. Please help me.

I will admit, sweetheart, that I don't know much about human nature. You are a great puzzle to me and I often despair of ever understanding you at all. You will have to help me understand. You tell me so little of what you feel that I can never hope to know much about you unless you change. My actions depend a lot on the impression you give me. So long as you make me think you distrust me I can never open my heart. You have never known how much l long to be able to tell you everything and to feel that you want to know and will understand; and I want you to believe that my sympathy for you is deep and that my interest is the same as yours. And I'll be so happy, darling, if such a time ever comes.

Now, sweetheart, knowing as much of you as I do and in view of all the hurts you give me and the mean things you say, if you and I were

468

back in 1917 and you were to ask me to marry you, I'd say yes so quick your head would swim. Never think for a minute I'm sorry for that. In spite of our quarrels I am happy and my suffering is mostly because *I know you are not happy with me.*

I think I get bigger and broader each year for I think more of other people and less of myself. I am still extremely selfish. Perhaps you do not know that I am very jealous of you. I think you like to flirt but I try not to blame you because I guess that was born in you. I think you must have flirted last summer just a little and I know Blanche thinks more of you than any single girl should think of a married man; and not in a motherly way either. Still, dearest, thinking this and knowing you are human after all, I would not object to your seeing her this summer and taking her out if you care to. I have enough faith in you to believe you will not wrong me. I trust you so much that I think you could do anything and then make me believe it was the only thing you could do.

And if you had such faith in me I'd rather die than destroy it. But you have not. And it puts a million little devils in me to know that I am distrusted and spied on. That is the only way I can explain last summer. I worked last summer not because I wanted to but because I wanted to help us go to school. I thought you would understand my motive. And when people began to tell lies about me you don't know how it hurt. I often lay awake all night, crying and thinking about it. Then I learned that your mother believed the stories and I swear to God there wasn't a word of truth in them. She spied on me. She used to go down the other side of the street and hide in doorways and watch me and follow me home. *I decided there was no use being a good woman because nobody would believe you good anyway.* And I knew all the time that you distrusted me too. You had Diana following me. She showed it in every act. More than that, I caught her in several lies. I knew you were writing to her and I was so bitter I thought of suicide several times. I had to take aspirin and soothing syrups to sleep and I felt so bitter toward you and didn't want ever to see you again. But I have learned that what others say about you doesn't matter; it's what you think of yourself.

Do you understand any better now or have I made things worse? You don't know how much I love you and I suppose you will always doubt my love. But when we get a home of our own, away from your relatives and mine, then we shall get to know each other and greater love will come. That is my dream and I am happy with it. I trust you; I am praying that you trust me. Please understand my faults and shortcomings, dearest, and help me to grow big. That is the prayer of your

Neloa

On a bench in Washington Park Vridar read the letter a dozen times. He thought it a remarkable document because in parts it was so sincere and wise, in parts so contradictory and evasive—because it was such a revelation of the woman and yet no revelation at all. He shuddered again at her preoccupation with suicide.

What he was now to do he might not have done if circumstances had been different. One of these was his deep shame at being a psychic impotent. He was a good lover with Neloa and had no difficulty embracing her—though he *had* had difficulty the first two or three times with her. But when other women manifested an erotic interest in him he turned frightened and cold. He did not know why. He did know that most men of his age had lain with a dozen or a hundred women; and what sort of stupid and contemptible man was he, that he should wish to flee when a woman offered herself!

Another circumstance was his family. His mother and sister, puritans to their marrow, looked on Neloa as if she were little better than a harlot. This he perceived only dimly, if at all. He was still the prisoner of a stern family integrity, with its Calvinistic view on sex. There was more than that, a great deal more, but this he did not know and was to learn only with bitterness and heartache. He thought his mother and sister were good women, women pure and wise, and he had listened too many times, and with too much credulity, to their counsel. He had not yet seen them for what they were.

In his middle twenties he was still a naive and bewildered child, neurotic, emotionally immature, obsessed. He wanted to be a man. He wanted to be like other married men. He wanted above all to break his paralyzing fear of women. He stuffed the letter into a pocket and headed for Jackson Park.

"Well," he said, "I came."

"You must not have wanted to come very much."

"I didn't."

"Then I don't want you now."

If Blanche had come to him with hungry mouth and thighs, he would have spurned her. Fear would have made him do that. But finding her indifferent he felt cold and able, and he seized her arm and jerked her to him. "Remember the big strong fellow who raped you? You liked it, didn't you? It takes a lot of ape in a man to make you women swoon!"

"You're breaking my arm!"

"You'll be lucky if I don't break your neck."

"Why are you so savage?"

"That's the way you like it." Then she smiled and surrendered; and he took her arm to lead her away, but he felt frightened and sick. They followed paths, searching for a leafy gloom back in lost jungle. They peered guiltily into clumps of underbrush. And Vridar felt more and more ridiculous and impotent. "I don't see," he said, "why the world makes such a hell of a fuss about sin. Virtue, in a city at least, seems well protected."

"But not in the country," she said.

"No. There they have buggies and automobiles. But how can a man sin in Chicago?"

"I know a place," she said. They went up a path and at a bench she stopped and sat on the bench.

470

"Now what is it?" he asked, hoping she was in her menses.

"It's there," she said, nodding at a tangle of darkness. "But I don't want to now. I'm afraid."

He looked at her and examined his emotions. He was excited but it was not erotic excitement. So far as he could tell, he had no more wish to embrace this girl than to jump into Lake Michigan.

"You'll have to wait a little while," she said.

He sat on the bench and put an arm round her. Neloa had said that he might take Blanche out, and what he wondered was he to do after taking her out? He drew her to him and lightly kissed her lips but there was no fire in the kiss. "I'd better go home," he said.

"No, please don't."

What in hell had Neloa meant anyway? She as well as any woman he knew was aware of what men had in their minds when they took women out. He resolved to work up an erotic frenzy. He kissed her lips and throat and drew her blouse down and kissed her breast. He saw that she was pigeon-breasted and shuddered but went on kissing.

"Oh, Vridar, don't! Ohhh please!"

As frigid as a polar cap he was playing a part, knowing what he should do and doing it with fine amorous fury; but the erotic part of him was as dead as charred wood on a grate. He pretended nevertheless to be undone and he kissed her with what she took to be savage hunger; and she gasped and struggled to be free. But he held her and persisted, letting instinct guide him, crushing her to him, kissing, exploring, his thoughts as hard and naked as trees in December. Once or twice he turned away and looked into darkness and grinned. He wondered what sort of man he was and why he could not like other men take an eager woman and be done with it. Blanche, aroused now, clung to him, her hot wet mouth seeking his throat.

"Let's go," he said, fighting against laughter. He rose and led her away.

They went into tangled growth and on hands and knees Vridar crawled and Blanche followed him. He took his coat off and spread it on the grass and leaves. Kneeling, he drew her to him and laid her on the coat and saw that her eyes were as bright as stars. He felt the quivering in her flesh.

"Vridar, please be careful. Don't hurt me."

He wanted to laugh. He might hurt a woman but not that way. The mirth in him was so sardonic and mad and wild that he wanted to stand up and roar at the sky. But he gathered her to him, with laughter like a flood in his being, with a deep and ghastly alarm under it. For he felt no passion. He was impotent with fright or conscience or something, that lay under the laughter, as water lies dark and deep under a surface stirred by wind. He lay against her and sought her mouth. He strove with everything in him to come awake, to deliver himself from the emotional paralysis, to be a man and claim his own. And as he fought he swung between self-loathing and laughter, the one destroying him, the other defining his terror. What, he wondered, did other men do when a girl waited? Some took her, a few like himself were thumbscrewed by furious impotence. A few like himself were sickly warped idealists who tried to laugh all passion out of them .... And all the while he kissed

471

Blanche, hiding from her the terrible conflict within him, thinking how different her lips were from Neloa's, how different her flesh, for Neloa's thighs were firm but Blanche's felt soft and almost flabby . . . .

And when he could pretend no longer, he rolled over on to his back and laughed and began to talk. "You know who Stendhal was? . . . . A great novelist and the great psychologist before Freud. He said, Pleasure is a luxury; to enjoy it, it is necessary that one's sense of security should not feel itself running any risks. Is that it, in me? He called himself babilan, an old French word for eunuch. Babilan Stendhal and babilan Hunter! . . . . Is that it?—that when a child bullies threw me down several times and almost castrated me? Do I feel subsconsciously that I *am* a eunuch? Or is it something else? Stendhal confessed that as a child he wanted to copulate with his mother. When only six or seven he used to sit on her lap and kiss her mouth passionately. But I can't remember that my mother ever kissed me . . . . Or is it my sister? I tried to embrace her when I was a child . . . . "

He heard Blanche make a sudden sound and turned to look at her. She was sitting up staring at him and in her eyes he saw disgust and loathing. He rose to his feet with foliage all around him. He swept the foliage aside and looked down at her and said, "Babilan Vridar!" Then he laughed. All his own self-loathing and pain and hurt came out of him in wild laughter, and he turned away and went laughing down the path. She called to him but he did not turn. He was convulsed by madness and grief. After entering his room he lay on the floor and howled and realized only after several minutes that his laughter had run into tears.

The next day he sent a note to Neloa:

Here is money for the fare. Come at once.

Vridar.

Then for three days he wandered about like a man in a trance. He went to his classes but he understood nothing. By accident he met Blanche.

"Let's take a walk," she said. She was excited. They went to Washington Park. "Vridar," she said, "I'm in trouble."

"What trouble?"

"I'm pregnant."

"Pregnant! Not by me. Not by Babilan Vridar."

"I was sick this morning."

He stared at her and slowly he understood. She had never been raped. She had contrived that fantasy out of her desperate hunger. She was so ignorant of these matters that she thought he had embraced her and that she was pregnant.

"Vridar, do you love your wife?"

"Of course."

"But you love me."

"Hell yes. I love all women."

"Why don't you divorce her and marry me?"

"Listen, Blanche, the first move you women make is to get a man to lie with you. The second is to get him to marry you. The third is to get children. The fourth is to choose your daughters-in-laws. Your fifth is to be a tyrant in an armchair. Your sixth and the only decent move you ever make, is to die . . . . Come to my room."

472

"No, I'm afraid of you."

"It's probably your father you're afraid of. Come tonight then."

At midnight she came. At once she sat on the bed and drew up her skirt to show him her legs. "Haven't I got lovely legs?"

"They're all right."

"Why don't you kiss them? You never have."

"I never will."

"Other men kiss them. Vridar, you're not much of a lover."

"I know it. I'm a complete fraud."

"You know how other men make love? They kiss women here—and here."

"The hell they do." He stood up, feeling murderous. "Come on, get out. Get out before I twist your head off."

"Why don't you love me?"

"I said get out!"

He went with her to the door and watched her go up a quiet dark street. Then in the bathroom he steamed himself in a hot bath and looked at his eyes. Hating what he saw in them, he put on his one baggy suit and walked north into the city, and everything about him was hushed in smoke and sleep. He walked fifty-seven blocks and turned westward and crossed a bridge and entered a station. An hour later he heard the thunder of a train and a few moments later saw Neloa and their son and the tears in Neloa's eyes; and with tears in his own he kissed her and their child and took the child in his arms. Without a word they entered the street and entered a trolley and rode south to the shabby little aparment which he had engaged for them. Without a word he drew his wife and child close to him and enfolded them and fell asleep.

XV

Feeling that his one and only attempt at adulterous love had been a shameful thing, he turned again to books. Two personalities within him—the idealist, credulous and self-pitying, and the thinker, ironic and ruthless—were becoming day by day more irreconcilable; and he was disintegrating in the struggle and knew it. He resolved to search books for some faith that would sustain him, some clue to his deep unhappiness. He read in many fields, and the books that he borrowed and returned to library shelves numbered hundreds. From philosophy, comparative religions, history, sociology, anthropology he made piles of notes, and day by day he kept a journal, recording his pilgrimage in search of God. Besides all this he carried a full course of graduate study. For a small dark two-room apartment he was caretaker of an old and stinking building, stoking the furnace, scrubbing the hallways and stairs, carrying the garbage out, fighting bedbugs, letting rooms, and collecting the rent. He studied French and German and labored on a thesis. He spent his Sundays writing on a novel. And two or three times a week, despairing of his health, he went to the gymnasium and worked furiously with rings and dumbells and bars, or ran for two miles on the indoor track. From early morning until midnight he drove himself to the last ounce of his strength. At the end of his first year blindness threatened him and his health was on the brink of collapse.

Neloa also overtaxed her strength. Her second child was born two months after she came, and though Vridar wanted to launder their clothes, including the diapers of their second child, she said no, and insisted on helping him carry out garbage and make beds and tidy up rooms. She kept their own little apartment immaculate, scrubbing its floor every day and keeping herself and her children fresh and clean. Many an evening he read to her or she to him and many an evening she listened while he talked.

"Kant!" he would say. "He was forever pursuing *Ding an sich* in the black wilderness of his moral consciousness, like a whale after a fish; and he spouted tremendously; and when he was done the sea leveled off and was as calm as before. What was wrong with him? He was a very small man. Are systems of philosophy erected by the babilans? Didn't Mill sum it up a hundred years ago?—an age which has been described as destitute of faith but terrified at skepticism, in which people feel sure not so much that their opinions are true as that they wouldn't know what to do without them . . . . "

He would talk about marriage: "Tolstoy said that in a successful marriage there has to be complete discord or complete agreement. We have neither. And Lewis in his novel *The Monk* says that possession cloys man but only increases the affection of women. Do you think that is true?"

"I don't know," she said, her dark eyes fixed upon him.

"Well, a Rolland character says that happy marriages are very rare, for the reason that you cannot bind together the wills of two people without mutilating one of them, if not both. And such mutilation, he says, doesn't even produce the kind of suffering that it is well and profitable for the soul to pass through. Is he right?"

"Do you feel mutilated?"

"Both of us, don't we? As I look back at the married people I've known, I think about all of them have been mutilated. My father and mother almost destroyed one another. Your father almost destroyed your mother. Is marriage, then, a huge failure?"

"Not ours," she said, smiling.

Vridar responded to her smile. His notes he abstracted under various categories. Under *Marriage* he had hundreds of statements that famous men and women had made about it; and now he looked through them. "It may seem funny but almost nobody seems to have had a good word to say about marriage. Meredith says marriage has a decent front and a hideous rear. Thackeray says when the love-lamp is put out and in common daylight we look at the picture what a daub it is. Marriage, says Peacock, is like pills and one is a dose. If marriage is such a dismal failure is it chiefly the man's fault or the woman's?"

"Both," she said.

"It is certainly both in the case of my parents. Is it both in the case of us?"

"I think it is."

"You mean we are both difficult?"

"Yes."

"In what ways?" When she did not respond, he picked up *Man and Woman* by Havelock Ellis. "I suppose this is the best book ever published on the differences between the sexes. Ellis says that on the psychic side women are more inclined than men to preserve ancient customs and methods of thought. You are conservative, I am radical. You would still be a Mormon, I would not. Ellis says the man's tendency is to diverge from the average; woman's, to prefer stability and the old order. He says this tendency in the male is physical as well as psychic. That is, his tendency is to wander but the woman's is to remain stationary. A man's home is the world, a woman's world is the home. Do you think that is true?"

"I don't know."

"But how do you *feel* about it? In a letter you said I like to flirt. I can't remember that you have ever seen me flirt, but I have seen you flirt. Now if you are happy in your marriage, why do you?"

"I guess all women like to be attractive to men."

"Yes. But that is one thing. When a married woman responds to an erotic advance, that is another thing, isn't it?"

"I don't," she said.

He looked into her eyes, wondering about her. "Well, Ellis goes on to say that the man's tendency to wander and the woman's to stay put complement one another. For the man, woman is secure and safe and predictable like the earth, and when he falls down and kisses her breast he is strong again. For the woman—but you don't like the wandering man, do you?"

"I think woman has as many rights as man."

"Yes, but only within her own nature. And as to what her nature is, Diderot says all women are real savages inside. Do you agree with that?"

"I don't know what he means."

"He means women can be more violent and cruel. Ellis says because they are savages the ascetics hate them with hatred so bitter and intense that no words can be found to express their horror. Men who love the artificial, he says, find women repulsive, and he quotes Baudelaire, that woman is natural, that is to say abominable. And Ellis concludes that the sexual differences add to the charm of life, and also to its everlasting difficulties." He laid the book aside. "To make our marriage successful, what should we do that we're not doing now?"

She was looking at him steadily, but her eyes were unhappy and baffled. "You don't love me," she said.

"Of course I love you. I've loved you ever since I was twelve years old."

"It's just the image of me you've built up."

He considered that. He knew there was a lot of truth in it. "But you don't love me either. You said in a letter you don't understand me. Nobody can love what he doesn't understand. So we don't love one another. Is that it?"

"We are learning to," she said.

He went over and knelt at her feet and kissed her two lovely hands. "Darling Neloa, we are trying to. For every man or woman in the world there is some man, some woman, who would make the best mate. Yet in our youth we develop romantic fancies and we marry one of only a dozen or twenty whom we know; and with the odds

475

piled against us we struggle to make a success of our marriage. That is why the most successful marriages are those of people who marry late." He arose and kissed her lips. "But we'll try," he said, looking deep into her inscrutable eyes. "We'll try and try hard." He picked up a book to read but after a moment he said: "Altrock wants to come to dinner. But how can we ask him? We have barely enough to eat ourselves!"

Many weeks before, Vridar had seen Dennis Altrock in the University's corridors and had looked at the man with interest; for he was the strangest graduate student in the school, a huge gorilla with long and hairy arms and an apelike face with an insignificant nose, large sensual lips, and small gray eyes full of simian alertness. His hair was short and roached. He wore baggy trousers and went about coatless, his shirt open, with a thicket of hair pushing above his shirt.

Vridar little suspected that this man was to become a close friend. It was not a friendship of his making. He preferred to live without friends, and when Altrock spoke to him, he resented the man and tried to ignore him. But Altrock, huge and uncouth, childlike in his ways, and with no sense of niceties in behavior, would not be dismissed. He walked home with Vridar, talking to him, and did likewise the next day and the third. "I don't like him," Vridar said to Neloa. "I wish to hell he'd leave me alone. He knows everything under the sun or he's a monstrous bluff. . . ."

Altrock was no bluff. He was a wolfish reader who had explored every field and whose amazing memory preserved a great part of what he read. He could talk for hours about any period of English literature, or Greek or Latin or French or German; or about trees and flowers and birds, volcanology or the organisms in the sea, the habits of spiders and ants and wasps or the philosophy of Buridan and William of Auvergne, or the theories of Wundt and Westermarck, or the Hamburg-Elberfeld system of charity, or the socialism of Engels. He amazed Vridar into complete and abashed silence. Again and again, after being both astounded and annoyed, Vridar would allude to some remote fact, to some name in a footnote; and Altrock would overwhelm him with an hour's lecture on the subject. Or now and then Vridar would slip quietly to a library to deny or verify what Altrock had said; but never once, even in the smallest matters, did he find him in error.

This man lived in a foul little room and ate only milk, honey, and cheese. He had taught in three colleges and had been dismissed from all of them. He did not understand why but Vridar knew. Altrock had no sense of irony, no humor, no understanding of himself or others: he was only a strange weird machine that devoured and catalogued and gave off what he had taken in, without coloring it in any way. For most persons he was an insufferable obtuse bore who talked endlessly and to no point.

"You've never learned to listen," Vridar said. "Until you learn to listen you'll be an ignoramus for all your knowledge."

Such rebukes made Dennis look unhappy. His mouth twitched and his small eyes glanced round him as if seeking enemies; but after a few moments he was talking again. Most of the time he annoyed Vridar or bored or enraged him. In the gymnasium Dennis would walk about, looking at his huge muscles and then with frank and withering contempt at Vridar's. With the vanity of a child he would say, "I

476

guess I can lift about ten times as much as you." Or he would say: "If we were to fight you wouldn't last very long."

Dennis was a Scot. One day Vridar borrowed a nickel and the weeks passed and he forgot about it. But Dennis did not forget. One day he said: "I guess you don't remember the money you borrowed from me."

"What money?"

"That nickel you borrowed on 63rd Street."

Too astonished for words, Vridar proffered a nickel and Dennis hastily took it. He dropped it into the toe of a sock that he used for a wallet.

"Do you want interest on it?"

"A debt is a debt," Altrock said.

Vridar also despised the man's way with women. Dennis was a great lusty animal, sensual and vigorous and unashamed. He never told obscene tales or spoke of women as if they were all legs and uterus; and his clean-mindedness Vridar liked. But the man took all the women he could lay his big hairy hands on and took them with immense zest. When he told about them his eyes would shine in lustful memory and his tongue would lick his full red mouth. He seduced his landlady, a woman with gray in her hair; and then one of her lodgers and the wife of a neighbor. In plain truth, though, the women seduced him. He did not flatter women or offer gifts. He merely took those who came to him, as years ago, when a boy in Texas, he had taken a negress.

"A negress is best," he said one day, his eyes shining as if he were remembering vintaged wines. "All white men prefer negresses. They titillate more."

"Nonsense," said Vridar.

"Another thing," Dennis went on, "they're more natural. There's no shame in a negress."

At the moment they were in Altrock's room. A woman entered, robed only in a clinging gown. She looked at Vridar with bold and searching eyes, and then Dennis drew her to his lap and kissed her breasts.

"Be good," she said, slapping him. "I have to save up for my husband."

After she had left the room, Dennis said, "She's passionate. Last night when I got through she wanted me to again right away. I told her I had to wait fifteen minutes."

"I suppose," said Vridar dryly, "you waited."

"I had to. Any man has to."

During these years there gathered in Washington Park on Sundays and often in the evenings a huge crowd. There were evangelists, crusaders, social workers; evening idlers from factory and home and shop; students from the University; thieves and pimps and harlots; and women who rode in great cars and men who wore diamonds and twirled walking sticks. Vridar liked to study these people, and when he had a spare hour the gathering-place became one of his classrooms. For here was the strangest assortment of zealots and cripples and halfwits, of sneaking plots and high purpose, of poverty and wealth side by side that he had ever seen.

One Sunday afternoon a man came up to Dennis and struck him. "You son of a bitch," he shouted, "what are you doing with my wife?"

477

Then Dennis knocked the man down and the man leapt up and disappeared. A few moments later Dennis was turning a hat over and over in his hands. Was it a good hat?

"Yes," Vridar said. "Where'd you get it?"

"His. That's the lawyer I told you about. I screwed his wife." With savage pleasure Dennis put the hat on and thereafter he wore it, though he preferred to go without a hat.

It was here one midnight that Dennis and Vridar sat under a tree. Dennis was telling of the whores he had lain with in France, in the first War, and of how he had thrust his bayonet into German bellies and broken it off, and of what the sound was like when a bayonet was shoved into a belly. There came up to them six young men.

"Where you from?" one asked Dennis.

"Texas," Dennis said.

"Where men are big and tough!"

Dennis got to his feet, and before Vridar could cry out a man dropped behind Dennis and another man struck Dennis a dreadful blow on his mouth. The men fled and Vridar pursued three while Dennis pursued the other three. After Vridar had run a hundred yards the men turned and knocked him down, and while he tried to rise, fists and heels were like stones in his face. Then the men fled and Vridar got to his feet and heard Dennis shouting. He went to Altrock and saw that he had a jackknife in his hand and that the open blade was red.

"I got it into one of them," Dennis said, grinning. "But I think I missed his heart."

"You damned fool! Do you want to be up for murder?"

"When I was sixteen I killed a man with a pitchfork."

"The hell you did! Well, wipe that off and put it away."

Dennis wiped the blade on his trousers. "You're bloody," he said. "They hurt you?"

"Not much. Take me home."

When Vridar entered his rooms, Neloa sprang up with a cry and came to him. He went to a mirror and looked at himself.

"Sweetheart, what have you been doing?"

"Just out with that idiot named Altrock." He washed blood from his face and looked at the blood on his clothes. "This comes from reading Leibnitz," he said. "His monad and nisi ipse intellectur." Neloa stood by, helpless, her gaze on his bleeding mouth. "I can't understand that God damned Altrock. He's nothing but a big ape, but he writes good poetry. He'd as soon stick a knife in a man as eat his honey and cheese, but he almost weeps when he talks about the Sistine Chapel or Conrad's description."

"Vridar, you're still bleeding."

"It's nothing. I want to understand Altrock. I'm an American and he's an American and we're both melting in the same pot. Why are we so different? I'm a babilan, but he would copulate with a cripple." He sat, holding a wet rag to his mouth. "Altrock is deep in a passion about you. He almost slobbers when he talks about the curves of your hips and waist. He would put you to bed if he could, yet he pretends to be my friend. How am I to understand that?"

478

"I don't like him," she said.

"I don't like him either, but he fascinates me. He probably killed a man tonight, but he will never give it another thought. Right now he is probably in bed with his landlady."

"I don't like him," Neloa said.

"Our chief task in life is not to like but to understand."

Finding in philosophy nothing that he could use, Vridar turned to religion and learned that the Old and New Testaments were largely a patchwork of ancient superstitions. The first was also, of course, a romantic history of the Jews. With his interest aroused, he read in the scholarship about Jesus, and while he was so engaged two Mormon missionaries came to his door. They had been instructed, they said simply, to fetch him back to his Church. They were typical missionaries of the Mormon Church: beardless, earnest, untaught. Neither of them had completed his high school studies. They knew no more about the Bible than about the *Opus Tripartitum* of Eckhart.

"So you're here to make a Mormon out of me. Sit down and fire away."

One of the youths grinned and the other scowled at his hands. Said the first: "We want to know why you left your church."

"Because its doctrines are childish."

"You still believe in God, don't you?"

"What do you mean by God?"

"Why—why, the divine father. The person who rules the universe."

"I see no evidence of such a person."

"You don't? Why, there's the Bible and the Book of Mormon."

"What do you know about the Bible? You can't tell me if Johanna is a book in the Bible or a woman's name. Do you know what the canonical gospels are?"

"The ka—ka what?"

"Or the Talmud?"

"The—seems I've heard of that." He turned to his scowling companion. "Have you?"

"No."

They were pathetic. They were only boys who had inherited the dogmas and superstition of their parents. Religion for them, as for most people, was an easy and lazy and selfish way to heaven.

"There's a Catholic priest out in Washington Park. Argue with him. Find out how little you know."

"You mean you don't want to be a Mormon any more?"

One evening Vridar heard the smiling young man argue with the priest. It was worse than pathetic. It was ridiculous. This beardless youth had only his faith with no reasons to support it; and when the crowd jeered him, he broke into sweat and lost his temper. He howled at the multitude and said they would all be damned if they did not join the only true Church. Vridar turned away, feeling desolate and empty, for he had abandoned his childhood faith and had found nothing to take its place.

A few weeks later he saw the birth and growth of a strange yet very ancient phenomenon. Among those who came to the forum meetings was a man named Ezekiel Tolles, a tall gaunt skeleton, ragged and foul, with a mouthful of rotten teeth. His breath was an unbearable stench. His fingernails were very long, with filth packed under them and his uncombed matted hair fell over his collar and his eyes were those of a crazed fanatic. He stuttered in his speech and convulsed his face and choked.

Tolles was a Catholic. Within his field—that of Church doctrines and history—he was a man of great learning, and his memory was almost as extraordinary as Altrock's. Unschooled, he had nevertheless taught himself Greek and Hebrew and knew them well. He had got so much of the Bible by heart that he could recite whole chapters. When he lost himself in zealous fervor, he stuttered only a little; and his learning, his opinions and faith and hope, poured out of him in quaint forceful rhetoric.

Because at heart he was only a child, there was in him no bitterness or malice or irony. He never worked, having no strength for labor; at night he slept where he could, sometimes in the park, often in sheds or hallways; and he ate what was given him or what he could find in garbage cans. When, as infrequently occurred, he was given a pair of old shoes to replace his leather rags or a pair of trousers or a shirt, his gratitude was simple and pathetic. For he had no vanity, no pride: in spirit he was most like the traditional Jesus of any person Vridar had known or was ever to know.

But for nearly all the persons who came to the forum he was only an unclean and homeless lunatic. They taunted and jeered him. They asked him questions and ridiculed his answers and whooped at his stuttering. Vridar closely observed everything that Tolles did, studied him with quiet pity, and learned to love him. He now and then took the man's part when Tolles was distressed by jibes or silenced by scorn. Seeing in Tolles what he himself had once been, he talked to him. Tolles, clearly e-nough, had been driven into religious fanaticism by a sense of guilt: some perversion or some incestuous wish had driven this man to an apostleship in the clan of Jesus; and Tolles cherished the notion, as Vridar once had, of prophethood.

Tolles was always at the meetings. He would come in long loose shambling gait, dragging his long thin legs—six feet and two inches of skeleton and fervor, rags and dirt. He would rout anyone who engaged him in serious argument on religious matters; when, smiling as a child smiles, he would look round him with morbid shining eyes, and if he saw a sympathetic face he would lope toward it, his whole body trembling with eagerness. Sensing the terrible hunger of the man, Vridar wondered if he had never thought of women. Tolles never spoke of them and he seemed never to look at them. Vridar looked behind the simple self-denial and knew that the man wanted a woman's love.

Among the hundreds of women who came here was a small withered creature with crossed eyes and a thin twisted neck, livid with scars. She hungered for love, too, and Vridar knew it, for he carefully watched her, noting every small thing that she did. She had an alert mind. She had read in many fields. But when men looked at her, it was to grin and shrug, or to stare, as Dennis Altrock did, in profound and utter astonishment.

480

Thinking that Tolles would be happier with a wife, Vridar went to him and said, "Come, I want to talk to you"; and Tolles went with him, his brilliant eyes full of questions. "Tolles," Vridar said when they were alone, "why don't you marry?"

"Muh-muh-muh-marry?"

"Yes. You need a wife."

"Buh-buh-buh-who?"

"Haven't you ever found a woman who would marry you?"

Tolles shook his head, his grin sheepish and pathetic.

"I know one," Vridar said.

Tolles was electrified. "Huh-huh-huh-who?"

"Myrna Farner. You know her, don't you?"

"Yes. Does she luh-luh-luh love me?"

"I don't know. Ask her."

This astonishing man, shaking now like a reed in a wind, turned at once to the multitude and explored it; and a little later Vridar saw him and Myrna withdraw to a tree and sit. An hour passed and the two of them sat there, and Vridar watched them, hoping that for both life hereafter would be less unkind. Then Tolles came to Vridar, so excited that he was unable to speak.

"Will she?" Vridar asked. Tolles nodded his head in a tremendous affirmative. "Fine. And do you really want her?" The man's answer was another vigorous head-nodding. Then, without any shame at all, Tolles confessed that she would marry him if he would bathe and clean himself up. Vridar grasped the long slender dirty hand. It was very soft and weak in his clutch.

But this is no part of the strange phenomenon that Vridar saw. It came later. Day by day Tolles questioned certain dogmas of his Church, until he was overcome by dark and awful doubts. He talked to Vridar about it and Vridar said little, for it seemed to him that the man's questions were silly and trivial. Tolles thought a few of the popes had erred in some of their pronouncements and that a few of the rituals were too infused with paganism; and after months of torment he resolved to leave the fatherhood of Rome and found an order on his own principles. And this he did.

It was the birth and growth of this new sect that Vridar witnessed, and perhaps nothing that he had ever seen or was ever to see, in books or in life, was to leave him so thoughtful or to teach him more. For this ragged filthy man in afternoons and evenings preached his new gospel; and one by one he gathered converts; and a year later he had six hundred. Many of these were dubious and a few came to laugh and make fun, but there were as Vridar counted them a hundred or more who were deeply sincere. Nor were all of these social outcasts. There was a lawyer among them, a dentist, a half-dozen university students, and several business men. If only the simple-witted had followed this new prophet Vridar would not have been a-mazed; but when he saw intelligence and worldliness enrolling with Tolles he was left speechless by the implications and the truths.

Tolles held his services in the park. One of his converts furnished him with sacramental wine; and Sunday at dawn, when the trees were full of birds and the eastern sky was a lake of amber, Tolles would hold mass. He did not stutter now, and when he spoke in Latin he was superb. Tolles tried to convert Vridar and offered to make him a cardinal in the new order.

"Already mixing politics with religion," Vridar said, grinning.

"I—I should be ashamed of that, shouldn't I?" Tolles said.

"It makes you understand some things," Vridar said to Neloa. "The kind of person Jesus must have been, and Calvin and all the rest of them. Some day I want to write a novel about Jesus."

"Ask him to dinner. I'd like to see him."

"But he stinks so."

"Did he marry that woman?"

"Not yet but he says they're engaged. How funny it is! You see, my dear, all any man needs is the right woman to take the prophet out of him. Any fanatic is dodging some sexual problem."

"You're a fanatic," she said.

"Well, so I am. I missed being a Tolles by only a hair. I had no sense of humor."

"You have a sense of humor now," she said. "Why are you still a fanatic?"

"Give me time, my dear. I no longer believe in the saint-and-sugar-beet doctrine of Mormonism. I no longer believe in Christianity except as a historical phenomenon. And some day I'm going to write books about this."

"But will anyone want to read them?"

"You remind me of a story about Shelley. When a friend advised his mother to send him to school where they would teach him to think, she cried, O my God, teach him rather to think like other people! That's how my parents feel about me. And you also, I suspect."

"You make me tired," Neloa said. "You never believe the same thing twice. One year it's this, the next year it's something else. How do you expect me to keep up with you?"

"I'm exploring and I'm changing. Remember what Havelock Ellis said about the woman's conservatism and the man's vagrancy. Ponds stand still but rivers run."

"They just run but where are they going?"

"All right, they don't stink. You know when those missionaries came to see me? I thought at first I smelled their breath. Then I thought you must be cooking cabbage. I know now that I smelled their minds."

XVI

Vridar renounced all orthodox religions. Whether, as Freud said, God was only a father substitute, he did not know, or whether Jesus was only the self-immolating son who out of fear yielded to his father. But he had now read enough in religions to see that they were all much alike. He stored in his mind Joubert's statement that the proof of the existence of a God have made many men atheists; and Meredith's that a frank acceptance of reality is the only firm basis of the ideal; and Goethe's that a man never knows how anthropomorphic he is; and Peter's: "Religious progress, like all purely spiritual progress, is confined to the few." But the conflicts within him were as bitter as ever, and it was during these months that he deliberated a life of crime. He thought of spurning everything in the smug social order and of entering the underworld where motives were as naked as a sword. Dennis was ready to go with him.

"I'm serious," Vridar said one evening, not knowing if he was serious at all. "To hell with respectable hypocrites. Sacco and Vanzetti will be murdered. Look what is being done to the Jew and Catholic and Negro. Knights of the invisible empire, realms and their kleagles, domains and their grand goblins—and the imperial wizard! Magazines illustrating seven kinds of kisses, and Negroes beaten until they give their land away. Freud is right. Sadism is the strongest motive in this country and is growing. Why do men like to flog and lynch Negroes? Because their sex-life is rotten. The Inquisition, witch-burning, lunatic-bating, and now the flogging of the black: it all passes under the name of religion and patriotism. Where is there honesty except among crooks? They pretend to be only what they are, apes with most of their hair gone. The more I see of respectable people, the more I admire the candor of the murderer. The more I see of good women, the more I respect whores. I'm sick of misbegotten imbeciles like Ford and dull scoundrels like Harding. I'd rather rob a bank than rob factory drudges of their wages. I'd rather cut Morgan's throat than be a cardinal in purple or the beet-and-babies president of the Mormon Church . . . . "

During a furious tirade Dennis seldom spoke. Vridar's outraged idealism he did not share, for he had never knelt at the feet of Jesus or been taught that human nature is good. And if he agreed, if he felt himself drawn to the underlands, it was because he saw simply and clearly that many virtues were vicious or because he felt no deep passion, no love, no faith. He was boyishly eager to rob someone. Vridar knew that if Dennis took to crime, he would not be protesting against the brutal indecencies of the civilized life. He would do it as he sat at a feast or embraced a woman or read a book.

"I know a man," he said, "we could start on. That Jew who comes to the Bug Club."

"The fat ass with the big diamond in his tie?"

"Yes, and the gold on his walking-stick. Let's crack him." Dennis rose, excited. He said he would go at once and prepare a sandbag. He crossed the park and after an hour he returned and drew the sandbag from under his coat. "Let's go," he said. "I'll lay him down and you get the diamond and his wallet."

They went to the forum meeting and saw the Jew, and Vridar could tell by the way Dennis eyed the man that he was eager to break the fellow's skull. When the Jew left, Vridar and Dennis followed him down a path into darkness; but when Dennis stepped forward, Vridar seized his arm. "No," he said, "not yet. Let me think."

Dennis was annoyed. He peered into darkness and then looked at the sandbag in his hands. "You're a coward," he said.

When in other hours they sat on a bench, Vridar looked at the women who passed, but Dennis, when busy with ideas, paid no attention to women at all. If, wearied by the talk about philosophy and literature, Vridar said, "Let's pick up a couple of women," Dennis would get to his feet, as eager as a bull. At the north end of the park was a great open space, an assignation spot for midnight lovers. One Saturday night they counted forty-seven couples dotting the field like cocks of hay in a meadow. When Vridar and Dennis walked among them, a few did not move at all, and some sat up, looking very foolish, and some fumbling with their clothes got to their feet and went away. Vridar said it was immoral and the police ought to do something, but Dennis just grinned and said it was all right. "They're just doing what I'd like to be doing," he said.

One night they took a dark path. Unable to see where he walked, Vridar stepped on a man and the man sat up and cursed. Then Vridar saw the naked flesh of the woman. "You bastard," the man howled, "get out of here!" They passed on and Vridar began to laugh. This situation, of a man fetched up suddenly and delivered to fury, Vridar thought delightfully ironic. "There he was, his wits scattered, and with Mother Nature as his personal attendant; and I stepped on him!" But there was nothing funny in it for Dennis. "My God, have you read Anatole France? This is as delicious as the salamander scene!"

"You're morbid," Dennis said.

Vridar wiped mist from his eyes. "You're a bull and you eat and copulate."

"And you," said Dennis, "don't eat enough and don't copulate enough."

"Remember what Swift said? A mind worth having wears its body out. Your mind, my fine bull, will never wear yours out."

"I'm a man," said Dennis, blowing up his great chest and lifting his arms to feel their muscle. "In a civilized society, where only those breed who are fit, I'd be chosen. You'd be exiled to an island."

"You studhorse. You God damned awful studhorse."

At the forum meetings was a girl who wooed Vridar. Her name was Miriam Boyd. She was short and too plump but attractive to some of the men who came here. Her mother, a huge furious tyrant, once strode into the meeting and glared round her at the men and took her daughter home.

"She won't let me marry," said Miriam. "I'm twenty-six and a virgin but a hell of a lot she cares."

"You tired of being a virgin?"

"Well," she said with a bitter smile, "it has become quite a burden."

Dennis instructed her in the names of all the flowers and trees and shrubs in the park, talked to her in Latin or German as if she understood, and recited to her endlessly from the poets, until Miriam said: "I'm ignorant. Tell me some big words."

Dennis was pleased. He narrowed his wicked eyes and pursed his sensual lips. "Saccharimeter. Know that one?"

"Lord, no."

"It's an instrument for measuring the amount of sugar in a solution. Ultimogeniture, where the youngest son inherits the estate. Xenogenesis, the notion that an offspring is like a parent. Protevangelium, the first announcement of a savior, as in the third chapter of Genesis."

Miriam turned to Vridar. "Do you know big words?"

Vridar was annoyed. "Dennis knows all of them."

Miriam was not interested in Dennis, and when spring came she sought Vridar one evening and with a twisted smile said, "Come on, teach me some French."

He walked with her through the park, not knowing at first what she wanted. She led him to dark undergrowth, and then he knew and he faced her, hands on her shoulders. "No, Miriam. That's not what I want."

She threw his hands off. "Then what in hell do you want?"

"Oh, a way of life that is decent and clean."

"You beast!" she cried, as if he had struck her. "You don't think I'm decent and clean? You cur!"

"Listen, I didn't mean—"

"You dog, to insult me that way! If I was a man I'd break your neck!"

"You didn't understand me."

"Ohhh! Me unclean? You lousy lowdown bastard!" She looked round her for a weapon, but her eyes were blind with rage and tears. "Go!" she cried.

"But I tell you—"

"Go, I said! Police! Help!"

Vridar went quickly away. When he entered his rooms, Neloa was in bed and he undressed in silence and lay at her side. "Neloa, I think I'm going crazy." When a mood like this was upon him, Vridar yielded to clowning, sometimes making weird faces and talking in a jargon of nonsense syllables; or capering in grotesque antics in imitation of monkeys and apes; or delivering his emotions into parody, pun, and epigram. Now and then Neloa laughed until she wept. Or she would lie through half the night and listen to his spontaneous wild overflow until weary of his monologue she fell asleep.

Now he said: "According to a pretty legend Patrick Henry said, Give me liberty or give me death. He is dead. And sin, my dear, is what we want to do and wish we didn't; and virtue is what we had to do and wish we hadn't. An optimist, darling, is a man who thinks he loves his wife; a pessimist is one who knows he does. I'm a pessimist . . . . Are you listening?"

"Yes."

"I feel tonight as if I'd swallowed Calvin and Casanova and they had one another by the throat and Calvin's hands were just a little larger. But whether I digest them or not, life will go on and we'll civilize all the savages so that afterward we can reform them . . . and our opinions of our enemies will continue to be the only trustworthy summary of ourselves . . . and civilization will still find an analogue in a man when he looks at a lovely woman, for he approves the modesty of her clothes and wishes he could see more . . . . A professor said today that when he addressed a group of club women he felt like a lion in a den of Daniels and that's the way I feel and you're the mightiest Daniel of them all. Poets I think are a bunch of asses and I'd put them all in skirts and glasses for in regard to them Plato was right. Did you know that the Devil, not God, has been generally regarded as the patron of art and literature? In fact, the Church in the Middle Ages opposed him on the ground that he believed in liberty and equality. Some critics have said that no person can write art if he doesn't have the Devil in him; and Blake said of

485

Milton that he made Satan out to be such a remarkable person because he belonged to Satan's side without knowing it . . . . Are you asleep?"

"No."

"I mean a poet has spectacles on his emotions, and I'd like to know whatever got me fixed in rimes and rhetoric. What I write is like a mixture of acid and buttermilk and the acid comes to the top and the buttermilk sours and my mind is like a sword in bright sunlight and my heart is like a plate of butter in a hot oven. An enemy, darling, is a person who sees your motive before you see it and a friend is one who pretends he is blind. Is there a truly admirable person in the whole world or would we despise everyone if we had a full view of him? I suppose we would. It all sounds like staphylorraphy or another of Altrock's monstrous words or an ichthyosis of the moral skin with virtue patched from her head to her heels but still chirping sweetly and with the night coming in great modest darkness to hide the folly of women and the impuritanical heavy breathing of men. And every last man of us thinks

> When lovely woman stoops to folly
> and shoots her virtue under par
> it is a dandy thing, by golly,
> if I'm the man she's stooping for

but if I or any other John Doe is not the man she's stooping for then it's

> Pin a scarlet letter on her,
> bawd and trull, for motherhood
> must live in chastity, doggone her,
> and every virgin must be good.

Darling, still listening?"

"Yes."

"A woman cursed me tonight because I would not lie with her. She called me a dog and a cur. The world would have cursed me if I had. So I'm cursed going or coming."

"Did you want to lie with her?"

"I suppose possibly I did. In this country if a man devotes himself to women he is a scoundrel, but in France a man who ruins himself for women is a great guy. As Havelock Ellis said, we males are vagrant but a woman wants babies and a nest. You are happy here with your children but I prowl around watching Tolles establish another heresy."

"Women like to prowl, too," Neloa said.

"Nonsense." He drew her two hands to his mouth and kissed them and then put an arm round her and kissed her cheek, whispering, "Women who like to prowl are more male than female but you are all female. Well, it's late and I must be up at daylight to carry out the garbage. We must sleep but here is a thought for you to dream on. Man is certainly stark mad, says Montaigne: he cannot make a worm yet he is busy making gods by the dozen. Or would you prefer Thoreau? I have never yet met a man who was wide awake, he says. How could I have looked him in the face? . . . . Darling, goodnight."

486

XVII

Spring came to Chicago, a green glory in the parks and a warm languor in the sky. Vridar told Neloa he thought they should go home for the summer; it would cost them less than to live here.

"To Antelope?"

"Yes.

"I don't want to. I don't want ever to see that country again."

"But this city is driving me mad. Think, to get up in the mornings and smell the dew and the firs and a clean river and a smokeless sky. To take blankets and lie together on a green hillside and sleep with the whole sky and stars above us . . . ." He thought of his homeland as a beautiful thing. He thought he would find strength and calm where he had suffered agony, vision where he had seen only the dark; but when the mountains of Wyoming came in sight and the prairies of sagebrush, he was filled with the old anxieties. "I am sorry we came," he said to Neloa, and for two hundred miles he did not speak again.

He stared at the country, hating and yet loving it, seeing in it both terror and peace. The loneliness of this earth was part of him. Sagebrush and pale sky, hillsides of cedar, great reaches of solitude—they were all written upon his heart and mind. Within them stood all the scenes of his childhood and youth: of Neloa on the Annis butte with the smell of juniper in the morning; his father wrapping the cat around the dooryard post; the fragrance of burning sage in a kitchen stove and the smell of blood; the shelters in which he knelt and prayed and wept. God, how he hated it! His parents were on the homeplace and his brother and sister, but he hardly saw them at all, for he had eyes only for the wilderness of the meadows, the Bridwell place, the pouring river, the blue peaks. Feeling at once that he would have to work at heavy labor to keep his sanity, he went with Marion to the benchland to build fence and almost severed a foot with an axe. When he drew the blade out, a jet of blood shot upward, boiling and red; and when he smelled the blood he fainted. He came to, sick with shame, and saw that Marion had torn his shirt off and was bandaging the wound. Then Marion went for a horse, and when he returned he fetched a bottle of wine.

"Drink it," he said.

Vridar drank the wine. Then he was helped to the pony and borne to the house and his parents came to look at the wound. It would soon heal, Joe said. Vridar examined his foot and saw that the axe had cut more than half way through the bone of his instep. He tried to move his toes, but the tendon of the big toe and the one next to it had been severed. Joe poured iodine into the wound and chewed a huge quid of tobacco and when it was soft and full of its juices he shoved the tobacco into the wound.

"The tendons won't grow together," Vridar said.

"Sure they will," Joe said.

"Damn it, I know they won't."

"Sure they will," Joe said. Only last year a surgeon had cut a great stinking cancer out of Joe's throat. The surgeon said he would die but Joe said, "Me die? Nonsense!" And to Vridar he now said, "It will be well in a jiffy."

Vridar looked at the bandaged foot and remembered with shame that he had fainted. He wondered why the odor of blood sickened him. His mother said it was because of something that happened before he was born.

"This is an age of science," he said.

"Don't talk science to me, son. You was afraid of blood when you was only a babe. Why, when you was a year old, if you saw blood you'd howl your head off. You'd go into fits. But if you hurt yourself and saw no blood you didn't seem to care."

"When I was only a year old?"

"Yes. I don't care what science says. I know. The day Mother died, it was the most awful of my life. She filled whole pillow cases with blood. She soaked the bed. She coughed streams of blood from her lungs and all day and all night I had to take care of her alone. The house, it was full of blood."

"What has that to do with me?"

"Listen and I'll tell you. The look in her eyes when she died! It was the most awful thing I have ever seen. That look, it's the same look you had when you were born and when you were a child. It's always been with you, that horrible insane look she had. That's why—"

"I wasn't born then?"

"I'd been carrying you six months when Mother died. Your science son, it can say what it will but I know. Some things your science doesn't understand yet."

"Maybe," he said. "You suppose all this has anything to do with my feeling that we shouldn't eat meat?"

It was all right to eat meat, his mother said. God put it here to eat.

"I don't especially care what God did," he said. "That Old Testament primitive—"

"Son, how you do talk!"

"That Old Testament skulker-around-in-the-skies."

"Stop it!" Prudence had turned pale. "Some day God will strike you dead."

"That's all right with me. He's the sort who used to sneak around and drop stones on defenseless people."

"Son! What has got into you?"

Unable to work and unwilling to be idle, Vridar resolved to read the Bible again, though he had read it several times in childhood. Like the country here, it was in his nerves and blood and brain. He told Neloa to find him the book of monsters and he would see if there was any sense in it. Day by day he read it carefully, studying the obscure passages, pondering its folklore and history, and keeping in mind all the while Arnold's thesis in *Literature and Dogma*. He made many notes. Now and then he spoke to his mother.

"You really believe this is the word of God?"

"Son, please stop talking that way."

"You believe all of it?"

"Of course I do."

"Have you read it?"

488

"Some. Not as much as I should."

"You believe God strolled down to sit on his rump and eat lamb stew?"

"Son!"

"Who liked the smell of burning flesh; ordered the firstborn sons sacrificed to him; encouraged his people to go to war; approved the cutting off of toes and thumbs of captives—"

"Son, that is enough."

"God says it's an abomination for a man to wear a woman's or a woman a man's clothes. Then this is an abominable country."

"It's an abomination to me," Prudence said.

"You're not to eat pig but you and dad eat it. You Mormons say, Follow the truth and it shall make you free, but the Bible says, Trust the Lord and lean not on your own understanding. And did you know that this book records about all the sexual perversions even Oscar Wilde ever heard of? Daughters seduced their fathers. Men seduced wives and killed the husbands. How can such a book be the word of God?"

"It's not all translated correctly."

"It's simply the embellished history of a primitive and ignorant people."

"I don't want to listen to you. You make me sorry I ever sent you to school."

Vridar looked round for his father, but Joe had slipped away, his eyes filled with pain. To his mother Vridar said, "I'll read you a verse. Listen. 'Hath he not sent me to the men that sit upon the wall, that they may eat their own dung, and drink their own piss with you?' "

Prudence gasped, as he had known she would. "Son, shame on you to use such words!"

"It's your own Bible. Look."

"I don't believe it."

"Well, here it is—Isaiah, thirty-sixth chapter, verse twelve. Read it." Like one who found herself in the presence of Satan, she looked at him and then at his pointing finger. She read the words. He saw her lips moving as she read, and the color filling her face.

"It's not translated correct," she said.

"There are other verses like it."

"I don't want to see them. It's wicked men who put in such words."

He knew that he was mean and stupid when he pressed these matters on the attention of his parents, but his leg had swollen to his knee and he was afraid of gangrene; but his father said it was nothing at all and his mother appeared to be unconcerned. One evening while suffering considerable pain, he propped his leg high and told his parents he had been reading in biblical scholarship. Did they want to hear what he had learned about this holy book? His parents looked at him with resentful unbelief, his sister with pain, his free-thinking brother with weariness. Vridar said the Bible was a romantic history, a collection of myths and legends, most of which the Hebrews had taken from other people. "The story of the creation, of the garden, of the flood was the common property of nearly all people in ancient times. The story—"

489

"I won't ever believe it," his mother said.

"You mean the great scholars don't know what they're talking about?"

Joe said angrily, "No son, they don't."

"Then who does?"

"Joseph Smith, he knew."

"Dad, you believe the first man was pure and woman led him into sin?"

"I know it!" cried Joe, his voice loud and angry.

"Mater, you believe your sex brought sin into the world?"

Prudence looked at Joe. "No," she said, "woman wasn't any more wicked than man was."

"Why, wife," said Joe, turning to her, "what are you tellun me? Don't it say right in the holy Scripture that Adam was pure till Eve tempted him?"

"Oh, hell!" said Prudence. "He wasn't any more pure than she was."

"Why, wife—"

"Mater, when I was a child you taught me that all women are naturally good, that it is men who make them wicked."

"It is," Prudence said. "I never knew a bad woman without some man was in it."

"Why, wife," said Joe, looking at her with astonishment and pity. "It was womern who brought sin into the world. Don't you know that?"

"I know men say it but I don't believe it."

"Then you don't believe the Holy Writ."

Vridar said to his father, "How do you know that part is translated correctly?"

"What part?" asked Joe, glaring at his son. But he knew. He withdrew now into outraged silence and scowled in turn at his son and wife.

Vridar said, "You two would rather your sons were Mormon bishops than great scholars or scientists or writers. Isn't that so?"

Prudence looked at him as if suspecting a snare. "We'd rather that you and Marion believe as we believe, for we know that we are right."

"How do you know it?"

"Because God gave the truth to Joseph Smith."

"And all the other Christians are wrong?"

Prudence appealed to Joe and after a few moments of sulking he growled, "Yes, son, all the other Christians is wrong."

In bed that night Vridar said to Neloa: "What a hell of a family we are. My parents have no more interest in truth than an owl has and they'll break their hearts over their sons, who refuse to follow them in their superstitions. And look at my sister. She rides a horse every day and I think there's a lot of titillation in it but she'd knock you dead if you told her that."

"Maybe she just likes to ride."

"I say, This man likes to pinch a woman's fanny, and you say, Maybe he just likes to feel human meat. You were right: I shouldn't have come back here. As soon as I can walk we'll go."

Late in August Vridar said goodbye to his people—he kissed his mother and sister, he touched his check to his father's face, he shook his brother's hand and looked for a moment into his gray cynical eyes—and returned with his family to

490

Chicago; and he again paid for the two small dark rooms by taking care of an old bug-infested building In some of the rooms when he pulled the wallpaper back he saw the bedbugs in a solid brown mass. He killed them by the thousands and swept them down and carried them out; destroyed them by thousands in the coils of the bedsprings; stoked the furnace and swept the hallways and bore the garbage to the back alley. The signal from tenants above was a certain number of raps on an iron pipe that ran from the roof to the basement, passing through Vridar's living-room. There were sixteen apartments and fifteen signals, from one blow to fifteen. One of the tenants, a huge and imperious woman, was forever pounding on the iron. Vridar would lay aside his book and climb to the fourth floor and knock and she would swing the door open and abuse him.

"Heat, janitor! I want heat!" Or again: "When my groceries come fetch them up."

"I'm not a delivery truck."

"You're the janitor, ain't you?"

The word stung him. He wanted to say, No, I'm a graduate student in a great university and you are a vulgar illiterate housewife. Most of his tenants were arrogant and stupid. The women asked him to run errands and some of them dumped their slop from the windows or choked the plumbing with it. He wondered why some women could never learn not to put six or eight kotex napkins into a toilet bowl at one time. He thought of them as the states they had come from. It was Kansas who blew a fuse one Sunday when he was writing on his novel and then pounded on the pipe. He climbed to the third floor and knocked.

"What's the matter your fuses? They all blow out."

"You must have a faulty iron."

"Don't tell me my iron is no good."

This woman had blown a dozen fuses. Vridar said: "I won't put in another fuse until you have your iron repaired."

"What's that? Listen, Robert, you hear this man?" Kansas himself rose and came to the door. He was short and bald and had an ugly temper. "Say that again," he said.

"I'm not putting in any more fuses until—"

"Listen, you kike, you can't talk to my wife that way. Get down there and put in a fuse."

Vridar went to his room and called Adolph Klars, the owner. He and his daughter Sally lived in a hotel overlooking the lake and rode behind a chauffeur. Adolph wore diamonds and a beaver coat and carried a stick. Vridar had said to him one day, "Understand that I'm not a common janitor. I kill bedbugs and lice and carry garbage out only because I have to because I have no money. Don't put on social airs around me . . . ." And now over the telephone he said, "One of your tenants has just called me a kike. He will apologize within twenty-four hours or you will get another manager."

Klars came over. He was a big kingly-looking fellow but illiterate. "Jones," he said, "is one of my best tenants. Mr. Hunter, don't you think—"

"An apology or out I go."

"But he says you insulted his wife."

"Nobody could."

"You mean—Mr. Hunter, who *do* you mean?"

"I mean I'm sick of the big stupid asses. If I'm your manager, then I'm going to manage."

"Yes, yes, of course. But they always pay their rent promptly, don't they?"

This evening Jones came to Vridar's room. His face was red. "I understand you think I insulted you."

"You call me a kike. You may be the Duke of Whimwham for all I know, but in that case you should live on the lake front. If you stay in this building you will act like a gentleman."

"Well, I didn't know. Klars just told me. I thought you was just a janitor."

The statement made Vridar furious. "A janitor is a man, isn't he? Where'd you get the notion that janitors are not human?"

"Well, never mind. What do you want?"

"An apology."

"And if I won't?"

"You'll have to move."

Jones looked at him, his face red with anger. Then he thrust forth a hand. "Well, I apologize. I can't afford to move now."

"You apologize like a gentleman."

"What—what do you mean by that?"

And so for two years Vridar's absurd pride suffered shame and outrage. At daylight he would rise and take the garbage quietly away and mop the entrance and the stairways, hoping that nobody saw him. He felt the degradation he had felt as a child when he went with his mother to peddle chickens and cheese. His underwear was so ragged that when he went to the gymnasium he hid in a dark corridor and undressed in haste; his shirts were so ragged that he never took his coat off when anyone but Neloa could see; and he had worn the same suit for nearly three years. Neloa, too, had little to wear. Her underthings she made of flour sacks. Her stockings save one pair were of cotton. She had no hat and no coat.

Vridar could have spent a little more for clothes if he had spent a little less for books. A wish to own books obsessed him. He would smile at Neloa and say, "After going up to Oxford Erasmus wrote that 'I am giving my whole soul to the study of Greek; directly I get some money I shall buy Greek authors first, and then some clothes.' But Erasmus begged shamefully from his friends. At least we don't beg." Now and then he went to secondhand bookshops and spent hours turning volumes over, wondering if he should buy. If he saw an old favorite, forlorn and unused, he had to buy it. He *had* to buy *Pierre et Jean* and Daudet's *Premier Voyage* and Artsybashev's *Sanine* and Hiene's works in German and Lamb's *Letters* and Hazlitt's *Spirit of the Age* and the poems of Keats. When he came home, hugging a book dear to him, he would feel guilty, knowing well that he had no money for books. "I couldn't leave it," he would say. "And I've found the Arabian Nights complete for only thirteen dollars. Should I buy it?"

"If you want to."

492

"But I shouldn't. There's so much we need."

"I guess we can afford it," she said.

He almost ran to the store, afraid that the books might be gone. So childlike was he in this matter that he never perceived how distressed Neloa was or how she hungered for a few things to wear. His great passion was not whisky, not women, but books. He dreamed about them. He saw himself in a great library of his own, with books everywhere, and himself searching them for a plan of life.

He was bent over *Hydriotaphia* one morning when he looked up to see Dennis Altrock staring at him. Dennis was so excited that he trembled. He said he wanted to tell Vridar something and Vridar left the library and went with him.

"I'm in a mess," said Dennis. "You remember Ellen Mavis?"

"Yes," Vridar said, calling Ellen to mind, a beautiful but very neurotic woman.

When Dennis was excited his gaze roved from side to side and up and down, as though following the course of gnats in the air or the images of dead cells on his retina. "It's like this," he said. "Ellen and Jack asked me to spend a weekend with them at the dunes. I went, just as a friend."

"And ended up a lover."

"Well," said Dennis, still gazing round and round the sky, "one night she came to my tent and crawled into bed with me."

"And you promptly shoved her out, of course."

"No," he said, with a foolish grin. "It's a crazy situation. She and Jack have been married two years. They were married just after he graduated from Yale."

"Yes?"

"Well, in all that time," said Dennis, his mouth twitching, "they've never copulated. Not once."

"No!"

"It's true. Jack actually doesn't know what he's supposed to do. Ellen tried to explain. She brought books and showed him pictures. Now he hates women."

"I read the other day about a case like that. Now, I suppose, Ellen thinks you're quite a guy. Is she in love with you?"

"Yes."

"What a world, Dennis, what a world. Are you living with her?"

"Yes."

"And Jack, where is he?"

"He fled."

"No wonder. Well, you ought to please her. She told me she likes hairy men, and you have enough hair for a mattress."

"Hair," said Dennis, looking at the heavy growth on his hands and arms, "is a sign of virility."

After telling Neloa about it Vridar said: "If any of us knew all the truth about human beings we'd be silenced for life. What would you do with a man like Jack?"

"I don't know."

"Would you boot him out?"

"I think I might."

493

"If it's better to burn than to marry, that guy ought to be a grand goblin in heaven. I suppose there are a lot of Jacks in the world. I almost became one."

"He must be stupid," Neloa said.

"No, darling, just well-trained." He then told her that Dennis had a mistress who was a masochist. "Dennis chews and beats her frightfully. I saw him one night after he had been with her, and he had blood all over him." He was watching her. "You like sadistic men too, don't you?"

"Not that sadistic," she said.

"Do you think it is normal in women to want to be bitten and manhandled?"

Neloa looked out the window and seemed to be thinking about it. "A little, I guess," she said at last.

"I'm a hell of a lover," he said. "Far from chewing a woman, I can't even eat meat."

Neloa turned on him that faint smile of pity. For a year or more Vridar had refused to eat meat. In his notes he had written: France's Coignard says, An honest man cannot without disgust eat the flesh of animals, and nations cannot call themselves civilized as long as slaughter-houses and butchers' shops are to be found in their towns. H. G. Wells thinks the sensitive abstain from meat because of the butchery: one wonders how many would eat it if they had to do their own butchering. Meredith says eating meat has never been to his taste but Gissing thinks there is an odd pathos in the literature on vegetarianism. But isn't there an odd pathos in all idealism? . . .

Vridar now looked at Neloa and wondered about her. Once in sexual embrace she had suddenly flung herself on him with her mouth wide open and in that moment he saw an aroused woman who was all primitive savage. She had amazed and terrified him. He had had to fight her off to keep her teeth from closing on his flesh.

"Well," he said, taking up a book, "I guess you'd better read to me. Some more Trollope. That dull bastard will kill both of us."

XVIII

For many months his eyes had been giving him excruciating headaches. Dark spots floated in his vision like swarms of bacteria, and when he looked at a page he could see words and then only a foggy blur, in which after a moment the words would stand sharply, only to dance and vanish, leaving a sheet of gray. When he closed his eyes, he saw intensely bright colors in strange brilliant patterns, or faces of people whom he had never known, coming and disappearing beyond his will. He told Neloa he would have to borrow money from his father and consult a doctor, for he was afraid that he was going blind. He went first to a famous professor in the Rush Medical College, who with an assistant examined him. They prescribed lenses and Vridar wore them but they did him no good. He returned to Dr. Reed and that man, tall and gray and weary, examined him again. There was nothing the matter, he said. "How is your nose?"

"My nose?"

"Possibly you need an operation on your nose."

So Vridar went next to a great nose specialist and he dipped a cauterizing iron into acid and took a part of the bone out of the septum. Vridar went home, praying that his trouble had been found, and waited until his nose healed. But his eyes were no better. Dr. Reed then called in two specialists and they peered into Vridar's eyes and nose and ears. "Perhaps," said one, "it's his teeth."

"Any abscessed teeth?" asked Dr. Reed.

Vridar then had his teeth x-rayed and took the negatives to Dr. Bixby Greenwood, famous dental surgeon. "These six," said Greenwood, "will have to come out. There are four others that possibly you can save." Greenwood thrust a needle into Vridar's gums and a few minutes later bent over him, instruments in his hands. Before Vridar knew what Greenwood intended, a blow shook him and he heard something strike the floor.

"What was that?" he asked anxiously.

"A tooth," said Greenwood. With a chisel and maul the surgeon had knocked one of Vridar's eyeteeth clear across the room. Such highhanded methods, it seemed to Vridar, were too like ancient trepanation when holes were knocked into men's skulls to let devils out. But he supposed the surgeon knew his business.

"You going to knock the others out?"

"No," said Greenwood. "I can't get at them that way."

The surgeon now set forceps on a molar and pulled. He almost lifted Vridar out of the chair. There was no pain but there was a sound of crunching in his jawbone. Greenwood broke the tooth off. "Damn it!" he said.

"What's the matter?" Vridar asked. He would not have been surprised to see his jawbone in the surgeon's forceps.

"Get ready," said Greenwood to his nurse. "I'll have to dig it out." For twenty-seven minutes by the clock on the wall Greenwood was busy, digging out the roots of this tooth. Sweat ran down his face. He whispered profanely in his breath or now and then exploded a great oath; and the nurse sopped into the hole with cotton, her face very grave. A deathly sickness filled Vridar. My God, he thought, four teeth to go! He fought to keep his wits, his courage, but he fainted, and when he came to the nurse was bathing his forehead and now gave him something to drink. From time to time he drank from the glass while the surgeon worked. "The worst damn teeth I ever saw!" Greenwood muttered. And when it was all over he gave Vridar some pills, saying, "There will be pain, so take these." Vridar took the tablets and sat for a little while spitting blood. On the long ride home he would hold in his mouth as much blood as he could, and then leave the trolley and spit the blood out and wait for the next car. He paced the floor all that night.

The pulling of his teeth cost him thirty-five dollars; the operation on his nose twenty-five; the x-rays and examination and lenses forty-seven; and his eyes were no better. Reed looked dog-tired when Vridar again appeared before him. "We can find nothing wrong. Have you syphilis?"

"Good heavens no!"

"You'd better go to Dr. Brown."

And so Vridar went to Dr. Brown and paid fifteen dollars for a Wassermann. There was no evidence of syphilis. "To hell with doctors!" he said to Neloa.

"They've whittled up my nose and yanked out my teeth and x-rayed me and blood-tested me and taken all my money! I'm right where I was, minus a half pound of bone. What do doctors learn in school?"

This winter was for Vridar a long nightmare. For his Doctor's thesis he had undertaken to read more than three hundred novels, and most of them were big fat novels, bloated with words. Besides all this reading to be done, there were his courses and his reading for them, and reports and term-papers and examinations. But he could not read at all. Even in the classroom he sat with his eyes closed; and the notes which he made he made blindly, without looking at the paper on which he wrote. In the long evenings and sometimes in the afternoons Neloa read to him, patiently, quietly, with never a word of complaint. She read novels to him, one after another, month after month, and the slow uninspired toil of it maddened him. She read to him while he cooked the meals and washed the dishes and did the laundry and scrubbed the floors. In the novels by Scott and Dickens and Trollope and Reade and Disraeli and Gaskell and Bulwer and Blackmore and Black there were long stretches of emptiness, chapters in which words buried a handful of meaning, sermons that lay in level dullness from page to page; but he had to listen to all of it, had to sit in darkness and make notes. "Stop!" he would cry now and then. "That monstrous insufferable romantic windbag! Where'd the notion come from that Scott is a great novelist?" Or again: "That's enough, Darling, don't read any more Dickens to me for a week. If all the self-pity were squeezed out of his books they'd be no bigger than one of Martial's epigrams." Or again: "God damn Trollope! I can't stand any more of him if I never get a degree. He's as dull and thick as English puddings." There were three novelists to whom he listened without protest: Austen, Peacock, and Meredith. "They had brains," he said. "Scott wrote because he wanted to be a feudal lord, Thackeray because he wanted to be a duke, Dickens because he wept over himself and hid his mouth in a beard, Hardy because he was insatiably fixed on virgins." Sometimes he would say, "Read that again," or, "Write that down for me." And Neloa would read again, "If you wish to win a man's heart, allow him to confute you." "Disraeli, the sly rascal, knew his queens!"

"What was that?"

"All of us are weak in the period of growth, and are of small worth before the hour of trial."

"Fine. Meredith had more to say than all of them. Darling, read the things you have written down from him."

Neloa read: "Shallow souls run to rhapsody. A little yielding to desperation shoots us to strange distances. Like all rapid phrasers, Mrs. Mountstuart detested the analysis of her sentence. It had an outline in vagueness, and was flung out to be apprehended, not dissected."

"Good. Read some more of the notes."

Neloa took cards and read: "The many are sacrificed to the few; that ninety-nine in a hundred are occupied in a perpetual struggle for the preservation of a perilous and precarious existence, while the remaining one wallows in all the redundancies of luxury that can be wrung from their labours and privations."

496

"Is that Peacock?"

"Yes."

"He had both heart and brains but nobody reads him now. They read Scott. Read Gissing."

"And why should any man who writes, even if he writes things immortal, nurse anger at the world's neglect? Who asked him to publish? . . . Every day the world grows noisier; I, for one, will have no part in that increasing clamour, and, were it only by my silence, I confer a boon on all . . . . Dozens of my books were purchased with money which ought to have been spent upon what are called the necessities of life."

"I, too," Vridar said. "Fools, both of us. Well, the apple-woman in *Lavengro* attributed the vices and follies of her life to being able to read. Her mother, she said, who could not read, lived respectably and died in peace. Read something from the Hazlitt cards."

Neloa was busy looking over the Hazlitt cards, and as soon as she began to read he knew that she did not like what she was reading. She read: "How few of the infinite number of those that marry and are given in marriage, wed with those they would prefer to all the world: nay, how far the greater proportion are joined together by mere motives of convenience, accident, recommendation of friends, or indeed not infrequently by the very fear of the event; and a man no longer lives to himself, but is a body (as well as mind) chained to another."

"Is it true?"

"No."

"The first part of it certainly is true. Now read Gissing—the one I like."

She was prepared for this. She had read it to him a half-dozen times. "It is so difficult for human beings to live together; nay, so difficult for them to associate even under the most favourable conditions without some shadow of mutual offense. Even love, in the largest and purest sense of the word, is no safeguard—"

"That's true, isn't it?"

"No," she said.

"Neloa, you know it's true—both Hazlitt and Gissing. It's certainly true that very few persons marry the one who would be best for them. Do you know of anyone who did?"

"We did."

"How silly! Where are two persons more mismated?"

"You just like to think we are."

"I've tried to think we aren't, and most of the fault I suppose is mine. My mother filled my head with a thousand sickly ideals. My childhood made a horrible neurotic of me. I should not have married. I'm probably the kind who should never marry. Marriage would be all right for you if you had a decent mate instead of the fool you live with. But you'll never have a decent marriage with me."

"I would if you'd let me."

"Neloa dear, why won't you be reasonable? If you would discuss these matters with me we might come to some sensible decisions. But you persist in blindness, in saying that everything will be all right. There are men you could be happy with."

497

"I'm happy with you."

"There you go! You're not happy. You get thinner and thinner. I make you wretched because I am wretched, and as far as I can look into the future I can't see myself as anything but the fool I am. I don't want to destroy you. I think if you had stayed on Antelope—"

"No! I wouldn't give one year with you for a thousand on Antelope!"

He looked at her. "You can't mean that."

"I do mean it, so help me God."

"I don't understand," he said despairingly. "I keep your world in an uproar. You belong in a decent home with husband and children. I am going to try to be an artist of some sort but of all the artists I've read about who were married, not a one had a happy marriage. Unless we except Browning. Shelley's wife killed herself and he never made Mary happy. Meredith's wife killed herself and his second wife was certainly not very happy with him. Look at Dickens, Thackeray, even Shakespeare. I don't know why it is true but it obviously is true that men who become writers are lousy husbands—or painters or musicians or anything in the world of art. In my reading I've searched endlessly for happy marriages in these fields, thinking if I found some I might discover what I should do. But I've found only Robert and Elizabeth and they married late. If you would only be reasonable, if for your sake and possibly for mine you would leave me now, while we both are strong enough. If—"

"You mean you want to leave me?"

"I mean—"

"O sweetheart!"

It was such a despairing cry that he went over and knelt at her feet. "Darling, darling, I only want to do what is best for us and above all for you."

"What is best for me?"

"Yes."

"Then stay with me."

"But you don't know what you are saying. Would you have us destroy one another, slowly, inevitably, in the way we are now doing?"

"We won't."

"But Neloa dear, we are doing it now. A blind man could see it. Even a thick-head like Altrock can see it."

"To hell with Altrock."

"Yes, you would say to hell with everything but blindness. If we had money for professional help, but we have no money. If we had some wise person to talk to us and assess the blame and tell us what to do. But we have no one. We are alone in the dark—and how dark it is you seem not to know. If I dared to ask Thurman," he said, meaning the chairman of the department of English. "He is a great man. Imagine an old brown tough parchment. Imagine that all the wisdom and suffering of earth were distilled and the parchment soaked in it and used as the covering of a man's face. That is Thurman. Except the eyes. You see such eyes only once in a lifetime. It is not their color or the big hedges they stand under. Remember what Thoreau said?—that he had never seen a person fully awake? Thurman is awake.

He has never married and he is now an old man. I've heard on the campus that he has said that few persons are qualified for marriage and that he is not one. Nor am I. But I don't dare bother him with our troubles. I've learned that I've paid the doctors only half their regular fee and that Thurman paid the rest of it. He's that kind of man. He likes me, though God knows why. He thinks I have a great future but he may be wrong. In any case I can't bother him with our childish woes."

"We'll settle our own problems," she said.

"We never have. They get worse on us year by year." He drew her skirt above her knees and kissed her bare flesh and then he sat on the floor, with his arms enfolding her legs. "Think about it, Neloa. Refusing to think about it will get us nothing but more of what we have too much of."

"I've thought about it," she said. "I just want to stay with you."

XIX

Vridar heard Lorado Taft, the sculptor, say of a friend that he had got a hundred poems by heart. Taft said he envied such a rich and invisible treasure, untaxed and undiminished, and ready to serve anywhere and at any time. Vridar thought, Then why in hell doesn't he memorize a hundred poems? He resolved to. He memorized a hundred and a second hundred and a third hundred, including all the odes by Keats, Wordsworth, and Dryden, several of Browning's monologues, and more than two hundred lyrics from Chaucer to Masefield. When in bed at night, sleepless, he would say them over and over, to fix them in memory. He was full of them when, early in October in 1923, he saw Athene Marvell for the first time. He was a teaching fellow this year, with two sections of freshman English, and his office was in a large room with the other assistants. He was sitting at his desk, reading Shelley, when he became conscious of eyes watching him. He looked up to meet a steady gaze, and for possibly a minute the two strangers stared at one another.

Then: "What are you reading?" she asked.

"Shelley's *Alastor.*"

"You like Shelley?"

"Yes. Do you?"

"Very much." She said there was a splendid line in *Alastor*: "Her voice was like the voice of his own soul, heard in the calm of thought." Vridar looked away and thought about it: yes, it was great poetry. Why had he not discovered it?

"Where you from?"

"Vassar."

"Oh," he said, thinking of his own wretched training at Wasatch.

"And you?"

"Wasatch College in Salt Lake City. What other poets do you like?"

"Keats and Browning and Milton and Dante."

"Milton? He had a conscience as big and sick as a hospital." Again they stared. "What is your favorite English lyric?"

"I don't know. What is yours?"

"Cynara."

499

"I love it."

This was the only woman he had known, and except Jake Arlow he had known no man, who liked that magnificent poem. For Vridar it was like Cowper's poems to Mary Unwin, the letters of Keats to Fanny. The next day, the next and the next they talked again, across the thirty feet between their desks. Then Vridar did what, looking back on it from a later time, he though an amazing and incredible thing to do. He wrote her a letter.

Dear Athene:

I have been wanting to write you as I feel. For most persons, more hardheaded and practical than I, this letter may seem to be the last word in bellyache; but the motive that prompts it springs, I feel, from the best that I am.

Six years ago I married blindly, madly: it was a childhood romance. I was brought up by a puritan mother and I was taught in almost every day to believe in the goodness of women; until my attitude toward them came to be idolatrous in the extreme. I came to feel indeed that they were different in kind from men in all those respects which have become a part of tradition. My disillustionment in the girl I was to marry was, in consequence, complete and overwhelming but I married her because I loved her.

For years I have been midway between desertion and suicide, yet have yielded to neither, thinking them both cowardly. My wife has many virtues: she is saving, neat, willing, and has more than human patience. She is beautiful. She reads to me many hours every day, well and heroically. She tries to see life as I do, tries to accept my interests and tastes; and fails, poor dear, miserably. Children, two of them, now complicate the problem.

Duty is the cardinal point in my philosophy of life. I detest the man who is cowardly enough to desert his family; but at the same time I detest the man who, because of false notions, is cowardly enough to crucify himself. I cannot see clearly what I should do. I need a friend, wiser than I, more dispassionate; but I have none. I suspect at times that my idealism may be very stupid and that all idealism may indeed be; but I cannot yield it until I find a way of life that offers greater decency and peace. Now don't misunderstand me: I am in the words of Bojer no stunted ascetic; but neither, on the other hand, do I see why sex must be dragged into every situation of life. Some may say I am 'sublimating' my desires. I may be. But it must be possible in this world to love beautifully, with sex functioning in full power, but purged of its smoking-car filth.

Now my struggle, as you must see, is between certain ideals on the one hand, and on the other a world which reduces all ideals to sickly impotence. I am not an angel beating my wings in a void. I am in fact a rather cynical and bedeviled and crazed person, seeking something that is worthy of a deep and fixed loyalty. My need to love and to trust completely in some unalterable goodness is the great need of my being. I have thought of Marxism but so far have rejected it. And Shelley is not enough, for there was in him much unworthiness that I find in myself.

500

In Black's *Princes of Thule* the heroine marries a man who does not understand her. One day she is found in a cemetery, weeping. Her husband tells a friend of the matter. "About what?" asks the friend. "Why, because so many people had died." Now for some there is in that only infinite silliness; for me it has infinite pathos. "There are many whose imagination never went the length of constructing any ideal, except that of a moor covered with grouse. There are others who have educated themselves into a useful indifferentism or cynicism. Unfortunately it is the nobler natures who suffer most." Black wrote that. I don't want to be a cynic but right now I am moving, and a large part of the world is moving with me, in that direction. Yet what is to stop us? Where is there a faith that intelligence can live by? I don't want to retire to Olympus with Meredith's Comic Muse nor to live in that wallpapered optimism of those who dodge truth and build around them a fortress of self-esteem. But what is there between the two?

Well, this is enough. I seek your friendship, believing you are sensitive enough to understand this problem which millions faced before I was born; believing, too, that you share it. If I am wrong, disillusion me without delicacy. If you feel this is a sentimental wail, hit me hard. But I have only one life to live and it is short and I don't want to thrash blindly forever in this endless catharsis that has no power to purge.

To this letter she replied:

I accept your friendship in the spirit in which you offer it. I, too, find life meaningless, and I, too, seek loyalties worthy of respect. Except doubtfully in books I find none . . . .

Vridar was pleased but he was not thinking of her as a female. She was a spirit, an ideal. She was a symbol, as unfleshed and bloodless as the word itself; and all that he wished, all that he hoped for, was a friend in whose high purpose he could believe—not a brutal sensualist like Altrock, but one with imagination, whose perception of excellence in poetry and art would be unerring. Athene's insight into poetry was so much sharper than his, and her own poetry so much better, that he listened humbly and gratefully to what she said. He thought he might find in her a friend who would lead him from darkness to light.

When he talked to her in the office or walked with her on his way home to the street where she lived, he was never conscious of her as a female, of himself as a male. He was lost in the bewildering and fantastic chaos of his ideals. She was a voice that spoke, and he listened; or he spoke and she listened. If he had been asked two months after he met her to describe her face or to tell what she wore, he could not have done so. He could have told only what she said. Emotionally she was far more matured than he. He could have told that she discovered for him "Hertha" and "The Man Against the Sky" and Baudelaire and Catullus. He would have known that she knew Greek, which he did not, and far more Latin than he knew; and Italian besides German and French. Never for a moment did he think of kissing her or wonder if she wished to be kissed. Never did he talk to her about anything but art and ideals.

501

One day he said: "My dream is to become all clear intelligence, for the reason that emotions have almost destroyed me. I want to be all clear functioning mind." He sometimes spoke so earnestly about these things that Athene was silenced and he thought she was convinced. How little he knew about her! How little he knew what she thought of his wild declarations! In one hour he would chart a course and in the next he would repudiate it. In one moment he would scorn man-woman love, declaring it to be the darkness of earth; but with Neloa he hung it upon the stars. He would say that writing was the greatest of the professions and then heap scorn upon it as the myth of vanity. Athene would protest and argue and he would demolish her arguments with his nimble and much more agile mind. And so he lived for two months, feeling restored, believing that clear and steady sunlight was upon his path. But he could not go on forever, drunk with poetry. The platonic phase of it passed and they found themselves in love.

Still, that is not the way of it. Vridar was not in love with her at all: he confused her with what she symbolized. And even after he became aware that she was a woman, with magnificent dark red hair and hazel-green eyes, and not a spirit out of Shelley, wandering far aloft; after he realized that the relationship for her was not wholly platonic, he persisted in his romantic worship of an ideal. When he became aware of her wish to be kissed, he resented it, for he had been living above flesh and spurning it. It happened one late afternoon in the hallway of the building where she lived. He knew by the way she looked at him that she wanted him to kiss her and he was dismayed.

But he said: "Shall I kiss you?"

"If you want to," she said. Her voice was surprised and hurt.

He gave her a swift unimpassioned touch on her lips, the kind he might have given to an angel; and then felt that they had degraded their friendship. He felt guilty toward Neloa. Trying to be honest with Neloa, he had told her about Athene and about what they said when together. In October: "I've met a woman who understands poetry. She's a teaching fellow, like me. She's a good critic." He was looking at Neloa and he saw that she was watching him intently. Her eyes were baffling eyes to read. "Do you care if I talk with her?"

"I guess not, if you just talk. But you'll be kissing her one of these days."

"Nonsense."

"Is she beautiful?"

"I really couldn't tell you." And in November: "I sometimes walk home with Athene. She's a fine person and I know you'd like her."

"I suppose you mean," said Neloa bitterly, "that she likes you. I suppose you intend to ditch me now."

"I tell you we're only friends. I never think of her in any other way."

"You will if you keep fooling around with her."

"We talk of books and nothing but books."

"Well, you can find just about anything in books."

In December, after the kiss: "Neloa, I have a confession."

"Oh? So I was right."

"I'm trying to be honest with you. Even if you learn to hate me I'll try to be

502

that, though confessions," he said, looking at her, "don't seem always to lead to honesty."

"No?" she said, looking at him scornfully.

"Well, here's the confession: Athene and I may be falling in love."

"Oh, really?" Her laughter was bitter.

"As for you and me, we're not mated, as I have said how many times? But you would go on, I guess, and let us make a mess of one another."

"You mean you don't love me any longer?"

"No. I do love you. I imagine I'll always love you. That may be my curse but you wouldn't understand."

"If you love me, why do you want to leave me?"

"You couldn't understand a man who would leave the woman he loves and go with another because duty demands it?"

"O my God, duty!" Her scorn was overwhelming. "Why do you call it duty?"

"What would you call it? . . . . Lust?"

"Yes."

He was furious. He paced the room, trembling. "I might have known you'd say that. That's what the world would say, wouldn't it? Did Shelley leave Harriet and go with Mary because of lust? That's not what his biographers say."

"They're men, aren't they?"

"Neloa, my dear, I'm trying to be honest with you and myself. Isn't loyalty to my talent—if I have talent—my first loyalty? Wouldn't I be a coward if I sacrificed it?"

"You don't have to sacrifice it with me. And if you think you do, why not leave me and go alone? Why get another woman if women understand so little about you Shelleys?"

"I need a critic."

"Then get a man."

"I'm no homosexual."

"Oh, you mean you want a bed-partner. Does a writer usually copulate with his critic."

He swung to her, saying, "You would put it that way! You drag everything into the bedroom!"

"If you go with this woman, will there be no bedroom?"

"You don't understand—"

"Oh, I understand far more than you know."

"What? It's all right with you for me to go on and be a mole in a dark place! If I never write a book in my lifetime, it's all right with you!"

"But I don't see why you can't write books and live with me."

"Of course you don't. You think books are written out of lemon pies and clean bedspreads. They're written out of blood and suffering—"

"You suffer enough to write a hundred books. You've done nothing but suffer ever since you married me. If suffering—"

"There's no use talking to you. And I wish to God I didn't love you. Then I wouldn't have to tear my damned heart out and throw it at your feet to be a free man!"

"You're right," said Neloa, shrugging. "I don't understand. I don't understand why you love me and want to leave me."

"No, and you don't understand why I want to leave you because I love you."

"No, good God I don't and no other woman could understand that either!"

"Women, what the hell *do* they understand?"

"Oh, but this—this Athene, she understands!"

"Go ahead. Say anything you wish. But I'm not going behind your back in this. I have no letter hidden away saying love as ever, Bob. If you know of another husband—"

"But other husbands don't leave their wives if they love them."

"Nor if they don't, the skunks. They run out and find a mistress. Here's a truth, Neloa, that will go over your head like an eagle: any man who wants to leave his wife, or wife her husband, and does not is a coward. That includes a lot of people past forty. Anyway, why do you want me to stay with you? You don't care for me much. You don't think I'll ever give you a nice home and fine clothes and all that. I'll probably always be a poor man chasing around for what he can never find. You'll get tired of that. So why live with me?"

"Because I want to."

"Would you live in an attic all your life and wear underthings made of flour sacks to give me a chance to write?"

"Yes."

"And be a social outcast without friends?"

"Yes."

"I don't believe it. You'd become a bitter woman—and doubly bitter if I never made a go of it—if at the end of our lives you looked back on nothing but dirt and emptiness. Even Mary became bitter about Shelley."

"But I wouldn't."

"Even now, Neloa, you complain because you don't have nice clothes; and with hardly a dollar in our pockets, you want a victrola. All right, we'll get you one. You want a lot of friends. You like that big cockeyed ox up front with his tum-tumming on a banjo and trying to write popular songs. I think popular songs are utterly banal. You like Horner, and what will he ever be but a talking-machine that plays the latest records? You like that big vulgar monster of a nurse who thinks the day lost if she hasn't found another dirty story. Why not admit these things?

"The truth, the simple truth—and in the name of Jesus I've told you this until it sickens me—is that our levels are different. I don't care about fine clothes and manners and pomp and strut and small talk. You hate the only way that I can ever have. You hate loneliness and living in starvation with books; but it's my life. So in heaven's name let's try to be honest with one another. Let's face this situation and meet it with courage. I'm sick of your pretending because you wish to please me. I'm sick of detesting you in one hour and worshiping you in the next. I'm sick of pinning wings on you, only to see you go down in a vulgar sprawl. You like dirty stories and I hate them. I've heard you telling them with this nurse. So let's be sensible and do what we should do."

"I'm trying," she said, quiet now. "I've memorized ten poems since you asked me to."

It was so pathetic, so heartbreaking a statement that he had to leave the room.

To Athene he said: "I don't know what to do. I talk with her, I try to reason with her, I try to make her understand that we are hopelessly mismated. She holds two threats over me. One is that she will kill herself. The other is that she will become a harlot. My God, what can I do?"

"But you don't think she would do either, do you?"

"Is it a matter of what I think? Isn't the matter this, that we cannot afford to risk such possibilities? Perhaps Harriet threatened Shelley with suicide. But he went. He had the courage and he went. The world has condemned him for that. Critics write about his ethical paradox. But I can see no paradox in it. And I'm no Shelley. If I knew that I have great talent, I might take the risk, but, not knowing, dare I?"

"I don't know," she said. She was deeply unhappy and anxious and almost terrified. He knew that she wished herself out of this old triangle of two women and a man and that she would withdraw from it with tremendous relief if he would only say, "Yes, that is best."

He simply did not know what was best, what was wise and brave. If he yielded to Neloa's importunities and threats, he felt that he would be an unspeakable coward; but would he not also be a coward if he left her and she killed herself and he then proved to be a man of no worth? How could any man, even a man as wise as Solomon, determine in a situation like this what should be done? Shelley had been justified, and Meredith and many others, for the reason that they were great men. But where was there evidence of greatness in him? In his middle twenties, older than when Keats died, he had not written a line in poetry or prose with the mark of great talent on it. Athene admitted that in her judgment this was so.

"Then what justification can I find for leaving a wife and children?"

"Only what your own soul tells you. You must look into it for the answer."

His brother was at Johns Hopkins, studying for his doctorate in psychology. Vridar wrote to him and Marion sent this brief reply:

> I have always thought it was an unwise marriage, and if you have the guts I think it would be well to make the break. But I don't think you have the guts.

"What a brother!" Vridar said bitterly to Athene. "I turn to him in desperation and he flings an insult!

"It all comes down to this," Athene said, "that you must find the answer in yourself. If you feel deeply enough that you should do it, even if I were not in the world or you had never known me, then you will do it eventually; but as long as you have these doubts—"

"Doubts? Only fools have no doubts. Have you none?"

"Yes, I have doubts but you are the source of them."

505

"That isn't true. If I had no wife you would doubt that you should go with me. Isn't that so?"

"Yes," she said after a long moment, "that is so. For you go over these things and you bury doubts only to see them rise again. You torture yourself to the brink of madness and you torture me, until I no longer know right from wrong. The past is too much with you, as it was with Wordsworth . . . . "

Yes, the past was too much with him. He had come out of a nightmare of loneliness and he was now lost to himself, with no anchor, no light. He still refused to admit the truth about himself and his fellowmen—the self-deceptions, the illusions, the cunning and greed and egoistic self-seeking; all the dishonesties masquerading as high purpose, all the vanity pretending to be what it was not. Truths had touched his intellect but not his emotions. He lived in absurd and pitiful disguises, with so much buried deep in his heart out of memory and almost beyond recall. He had read Freud and had thought that many of his premises were sound. There now and then came to him, like showers of flame out of darkness, the bright intimations of what was true, about himself and others; and he would gather them into appalling certainties, until he began to see his own pitiable soul stripped, one by one, of all its masks. But instead of holding to the truth and going boldly to the depth of it, he recoiled in disgust. He recoiled because in a moment of light he would see the awful certainty of his erotic love for his sister or the ways in which Athene was so unmistakably like his mother; or he would catch an illumination of the ancient depths of brutality and cunning, in himself and in mankind; or he would sense a dark and shameful hatred of his father. These were the dark gods of D. H. Lawrence, and they filled him with heartache and despair. Then, turning away, he would lift his self-pitying heart in prayer to the sophistries of Spinoza or the vast and cloudy nonsense of Plato; or from his notes and the books he had read he would summon to his comfort and peace of mind the specious products of vanity and pride. "I'm not just an animal!" the coward in him would cry. Or he would tell himself, "I've had no wish to copulate with my sister!" and the deeper truth would give answer, "Incestuous thoughts lie in the subsconscious of most adults." Was it not preposterous to say that a babe was erotic? But if there is no truth in Freudianism, why does it make you furious? To get an explosion you have to pull a trigger . . . .

One day he said to Athene: "As nearly as I can tell, my personality has become almost split. I think of them as X and Y. X is the credulous and bellyaching fool who believes in the high motives of people and seeks what he calls the beautiful and good. He is the idealist, the poet, the child, but there is so much of him that his poetry is no good. But Y—do you know what Y is like?"

"I've seen him," she said.

"He's the realist. He knows what human beings are like and he looks at them with the detached spirit of a scientist. X sees the earth peopled with fallen saints, struggling desperately to regain their heaven. Y sees a vast spawn of apes—for what man who has studied the apes fails to see them in the faces of his friends? For X there is a great and noble purpose in life; for Y there is only greater and greater complexity in the bungling and blundering that makes up the human record. But there isn't enough of Y and you don't like what there is. Do you?"

506

"No. He has no heart."

"If he has enough mind he doesn't need a heart. I want Y to grow and X to diminish, but if I am able to accomplish this you would not stay with me."

"There is so much of X, Vridar, that you will never destroy him. Your task is to reconcile the two."

But the two were unreconciled. They were bitter, almost vindictive, in their feud which was the core of his struggle. When with Athene or with Neloa, the one personality or the other was in power. In one hour he was a lonely person with haunted eyes and a haggard face and a tremulous wish to love and be loved. "All I want, Athene, is to be with you and my work, even in poverty, even if I am a social outcast. But you would not like to be with me if we were outcasts?"

She hesitated and said, "I'd not want to be an outcast."

"But Shelley was. How can you give your heart to his poetry and at the same time disapprove his conduct? You can't separate the two."

"That is sophistry. To like Villon's poems, do we have to approve his shame? Is the great compassion in Dickens the same thing as his brutality toward his wife? Vridar, I've never known a person so facile in sophistry as you. I sometimes think you are very superficial."

Her rebuke would abash X, and Y would come to the foreground. "Then why in hell do you think you love me? Is it because to endure your damned prim virtues you find wickedness fascinating? Or are you another Narcissus?"

"You're unfair!" she cried, her eyes filling, and turned and left him.

Or watching Neloa in their home he would say: "Do you hate me yet?"

"I guess so."

"Darling, don't hate me. I'll always love you."

"Bosh!" she said.

"You must not have loved much if you can hate so quickly."

"What is there left to love? You go out and see her, and then you want to come home and love me!"

"It's true," he said. "Do you care if for a few minutes I put my head in your lap?"

"Why should you?" she asked, her eyes hating him.

"Because I love you. Darling, please."

"I'm not your darling. Call her your darling now."

He went to her and put his head in her lap and drew an unwilling hand to his lips. She took her hand away. He looked up at the pitying scorn in her eyes. "I guess," he said, looking back through the years, "I was a child who had no affection. I can remember none. When still a boy I fixed all my soul on you, and with such intensity that I must always love you, in some fashion. Not all of life can take out of me the devotion to you that so many years built into me. That is what I mean when I say you don't understand. That is what, if Athene sensed the depth of it, would turn her away."

"Then why don't you tell her?"

"I have but she doesn't understand either. You had affection as a child, and she. How could either of you understand.?"

Or when the other personality held him: "Athene, sometimes I smell in you a

507

yearning for social eminence. Do you find any value in a silver tray with a calling-card on it?"

"Every woman," she said, "is interested in such things. But neither that nor anything like it is my chief interest."

"There's the fop I saw the other day who married one of your relatives. His social graces please you. So I sometimes wonder if there is much between us after all, except our interest in poetry. You have, for instance, very romantic notions about love."

Athene was looking at him with her steady searching eyes. When he was in this mood, she did not like him and he knew she did not like him. "You can be very unfair," she said.

"But have you ever considered the relationship between perfumes and erotic odors?—or the obvious erotic element in most dancing? How much are you hiding from?"

"I said you can be very unfair."

"Perhaps, but I am distressed by your romantic notions. When we are intimate, if we are ever to be, you want the situation to be romantic, with roses in a room overlooking a garden and with moonlight and all that stuff. Isn't it true?"

Or when with Neloa: "Here we are, with our marriage ark tossed up like a rowboat on a reef. In midocean and we don't even have oars. Don't you think it's pretty funny?"

"No, but you seem to."

"Well, think a moment. Two adolescents fall in love. That means chiefly that they want to copulate. They think everything is going to be sweet and perfect with them, but a few years later they find, as Meredith says, that they have a decent visage and a hideous rear. That's what most marriages come to."

"But you," she said scornfully, "are in love again. You think it will be perfect this time."

"Oh no I don't. You have taken the romantic notions out of me."

"You didn't have much to begin with."

"And do you think your next marriage will be better?"

"Why not? Not all men are like you."

"You women should thank God for that."

"Does this—this Athene think she'll be happy with you?"

"She's finding out what a fool I am."

"Bring her to me: I'll tell her."

"You women like one another, don't you? What did Dekker say? There's more deceit in women than in hell. Ask, says Meredith, how innocence and uncleanness go together in women. Says Eugénie de Guerin, there's nothing fixed or vital in the sentiments of women for one another. You and Athene would detest one another, but you may meet for all I care any time you wish to. In your detestation of one another you might both find some sympathy for me."

But when the two personalities together possessed him they rent him with conflict and bred violence. Then he loathed himself and wished himself dead. He thought it might be best to flee the city, to go away somewhere and try to find himself. He told himself that if he were to leave Neloa he should not marry Athene, that he should not marry for a long time, if indeed ever again. James Breslow Thurman was right: marriage was only for the few, only for those qualified for it. But he did not have the strength to flee. He was now the prisoner of two women, and he could only go ahead in his blind desperate way and let time build the crisis.

XX

It became known in the Department of English that Vridar and Athene were much together. Knowledge of this Vridar saw in the eyes of his instructors, eyes amused or pitying or grave with doubts. To Athene he wrote:

> I think it best for us not to meet at all. Out of an interval will come to you a clearer recognition of what you should do. If doubt or duty or a combination of these declares the folly of pursuing our course I will accept your judgment. Let time clarify what we have no power to see clearly. For we both know that we must do the honorable thing.

Athene replied:

> I think you are right: If we meet less frequently or not at all, we shall see more clearly what is the best thing to do.

That was in January. For two months they rarely met but they wrote to one another long letters, recording their doubts and despair and their struggle to be honest. A subject Vridar touched on again and again was doubt of himself. "If I don't have in me the stuff of a writer I should stay where I am and mow lawns and play bridge. And how in God's name am I to know? You say to look into my soul and I do and find it empty. It is this one uncertainty to which I can find no answer . . . "

Athene replied:

> If you fall short in achievement you will think you could have served better where you were. There is only one answer. Search yourself, feel beyond the shadows, look at past achievement in an effort to measure your capacity, and so find something for faith to rest on. In my moments of strength I see the future as something that must be achieved by suffering, struggle, and doubt even; and in my moments of weakness we seem to be only two romantic fools. You feel that only the strong can face the future with heavy odds against them. I see it this way: courage to recognize and admit mediocrity in oneself is a mark of greatness; and on the other hand, it is stupid cowardice for one who knows he has wings to refuse to use them. I can say I believe in you; but that, I realize, is not the certainty we need . . .

Or he would write of his children, saying they would be as well off if they never saw him again. "I've been a hell of a father. I've been too turned within, too wretched, to give them a father's care. And besides, the paternal affection in me seems dead or unawakened." And she would write:

> Although you deny a strong affection for your sons, they are much closer to you than you will admit. Their education, and

509

the appeal to the best in your wife are what worry you. If you are to miss the star you aim at, you had better have fulfilled old responsibilities. Often I think that if we had parted a month ago we would have been wise. The generosity in you and your fear of doing the wrong or the cowardly thing keep you in doubt. I think you cannot stand the strain of another year. Most of your agonies, I know, you keep to yourself and I want to share them; for we must see our way through this in common understanding if we are to see it at all . . . .

Most of his agony, it is true, Vridar kept to himself; but now and then he poured his heart out:

Great God, I've suffered today! I'm desperate! If suicide were not cowardly that is the way I would take. For I know deep to the bottom of my soul that you wish to get away, that you wish you had never met me. I know! I'm sick of reaching to you and finding you are not there. My thesis on which I have worked for two years has been rejected. My eyes are worse. My doubts multiply. Athene, I don't want you unless your conviction of right is deep and unshakable. As it is now, I'm only a pitiable boy, and you're only a mother who pats my head.

Then he added:

Postscript by Y: X, the insufferable fool, spent a bad night but will kick out of it. Don't be alarmed. I'll poke an ironic finger at his prodigious bellyaches and fetch him around. He will write again in this mad and chattering vein; and he will plan, laying great ideals to his feet like a carpet; and he will hate and blaspheme until he is white. But I'll let you know, my dear Miss Marvell, how his pulse trots. And believe me, dear lady, in this affair which so distresses both of us, your faithful
                                                                              Y

Ignoring the postscript, Athene replied:

It is the bitterest thing of all to know that in your hour of deepest need I am somewhere alone, thinking of you. Believe to absolute knowing that you can come to me anywhere at any time and be sure of my response, as I am sure of yours. Please see me today for just a little while.

That evening Vridar went to her home. She was living with a married friend— he had thought she was a relative—named Janice Storr, and her husband Arthur, a small immaculate prig whom Vridar despised. They affected radical points of view and talked about the miseries of the working-classes and yellow-dog contracts. Vridar knew that Arthur wanted to seduce Athene, and he knew that Athene was flattered. When two days later Athene told him that Janice thought him unschooled and uncouth, he hid his fury but hours later wrote her this letter:

I care no more about Janice Storr or her opinion than I do about the earth under her—which is hard on the earth, for I love it. Her superficial brain, her shadow-boxing with theories, her fatuous social graces, all these I detest in her as I detest mucus.

510

But what concerns me is not this empty and pitiable friend of
yours but what I so clearly saw in your eyes and heard in your
voice. In telling, you rebuked me; because you, too, find me un-
mannered and wanting in grace. Let me make it plain: you wish
I had more of what your friend clearly perceived I do not have.
That I am unpolished I admit and I do not take pride in my
boorishness. I do not dislike social graces merely to dislike. I
prefer a woman beautifully gowned to one who is dirty and
vulgar; yes, provided that her refinement is not nourished
by vanity and scorn. Give her a parlor to sit in if her husband has
not exploited the weak to get it. The ugliest thing in life for
me is persons sitting in immaculate duds and talking their superficial cant about suffering in the world. I prefer one dirty
unclean fellow talking in a drizzling rain to the unhappy and
homeless of Chicago to all the cat-loving Janices that Noah could
put into another ark. I prefer the respect of one honest man,
doing a man's work, to seventeen thousand Janices sent from
hell to add silly chatter to confusion. Now I care nothing for
Walt Whitman and I take no stock in Bobby Burnses. My place
nevertheless, and understand this, is with the common people.
I came from them and will never be coward enough to repudiate
them. There are murderous Fourniers among us who carry squirrels on their shoulders; Marats who rear doves; and thousands
of women who kiss cats and hate their own kind. Let them be.
Blood and revolution will record them in the footnotes where
they belong. If there is any Janice in you our ways lie apart. . .

After posting the letter he wrote another and signed it **Y**:

Dear Hardy's Sue:
Here is an analysis. The most striking omission in you of
values which make for a sane life is a sense of humor. What you
have runs to the funny and superficial, rather than to the ironic
and profound. You perceive incongruities, deficiencies in outline
and form, certain improprieties; and the aesthete in you notes
and smiles. You miss the distortions, the posturings of vanity,
the ego's cluck and strut. In any serious preachment of the gospel
of love, comedy lies in great abundance; but not for you. Our
own affair, dear lady, is high comedy, and we are, from any rational point of view, two side splitting clowns.
And, too: you have not learned that thorough deliberation
makes action impossible; because resolves, when deliberated, are
revised or endorsed by different moods; and the Ironic Muse
allows only fools to arrive at certainty. Nor do you understand
this X whom you profess to love. He, who loves humanity, a-
voids it; you, who rather despise it, want to be a butterfly in its
suns. The great lovers of humanity have always withdrawn from
it. X is wholly unconventional and you are conventional to your
bone. A Harvard professor once said the crowning glory of
civilization is a group of persons in elegant clothes talking in a
drawing-room. You fall hard for such sophomoric trivia.
Now all of this you should understand. Love X if you must
but realize that he is a volcano. I, who sit on Olympus, you
scorn, and that is very well. But do not scorn this attempt to

511

clarify for you the headstrong fanatic whom you profess to love. For my part I find him amusing and sometimes tolerable, and quite the sort whom romantic schoolgirls would adore. I find in him the artist and zealot and the martyr of all ages: a sometimes lovable, a sometimes most incredible, fool: humorless, drunk with ideals, mad. Out of his sort you make the Shelleys; out of my kind, the Bismarcks. As always, in this most unhappy affair, your faithful

Y

Athene's reply X read with his heart pounding; Y, aloof and amused.

I do ask at times if it is all worth the effort. But the thought of poverty or of social ostracism does not bother me. I am not sure that I love you as deeply as I desire to and I fall in a rage with myself for sleeping soundly when I know you are pacing the streets. I don't doubt my affection for you; I doubt my depth. I have never loved anyone to the point of great sacrifice; and I wonder if any of the girls who have wanted you would still want if they knew what their love would have to face. I doubt it.

Call me a moral coward. But I like the ideal figure of Emily Brontë: the world has never learned more about her than the barest facts. It seems to me that many of our greatest have left little knowledge of themselves for condescension to pity. I guess that is caring what the world would think. But to me the beauty of Shelley's elopment is that no one knew how it came about and no letters remain.

I ask: if Vridar were to die would I return to the herd? Indecision in this whole matter is playing hell with me. Every step of the way I have refused to decide anything until you forced me. I have wished I had the courage to renounce you but I cannot because I cannot convince myself it would not be cowardly. As it is now, you have fought desperately to awaken my latent radical tendencies and you are worn out. It is time for me to stand on my own feet. Ever since we met you've been holding me up and leading me and giving me courage. But, damn it, when I think of your children I'm shaken. If we strike out to-together at so much cost to others, *we must* be right, and who is to say? It is a matter I cannot settle in a few weeks or perhaps even in a few months . . . .

Vridar had known of these doubts in Athene, these hesitations; he had known how deeply she wished that they had never met. He had known her gnawing fear of public disapproval, her desire that no one should know about this clandestine affair. He had known that she doubted her love for him, for in how many times had he doubted it! And he had known how deeply the mother in her was concerned about the children.

Now, after reading her letter—which he knew was a farewell if he wanted to make it so—he entered an afternoon of storm. He walked bareheaded in wind and sleet and came to a drugstore and bought a pint of whisky; and drank and went west with the wind to Washington Park. All night he wandered there. The wet snow soaked him to his skin and he was cold. Toward dawn while crossing a street he was

512

struck by an automobile and left for dead. "I'm all right," he said aloud, lying in a pool of mud. "A drunkard never gets hurt . . . ." Dawn was coming now. He crawled to the curb and stood up and felt over his bones. He entered a wet wilderness and took his garments off and twisted the water out of them and shook in the wind. Then he left the park and walked the streets. A smoky field of light was spreading in the east above Lake Michigan. He was standing on a corner, trembling in the wind, when he saw Athene. She was running toward him and he knew it was Athene but he did not care. She came up and stared at him with anxious eyes; and when she saw that he was wet and the mud all over him and the blood and bruises on his face she put her head to his breast and moaned with grief.

"I knew!" she cried. "I knew you were alone in the night! O Vridar!"

"I'm all right," he said.

"Vridar, what has happened?"

"Nothing."

"Tell me! Has she—?"

"No."

"Thank God! Then what is it?"

"Nothing."

"You've been out all night. I knew it."

"How?" he asked, without interest.

"I knew. I couldn't sleep. O my God, I thought you had killed yourself!"

"You did?"

"I—I thought—I was afraid—"

He came suddenly to life and swung to her and looked into her eyes. He read the truth there. He was amazed. "So that's it! You thought I was dead and you—you were afraid a newspaper would get hold of your letters! Is that it?"

"Yes," she said, moaning.

"You God damned coward!" He turned and left her. She ran after him, crying for him to stop; but he pushed her aside and went on. He turned once and saw her far down the street under rain and fog, staring after him. He despised her. For in this matter he was not afraid of public opinion and he had had no wish to spare himself. To learn that Athene, believing him dead, had entered the night hoping to recover her letters—!

Going to the basement, he stoked the furnace and stood in its heat, drying his clothes; and then like a man in a trance he carried the garbage out. When he entered his rooms Neloa was preparing breakfast. He looked once at her eyes and saw triumph there.

"You must have quarreled," she said. "Or are you in love with a third woman?"

"No dear. Just convinced that you women are all alike."

"You mean you're finding out she's no better than I am? Oh, that's too bad."

"Byron was right. He slept with you and then booted you out."

"Really?"

"Women live with their viscera and chiefly with the lower half of that."

"You don't say. Well, I'm glad you found it out. If we're nothing but guts, you just as well stay with mine."

"A sensible man doesn't stay with any of you. He lives alone."

"Or a sensible woman either, I guess."

He sent this letter to Athene:

> By insured mail I'm returning everything I have of yours. I don't want mine. What I've written the stupid world may read any time it chooses. You are free. We cannot go on together if either of us is afraid of the world because cowardly things would be said about us and we would have few friends. To go with me a woman must have courage, and that kind of courage you obviously do not have. Goodbye and good luck.

Two days later he received her reply:

> I will come to you in the way you want me to come. Everything that I am or might be must go with you or must die. I cannot accept the freedom you offer: If I did so I'd not love and I do love. I do have the courage. I'll face anything. I've fought this thing through and this is my answer and I am ready.

Was she ready? Vridar had watched her vacillate too many months to believe that. He would have to give her courage to face, if not scandal here, then in her own family. Her parents had died when she was very small and a maiden aunt had served as mother. She had a sister and two brothers. Vridar had seen only her aunt; he knew that she did not like him and he suspected that she would never like him.

"Very well," he said, when he saw Athene. "If we are convinced we are right we must burn our bridges and shut off all retreat."

"That," she said, "would not be the worthy way. If we want to retreat we should."

"There you go again. In moments of weakness persons always want to turn back. The perceiving mind must chasten the doubting heart. Among the great hasn't it done so? The pilgrimage to higher things has always left behind it the bones of the weak . . . ."

Day after day he reasoned with her or spurned her and she remained unconvinced. She could not forget his children, his wife; but was that all of it or even the deepest part of it? "Why do you always bring up my children? I'll take care of them."

"But your love for them, what of that? You cannot be with them."

"True, but I can't have everything. Anyway, I'm not a doting father. I don't regard it as a miracle that I sired a son. It might be better if children were taken from their parents. I think it would have been better for me."

"Just the same, I can't feel right about it."

"No, you'd feel right only if I were unmarried, only if there were no obstacles in our path."

"I can't destroy in a moment what twenty years have built."

"Athene, you're dodging again. If you want an end of it, say so."

"I don't. I'm merely trying to look into the future. You think there isn't much paternal love in you but it's dormant, that's all."

"Is it so much a matter of love? I thought it was a matter of duty."

"Oh, I know. It is with me, too. But if I take a father from his children, what have I to give? How can I know I'm worth it?"

"Look into your soul. That's what you've asked me to do. How can I know *I'm* worth it? If we have the courage we're worth it, and if we haven't, we're not."

"Anyone could say that. You can justify anything by that."

"It's hopeless," he said. "You'll always be turning back to might-have-beens."

"And you, won't you ever?"

"No." How little he knew himself in that!

The question of his worthiness filled him with desperate heartache. In a thousand hours and in almost as many ways he tried to see himself clearly and to judge of his power. He would read his verse, his prose, and fling it from him. He would sit, brooding, trying to sense his depth and reach. He would talk to himself: "What if I do become a writer of significance? It is all vanity and ego and nonsense." And the reply: "But nothing we know of is greater than a great person."

"What of it? Flies perhaps envy wasps but what do wasps amount to? Let the wasp aspire to the eagle, the eagle to the stars; but even stars are only meaningless lights in an empty darkness."

"And who is to say what the best is? Is the writing of a great book better than being a devoted husband and father?"

"The greatest minds have thought so."

"History shows that the greatest minds have been wrong twenty or a hundred times for every time they have been right . . . ."

In April the doubts between them reached a small crisis. Vridar took Neloa to a dance. Now and then he had taken her to a theater or a dance because her unhappiness tortured him. This evening she outraged him and he hated her. After taking her home he called Athene and she met him in the park.

"Well, she wanted some ice-cream. I had only fifty cents and told her so. She chose a twenty-five cent dish and ordered two. The bill when it came was sixty cents. I suppose I'm a fool about such things, but the awful poverty of my childhood would explain that. I told the waitress I was short a dime but would bring it in a moment. Neloa said, Oh, go get it now! I knew what she was thinking, that others watched us, that they and the waitress thought me cheap. I said, It should be only fifty cents. It says so on the menu. Neloa said, Do you expect service for nothing? Then God damn it I was mad, for I bought the clothes she was married in! And she thought I was cheap. What a mess, what a fool's life! If only I had no children I'd kill myself, for I'm sick of it, sick of it. I can't go on this way. Every time I see you, you have a new litter of doubts. You are arguing us both into lunacy. You say we'll take months to settle this matter, but we've got to settle it soon, one way or the other."

Athene talked to him gently, quietly, and a part of the bitterness left him. The self-pity left him, and his mind looked out, sharp and cynical. He despised himself for calling her out here to listen to a shameful and contemptible confession. After a few minutes he became annoyed, for he did not want gentleness and pity. He wanted to be scourged.

"Listen, Athene, I need a woman whose mind will strip me to the bone and help me to find a decent strength. I don't want pity. Haven't you understood that?"

Athene was furious. Never had he seen her so angry. "Listen, are you trying to unmake what you've done to me? When I try to lose self in you, then you reproach me! I think you're not worth it. Damn it, I think you want me to be a woman, a co-quette, a siren! Listen, my dear, one part of you is laughing at both of us all the time. The poet in you is frenzied; the mind is ironic and bitter. If I appeal to the poet, you try to murder me with epigrams. If I appeal to the thinker, you say I have no heart. Now just what in hell do you want, anyhow? You'll force me to my former conviction that the only way to handle a man is to be unattainable. I know: my partial surrender is cooling you. You don't want me when you think you can get me. Is that it? Then you scrutinize our love and laugh.

"But understand this: whatever happens, you have shaped me to an attitude of life to which I can never be false. I'll live by that. Right now you make me doubt, not your nobility—I'll never doubt that—but the worthiness of your interest in me. Well, if most women do not seek goodness, neither do most men. Always till tonight you've stood immeasurably above other persons; tonight you're at their level. And don't think I can't be all mind if I try. But you wouldn't want me then. I wonder, Vridar, if you really know what you want."

He shrugged, feeling mean and worthless. "I don't know. I wish to hell you would despise me—you and the whole world. Then I'd have a definite foe, out in the open. As it is now I fight in the dark."

He thought of what she had said and he knew there was truth in it. He knew also that Athene had the strength to follow but not the strength to lead, and he decided that he would have to take most of the responsibility and find in himself most of the courage. "If honesty and right are to survive in this world," he wrote in his journal, "they must have ruthless advocates who will show to cowardice and stupidity no quarter. Every generous heart must have a small Machiavelli in the mind. Otherwise it breeds only compromise and distortion . . . ." But how could he hold Athene unwaveringly to the course they had chosen? It seemed to him that only sexual intimacy could do it for a woman like her: she was a virgin and inordinately proud of it.

His decision was not related at all to passion. He had had no wish to embrace her, and he had never been shaken when she stood against him with his arms around her. Sexual passion in him when aroused was a violent hunger, as it was in Neloa, with all his blood wild and undone. But during all these months he had been so fixed on being worthy that sensual pleasures had been exiled to the dark. If they lived in him, if they ever reached out to Athene, he was unaware. Nor did his decision have anything to do with joy: like Wordsworth's Ode to Duty, which had been such a force in compelling him to these ends, it was stern and unpitying. It was the shadow of God and right.

"Call me an ordinary male," he said, after Athene had reproached him. "Sexual embrace for you is a sonnet, as it is for a lot of poets."

"Vridar! You know that isn't true."

"You're a God damned narcissus bogged down in platonism."

"Oh? And who taught me but you? You were the platonist. It was you who said we'd have only a beautiful friendship."

"True, but that was many months back. We decided it could not be. You helped decide that. And you're the first of us to think of kissing."

"I'm not so sure. You've decided nearly all these things."

"I'm speaking of your shallow emotions, your horrible self-love—"

"You're being dishonest."

"Then why—"

"Because I didn't want it like that."

"Oh no. You want to be banked around with roses. Or is it lilies?"

"You're being childish."

"And you're being romantic. We have to be realistic in this matter. We can be intimate here in the park. Thousands have been."

"Which is one reason I don't want it."

"We could find a place but you are dodging again. What is your real objection?" She looked at him, ill as ease, her eyes doubting him. "Let's be frank. Tell me."

"Well," she said, "you don't really belong to me yet."

"What do you mean?"

"You know what I mean. You still live with your wife."

"You sophist! I haven't been intimate with my wife in a long time. And four walls don't make a wedlock. Is it because you set too great a value on this that you have to give?"

Time after time they met and argued. They had come—this he perceived unerringly—to a crisis in their relationship: if Athene did not surrender now, she would never yield to him. They would go on, week after week, adding evasions and confusions to their problem.

"You may as well admit, my dear, that you don't want intimacy with me."

"But your wife?"

"My wife has got a job. She's seeing men. I don't know what she's doing and I don't ask. You know I've a good mind to rape you. That's what you want. That's what women want deep in their hearts. You're like hens. My mother once observed that a hen will flee frantically from a rooster but when overtaken yields readily enough and looks happy."

"Really?"

"But I couldn't do it. I'm a psychic impotent, you know. I could never take a woman against her will."

"There's no use talking when you're like this."

"You reject the recognitions that the years have shoved down my throat. If a man breaks a woman to it she loves him."

"Oh, you think so?"

"I know it but I'm a babilan. If a woman resists, I'm the kind of kindergarten oaf who thinks she means it. Some biology goes deeper than my will or my powers. Right now I know you want me to take you and I'm a fool not to do it . . . . Shall I?"

"If you insist."

"There it is! It must all be my doing. Your conscience must have an out . . . Well, I don't want you that way."

"I knew you wouldn't."

And again: "Athene, it is obvious that we must have more than idealism and rhetoric. Can't you understand that?"

517

"I know what you mean. But if we must be intimate to keep one another, our relationship is not worth keeping."

"Always the romantic! And I retort that if our relationship is so damned timid and wavering, it is not worth keeping. So let's say goodbye and be done with it."

"You don't mean that."

"You wish I did. We're being miserable cowards. If this doesn't mean enough to mean everything, then let's forget it."

"You're an extremist, as usual."

"History has been made by extremists. Anyway, if we're to be only friends, all right. If we're to build our lives together we'll start now. If you feel I'd be disloyal to my wife, I'll tell her about it. That's more than she would for me."

"No, you won't tell her. If we do this, it's to be between us."

He looked into her eyes. "Why?"

"Because I want it that way. I insist."

"But it would be my way to tell her."

"No. I'm too sensitive about such things."

"Very well, then. Tomorrow afternoon or when you please we'll go to a hotel."

It was not a mating of passion. For Vridar it could not possibly have been. Thereafter, but only infrequently, they met in intimacy of the flesh, and these experiences did for Athene what he had suspected they would do. They fixed her heart and courage. She was now ready to have relatives and friends renounce her and to face the scorn of the world. And Vridar, with Athene ready to follow where her heart led, now turned to his most difficult task. He had to reason with Neloa and give her philosophy and strength and he had to tear out of his being this girl whom he had idolized for so many years. He imagined that he could do this. Y said, When there's a sickly adolescent to be hanged, hang him. But X recoiled. The child in him, the zealot, still sat at Neloa's feet.

Because of forces beyond his control or motives that blurred his recognitions, his struggle became as desperate as any struggle of his life. Not his sufferings in childhood or his agonies of self-pity and rage after Neloa's first confessions were worse heartbreak than this in the weeks ahead. This fight he made alone. Athene had been driven to decision and was ready—indeed, now that she had surrendered, could *not* turn back; and Vridar perceived how pitiably ironic and silly it would be to go to her and say, This struggle is killing me: I want her, I want you, I need you both. And he did need them both but not for reasons that he had even dimly suspected.

Hour after hour he talked to Neloa. She had never been convinced that he loved Athene or would go with her, but one summer morning she became convinced. She rose from a chair, shaking as he had never seen her before; and she looked at him and tears filled her eyes, and in a voice of utter despair she cried: "O sweetheart!" The cry went into him like a knife. He wanted to rush to Athene and say, I can't do it, I can't do it! In the silence he looked at Neloa, wondering if she really loved him after all; and there was nothing to be said, nothing to be done. If only she had scorned him, if only she had heaped abuse upon him . . . . But to have her cry out of that awful heartache, to wonder after all these years of doubt if she loved him: and to have love spring within to answer love, this he could not endure. He turned like a whipped thing and left the room.

In this hour, in these weeks to come, it was only thought of duty that kept him alive. He believed that he was worthy of neither woman and to make both of them happy he would have laid down his life, in utter content. If he could have done so, he would have turned time back to that October when he first saw Athene and he would have erased all that had happened since. But now he owed a debt to still another woman. Athene did not know of his desperate mad love for his wife. She did not know of his struggle now. He could not go to her and say, "Look, I've blundered. I love my wife and I'm more convinced than before that she loves me. I must go to her." How could he say, "I'm sorry, deeply sorry. I'm a fool, born to the tragic, and you must learn to despise me as you should have despised me from the first." For Athene would reply: "Your nobility is something I shall never doubt. If you must go with her, that is for you to say and not for me . . . ." Or how could he say to himself, to his own integrity and self-esteem, "You had the courage once to break free and give your life to higher motives. But now you have faltered. You haven't the strength or the courage and in all this time you have been self-deceived . . . ." He could not admit that and still live with himself. And so he was caught between two forces that he could neither understand nor conquer: an unreasoning love on the one hand, a conviction of duty and courage on the other. He had set the stage and shaped the plot. "All these matters," he said to Athene, "Shelley and Mary discussed in the graveyard. He had children. I suppose he loved Harriet. But a higher purpose called him and he went."

XXI

After that one moment the only moment in all her years with Vridar in which he saw her spiritually naked, Neloa withdrew again into scorn. It was her defense and he knew this and he prayed that scorn would support her. He encouraged her hatred and abuse.

"I've told you I'm not worth your love. You should have come to your senses a long time ago."

"I know it. Good God, I've known it all the time. You're made of clay and cheap clay at that."

"I admit it. I'm a stinker at heart."

"I feel sorry for her," Neloa said. She had said this many times. "The silly fool! I'd like to meet her and tell her some things."

"I wish you would. I wish you would get some sense in her head. But don't fight over me. I'm not worth a fight."

"Don't fret. I'll just tell her the plain damn truth and be friends with her."

"Do it. I ought to be punished from sunup to sundown and flogged while I lie in bed."

"You're not worth a woman's love."

"I know it."

"You're just a plain damn hyprocrite."

519

"I know it."

"And I hate you."

"How else could you feel toward me?"

Or he would talk to her about what she would do. "You'll marry again and of course you should."

"Of course I will. Do you think I will ruin my life over a rotten egg like you?"

"That would be silly."

"I'll get a decent man next time."

He looked at her, thinking of her in the arms of another. "Of course you will choose a man who'll be decent with our children. I won't let any man abuse them."

"Oh, you won't?"

"No, Neloa, I won't."

"That's my business. I'll marry the man I please. I didn't pick your woman for you, did I?"

"No, but the children are going with me. Let me have the children and the man you marry is no business of mine. But if he's the kind—"

"Oh yes?"

"Yes!"

"Why should you pick my husband if I don't pick your wife?"

"I'm not. I repeat, let me have the children—"

"No. They are mine."

He stood up, shaking. "Then they must have a stepfather who will be decent to them. I've seen some stepfathers. No son of a bitch knocks my kids around."

"No?"

"No!"

She always came to the same question: "If you feel that way, then why don't you stay with us?"

Now and then, because Neloa wanted them, Vridar invited guests in. They were tenants in this building of which he was still the janitor. Ash Bingham and his wife Dolly were a strange pair. Ash was enormous and fat and had a glass eye; Dolly was a short plump dumpling with one leg four inches shorter than the other. They had been in vaudeville. The consuming desire of Ash was to write popular songs, and when he came to their rooms he brought his banjo and strummed and sang. His one eye would turn, looking now at Vridar, now at Neloa; and the other eye remained fixed.

> "Ohhh, it ain't a-gonna rain no more no more
> oh it ain't a-gonna rain no more!
> How in hell can the old folks tell
> that it ain't a-gonna rain no more . . . . "

"You think that's a swell song? How much you think the guy made off of it? I got one as good or I'm a cheese. Ain't I, Dolly?"

"You're a cheese," Dolly would say, smiling.

Then Ash would fiercely thump his instrument and turn his good eye on Vridar. He would gather fresh ardor. Often when he sang he would shut his good eye and leave the other to stare straight ahead, fixed and unwinking.

Ohhh a man laid down by a sewer
and by a sewer he died
and the coroner said I guess by gosh
it must be sewercide!
Oh it ain't a-gonna rain no more no more . . . ."

Neloa was greatly amused by his clowning and singing. There also came in a nurse and midwife named Kate Ryan; she was a huge fat but very spry woman who carried within her a great hunger for men. Neloa said one day to Vridar, "You know when you went in to fix Kate's radiator? She says she could hardly stop throwing her arms around you. She says she's mad about you."

"The hell she is."

"Of course," said Neloa, looking at him with feigned astonishment, "I don't understand. Why women chase you, I mean."

"Neither do I. Why don't you ask the women?"

"I asked Kate. She doesn't know."

Vridar did not like Kate and he did not like Neloa's close friendship with her. Kate had a lewd and spermy mind; she made an obscene jest of everything related to love. She had a husband somewhere. "Once in a while he blows in, his breath smelling of raw eggs and oysters. He makes love like the devil for one night and then he's gone. But O God he's some man when his steam is up! . . . "

And there were the Haddocks. Albert Haddock had been shellshocked in France and was now living on a government pension. His wife Maude, larger than he, was a dull stupid woman with a cynical smile. The minds of both, like Kate's, ran to obscene little parables. Vridar saw that Albert was infatuated with Neloa, and Neloa a little with him, and that Maude looked on with cynical astonishment. One evening when Kate and Albert and Maude were in, Kate said, "Today I saw a white woman with a Negro." "The hell," said Albert. "Well, maybe she has a little Negro in her." "Not yet," said Kate, "but she soon will have." And they all laughed, while Vridar looked at his wife. A little later Neloa said she ought to eat malted milk and eggs so that she could put on weight. Albert said, "You know what I'm thinking?" He looked at Vridar and added, "I'll bet your wife does." One day when Vridar was present Neloa and Kate were talking. Haddock, Vridar gathered, had cut Kate's hair and while cutting it had said, "I cut Mrs. Johnson's too." Kate said, "Oh, I thought I cut hers." Vridar could see nothing funny in it and was wondering why the women laughed, when Neloa turned on him, crying, "Well, you dumb egg!" After a few minutes it became clear to him that Mrs. Johnson had recently given birth. He had not known that women were shaved for that and he did not think it funny. He would stare at Neloa and wonder about her, as he had wondered so many times.

He never spoke to Neloa about her relations with Haddock. Perhaps, he thought, they were only gentle flirtations in the halls or friendly talk in the evenings when he was away. He was trying with all his strength to set her free and let her go, but in spite of all he could do he caught himself turning back into the old bondage, into his bitter dead years.

One evening Athene cried, "Listen, Vridar, what do you mean by your sheepish statement that this is not your night out? You sound like a pitiable dog, double-leashed—to me and to her. Can't you understand that I don't want the gestures of love and the cheap disguises? The trouble with you is that you have lost the conviction you are right. You know that. Until you find it again there's no use to think of our going on. There's only one life I want to live; but I could go with you and not have you, and I could leave you and you would always be with me. I won't be tortured any longer! I won't, I tell you, I won't!"

He knew that her reproaches were just. "Please!" he said, for she sounded hysterical.

"But I can't stand it any longer! There's only one way to be honest with me: take me into your heart and keep me there or let me go! I know now that you love your wife but I don't know why. You've told me so little about it. If you don't want me, in God's name say so! I won't stand this doubt."

Yes, he knew that he deserved it. "But I do want you."

"You can't have us both and you're deceiving us both! Is it because I'm not so lovely as your wife? The smell and touch of me and the sound of my voice are still strange. Is that it? The love between us has sunk no roots. Is that it? Well, we can quickly undo all that we have done."

"That would be to admit that I'm a slave to unreason. I can't admit that."

"Well, I'm tired, Vridar. Take me or let me go. I can't endure this. More and more of late you come to me and you don't want me. Your heart is with her. I can feel it. Don't you think I can? Great God, don't you think I have any pride? I've been trying to be fair and generous but I won't be a fool."

His face white and his heart sick, he faced her. "With all the strength I have, Athene, I'm trying to be honest with both of you. If you want to leave me I shall not say a word. But I'll not go back to her. I'm going to leave her if it kills me and nothing in life is more certain than that. But I must do what I must do. I must do what I can to put her on her feet. She threatens me with suicide. I think the threat is a bluff to hold me but I don't want to blunder in this thing and you don't want me to. I don't want to suffer the agony that Shelley must have suffered nor have you suffer with me. I'd do the right and brave thing if I only knew what it is. I have desperate struggles that I tell you nothing about. I have scorn and torment in my home from waking until sleep again. I'm doing my best. I talk with her and try to reason with her every day. I'm drawing on all the courage I have. If I lie in that, may God strike me dead. But if you think it best to leave me, do so."

"I don't want to leave you."

"Then be patient. As soon as I think she will do nothing rash, I'll come to you and we'll go."

"Then you will never come. She will always threaten you."

"Not if I can teach her to hate me."

"But dear, that isn't the real trouble."

"Then what is?"

"Her threats are not it."

"Then what is the trouble?"

Athene's gaze was steady and searching. "It's this: you've turned away from me and back to her."

522

Was that it? "No," he said, "that isn't it."

He erred but he did not know that he erred. He *had* turned back to Neloa and he had been struggling in her power like a thing in a trap. And Neloa knew it. She was now working in a fashionable downtown cafe. Vridar was not in school now and he did most of the housework and took care of their sons. She was paid nine dollars a week and she received almost that much in tips; and she spent all of it. She bought cosmetics and hairwaves; and inexpensive dresses until she had a closet full of them; and hats until she had seven. She affected long nails and polished and colored them. She rouged her cheeks and mouth, put mascara on her lashes, and perfumes and powders on her body and clothes. Vridar watched her and said nothing, feeling that he had no right to speak, but believing nevertheless that she was ridiculous. She now treated him with gentle scorn and pity.

"How do I look?" she would ask, and he would sit like a mournful clown and stare at her. "Am I as beautiful as *this other?"*

She told him of men who proposed to her in the cafe; of men who gave her large tips; of men who strove to kiss her or drive her into the country after work; of men who followed her home. He never imagined that she told all of it. He wanted to say, "Get that damn stuff off your face! You look like a harlot." But he had no right to say that. He had maneuvered their two lives, and this radiant girl who smiled at him and said, "Goodbye, my dear, I'll be home, I *guess"* was part of the result. She mocked him and pitied him and he looked at her and said nothing at all.

One morning, seeing her so lovely, so vital with warmth and womanhood, he wanted to kiss her. She rebuked him with magnificent scorn.

"Go to *her,* my dear. She's your sweetheart now." Vridar sank to a chair and looked at her. "My dear, have you quarreled?" Neloa asked, her eyes for a moment large and bright.

"No."

"You're getting tired of each other so soon?"

"Oh, to hell with it."

"I thought you said she is a middle-aged woman."

"I never said it."

"Well, I've seen her. She's so young, the poor silly thing."

"Where did you see her?"

"That's my business. I see a lot of things."

"Men, you mean."

"Men too. You'd be surprised to know how many want to sleep with me."

"A lot of men would sleep with anything."

"Oh, I don't know. You think I look so bad?" She turned round and round, smiling at him. "For a mother with two sons I could look a lot worse, don't you think?"

It was in August when she said: "I'm pregnant. I want an abortion."

"Pregnant!" he cried. "How in hell could you be?"

"You," she said.

"Me? Why, we haven't been together twice in the last four months."

"Once is enough," she said.

She was not looking at him but he was staring hard at her. Was this his child? He did not believe it. He knew a lot more about contraceptives now and he had been extremely careful. If the child was not his, then who was the father? Was it—?—but he put the thought away.

She was saying: "I'm going to have an abortion. Kate will arrange it."

And she had an abortion one afternoon at a local hospital. Vridar was now so beside himself that Athene thought he was close to collapse and suggested that he go to a famous psychiatrist in Boston. It is impossible to say what he might have done if another man had not entered the plot. He was Heinrich Thom, a German immigrant. Neloa said she was going to marry him when she got a divorce.

"Do you love him?" Vridar asked.

"Oh, I don't know. He'll be good to me. He's crazy about me."

"Will he be decent with our children?"

"Of course."

"I'll have to be sure. I'll have to size him up."

"All right, go see him."

But Vridar did not go to see Thom. He sat in jealous misery, thinking about the man. He wanted to say to him, "Listen, I love this woman as you will never love her. Be good to her or I will kill you." But he said nothing. Most of the evenings he stayed home and Neloa went out with the nurse. He did not know where they went. He did not ask. He would take his sons to his knees and talk to them or he would try to read while sitting by them on their bed. He would look now and then at the clock. Sometimes she did not return until after midnight. Now and then she borrowed Bingham's banjo and took it with her and early one morning when she returned the banjo was broken. He did not ask what she had been doing or how she had broken it. It's none of my business, he thought. I must be fair to her . . . .

But the day came when he could endure no more.

XXII

He came home one afternoon early in September and found Neloa there with Kate and Heinrich Thom. Thom was playing the victrola which Neloa had bought. Kate, huge and calm, was listening to 'Dream Daddy' and Neloa was sitting on a couch by the window. When Vridar came in, she looked startled, for she had not been expecting him. He glanced at her and at the man and went to the kitchen and stood there a few moments. Then he came to the doorway and fixed his gaze on Thom.

Neloa did not introduce the man. In one moment she smiled at Thom's broken English; in the next she looked alarmed, as though a hand had touched her, and the smile left her face. Thom had come in and taken possession as if he lived here and Neloa were his wife. All this Vridar sensed at once. He saw after a little that this man was both arrogant and vulgar; his witticisms turned on the obscene and his loud laugh was one of self approval. Vridar's heart sank. How could he let his wife and children go with a man like this!

He stood in the doorway, looking at Thom. This was the kind of man he had always despised, an empty braggart in love with himself. Thom's cockiness, it seemed to Vridar, was amazing. The man played the machine and chattered or got up and did dance steps; or he went over to Neloa as though she belonged to him in the way of his necktie or his shoes. His nonsense made her smile, even made her laugh, save in those moments of alarm when her gaze turned to Vridar.

"Vutt ish de matter?" Thom asked, cranking furiously at the victrola. He fell to his knees and peered under it. "Vutt can zee matter be? Neloaha, do you understand? Mein Gott vass it? I veel all—all like a vumman mit her panz down!" He glanced at Vridar. "Der Geshcmack ist verschieden," he said.

This thrust made Vridar furious but he did not speak. Neloa did not understand it but she was laughing like a child, and Kate was roaring as if she were all diaphragm and sound.

"Ich can nicht unterstan," said Thom, and with elaborate curiousness he looked behind the machine and all around it. "Haben Sie die Güte zu tell me, Kate. Es muss etwas los sein. Himmel!" Again he glanced at Vridar. "Mein Schätzchen, nicht wahr?"

Vridar ignored the question. He knew now what he had known all the while. He knew that Thom and Neloa had lain in sexual embrace and this certainty filled him until it was the only recognition in his mind. He turned away, his senses swimming, with Y saying, She has done only what you have done. Yes, that was true. But he was thrown back to his suffering after her first confessions, back to her waving to the man by the water-tank, with whom she had lain only two weeks before; back to her desertion of him in Swan Valley the night he was beaten senseless; back—He paced the kitchen, knowing that he was close to collapse, knowing that he would have to fight out of this, now and quickly, or be forever lost. When Thom and Kate left, he entered the room where Neloa was sitting. He stood before her, trembling, fighting against the darkness that possessed him. His eyes were so blurred that he could barely see her.

"So—so you have given yourself to him."

"I have not!"

"And you still lie. After all these years you still lie to me."

"I'm not lying!"

"Neloa, please don't lie. You've lied to me so much."

She stood up with terror bright in her eyes and tried to face him. But she would not look at him. She sank to the couch, trembling.

"Neloa, don't lie."

"All right, and what if I have?"

"Nothing. It's not my business—but that you should give yourself to a man so vulgar! For you don't love him, Neloa! If you loved him it would be different or if I did not love you. May God curse me, may my heart be torn out and fed to wolves. Everything about you has been so dear to me but you treat it like a common harlot. You—I have no right to speak, no right but that of love. I'm not rebuking you.

525

I'm just saying that if only you had chosen a man—for you could choose among many—"

He stopped. He could not see her now. She was lost and he was lost and he no longer understood that he was here in a room, speaking to her. There was no meaning now; and he and this girl, here in silence, with only her eyes alive of all the things around him . . . . He was not here but in Antelope, kneeling at her feet, begging her to say it was not true; and in Idaho Falls lying with her on a bed with his face in her hair and his heart in her heart; and alone on the gray hills, listening for the sound of a cowbell: all these years were in this moment and they buried him and there was nothing else. He swayed and the world turned black and unknown to himself he dropped and was still.

When he came to he was in bed in the room where he slept alone. Perhaps Marion had put him there, the cynical Marion who took women as his right, who looked at his brother with scorn and pity. Or perhaps Albert had put him here. He sat up in bed, wondering what the time was and if Neloa was asleep in the other room. He felt very weak but after a while he left the bed and went tiptoe to Neloa's room and saw that she slept. Thinking that he must have been unconscious for hours, he went over and knelt by her. He kissed her hair spread darkly over the pillow and one of her hands. He looked at his sons: they were asleep too. For an hour he knelt here, looking at Neloa's face and kissing her hair and wondering what curse was in his blood that he must love her so. Then he returned to his room. He sat on the bed with his face in his hands.

Rising at last he entered the hall, moving quietly, wondering what he intended to do. As nearly as he could tell he intended to kill his family and himself. But how? he asked, softly, patiently, within the quiet of his mind; and looked for a weapon. He had no gun and he could not use a knife. Going to the basement, he searched there, lost to himself and lost in wonder about what he would do. A force stronger than his own will was leading him and he was a child, eager to obey. He found clubs but he could not use a club. He would have to kill them in a swift clean way, without blood and pain; and with a club he could not kill himself. How can I? he asked, whispering. Going to the furnace he read the meters; he saw piles of newspapers and these he baled; and all the while the thought of murder and suicide was a waiting and patient thing. When the baling was done, he explored again and climbed the stairway and went into empty rooms, looking for a gun. He went into Neloa's room and looked at her.

Then he put on his shoes and left the building and walked the streets. He stared at houses, wondering in which one Thom lived. It seemed to him now—but the thought was very quiet—that he ought to kill Thom. Then he knew that he did not wish to kill this man. Returning to his room he sat on the bed, shivering, and wondered why he had never bought a gun. Daylight was coming now. Going to the bathroom he thrust his head under a faucet and let cold water pour over the back of his neck; and he let it run over his wrists and the veins in his temples; but it was of no use. Water had no power to cool this fever in him. He wanted to look in a mirror but he did not dare: he was afraid of his eyes. Taking all his clothes off he sat waist deep in cold water but he did not feel the cold. He was annoyed and he let the cold water flow away and sat in hot water but he could not feel the heat. He could not be sure which was hot and which was cold and he thought that possibly both were tepid. Leaving the tub, he rubbed himself vigorously and dressed, wondering all the while where he could find a gun.

When he entered their rooms, Neloa was getting breakfast. He sat on a chair and looked at her; and little by little the drugged patience left him. He began to shake and he shook so that he had to stand up; and sweat burst from him and his face was like wet chalk.

"Listen," he said, his voice shaking like his body, "don't you understand that I can't let my children go with him? You go if you want to. But if you go with that man, the children must stay with me."

Neloa had withdrawn from him but now she rose to her fullest height, like a snake ready to strike, and came toward him. "You can't take my children!" Her voice rang. Her eyes were terrible with fury and hate. "I'll die first! You'll have to kill me!"

Vridar faced her. "Our sons can't go with him!"

They stared at one another and Neloa faltered and broke. The fury left her and she looked haunted. She sank weakly to a chair, her gaze on his face; and Vridar spoke out of the bitterness and despair that choked him.

"For sixteen years I have loved you. I've been a fool and you have put me through hell. But our children must have a decent life and I mean that if I have to kill. I won't let them go with Thom." He was silent, looking at her. "If you want to go with him, go, but I don't understand why you should. You are beautiful and many good and worthy men would marry you. But if you insist on going with this man, I must keep the children."

Again he was silent. Then he said: "I could never have left you. I know that now. For months I have fought to get away but I have been bound to you. I couldn't have gone with Athene. I could have died and only that. If you—if you, Neloa, had had patience, if you had behaved with character, with dignity and pride, I would have come back. That is all you had to do to win. That is all you had to do to erase the past. It was your great opportunity but you did not know it. On the contrary you, the very heart of my life, gave yourself when there was no love. No dignity, no pride. And I must go now. If only during these God damned haunted desperate months you had been too devoted to be mean, too proud to be cheap, I would have been yours. The whole past would have been wiped out. I know that now but now I must go, for you have given me no choice." Wavering, he turned to the rear door and left the house.

He had not gone more than thirty or forty yards when he heard her call his name. She cried *Vridar!* and the cry was ringing and wild. He stopped as if he had been struck. He turned. She stood on the back porch and she looked like a strange wild goddess; and high in her right hand she held a full glass. And while he stared, paralyzed, she cried, "Look!" and drained the glass. Then with a magnificent gesture of disdain, she hurled it at him and it rolled to his feet.

527

For another moment he could not move and in this moment he doubted, not knowing if she had drunk poison or had pretended to. When at last he came to sudden wild life, he seized the glass and smelled of it and the smell was of lysol. He dropped it and leapt to the porch and he swung the screen door so violently that it was torn from its hinges. In almost the same instant he was standing before her and she was sitting on a chair, her arms folded, her face set in a strange smile.

"Great God!" he said. "Neloa!"

He sprang from the room and leapt up the back stairway, four or five steps at a time; and on the third floor he yelled, "Marion, come quick!" and turned, leaping back down the stairs; paused on the second floor and flung wide the door to Haddock's apartment, shouting, "Haddock, come quick in God's name!" and in less than ten seconds was facing Neloa again. She sat as he had left her, smiling, her arms folded on her breast.

"Neloa, Neloa, why did you do it!"

The next few minutes were nightmare and he was a wild man. Yet he moved swiftly, unerringly, without a fumble or a lost movement. It was madness all around him and in his mind and heart; and it was clarity, too, as vivid and certain as a naked blade; and he cut through the darkness, knowing everything that he did, everything that he must do, yet knowing nothing at all. He sprang first to the closet and seized a half-pint of whiskey there; and before Marion came in he had poured it all down Neloa's throat. He leapt to the closet again and came out, smashing eggs into a bowl; poured milk over the eggs; crushed the eggs and milk with his hands; and grasped Neloa and poured the bowlful of stuff down her. And he was thinking, She had planned this, for the glass was ready before I came in! Albert was there now. Marion was there. But their presence Vridar sensed only dimly: his whole being was fixed on Neloa and he was begging her to fight.

"Sweetheart, please! In God's name, please, please! . . . ."

She did not want to try to vomit or to help herself and he was frantic. He raced round the kitchen, looking for other things to pour down her; he sent Albert scurrying for a doctor and called Marion to his side. "Help me make her vomit!" He shouted and he dragged Neloa to the sink and thrust a finger down her throat; and failing in this to make her vomit, he shoved a greasy rag into her throat and then a piece of soap and shook her and called to her all the while to fight out of it. But she was scornful of his efforts and she laughed. Her laughter was so bitter that he was horrified and he shook her with all his might and shoved stuff into her throat and talked to her, begging her not to die. In hot water he swiftly washed bars of soap round and round and then poured the stuff down her. There was foam on her lips now. She was bending over the sink and he was by her, his arms round her, his stricken eyes watching her face, his wild voice ringing in her ears.

"Sweetheart, please help, please help! For me, for the children! I'll do anything! I'll be your slave! I'll give up writing, everything! Neloa, I love you, love you! Please, please, for me! . . . ."

She was retching now but she could not vomit. He poured soft grease into her mouth, and with her eyes shut, her body shuddering, she swallowed it.

"Darling, darling, fight, for me!"

She raised a hand and wiped foam from her lips. She was convulsed with agony and she sank, trembling in his arms; and he lifted her; and in this moment she spoke.

"Not even for you now," she said. "Not even for you."

If the words had been a knife that had laid his heart open, he could not have cried out with more terrible anguish. He glanced round him for poison, intending to drink it but he could find none. Gathering her in his arms—for she could no longer stand—he carried her to a bed.

"Where's the doctor?" he yelled. Everything was dark now. The world was mad and there was nothing in it but horror and death. Marion cried to him that they would take her to a hospital and Vridar seized her and with his brother's aid carried her down the hallway and to the street and put her in a car. He got in with Marion and held her in his arms and the car went down the street. It came to Midway and stopped and Vridar shouted, "Go on! For Christ sake, go on!" It seemed to him that they waited here for ages. He broke into hysterical profanity and cursed so horribly that his vision darkened; and after they had crossed the Midway and were going down Sixtieth Street, the driver stopped and said he was out of gas. Vridar leapt out and called to Marion to help him and together they carried Neloa down the street. They were white with exhaustion but they ran with her and came to a hospital and carried her inside and laid her on a bed in a small room. Then Vridar ran down corridors, shouting for doctors; and found a doctor and laid hands on him and tried to drag him to his wife. The doctor angrily threw his hands off.

"Come, come! My wife is dying! She took poison!"

"I'm busy, I told you! You'll have to wait!"

"But I can't wait, she's dying!"

Frantic, he ran through the hospital, seeking other doctors. He found others and begged them to come but they all said they were busy. Hating doctors as he had never hated anything, he leapt up a stairway and found nurses and begged them to come; and some of them looked at him with amazement, some with pity; but none of them came. He laid violent hands on them and begged them, his voice hysterical. They said he would have to wait. Wait, with Neloa dying! He became so desperate that he ran to every person he could find, and his voice and his appearance terrified them. He followed them. He ran up stairways and down and up again. Not for a second did he pause in his crazed effort to find help. Sweat was pouring off him. It was running down his body and arms and it had drenched his clothes. His mouth was bloodless and wet and his eyes were such eyes as nobody could look at. And still he ran, a trembling drenched apparition, begging for help. Then Marion came to him and said, "The doctors are with her now."

"Thank God, thank God!"

Vridar ran to a door and looked in and saw doctors with Neloa. All the emotion of his being was now gathered and banked round his heart and he found it difficult to breathe. He felt that at a touch, a word, the emotion would blow him to pieces; and in the power of it he shook so that he could not stand, but had to lean against a wall. He bowed his head, moaning. The frenzy in him was waiting—waiting to break and destroy. He stood by the wall, shaking uncontrollably, with froth and slobber on his mouth. He knew, he realized in the deep dark part of him, that he was at the point of breaking, and that if he broke he would be mad. He fought against this darkness, this sucking at his mind, this terror of blood pouring through his heart; and now as in former years he tried to speak, hoping to break the silence. But he could not speak. He could only shudder and moan.

Then Marion came to him and spoke. "Buck up, old man," he said.

"You mean—?"

"It's all over."

One moment Vridar wavered. In this instant he could have been swallowed by darkness, hopelessly, forever; or the awful flood could have poured out of him in wild grief. He stood, transfixed, between the two. Then with a cry he broke and fell, and out of him in grief that was screaming came all the desolation of his soul and his years.

XXIII

Most of what he did in the next few days or indeed in the next few months he could never remember. Darkness closed in and he was lost. His grief was the deep and tearless grief, the strange and unreal grief of a person who walks from a death-cell to a scaffold. It was the same horror fixed in a world that was unreal because it was so soon to vanish. For him the whole world had become mad and he saw it a-round him not as human beings and machines but as aimless movement; heard it as meaningless patter and cry; smelled it as lysol and hospitals and morgues. It was in a building advertised as A Home for the Dead that he faced a coroner and a jury, though he was never to know why; and heard questions that he did not understand and did not answer; and looked at the coroner and men and did not see them. Marion took him away. Marion took him to a hotel, and he and Albert spent the night with him and drugged him to make him sleep. News reporters came but after looking at Vridar they asked no questions of him and only a few of Marion and quietly let themselves out. It was this night—or was it the next day or the next night? —that he slipped away from his guardians with only one thought in mind. He went to the dingy little apartment expecting to see Neloa there. He entered and softly call-ed her and when he heard echoes in the walls he thought she was here; he was con-vinced that she was here; and he ran from room to room, looking into closets, soft-ly calling her name. "Neloa!"—and he would listen, as years before he had listened for the sound of a cowbell. From room to room he went and he felt among her clothes to see if she was hiding or looked under the beds or went to the back porch. There he saw the glass. He picked it up and smelled it. Then he knew she was not here, and he began to shake and there was another thought in his mind. He went to the kitchen and searched for poison, looked among all the dishes and in the stove, in closets and in trunks. Finding no poison, he looked for a knife but all the knives had been taken. Then as quickly as it had come, the wish left him and he knew that Neloa lived. He went to the basement and looked into boxes and behind bales of paper and the furnace; climbed the stairways and searched in the vacant apartments and rooms, all the while whispering her name. He came to her clothes again and felt of them and kissed them and thought the odor of cheap cosmetics in them was good and pure. He was still searching when Albert came and led him away . . .

This day —or was it the next?—he was taken by Marion to The Home for the Dead. A man there was very friendly, he jested or whistled, and Vridar was afraid of him. Vridar understood that Neloa was somewhere near and he wanted to see her. He told Marion he wanted to see her, and Marion went to a man and the man led Vridar into a hallway and opened a door. Vridar now expected to see Neloa a-live. He still had no power to understand that she was dead. He trembled as he step-ped into a room and closed the door behind him; and he stood by the door shaking from head to feet and looking round the room. He saw Neloa across the room and she was very quiet and he did not understand. "Neloa?" he said. He waited; and then, "Neloa?" Slowly he tiptoed toward her, his eyes on her face. She was lying in a white robe with her arms at her side. Half way across the room he stopped to look at her, and again he said, "Neloa?" but very softly now. Again he tiptoed. He came to her side and looked down at her. Her eyes were closed. There was a smile on her white face and it was the smile that he had known and loved; and there was brown stain on her lips and chin but he did not know what it was. "Neloa?" he whispered.

Then he heard a sound and he listened, with wonder taking him; and then he screamed, so sudden and terrible was his joy. "Neloa, I knew you weren't dead!" He bent over her, waiting for her eyes to open, her lips to speak. For a minute he must have waited, scarcely breathing at all; and then he felt surprise and the sur-prise grew into astonishment, for Neloa did not open her eyes or speak. He bent lower, his face close to her heart; and in this body that he had idolized, looking so queenly under the white robe, he heard a strange gurgling. Swiftly he touched her hand and it was like ice; her white cheek, her throat; and shrank back, horrified. Then he sank to his knees with one arm reaching over and around her, his hands searching her for life; and his hands came to her hair, spilled around her, a dark mass under the whiteness of her; and he clutched it and smelled of it and it was a-live. He buried his face in her hair, breathing of it, until he felt again, deeply, that she was not dead; but when he looked at her he saw only the awful calm of her face. Again he touched her flesh and found it cold; and again buried his face in her hair and sucked into him its familiar and fragrant life, trying desperately to make her live again as her hair lived. It was the same hair in which night after night he had laid his face, the same which in all their bitter years together had hung round her and been his. And it was alive . . . .

A man knocked on the door and, startled, Vridar rose to his feet. Then he re-membered. He remembered that scissors had been given to him and he drew them from a coat pocket and from her head he cut a handful of this which still lived. He shoved the hair into a pocket. Then he kissed her cold white arms and hands, her burnt mouth, and the eyelids upon her closed eyes; and he patted her gently and said, "Neloa, I love you!" He crossed the room to the door and stopped to look at her again; and all the anguish of his soul broke into a cry. He ran back and put his arms around her and knelt, with his cheek to her cold cheek. He was still there, kneeling, holding her close when two men came and took him away . . . .

This day—or was it the next day?—he was in a car with a man, riding through the city. Was Marion with him? Looking back on this hour, Vridar could never be sure. The man talked but Vridar did not understand what the man said. The day was wet and gray, with rain falling, and with Lake Michigan rolling in gray surf. Vridar rode along the shore and looked at the desolate waters. Somewhere in another car Neloa was riding and Vridar could think only of her, alone in a cold hearse, going through this gray wet city; and of these surging waters, beating at the piers. Then the car left the shore and in a little while it stopped. Vridar got out and saw that he was in a lonely place with a strange building. With the man he entered this building and he heard a great roaring and at first he thought he heard the lake. Then he knew that he was listening to a furnace; he knew this was the crematorium; and he saw a long box and knew that Neloa was in the box. He went to the box and laid his hands on it; and when the man came to him he said, "I'd like to be alone with her just a minute." The man left the furnace room and Vridar stood alone with his hands on the box where Neloa slept. A romantic to the last he knelt by the coffin and made his vow:

> I'll try to go on and do my work and care for our sons. I'll try to have the courage and strength. I will take seven years— because we had seven years together. I will spare myself nothing and I will be as honest with myself and others as I can be. If at the end of seven years I think I have failed and that your sacrifice was for nothing I will follow you into death. All this, Neloa, I swear by the love I have for you. You, darling, wherever you are, let your spirit be with me and support me.

He rose, shaking, when three men entered the room.

"Are you ready?"

"Yes," he said.

A great iron door was swung wide and he looked into a red and raging furnace. The men grasped the box and raised it and with a cry Vridar sprang to stop them; but two other men came and held him, and with horror he saw the box shot into the flames and saw the great door close. Stricken by sickness he fought toward light and air. Behind him he could hear the roaring of flames, and suddenly he vomited, while two men held him and wiped his mouth. Then he rode by a desolate shore, under a desolate sky. Wind whipped at the car, rain was driven against the windshield. Wind was driving over the lake, piling water in long reefs and foaming crests. Far out, boats were tossing against a gray sky, and there came to him the lines, And the stately ships go on to their haven under the hill. But not here, not here. There was only a waste of sky here, and blind rain on the windshield, and blind streets. Neloa was out in the sky now, a part of the desolation; and all this that he saw now was the backdrop of their lives together and of their farewell. She was beyond reach and at peace—But O for the touch of a vanished hand and the sound of a voice that is still —and he was still here in the anguished darkness of a wild earth. Never again would he hear her voice or feel her touch—never, in all the eternities of time. The absolute finality of such a farewell he was unable to understand, or believe in; with all the passion and desperation in him he wanted to flee to the two gloomy rooms on Ellis Street, to see if she was still there. He fought the beating rain and the sound of the furnace and the sound of the sea. He bowed his head and drew deep into loneliness, wishing to the bottom of his heart and soul that he had been with her in the flames, that he could be with her now in the sky . . . .

BOOK II

OURANIA APHRODITE

PART I

Cinderella

"In several parts of Europe the story of Cinderella is known as 'The Brother and Sister' and the heroine's adventures arise from her refusal to entertain her brother's proposals"—Bayley

I

They told him Neloa was dead but he refused to believe it. His cynical Paphian brother was jesting, yet in his more lucid moments he recalled having knelt by her somewhere; having kissed her cold eyelids and cheeks and hands; having filled a pocket with her beautiful hair; having ridden in a drizzle of rain and fog by a wild lakeshore; having seen her thrust into a huge red and roaring furnace; having heard an iron door close. But he knew she was not dead. His emotions wild and delirious, his world broken, he walked the streets of what they said was Baltimore, looking for her . . . .

When now and then, in a clear moment of reason, he knew that she was dead, he turned despairingly to any strength that might support him. Like Carlyle he had worshiped Heroes—the great persons of the past who had suffered terribly in fighting for the right: not the Cromwells, Napoleons, and Caesars but the gentle men of compassion—such as Spinoza and Keats; and even more, such as Abelard and Roger Bacon, whose incredible courage had sustained them even in the deepest suffering. But among his friends was there one? Or would he have to endure alone this purgatory of which Tolstoy had written to Rolland?—through which Shelley had passed, and Carlyle and Meredith and many more.

He had actually forgotten, so soon, that when in Chicago the urn was handed to him and he had kissed it and then had found his lips gray with bone-dust. He had held it to him, thinking, This is Neloa, the ashes in this can, this and the hair he had taken. Nothing else remained. Of her vibrant womanhood, of all that he had known and loved, there was nothing anywhere except this bone-dust, a few strands of hair, and the faint odor of her flesh somewhere in the sky. When his mother had come, she had wanted to see where Neloa had lived and he had taken her to the ugly old building and had entered the backyard. His younger son, a lad of three, had looked up at Prudence and said gravely, "My mama doesn't live here any more." No words had ever gone into Vridar so like a knife, no words ever would again. He murmured them over, thinking, How unconscious, yet how perfect the pathos! My mama doesn't live here any more . . . .

Prudence had taken the children to Idaho, and on the day she left, Vridar took up the cigarette habit. He would smoke one cigarette after another, staring at Athene, his eyes empty of all but loneliness. He said he had been a coward and he supposed he ought to kill himself. That, Athene said, would be cowardice.

"What else can I do?"

"Your duty. You have two sons."

"But can a man live without faith?"

"Have you so soon forgotten Leonard's sonnets?"

No, he hadn't forgotten them. He had read them a year ago in an edition privately printed and had memorized a number of them:

> She opened .... with a vision on her face,
> And hands uplifted to immortal things,
> And past me flew .... upon her toilet case
> An emptied glass with foam in awful rings ....

He hadn't forgotten:

> We dare not think too long on those who died,
> While still so many yet must come to birth.

He said, "But Leonard teaches at the University of Wisconsin. He has friends with faith in him."

"Shouldn't you try to have faith in yourself?"

"In myself? How can I!"

He had then bowed his head, his world swimming; and he had muttered, "If only there were someone to see me for what I am and tell me what to do! If I'm only a weakling and a fool, there's no reason to go on living, for the world is choked with the foolish and the weak .... " Then he thought of one. He thought of the chairman of his department, the small man with the magnificent eyes. He would go to him. This man would be his judge.

"Vridar, try to be rational!"

He stood before the bench on which she sat. He was white, he was trembling. "I'll tell him everything," he said. "He can judge me."

"No!" Athene moaned, despairing. "This is our problem."

"I tell you I'm going to him!"

"O God, listen! Let's not expose our shame!"

"I'm going to him."

With Athene running after him, he had gone swiftly across Washington Park. When he came to the Midway, he waited for her.

"Please, O God!" she cried, supplicating him. "Let's talk this over!"

"There's nothing to talk over."

"Will you listen?"

"No. I'm going to Thurman and he can judge me."

He took her arm and together they crossed the Midway and went south on a street. They came to a front door and Vridar stood by it, trembling all over. Then he pressed the bell. The housekeeper ushered them in and they stood in a large room, with books everywhere; and after a moment Thurman entered, his brilliant eyes questioning them.

"I've a problem," Vridar said. Thurman waved them to chairs and fixed his gaze on Vridar. It was only with an effort almost spasmodic that Vridar was able to speak. He said he was in trouble and needed a great and wise person. — Then his voice broke. He glanced at Athene: she was looking at her lap and making movements of deep anguish with her hands.

Thurman's face was sympathetic. He said, "How can I help you?"

Still Vridar hesitated. He felt that his tragedy, his loss, was trivial, almost silly, when measured against the infinite sum of human heartbreak. Millions had come to such grief as this. Millions had suffered and died and been forgotten: in the eternal record of striving and defeat, not even a footnote remained, much less a head-stone. Every year thousands killed themselves, all over the world!

"I don't want to weary you," he said at last, fighting for control of his voice. "My wife killed herself. How much we are to blame, this woman and I, we don't know. We've tried to act with courage and honor. Now—I haven't come here to try to justify myself. I—I guess I came to be judged."

"Are you reproaching yourselves?"

"Oh, more than that. I mean this," Vridar went on desperately. "If I've been dishonorable I'll take the punishment. But what should the punishment be? I thought perhaps you could tell me."

Thurman was looking at him with steady searching interest. "I rather imagine," he said, speaking quietly, "that you're making too much of the matter. Probably nobody is to blame. In any case, to reproach yourselves now for what is done is pretty futile, isn't it?" Thurman lit a cigarette and when he spoke again his voice was throaty with tobacco smoke. "What are your plans?"

"To leave Chicago. I can't stay here."

"And later?"

"I—Sir, I don't know."

Thurman turned to Athene. "Are you going with him?"

"Yes."

For a moment shrewd gray eyes studied Athene.

"I often wonder," Vridar said, forcing himself to speak, "if I should ever marry, or live alone, for I suspect that no woman can ever be happy with me."

Thurman smiled. He doubted, he said, that Vridar was the kind who could live alone. Some men could but most men could not. As for marriage, he had never thought highly of it as an institution. For a few it seemed to be all right, but in most people it nourished unhappiness and frustration. "You will have time to think it over," he said. He rose, and in rising, Vridar knew, Thurman was dismissing them. But he went to the door with them and there was warmth in his goodbye and in his handclasp. He said he hoped that Vridar would return to the university to complete his work. He hoped he would be able to summon his sense of irony. "Let me know how you get along."

"Thank you," Vridar said. He and Athene went down the street in silence and came to a park bench. Vridar said he loved this man. This was the only great man he had ever known, this scholar who had given most of his life to Chaucer. He was remembering how, a year ago, when Vridar thought he was going blind, Thurman had sent him to his own doctor and himself had paid the bill . . . .

Now, in Baltimore, he had forgotten the scene with Thurman; forgotten how for several days he had slept drugged with veronal, and the long ride to Baltimore. He had forgotten how day and night in wretched verse he had poured out his selfpitying unreason, heaping upon himself abuse and loathing, and enshrining Neloa among the pure and holy—

> And after I am dead leave me to rot
> where I have fallen; and let no one mark
> the hair of Neloa within my hand.

539

> Let no one curious find the lonely spot
> to see my eyes and try to understand
> the face of Neloa in the sightless dark!

He would hand the verses to Athene and eagerly search her face for approval. "Is it any good?"

"Does it matter now? You'll be a great writer some day."

"A colossal steer," he said. "A gargantuan babilan."

He wrote dozens of poems to Neloa, all of them bitter with the desolation of his soul. Only once in a while did he write something that Athene found good:

> You are dead now: but a short while ago
>   fell the year's roses too,
> deep around you, even as lovely,
>   Neloa, as you.
>
> Things like me remain, ugly for living,
>   while death uncloses
> to gather his choice of all that is most lovely,
>   you and the roses.

They had taken two small rooms on Charles Street, uptown from the bridge. Now and then leaving a nightmare of sleep, Vridar would sit in night-dark by a window and look out at the lonely dying of autumn. In such hours he sat deep in the belief that he was a fool. He would think of the millions of human beings who were striving as he strove, blundering in ignorance, self-pity, and vanity; and the overwhelming picture of it would chasten and hush him. In the dark he would reach for his pen and scribble his lines:

> But that you should go, silent and alone,
> down into death, with scorn across your brow,
> doubting I loved you and your love of me,
> and leaving no way for love to reach you now:
> this will I not forgive until I see
> the last dull dogma choked upon its throne!

He would read the lines and then tear the paper into shreds and stuff the shreds into a pocket. He would glance over where Athene lay, asleep or awake, though in these weeks, turned inward to his own despair, he was not often conscious of her. At daylight he would begin to type in frenzied haste, muttering all the while to himself, "A great writer! No, a colossal steer! A goddamed Christian eunuch!" After a while he would walk the streets and standing on a corner he would search for Neloa's face. After weeks had passed, he knew she was gone forever beyond his touch, yet still cherished the tender belief that somewhere she lived and waited, somewhere he would find her. He would enter buildings, stare at faces in windows, mingle with the throngs. Once he thought he saw her and his blood leapt in such delirious surging that his passions choked him. Once he thought he heard her call his name.

A river flowed through Baltimore and close by his lodgings it was spanned by a high bridge. The distance was about a hundred feet from where he stood to a shoulder of rock below, and this huge stone he looked at so often that he knew its lineaments as he knew his own face. In fancy he saw again and again every moment of his death, and felt every emotion: he stood poised on the side of the bridge, he plunged, he struck headfirst upon the stone. Athene and Marion came running, policemen came to gather up the broken mess of him, his mother hastened eastward by the fastest train, and his younger son said, My father doesn't live there any more. He would visualize the scene and then shrink back, loathing himself. In feeble defense of his wish to die he would reflect that thousands every year killed themselves, because they had burdens they could neither carry nor put aside. He wondered about them—their struggles, their heartbreak, their swift end. If he were to kill himself there might be a brief note in the Baltimore Sun:

MAN PLUNGES FROM CHARLES STREET BRIDGE

There might be:

> Early this morning a Baltimore and Ohio switchman found on the river rocks a man who had leapt or fallen to his death. He has been identified as Vridar Hunter, until recently a student at Midwestern University. His parents are in Idaho, where Hunter was born. He has a brother in this city and a common law wife. Both are unable to explain the rash act . . . .

People would read the words and yawn over their morning coffee. A husband would say, "How many damn fools have jumped offen that bridge anyhow?" And his wife, listening for sounds of Junior in the bathroom, would reply, "We seem to read about them all the time." In a speakeasy a man would say, "That's quite a jump." And another, wiping beer off his hairy mouth, "What a splash of brains— if he had any brains." With such words people would note his passing and forget him. Athene would be stricken, but she would recover and love again. Or would she? She had not wanted to love or to marry. She was the bachelor-woman kind. His brother would hardly miss a stride in his pursuit of women. His sons would grow up in ignorance of both parents, saying, "We didn't know them very well." That was all. If that was all, why shouldn't he do it?

He looked round to see if anyone was watching him. The policeman was. This officer had been watching him for two weeks now. Angered, Vridar went over to him and said, "Why do you spy on me?"

Cold clear eyes looked into his eyes.

"You spy on me when I come here."

"Why do you come here?"

"To look at the river."

"Look, Jack, cut it. You don't like the river that well. You figger to jump off, that's it."

"I—How did you know?"

"I've watched them for thirty years."

"You mean I act queer?"

"Look, Jack, ain't you got a home or wife or nothun?"

"Why should you care if I jump off?"

541

The policeman shrugged. "I don't, Jack. But I thought if I stopped you, you'd change your mind. They usually do."

Vridar looked into the cold clear eyes. "They usually do?" he said.

He never went to the bridge again, but he still felt driven to destroy himself and get his dark little life over with. He thought of trains and his childhood. On the edge of the city was a railroad track hidden by a jungle of forest. He went there and sat on a pile of ties. One evening in November he heard a locomotive approaching and he got up, shaking all over, and sat by the nearest rail. He was thinking, When the train draws near I can fall over the rail and in a moment I'll be dead. As the engine came in sight around a curve, he seized a handful of gravel and rubbed it sharply into the flesh of his palm. The engineer saw him and warned him with blasts of steam; the brakeman leaned from the cab and seemed to be shouting. But Vridar did not move. He could hear the screeching and wrenching of steel on steel under the impact of brakes and he could feel the hot wind from the engine. Then he heard Neloa call his name. He leapt aside and in that moment the wind from the engine struck him, hurling him down the bank and rolling him over and over. He saw three men leaning from the black cab, looking back at him. Then he ran away, thinking in his horrible lunacy that he would find Neloa; but it was Athene . . . .

She was running toward him, and he saw as she came up that her face was terribly white. She looked up into his eyes and what she saw there made her cry out with pain. "Vridar!" she said and covered her face.

He was trying to understand that it had not been Neloa but this golden-haired woman. Athene had sunk to the earth. He sat by her and said, "It was you."

"Only me," she said, her smile bitter and twisted.

"You followed me out here?" he asked, still trying to understand.

"Vridar, I can't stand this much longer!"

"You can't?" He thought about it and said, "Yesterday you were canning fruit."

"O great God! That means I'm happy, I suppose! Tell me, did you come out here to kill yourself?"

"I guess that was my thought."

She began to weep. "I can't stand it!" Her grief was so terrible that he wished he was dead. He looked round him at the hills and heard the sound of her sorrow and waited. Suddenly she shook her red hair back and seizing him with both hands tried to shake him. Her voice rang in his ears. "Vridar, you fool! Look at me!" He met her eyes. Then she got to her feet and tried to drag him up. He arose and she faced him, and he was aware of her trembling on his arms, of her tears falling to her cheeks. She turned away, leading him, and they went back to the city. On their way across the bridge he realized that she spoke to the policeman, that the policeman spoke and smiled. He thought that was strange. In their room with frantic hands she undressed him. She led him to the bathroom and shoved his scrawny body into the tub. She turned water on until he sat in it to his waist and then she massaged him, her hands moving in furious power over his flesh. "You're only skin and bones," she said. "You're starving to death."

"I'm all right," he said, wishing she would leave him alone.

Then she went to pieces. While Vridar put his clothes on, she sat in a chair, shaking horribly and moaning. He was so appalled by her face that he knelt at her feet, saying, "Please, I'm all right now." She poured her woe out with such hysteria that he was frightened, recalling in this moment the vein of insanity in her father's line. He tried desperately to comfort and reassure her. For a little while she would stop shaking and he would think she was all right; but then she would turn rigid and the horror in her face would unnerve him.

It was hours before they were both quiet. She then forced from him a promise that if he decided to kill himself he would tell her. "After this I must go where you go."

"Like Ruth," he said.

"But I won't trail you like a spy. I won't do that."

"I'll give you no reason to."

"Do you realize that you're not in your right mind?—that you think Neloa is alive?"

With one of the deep insights that so frequently came from his childlike nature, he said, "It's that I can't afford to think she isn't. Not yet."

II

This night he dreamed a dream that he had dreamed before, that he was to dream again. It was a variant of a dream his mother had had. She had seen Neloa as a harlot in a big city, she had seen Vridar spurn her, she had seen her turn away, pale and forlorn and friendless, with the look of death on her face. Vridar saw her that way in his dream. He did not spurn her. He only stared at her and wondered about her. He said to himself, "She's a whore, yet I never knew it. She has had lovers and now she comes to mock me, yet I see that she is not happy. I see that she is headed for suffering deeper than I have known. So why is this? . . . "

The experience was so bitter and so dreadful that he first whimpered and then cried out in his sleep. He awoke, his whole being full of the reality of her and their relationship, and all the pity and pain of it. He lay softly weeping, remembering— remembering her as she had come, her walk, her appearance, the mocking challenge in her eyes, and behind it the hopelessness. In this moment he came close to one of the central truths of his life. He felt it but could not grasp it; it was there a moment, and then gone . . . .

He sat up, tortured, trembling. How ghastly it was that she whom he had idolized should come to him out of the gloom of Chicago's west side, the marks of other men on her, the pallor of death on her even while she scorned him. All night, night after night, he would see this picture of her and tremble. All night, night after night, he would come close to the truth and miss it.

One morning he arose early and began a long poem to Neloa, using without shame the wonderful stanza form of Meredith's great poem, "Love in the Valley." He wrote morning and afternoon, pouring it out:

> Deep breathes the summer; on the haze the blue-wings,
> silver-spots and orange-tips hang like lucent gauze;
> stridulous the locust! shy behind a serviceberry
> sits the silvered ground squirred with breakfast in its paws.

Dust-choked lies the long road, hill to hill top cable;
swift skips the chipmunk, loud shrieks the loon;
through the seas of sunlight flashes scarlet tanager;
in the western sky there hangs the memory of a moon . . . .

He was studying some of the lines and telling himself that he would never be a poet or a novelist or anything worth shooting when there came to him the sound of voices, low and insistent. He knew that he had been hearing them for an hour or more. He became aware that they were talking about him. He went softly to a wall and listened.

"Understand," Marion was saying, "that a person can be insane and still know what he's doing. He's been insane ever since she died, but I don't think he'll kill himself. He's just too damned full of self-pity. . . . ."

O brother, dear wonderful brother!

"If only you understood him—"

"I do."

"The way I understand St. John."

"I understand St. John too."

"You take St. John and I'll take him. All his life he's been half-crazy with a wish to reform the world. He's the kind of half-baked adolescent they call a liberal. He'd die to make the world better, but it wouldn't be any better. It would be worse. It always is when the reformers get through with it . . . . "

O brother, dear brother!

"Has he told you about his childhood?"

"A lot, yes."

"We had much the same childhood. I became a psychologist, he a poet. You know why a person writes poetry?"

Athene said stiffly, "I wouldn't agree with you."

Vridar hastened over to strike the keys a few times, so they would think he was typing. On returning to the wall he heard his brother saying, "The driving force in the reformer is a sense of guilt. You idealists!" His tone was contemptuous. "Both of you writing what you call poetry when what you need is better lovers. Anyway, I wouldn't worry about him. Just try to keep his mind off himself, for he has too little mind and too much self."

O wonderful brother!

"It would be a good thing to trot him around and make him see people. Force him to stop looking at his navel. You've met Becky Hammond?"

"Once"

"Let's take him over there tonight. She'll be good for him."

Vridar returned to his machine and when Athene came in he pretended to be absorbed by his stanzas. He recalled having heard earlier, "Praise his stuff, even if it is bad." Athene now read a few lines:

When the world of twilight lays its fields of darkness,
heaping dusk in mountain coves, blue upon the hills;
when a splendid wind rolls against the heated sunset . . . .

"Don't speak!" he cried, staggering up. "Everything I write is bad and I know it."

544

"Not everything."

"Don't lie to me. If it's bad say so and keep on saying so and you'll have a job for life." He pulled the sheet of paper from the machine and destroyed it. "I'm only an imitator. I read Meredith and write like Meredith; Robinson and write like Robinson; Swinburne and write like Swinburne. I see a man with a limp and for weeks I limp; with a tic, and I get a tic; with a mustache, and I can feel the hair on my lip!"

"But now and then you're Vridar."

He snorted. "As when?"

Sitting on the floor she examined a pile of manuscript. She chose a sonnet and read it aloud:

> "Too well I know, my dear, that you are dead:
> I saw you lying rigid with the brown
> of poison on your throat where it ran down;
> I saw you later, stiff and white and bled.
> And once again I saw you, still the same,
> when with your hand in mine I made a vow;
> and then the furnace closed, and even now
> I hear the wild red hunger of its flame.
>
> In what brief while I learned how beauty slips
> to death and darkness, and by what strange way.
> Last week my pulse was in your heart; now only
> a copper urn of ashes, and one more lonely.
> A week ago I kissed your flesh; today
> I raise my head with dust upon my lips!"

Athene's voice broke. Quickly she left the room.

That evening Vridar went with her and his brother to Becky Hammond's. He had seen her once or twice, years ago—a tall long-legged woman, flatchested, lanky, with a small child-like face and a small topknot of hair. On a Montana ranch her husband had gone mad and killed himself. She had gone one summer to the Hunter ranch with Marion and there they had built fences—"When," Marion had said with a leer, "we weren't doing something else." Always when Vridar saw one of his brother's mistresses, he marveled at his taste in women. Or lack of all taste, for the man seemed to be completely impartial. Last summer Vridar had seen him with a woman so skinny that she was little more than hide and bone, and a week later with one so monstrously fat she could barely walk. There was nothing attractive about Becky. She stretched her long legs and smiled at Vridar, saying, "You take things too seriously. I've been through hell and high water and it was damned high water. I can still grin, for life is essentially a jest. Res est sacra miser. Are you trying to become saintly?"

Vridar responded with a thin smile. He was annoyed. He wondered why he had been fool enough to come here.

"What is life for me?" Becky was saying. "I sleep, I eat; sometimes a man is gallant enough to lie with me. I'll take my doctorate, I'll be a professor, I guess. My students will pity me, thinking I've been a spinster all my life. Vridar, you need a hobby."

545

"He has one," Marion said. "He's going to reform the world. He's one of these half-woman things called a liberal."

"I mean a small hobby—collecting bugs or stamps; writing limericks or seducing women. Translating is fun. I've just finished one of Sudermann's stories and I'm studying Russian." She turned to Athene. "How about a drink? You drink?"

"I never have," Athene said.

Becky rose and stretched her tall flat body. She was so un-female in appearance that it pained Vridar to look at her. She returned from the kitchen with brimming glasses. Vridar gulped his highball and felt more wretched, but because his mother had taught him that politeness was next to holiness he forced himself to listen. Becky was telling about a prize poem by a Baltimore youth. It was called hot days have been in Montana or something of the sort and had been given a prize by a journal called *The Nation*. Becky read it aloud. Vridar thought it was the worst stuff he had ever heard.

Tossing it to Vridar, she said, "Alia tentanda via est. Study it, Imitate it."

Vridar glanced over at Athene.

They all drank again and Becky's tongue got looser. She was assistant to a famous psychiatrist and she loved to tell of patients who came to Dr. Zwing: of a woman with a tic in her left eyelid who was going crazy because she was thought guilty of winking at men; of a huge man who was breaking his heart and his mind because of his belief that his penis had a crook in it; of a dentist who had decided that it was his religious duty to pull all his wife's teeth. The funniest case for Becky was that of a middle-aged spinster haunted by fear of a burglar under her bed.

"She goes out every evening and stays until midnight, giving burglars every chance in the world to get under her bed. But they never do. If only she could catch Casanova there! Her name is Hannah Border. There are thousands of Hannah Borders in the world and not enough burglars to go around. Now this Hannah—Vridar, another drink?"

"No, thanks."

"Does thus. She comes to her front door and listens. Softly she opens it and tiptoes to a closet, which she has had built for burglars to hide in. Softly she peaks into the closet and stirs the clothes, while one hand comes up to her flat chest, as flat as mine. Who wants a drink?

"Well, she stirs the garments. The swishing of the dresses makes her swoon a little. Once she fainted clear away and on coming to found the window open, and heard a man running across Baltimore. It might have been Mencken. She ran out and chased him with a broom but he misunderstood the symbolism of the broom." She turned to Athene. "Are you a Hannah?"

Athene's color deepened. She had not touched her drink.

Pale blue eyes studied her. Thin lips smiled. "I confess," Becky said, "that I like to-go-walking after midnight, hoping some man will pursue me. It isn't as easy to be sinful as people think. At least I've never found it easy. All women like to be chased but you seldom see a man chasing one."

Having brought the color to Athene's face, Becky turned to Vridar. "I know what you should do. First, stop feeling virtuous. Then seduce a lot of women—for how can you ever write anything any good if you don't?"

"You're wrong there," said Marion a little sharply. "If Vridar ever commits adultery, he'll be through as a writer."

"My God, you don't mean that!"

"You don't understand my brother."

Becky stared a few moments at Vridar's red and annoyed face. "I don't know what he has to feel morose about," she said. "He doesn't have to squat when he makes water . . . . "

The next evening they took Vridar to the house where Marion lived. For his room and board Marion had become guardian of a lunatic who, in his violent moods, was determined to kill his wife. Athene wanted to know what was wrong with the man. A lot of things were wrong, Marion said—feelings of impotence, ideas of persecution, insane jealousy. He thought his wife had lovers. For a moment Marion leveled his gray rather cynical eyes on Athene.

"Why doesn't she put him in an institution?"

Pride, Marion said. They had been high in society. She thought he would get well and put on his white tie again. But he never would. Sometimes, Marion said, the man chased him out of the house. Once with a long knife he chased him through every room and then through a window and halfway down Charles Street. Listening, Vridar did not doubt it. When Marion was only nineteen or twenty, he had returned home from Oklahoma with the furrow of a bullet across his skull. Choking with laughter he had confessed to Vridar that an enraged husband had caught him with his wife and had emptied a sixgun at him. Marion would wear the scar of that escapade to his death.

When they entered the house, large and overfurnished, Vridar saw a man by a reading lamp. The man looked up from a book and scowled. A woman came forward to meet them, a rather attractive woman whom fear and anxiety made to seem almost stupid.

"You go now," Marion said. "He'll be all right."

The wife withdrew.

"Mr. Cortland," Marion said, "meet my brother . . . . And his wife." Cortland rose and bowed stiffly, his morbid gaze on Athene. "We'll now leave you two," Marion said. "Cortland is a lover of books, so you two ought to have a fine talk." Marion and Athene left the room. Marion's contempt had been so plain that Vridar was furious.

"Have a cigar?" asked Cortland, glancing up and down Vridar's shabby garments.

"No thank you."

"A cigarette?"

Vridar took a cigarette. The two men smoked and looked at one another, Vridar politely, Cortland with morbid earnestness. His stare, it seemed to Vridar, was that of a man filled with murderous suspicious.

"Where did *he* go?" Cortland asked. He indicated the door through which Marion had passed.

"He's with my wife."

"You trust him with your wife?"

Vridar was startled. In later years that question was to come down through memory again and again. Even now his thoughts went back to footsteps in a certain night in Salt Lake City. He said, "What were you reading?"

"Where is *my* wife?" asked Cortland, staring at the door.

"In her room, I suppose."

Cortland fixed his mad glittering eyes on Vridar. "You liar!"

Vridar was so shocked that he dropped his cigarette. Recovering it, he stood up. He called to his brother. A door opened and Marion looked in.

"Isn't Mrs. Cortland in her room?"

"Of course."

"Mr. Cortland wanted to know."

Marion came over on long strides, looking arrogant and angry. He stared at Cortland, and Cortland shrank from him and looked whipped. His whole face began to twitch. On Marion's face was a malevolent grin.

"Cortland, I brought a man to talk poetry with you. He's just as sane as you are. As for your wife, she's tired, she went to bed."

Staring up at Marion, Cortland nodded but his face still twitched.

"Cortland is a poet," Marion said, turning to Vridar. "Maybe you'd like to see some of his masterpieces."

Marion swung and left the room. Vridar now saw hatred and terror in Cortland's eyes, and looking down saw his hands trembling on his knees. He asked him what poets he liked, but he knew that Cortland did not hear. The man was looking at the door through which Marion had passed. He was listening, as a man might listen with his whole body, or with the memories of a thousand betrayals. Without turning to Vridar he said, "That lecher is with my wife."

Most of this night Vridar lay awake, thinking of Cortland—of his terrors and tortures and loathings. When morning came he did not go to his typewriter. He said to Athene, "Were you ever under ether?"

"No."

"It's a nightmare of dreaming and waking. Awareness envelopes you like a dim light in a vast darkness. You feel as though only certain parts of you are alive, and not wholly. You have memory of pain. In the blackness that engulfs you, you have feeble flashes of meaning, as you struggle, trying to come awake. That's the way I feel now." He looked at her, his dark child eyes clouded, "I wish something would shake me out of this."

"Marion says it might take you a year or more."

It was Marion who shook him out of it. Marion had been over to see them and had left one of his notebooks. Vridar was looking through it when he came to what he took to be a journal. He was astonished, for he had never known that Marion kept a record of his thoughts. Turning the pages, reading here and there, he at last came to this:

> Sept. 14. We're on the train to Baltimore. Vridar is writing sonnets to Neloa. He writes one and then another and then another. He doesn't know that he seeks atonement or what at-

onement is. He's insane. I don't know what to do with him.

> Sept. 19. Vridar is getting worse. He spends all his time think-
> ing of Neloa and suicide. Like all poets his ego is too big for his
> mind. All martyrdom is self-pity and he's hellbent on being a
> martyr. If an outraged world would burn him at the stake he'd
> die happy. He wants to be enshrined with the sainted fakirs of
> history. If only for a moment he could see what a colossal jack-
> ass he is . . . .

Vridar looked up and glanced guiltily round him. He read again:

> Nov. 6. Whether my brother will kill himself is a tossup. If
> he does he'll never know why he did it. There's the poet for you.
> For what poet ever looked into his motives, or dared try? Does
> the child? Self-loathing, which is a form of self-pity; self-preoc-
> cupation, a form of looking at the navel; a yearning to suicide
> and death, all aspects of morbid self-love . . . .

Vridar read a number of the statements over and over and then closed the journal, wondering if his cynical brother had left it here for him to find. He was sunk in
thought when Athene came in. When she showed concern for him, he told her to
go away. "I'm all right," he said. *His ego is too big for his mind.* He looked over at
Athene and said, "I'm going to be all right." *If an outraged world would burn him
at the stake.*

"Have you been writing?"

"Why should I? Hasn't the world enough Prousts?" *Self-loathing, which is a form
of self-pity.* "What day is it?"

"November the twenty-third."

"From September eighth to this day my life has been a complete waste." *A yearning to suicide and death.* "Well, today marks a turning point in my life." He was
looking curiously at Athene. Marion had said that she was not the kind of woman
he should live with. Vridar was thinking about the inside of her—her emotions, hungers, prejudices . . . . Marion had said to her, "What you need is a lot of good
screwing." Vridar said, "Have you found me all right as a lover?"

"Why do you ask that?"

"Because of something Marion said. But don't answer it. I know I'm no good for
that either, compared to him. What did he tell us about Shirley Rae, his present
mistress? When he asked her to do it she said other men had tried and couldn't but
he could try if he wished to. She said she was abnormally small. You remember the
look on his face when he told us? Can you imagine how easy it was for him?"

Her voice rather sharp she said, "What's wrong with you?"

"Just about everything, I suppose. You want to know what happened? I have
been trying to sum it up in an epigram. It goes like this: Vridar lies here, the pitiable fraud who entered a partnership with God; searched for himself on the cross
eternal, and found himself in his brother's journal."

"His journal?"

"There. He left it for me to read, I guess. You want to read what he says?"

"That would be dishonest."

"It appears, then, that we can win victories from dishonesty, for I'm not going to be what I was. He says I'm full of self-pity. He's taking a doctorate in psychology. Maybe he knows. He says I yearn for martyrdom. I suspect this, that the deepest grief refuses to be observed. I'm not sure I have that depth but I'll find out what made me this thing I am."

He got to his feet. "I'm going for a walk now. Alone." He put on his battered old cap and left the room, thinking, It's the way it has always been: she wants me but doesn't want me; wants me to keep her, yet wants me to let her go . . . .

III

He left the city and went to a wooded hillside and sat where he could smell water and trees and look at the sky. He lay back, and on the sky he imagined scenes from his past. His first memory was of his father gently caning him because he had refused to count; his second was of himself paralyzed with fright, as he sat on a high stool. He was then three. His third was at the age of five or six: his Aunt Agnes had scared the daylights out of him with threats of Hell and the Devil. Those were the only memories of his first six years and they were all memories of terror.

After that his memories for a long time seemed to be chiefly of guilt, pain, and cruelty. Was there a pattern in it all? He looked for one as events came to him in pictures, each with its sight, sound, and smell: of a sheep with its head pulled up and back, its throat butchered open from ear to ear, its blood pouring out; of an enraged father grasping a cat by its heels and crushing it around a post, the squawk of it when it struck, the smell of it, the sight of its open eyes as it lay senseless in the yard; of the corrals—of his father after days of heavy rain wading in manure almost to his knees and being kicked over, and then rushing at a cow with a heavy club and roaring, "So, you son of a bitch when I say so!" Of his father smiting with all his great power across the cow's skull and knocking her sprawling into the awful depth of dung, while his mother cried hysterically, "Joe, you damn silly fool you!" There came back to him the stench of burning hair and hide and the agonized bawling, the branding iron, the knife, the blood; Joe's brutally slow deliberate way of cutting off half of the scrotum—his slow deliberate way of cutting open the testicle and squeezing it out of its sac and scraping back along the cord with his knife, as the poor beast's eyes almost exploded from its skull; of Joe's slow way of tossing the bloody dripping testicle out to the flies and then bending to the other; of Joe's slow deliberate way with a dull saw as he sawed slowly through a big handsome horn, close to the base of the skull—of the round horn-hole then, full of blood and bone dust—and the poor thing's eyes, glazed with amazement and horror . . . .O God, how it all came back to him!

And the nights under downpours, with water and chunks of mud falling from the ceiling to the untanned deer and elk skins on his bed; the smell of the hides and the smell of water filling the room; the trails down in jungleland lying through marsh and bog, the depthless springs into which unwary beasts vanished; the smell of stagnant water, of kinnikinic and birch and willow, fir and aspen, cattails and tule, and grassy beds where wild things had lain; the smell of great waving trees in a wild storm, and of the river in spring floods, and of pelts of wolves and wildcats, muskrats and minks and beavers, spiked to the house walls; and the smell of chickens with their feathers soaked, huddled in baskets by the stove; and of cows with steaming hides, and of his parents in from milking, with corral manure all over them. . . . It all came back now—the velvety feel of rose petals, the wonderful textures of different barks, the sharp thrust of briar and thorn; the cool liquid feeling of water and the round smoothness of a deer's thighbone; of heavy quilts or skins under nightmare and the feeling of pain in his own loins when he watched the horrible castrations, but never the feel of a mother's kiss, for there had been none. There had been none in all the years of memory . . . .

The taste of gilia petals, of wheat chewed to gum, of oats in oatmeal, of wild strawberry and gooseberry, currant, serviceberry and chokecherry, and of huckleberry above all; of aspen bark and yarrow and wild graperoot, all brewed to make a tonic; or dead leaves in autumn, or rose hips, of rock salt placed for the cattle to lick and the smooth saucers their tongues had made; of old tobacco quids which his father had put on the house logs to dry; of venison and mallard duck and black bear, rainbow and cutthroat trout, elk, moose, sagehen, grouse; of soured milk in vats, and of curd and cheese, and of the weed seeds which he had bottled and called vegetables and fruits . . . . The sound of river waters and nightwinds, of wolves and coyotes and mountain lions; of calves bawling and of chickens fretting at dawn; of a horse screaming because of the turpentine poured into his bowels by the Bridwell boys; of a rabbit screaming when overtaken by a dog; of his brother screaming when he stepped on the redhot iron and went hopping away with it buried in his flesh . . . . It all came back now — the chickens hopping madly after their heads had been chopped off and the look of the eyes in the heads when, hiding in the bushes, he studied them; and a hog running wildly with two bullets in its head and Joe desperately chasing it with an ax—and then the sound of the blows on its skull; and the wild things shrieking in traps and the castrated yearling bulls standing alone, their heads matted with blood and bone dust, a pool of blood under their bellies. It came back —the sickening smell of mice and rats and of wet chicken feathers and of cat dung and of cattle breath; the insane droning of flies in yellow sunlight and the insane sound of winds round the corners. The feeling of a young bluebird, wounded and dying in his hands . . . .

Such were the memories of life from his sixth to his eleventh year: the chief meaning seemed to be loneliness, pain, and terror—the frantic movements of the living that would go on living, the awful stillness of the dead. Could he recall no moments of tenderness, no hour when he wanted to sing? There was almost none of that. It had been American pioneer life, raw, brutal, earnest, unpitying—not Willa Cather's foolish romanticism, not the customary glamorizing . . . . It was a life that thousands had lived with zest and appetite, but he had been a sickly child, a child terrified from birth—for his mother said that he had screamed and had convulsions as an infant; a child so abnormally sensitive that it broke his heart to watch what strong men loved—such as pressing a huge redhot iron into the hide and flesh of a quivering calf. He had lived in fear—in fear so deep and constant that only those could find it credible who had known it. He had been deeply afraid of his father, even afraid of his mother; and he had simply been paralyzed with terror in the presence of the Bridwell sons . . . .

Smell of cedar on a gray butte, of sand and gravel under a hot sun; the stink of outdoor privies; the sounds of Agnes and her man sunk in sexual embrace, Agnes gasping and her man grunting like a mounted boar; the feel of chalk and books and blackboard, the sight of school bullies waiting at the bridge; a big naked hairy Swede holding his thing up and neighing like a stallion and his wife giggling hysterically; the smell of red ants swarming over a mound, of Easter eggs and their paint, of wet diapers; and a picture of Neloa, a slender child with long black hair and dark eyes and red cheeks. Was that his first memory of tenderness? Surely there had been tenderness before then, but he could recall none.

He had loved her, even then, or he had needed love. That was it. He had idolized her as something pure that stood above the welter of stinking corrals, castrating knives, and branding irons, and magpies drooling with their tongues cut out. She became for him, he supposed, a symbol of all that was lovely and good: his testaments, his church, his prayer and passion. For years he had been scared out of his wits: hungers had grown to be obsessions, loneliness to be nightmare; and she came along and was all things. She and books had become his idols; in a world that had proved friendless and evil, she had become the light and the way, until she was no longer girl or woman but the center of heaven and the heart of God. He married her, he refused to see what she was, he drove her to her death.

That was it and it was folly to pretend that that was not it.

How had it been? Twenty years had led him to see life as a brutal and terrifying struggle, with only a little good in it, and that seldom triumphant: a world in which beauty was as insubstantial as the fires in a sunset, in which peace could be insured only with death. How had he come to be such an idealist in such a world? It had been his mother's work, and the Bible's. Having little else to read during those years before he entered school, he had read the Bible three or four times and parts of it many times; and alone when at his chores, or lying awake in bed, he had pondered its meanings hour after hour. The Bible and his mother had made an emotional imbecile of him.

He didn't see it all yet; he suspected that he saw only a little of it, but he would see it all some day. He would persist until the truth came plain. He took pencil and paper and began to make notes, and after a while his effort to see himself for what he was became such a monstrous silliness that he put his digust in verse:

> Vridar out there is making notes
> with their addenda of morgues and motes;
> tots up his ideals, reflects a little,
> and finds that he has two jots, one tittle.

He got up and walked back to the city, and not far from the bridge he met Athene. She had brought a letter. He opened it and read it. It was from the woman Dennis had lived with in Chicago: it said that the two of them with their infant in a baby carriage had set out for Mobile, with Dennis pushing the carriage. It said that in Tennessee the Klan had seized Dennis and thrown him into jail, and she had been left, as she put it, to the tigerish virtue of the town. The letter was wild and abusive. The next day another letter came. It said that Dennis had got out of jail and was hotfooting it to Baltimore. It said: "He loves you more than me so send me some money. Money can't pay for what you've done to me but it can help me out of this God damned nest of puritans . . . . "

"If I'm responsible for her being where she is," Vridar said drily, "no doubt I'm also responsible for Teapot Dome. What an idiot he is! Imagine setting out to push a baby buggy two thousand miles! And now the neurotic bitch wants money."

"There's a baby," Athene said.

"O God, isn't there always a baby? Where does the fool think he's going?"

"To Baltimore" she said.

"Well, I'll head that off. She gave an address here where I can reach him."

Vridar wrote a sharp note to Dennis, telling him to get back to his wife and child. He was never to see him again.

"Why should he want to come to me?" Vridar angrily demanded. "Does the fool think I have wisdom?—or you?—we with our sickly mating of illusions and poetry! What an ass! He's simply too damned lazy to use a contraceptive—or too selfish. Or is it that some men are hellbent on knocking women up? Well, he's taken the bloom off her now, he'll be sorry he met her, he'll leave her some day with six kids. And that reminds me, are you sorry you met me?"

She made the quick movement that was typical of her when forced to be unhappily aware of herself. "For her," she said. "Not for myself."

"But you've cut yourself off from friends—your relatives, your brothers."

She stared at him. He was making her very miserable.

"You want to leave me?"

Her spirit flamed for a moment. "Weren't you always asking her that question? Was it because you wanted to be honest or was it because you wanted to leave her?"

"Maybe both," he said.

"Then never ask the question again."

"All right, but there are a few things I should say to you. They're the kind of things nobody can say without seeming stupid. I've been out in the hills thinking, and I can see that I've been a romantic fool and that I've been breaking my heart over what I can never change. I must now become a rationalist and a realist, but I'm not sure you'll like that kind of man. You have in you so much mysticism. You like the Gospel of John, for instance, and Plato. I probably shall come to detest both.

"And there's this. I don't really know why I was attracted to you, or you to me. In my case was it because you seemed to have more quality?—because you had gone through a firstrate college on fellowships, and were writing poetry, and loved books? Why were you attracted to me?"

She again made the movement of distress. "I don't suppose I know."

"Don't I seem to you to be a fool? But would you admit that Swinburne was, driven headlong into rhetoric by his fear of women?—or Byron, driven to wandering by incest?— or Swift, turned into a fury because of disgust for his natural functions?— or all the others, for the list of them is as long as the roster of the famous."

"You'll probably become obsessed with the idea of knowing yourself."

"I suppose I'm the kind who could. I'm an extremist."

"Wouldn't that be another form of self-pity?"

"I suppose. But what's the mind for if not to use? And if we use it, is there any plainer way to the civilized life than an understanding of our motives?"

She was looking at him in a way she had looked so many times. It perplexed and annoyed him. He thought he perceived that the core of this woman, which he had never reached and no man would ever reach, was narcissistic. It was with pride that she had told him that her hymen had grown together after the rupture and had to be ruptured a second time.

She now said, "Nobody can predict what extreme you'll swing to."

"Why aren't you an extremist?"

"I'm a Greek."

That also annoyed him. She was, it seemed to him, inordinately vain of her knowledge of Greek and of the Greek philosophers. "But isn't life a matter of extremes? —from June to January; from the north pole to the equator; from birth to death. I don't suppose you'd ever want to share a ruthless and unpitying exploration. Would you want to lay your motives as bare as your palm?"

She was looking at him, her eyes troubled. At last she said, "No."

"You distrust thinking, don't you? You prefer to fall back on the faculties of the mystic?"

"Oh, I wouldn't say that."

"You're an idealist?"

"Of course I am."

"Well, I suppose that our views will steadily move apart, as we grow older. Our marriage—"

She cut in a little sharply, "You've said you wanted to be a poet. Thinking without poetry is sterile." When Athene made what seemed to her to be a profound statement, she was never able to keep an emotion of gentle triumph out of her face. It was there now.

Vridar noted it and said, "I'm only saying really that I've been a sentimental fool and am weary of it. By a mother and the Bible I've been betrayed. But must I be a fool all my life? Should I not look to the sources of my beliefs, or take them on faith? Shall I assume that I have my mind as I have my legs to use, and use it?"

"For the right and true things," she said.

Her words startled him. He met her eyes. "Oh, come now! Who knows what are the right and true things? I sometimes suspect you of being an orthodox Christian and of hiding the fact from me."

"I think there are certain truths that we don't need to inquire into."

Astonishment was growing in him. He had not seen this side of her before. "Such as what?"

"I don't want to talk about it. You're in a belligerent mood."

"Only a determined mood, my dear. So help me God I won't go on in self-pitying evasions. I'm tired of being the fool. I have a notion that one phase of my life has ended, that another has begun. I've a job to do and I'm going to do it. You'll be surprised to hear what the first move is."

554

Looking at him uneasily she said, "I don't doubt it."

"I'm going to take my doctorate. I'm going back to Chicago."

"Oh no!" she cried and her face paled. "You could never stand it there!"

"I have no choice. Can't you see that?"

"You have no—"

"I have no choice. If I can't face that, do you think I can face a search into motives? Is my first move to be one of cowardice?"

"But you can't stand to go back."

"Then let me break."

"You will break, Vridar! Please, is there any sense in this?"

"Would you have me be a weakling? Would you have me flee? Could you live with me if I were too cowardly to go back and finish the job? It is simply a waste of time to try to talk me out of it, for I am going back. First I'll do a thesis in the Library of Congress and for that I'll have only two or three months, and then back to Chicago. So let's get our junk packed and be off."

IV

They went first to Washington, where Vridar hoped to do a thesis, and they lived in one small cold dirty room close to the library. It had a gas plate, unclean bedding, cockroaches, and tattered wallpaper, but Vridar asked how they could afford anything better, having so little in funds. They would eat and sleep in it, that was all. He looked out the window at an area of junk and filth and said, "I'd think Uncle Sam would clean up his backyard."

They did not spend much time in the room. For Vridar the library was a magnificent storehouse of minds, and after getting a stack permit and a table he spent most of his time there. And every hour he was there Athene was right at his side, helping for all she was worth. They were at the library every morning before the doors were opened; they remained there until the doors were closed, long after dark.

He had made a stern resolve, he was determined to dredge all the weakness and self-pity out of him, but many a night from midnight till morning he tossed in dream and delirium. He was only a skeleton of a man now, with sunken morbid child-eyes; a big thrust of nose, a pale thin mouth. Athene yielded at last to his wish to drug himself for sleep, for if she protested he always gave the same reply, "Swift said that a mind worth having wears its body out." Early in January he was stricken with dizziness and it took him an hour, groping and staggering, to find the way from the library to his room. He told Athene he needed exercise and went down Pennsylvania Avenue to the Y.M.C.A. gymnasium. He came out an hour later feeling a little better, but in the cold and sleet on the way home he was taken with chills. When he entered his room he was deathly sick. This night he was delirious all night and at times violent. Desperate, and halfsick too, Athene worked with him until morning came.

"I wonder what's wrong with me," he said, looking at her.

"You're sick." She began to weep. She wanted to call a doctor, but he asked how they could afford a doctor. He said he would be all right soon and he left the bed and dressed. He tried to eat an orange, he drank a little buttermilk. He gathered his paper and pencils.

"Don't go to the library today!"

"I must," he said, half out of his mind. "I'll be all right."

"You're sick, damn it!" Her eyes were wet and angry. "You'll kill yourself."

"All right. Marion said it. Let's see how he stands up."

"Vridar, look at yourself."

"No," he said. "I've never liked the look of myself." He entered the tiny bathroom and doused his face with cold water. He returned, saying, "In high school I looked so ghastly that I put red ink on my cheeks."

"You're ghastly now."

He sat on the bed, wondering what to do. They had only a little money. He would have to get his degree soon or go out and find a job. He rose, and at the door she clung to him but he went to the library anyway and bent over old bound volumes of the London *Times,* thinking he would be all right. Then suddenly, almost without warning, he was stricken with vomiting sickness. He left the building in haste and bent over a gutter, puking bitter foam to his lips. He went to a bench and sat, now trembling all over with chills. He again entered the warmth of the building but the nausea overwhelmed him and he hastened out.

For two weeks he fought this sickness but went to the library every day, determined to gather the materials and write a thesis of more than a hundred thousand words, all in two or three months. He would teach his damned cynical brother to charge him with self-pity! Athene argued with him, wept over him, despaired. She believed that a sick person ought to be in bed. For her the body was a thing to cherish and care for.

But Vridar growled, "Sickness never put either of my parents to bed. They went right on working and got well. My father blew the palm off a hand with a shotgun but never missed an hour's labor. He just filled it up with tobacco and went on."

"They'll pay for it in their old age."

"Nonsense. They'll live forever. My mother almost cut off a finger and for days her dish water was red but she never paused. My father—"

"If you drive yourself to a breakdown, will that be honest?"

"Look. I should be in Chicago now. I have more courses to take. I may have to rewrite the damned thesis a time or two. Isn't there some medicine that might fix me up? Get the kind that tastes the worst. My father says that is better."

Athene fetched medicines but they did him no good. They only made him vomit. Then he would rest a little while and return to the library stacks, with Athene at his side. Every night he talked out of delirium and the next morning would ask: "What did I say last night?"

"About her. You seemed to think she was with you."

"What did I say?"

"I don't want to talk about it."

"Athene dear, indulge me a little longer. I'll fight out of this. It might help to know what I say."

"Oh, it's just despair, bitterness—love sometimes." She rose and went to the bathroom.

Vridar lay back, sick, dizzy, thinking. Nearly every night since Neloa's death he had dreamed of her and awakened filled with her presence. He knew this was stupid and cowardly. He knew that she had never been worth such devotion. He knew that dreaming of Neloa was no way to be loyal to the woman now with him.

What were the dreams? Some of them were their meeting on the Antelope hills, when Neloa had come to him through sunlight and birdsong, their sitting by the old millstream when he thought she was too pure to touch, their riding over the hills. But these were not the dreams that left him shaken. The dreams that shook him were those in which he searched over the earth for her and finding her knelt at her feet; or in which she came to him smiling and said it had all been a jest. Some of the dreams were hidden in symbols.

There had been a terrible one in the land of his youth: he was carrying a gun and his father was with him, they were hunting deer. They flushed a herd and marking the loveliest of the does Vridar shot her. Then the wounded thing, wild and beautiful in the morning, ran from hill to hill, leaving a path of blood; and Vridar ran after her, trying for another shot. But as he ran he was filled with sickening realization of what he had done, and he wanted to catch the doe and heal her wound. He began to weep and ran weeping over the hills. And the stricken deer vanished into a great dark canyon and was lost.

While thinking about the dream, there came to him in a flash Cowper's famous line, "I was a stricken deer that left the herd. . . ." Then he knew! The deer had been Neloa and the dark canyon had been death. He had been an eager and thoughtless huntsman. How simple the symbols were! But this too was cowardice, he told himself; this would never do. When Athene came in, he asked her to sit by him. He said:

"It would be a good thing to study our dreams, wouldn't it? We could discover things about ourselves." He saw that she did not want to. Talk of self-exploration always wearied her, for she was a mystic, she thought truth came from God.

Hereafter, before falling asleep he told himself that he would dream plain naked dreams without symbolism and disguise. Let it all come out of the dark and the depths. Let all of it, the fears, the terrors, the evasions—

And something came. The moment he awoke, he knew that something had come out of his buried mind, and had shown itself, clearly, for what it was. It filled him with wonder and astonishment, for he had never suspected that he had such a wish. He thought about it until it was all clear, and then to the woman at his side, he said, "I want to tell you a dream."

She did not speak. He supposed she did not want to hear it. But he said: "I was somewhere—I don't think the place matters—with a negress. I was out with her, to a party or dance or something; people were staring at us, I felt ill at ease, I felt shame. I said to myself, Why feel shame?—for you've said there's no prejudice of race in you. It seems then to go back to something that happened in Chicago two years ago. A white woman walked with a black man one Sunday

557

along Lake Michigan and a crowd followed, looking at them. I went with the crowd. I said to myself, Here are a woman and a man, one white, one black, and these people don't like to see them together. I didn't either but I didn't know it then.

"Well, that part shows that I had fooled myself about race prejudice. The other revelation is more important and more difficult to confess. We were somewhere alone and she wanted me to make love to her. I looked at her huge lips and thought, O Lord, I can never kiss those! But she was so insistent, so primitive in her ardor that I did kiss her and then I felt ill. I kissed only a part of her lower lip, knowing that I could never envelop her whole mouth with a mouth like mine— so I just kissed her lip as I might have kissed the side of a house." He turned to Athene. "I'm feeling pretty silly, and the worst of it is still to come. Stand up to it, Hunter; drag it out."

He was silent a few moments. Then: "I kissed her cheek, and it was like kissing black rubber. I was repelled. But at the moment when I was ready to flee, she did something. With her mouth, I mean. She didn't use her tongue. It was somehow the quality of her mouth—something deep, ancient, and unashamed; and a great passion seized and shook me. I kissed her again and was amazed to find what pleasure it gave me. I began the sexual embrace and was so overcome that I fainted with joy. About then I woke up."

Again he was silent. "Well, what does it mean? Time and again I've heard men say that the sexual rapture is deeper with a negress than with white women. Dennis said it, O Lord, a thousand times. Gourmont says it in one of his books. I've always been rather outraged by the statement *because I was afraid it might be so*. I suppose it's largely in the man's mind, though ardor in a sexual partner does shake us. Did Richard Francis Burton have it or just look it? Does my brother have it?"

She was silent.

"Well," he said, beginning to dress, "I think I'm on my way. No doubt it will be a long and a hard way. You sit on the Gospel of John, but I'm going down into my subconscious in any way I can. I'm going through my evasions like a war tank through a French hedge—and the time will come when not many eyes can look into mine. And I sense now that this search can be a very wonderful thing—the emotional counterpart of the Lewis and Clark journey. Another world, Athene, is opening to me." He was bending over, putting on his shoes, talking. "What a thing I am, overborne and nearly choked by this heavy Hebrew and Christian heritage of evasion. What a fraud! I'm pretty thoroughly damned sick of him. The poor stupid thing, ashamed to be decent. The gargantuan imbecile, emotionally. An emotional halfwit, that's what. An emotional illiterate." He turned to look at her unhappy face. "That's it—an emotional illiterate; and I suspect now that emotional illiteracy is the trouble with the whole damned Christian world. Oh, I have an intimation of it now!"

He stook up, still looking at her. "A nice boy," he said. "My mother always said so and I believed my mother. A nice boy with nice ideals—unselfish, manly, compassionate—in short, a fraud. I'll get all that puritan cant out of me. I'll breathe air that hasn't been breathed by the popes and Calvin and Luther." He was brushing his hair. The hair fell down over his eyes, and through the hair he looked at her. "You may always be the same woman, for you seem quite satisfied with what you are; but I'll not be the same man. We may as well realize that we shall not always be together."

She sat up. "You mean you're warning me so early?"

"That's a crass way to put it. I mean that this evasive self-pitying thing before you is not what I'll be before I'm done. And what I become you may not want. My way for you may be too—too ruthless. I'll never bed a lusty negress, but not forever will I be the mewling thing that is afraid to. Marion could, couldn't he?"

"I'm not interested."

"Of course he could," Vridar said, as though she had denied it. "Hell, he probably has. Some day I'll tell you about him. Now we must have a huge breakfast—wads of bacon and eggs and fruit and coffee and a small mountain of toast. Come, we have a job to do, so let's be at it."

V

But his vision of a new world and a new purpose did not burn steady; it came and he lost it and it came again. He was like a sick man living in a room with shades drawn, sensing the health and all the health-odors of a world beyond the window. With Athene at his side in the stacks fifteen or more hours every day, he completed his reading and wrote his thesis, but when the hour came for the return to Chicago he felt sick with despair. He told Athene to go first, he would follow on the next train. In a night of fog and drizzle he saw her off and then walked the streets till dawn.

Twenty-four hours later he arrived in Chicago and rode a trolley to the University; and when, passing Washington Park, he saw spots where he had been with Neloa, old trysting places with Athene, he was so sick with all the old heartbreak that he could barely endure it. Having read *Crime and Punishment* twice, he had supposed that he would have to go, at least once, to the dingy drab apartment on Ellis Street just to convince himself that she was not there. He fought against the madness, but after he had checked his luggage, he walked swiftly to the building, his heart in his throat. It was so familiar, every ugly brick and stone of it, yet it was something out of nightmare and the dark. Softly, as though she might flee at his approach, he entered the front door and stood in the musty familiar odors of the hallways; entered the basement and looked round it—for here he had stoked the furnace, baled papers—the machine for baling was still there and the same old garbage pails, the same old irons with which he had shoveled coal. He went to the back yard and stared at the windows of the rooms where they had lived—and heard again the words, My mama doesn't live here any more. He tried to fight down a wish to enter the rooms, but he might as well have tried to stop his breathing. Looking at the spot where the glass had lain after she hurled it, he went to the porch and stood where she had stood when she called his name; and then softly he knocked on the door. There seemed to be no one home. He

559

tried the door and finding it unlocked let himself in. Other persons were living here now: the furniture, the carpets were different, but the presence of Neloa filled the two small rooms and would fill them as long as the building stood. With hot desperate grief all through him, he went from one room to the other, remembering where she had sat when she read to him; when she combed her long hair; and then to the closet where her clothes had hung and he could still smell them, as he had smelled them in those days after her death. He pressed his cheek to a bare wall, knowing that she had touched the spot; to the knobs on the door, knowing that many times her hand had clasped them; even to the faucets on the sink, knowing she had touched those. "Neloa!" he whispered, his heart breaking.

Suddenly, unable to endure it, he rushed from the building. He was hastening away without looking back when a voice called him and Arnold Johnson smiled a greeting. Johnson was large and fat, with a fat pimpled face that always looked as though it had just been massaged with oils. He breathed heavily through his nose, especially when at ease. Now he bellowed a welcome and slapped Vridar's back, knocking mist from his eyes.

"You old son of a gun. Say, my God, you look bad."

"I'm all right."

"Where you staying?"

"Nowhere yet. I'm looking."

"Fine, why don't you come live with me?"

For an hour or more he walked with this man, unable to throw him off, driven mad by his empty flow of chatter. "I'm married, did you know? Swellest girl you ever did see, but she's a nurse and we can't live together. That's heck, I call it." He laughed. When Arnold laughed, he backed off a little, as though afraid he might blow a man down. "What you think of Coolidge. You taking your degree this spring? You got a job yet? I want to teach but my wife doesn't want to leave her nursing. I'm between Scylla and Charybdis, I call it." He laughed again. "My wife's name is Lorraine. She calls me Alsace. But that's my honeymoon name and is just for private use. She's a witty kid, my wife. She said, Alsace, we Metz, and just over the hill is Verdun. Danged clever, I say. She says, When I met you, Alsace, I was Lorraine, but now I'm John's daughter and you're Johnson." He roared. "You know, Shakespeare was a punny man but my wife is punnier. You know Louis Untermeyer's?—that the Russian revolution was a danged poor piece of Marxmanship. My wife has a hundred better than that. She'll get a legacy in two years, but says the whole country is getting heir-minded. She says John Donne a heck of a good job with the man drake's root—"

Vridar stopped and turned, unable to endure more of this. "Look, Arnold, I'll have to live alone, for I want to take my degree in a couple of months. I'll be working day and night."

"Oh sure," said Arnold agreeably. "Dang it, man, you sure look sick. You all right?"

"I'm all right. Been working hard."

"I want you to take lunch with us. Lorraine—"

"After I'm settled."

"Sure, that's what I meant. Lorraine—"

"I have to go now."

"Dang it, man, you sure you're all right?"

Vridar went to the University and asked for his mail. There was a note from Athene, giving her address, and an hour later they sat together in Jackson Park. The moment she saw him, she was appalled by his appearance. She said he should not have come here.

"I'll be all right," he said.

"You're all right and it's senseless to say you are."

Unknown to her he was looking toward the building where Neloa had lived. "I'll be all right," he said. "I'll read Voltaire and Swift."

He decided that that was what he needed—a literary tonic to set him up. In the library he came on a slender volume called *Ph.D.'s,* by Leonard Bacon, and the reading of a page convinced him that it was what he needed. He went to his room, reading as he walked; and this story of a young woman who so adored her professor of Shelley that she yielded her dream of marriage and a home to work under him for a doctor's degree was so apt, so devastating in its bitter truth, that Vridar began to laugh. The final scene drenched him with sardonic mirth: the deluded creature, after years of devotion to petty details, happened to pass the open door of a classroom and saw there another girl, much like what she had been, listening with wide rapt eyes to the same professor. Vridar lay back and howled. Then seizing the book he went to find Athene.

He told her it was something she must read, she simply must; for she had had a professor of Italian whom she had adored with pure sexless ardor. "Or was it so pure?" he asked. "And how about your professor of Latin, with his bedridden wife, who gave parties to his girls, acting as benevolent godfather and host, yet pinching them in delicate places and kissing them goodnight. You thought he was only a scholar with a white beard? Well, here's a book for you, and for all the other well-pinched nuns in Hunter, Barnard, Goucher, Bryn Mawr, Smith, Mills, and Stephens. It shows how scholars are made of virgins."

Athene did not want to read the book. She disliked anything that aroused in him such sardonic glee. He would read a few lines aloud and demand, "Haven't you any sense of the ironic?" She would stare at him, her eyes unhappy. "Damn it, this story's perfect. There are thousands of instructors like this fraud. And the girls adore them! What platonic plundering of their wits prepares them for the pinch on the hindend and the goodnight kiss! Did you adore that professor of Italian."

"Oh, some of us, I guess." She was vexed.

"The women's colleges! What pastures for the Don Juan bulls. If my brother ever gets into one, there'll be gone virgins under every bush."

"You sound envious."

"Don't think I'm not. Didn't this Italian ever seduce any of you? Was all his pinching wasted?"

"He didn't pinch," she said, a little sharply.

"Oh no, that was the other one. The Italian asked you to his apartment to see his library and wooed you with d'Annunzio. You don't want to read this book?"

"No."

"All right, I'll take it along. I'm going to write."

He hastened to his room and sat at his decrepit portable machine. Still a shameless imitator, he chose the stanza form made famous by Byron, and used by Bacon. Sometimes, for twenty minutes or a half-hour at a stretch, he poured it out of him almost as fast as he could type:

> There still are those who like a painted sky
> and books with heroes, tall and pure and many;
> though Time, the jester, I observe, disguises
> oblivion nicely with awards and prizes. . . .

That, he hoped, would take care of a recent Pulitzer novelist, whose book when he tried to read it made him ill. He wrote the afternoon away and far into the night, forgetting his hunger, his weariness, his pain and grief, and even himself, while his satire on mankind flowed from his brain to his fingers:

> As editor I make a fair pretension,
> though doubtless not so learned as Morize.
> A lex non scripta urges me to mention
> the garnering of almost four degrees.
> Two I now have and am agog with tension
> over the prospect of some LL. D.'s.
> Coolidge, I know, has all the laws allow
> but the politicians lead the scholars now.

He was sending Joe Doe to Mars, there to have him discover a civilized creature quite unlike himself. Because of Joe's self-love and prejudice he would be appalled at the appearance of the Martians; and over the implications here Vridar snorted with joy as he paced the room smoking and composing :

> He leapt the rivers and the estuaries
> like moralists who smell an assignation;
> and clinging to his shoulders as he went
> was a picture of filmed teeth—and Pepsodent.

Seizing a batch of stanzas, he hastened over to Athene, who lived only two blocks away. Bursting in, he asked her to read them. She read, looking frozen at first, but then smiled. He wanted to know if they were any good. She said they were satanic. She said that they were lightning flashes that revealed the worst in mankind but never the best. It was the worst he was after, he said. He would leave the best to the Pulitzers. "You mean this sort?" He read aloud:

> "Their heads did not grow down beneath their shoulders
> like those of pigs and anthropophagi,
> but sat above, like queerly suspended boulders
> somewhere between their bodies and the sky.
> With vast attentive ears like leather folders;
> with great bold eyes, each asking where and why:
> (for my part, whether liar, thief or bawd
> I do think man's an image of his god)."

"No, no," said Athene. "Can't you be whimsical and gentle?"

"When attacking selflove? When attacking this absurd creature who thinks he's the center of the universe?"

"It would be more effective—"

"But I'm not a whimsical and gentle person."

"You can be," she said, and picked up a sheet. Over her shoulder he read with her:

> Let that be censored. Now and then I shed
> a witticism, or fall into surmise.
> For one with suffixes accredited
> to ponder on the loveliest of lies
> of all the best that has been thought and said
> between the inspiration and the prize,
> must leave some dogmas on the printed page
> to flush his youth and castigate his age.

The couplet, she said, was one that Pope might have accepted, though the words dogmas and castigate might not be the inevitable ones. He would revise it, of course.

"Oh, of course," he said impatiently. "But I can't make it light and whimsical."

He could make it lighter, she said. This rebuke to Edna Ferber was not too bad:

> Nor had the women any breasts—or drifts
> of snow, Pulitzers call them; nor of hips
> more than the bone and shank; nor any shifts
> of parentheses upon the brow; nor lips
> like summer's crimson rosebud where it lifts
> to hungry bee-tongue. (They had finger-tips;
> the same I'm-hungering look upon the street;
> the same biology—and they had feet).

No, she said, studying it, that stanza would not do. There was something brash and immature about it. But quickly, while he was staring down from her pointed finger and observing that even her fingers were freckled, she said the couplet about Elizabeth was good. Under his breath he read, "Nor placed a coat for one upon the mud whose mind was far less royal than her blood."

"But this is too bitter," she said. She meant:

> These Martians, heavens yes, had come to feel
> the price they paid for statesmen was too high:
> ten million slain, a million tons of steel,
> the red wet smell of young men in the sky;
> leagues and speeches, covenants and repeal,
> and poppies redder where men went to die:
> a statesman was a glory, but the Christ
> had cost no more of people sacrificed.

He said he thought it was good. He said it ought to be printed on bales of coarse paper and the men who led their nations to war ought to be forced to eat a pound or two every morning for breakfast. He seized a sheet and read aloud to her:

> "Nor had they any culture such as ours:
> I now allude to that wherein the rich
> are troubled by the proper size of dowers,

563

> the poor by misplaced pennies and the itch;
> where some lie swathed in silk in penthouse towers
> and some, alas, sleep naked in a ditch:
> the culture Bismarck's fingers held till lo,
> it crossed the Rhine to Tiger Clemenceau!"

Without waiting for her to make a response to it, he fled back to his room, thinking on the way of his Mormon heritage—of the gross presumption of the stronger males who took mates from the weak. It was done throughout the animal kingdom, of course, but only men had made it an act of God. In a frenzy he typed off the lines:

> And next a boar whom lechery had turned
> into a prophet married forty sows;
> and all the little runts rose up and spurned
> polygamy, swearing that the Law allows
> to each one wife, else had the Great Pig earned
> the name of traitor! Why let one espouse
> two score of females when the sexes are
> divided as evenly as peace and war?

He turned next to the Ten Commandments and parodied each; then turned, exhausted, to Apuleius, Swift, Aristophanes, Rabelais, Cervantes, Lucian. Swift, it seemed to him, had written the greatest of the satires, saying with the finality of genius all that any man could say. What, he wondered, lay behind satire?—how much emotional sickness, how many evasions. Swift had hated mankind and that meant chiefly that he had hated Swift. He had despised fraud and sham, liars and hypocrites, stupid moralists, cheap ideals, possibly because he had found them all in himself.

Lying on his bed Vridar tried to distill it all in a few lines and at last tasted these over and over, as he liked to taste the Odes of Keats:

> If you could see me as I am
> you'd slay me with an epigram;
> if I could see you as you are
> I'd wonder what you're living for.

That didn't say it, not perfectly, but he was worn out now, he would sleep, there would be another day.

VI

He kept writing satire because it was his strength, it refreshed and restored his wits. Besides a full course of study, he was rewriting parts of his thesis, reading books to prepare for his final examinations, and memorizing dates until he would know a thousand of them. One day that great man, the chairman of his department, the one he had asked to judge him, put a hand on his shoulder and said, "You're working too hard. Get more rest." When Vridar turned away his eyes were misted. For the first time in his life he realized a fundamental truth about himself, that he was seeking a father-image.

Thought of the final examination almost paralyzed him. A woman candidate had fainted dead away. A man had emerged looking as though made of chalk. Vridar would have to face not only the greatest scholars in his own department but in allied departments. He would be expected to have a general knowledge of Greek and Roman, Italian and German literatures, and of the histories of these peoples. He would be expected to have a general knowledge of philosophy in all its periods. "The Inquisition," one trembling student had said, "and we're all relapsed heretics." Vridar was reading eighteen hours a day and when words became meaningless he would write a few lines:

> All I could see from where I stood
> was three bootleggers making good.
> I turned and looked the other way
> and saw three smugglers in a bay.
> So with my eye I traced the line
> of Prohibition, wet and fine,
> from east to west till I was come
> back to where I'd started from;
> and all I saw from where I stood
> was more bootleggers making good.

"Forgive me, Edna Millay," he murmured. When the evening of his examination came, he was gaunt, white, and trembling. He drank strong tea, took aspirin, and sat on a bench, smoking, and hoping that the more formidable examiners would be ill. He was in fact afraid of all of them—of their vast learning, even more, of their poise. He drank more tea and took more aspirin and saying goodbye to Athene slipped away.

The examination lasted two hours. He was never able to recall clearly more than a few trivial things: with two or three witticisms, he had made the chairman and one or two others laugh; he had irked the famous Celtic scholar, who'd never liked him; he had stumbled on a passage in *Beowulf* that he knew as well as his own name. He was sent outside to wait, and stood in the large chamber where he had first met Athene. Then the chairman came out, his craggy face touched by humor, his magnificent eyes on Vridar as he strode over to him. He put an arm across Vridar's shoulders and gave him a little hug, saying that he was to receive his degree magna cum laude. Vridar was so staggered by this that he was hardly conscious of Thurman's words, "You read too much. Read less and think more." He felt Thurman's handclasp. Then, his eyes blinded, he swung and hastened away. Athene was waiting at a park bench. He threw himself at her feet, weeping —weeping and laughing, laughing and weeping, while convulsions from aspirin and tea ran through him. He gasped out to her that he was taking his degree with high honors! O Lord! He had not expected even a cum laude. He had expected to be flunked! But here he was, Vridar Hunter Ph.D. magna cum laude—a scrawny wretch of skin and bones shaking all over and doubting his senses. He became conscious then of pride in her voice, and he clasped her knees and said against her dress, "A man wants to be president, does he?—and then to conquer the world—and then to overthrow his Pa up in the sky. There is no limit to human vanity. To hell with the doctor of philosophy! I want to be a writer!"

"Vridar—"

"I don't want it!" he said, knocking tears from his eyes. "I want a garden, an orchard, two horses, a few hens, a berry patch—and let vanity have all its childish posturing in the pages of *Who's Who!* To hell with it."

"Doctor Hunter—"

He was on his feet, his arms flung wide. "Don't you dare! Don't you ever call me that, even in jest. I gave four years of my life to this degree, because I had a wife and two children and thought I owed it to them. There isn't much left of that, but here I am with the degree and high honors and I'd trade it all for Stevenson's epitaph."

"You're foolish," she said. "I want one too."

"A Ph.D?"

"I'll have one some day."

Vridar lit a cigarette and they walked through the park. He tried to think of himself as a Doctor of Philosophy now but his mind turned to satire. The pompous strut and ceremony of graduation exercises in American schools always wearied him: when he took his Bachelor's degree, and later, his Master's, he had been excused, pleading sickness in the first and unavoidable absence in the second. On the second occasion he had sat in the audience with Dennis and had had to hide his face in his coat to muffle the sounds of his mirth. The President, robed in black and looking as stiff as he might have looked if his skin had been poured full of concrete, got mixed in his Latin; was prompted by a fluttering and anxious assistant; got mixed again and then abandoned Latin and fled into English. Vridar wondered why human vanity indulged in what seemed to him to be silly rigmaroles of conduct—of the solemn and outlandish dignity of apes, some as grand goblins and kleagles, or as gaudy regents of Church and State—or as professors, deans, and a president, robed in medieval black and looking as grave and unimportant as owls. It was, he knew, the heritage of primitive customs, all darkly related to prayer wheels and euchologies, exorcisms and cabals and golden calves. . . .

Was all that, he wondered, the buried life that Matthew Arnold had written of? For see us, he thought: a people pretending to be civilized, yet in our blood are mumbo jumbo and voodoo, the evil eye and death lights and fetishism—and that is what it was, the fetish. Everywhere under the surface was the fetish. What had Maitland said?—"We study the day before yesterday, in order that yesterday may not paralyze today, and today may not paralyze tomorrow." As though study had removed the paralysis! What had a great sociologist said?—"In probably no region of personality do we find so many residues of childhood as in the religious attitudes of adults." The childhood of the race, he meant. He had sometimes tried to see himself with a rabbit's foot in his pocket, or a horseshoe above his door, but saw himself now with a cardboard hood on his head, running through the dark after a witch and pausing to lynch a Negro. He shuddered. As long as they kept all the fetishism in commencement exercises, why pass laws against lynching?

He wrote to the president, asking to take his degree in absentia. The reply, a curt note, said he'd not be allowed to take his degree in absentia, even if he were in China. So for three dollars he rented a gown of black and gold and purple; and for five dollars he bought a hood because nowhere could he rent one. "Think," he cried angrily to Athene, "of the books I could have bought with the five I paid for that God damned thing! Heine's complete works in German cost me less, with half of Goethe thrown in." Long before the exercises began, some of the doctors strutted about the campus, looking to Vridar like justices of a supreme court. They were a little self-conscious but oh, they were proud! Families and friends stood in awe and watched them, and in not a single face could Vridar see a flicker of amusement. Also garbed, he felt too ridiculous for words.

He met Abraham Isaac Smith, a Mormon professor from Wastach College. Abe had a neat patch of hair on his upper lip; he walked with the dignity of an earl. While looking at him, Vridar thought of another Wasatch professor who, on taking his doctorate, had sent Christmas cards with Ph.D. after his name. He thought of the faculty rosters in university and college catalogs:

John Brown Doe, A.B., A.M., Ph.D.

What envy in those without the doctor's degree, what condescension in those with it!

"I suppose you're feeling pretty damned silly," he said to Abe.

"Silly? Why should I feel silly?"

"You look like something out of the Middle Ages."

As solemn as an owl, Abe looked at the folds of purple lying across his arm. "Did you buy your gown?"

"Oh Lord no."

"You should have. You'll need it in the Wasatch faculty parades."

"Those parades will get along without me," Vridar said. Abe gave him a sharp look.

The address to the graduates was given by M. Jusserand. An ambassador now, Jusserand had formerly been a scholar and for some of his writings Vridar had felt warm esteem. His admiration for the man died in the next hours. Jusserand, a small fat toad of a man with a goatee and eyes bugged out, pitched into wild shrill abuse of Germany and an almost tearful defense of France. He said the United States and France were sisters—and Vridar wondered why people gave sex to lands, continents, oceans, mountains, rivers. There was a deep truth in it that he would try to dig out.

Jusserand, it seemed to Vridar, was so wildly foolish in his patriotism, so sure that France was the beacon of Europe, the haven of the oppressed and the hope of the world, that after a few minutes he could stand no more of it. Bowing low with paper and pencil, he began to write. Using the frame of "Kubla Khan" he wrote a satire on France and Germany and the League of Nations. Kickapoo Klac devised a peace between the two old feudists, and treaties and mandates and a league; but nothing worked out according to Woodrow Wilson-Kickapoo's plans. Affairs went from bad to worse until

> Fragments of treaties then tumbled down
> as large as an ordinary town;
> and the Little Entente then waltzed and sang
> till Italy smote it with a bang.

567

> The Rhine, the same but for a little red,
> and as calm as any boundary could be,
> gathered the League of Nations to its bed
> and flowed away serenely to the sea. . . .

He would write, and then peer hard at M. Jusserand, wondering how a scholar could bug his eyes and grow apoplectic over a matter so partisan as love of country —which he began to see now was another aspect of the father-image. He was bored stiff by the time he came to the conclusion:

> A moral, sir, is here for you:
> A German said scat, a Frenchman jeered.
> Another war now comes in view,
> as Jusserand weeps into his beard.

The next day he had to leave for home and his sons, and he felt loneliness that was almost unendurable when he stood with Athene on the bridge near the railway station, looking down at an ugly river that was only a sewer. Athene had been granted a scholarship and was to remain in Chicago to pursue her studies. They would both be lonely, he said; and she said quickly that they would both be working hard. She began to weep softly, and he could feel his own eyes misting over. He would rather have died than have left her, but it was a matter not of what they wanted to do but of what duty compelled them to do. Remembering his brother's scathing words, he had said to her, "We'll do what it takes the most courage to do." They both knew that separation would take the most courage, for they would be apart a year, two years, or more. Sobbing quietly, she begged him not to work too hard.

Trying to control his voice, he whispered at her ear, "Don't weep. I don't want to take with me a picture of you in tears."

She glanced at him. "You're weeping, too."

Vridar put an arm around her and tried to hide from her the sudden rush of dark emotions. He looked at the station clock. "It'll be only a year," he said but he knew that the year would be an eternity. "You'll be far along to your doctorate when I see you again."

Athene was not an impulsive person like him, but she now touched her lips to his ear and whispered, "Please do nothing rash!"

"I promise," he said. He turned her to face him and tilting her head up looked into her eyes. They were beautiful eyes—wide apart, hazel green, intelligent, steady. He drew her to him, whispering against her hair, "Darling, we'll work it out."

"Yes!"

"We'll both be strong."

"Yes!"

He glanced again at the clock, but his eyes were now so wet that he couldn't see the time. Then he heard a train whistle. He folded her in close and kissed over her wet face and lips and over her beautiful hair. Then he swung away from her and ran but turned once to see her standing alone on the bridge. It took absolutely every iota of courage and strength he had to keep from running back to her—to turn toward the station and run again.

In the long journey westward he sat with his typewriter and the ironic muse save when he slept or ate sandwiches from his bag. He had so abused himself in the past months that he was ill. He had so many pains that he was afraid he had impaired some of his organs. Thinking of doctors, he typed:

A pang and a groan; a gulping of pills
and tonics and pastes; a dark wild hope;
a clear calm voice with nothing in it
professionally talking of aches and ills.
A prayer and a moan and a frantic clinging
to a lance of light, and far bells ringing.
Then a form bent low with a stethoscope
and a calm voice saying, "In another minute. . . ."

Hour after hour he had to pour out the bitter or scathing lines to save his sanity. He had to write to keep from thinking of 5622 Ellis, the morgue, the hospital, the furnace; and of Athene on the bridge. After he arrived in Salt Lake City, he never dared relax for a moment the vigil of mind over heart. He had been insane in his time, and he knew all the signs when the old lunacy was about to engulf him and obliterate his mind. It was as though he lived with a lunatic, sharply watching every move, anticipating every impulse toward violence, rebuking every moment of loneliness, crushing at its instant of starting every moment of passionate grief. He knew well that if he once surrendered to the great heartache that threatened every day to overpower him, he would be forever lost.

He found a room in a house where a tall gray woman lived alone with an imbecile son. The son, a man of thirty, was a dwarfed creature with hideous teeth and abnormally long arms. He loved gaudy things—crimson suspenders, purple ties, pink shirts and green trousers, yellow socks and red shoes. Every day he was allowed to dress in his most splendid regalia and strut up and down stairs and through the rooms, stuttering and gesticulating and caressing his brilliant colors. He helped Vridar to keep a grasp on life.

"Hello there," Vridar would say, and two small stupid eyes would stare at him. Two short thick hairy hands would smooth the pink shirt. A thick tongue would try to express the one hunger that consumed him. "Gu-gu-gu-girl!"

"Girl, my eye. What would you do with a girl?"

"Gu-gu-gu-gurl!"

"I wish you had an imbecile in the house with you," Vridar wrote Athene. "He reduces my egoism to nothing. When I come home, saturated with gloom and woe, there he is, a gorgeous spectacle of mindless happiness, stuttering in a mirror and admiring himself. God Almighty, how he wants a girl! His small hog-eyes simply glow with lust. His thing seems always to be up. If I don't respond to his girl utterings, he flies into one hell of a fury and wants to murder me. If I show him a picture of a lovely girl, he stutters with lustful joy and slobbers all over his pink shirt and keeps poking a finger at her pubic area. Apparently no male can be so stupid as not to know where to find it. All in all this idiot is almost enough to turn the mind of anyone who observes him away from lustful thoughts for life. . . ."

Vridar was teaching again but not as formerly. He still felt that teaching should be noble work, but to the classroom now he took a sardonic mind and a biting tongue. His students seemed not to know what to make of him. They did not know that under his mask he was so shy and frightened that he felt ill; so unsure of himself that he lived in chronic despair. They did not know that often before he could screw up his courage to face them he would go to the men's room and try to urinate when there was no need; or waste the ten or fifteen minutes before classtime looking at a clock, opening and shutting books, opening and closing drawers in his desk and making such an ass of himself that he could think of himself only as the world's worst fool.

Not many weeks passed before he was in trouble. One day in class a girl with a lovely innocent face asked him a question. "Dr. Hunter, don't you believe in God?" He had looked at her, and the class had waited. Most of these students were Mormons.

"Why do you ask?"

"I just wondered. I don't think you do."

Vridar turned to the blackboard and wrote on it:

> The proofs of the existence of God have made
> many men atheists—Joubert

To the girl he said: "In schools supported by public taxes, we're not allowed to discuss such matters. There are perhaps a thousand definitions of God. The concept means different things for different people. But let's not go into all that."

Two days later he received from a powerful business man in the city this curt note:

> Dear Sir:
> I am told you devoted an hour, or period, last week or recently in your class telling, according to your view point, why Jesus is not divine. Please advise me if this is so.

With amazement Vridar read the letter again, and a third time. He had come headon with the problem every American teacher had to face—to be honest with his students, or to dodge. He wrote Athene, asking her what he should do. She replied that he might tell the business man what he conceived to be the purpose of a university.

Vridar thought of the matter several days and then wrote:

> It is not my habit to declare my personal opinions in the classroom. I have no students who know what I believe on any subject but some of them may cherish unsupported convictions.
> It may interest you to know what I conceive to be my duty as a teacher—to arouse my students to an intelligent interest in contemporary affairs; to awaken them to the possibilities of their own minds; to suggest to them the folly in believing something merely because someone else believes it. I want them to think, not as I think, and not necessarily as you think, but as they must honestly think after they have examined the evidence.
> Of importance to them is fearless and honest inquiry into the facts and superstitions of life. To that end it is imperative to be acquainted with the principal currents in modern thought. It would be shameless

perversion of my function as a teacher if I were to deny to them the sources of the knowledge they seek. One of my students did manifest an interest in the historicity of Jesus and I suggested two books by distinguished scholars, one of whom supports and one of whom denies it. If I erred in that, then the college I serve errs in calling itself an institution of learning.

He sent a copy of his letter to the president. The business man ignored it. The president wrote:

I am not writing you in any sense of criticism for what you have said and done, because I do not know the nature of it and would not presume to say until I knew the facts. My tendency always is to freedom of discussion in the classroom. At the same time I am calling your attention to the law so that you will not say anything that will bring down criticism on you.

The letter filled Vridar with misgivings. What was the law? He thought he saw an end of him in the academic world, at least here, and the thought was bitter, for he had worked so hard and long to qualify himself for teaching.

He stayed off the subject of religion, he tried to be prudent, but he blundered again. There came to him the editor of the school's literary journal. She had a short story. In the story was "my gawd" and this, she said, would never pass the censors. The author would not take the word out.

"He won't use my gosh? Gosh and God mean the same thing. Heck means hell, gewhiz means Jesus, gol-darn means God damn. Don't the censors know these things?"

"They won't let that pass unless I have support."

"They want your stories to say bad woman for whore, female dog for bitch, agent provocateur for pimp?"

The editor made a face. She was not amused. She had an angular frame, a strong chin, and hair on her upper lip. She said she would publish the story with the word in it if Vridar would back her up.

He said he would.

"You'll have to put it in writing."

At an office machine he typed these words:

Dear Miss Arnold:
"My gawd" is a vulgarism but surely it is not too offensive in a college journal. I suggest that you let it stand. If there are objections, refer the purists to me.

So ignorant was Vridar of the inner workings of a small college supported by public taxes that he expected to hear no more of the matter. His astonishment was boundless when he received from the censors a summons to their office. He found himself facing three hostile men.

The chairman said, "Am I to understand that you approved of this profanity?" He was tapping a page of the literary journal.

Startled to find a full professor using "approved of," Vridar looked the man up and down. "I approved the use of my g-a-w-d." He spelled the word.

"Are we to understand that you approve of profanity in a college paper?"

571

"Would my gosh have been acceptable to you?"

"Why yes, I should say so, yes."

"My gosh and my gawd mean exactly the same thing. Do you think the Almighty is so simple as to be fooled?"

The chairman reddened. "And just who do you have in mind by the purists?"

Vridar paused to note the man's grammar. "Censors," he said.

There was silence. Then Vridar rose to his feet, saying, "If you establish a suffocating paternalism over college students, you will only drive them off the campus, it seems to me. I can't see anything offensive in my gawd, particularly in a story that tries to offer an honest portrayal of life." He went to the door and turned.

"After this, Dr. Hunter, you'll leave such matters to the committee appointed to handle them."

"Is that all?"

"That is all."

Furious, Vridar went to his room. Almost at once the door was opened and the imbecile looked in. "Hello, Bob," Vridar said.

"Gu-gu-gu-gurl?"

"Bob, you should be a censor. You have just the brains for it."

"Gu-gu-gu-gurl!" said Bob, and grinned to show his bone-snags.

A few days later Vridar met the president on the campus. He liked Tom Lewis, a stout florid Welshman with small twinkling eyes and blunt speech.

"You have a student named Edith Sedgwich?"

"Yes sir. Why?"

"You advised her not to read the Bible?"

"O Lord no. I advised her to read it. Like most Christians she knows nothing about it."

Tom Lewis regarded Vridar steadily a few moments and said, "You know Ronald Martin?"

"He's one of my students."

"He was. His father has taken him to another school." Lewis stepped close to Vridar and spoke quietly. "When I taught sociology before coming here, I taught evolution and got away with it. I said I'd present all the theories. All the bright students ended up believing it. Hunter, your trouble is lack of prudence. You can teach anything if you know how."

"Maybe I'll learn how."

But Vridar was not and would never be a prudent man. If a student came to his office, seeking advice, and seemed to be intelligent and sincere, Vridar went right to the point.

"My people are all Mormons," one young man said. "But I can't see it. Can you?"

"All my people on both sides are Mormons. Some of them on both sides came over the plains with Brigham Young. My brother and I left the Church long ago. But I've no doubt it's a good faith for a lot who believe it."

"Isn't it stupid?"

"Oh, come now. You mean it smells too much of babies and sugar beets?"

A few days later Vridar was summoned to the president's office. Tom Lewis was

572

in an ugly mood. His face was red and mottled, his eyes had lost their twinkle.

"Listen, Hunter, what do I hear now?"

"I can't imagine."

"Have you been telling your classes that Mormonism smells of sugar beets and babies?"

"No sir."

"You didn't? The Mormon president has been up to see me and he raised Cain. Just what in hell did you say?"

"I made some such remark privately to a student who wanted to talk to me about his religion. I didn't know he'd run off and blab."

"Good God, Hunter, what a thing to say! Do you have to try to be witty about a religion? Smells of babies and sugar beets! Do you expect to talk that way and teach here? You're giving me altogether too much trouble. I have work to do. I can't spend all my time talking to Mormon leaders and outraged taxpayers."

"I realize that."

"All right, then. After this watch your tongue."

Vridar did watch his tongue. Teachers in the deep South, he had heard, hardly dared say anything at all. In the Mormon empire, they did not dare say much. Even in the Northeast Robinson, Nearing, and some other distinguished professors had been dismissed. It was the winter of 1926 and the country seemed to be swinging away from the idealism of Woodrow Wilson, disillusioned by a foolish crusade to make the world safe for democracy.

If a student came for advice, Vridar would say, "I'm sorry but there are subjects which it is not prudent to discuss with you. You students run and tell your parents and your parents run to the president."

"I promise to tell no one. Please, Dr. Hunter! My people are Mormons—"

"Not another word. I'll not listen to it."

Off the campus Vridar talked, and not always discreetly. He was invited to read a paper to a liberal club, and chose as his subject the function of education in a democracy. His audience was small—doctors, lawyers, merchants, most of them Unitarians. After the paper was read, the discussion turned to sex and a doctor spoke of girls who worked their way through college. Some of them, he said, were plain gold diggers.

Vridar said that reminded him of a student who, for a course in sociology, had made a study of prostitution in the city. This student said a half-dozen college girls were supporting themselves in part by selling their love. The doctor said he imagined that such a condition prevailed everywhere. A lawyer said that any gold-digging girl was a harlot. It didn't take three dollars. A gift would do. "If a man takes a girl out and buys her candy and flowers, and with his favors seduces her, she's a whore, isn't she?"

Such whores as that, the doctor said, would be common on any campus. He said slyly, "Perhaps we've all given flowers, with something in mind."

Vridar forgot the matter until out of the blue came a note from the president:

> Did you or did you not in an address before the Delphic Club make the statement that some of the girls in Wasatch College are harlots?

Flabbergasted, Vridar's first impulse was to resign. His second was to go at once and face Tom Lewis in his office. His third was to write it down, so that he would have a record of it.

> In our discussion [he wrote] I said that a student of mine (John Ellerton is the name) stated in a thesis that a half-dozen girls on our campus are supporting themselves in part by selling their love. I did not ask to see Mr. Ellerton's evidence. I did not say that I thought his statement is true. The members of the Club found nothing incredible in it . . . .

From the president came a short angry reply:

> It seems to me very strange that a member of our faculty, with your dignity and standing, should repeat the word of an itinerant student and cast insult at the fair womanhood of this school!

Vridar read it and groaned. There it was, the Nordic tradition of chivalry, the fair blossoms of purity, the virgins, the mothers of men! A whore in an American university? Unthinkable! Whores were another order of being who took men behind billboards. All university girls were virgins; or if not virgins they were married; and if neither virgin nor wife, they were still somehow the fair womanhood.

In a long and carefully worded reply Vridar made a statement that brought matters to a head:

> Your position is, I understand, a most difficult one. You have to placate the outraged prejudice and stupidity of a community, and you have also to stand behind academic freedom and the integrity of your faculty. These are two positions that it is almost impossible to reconcile. . . .

Then came the thunderbolt:

> I have carefully noted the letter in which you accuse the president of moral cowardice.

Vridar was so distressed that he could neither eat nor sleep. He wrote to Athene, saying that he might as well resign and find another kind of work. He walked the streets. One night he met a colleague, William Morton, member of an old Mormon family. Morton was whimsical, tactful, shrewd.

"Vridar, you look troubled. What's the matter?"

"Nothing."

"No man can look so sad over nothing. Getting along all right in your teaching?"

"No, I guess not."

"Aren't you taking it too seriously? Like a drink?"

"No, thanks."

"Well, cheer up. Nothing is important enough to make a woman cry, or a man take long walks alone."

Returning to his room, Vridar lay on his bed, trying to think his way through it. Letters from Athene implored him to be prudent. But what was prudence? He recalled how, when he first entered this college, he was speechless with awe at the wonder of it. He had thought that all college teachers were men and women of great honesty, courage, and character. It had been bitter disillusionment to learn that they were not. Should he try to be one, or should he learn to be a bland and urbane stinker, playing the game?

As a student he had seen of the academic world only what a student sees. As an instructor five years ago he had been without professorial rank and had not sat in the councils. This year he learned what went on behind the closed doors. He still found it difficult to believe that the teachers of a nation's youth could be sly petty tyrants who fought among themselves for privilege and prestige, who stooped again and again to deliberate malice, or who wasted hours in grave deliberation over trivial matters.

A hundred and fifty men and women were called to a special meeting because Henry Roe, a senior, had petitioned the faculty for the privilege to graduate with only five and seven-tenths hours of physical education, instead of the required six. "You have heard the petition," said Tom Lewis. "What is the pleasure of the faculty?"

Dr. Allerbeck was recognized. He said: "Mr. Roe has been a student of mine in several classes. He's a good student. It wasn't possible to arrange his schedule of study so that he could complete his physical education requirement. I move that we grant the petition."

"It has been moved—"

"Mr. President?"

"Professor Ames."

"I question the wisdom of establishing such a precedent. If we allow one student to graduate minus three-tenths of an hour, another may wish to graduate minus a half. After a while they'll want to graduate without any at all." There was laughter. Ames looked around him and smiled. "Then some students may wish to graduate without fulfilling the requirement in some subject more important than physical education. In physics, say, or botany. To make an exception of physical education merely because it is not important—"

"Mr. President!"

"Professor Ames has the floor."

But Becken, a short scrappy man, whose eyes looked as though sparks would be flying from them, was not to be put aside. "I'd like to know what Professor Ames means by saying physical education has no importance." He paused and a hush fell. The more timid faculty members looked toward the windows. "In my opinion it's of greater importance than any other subject. Physical education—"

But Ames, professor of physics, was speaking again. "I agree with Professor Becken, who teaches physical education, and so must believe in it—"

"I resent that!" cried Becken, glaring at him.

"Any young person," Ames went on, "can get his exercise off the campus. Will Professor Becken tell us just what the value is to Student Roe of another three-tenths of an hour lifting his legs up and down in a gym?"

Some of the professors were grinning. Some of them, Vridar had learned, liked these bitter feuds between departments.

"Mr. President!"

"I wish two of you would sit down," Tom Lewis said. "Professor Ames, do you yield to Dr. Saunders?"

"I yield," said Ames and sat.

Saunders was another scrappy teacher of physical education. His use of the English language always brought smiles to faces. "Puffesser Ames asks, as I understand him, is physical education necessary. Mebbe he doesn't know much about physiology. Mebbe he thinks a rule in physics is more important than a sound heart. Mebbe—"

The argument ran for another hour. Two hundred hours of faculty time were given to the matter. The petition was granted.

Vridar marveled at the feuds. Some of the professors detested one another with a candor as plain as their bald heads. The dean of education and the dean of science had long been enemies. On the side of the first stood many of those who taught the social sciences and the arts, and on the side of the second stood every physical scientist in the school. Vridar rather liked both men. James Monson, dean of education, was a quiet devout Mormon, with a pink bald head and a round pink face. William Tergaud, dean of sciences, was hot-tempered, impatient, and stinging. He saw little sense in what was called art, and for pedagogy his contempt was simply unutterable. For him life was scientific, or it was morbid. Vridar admitted to himself that those who taught the physical sciences were far less neurotic than most of the other instructors. He wondered why this was so.

At every opportunity Tergaud buried his witty harpoons in his pink sensitive foe. He overlooked no chance to tell what he thought about graphs and charts, intelligence tests and courses in how to teach; and when he grew weary or his wit failed him, other scientists rose to the attack. One afternoon there was almost a rout. Dean Monson, dignified, soft-spoken, but implacable, had placed before the faculty the program of his department. He asked for more money and an expansion of facilities. Albert Duncan, professor of chemistry, was the first to rise to his feet. He was lean and aggressive and given to scathing diatribe. After making a brutal attack on pedagogy and all that it stood for, he closed with the remark: "There are some of us who feel that in this college we have education—and something else for which I can think of no better term than pedagogy. If pedagogy continues to win popular approval, education in this nation will come to an end."

For a few moments there was silence. Here and there a professor put a hand to his face and smiled behind the hand. A few of them looked through windows, as though suddenly interested in the world outside. Up the pink neck and face of Monson blood crept like dark shadow, and slowly, wearily, like one sick of scientists and their cult, he rose to his feet. His remarks, though touched by anger, were not personal.

This was the most bitter feud but was by no means the only one. Every chairman fought for the prestige and advantage of his department and actually believed, it seemed to Vridar, that his department was the most important one in the college. The success of departments was measured, not by scholarship, not by the esteem or want of it by which they were held in other schools, but by the size of their enrollment. The president looked on small departments with suspicion. There was

576

that of ancient languages: its chairman was a shy and studious man but possibly, Vridar suspected, the greatest scholar in the school. But this man stuttered, he was unpopular with students, and his department lived from year to year under threat of extinction. In contrast stood the professor of geology: students flocked to him to hear his tirades against cigarettes and his boast that no smoker could climb to the top of a mountain as fast as he could; his tearful blessings upon young marriages and large families (for he was a Mormon); or his vulgar story of his own courtship.

After one of Tock's harangues, a girl came to Vridar with tears in her eyes. Wiping at her lids, she said that maybe she was a silly thing, but Professor Tock had made most of them weep. Oh, he was wonderful! His talks were so inspiring!

Vridar looked at her; observed the patches of lipstick stain on the handkerchief she used on her eyes; noted a gold brace on her upper front teeth; and waited.

"Today," she gasped, tears again flooding her eyes and spilling down over her face, "today it was—it was young love! He is like a father and oh so nice! I wish you was that nice. . . . Ohhh! You know what he does?"

"I can't imagine."

She wiped hard at both eyes and gave him a brave smile. She said that when Professor Tock had completed his lecture, he stood at the door and shook the hands of his students as they passed out. And oh dear, he was crying too! He actually was. "But you," she said, "you're cynical."

"He must be a very remarkable teacher," Vridar said. And inside he said to himself, Be prudent, damn you.

"Oh, he is!" she said, her eyes wet and glowing. "I never liked science till this year. Now I love all the rocks." She turned sly and cold then and looked at him rather hard. "You don't love people, do you?"

Be prudent, he thought. Damn you, be prudent.

Or there was Ellen Dobram, professor of speech and dramatics. It was said that she had been a polygamous wife and had a child hidden away somewhere. She would engage for her department no man who smoked, and she looked down her long thin nose at anyone who ate pepper or drank coffee or tea. She was another Mormon. For the most part she employed only her satellites. Her specialties were culture and the Boston dialect. She loved to give public readings, and it was said that once when impersonating Juliet she had swooned with such ardor that she fell off the balcony. When Ellen rose in faculty meetings, far more intent on her dialect than on what she was saying, professors exchanged sly winks and some began to doodle.

Or there was John Bleecker, professor of French and chairman of the department; a man who said again and again to his students, "When I was in Paris I asked myself, If a Frenchman can speak French perfectly why can't I? I did. I do. I've been told my French is more Parisian than that of the Parisians." He was a Mormon, too, and another dictator who employed none but satellites, if they could be found. He had a new way of teaching languages and forced all those in his department to use it, as well as his own textbook. He had hired a brilliant Jew who wished to teach French his own way, and use a text of his own choosing.

577

Arnstein was soon in trouble. Hearing that the man was to be fired, Vridar went to see him and found himself facing a sensitive and rather sophisticated person.

Hearing that Vridar had come out of sympathy, Arnstein shrugged. A hand as hairy as an ape's reached for a cigarette. It was nothing, he said. Bleecker taught French by one method, he by another. He was to be dismissed.

"Fired, you mean?"

One word was as good as another, wasn't it? The president had called him in and said, "Arnstein, you'll be recommended for appointment next year if you give me your resignation first."

"Why, the stinking coward!" Vridar cried. "You don't mean it?"

That, Arnstein said, was the way the thing was commonly handled in American schools. Nobody then can say that a man was fired. His record is clean.

"You're not going to do it?"

"Why not? Jews aren't wanted here. Besides, I've no taste for brawls."

"I wouldn't do it," Vridar said. "I'd fight it."

"You," Arnstein said, politely, coldly, "aren't a Jew."

In his room Vridar sat in thought. By all the gods, what was this academic world anyway! He told himself that rather than stoop to such moral cowardice he'd return to the Antelope hills and follow a plow—or take up bootlegging again— for he was beginning to see that in the ranks of the respectable there were worse creatures than bootleggers. He wished he had a pint of whisky. He wanted to get drunk. He began a letter to Athene, "I can see the end of me in the academic world, if all faculties are like this one. I'm trying to be prudent but I'd rather die in a whorehouse than live at the level of some of these people. . . ." Then he tore the sheet into shreds and lay back, saying, No, no, it's the ironic muse I need now! He began to put words together:

> H. G. Wells, only the other night
> I saw your utopia like a great ring of light. . . .
> but I was pretty tight. . . .

VII

During this academic year Vridar taught a full load and wrote two novels and a pile of ironic verse. He took walks up the mountains, for he loved mountains. He wrote many letters to Athene, letters to his sons and parents, but no letter to his brother. He searched himself for motives and studied his dreams. And month after month he studied his colleagues.

He was sitting in his tiny office one morning when the door was opened and a masklike face thrust itself inside. It had large pale blue eyes, a wide colorless mouth, a small nose. The mouth said:

"DIAMOND BRAND WALNUTS!"

The face withdrew. This was Max Ohm, an instructor in English and a specialist in whimsy and bombast. Vridar later learned that Max had poked his head into every office up and down the hall and had uttered the same words, because in an advertisement he had read, Diamond Brand Walnuts are good, tell your friends.

Once in a while Vridar accepted dinner at the Larmonds. George Larmond had been a teacher of English a few years, after returning from a Mormon mission, but had switched to law. He was a fat bald man of thirty, with a very large forehead, bulging pale eyes, a rather foolish dished nose, a full sensual mouth and heavy jowls. He had a logical but not an intuitive mind. He believed in man-woman Love with a capital letter; and in moonlight and Walter Raleigh's cloak in the mud—a solid middle-class bore who loved more than anything else to go at day-light to the state prison to see criminals shot through the heart. On hearing George confess this, Vridar thought of Thackeray's words after going to an execution: "I feel myself ashamed at the brutal curiosity which took me to that brutal sight." Thackeray had not been able to forget the calloused indifference of the people who watched, or the expression on the pale face of the condemned man. Thackeray was an artist. George was what would later be called a Babbitt.

His wife was older by six or eight years. Married before, she had had no children by either husband, nor ever would have a child, because her uterus had been removed. She was intuitive, sharp, bitterly unhappy, brutally malicious, but could be charming when she wished to be and had an infectious laugh.

Vridar took them the manuscript of one of his novels. They told him when he saw them next that the story had so offended them that they had hidden it in a closet. This was Freudian cant and phobia and hysteria at its worst and had no relationship to life. Why, George demanded, shaking a fist at Vridar, did the hero say that most American men thought of love without a petticoat on? Couldn't he express it poetically? He liked wholesome books, George said, fixing Vridar with bulging blue eyes behind thick lenses. He liked books that raised people to the stars, not the Drieserian kind that dragged them down into the sewers.

Maxine was the kind of woman whose eyes darted swiftly from face to face, reading the emotion in them before making up her mind what her high-pitched voice would say. Her gaze now swept back and forth between Vridar and her husband.

"George is right," she said at last. "Your story's obscene."

Vridar looked at them in turn. He had heard these two tell jests filthy enough to choke a condor. This evening at dinner there were two other guests and the four of them swapped unprintable things about the body's natural functions. In a milder one the male guest had said that he envied George his philosophic calm. "Every bone in his body is restful and at peace."

"Every bone but one," George had said. Maxine had exploded with such force that she had blown half an olive across the table. When George laughed, he laughed all over: he now sat back and shook like a great mound of jelly wrapped in expensive broadcloth. He wiped a tear from his eye.

"I'd like to know," Vridar wrote to Athene, "how intelligence can live in such lush moral imbecility. Why does George become so furious at me because I try to portray a sickly idealist (myself, of course), yet every time I meet him have some stinking pieces of privy filth to tell? Ah, and he tells it with such lewd lustful licking of his lips, as though as a male he spent half his time on hands and knees.

579

"Well, I've finished Amy Lowell's book about the tragic Keats—his renouncing of Fanny and going to Rome to die, alone; and his patience in dying. That sort of thing makes up for a lot of Georges. I was moved deeper than tears by the pathos of it and I wanted to take a kick at Amy's big New England hindend for trying to prove that Keats did not have syphilis. To whom could it matter but the Amys? I then turned to a bit of Tschaikowsky: on his deathbed he looked at those around him and said, Gentlemen, I'm afraid I'm an unconscionable time dying. How fine, if he said it. With so many terrors in me, I'm afraid I shall never be able to say it. I've been reading about Liszt, Grieg, Wagner, Beethoven, and others all of them so mad that they occupied abnormal worlds. Knowing what madness there is under my mask I dare hope at times that I have a great talent but look at the age of me with nothing accomplished! Keats, Shelley and how many more never lived to be as old as I am now, yet what glories they left upon the page!

"I try to look normal but I can't. People remark on my appearance—so many of my students have said how sad I am, what haunted eyes I have, and then I turn for strength to the only strength I have now, the bitter muse:

A RADIO ANNOUNCER GOES TO HEAVEN

A lunch of snow-white milk and honey,
a small weird sense of feeling funny;
a startled look at his old wife who
lived forty years after he was through;
 and a stroll to learn if the aches and ills
 of heaven were cured by Phooier's Pills.

The angels were looking a bit rococo
and filling their tanks with Standard's Conoco.
One played a harp, one sang a ditty,
and one blond chicken looked gol-darn pretty.
 He saw an enemy whom once he feared
 and Moses stark naked except for his beard.

To life, he thought, it was a hell of a sequel
to make all the angels exactly equal.
It was heaven, they said, but where were the Packards,
where were the billboards and posters and placards?
 He said to the Lord, If I had my way
 we'd develop this country and make it pay.

He looked again, for he had not seen
a sign of Lux or of Listerine.
No Crazy Crystals or M J B,
No Maxwell House, no Lipton's Tea.
 No Lucky Strikes and no girl with a pose
 ardent and eager within its clothes.

He sought God out and he said, Great Sir,
we need some testimonials, some whirr!
I know a man for a thousand dollars
will speak right up for Arrow Collars.
 I mean it's pretty confounded surprising
 you don't do a damned bit of advertising!

"My dear Athene," he went on, "your dreams worry you and now they worry me, for they sound to me like birth phantasies. I hadn't known that you want a child so deeply; or is your subsconscious reproaching you for that abortion? Are you such a mystic that you think a child was slain? My own dreams I try to probe but much of the symbolism eludes me. I read the other day that in Europe there is a legend that most of Cinderella's adventures arose from the fact that she spurned her brother's erotic advances. After reading that, I had a dream in which (I cannot doubt this, nor wish to) Cinderella and my sister were one. Contributing also to the dream was a statement by a psychologist that the guilt-feeling in Orestes, which his sister Iphigenia takes away by touching him, had come from his touching his sister; but I don't know if it is implied that one incestuous act cured another!

"My novel came back yesterday from Mencken with a short note saying that his eyes had failed him so that he could not read it. I should know better than to presume on the time of a busy critic but should have liked it better had he said, My dear scribbling ass, thousands of young upstarts like you ask me to read their stories. I've no time for it. Six publishers to date have said no, so I assume that my story must have a deep illness. When one declines I get all through me such a sick haggard lost feeling that I'm convulsed by nausea and would like nothing better than to be dead. This means, I suppose, a very deep doubt of my talent; and when I consider the background out of which I have come, and that out of which most writers have come (so often with wealth and the best of education) I find no reason why I shouldn't doubt.

"I heard today another astonishing thing about Pres. Tom Lewis. This Max Ohm (it is freely rumored over the campus that he is a homosexual, whose current lover is an aviator) is doing an article about this college for the *American Mercury*. Lewis, hearing of it, called him in. Max says he couldn't have been sweeter if he had come headfirst out of a maple tree. He put an arm round me and I thought he was going to ask me to dinner. He said I'm a brilliant teacher. So lies are forced from the throats of presidents because they are afraid they'll be written about . . . . Made the mistake of going to the Larmonds' for dinner and they both pitched in. Vridar, you unspeakable egotist, you think you're a genius but you're only a dinky professor in a dinky school. Vridar, you bore us. Why don't you sink down to your size and relax? I was frightfully annoyed; but while they strove to exacerbate my hide off, I spoke inwardly, saying, Hunter, if they were to say, You're a great man, some day you'll shake the earth and knock the moon out of its orbit, why then you would feel, These people have minds! Stand up to it, **boy, and take it.**

"We were playing cards (I hate cards) and Maxine said, with the hauteur of a duchess who felt imminent bellyache, George dear, will you get my coat? Her coat was lying on the sofa where she sat, practically within reach. But George hopped up as though he were about to be knighted and draped the coat around her shoulders. When she pulled him down to give his fat cheek the touch of her thin lips, if not her devotion, her eyes, full of amusement and malice, looked at me as a wife for whom her husband is a boy and a bore; and with her throaty most charming laugh she said, Vridar, don't you think he's a darling?

"I think he's a damned towering ass, I said. Then the deluge. They both pitched

581

into me, and when I was able to break through I asked George if he was not aware that women of quality haven't much taste for cavaliers who spread their cloaks in mud? Zounds and furies! said George. Was I as backwoods as I sounded? asked Maxine. They have enough brains to know they're unhappy but not enough to look into the reasons. What, George asked, should he have done? Mon amie, get your own God damned coat. I said he reminded me of a big eager houseboy who carries roses home and quotes love verses from the woman's page in the local newspaper. I've observed that when a man talks that way to a husband, the wife (if she has the brains of a yak) looks at him with speculative eyes, wondering what kind of lover he is. They had told me earlier that George feels that his penis is abnormally short (or maybe it was Maxine who felt it, and I don't intend a pun) and fairly wears himself out trying to appease her ardor. This evening they assured me with faces almost reverent that their marriage is as indissoluble as that of Pickford and Fairbanks. Then out of the blue Maxine said, 'Honey, Vridar is right. You really *don't* understand women.'

"George was simply and completely astounded. 'I don't? . . . I don't understand *women?*' She called him honey again and said no. I felt pity for George then. He had been so sure that he knew all about women. The more I see of the Maxines, the more I do meditate on women and what they want. There must be a lot of them in this country emotionally halfdead, and many wholly so: with a fervor that is barely tepid even to the most sensitive finger (I intend no phallic symbol) and an imagination that hasn't absorbed even the most commonplace things around them. For them a man is a household article. Maxine always calls to my mind the Millay sonnet in which the woman is caustic about her under-position; and Becky's repeated statement that a man doesn't have to squat when he makes water. Deep currents are running down under and I suggest that you try to bring to the surface your own unbidden insights.

"This Ohm creature (among the ditties he hums through his nose, Mid Adeline and Alices though you may roam, be it ever so humble there's no place like Ohm) has a hugely developed sense of the diabolic. He is a man largely abandoned to mummery (because he's a homosexual?) Yesterday he thrust his expressionless face into offices up and down the hall to ask:

> "Did God tell her ere she went
> she had borne a president?
> Did God ever let her see
> little Calvin's destiny?"

"Those lines, I'm told, are from Edgar Guest's epitasis to Coolidge. Last fall Max ran a series on Red Grange, almost the most recent of American idols:

GRANGE IS CARRIED TWO MILES BY STUDENTS

The second:

GRANGE'S FOOTBALL JERSEY IS TO BE FRAMED

"By this time we were all expecting a third:
"There were three or four others before the conclusion:

582

GRANGE IS PRESENTED TO COOLIDGE

Will Jehovah let him see
little Calvin's destiny?

"This, he said, completed his course of lectures on contemporary American culture. Almost daily he thrusts his face in to make an announcement or ask a question. At the moment I recall these:

BRUCE BARTON SAYS JESUS WAS THE FOUNDER OF
MODERN BUSINESS
THE METROPOLITAN INSURANCE COMPANY SAYS
THAT MOSES WAS ONE OF THE GREATEST SALES-
MEN AND REAL-ESTATE PROMOTERS THAT EVER
LIVED
GLORIA SWANSON HAS MARRIED THE MARQUIS DE
LA CORDUROY

"Last week he gave what he called a snapshot course in American aesthetics. His first:

OFTEN A BRIDESMAID BUT NEVER A BRIDE

His slab of granite face the next morning said:

POOR EDNA'S CASE WAS REALLY A PATHETIC ONE

Of his ten 'lectures' I recall at the moment only one other:

I THINK HE'S QUOTING FROM SHELLEY

He has said in his solemn way that he is educating his colleagues. Some of them think him insane; some dismiss him as a schoolboy nuisance. I am reminded of the words of one of our philosophers. There is no other country, Santayana has told us, "in which people live under more overpowering compulsions . . . . Even what is best in American life is compulsory, the idealism, the zeal, the beautiful unison of great movements. You must wave, you must shout, you must push with the irresistible crowd: otherwise you will feel like a traitor, a soulless outcast . . . . in a country where all men are free, every man finds that most matters have been settled for him beforehand.

"Like me, Ohm is in trouble here. Donnaugh, his chairman, called him to the carpet the other day and Ohm's account of it goes like this:

> He called me to his office and I sensed at once that I was in the presence of another man of destiny. Ohm, he said, I hear unfavorable things about you. I looked as innocent as a priest with his hand in a woman's bodice. He then charged me with having said that the president of the Mormon Church thinks he's a little tin god.
> Oh, I did not, I said. With the candor of a diamond back looking into the eyes of a sparrow I said, Positively I did not. He had a dozen students, Donnaugh said, who would swear that I did. That I did what? I asked, not because my memory is so poor as because I wanted to hear the wonderful words again. That you

called the president of the Mormons a little tin god. I denied it again and demanded a jury trial.

You deny it? he asked, opening his Nordic blue eyes another inch. I deny it. I execrate it. Like Miniver Cheevy he thought and thought and thought about it. Ohm, you mean to tell me there's no truth in this, even though I have a dozen students who will swear you said it? No truth at all, I said, beginning to pity the man. His forehead was bursting with dew. I took pity on him. I took pity and threw it at him and it was like a halo round his head; and when I looked out I saw a star in the East, and three wise men walking across the campus.

Then what *did* you say? I said the president of the Mormon Church thinks he's a little tin Jesus.

"That's Maxwell Ohm for you. He sends stuff to Mencken's Americana; writes parodies of the Congressional Record; love poems that almost kill me; and sleeps with an aviator. He's popular with his students for the wrong reasons. He will stop in the middle of a lecture and groan as though in pain, his gaze turning to the outside world. For perhaps ten minutes he will stand motionless, every student looking at him—and with what amazement you can imagine. Or he will affect a sudden uncontrollable fury and smite his desk and demand in a high squeaky voice, Has the damned Sphinx ever found out what he thinks? Then he will stride out, leaving his students breathless.

"Am glad you liked the hatrack article in *Mercury*. It raised a great storm here, and because I asked to have it available to my students I'm in trouble again. Imagine a whore of one Christian sect taking her patrons into the cemetery of another! Writers can't contrive ironies so delicious. Ohm says that when he contemplates the exchange of amenities between the Catholics and Mormons he knows that mankind has a future.

"Ohm is a fine pianist. I was in his room the other day and he played something and asked me if I like it. I said it was one of my favorites. He took the sheet of music and with slow deliberation tore it in shreds; and turning on me the nastiest sneer I've ever seen he said, If you like it I know it's no good. I was furious but I said nothing. His aviator friend came in, a handsome rugged young man. I thought their attitude toward one another had a subtle intimacy in it, like that of lovers, and I recalled Ohm's statement earlier that sexual embrace with a woman was for the man only a poultice of warm guts. The statement shocked me, and shocks me again to record it; and reveals about this man more than I'll ever know. Would that be the common homosexual response to it?

"Publishers are amusing fellows [Vridar was writing far into the night]. One of them sends my novel back with the remark, Do not suppose that we never publish books that will not sell. As an instance he cited E. L. Grant Watson's *The Contracting Circle* of which he says that it is a far finer book than *A Passage to India* but so subtle that it could never sell. But note: Watson had published at least five books before this one. He cited Niven's *Justice of the Peace,* 'A book that has been hailed on both sides of the Atlantic as one of the great books of this century but which because of its ruggedness could not possibly sell.' Niven had published at least six novels and the one cited *is a reprint* and carries two prefaces, one by the ubiquitous Morley and one by his British twin, Walpole. He cited Updegraff's *Dancers in the Wind,* 'One of the most whimsical and charming books It has been my pleasure to read in a long time. But we knew this book would have no sale.' Updegraff had already published at least four books. I got Niven's hailed-on-both-sides-of-the-Atlantic masterpiece and bogged down in the first chapter. I struggled deep into it and decided that if this is great writing I should never have left the Antelope hills.

"Spring is here. I feel the old gypsy pulse in my blood and smell the open roads. Soon we'll meet again. I'm still a colossal ass but I think I'm making progress: self-pity is Ruskin's pathetic fallacy and seems to be the heart and soul of this nation's popular fiction. Can I ever get it all out of me? More important than that, can I keep it out of what I write? Richard Trench said to Monckton Milnes, 'I will own that from having worshiped false gods I am now an iconoclast.' But I must be more than that.

"You once asked if I had an incestuous fixation on my mother. I think not. She was too busy, and at her center too frozen, to give love and tenderness. Those yearnings in me were fixed on my sister, and hers on me, though she would deny it for she is an emotional halfwit. I feel that incestuous yearnings are not so much the trouble with many sons as the failure to come out of adolescence. I must come out, though sometimes feel that if you don't come out when you should, the door is then forever closed to you. I look round me and see that many adults are still in their emotional childhood. No wonder they throw such tantrums in the face of Freud! The past year I've made it a habit to study the faces of newlyweds in the local newspapers and have been astonished to find more than half of them looking like brother and sister.

"Sydney Smith said, 'How few men are on the right rail' and Milnes retorted. 'If you have continual collisions you should perhaps infer that you are on the wrong one.' So many take pride in confessions of their weakness. They seem not to realize that an intellectual apprehension is one thing, an emotional recognition that goes to the roots, another thing. On the intellectual level I'm prepared to admit almost anything; on the emotional, there's little that I've yet realized deep enough to make it my own. I know that when an author like Dickens or Hardy broods in vast tearful grief over his characters he is merely brooding in vast self-pity over himself, and I suspect that the irony of such as Meredith and Cabell is only the other side of the shield. So what do *I* have? So little that I often recall Dionysius of Tarsus, 'Here lie I of Tarsus never having been married; would that my father had not.'

"Before you return, I want you to have no illusions about one thing; some would call me an agnostic, some an atheist, but I prefer to be thought of as a free-thinker. This doesn't mean I'm not religious: Maxine tells me that I'm a deeply religious person and has forced me to some thinking there. But I'm forever done with such ancient primitive concepts as Father, Son, Mother, revelation—and on rereading it the other day I was not warmed by the Gospel of John. I raise these matters having sensed a fundamental difference in our attitudes. You've been away from me a year. You've had time to see yourself more clearly in this relationship.

"Since our separation I've been what the world calls faithful. I've had to be, not only for honor but for the knowledge that I'd have been impotent with your image before me. The source of this gagged and castrated feeling when an attractive woman calls to me (as quite a few of them here have) I've not yet reached, but will. I know that looking into myself at that depth is not going to be easy—I recall too well and too often Nietzsche's words, 'Deep wells take a long time to realize what has fallen into their depths.' I think the most important thing to come out of my tortured thinking this past year is a belief that the intellectual quest can be more exciting, for any person with the mental equipment for it, than a quest that primarily engages the emotions. If right in this, and if I can find a quest to challenge all my faculties, I shall have won a singleness of purpose to which I can cling. What that quest is to be I don't yet know.

"I love you, dearest Athene. I say it and instantly recall how Lady Ashburton cut Mr. Byng short by saying that the most dreadful thing against women is the character of the men who praise them! I love you. You have some remarkable virtues, a-mong which is your abiding patience with me. I'll try to be worthy of it. You're far more conventional than I and have little patience with some things in me: I ask you to bear in mind what a biographer said of the terrible-tempered Landor, that the traits which make men most difficult to live with are often the ones posterity hangs laurels on. When we meet I hope we'll both find, with the person in the Millay poem, that we're a little taller than when we went. I hope we both go on growing.

"And now I must get some sleep. Goodnight.

Vridar"

VIII

To Vridar's office came girls from his classes. He was again and again astonished by their innocence, for they pretended to seek advice, yet their eyes said that advice was not what they sought. There was Sylvia Ashley. If he didn't mind, she said, she'd like to have some things explained. She did not understand some things he had said in class. She was looking through her notes and while she was thus engaged, Vridar glanced down and saw that her ankles were thick. The unlovliest thing about Neloa had been her thick ankles.

Sylvia read: "When people are angry they say what they mean and then of course are sorry that they mean what they said."

"You don't understand that?"

"No." Their eyes met and he saw in her eyes what he had expected to see. What a subtle and elusive thing it was, that magic in a woman's eyes when looking for a mate! She looked away, saying, "You told us if we can't be right to be righteous. Aren't they the same thing?" Again for a moment she met his eyes. "I looked both words up. Right comes from the Angle-Saxon r-i-h-t which means straight. Right-eous comes from that and w-i-s, which means wise. So righteous means straight and wise."

"Few abstract words mean what they used to mean and no two of them mean the same to any two persons. What else has troubled you?"

"Well, you said the other day there are bad people and good people, and the bad people feel sorry for the good people and the good people feel sorry for themselves. Did you mean anything by that?"

"Only what it says. You believe there are bad people and good people?"

"Of course. Aren't there?"

"You and I are good people?"

She looked astonished. "Aren't we?"

"And who are the bad people?"

"The bad people?" She was annoyed. "You know who they are. Why ask me?"

"In fact I don't know. I'd like to."

"You don't think all people are alike, do you?"

"In the way apes are. Some murder and some only wish to. Why do we punish the lone murderer and build monuments to those who murder as a group?"

"You have peculiar ideas. Would you think a—a—"

"Prostitute? Some are fine women. I knew one. The trouble, Miss Ashley, is that most persons live by traditional ideas which they take for granted, yet these ideas lead us into wars, fill our asylums and our jails, drive millions insane and other millions to suicide. Wouldn't it be a good thing to examine these ideas and try to understand where they came from, and why, and why we cling to them?"

"You're radical," she said.

"Are cows?" He reached for a dictionary. "Radical means coming from the root; that is, original and fundamental. Now we imagine a more intelligent cow. She says to the herd, As long as we go on four legs and move between a pasture and a barn we'll always be cows. So let's learn to stand up, clean off the lice and dirt, and at least see if there aren't better pastures somewhere. Some day, says this cow, getting to her hind legs and looking round her, we may learn to fly. The other cows are horrified. They call her a radical and they all rejoice when she's shipped back to Mr. Swift."

Sylvia was staring at him. "But even if she learned to fly she'd still be a cow."

"She'd have another name then. We don't call ourselves apes, do we?"

Now she was horrified. Barely above a whisper she said, "You don't believe we came from monkeys?"

Some of the Mormon sons and daughters found a gospel of babies (all the babies a mother could have) and sugar beets and Zion a little dull. But Vidar refused to talk about Mormonism. Now and then a girl came because she wanted physical love. There was Patricia Arnon, member of a distinguished Mormon family. She came and sat by Vridar's desk and fixed on him a disturbing scrutiny.

"What can I do for you?"

"A quite a lot, if you will."

Startled, he met her gaze. "What do you mean?"

Her flecked brown eyes were studying him. "Do I embarrass you?"

He was annoyed. He thought her question impertinent. "I imagine that after a while you'll say what you came to say."

She inched forward. "Dr. Hunter, I could come and talk as other girls talk who come to you—oh, I've looked in now and then and seen them. What these girls don't dare say I dare say. Will you listen?"

"I'm listening."

"I have a secret. I think you've guessed it. You've noticed my confusion in class and you've known its meaning."

"I haven't observed confusion in you."

"Oh come now. Your eyes miss nothing. Are you going to meet frankness with evasion?"

"Assume then that I observed it. What does it mean?"

"You know what it means. You know I'm in love with you."

Astonished, Vridar pushed back from his desk. For a few moments he looked through a window, then turned to Patricia. He said a stupid thing, for the reason that he could think of nothing to say. He said, "Your irony is dreadful."

She flushed over her entire face. She was very angry. "I didn't expect such a cheap retort from you!"

"I'm sorry," he said. "You're right, it was cheap." He was now surprised to see her trembling. "Miss Arnon, when I was a youth I had the conviction that no girl could find me attractive. Besides, I was sure you were jesting."

"Is a woman in love with a man a phenomenon?"

"Wait a minute now. Just what in the world do you mean by love?"

She staggered him again. "Physical love. Is there any other kind? I came here without shame to offer myself to you. I didn't expect you'd take me." Vridar was staring at her. "I felt," she went on, "that at least you'd understand. You're not a pious moralist who does all his seducing in the dark. I sized you up as a man for whom sex is a decent daylight thing. Anyway, I'm tubercular. I don't have long."

Pity went into him now but still he could find no words.

This strange woman continued: "This is the only life I'll ever have. I'm twenty-two. The doctor tells me I have a few years. I'm hungry, but I don't want love with a man who thinks it's smart to write dirty verses on privy walls. I don't want those who idolize their mothers and go to whores. I've had two lovers—only two—and my experiences with them I don't like to remember. All they knew of love is what a bull knows. Do I embarrass you?"

"No," said Vridar, trying to conceal his embarrassment.

"I'm not proposing marriage. I had thought that—well, maybe we could be friends. But if you have a mistress—"

"I do have," he said.

"Believe me I didn't know that." The woman paused a moment and asked: "Is she here?"

"In Chicago."

"Well," said Patricia with a wry smile, "that settles it. Forgive me for being curious: are you always going to be so monkish when she's away?"

He was silent. He didn't like the question.

"Would she care?"

"Women do, don't they?"

She rose and smiled. "Well, more ado about nothing. We resume our former relations of instructor and student—Dr. Hunter and Miss Arnon." The smile left her face and he thought she was going to weep. She went to the door and turned, saying, "Credula res amor est," and let herself out.

588

Vridar sat a little while wondering about her. She was not an attractive woman her figure was too thick, her complexion too sallow. But in his class she was an A-student, even an A-plus. She sat on the front row and he had known from the start that she was intently studying him.

Wilma Reagan came one evening to Vridar's room, bringing with her a short story. She said she wanted his opinion of it and her excuse was so palpably silly that she threw the story to the carpet and stood on it. "To hell with it," she said. "Can we talk?"

"About what?"

"They're going to kick me out of this whistle stop school." She sank to a chair and lit a cigarette. "You poor unfortunate man, you're about to hear the story of my life." She inhaled a few times and went on: "I'm twenty, father dead, mother in St. George—good Mormon family, so good that for sixteen years I never tasted pepper. I got seduced when I was fourteen and I liked it. My parents decided to make an educated woman of me but their money ran out. Now I work for my board and room for a Mrs. Nevens, a good fat Mormon soul who thinks I'm wicked. She says I lie and she's right. So the school is going to boot me out."

"What for?" Wilma was another unattractive A-student who sat on the front row and studied him. She was a big girl, with a heavy peasant face and small laughing green eyes.

"Because of things I do, such as coming to your room." She smoked and looked at him. She leaned forward and her blouse fell down, revealing the upper part of her full breasts. He knew that the green eyes had seen his glance. She said, "Will you help me?"

"How?"

"Call Mrs. Nevens and tell her you're my guardian."

Wilma stayed until almost midnight. She confessed to him that she was a shameless liar, a shoplifter, and a man-lover and suspected that she would end up as a whore. When she rose to go, he saw in her eyes what had been there ever since she entered the room. She read his mind.

"I came," she said, "to go to bed with you and now am glad I didn't. Goodnight."

A week later Vridar received a letter from Patricia Arnon:

> My dear Dr. Hunter:
> I'm very unhappy and am leaving school. I wonder, as you must now and then, if physical love is worth the candle and if not, what one can put in its place. And I wonder if the common notion of the over-erotic tubercular is legend or fact. I even wonder if D. H. Lawrence knows.
> I told you that my lovers were stupid. It's rare that we women meet men who haven't forgotten that we are females, or who, discovering that we are, know how to act like normal males. I fully believe that every college and university needs a course in love-making for men—with women instructors, of course.
> Other girls talk with you and they want what I want but they hide it in questions about gerunds and Pater. It is supposed—but there's no truth in it—that women like safe tidy men who thrive on platitudes and biscuits. What we seek in spite of our training is flood and whirlwind, and then a baby and a nest for it. I feel all through me a dry humor when I think of

the girls who troop to your office, seeking love that will be tender dynamite, yet trained to marry those queer and properly buttoned creatures
who will be their husbands and eldest sons.

Remember me with gentleness, for I shall never see you again.

Goodbye

Patricia

When walking alone or lying on his bed, Vridar would think about Patricia, Wilma, and the other girls who seemed infatuated with him; and about himself; and
would wonder why they were attracted to men with a scathing and ironic tongue. He
would wonder why men had glorified chastity (in the Christian world) and why so
many American women seemed to have contempt for their husbands. He would
wonder about Neloa. He knew that she had lied to him again and again. He knew
now that he had not been the kind of man she wanted—that she had taken him because of those who had offered marriage he was the only one who had gone to college. The potential mother had a sharp eye for the most promising nest-builder!

Lying in darkness, alone, trying to face himself, he asked if he had tried to force
upon her his own Calvinistic morality. For she had been a pagan really who loved
lewdness and earthy jests, and males who looked at her as the oat-fed stud looked
at the mare. He asked himself if he had wanted to go to bed with Patricia and Wilma
and the other girls; and his answer was no, but only because they had not been attractive enough for his taste. He was not a Marion, who impartially took all of them.
Patricia and Wilma were the kind whose aggressiveness masked and hid a contempt
for their sex. Such women repelled him. Trying to figure it out he thought that the
quality in woman that most appealed to him was an unneurotic happiness in being
female. Neloa had it. Athene did not have it. Added to that he wanted a good figure,
a lovely face, and a personality abounding in *femaleness*. . . . .

Trying night after night to see his way through this, he came at last to a question:
had Athene been a mother-image, a Prudence-image?—or had she appealed to him
because from the first she had so obviously been attracted to him, because she shared his literary tastes, and because (was this the most significant part of it?) she had
come from a way of life that was culturally above his own?

Such self-searching caused him so much pain that he took a book from his table
and read till he fell asleep. The last thing in his mind was the confession of Lawrence of Arabia, that an abnormal sensitiveness to terror and pain had been his obsession since childhood . . . .

IX

It was almost the end of the school term when he met Carlos Noyce. He didn't
like the man and he tried to avoid him, as formerly he had tried to keep away from
Dennis. For one thing he didn't like Carl because the man overflowed with effusions
and enthusiasms and lusty radical resolutions to reform the earth. Carl was to say
later that he was Welsh and Spanish but behind his back there were some who said
he was part Indian. Some thought him handsome; some, as ugly as a toad: he had a
large curiously misshapen head; a big bulge of forehead; an abnormally wide mouth
which in a grin ran far into either cheek; a long nose thin and pointed that reached

down almost to his mouth; flashing black eyes set far apart; and beautiful dark brown hair shot full of golden tints. He wore a tiny patch of hair in the middle of his upper lip. It was the contour of his high cheek bones, his eyes and his complexion that made some people think of the American Indians.

Carl had been kicked out of a couple of colleges and looked back on each dismissal as a badge of honor. He had so much gusto that Vridar found him obnoxious. He was so completely extroverted that Vridar thought him absurd. Carl loved disputation, handsome clothes, alcoholic drinks, women, middle-class homes and food, somewhat in that order. He had no tact at all, no sense of prudence. Some of his colleagues looked on him as a noisy and tiresome vulgarian, but most of his students swore by him and brought him gifts.

He was only in his middle twenties when he accosted Vridar on the campus and blew bad breath into his face and talked him into a torpor. Carl's chief interest at this time was the vanities and obscenities of the academic world. With the relentless curiosity of an Upton Sinclair he nosed around in dark places, ferreting out the secrets, rattling old skeltons and alarming those in the faculty who had buried lives. Of the things professors wished to keep concealed, Carl learned more in a month than Vridar would have learned in ten years. He had learned that this dignified old owl, with a wife and ten children, had tried at a conference to lie with an amorous woman and had been impotent; that this stately image of a New England gentleman held the hands of his girl students and that one of them had fainted across his lap; that this man who taught in his Church and adored God publicly had a bastard son hidden out in southern Utah; and that Ellen Dobram was not the virgin she pretended to be. With great snorts of joy Carl told Vridar all these things. He wasn't content to drag out only the academic skeltons; he went to the city clerk's office and elsewhere and exposed, for himself and a few friends, enough shameful and hidden things to have rocked the city for years.

One evening Vridar found himself with Carl and Max, the one with his bloodless chalklike face, the other so flushed and Indian-red that he looked about to burst. Max had memorized some of Vridar's satiric verses and at unexpected moments would intone a line or two, or would utter some shocking obscenity about women. His favorite definition of woman was a wet dark place where he had spent his first nine months. "A woman," Ohm said, "is the charm that attracts and repels, especially in a dress like the corolla of a rose." Carl made prodigious efforts to be witty but he was not a wit. He was at his best when telling outlandish stories about former colleagues.

"I'll now tell you the tale of Professor John Armstrong. John got himself a wife. My God, you should see his wife, but not when you have a hangover. They honeymooned. One night, weary of the honey, Bertha Josephine said to John, Darling, I'll turn on my stomach now. John said, God damn it, I didn't know you had ever turned it off." Carl exploded with laughter. His laughter, though shocking in its violence, was inoffensive because it was so spontaneous and boyish.

Max, looking like a sleepy owl that had its blood withdrawn, softly intoned: "I can't even guess what they fed honest Abe but Herbert Hoover was an ovaltine babe."

591

Carl would then stare at Max with affected amazement. "Now Jerry Dorwald," he said, "was a gentleman who liked co-eds. He had a wife. The telephone rang in his office and Jerry was fool enough to answer it. A sweet girlish voice said, Jerry darling, I missed you last night. And what did Jerry say?" asked Carl, pivoting on one foot, swinging his long arms, his black gaze darting from face to face. "He said, Honey, who is this?"

"Have you ever heard of Bingham Bosworth?" asked Max suddenly.

"Sure," said Carl, "I've heard of him."

"I was hoping someone had." Max thrust his scrawny neck out and said, "Tell me, are you constipated? And don't start singing Ohm sweet Ohm when you look at me that way." Max pulled himself to the piano and played and sang: "I've tried spinach, I've tried yeast; of oils I've drunk some twenty tons at least. I've eaten bran, rose hips, stovewood and figs. I've ridden in a Ford and I've danced jigs. I've dug deep ditches and I've pulled down garages, I've tried rubs, kicks, grunts and massages. I've stood on my head and I've bent over double, but I still have—the—same—old—trouble!"

Max fixed Vridar with an accusing leer. "What do you use?"

Vridar had not yet heard the term, The Lost Generation. This was the late spring of 1926.

He listened to these two clowns, wondered about them, envied them. He envied their ability to *project* themselves without the slightest trace of self-embarrassment. With him self-awareness was such a disease and such a curse that the mere act of speaking caused him acute uneasiness. And because he suffered so his study of others took on the intensity of an obsession. Among his students was a girl with short chunky hands, like his own, which she hid in the folds of her dress; and one who had bad teeth over which she pulled her lips tight when she smiled; and one with huge ears over which she dressed her hair down in bangs. There was a professor no larger than a boy who had double heels on his shoes and walked in a curious brisk manner like one about to break into a run. All such simple things Vridar had learned long ago to read in people, as he read them in himself: the meaning of smiles and shrugs, laughs, coughs and sneezes; the movements of hands and legs; and facial mannerisms and tics, whether genuine or feigned. He understood the girl who when talking to him unconsciously kept drawing her skirt little by little above her knees; and the shy and tortured young man who doodled phallic symbols in his notebook while Vridar pointed out the errors in his composition.

All these things he knew and now he wanted to look deeper, much deeper—to understand why Carl was a rabid crusading Socialist; why Max had such unspeakable horror of women; why Maxine so implacably detested her husband; why George, who graduated from law with high honors, was such an obtuse ass around women. He was studying them and others and himself, and reading many hours every day and night, when Athene was appointed to a position here and in June came west. She took a small apartment near the college and Vridar lived in a room a few doors away.

They agreed that they would have to be very circumspect. If they married, she would lose her position; if they were suspected of being lovers, they would both be fired. "Every person," Vridar said, "who blunders into marriage wants all other persons to blunder in and suffer with him. The reason they get so furious about free love is that they want it to be bought and paid for."

He knew that Athene didn't like to live what she called a double life. The thought of deception repelled her.

"I'll shyly woo you," Vridar said. "It'll be rumored we're falling in love. Then the eyes of the gossips will glow upon the vicarious consummations. I used to be such an ass. The idea of free love made me furious—because I wasn't in on it. I'd have made a fine Anthony Comstock, only one year ago, this very day."

He was so allusive in his talk, often so dry, sometimes so obscure that now and then he wearied her. Under cover of darkness he would slip to the back door. In her apartment they would speak in low voices, almost whispering. If now and then Vridar raised his voice she would rebuke him and he would yell, "To hell with the Puritans."

"Vridar!"

"I say to hell with them."

His mother came down from Idaho to visit him. Her cold blue eyes studied his face and saw guilt in it, and she then wept and reproached him. "I never knew a son of mine would do such a thing! I'd rather be dead, son, dead, than see you this way!"

He thought, If only you could see your other son. He said, "What way?"

"Living in sin with a woman! Living in lust like a common hoodlum! O my God, I would never have believed it! I also had such dreams for you," she said, wiping from her eyes huge tears of self-pity. "You were always such a clean and noble boy with such noble ideals!"

He wanted to say, Horseshit! He said, "I was a pious little stinker."

"Oh no!" she cried, fixing him with eyes in which stood the boy he had learned to detest. "I knew my sons but you're not my son any more. I can see the guilt in your face. I can see —"

"A person like you would make God himself feel guilty. Listen."

"There's not a thing you can say, son. You've broken your poor old mother's heart. All my life I slaved for you. I worked like a slave for my children and I trained them to be pure and noble. And now—my God, I wish you had killed me instead!"

Yes, yes, she had worked like a slave for her children! How well he knew it! "Mater, will you listen?"

"Please don't talk to me, son. There's not a thing you can say. I wish I was dead, that's all."

Vridar looked at her wrinkled and anguished face, at her golden hair turning gray. "It's true that you slaved for your children. They'll never forget that. I think you labored for us as few mothers have ever labored. I think—"

"And for what?" she cried angrily. "You think I'd have slaved that way if I had known you'd come to this? All them years in that lonely place? I wish to God I'd never been born!" She choked up.

"Mater, you make it so hard for me to be honest with you. I could have lied about it, as possibly most sons would have done. I—"

593

"Oh no! You never could lie. Thank God for that."

He thought, How little parents know of their children! He said: "Yes, I could have lied. I'm trying to be a son worthy of you. If there are some things we don't see alike—"

"O my God! Sin, my son, is sin and it will never be anything else!"

"I mean," he said patiently, "that like most mothers you want me to go through life with your belief. I don't think I'll ever pretend to you or lie to you. I have a life to live and I expect to live it decently—"

"In sin with a red-headed woman!"

"Is red hair more wicked than black or brown?" But he knew the pain in her. Her own hair had been reddish and her husband preferred red hair, and detested black hair because his own mother's was black. "Mater, as for marriages, I know some that are really sinful. In fact I now suspect that the most sinful persons on earth are married."

"Son, what are you saying?"

"The truth, mother dear."

"You can talk till doomsday but you won't change me. Sin is sin and I know it when I see it."

"If nobody can change you why expect to change me? I'm my mother's son."

"You're the son I'm ashamed of and I wish I was dead. I wish I was dead a thousand times rather than see you like this!" She flung herself to his bed and lay there, moaning out of desolate grief.

He thought, What a strange and terrible thing that Christian parents try to manage their children even when they're past thirty, past forty or fifty! The deep truth I seek may be there, if I can find it.

He went to Athene. He told her what his mother had said and was then annoyed by what he saw in her eyes. He knew that again she was computing the cost of the life she had chosen.

"Don't look at me that way!" he cried. "Can a man be indifferent to his mother's grief? Oh, I know the source of it is in ignorance, prejudice, and erotic sublimation and I hate all that; but she suffers, she was a slave for me, she came among my father's lewd people, she lived on a lonely river outpost. If she could have her way I'd be a Mormon bishop. Yes, I know it all! But it's you I wonder about now. I wish you were out of this situation."

"I don't."

"I saw it in your eyes, what I saw that night in the Chicago rain." She was silent. He looked into her eyes and said, "You're conventional, you're afraid of public opinion. I could lay myself bare to the world. You never could, could you?"

"I can see no reason to."

"There was no reason for Stendhal to do it? Look, my mother will have contempt for you now. She thinks you're a wicked woman. Can you endure all this? Can you stand up with me and fight for what we think is best? That means that we have to resist a great deal of what my mother stands for, doesn't it?"

She was looking at him in her strange intent way. She said, "Already in your life you've had enough inner conflicts to wear a dozen persons out. Why do you wish for more?"

"I have no choice."

"What is it you want to win through to?"

He turned and left her and a week passed before he saw her again. He would sit alone, asking himself what it was that he wished to win through to. He felt that a persevering and unpitying exploration of himself was necessary if he was ever to be a writer of any stature. Athene wanted a life free of turmoil. She wanted peace. She was pained by his acid tongue and his corrosive moods. She resisted his probing.

One evening she said, "Women are naturally franker about sex matters than men. We'd be decent if you men would let us."

That dashed Vridar a little. "You'd be pagan, you mean?"

"You made me feel more shame than I'd ever felt."

Drily he said, "I had precisely the training for it. I should have been Adam. When Eve whispered the naughty suggestion in my ear, I'd have run complaining to God."

"Oh no. You've always liked the naughty whispering. I don't think you've ever been ashamed of sex really, but ashamed because you were not ashamed enough."

He stared at her and broke into a wide grin. "You know, you may look like a simple woman but now and then you look deep. If you'd only look that deep into yourself. I once thought when I read the Bible that Moses should be sued for libel. Men who dote on married life aren't much to kiss their wife. Is that it? Marriage gets a man melancholy and listless, but he sure picks up when he gets him a mistress. If she's a redhead. How my mother would love that!"

Athene was looking at him, her gaze steady and unamused. "In writing so much satiric verse, aren't you hiding something from yourself?"

"I think so. Have you any notion of what it is?" When she gave no reply he went on: "I have, I suppose all men have, impulses to rape. I also suppose that you women like it. I recall what my mother once said about hens. She said they are like women. A hen will run wildly at the top of her life, but when overtaken she submits and looks happy about it. Isn't there a lot of that in women?" When she was still silent he said, "Does rape appeal at all to you?"

"You're being silly."

"Oh? There are no frailties in Athene. I'm just about convinced you're a narcissist. There is the time you told me—"

"Stop it!" She had turned a furious red over her whole face.

To cover it all over Vridar went on quickly, "As a virgin I had a lot of hymens for life to get though. I believed in brotherhood and equality and virtuous women. All married men who feel that they must be faithful to their wives want all other women to be virgins. I actually thought a lily was more unimpassioned than a rose. In a review of a novel the other day a man said the hero was a fatass and a stinker. He couldn't understand why the heroine loved him—which meant that he thought himself the sort she should be attracted to. I read a review by a woman. She said the heroine was a fool and an idiot. She meant she was the sort the hero

595

should be attracted to. I used to read novels and think the hero was an ass—which meant that he was not what I thought I was. Vridar Hunter, how noble in reason! How infinite in faculty! In form and moving how express and admirable! In action how like an angel! In apprehension how like a god! Or take Walt Whitman who apostrophized through a thousand pages proclaiming the greatness of Walt Whitman. Why Americans are so fond of such moonshine I'll know some day."

Athene's color was fading. She was smiling faintly. Vridar knew that she knew that he was clowning to absolve the crassness of his statement. He also knew that it was the clown in him that she liked best. Her pet names for him were those of clowns, particularly from Italian plays.

"How like an angel I was when I was pleased to observe that a doll was sexless. How infinite in faculty when I failed to perceive that the only obscenity is in a person's mind. How like an angel when I staggered away with that case of beer into an alfalfa field and got drunk. What a paragon among animals when I leapt out of a nightmare and went away screaming into the night. How noble in reason when I figured out that men in books were admirable in proportion as they were like me."

"You don't like Stendhal? They're saying now he was just about the greatest novelist of the past century, but what did they say when he lived? The novelists praised to the sky were such as Janin, Kerr, and Sandeau. Ever heard of them? A Stendhal novel sold twenty-two copies. Even *The Red and the Black* never reached a second printing in his lifetime. I hope I remember these things if book reviewers give me a lot of trouble. He was viciously denounced because he admitted that as a child he had an erotic interest in his mother. The dirty cowards who denounced him didn't have. Oh no, they didn't have. They're forgotten now, but his books are a joy to read because in dragging so many things out of himself he anticipated a lot of the truths now taken for granted. Is that a good enough reason for my probing?"

She was silent and again he spoke. "You have the idea you're the center of the universe?" She gave no reply. She knew that the sly rascal set traps for people. "You do, of course. My students deny it at first but I say, There you sit and it seems to you that the universe is equidistant at all points. When you move you take the center with you. Aren't you ashamed to be carting it around this way? . . . Well, then, you feel no enthusiasm for this exploration?"

"Do you expect to put in print everything you find?"

"Everything." He gave her the swift sad smile of the little lost boy. "My fear is that I'll put in more than I find. I'm beginning to suspect that I'm a masochist."

"Why do you take caustic thrusts at men with hairy chests?"

He looked at her a few moments; then said, "My dear, that's kindergarten stuff. You say you believe in the Bible but so far as I know you've never read it. If you had studied it, or had read some of the ablest scholarship about it, you'd know that the ancient Hebrews associated hair with divinity. They practically worshiped it. The Christians have taken over a lot of that attitude. There's my father. He's as hairless as I am. When a young man he was so determined to grow a mustache that he rubbed cream on his upper lip and let a cat lick it off—I did so a few times myself; and in the photograph of him, taken when he was about twenty-five, he has a mustache, a horribly ridiculous reddish thing that he paid the photographer to paint on. For Jews and Christians, hair, my dear woman, means virility."

"You have enough virility."

"But wouldn't you like it better if there was hair on it?"

She was showing distaste. She was more than a normally hairy woman herself.

"You see," he said, "I'm half-woman and you're half-man. Not homosexuals— that's something else. My brother, I think, put it well in one of his bitter jesting moods when he said that he was scared to death that he'd get knocked up before he died. He's a smart monkey. He meant that he and I got strongly identified with the opposite sex, because of a mother who dominated everything in our lives, including in a way our father. We have to correct that over-identification, or at least, good God, to understand it, as Stendahl did. It seems pretty silly to me to write novels if you don't understand what you're writing about. And how many do?"

"You really expect to understand all these things?"

"Well, a lot more than college teachers understand. Have you ever studied *them?*"

X

There came to the college as an instructor a young man named Carlyle Orcutt. His wife's name was Elsa. Carlyle, actually twenty-three but looking about seventeen, was a small foppish prig, a Rhodes scholar, who loved to work in a kitchen over fine gravies and sauces, or to drop the names of various celebrities whom he claimed as friends. It was in Europe that he met Elsa, who said she was German-Irish but who looked part Jewish. Elsa had taught French in Nice and spoke French like a native. She was tall, willowy, flatchested, lean-shanked, with beautiful hair, lovely Irish-gray eyes, a weak tremulous mouth, and a weak foolish chin. The Orcutts took a fancy to Vridar and insisted on teaching him to play bridge, all the while with malicious innuendo or open thrusts rebuking his blunders, catisgating his rural heritage and sneering at his clothes. Now and then he seethed like a cauldron but tried to conceal his fury. Then at last he saw the irony of his situation, saw that he was angry because much of what they said was true.

When he blundered in his playing—and because of his tortured self-consciousness his blunders were many—Elsa would murmur in her bright malicious way, "They're walking the streets of London, Orcutt." Carlyle's small dark brown eyes under black brows would fairly glow with malicious joy. When Vridar and Athene lost, as they always did, Carlyle's triumph was as huge and undisguised as a child's. He would add up the sums and say, "We won six dollars—that is, if we'd been playing for money." Then he would wrinkle his small nose and suck air up it in short furious snorts.

When alone with Athene Vridar would sputter and say, "The God damned gall of it! Did you ever see two persons so completely dominated by bad taste?"

"Why go around them?"

"I haven't started running yet."

Now and then Carl Noyce would watch the playing. He despised the Orcutts.

597

At the top of his lungs (he had a voice like an auctioneer's) he would roar at them, "Cut out your damn posing! Where did you pick up that eyether and nyether stuff? Does this Mormon valley look like Oxford to you?"

When so directly assaulted, Carlyle would redden with anger and stride about, puffing his cigarette, wrinkling his nose and snorting up his hairy nostrils, or turning his full lips out in a red pout. His small eyes would flicker with spite. Elsa, far more intuitive and inscrutable, would reveal only in her eyes what was in her mind—and in the tremulous movement in her lower lip when she put a cigarette to her mouth. Carl, it seemed to Vridar, was too brutal. These Carlyle's were only children.

"If you're going to smoke," Carl would roar at Carlyle, "then God damn it why don't you smoke? You're just a fussy little old grandma in British tweeds who doesn't inhale!"

Closely watching the Orcutts, Vridar saw little things that betrayed their inner emotions: Elsa's trembling hand when she reached for a cigarette; a sudden brief quivering, almost a spasm, in her lips; a haunted and desolate expression in her eyes; the nervous moving up and down of one long foot. . . . In Carlyle's one-syllable cough, which was frequent; in the wrinkling of his small nose; in the sharp sucking in of breath followed by a narrowing of his eyes—in these and more Vridar read his emotions and mind. Anger yielded to compassion, though he found some of the sneers hard to take: "I've heard you expect to be a writer. How can you write before you've lived?"

Among the students was a lean ungainly long-legged pimpled youth of twenty with a sharp and bitter mind. His mother was a Jew, his father an Irishman. His name was Moses McGuire. Everyone called him Mac. Mac was so full of bitterness and hatreds and conflicts that he lived in torment day and night and spent a part of his time trying to be an Oscar Wilde. One day Vridar invited him to his room.

Mac had been reading Freud and Jung and other well-known psychologists. He was trying to understand his compulsions. When he walked the streets he had to count all the squares in the pavement; to measure his long strides to the lines in the walk; to count windows and doors and trees, and the number of persons who passed him. He cultivated the sardonic gesture. One afternoon he wanted cigarettes and Vridar walked with him to a drugstore. Mac strode to the rear counter and fixed his cynical sneering gaze on the pharmacist. "Camels," he said at last, "and an ounce of carbolic acid." When he was again on the street he set the bottle of acid on the concrete and ground it under his heel. "I have a suicide compulsion," he said. "I have to crush it." He laughed, or at least made a sound that some people mistook for laughter. It was a harsh cawing, bitter and mirthless. Now and then he came to Vridar's room and pacing back and forth talked till past midnight.

"Am I a fool because I'm half Jew and half Irish? That lush overgrown ass Ludwig Lewisohn would say so. Is it because I play chess and smoke a pipe? Is it because my chest is hairless and one testicle hangs four inches below the other? Is it because when a boy I tried to see under the dresses of girls and my mother roared at me like a fog-siren? She would take me in and kiss my erotic little cheeks and put my erotic little hands up to her big bosom and slap my erotic little hindend. The virgin and the child! How pure our love was!"

He cawed again. Never in his life had Vridar heard such laughter.

"There's a law of compensation according to an old deacon named Emerson: because my old man screwed everything in the block, I take a maid out and am abandoned to the sagebrush and the owls. Lovely women stoop to folly but my name is McGuire. What is wrong with me, Hunter? Something should be done about me or I'll be another Leopold or another Loeb. I've read all the psychologists but they need psychiatrists themselves, and none more than that unbuttoned old Fraud over in Vienna. How can you live among these Mormons, who meander through the pastures of Zion, belching their platitudes! And look at that campus. The halfbacks of the academic world, the rah-rah boys of Sigma Chi, who read Frank Crane and Elbert Hubbard and Mark Sullivan. Oh yes yes yes, and Bruce Barton."

Lying on his bed and looking at Mac, Vridar thought of Stendhal's words, that though sincerity was harmful to wit, it was indispensable to art. Mac spent half his time trying to formulate devasting aphorisms.

"I ask myself, is it paranoia or dementia praecox, paresis or anorexia? Algalagnia? Of course, Hunter; you're bright enough to see that." The cawing again came in sunken violence from his thin chest. "A recent study of ten thousand M.A. and Ph.D. women in Germany discovered that ninety-four per cent of them were masturbators. What a picture of fair womanhood!—and can you imagine all the ways they do it? I sit in the classroom and look at my professors and tell myself it is a masturbating world. When they see me looking into their bowels, they become disturbed and frightened, and then I look all the harder.

"I've read enough books to have learned that the human female has a bulbous penis and a loose vagina, the bull a spear and the cow a tight one. No, damn it, I mean the human male has the bulb. Why these differences? Because long ago the bull and the cow were in danger of being eaten while they copulated and so had to get it over fast, whereas our ancient papa seized a big club and took his time. I've learned that clothes originated not in modesty but in adornment, and that an old woman today loaded with jewels is trying to compensate for the gray in her pubic hair. I've learned that all ancient peoples thought they were the center of the universe and that all other peoples were barbarians. It wasn't only the Hebrews who had that halfwitted notion. I've learned that at the primitive level good intentions were of no worth at all compared to the ritual—and they still aren't. I've learned that in some parts of the earth girls are still deflowered before marriage, but I still don't know why men in Judaism and Christianity make such a hell of a fuss about virginity.

"I've learned," said Mac, still pacing, leering, cawing, "that the odors a person first associates with sexual excitement are those he'll find most exciting throughout life. If a man seduces a girl in an outdoor privy, does it mean he'll have to take his wife there? Heine says the Devil is the apostle of Reason. Hunter, God damn it, what is wrong with me?"

"You're trying awfully hard to be witty and profound. Are you a babilan?"

"And just what is that?"

"It's Old French for eunuch. Pleasure is a luxury, Stendhal said; to enjoy it it is necessary that one's sense of security—I mean that one should feel safe from his enemies. He thought of himself as a babilan, not because he was a eunuch but because in any situation where he felt he might be discovered he was impotent."

Mac turned to stare at Vridar down his long sallow nose. "Are you a babilan?" When Vridar hesitated, Mac bellowed, "You can trust me, Jeremiah! And isn't that what you'd like to be?—another Jeremiah?"

"Yes, Moses, I'm a babilan."

Mac stared at him a long moment. "You know Shirley. I've been trying for a year to seduce that bitch. Not that she isn't willing, or was, but now she hates me. That feeling of about-to-be-discovered was always there; I could hear the fog-siren of my mother's lungs and see that huge mattress front coming after me. And I couldn't do it. Hunter, there's nothing on God's earth a woman hates so as a man to whom she offers herself who can't do it. Nothing else on earth makes her look like such an incredible fool. Jeremiah, am I right?"

"Yes, Moses."

There was Pyke Rowe, son of a distinguished surgeon. Pyke was also a brilliant student and like Mac was at loose ends. He imagined himself to be fascinated by ugliness; he said he followed certain women around to stare at them and delight in their gawky malformations. He said he was fascinated by offensive odors. "I was sitting by a girl in class today and her stink enraptured me. She had a blend of heliotrope and sweat." Of Prof. Dobram he would say, "Have you ever really smelled her? What an epithelial membrane she must have!"

Pyke wrote an essay for the school's journal. In it he said:

> Our St. Georges of the academic middle ages know less than nothing of what goes on around them. They doubtless remember that they spooned when young and closed their eyes on the succulent kiss. That was all very well. That led to babies and helped to support the patent medicine industry. It was through some such ecstatic maneuvering that I got her.
>
> But in this school there is, in my humble opinion, an excess of amatory erotica and a conspicious lack of the best that has been said and thought. In automobiles around our campus, fair maids, after enduring a lecture on life is real and life is earnest, and handsome gentlemen, in from a cultural workout on the football field, do retire to closed sedans and draw the shades. And there they do suck tongues and exchange spit. . .

The whole college quaked with consternation and rage and the committee on censorship met in secret. According to Pyke's story he was called in to face the inquisitors but after half an hour of pious windiness lit a cigarette and said to them, "You witch doctors bore me. You object to my gawd in a short story and turn away from what goes on behind the shades in the limousines. It doesn't seem likely to me that you know much of anything. Gentlemen, good day."

No, Vridar had not yet heard that this was the decade of the lost generation. He little dreamed of what was yet to come. He little knew the causes under the profound unrest but did perceive that he was a part of it. During this year and the next he and Athene went to weekend song-and-bootleg parties. Athene didn't like to drink or to be around drinkers, but Vridar found the parties stimulating, for there he saw persons without their masks: saw Carlyle chainsmoke while staring with morbidly jealous and frustrated eyes at his wife; saw Mac slouch low and leer with contempt at the loveliest of the women; saw Elsa flirt in ways so subtle that only the sharpest observer was aware of them; saw Carl Noyce when full of brandy manifest an eager interest in seduction. . . .

Their liquor was sold to them by a strange halfblind man who was known as Utah's official bootlegger. He had police protection. A few miles from Salt Lake City he made a peach brandy by the barrel. "Next to sugar beets and babies," Moses McGuire said, "Jason Tooms is Utah's greatest industry. The fact that he is a Mormon is only incidental." A State official gave Vridar and Carl a letter of introduction. It said:

> Dear Jake:
> These men are college professors.
> Sell them anything they want.

Vridar and his friends bought an excellent peach brandy for six dollars a gallon. The group usually met at the Orcutt home, and it was there one night that Carlyle drew Vridar aside and fixed him with small malicious eyes. He said, "How are your boy friends?"

Vridar looked at him, wondering what he meant.

"I mean your boy friends Mac and Pyke. Aren't they up to your room a lot?"

Vridar then imagined that he understood. His first impulse was to seize the frail little man and shake him out of his expensive English tweeds. His second impulse was pity. He turned away.

"But I won't continue to take his impertinence," he said to Athene.

"If you get angry, he'll be convinced."

"Of what?"

"That you're a homosexual."

"Why did he ask the question? Does he think Mac and Pyke are?"

A week or two later, after Carlyle and Elsa had been needling him all evening, Vridar pushed his chair back and stood up. "Listen," he said. "For more than a year now I've passed over your damned stinking little ways. I've had enough. If you can't be decent friends, we'll not be friends." He looked at them and they looked at one another. He said, "Does either of you know the source of malice?"

"Orcutt, he thinks we're malicious. Fancy that."

"Malice," said Carlyle, flicking an ash off and glancing at his wife, "is not the same as mental alertness."

"Bravo!" cried Elsa.

"You mean you're mentally alert?"

"Oh, much more than you are."

There flashed through Vridar's mind the words, When you dispute with a fool the fool has all the best of it and he knows it. But he persisted, despising himself for persisting. "You mean you've been to Europe and like to tell everybody that you saw two writers in Paris named Hemingway and Stein? Orcutt, you know no

601

more about life than an earwig knows about a cherry tree. He gets a living out of it—"

"Hear ye! hear ye!" cried Elsa. She had got a dictionary and now in her tremulous voice was reading from it: "Malice from malus meaning evil. One, enmity of heart, malevolence; a malignant design of evil. Two, law. State of mind shown by intent to commit an unlawful act. Orcutt, have you been contemplating unlawful acts? Do you," she asked, glancing at Vridar, "accuse my little Carlyle of that? And me trusting him!" Vridar could not restrain a smile. "Synonyms, the book says: ill will, spite, grudge, rancor, virulence, venom. Orcutt, do you have all them-there things? The book says see resentment."

Vridar shruged his shoulders and sat. He was feeling ridiculous.

"R-e," said Elsa. "R-e-m, r-e-n, r-e-p. Requiescat. Maybe," she said, glancing at Vridar, "that's what you meant." Vridar observed again as she looked up that she had long lovely lashes and beautiful eyes behind them. "Resentment, a feeling of indignant displeasure because of something regarded as a wrong, an insult. That," she said, glancing again, "seems to be what you feel. Synonyms: anger, choler, indignation, enmity, hatred, ill will, animosity, dudgeon—that's a slick word—malice, spite, grudge, rancor. A deep dudgeon. Orcutt, that's what he's in."

Carlyle was wrinkling his nose and sniffing up it.

Vridar said to Athene, "Let's go."

Outside, walking homeward, she said, "I told you it would do no good."

"It'll do plenty. Wait."

Two weeks later the Orcutts came to Athene's apartment and Vridar was called over. They were chastened. "My chin," said Elsa, her hand trembling as she raised her cigarette, "is nothing. I hate myself for being chinless. Carlyle is chinless too. If we ever have a child it'll be chinless." She looked over at Vridar, sitting back in shadow. "Orcutt, could you stand a chinless son?"

"Huh?" said Carlyle, wrinkling his nose. He was a little deaf.

Elsa talked for half an hour about the imperfections or frailties in the Orcutts, until at last Carlyle said to Vridar, "What's algalagnia?"

"I don't know," Vridar said. "Some term Mac picked up." Vridar studied Carlyle a few moments. "Did you think it meant homosexuality?"

"I wonder what it meant to you."

"And I wonder where you got the idea I'm a homosexual."

"You seem to spend a lot of time with Mac and Pyke."

"You spend a lot of time in the kitchen. You have a mincing girling walk and a waggle in your hips. You haven't the slightest interest in any manly exercise, and when you boast that you take two hours in the sexual embrace you sound a bit suspicious. But I've never thought you're a fairy."

"I saw a lot of fairies in Europe," Carlyle said. "Most of the British poets are fairies."

After they had gone Vridar looked at Athene. "Have you ever thought there's any of the homosexual in me?"

"No."

"Did Marion ever suggest that he thought so?"

"No. He said you're both over-identified with the opposite sex, whatever that means."

"The meaning is simple enough. Those who identify with the opposite sex tend to accept their values and attitudes, over those of their own sex. It means you're half-man and half-woman."

"I don't think I am."

"Oh, of course not. You feel very feminine with that big aggressive chin and all your masculine strivings. And I feel, of course, like a Jack Dempsey, with all my womanly tears and compassion, and so complete a loss of individuality that I'm the captive of every situation that evokes my sympathy."

"I feel like a woman," she said.

"I can't imagine how you can know how a woman feels. As for the Orcutts, it's true that it's our enemies who make us grow, not our friends. They made me do some thinking."

"Why, then, call them enemies?"

"It was a stupid way of speaking. I suppose my biggest enemy is my mother, who, pretending to love me more than any other person on earth, would destroy me. She'd actually rather see me dead than living in sin with a redheaded woman. She wouldn't mind it half so much if you had black hair, for her hair was almost red when she was young. Does it amuse you!"

"Not at all."

"It takes a lot to amuse you. Shall I go get us a drink?"

"I'd rather not."

Vridar stood up and after looking at her a few moments kissed her beautiful hair, her cheeks, her lips lightly and headed for his room. There were times when he couldn't for the life of him tell what in this woman had attracted him. Once or twice he had wondered— no, not that, not yet.

XI

At the end of his second year in this school, Carl was fired. With tireless and stormy eloquence he had opposed military training, and with Vridar had been guilty of spending an hour with Scott Nearing, when that persecuted man came like a thief in the night. Carl said he was a queer fellow, for he didn't like to see men trained to kill. The school was so eager to get rid of him that it gave him fine recommendations to other schools.

Carl abandoned his wife, picked up a mistress, and headed for a labor college. He sent Vridar hilarious descriptions of his new colleagues:

> I must tell you about Prof. Leonard Ayres. He's deaf. He packs around an ear apparatus as big as a phonograph. He loves privy dirt. His ears come forward like a staghound's when he sniffs an erotic odor. But you have to shout at him, so his pal Prof. Arnold Hoag takes him up to the roof. As eager as the Utah librarian on the trail of the hatrack article, Hoag hikes up the stairs and through the roof door, with Ayres panting at his heels. Ayres adjusts his apparatus and Hoag shouts into it some stuff that would make a traveling salesman turn sick in his belly. Then the two

603

great minds come back down. Hoag is the one who thinks Shakespeare should be expurgated. . . .

O God, I must tell you about Prof. Adam Brown. He teaches the modern novel here and thinks most modern novels pretty lousy. He means immoral. He was reading a French story in which a man rapes a woman. That set him to thinking. He decided the French author was a fool and determined to find out if a man *could* rape a woman. He used his wife in the experiment. He told her simply and straight out that he was going to rape her if he could, that she was to resist with every means at hand, including the portrait over the mantle of Prof. Adam Brown Senior. Well, Brown (he tells all this himself) chased that poor skinny mother of six all over the damned house. She screamed, she fought; they shattered furniture; and when the battle was over, there lay Adam Brown on the floor, unable to wiggle a finger, much less his unmentionable; and there stood Mrs. Brown, breathing hard but triumphant. Half her clothes were off but none of her virtue. Brown now tells his students that the French author dealt with an improbable situation, that art should concern itself only with the probable. This man reviews novels, and so may meet you somewhere down the years. . . .

After leaving Utah, Carl wrote and published a number of essays about his Utah colleagues. One morning Vridar saw an office door open and a furious professor hurl a magazine down the hallway. One of Carl's former colleagues was throwing the portrait of himself to the janitor. It was this same professor of history who had thrown *Elmer Gantry* through his open window. Carl was not content to write scrathing portraits; he did an article on Wasatch College for a liberal journal in New York City, and the editor sent it to President Tom Lewis. The editor then sent a copy to Vridar for his opinion, and a copy of Lewis's reply.

With astonishment Vridar read what Tom Lewis had written, and then said to Athene: "The man tells lies. Shall I answer him?"

"If you do, it'll mean the end of you here."

"What, then? Am I going to start crawling?"

He wrote and rewrote most of the night, and sent these words to the editor:

What I say is significant for me less in its bearing upon this school than in its implications of weakness in our educational system and our national life. But first I wish to correct the President in a few of his statements.

What he says about the training of Carl Noyce and his ability as a teacher is, in my opinion, beneath the dignity of his position. The President must know that it takes more than a Master's or Doctor's degree to make a good teacher and he should not forget that many of his present faculty were trained in this school when it was hardly, if at all, more than a Mormon institution. To point out that Noyce is a graduate of a denominational college seems to be ungracious and beside the point. The President says a Master's degree or a year of graduate work is demanded of instructors here but he has a number now teaching here who have neither.

He says Noyce asked for a leave of absence and was denied because a leave obligates the College to reappoint. This too is an evasion. I left here in 1921 with a leave and when I asked to return the following year I was told that my leave had been a formality only. The President says the "turnover in the faculty the last six years is about as low as it could possibly be, and only for better salaries." That is false. I can give you the names of several who left the College because it would not reappoint them. The President says that men "of all views are allowed to go on in their work here unmolested and affiliate themselves with local groups" and that he has no control over his faculty "religiously, politically, economically, or ethically." Both statements are false. No man could keep his job here if he were to tell his students about the travesty of justice in Massachusetts, or our cowardly interference in Nicaragua, or the real truth about Prohibition in this city, or a thousand other facts which students in the interest of wholesome government ought to know. It is true nevertheless that the President is himself a liberal and would, I believe, staff his school with persons of integrity and courage if he were not restrained by the ultra-patriotic groups which endow the school with their patronage.

And that, after all, is the only significant thing in the whole matter. Education in a democracy, supported by public taxes and directed by boards of business men, must defer in all important and vital matters to the prejudices and superstitions of the community. It is idle to deplore want of education in a country in which there is no demand for it, or to abuse professors and presidents because they do not do what they have no power to do.

Our President has written you an evasive letter but there is nothing surprising in that. He is the best president by far this school has ever had and he would do many things that this community will not allow him to do. He has written you, I observe, about a thousand words of mild abuse of me and not in a single instance has he told the truth. He has given you the gossip of persons in the city. But what of it? I perceive at last that he is not my enemy, nor are my enemies to be found among the timid and quaking souls who teach here. My enemy and the enemy of Noyce is that neurotic Calvinism which is the god and holy ghost of this country; which has so nearly strangled it that art is almost dead among us, and joy is an obscene thing, while our asylums and jails fill to overflowing with the evidence of our shame. This College is one of its paid instruments. To publish an article about it, exposing its meanness, would be about as sensible as to try to cure a man of syphilis by pointing a derisive finger at the disease.

As Athene read the letter her face clouded with dismay. Vridar said, "Oh, I know! I know it means the end of me here but if I don't stand up now I'll never stand up." He sent a copy of his letter to Tom Lewis. Two days later Lewis summoned him to his office and to Vridar's amazement he found not an angry but a chastened man.

"Dr. Hunter," he said in his abrupt way, "I've always admired you for two things. One is your frankness. The other is your ability to get things done."

"Thank you," Vridar said. "You're a pretty frank man yourself."

"Well, sit down, I want to talk to you." Vridar drew a chair and sat. "About Noyce. You overrate him. In my opinion he has only an average mind. To be frank, not above the average of our college graduates here."

"I can't agree. I know him better than you. In my opinion he's abler than most of your faculty here and beyond all question he has more honor."

"I don't think he could get a doctorate in a good school."

"I think he can and I think he will."

"Did you approve the article he wrote?"

"It was too exuberant but essentially it told the truth."

"You think it should be published?"

"In my letter I said I did not."

"I'd like," Tom Lewis said bitterly, "for some of my critics to tell me how I can do more than I'm doing now."

"But do you have to evade? Couldn't you say, Look, this college is supported by fanatics. Much of the truth they don't want taught here. If they don't get what they want, the legislature will withhold appropriations—"

"Yes, that's it," said Lewis impatiently.

"Since we're being frank with one another, let me ask, Do you want me to resign?"

"I've never asked you to. Haven't I stood behind you?"

"You listen to malicious gossip."

"When enraged taxpayers come to my office, I have to listen."

"Yes. I suppose," Vridar said, rising, "it would be best all around for me to leave. I'm told that the president of the Mormon Church is determined to force me out. Only one member of the Board of Regents now supports me. The writing on the wall seems to be pretty plain. . . ."

A few days later Vridar met Abraham Moses Smith, who for him was another Flammonde, with news of nations in his talk, with that in his manner which tradition owned to more than fifty Mormon years. He had been promoted twice and there were those who thought of him as a future president.

He drew Vridar aside and said, "How you getting along?"

"I expect to be fired."

"You're not selling yourself."

"I'm not for sale."

"Oh, come now. In this country a man has to sell what he has. You're a well-trained man, a magna doctor from one of the greatest schools in the world, yet you're on no committees, you've had no promotion, and you've made enemies everywhere. You have something the world wants to buy but you have to present yourself in the market—"

"As though I were a toothpaste or a toilet paper?"

"You don't meet this problem with levity. As if you were a trained man ready to fill a big job, as in fact you are. I've watched you. Your first year you had only one course in composition. Your third year you have three. You know what that means?"

"Yes. My chairman loves me and by piling work on me hopes to force me out."

"It's your fault. You don't play the game. What friends do you choose? Such renegades as Noyce and Orcutt and Ohm. My God!" he said. "Two fairies and an I.W.W."

"I guess," Vridar said, "the world isn't what I thought it was."

"God's world is fine. It's a beautiful world. Why don't you love it?"

Vridar almost chuckled. "I try to," he said.

"The truth—it may not be pleasant but it's the truth—is this, that men who get ahead are men who keep their mouths shut and take advantage of other men's blunders. Did you have to let people know that you sympathized with Sacco and

Vanzetti? Did you have to sneak down to the hotel to see Scott Nearing? Do you have to keep defending this wild radical named Noyce, even after he has gone? Moral indignation is fine but it doesn't butter our bread."

"But the human spirit doesn't live on butter."

"Look, Vridar, you might have become chairman of your department. I was pulling for you. Now I'm afraid you're out."

"Well, when I'm an old man I don't want to have to look back—"

"Oh, don't bore me with that. You have children. You should be a responsible man. Yet you've gone to the home of a Unitarian minister who makes beer in his cellar."

"It's good beer," Vridar said.

"Do you have to defend Margaret Sanger in your classes? Do you have to put *Marriage and Morals* on your reading lists? Do you have to risk your own neck defending such showoffs as Pyke Rowe? It's such things that are driving you out of here."

"I know it, Abe. I do appreciate your friendly interest. . . ."

Walking across the campus Vridar lifted from memory the sextet of a sonnet:

I'll be a dean when I accept the task
of keeping truth and honor underground.
I'll be polite, and that's enough to ask.
I'll speak, and there'll be nothing to astound.
I'll smile, and friends will like my gracious mask,
I'll laugh, and they'll be pleased with empty sound.

Anson Ward, chairman of Vridar's department, was playing the game. Vridar had heard a girl say that Ward had a large paternal brooding erotic interest in lovely girls but never made passes. He read Tennyson to them until the girls' senses swam, and one of them, it was rumored, fainted. Who could object to a Harvard man's reading Tennyson to his students? Every point Ward made, the girl said, he supported with half a mile of perfectly metrical platitudes. He had what Mac McGuire called the mystical orgasm. Anson played the game but Vridar was not sure that *he* knew how to play it, even if he had wished to. Athene, he supposed, wanted him to. . . .

Well, he was on his way out and what would he do then? In three years he had written five novels and all of them had gone forth and returned a number of times. Then, one April day, the fifth one did not come back. With a letter he ran to Athene.

He kissed her. He said, "Did you taste the Who's Who in me? Smell me," he said and sniffed a sleeve. "That's the Hall of Fame odor. If you'll compose yourself I'll now address the universe, because Monckton and Snafflin have accepted the novel."

"Vridar!"

"Don't forget yourself. I'm almost a distinguished man now. The best thing of its kind, they say, since Cather. Soon I'll be up there with Will Durant. Remember his lecture on our Master Mind series? I now have personal relations with destiny. I'm about to add to the burdens of librarians, and to the joy of the manufacturers of paper. This time next year I should be endorsing a cigarette, and the year after that, a soap. I'll give lectures on art. And after I've published twenty books some exasperated critic will say of me:

"A word is necessary at this point to dismiss the elaborate pretensions of one Vridar Hunter. A morbid upstart from the Antelope hills (these seem to be somewhere in Idaho), he has managed with dogged and humorless effort to get a part of that dreary land into his tomes. His personality, a kind of grim skeleton of Calvinism, he has padded and fattened with all the distortions and horrors he has ever heard of—"

He broke off suddenly and turning left the room. He was weeping. He went to his own room and flinging himself on the bed tried to weep out of him an awful sense of desolation and loss. What, he wondered, after he lay exhausted and breathing hard, was the meaning of this? One of the oldest and most distinguished publishers had accepted his novel and written him an enthusiastic letter—and he had wept. What did it mean? What is wrong with me? he asked, sitting up and staring angrily round him. He knew that the meaning of this, whatever it was, went deep in him. It went clear to the bottom of him. But what was it?

He sat at his typewriter and wrote:

> I teach the cheap morality that lends
> its uses to distrust and war and hate;
> that makes of flatterers our dearest friends
> and sycophants of men who educate;
> that dwarfs religion to the foul estate
> of casuists and fools, and apprehends
> a skulking vengeful god to lie in wait
> for us and potter with our tragic ends.
>
> Ah, beautiful are these: the child that grows
> to be a deacon or a doctrinaire!
> And Elbert Hubbard's sweet arpeggios
> of rhetoric; and all the earnest prayer
> that breathes throughout *The Man Nobody Knows!* . . .
> Upon my desk are Lucian and Voltaire.

XII

It was the decade of the Lost Generation but he found it hard to think of it that way. He saw it as a time of intellectual unrest and moral questioning, a time of great cleavage. What should be abandoned, what cherished? Knowing that he would be forced out, he resigned and accepted a position at Manhattan College in New York City. Orcutt also resigned and headed east. Noyce left the labor college and came to Idaho, where Vridar was visiting with his parents and sons, and prepared to go to New York with him. Marion was already teaching there.

On the way back Vridar wondered if society was actually sick, as some of its critics were saying; and if so, why. Was it because it persisted in living by various illusions that rational minds could no longer accept? Was it because too much

608

civilization had been laid too quickly upon Adam and Eve? Was a nobler way to be found in a rational or a mystical view?

As for himself, three years of self-searching had convinced him that his subconscious mind was the significant part of him. It seemed to have depth and spaciousness, as if whole worlds were there, both contemporary and ancient. He wanted to explore those worlds but could find no way. It was folly to think that the conscious mind could do it: all that mind could do was to read, and most of what it read was abandoned or buried. Below that superficial surface mind was the wide dark reach of all that he was, lying to the farthest boundaries of time and space; for he had been all things and he was in all things. He sensed his ageless heritage; now and then intimations came out of it and were hauntingly familiar, yet strange. Now and then he seemed in dreams to wander deep in it, to go far back, to lose himself in the primeval, where only his muscular self had meaning and use; where his only hungers were the eternal hungers—food and female; and his deepest emotions were fear and terror. Sometimes when awake he tried to project himself back into the black night of it; to imagine himself sitting in idolatrous worship by a fire, reading in its flame the soul of the world around him.

He had clowned so much—but only when alone or with his woman—during the past two years in Utah that he had brought Athene to the brink of despair. Now and then he so mixed the past and the present in his projections that he got himself lost; and being lost he was frightened; and when he came to his senses he was subdued. He had indulged in outpourings of meaningless syllables, in wild harangues in words that were found in no dictionaries, in contortions of body and face, hoping in an unanticipated moment to catch a deeper revelation of himself. All this, Athene had said, was lunacy, pure and simple. He had retorted: "All right, what is Scott Fitzgerald doing? Observing and writing it down, but he knows no more about it than a photograph knows." He told her that in these emotional storms he sometimes touched something so vivid and elemental that the power of it, the deep unthinking logic of it, first amazed and then restored him to the sterile calm of thought. He would stand then in quiet, trying to recapture and intellectually look at that ancient meaning; trying to keep it undiluted by the superficial and civilized externals. He wanted to work out some art-form that would allow him to draw from the prehistoric reservoirs of strength and sanity but he was not able to, not yet, and doubted that he would ever be able. "That for the writer," he said, "is what makes writing such a nightmare—these intimations of reach that so far exceed our grasp that we want to shatter our brain-case and remove it and let the mind out . . . "

When he moved in the civilized patterns of restraint, offering the empty smile, the polite word; when he spent his hours in the spiritually unnourishing details of eating and reading themes and going to bed; and when he saw around him so many persons who seemed stiff and formalized and unreal, he then felt unreal too and would rush to his machine and write. There would then open to him and obscurely to memory the vast ancientness out of which he had come, but his groping for words left it too long, waiting, and it would dissolve like a death-fog and go away. It was then that he would, alone, throw himself into a wild tantrum, half-contained, half beyond his control; and the fuller meaning of himself would seem to roll in upon him, like a darkness touched by lights out of a deeper darkness; and his emotions, struggling out of their dungeon, would for a sharp and terrible instant stand in magnificent integration. All the traditions of evasion in human civilized life would seem to fall away for a moment, and he would stand plain for what he was. That momentary vision of himself was overwhelming in its splendor and terror. Was that, he wondered, the instant of light that Whitman had seen?

And then, becalmed, he would ask if he and the human life around him were regressing to a more primitive level, where to escape from madness the soul could simplify its forms? For this above all else was a century of war. Or did he err? Was it only a struggle in himself between two personalities that he had never been able to integrate? That, or a terribly pathetic and delicate civilization resting upon the seething and smoking craters of the past?

He would stand in the Woolworth tower looking down—seeing below him, as though transfixed by violence, the ocean of roof and spire, abutment and smoke-stack, abysses and gorges and ledges, as if a sky of brick and steel had fallen. Among the crags of iron and stone were the streets, lying in fog and smoke like the sunken backs of ruin. Trolleys like green toys disappeared into caverns; elevated trains like huge iron reptiles crawled headless and tailless along their darkened gorge; and human beings everywhere looked absurdly small and nervous and aimless. What an anthill it was!

He looked into the east and saw on his left mammoth bridges swung over East River on ropes of steel. Beyond lay Brooklyn, a vast smudge of dirty walls and blackened towers. He looked to the south and before him lay the harbor, with the Statue of Liberty standing in cold fog. Tugs and barges plowed furrows through a gray sea. A passenger boat was bearing upon Ellis Island, lying like a pile of shadow on the harbor's breast. He moved again and before him lay Jersey City, another blur of pinnacles and blind walls. Above it the sun was a burning disc in smoke piled upon the skyline. In the foreground was a long ragged wharfage of piers and docks, with a few boats lying in; and fronting it was another on the opposite shore; and between the two lay the turbid and gloomy Hudson, deep and poisonous and darkly green. In his mind some verses had been taking shape,

> One by one the gods have gone to rest
> the Magna Mater, and Ceres with her plow;
> Eos and Zephyrus and Melpomene,
> and Cronos of the Islands of the Blest—
> not one of them is on Olympus now!

A young man and a young woman were spitting. The man said, "See how far I can spit" and with an ugly sound he drew phlegm up his throat. The girl laughed happily and leaned against him. Then she spit in turn and wiped her mouth with the back of a gloved hand. Another man thrust a coin into a fixed telescope and peered through. "I can't see a damn bit farther," he complained to no one. "This thing is a fake." He looked into the slot where his coin had vanished. "If I could spit on a bald head," said the man with the girl. "Jesus, would he jump. See how far up we are." "Only think," said the girl. "Only think what man has done. With just his hands." "If I was to jump off," the man said, "how long would it take me to hit?" He leaned over as if to see. "You know, in Japan they jump into craters. When we get on a high place why do we want to jump?" The other man was saying, "I tell you this thing is a fake . . ."

Vridar moved again and looked north over the blurred scene. In his ears was the deep and troubled sound of an iron city, in his nostrils a pungent ocean wind; but in the wind's eddies was the smell of the breath and sweat of the city's millions. On the streets below the odors for him were like those of seaweed and pond water, unventilated bedrooms, wet chickens and old bones. It was true that some of the skylines and some of the spires were lovely when seen in mists, for they then were as soft as Turner's "Snow Storm," with all the ugliness hidden . . .

He descended and entered Wall Street, a deep narrow gray canyon. At its head stood Trinity Church, which once a year spilled Christmas chimes against the stone walls. Were these the chief symbols of his country?—or Beethoven's Academy of Music, whose professors were mythical names on a letterhead? Or the Village? Once it had been packed with talent but was now a smoky area of decaying roofs and crumbling walls. It had a few dens and speakeasies under quaintly silly names, among them Romany Marie's, a snuggery for artists who cultivated poses. There one evening Vridar had seen a writer sitting among Chinese lanterns, sucking tea through a reed six feet long. Across from where he sat a wrecking gang had shattered an old building and it stood now as a pile of ruins. The stink of them was unbearable.

He walked along Sixth Avenue. Overhead an elevated thundered upon its iron path, shaking a mist of grit to the street. In a newstand an old woman was huddled in rags, her face like wrinkled cowhide, her hands like claws. Up and down the sidewalk paced an unclean fellow, advertising halfsoles. A legless beggar looked like a man sitting in stone to his crotch. At the entrance to the subway was another creature, foul and old, with pencils in her lap and a few pennies. Her upper lip was wide and yellow. On glancing back Vridar saw that one withered leg came like a root from the folds of her dress. He dropped a nickel into a slot and swung an iron turnstile. He went down a stairway of stone and stood on a stone platform, waiting for an iron train. He shouldered his way in and was wedged between a large soughing fat man and an old woman with pouches under her eyes. A little way off was a girl, her mouth scarlet, with a tall amorous youth hovering over her. Another man, hanging from a strap, seemed to be trying to insinuate his knee between the legs of the girl who sat before him. Down low, among the hips and bellies, were the sober eyes of a small child. Vridar smiled but the lad only looked up at his mother and again at Vridar. Vridar then turned a little to watch the man trying to invade with his knee.

A New York phychologist had said that subway riding was the largest group perversion of sex in the world. It seemed to Vridar not to be perversion at all. Hundreds of men, jampacked into these savage journeys, hugged tight against women and moved a little this way, a little that, as the train rocked and shuddered: hips against hips, bellies against backs: Bergson's élan vital and Freud's libido . . .

O Lord, for the clean Douglas fir odor of the Big Hole mountains! To lie in a huckleberry thicket, crushing purple juice against his lips, or in a semiarid sagebrush area, wide under sunlight and with a fragrance as sweet as the world's soul! It took him only an hour or two wandering through New York City to realize again, and at greater depth, that he was incurably a mountain man, a man of the American West.

He left the train and followed a stream of humanity to light and air. He turned east and flowed with the crowd, his feet lost in a current of feet, his identity muffed in a void of sound. Around him were men carrying large stomachs, with jowls overhanging their collars; women entombed and panting; girls with complexions fighting poison and smoke. "Short skirts," said Moses McGuire, "show how crooked the world is." Turning south Vridar passed the glittering Chrysler tower and came to a dark street that smelled of rain dripping from henroosts, of rubber scaled against stone; turned a corner, hearing a murmuring as of far seas, smelling an odor of wet rags. He reflected that if Manhattan could stand up, with its feet in Battery Park, it would have Harlem from shoulder to shoulder across its heart. The Great White Way would lie between its navel and its knees. Yes, indeed, the United States contrived its ironies with incredible perfection: Trinity looked into Wall Street, Ellis Island lay almost within the shadow of the Goddess of Liberty.

When he could find time, Vridar walked the city for hours, trying to catch the spirit and the meaning of it. Was it, like Baudelaire's life, an oasis of horror in a desert of ennui? He paraphrased Auslander: This city is dead. Everything that you can say has been quite definitely said. But it was not dead. It was horrifyingly alive, like six million huge ants shaken out of their hills. It ravaged countrysides and sucked them into its suburbs; buried wooded hills under brick and stone; turned clean lovely streams into open sewers. How many thousands of tons of human excrement were dumped into the two rivers every week!

All its favorite trademarks and shibboleths were cacophonous: tabloid and subway and dock, frigidaire and macadamized bridge, girder, skyscraper, progress. What ugly words! In contrast was the liquid loveliness of a world so unlike it that they seemed not to be on the same planet—the dells and hills and melodies, skylark and warbler and wren, sunlight-on-peace. In time there would be, an architect said, a city of twenty million—with multiplied towers, subways under subways, underground electrified caverns, sidewalks tier on tier. This mighty sarcophagus of steel and stone, phychiatrists said, would be a mammoth bedlam, in which the doctors of emotional ills would be busy analyzing one another. Why, he wondered, why oh why did human beings want to multiply their numbers into such nightmares? It was so plain to him when walking the streets that most of them detested one another—why, then, did they want all the women to have all the babies they could have? What underlay this appalling lunacy? He came close to the secret of it but it eluded him and he walked on, struggling, but in vain, to formulate it. Should he say—

Our ribs are now the ribs of steel,
our flesh is flesh of iron and stone;

612

we stir like mortar when we feel,
we feel the rivets in our bone,
The roar of industry, the whine
has shaped us and has shaped our art:
we feel the girder in our spine,
we feel the motor in our heart . . .

The Communists among his teaching colleagues said it would not be like this in Russia. They said a utopia was at hand. In Russia, Lesbians did not shake their "implacable" thighs; dealers in seafood did not sell gin in codfish packages; bootleggers did not wear Hoover buttons. There were no wells of loneliness, none of the stuff Maisie knew. Here, they said, millions of persons worked as slaves; ate, slept, bred, died. Millions rode the subways and where did you see a happy face? Those with the loot slept in sumptuous apartments high above the smoke. Columnists lived up there who wrote about the romance and beauty of Forty-Second Street—but they spent their winters in Florida or Nice. So the Communists said.

"You should join us," one of them had said to Vridar. "In Russia writers are given the pay and position they deserve. You spent thousands of hours on a novel and how much did you get out of it? Six hundred dollars. And Monckton and Snafflin don't want your next one because they think it won't sell. In Russia it would be published and millions would read it and you'd be acclaimed as a great benefactor. Why don't you join us?"

Vridar was thinking about it. He knew that a lot of people were thinking about it.

"The sun has risen," the Communists said. "It's shining over Russia but setting here. The future is yonder, the shape of things to come. We need people like you. Come with us."

He was thinking about it, but he had been so bitterly deceived in the teachings of the Bible and his mother, his disillusionment had come so close to unseating his mind and he was now at such loose ends and so full of despair that he was resolved never again to hug to his heart anything that could not stand the searching scrutiny of his mind. Yes, he was thinking about it and he was looking hard at it. There would be nothing else in all his life at which he would look any harder.

XIII

Among Vridar's students in Utah there now and then had been a Jew. "Give me all Jews," he had said to Athene, "and I can teach. These damned self-adoring Christians wear me out." Most of his students now were Jews and when he entered a classroom he faced intelligent men and women who were not slumped down staring at their watches. These students had come to learn. Most of them were skeptical, even cynical. Vridar had been trying to teach boys and girls from Mormon countryside and town, who actually believed that they were the latter-day saints, and that their Utah valley was the zion of a chosen people. Now he faced Jew, Turk,

Arab, Armenian, Italian, Negro . . . and he was amazed at the difference between what he had left and what he had come to. That both student bodies could be American, living under the same flag and in the same year, was beyond belief. In Utah he never dared to approach certain facts; here he dared not evade them. If he was prudent a challenge was flung. A challenge was flung if he tried to soften with a euphemism. The derisive laughter shocked and frightened him, as when, seeing the name Lipshitz, he deliberately mispronounced it. "My name is Lipshitz," said a voice. "You mispronounced it. The last syllable is shitz." "I'm sorry," said Vridar, and felt a cold dampness on his forehead.

He learned that these students like this city were feverishly awake. They were neurotic, frank, loud, and by his traditions, vulgar. He observed the bold love-making—the way some of the men backed girls against walls and thrust at them and pushed their heads back to kiss them. One evening a woman about thirty years old entered Vridar's class and sat on the front row and doodled. When the class was dismissed she gave the paper to Vridar, saying, "I do this all the time. Why?"

Vridar stared at a whole page of phallic symbols. He gave the page to his brother. Marion said it was the best example of unconscious drawing he had ever seen.

In the same class an attractive Jewess sat alone at one side of the room. One evening in the presence of twenty students she astonished Vridar by saying, "Why do all the men in this class sit on one side and the women on the other?" She looked over at the men and said, "What's wrong with the men here?"

Almost every day Vridar was flabbergasted by some revelation. He had read a composition and was talking about it when a Jewess stopped him. "Professor, you know what I think is wrong with you?"

"Is something wrong with me?"

"You're a puritan. You're afraid of women."

His face turned red. God, he was beginning to hate teaching here!

This girl came to his office desk and would talk only about herself. The other woman whose name was Rose, even followed him to the street and said she was going home with him. She said she would do his typing.

"I do my own typing," he said.

"Then talk to me and I'll listen."

He tried to dismiss her, to walk around her, but she faced him at every turn. She seized his arm. She mocked him and taunted him.

"Is your time so precious that you can't give me a little?"

"Just what do you want?" he asked impatiently.

"You to listen to this," she said, walking backwards ahead of him. "I was at a party the other night and I was drinking. I ran to the bathroom and locked myself in. I kicked around in there and broke everything. When a man came to the door what did I do? I tore my brassiere off and threw it in his face. Why did I?"

"You must be a virgin," he said.

"Why did I do it?"

"It was your hymen," he said. "Now go on home." He came to the building where he lived and entered, shutting the door in her face. He went up the stairway, feeling pretty foolish.

The other girl, Sonia Cahan, asked Vridar to her room. Unlike Rose, she was fairskinned and flaxen-haired and looked like a Swede. He wondered why so many people called themselves Jews when most of their blood was not Jewish at all. Sonia was about twenty-four. When Vridar refused to go to her room, she came to his office desk. This embarrassed him because with thirty colleagues and the chairman he sat in one huge room.

Sonia said, "I'll tell you a story that'll amuse you."

"I'd rather you'd tell some other instructor. I'm busy."

"It's this, I'm afraid of men. I'm still a virgin, so this is what I did. There's a nice boy I know. He's only seventeen but he's tall, he's a man. I—" She broke off, looking at him.

"Yes?" Vridar said, trying to read a theme. He knew that his chairman, who sat at the far end of the room, was watching him.

"His name is Simon. Simon is living with me. We're in a large room and each of us has a bed. He's on one side, I'm on the other. I told him never to approach me or I'd scream."

For a moment Vridar met her eyes. "You haven't screamed yet?"

"Don't laugh, please. It's not funny for us."

"No, it isn't funny," Vridar said, again meeting her gaze. "How long has he been living with you?"

"A month. No, I won't lie. Two months."

"Would you scream?" Vridar asked.

"Don't be silly. Of course I would."

"No wonder you called me a puritan," he said.

But he knew it was not that. He knew that it was something deep in the Jew that he didn't yet understand. Marion said it was because of the closeness of the Jewish family relationship. Vridar asked his deskmate, Jack Farlane, what he thought. Jack was a minor poet whose wife, the book editor of a liberal journal, lorded it over him. Jack tried to turn everything into witty smut. Looking at Vridar now he said, "March, Maxwell House coffee, Chesterfields." When Vridar looked blank Jack said, "You're thick. In like a lion, out like a lamb; good to the last drop and they satisfy." He yawned at Vridar and said, "You know Brownell's statement? This generation isn't emancipated, it's merely unbuttoned."

Vridar turned to his work. Merely unbuttoned. That wasn't bad at all. Another instructor had told him that seducing students was big business with faculty members here. That was why the chairman in this department had them all in a large room where he could keep his eye on them. There had been an instructor a year ago, the kind who talked to giddy girls about poetry and art and the wonder of life; who invited them to his apartment to see his art objects or hear his records and who, after the girl was at ease, gently enthroned her at the fireplace. He set her in a chair and draped her with a Turkish shawl, took off her shoes and put on her feet a pair of Persian sandals, gave her a Chinese cigarette holder and put in it an Egyptian cigarette. He urged her to sip cointreau from a delicate chalice. He burned incense. He sat at her feet, robed like a mandarin, and talked about beauty. After a while he gently undressed her and brought Japanese pyjamas and laid across her knees a fur-lined pelisse.

He seduced as many as four students a week, said the frail young man, his eyes sharp with envy.

Vridar was not interested in tales about lechers. He wanted to understand Jews, for he had a notion that the Jew was at the core of the Western riddle. In the middle of a lecture one afternoon he was stopped by a voice that said, "Dr. Hunter, I don't think you know what you're talking about." "I probably didn't," Vridar said to Athene later. "But it's a hell of a shock to have somebody tell you so." He soon discovered that Jews liked sharp intellectual skirmishes. They liked wit. And they were as quick to turn on one of their own as on a non-Jew, if they found him ignorant or dull. Marion was teaching in the department of psychology. One day Vridar asked him, "What's the psychology of the Jew?" Lack of ego-identification, Marion said: the Jew had neither country, land, nor home.

Was that it? Having been kicked around for centuries, as though the earth were a stadium and they a football, were they emotionally and mentally more awake than other Western people? Vridar now developed a statement that he was to repeat often: "If there are no stupid Jews it's because all the feebleminded perished in nineteen centuries of Christian persecution. For that if for nothing else Jews owe Christians a great debt." He would look round him a moment and add drily, "It's obvious everywhere you look that the Christians haven't been persecuted." Jews, Vridar perceived, had a deep sense of insecurity, but instead of sulking when set upon they took their blows as education and learned from every blow they received. They didn't want to be gentiles, as some gentiles imagined; they wanted to keep secure those values which alone could give them a sense of integrity and permanence. It had been the nineteen centuries that had driven them into family relationships so intimate that what they had entered as a refuge had become a curse.

Jews opened to Vridar another revelation of the human mind and heart. They forced him to revise or abandon some notions that he had been taught to cherish. Though he strove to be, and by most persons was taken to be, an aggressive person, he was at heart a submissive person who had made a great virtue of modesty; for his mother had taught him not to be self-seeking, bold, vulgar, ill-bred. Self-depreciation had become a law of life. He was aware of the typical American rebuke, "How you love yourself!" and in time came to see it as a part of the leveling of the uncommon base. He had been taught to despise hogs of all kind: the table-hog like his father who had no sense of his fair portion; the love-hog like his brother, about whom it was already becoming known that he lay with some of his patients; the property-hog like most Americans, who laid their hands on everything they could seize. He had gone to another extreme: self-denial with him had almost become a religion. He had been taught to believe that it was far better to give than to take, to listen than to be heard. Self-effacement had become his golden rule.

That much he now understood but not the sources of it. He asked himself if modesty was only another evasion. And who dared to be modest, save the one who felt insecure! Had he so detested aggressive persons because they made him feel inadequate? Were those who hotly denounced insolence, smugness, and conceit afraid to stand up to the grim competitive struggle? Was Communism a refuge for the intellectual who was a physical and emotional weakling? There, he felt, he was coming close to it but it still eluded him!

Was it centuries of persecution that had made Jews such an aggressive people? For their self-pitying and self-effacing persecutor, were they really insolent? While thinking of the matter Vridar recalled a story told of James Joyce—that on being introduced to Yeats he said, "We've met too late. You're too old to be influenced by me." Could any human being be *that* arrogant and still be *great?* The thought troubled him and deep in his soul he confided, "If talent must be arrogant, I have none . . . ."

Carlyle, Carl, and Athene had all been appointed to teaching positions in the College and were facing classes composed largely of Jews. One day Vridar laid his woes in Athene's lap and said, "Why have I made such a virtue of modesty?—and will I perish by it?"

It had become Athene's way to look at him like one bemused; her eyes steady but luminous with her opinion of herself, her face smiling a little, her whole manner giving an impression of mirth barely restrained.

"Didn't your mother teach you that?"

"There's something more. It's related somehow to my life with my brother but that escapes me."

"Why not ask him?"

Ask him! He thought of his brother as a patronizing ass. At a party Marion had proclaimed to everyone who would listen, "My brother here is a one-woman man. If he ever commits adultery, he'll be dead as an artist." Vridar had wanted to say, You blockhead, don't you know that artists are the most adulterous people on earth? And what do you mean anyway except that men like you should have all the women!

"For times like these," he said, "Moses McGuire is a better spokesman than I can ever be." This was the decade, drawing to its crisis and its close, that in a few years would be summarized as the Jazz Age, the Decade of the Flapper, the Glamorization of Gangsters, the Big Nonstop Business Boom, the Era of Silent Cal, the Great Emphasis on Sex, the Invasion by Freud . . . . It was the decade in which seven hundred ministers and theological students revealed, when polled, that more than half of them believed in the literal biblical hell, and sixty per cent of them thought that Satan was an actual being. It was the era of Jamaica Ginger, Bathtub Gin, Jake, Jackass Brandy, White Lightning, Soda Pop Moon, and Panther Whisky. In New York City alone there were thirty-two thousand speakeasies, most of them clip-and-roll, protected by a mayor whose popularity waxed exactly in proportion as his venality became more odious. It was the decade in which a cabinet member was found guilty of national betrayal, but in which, on his conviction, the wife of a juror ran screaming at her husband, "You miserable rat."

When Vridar was busy at his typewriter, Mac would burst in on him, sneering, "I come with a stipend from the National Academy. What are you writing now?—The Great American Novel or a letter to your Dear Mother?" He shoved a pile of books from a chair and sank sprawling. "Where's your gin?"

617

"In the bathroom."

Mac went to the bathroom and drank and came out. "If you want a popular book interview fifty married women and find out what their husbands did on their bridal nights. Call it Consolations for Old Maids." Mac cawed and with a trembling hand lit a cigarette. "Hunter, the clue to the Western world is the Devil. The Christians are right in believing that Satan created the earth. The great writers have always known it. Goethe said he did. Blake said it. Byron said it. Baudelaire and deVigny and a host of others realized that nature in its essence is infernal. That's the original sin." He sucked at his cigarette and looked at Vridar. "As for Jews, didn't the Christians of the Middle Ages say they worshiped the Devil and that synagogues were his temples? Isn't that the clue we're looking for?"

Vridar was silent.

Mac cawed again. "A pessimist thinks all women are bad, an optimist hopes they are. You know, I'm sick of being only another Oscar Wilde. And I'm sick of coming here and seeing you with these tail snarls from your spavined pegasus. Have you read what the critics think of your dull novel? Keats was dead at twenty-five, Shelley at twenty-nine. Congreve at your age had thrown his pen away. Marlowe had written his mighty line. And so has a guy named Hemingway. Have you read his farewell to screwing?"

Mac went to the bathroom and came out wiping his mouth. "Good God, Hunter, is there really any hope for you? Evangelists and artists both leap like jackasses out of repressions and bray, and you want to lead one of the packs. Did you ever observe that a woman poet always writes twice as badly after she marries? Rest your Mormon hindend on a soft chair and meditate on that. Have you ever seen the Round table group?" He meant the writers who gathered at the Algonquin Hotel—Alexander Woollcott, Robert Benchley, Dorothy Parker, Heywood Broun, George Kaufman, and a few others. "Just to look at them trying to make books out of a pinch or two of talent is enough to cure any man of the itch to write."

Vridar slipped a paper into his machine and typed.

> Dear Mother and Dad:
>   Broadway at 42nd may be the center of the world but not of my world. At the moment I am seeing again all the lush wealth of a countryside —the fields of golden wheat upon which a breeze is a dimpled journeying; hills like banks of blue fog; clouds heaped like masses of dandelion bloom; and a sky aflame from sunset to zenith. I see again the fragrant roads lying upon

"My God!" said Mac, leaning forward to sneer. "The golden complex is flowing into prose."

> distance; smell the drip of orchards, huckleberries, peeled aspen bark, fir gum and kinnikinic, crushed yarrow and sage leaf and badger hole. I asked my students where, if they had a day to spend as they pleased, they would go. Not a one went to Europe or the South Seas. Most of them said they'd go to the country and lie under a noble tree. Some of them wanted to find old log bridges, sunk, overgrown with moss, under which sweet water gurgles along its path through the cress. The air under such bridges I recall is sweet with hidden growth and clean decay. An old

bridge sunk in a meadow (I know one!) or lost in an upland pasture of clover is a lovely thing, aged and mellowed in its own quiet being, golden rust on the spikeheads and moss on every scar of the ax. And roads disappearing into thickets of aspen, mallow, gilia and goldenrod; and the sagebrush prairie in the heat of midday sun, when all its marvelous incense rises heavenward.

He stopped typing, pulled the sheet out and tore it up and went to the window. Mac had been to the gin again and was now staring at Vridar. "What a picture you made," he said, "scribbling like any spinster, all your thoughts arranged and marked like merchandise in a Woolworth store. Was that a part of your materia amorosa?" When Vridar gave no reply Mac went on. "You know what an intellectual colossus named Elmer Davis said?—that not thinkers today but rich men rule the world. Maybe Elmer would tell us when thinkers ever ruled. And Henry L. Mencken says his greatest regret is that the Japanese haven't yet burned Los Angeles. Hunter, why don't you write some poetry? *The Saturday Review of Literature* has just given a prize to a bird named Oscar O'Kelleigh for a thing that is nothing on earth but a paean to a stock market that has now fallen on its face. The tape flows like soft May days that pass to summer. Some of the guys jumping out of windows must have loved that."

Vridar wished that Mac would go. His callow cynicism wearied him. He supposed that Mac wanted a father, which meant that he wanted God. Mac said he loved this city. Vridar hated it. He wanted to go again to the mountains and clean rivers and trees that were not fighting for their lives against smoke and poison. One of his colleagues, a Communist, would stand by a window and look out at the stunted half-dead trees in the square, rub his soft white hands and exclaim, "How bee-utiful this morning!"

"Hunter, is alcohol good for me?"

"William James," said Vridar without turning, "said that it brings its votary from the chill periphery of things to the radiant core. It makes him for the moment one with truth."

"From a great psychologist that's good enough." Mac disappeared and came out wiping his mouth. He would buy Vridar a few jugs, he said—and added: "I write letters to my mother and she sends me money. I'm absolutely shameless. I'd spend her last dime on a bottle or a whore." He paused only a moment. Then: "I can't get over what Jane Welsh Carlyle said, that all of a sudden the clothes come off and in fancy she sees them all naked, standing straddling in ludicrous postures. And Flaubert, he said that he nearly fainted when for the first time he saw the two naked breasts of a woman. Now women are pulling their skirts higher and higher, apparently determined to show their crotch. Suppose a woman's breasts were just in front of the hind legs, like those of a cow. What monsters we'd think them!"

"Of course," Vridar said, still looking out.

"But would we if the vagina was in the navel? Your stupid friend Carl Noyce now charges two-bits a person at parties to see his navel and I expect him any day to say, Who put the wound in me? Does he know why he shows off his navel?"

"Because it's full of hair," Vridar said.

"Well, don't forget to read O'Kelleigh's masterpiece." Mac looked a few moments toward the gin but shame won in him and he left the room.

After he was gone Vridar sat, feeling depressed, and looked under his bed at a small leather bag that had been with him for five years. He had never opened it. Within it, quiet and dark, were Neloa's letters, her cookbook, and a few locks of her hair and a copper urn. So many times he had thought of Leonard's lines,

> Did I not know
> the use of crepe, the etiquette of woe?
> Yes, but I'd business more severe than that:
> Knowing how hungrily death leered for me
> I seized on life wherever it might be.

To get away from himself he turned to letters from persons who had read his book. One was from a bachelor who had withdrawn deep into solitude and wondered if Vridar had "not found some positive faith the nature of which you will, if I do not presume, suggest to me." Some positive faith! He, who wouldn't have bet a silver dollar that he could keep his sanity another year! Where was there a positive faith? In Communism? In moribund churches? Another letter abused him: "You should hide in shame for having written such a brutal book." Brutal? Some of his friends had said that his book was brutal and to them one evening he said he wanted to tell them something.

"First," he said, "let me read this. Hang the bird from its feet from a cord or shackle with the breast toward the killer. The head of the bird is then grasped by placing the thumb and forefinger of the left hand between the eye and the ear on each side of the skull. An ordinary sharp knife, preferably with a blade about two and a half inches long and one fourth of an inch wide, is then inserted through the mouth in such a way that the point is just back of the skull and toward the left of the killer. The killer now presses down with the point of the knife, draws it slightly forward and across the base of the skull to the right. Ordinarily if this cut is carefully done the jugular veins will be severed and a stream of blood will flow immediately out of the mouth. When the killer sees that the stream of blood is flowing nicely he then debrains the bird. Debraining is done by inserting the point of the knife through the groove in the roof of the mouth and then forcing it backward on a line midway between the eyes and ears. After the knife has been inserted far enough to reach the brain, it is twisted slightly. If it has been placed correctly the bird flops and usually makes a distinctive quack. This——"

He stopped. There was shrill outcry from the women, one of whom was crying, "I suppose that's from your next book!"

"That," said Vridar, "was taken from a booklet from a cold storage company. It is called How to Dress Turkeys."

That was the only way to kill a turkey, Carlyle Orcutt said. It spoiled the meat to cut the head off. Carl Noyce was glowering round him and affecting a great fury. These sickly sentimentalists, he said, reminded him of Alexander Woollcott reading "A Christmas Carol." "The tiger eats the antelope, the spider eats the fly, and you eat the turkey. You boil lobsters alive. You press ducks. The Romans jumped up and down on the bellies of live sows to make their tits tender!" He was turning on

620

one foot, then on the other, scowling, his black eyes like fire. The woman who howled the loudest about brutality, he said, had a buried wish to beat her husband. She who was most shocked by sexy stories was the easiest to seduce. The torturer and the zealot always filled the same skin. He turned to Wilma Reagan, who with a few other Utah students had come to the city. "You big fat pile of womanhood!" He was swinging a bottle of gin above his head as a baton. "Come now, let's sing as the birdies sing—tweet—tweet-tweet—tweet-tweet . . . ."

Mac had been sprawled out, sneering up at Carl. "What frauds you all are!" he moaned, sucking at a cigarette. "Art has become a eunuch with homosexual tendencies. Infantilism is its Mother, Priapus is its Father. This big fat eunuch Woollcott tries with vicious wit to cut all competitors down, yet bawls like a rainstorm over 'Mammy.' That's this age for you, Hunter: the hired killers one night bawl over 'Mammy' and the next night murder a stranger for a hundred-dollar bill. You—"

"Oh God damn!" Carl roared, glaring down at him. "Sew up that wide loose mouth of yours!"

"If I told you what your mouth reminds me of, with that hair around it—"

"Shut up!" Wilma cried.

Mac turned to sneer at her. "One would think you must be all female genital area, you look so obscene. Wilma Reagan, the Sappho of Manhattan, writing verses for Christmas cards! Wilma—"

"Shut up, you loose-lipped imbecile! We didn't come here to hear your psychopathic lispings. Come, you people! Let's sing as the birdies sing . . . ."

"My God!" groaned Moses McGuire. "They allow this man to teach!"

XIV

Vridar decided that he had to get away from it for a while, and when an academic year ended he told Athene that her babilan was going west. Was he going alone? No, with Carl. Athene was his wife now. When she came to New York she had her heart set on marriage, and they had gone to a city building and stood for two hours in a line-up.

Now she did not ask if he would see women. When he called himself babilan, she had known that he would. He wanted to shake off the curse that hung over him, but he was not going west primarily to see women who might welcome him there. He had to see his sons and his parents. He wanted to see the mountains again, the rivers, the sagebrush plains to discover if he was now idealizing them, or if his greatest strength lay out there.

He and Carl went first to Salt Lake City, and when Vridar found that one of his former students was happy to see him and eager to go to bed with him, he called another, and still another. The first one shocked him by clutching at the sac that contained the semen. The second one, daughter of a distinguished Mormon family, met him the next noon for lunch. Smiling up at him, she said, "Do I look the same?"

"So far as I can tell."

"I looked the same to me this morning. But how, I thought, can that be?—for yesterday I was a virgin, today I'm a gal what's been laid." Vridar glanced at her and said nothing. Jean went on: "I expected my father to say, What on earth has happened to you? But he said nothing. The same father, the same breakfast, the same Jean."

"In what way did you expect to look different?"

"Transformed. I expected to *feel* different but I don't."

After lunch they again walked side by side, Jean studying his profile and saying at last, "Do you love Athene in a big way?"

The question disturbed him. "I suppose so," he said.

That was all. Without speaking again they came to a corner and Jean said, "I leave you here. Goodbye."

"Goodbye," he said. She went up the street and he stared after her as long as she was in sight. Not once did she look back. He understood that she had forced herself to ask that question and had taken his answer as final. If his answer had been different, she might have said, "Shall I see you again?" She might have said, "Could you ever love me in a big way?" It was the frankness of the American coed in the postwar age. He had never known that Jean was attracted to him and he now felt unworthy and foolish and stupid.

To put her out of memory he called Betty Gardner a few days later. Betty too was from a prominent and in this case a wealthy Mormon family. She said she'd be happy to see him. For two or three hours he sat alone with her in a big house and they talked about various faculty members, some of his former students, and New York City, while sipping drinks. He thought her quite a beautiful woman: she had a splendid mass of lustrous brown hair; dark gray eyes under heavy lashes; a fine nose, mouth, chin and a lovely figure. When he stood up to go, she arose and put arms round his neck and in the most matter of fact way kissed him. He put arms round her and kissed her. He looked inward to his emotions but nothing erotic seemed to be coming to life. Nevertheless he said, "Shall we?"

"I'd like to," she said.

He was to remember that once she thrust a leg beyond the cover and asked, "Have I a beautiful leg?" and without looking at it he replied, "Yes." She had said, "You're nicer than Paul," and he had wondered who Paul was. He slipped out the back way just before daylight. She called him that afternoon, asking him to come again, saying that she would ask another couple in. On arriving Vridar found Walter Kurtz, a man who now and then had been at parties with Carl and the Orcutts; and a stout wide-faced blonde named Lillian MacGregor. Walter was a sandy man and when that was said, everything about his appearance, it seemed to Vridar, had been said: his hair and eyebrows were sandy, his complexion, and all his clothes matched his complexion and hair. He was a quiet, whimsical, witty, and gentle person who was never obnoxious, even when drunk.

They rolled a carpet back and spent an evening drinking and dancing. About midnight Betty and Lillian entered a bedroom and went to bed. Walter sat in the kitchen with a full glass. Looking drunkenly round him Vridar said, "They've ditched us." Walter nodded. Vridar stood a few moments thinking about it and then went to the bedroom. He found the door open. He looked in. He went over and stood by the bed and looked at Betty. "Where do we sleep?" he asked her.

622

"In another room."

"I think I'll sleep with you two."

Then all hell broke loose. It happened so fast that he didn't even have time to get his hands up. She was there like a tigress, in a white gown, and her first blow shattered the frame of his spectacles. The next blow was the flat of her hand on his cheek and it stung like flame. Then it was blow after blow, her right hand, her left hand; her face ugly with distortion; her mouth curled with contempt and fury; her breath at last coming hard as she still struck, right and left and right. Blood was gushing from his nose and her blows scattered it all over him. When exhausted at last she stopped, glaring up at him; and quietly he said (for he was sober now); "Go on, kill me, if that's what you're trying to do." She broke into wild weeping and ran away from him.

He hadn't known that this woman loved him.

Turning, he saw Walter framed in the doorway, smoking a pipe and looking at Vridar with quiet amusement. Going to the parlor Vridar found his hat and let himself out. He walked toward the city and his hotel, trying to look to all the sources of Betty's fury and wondering how many novelists really knew anything about people. He was bruised and bloody and full of disgust and shame. He stopped at a fountain and tried to wash himself off. What a crass bastard I was! he thought and went on.

In Idaho two weeks later he was visiting his sons when he received a letter from her. It began, "Je suis enciente." It said she would have to have an abortion. She could think of only one way to get it legally and respectably: Vridar would have to come to Salt Lake City and swear before her family doctor he had Negro blood in him. Nobody, she said, would expect the daughter of so distinguished a family to suffer the shame of a bastard by a Negro father.

Vridar was speechless. How, he asked, could she know she was pregnant in only two weeks? Anyway, if she was pregnant he was not the father, for he had done in the situation what all decent men did. Two weeks later another note came, saying she was not pregnant after all. "Le estōy a ustēd muy agradecído," she wrote, switching to Spanish.

There were other women in Vridar's life this summer, including one of Neloa's cousins, a fat young woman who asked Vridar to marry her. Carl wanted to return by way of Denver, where he expected to have an assignation. On the way there Vridar sat by a window looking at the magnificent Rocky Mountains, at an elevation of twelve thousand feet. He was thinking back on what he had done. The babilan in him was fading out but he felt guilt. He tried to think he did not but it was no good, the guilt was there. He knew now that it took a man and a woman months or years to work out this relationship: the casual thing was only a conquest, it enhanced the ego, it put spit in a person's vanity; but that was all. There was so much risk, so much bother, and so much of what Carl called fandango in the build-up that the experience was simply not worth it.

In Denver Carl had a former student waiting for him. On the train going west Vridar had met two high school teachers, one of whom, Mary Carter, had taken a fancy to him. Because Carl wanted a little party in Denver, Vridar sent a wire to

Mary, asking if she would meet him there, for she taught in a town nearby. Both girls were at the hotel waiting.

Vridar thought Carl's girl one of the most beautiful women he had ever seen. She was stunning in both face and figure, and she had intelligence and charm. Compared to her, Mary, a blonde whose hair was tinged with red, looked plain, almost dowdy, and seemed stupid. They drank in Carl's room. Carl and his girl devoted themselves to one another with such ardor that Mary became miserably unhappy and begged Vridar to go to her room. He didn't want to go to bed with Mary. Oh, she was warm and womanly, she was ardent, and above all she was decent. Though twenty-five she said she was a virgin and this summer he had got enough of virgins. He wanted to sit and drink and talk but she would not have it that way, she dragged him to the door, she got him to her room; and then she flung herself to his lap and began to kiss him. She kissed his mouth and all over his face and then began to undress him, and to undress herself; and when he saw that she had a tuft of hair at each nipple he felt unspeakabley mean and wretched. But he allowed himself to be pulled into bed . . . .

It was Mary who leapt out, a half hour later, with a cry of amazement. Vridar then sprang out and turning to look was appalled. His first thought was sardonic: If Moses McGuire was here he'd count the spots! His second he uttered aloud, "Cold water." But there was no need to. Mary was an efficient level-headed woman. She yanked the sheets off and began to wash at the bowl. Vridar watched her while dressing and then went over to take her naked body in his arms and kiss her goodnight.

She looked up at him and said, "Will I ever see you again?"

"Mary, I doubt it."

"Will you ever come west again?"

"I doubt it."

"Well, thanks," she said and tiptoeing kissed him again.

His last memory of her was to be of a woman standing naked at a washbowl, looking short-legged and low-buttocked, rinsing a sheet. He went to his room. Carl was not there but came in before morning. Carl was a sleeper who lay on his back and snored like a hog, and for a person like Vridar, exhausted, unhappy, and nervous, his snores were intolerable. He entered the bathroom and putting all the towels and mats under him slept there.

A few days later he sat with Athene and told her what he had done. All the way east he had wondered whether to tell her: honesty, so plain and literal for his mother, had become all symbol and parable for him. If he confessed, would that be only another form of self-pity?—a still more contemptible form of exhibitionism? Carl never told. Marion never told. Vridar supposed that few men ever confessed, or women either; but as briefly as possible he told her and watched her eyes fill with tears. Were her tears, he asked himself, only another form of self-pity? Good God, was there no plane of conduct on which the human ego could be decent?

He said he was not aware of all the buried things that had compelled and directed him. He was not yet sure what had made him babilan. Was it merely a sense of guilt that paralyzed the will?—or was it, as Stendhal thought, the need to feel secure while

624

consummating the act? Was it fear of his mother's reproaches and his own shame? Was it his erotic interest in his sister, long years ago?

Had he done himself any good? "I'll have to wait and see what my subsconscious does with it."

Athene said, "How many women did you have?"

"It doesn't matter, does it?"

"Do you love any of them?"

"Athene, I don't know what love is. I found myself thinking that the company of two of them I could enjoy for a while. They had qualities that appeal to me. Does that mean I'm fickle?"

"I think you're fickle," she said. And she threw at him a taunt that she was to throw again, in the years ahead: "You old Brigham Young!"

He was annoyed. She had called him superficial and she now called him fickle. "Just what is it in me that you like, if anything at all?"

She was drying her eyes. "I sometimes wonder."

"Is it not your self-idolatry that keeps you with me? The more I know of you, my dear, the more I perceive that you're much like my mother. Why had I never known that?"

"Your mother has some wonderful virtues."

"You mean—"

"Oh, I don't want to talk about it!"

He went to a mirror and bowed low, trying to see the top of his skull. "I can't imagine," he said, "why any woman should be attracted to me—nor to his great delight can Carl. Still, he's the one who loves what he sees in a mirror and devotes hours to the care of it. It is no surprise to him when a woman surrenders."

Athene was looking at him in her amused pitying way. He knew it but he pretended not to know it.

"Well," he went on, still trying to see his bald spot, "I've rubbed about everything into my scalp I've ever heard of. I've sat in headgears and in a burning sun. I've read bales of literature on baldness. Dr. Sabouraud found only one bald eunuch in a hundred and forty-seven, and so related baldness to virility. Dr. Muller says soul emotion is the cause. Nessler believes in hair migration. I do know that every time I lose a handful on my head I get another brave solitary sprout on my chest."

"Vridar?"

"Engelbach relates baldness to the endocrine glands, Goodman to nervous shock, McLeod to the wearing of hats. The hat industry must love that guy. Do you know how many shops in New York devote themselves to the bald head? Do you know how many women are as bald as a baby's rump? I slipped into one of those places and was floored. What a sight a woman is with no hair!

"Well, Carl has all his hair and all his teeth. So has Carlyle. They find it very amusing because I have bridgework and potter around with it, using a file, chisel and pliers. They find it amusing because I eat bran and figs, or psyllium seed; but I'd rather be a jest for my friends than be constipated—and someone by the way ought to do a thesis on the relationship between constipation and art. Carl says proudly that when they embalm his body they won't find it full of psyllium seed."

625

He turned to look at her. There was on her face that soft almost tender smile of pity. She said, "What are you hiding now?"

That angered him a little. "Athene, look. I'll leave the Gospel of John to you but you'd do well to leave the psychology to me."

"You're not evading something?"

"Aren't we all the time? How was it with the saintly Florence Nightingale, who put Milnes off year after year?—but who said, on finding him interested in another woman, 'I hoped to find him longing to keep open another decision.' The real truth about the sainted and idolized woman would gag even a speakeasy operator. Who curses worst when drunk? The one who when sober would rather be thought stupid than say damn. Who when drunk drools worst over women? The one who when sober thinks Anthony Comstock the all-American father."

"Well, that isn't true of your brother."

"Oh, my brother. If you know so much about him tell me why he is always in such a passion to seduce my wife. It was so with Neloa. If I have a third it will be so again."

"Let's not talk about it."

"There are so many matters that you don't want to talk about. Drunkenness. You profess to find it very disgusting but maybe alcohol is keeping a neurotic nation from becoming psychotic. What is our land today but a mess of cults, of charlatans and impostors, of nationwide whoring under the precepts and prohibitions, with brigands like the Morgans and Insuls standing on top of the pile? What is it but a nation driven into cellars and made to feel vicious? And what drove it there? Don't you nourish a secret conviction that all people should go to heaven?"

"Go on talking," she said. "Maybe you'll come to the thing that's bothering you." She was sitting back looking at him, with that faint smile of amusement and pity, that indulgent knowledge of him in her eyes. It was, he thought, the way a mother might look at an erring and not-too-bright son.

He went on, more to tease her than anything else: "Has God nothing better to do than stand up there and fix his face in a puritan's scowl? Have we as a people nothing better to do than accept the doctrine of cowards that we're born depraved? We can no longer read advertisements without reading perjury; no longer listen to radio without hearing the ingratiating whine of some soulless hireling. Where are the affirmations today? Where is the joy? Not in Vridar, the poor miserable bastard with his bald head and bridgework and babilan complex and heaven knows how much he has not yet looked at. Not in his brother, not in his wife—"

"I say, when are you coming to it?"

"I came to it and passed and you were not there. Shall I put it in a limerick? Remember Jane Rinks, that flat yellow virgin who made A's in all our classes, yet fainted one day when she thought a man had made a pass at her. There is a young virgin named Rinks, and she thinks and she thinks and she thinks; and all that she knows is the desert that blows its sand in the face of the sphinx. And who knows any more? Our next project is to go to Europe."

He had gone west, he now wanted to go east, for he imagined that what he sought was not where he stood. He did not know that with Black Thursday there came the end of an era.

XV

They were in the apartment of Wilma Reagan, the stout blonde with the heavy thighs and flat feet and the big square face. She was a hack who wrote and sold Christmas and birthday greetings, sentimental verses, true confession stories. On one side of her desk she had a photograph of Anthony Comstock; on the other, of H. L. Mencken. She said she loved the ironic juxtapositions. She said she had worked out a Hoover cocktail that was a darling. It had inspired thirty-six Christmas greetings, three stories on wallpaper for bedrooms, three confessions of virgins who done wrong . . . She liked to quote Housman's line, We lay hands on our hearts when we think. She loved Caroline Norton's words, "The saddest moment for me is when a man seems uneasy at being left alone with me, when his voice lowers and he draws his chair nearer—I know I am about to lose a friend I love, to get a lover I do not want." "These bags!" she would say and jiggle a breast up and down in her bodice. "This belly that some day will swell up like a bloated ox, these old tits that some kid will pull at. When I was fifteen a man said, Come on, babe—with one thunderclap I'll knock you higher than a kite . . . . "

Someone would groan. From somewhere in the dark a drunken voice would say, "Lord, O Lord." Vridar would listen and ask himself, Where have all the values gone to? Where were those things that the Victorians took for granted? Was Wilma saying it?—"For people now have shut the door that opened on the Hebrides, and like strange dead things from the seas their youth and hope are washed ashore. They get urbanity with doubt; they mellow—which may mean that sand has filled the footprints down the strand where braver feet once ventured out." "Lord O Lord!" someone said, full of gin and woe. "Ah, they have wise sepulchral airs: they say, grow old along with me, these phantoms marching to the sea who scatter proverbs in their prayers . . . . "

The proverbs were wisecracks now.

Vridar at parties usually sat back and studied those who were present. Carl would charge two-bits for a look at his hairy sunken navel, or exhort all patriots to come to the aid of the Republican party. He had a hungry wish to lie with women besides his mistress but in his love-making he was never crude and offensive, nor even normally aggressive, Marion said. Marion when drinking seemed to be interested only in the sexual life. His way with women was bold, sometimes crass, but most women, Vridar observed, seemed to like it. He would test a girl's knee-jerk (this was his favorite approach), urging her to draw her skirt up a little farther; looking deep into her eyes a moment and suggesting a little farther still. He would grasp an ankle to move her leg, and again look into her eyes when he felt the thrill go through her. He would pat her naked thigh. No other man known to Vridar and Carl, no other man who would ever be known to them, had more than a small part of Marion's skill in seducing women.

Marion's wife was a Southern blonde with a honey-chile accent. She had a great

627

mass of hair the color of honey; blue eyes so pale they looked a little reptilian; a nose that turned up a little; a ripe voluptuous mouth and good teeth; and a good complexion. She had won a beauty contest in her home university. Her name was Mollie. Mollie was so conscious of herself as a woman attractive to men, so vain, so spoiled and indulged, that she could not look at a man without thinking of him as a male, of herself as a female. With her, to be conscious was to be flirtatious. She had a smile, and a laugh, that most men found disturbing. When Marion tested knee-jerks, or with a grandiloquent presentation of his professional card suggested that a woman should call at his office, Mollie flirted with men in the kitchen.

Among the guests was Larry Hopkins, who had a Doctor's degree in psychology from a great school. Vridar thought him the most obtuse man he had ever known and marveled every time he saw him that one who knew nothing about a subject could get a high degree in it. It was Larry's custom to get a room overlooking an apartment in which girls lived and to spy on them with glasses. If he saw a girl naked, he went into a kind of trance and fell off his chair. That was what Marion said. Larry laughed a great deal. His laughter was a kind of stifled giggling that flushed his round fat face.

If Elsa sneezed twice the same evening, Carlyle had to kiss her hand. She now waited, her face puckered, and a second sneeze came. She thrust her hand out. "Here, dearie, kiss your darling's hand."

"Kiss your own hand," Carlyle said. "You're closer to it."

"Oh, you beast!" she cried, pretending to be hysterical.

Carlyle wrinkled his nose and looked at her with charming derision. He shuffled over and kicked her shin. "You skinny old bitch," he said. He looked round him, wrinkling his small nose and affecting disgust. He bowed over her hand and kissed it. "I've nearly worn her hand out," he said. "It used to have some meat on it."

Wanda Jewett in her throaty alto was singing, "My father sells snow to the snow-birds, my mother makes synthetic gin; my sister makes love for a living! My God, how the money rolls in . . . . "

Wanda, related to one of the Mormon presidents, had a doll-like face and small shrewd hazel eyes. She liked what an American poet had called smubtleties, but was, Moses McGuire said, one of the ineradicable virgins. After singing she listened again to Johnny Hart. Johnny was a Communist. He said the American system was outworn, that its only contemporary writer of any worth was Dreiser, that its morals were decadent. The center of his universe was the Kremlin. Vridar listened to him and looked back to the time when he had been a Socialist. Johnny had an uncombed shock of dark hair, dark intense eyes, a small frame like Carlyle's, and a capacity to verbalize that in Vridar's experience was unmatched.

Sitting back in shadow with Athene Vridar said, "Listen to him. That's what I was a few years ago. The horror of it is that when fifty I'll look back with shock on what I am now; when seventy, on what I was at sixty; and realize that on the day of my death I shall have come to nothing."

Wilma was crying at Johnny, "You make me sick. Honest to Cotton Mather you make me feel like I'd eaten beetles. Why don't you get a woman and go to bed?"

Johnny's small boyish face looked offended. "I see before me," he said, looking round, "a typical segment of the bankrupt middle class. You've had your October twenty-eighth. It was the inevitable climax of a system that elects a Coolidge and allows a few robbers to possess everything, while most of the country's children don't have milk to drink. This morally bankrupt remnant before me—"

"Oh, to hell with you!" Wilma said. "You're as dull as a priest and a priest is what you are. Go join a church."

Looking at Johnny, Vridar thought of Gibbon's aunt's friend who, Gibbon said, might have ranked high as a writer, had not his vigorous mind been clouded by enthusiasm. He always thought of the words when he looked at David Hawke.

"You," said Johnny, swinging to Vridar, "will go on voting for Hoovers and writing books about a degenerate system—"

"I voted for Smith. Johnny, you remind me of Herbert of Cherbury. He said that as an infant he knew how to talk long before he spoke a word, but did forbear to speak, lest he should utter something that was imperfect or impertinent."

"That's Hawke. That's in the fourth chapter of his novel. Now tell me, if a capitalistic system can produce only the great robbers—"

Wilma sprang up and seizing his handsome dark hair kissed him. She held the struggling Johnny close to her and looked round, saying, "Why should any woman have children, as long as so many already born need our care?"

Johnny broke loose and found himself facing Mac's sneer. "You have Korssakow's psychosis," said Mac, his face, sallow with evil, breathing above the panting Johnny. "Have you read Krutch's *Modern Temper?* Read it, you poor orphan, reaching out into the darkness for Papa Stalin. Papa Marx and Papa Pope!" Mac glanced round him to see how many persons were listening. Vridar sensed that he had been preparing for days for one of his mighty moments. When Johnny again tried to talk Mac exploded a cawing sneer in his face.

"This halfwitted disciple of a London Jew says the capitalist system has gone to the dogs. It has merely gone to the House of Morgan. Life for this child, as for all of us who screw other men's wives, has become a deafening frog-chorus of small egos. Latrante uno, latrat statim et alter canis. When one dog barks they all bark." Again there came his harsh cawing laugh, slow in measured sounds to express his full loathing. "Babilans! That's what the Communists are. Why do I have to explain such simple things? When the lovely girl Alexandrine was forced on Stendhal he was impotent, to the delight of all his male friends. If he had heard of Marx he would at once have become a Marxist. Do I have to tell you that the clue to the Communist is to be found in incestuous yearnings? I'm goint to have to write the sexual history of politics . . . ."

They were at Marion's apartment. On a couch sat a man named James Shard. He strummed a banjo and sang softly to the mistress at his side, and now and then laid the banjo aside to kiss her. After he had kissed all over her face with full moist lips, she would take paint and powder out of her bag and daub at herself while looking in a mirror. If she saw Vridar watching her she would interrupt what she was doing and look at him intently a few moments, then shrug her shoulders at James. Marion said that Shard had spent years in an asylum and had twice tried to kill himself.

Across from him sat Tony Scarvelli, a small timid man who was a slave to heroin.

He was another of Marion's patients. Standing up and looking round him in a coldly calculating way was Kenneth Charwick. He boasted of having lunched with Chaplin, played golf with senators, vagabonded with Jim Tully and been a political prisoner in China. So far as Vridar could tell, Chadwick believed that his thoughts were hidden when, his eyes half-lidded, he looked speculatively at a woman's ankles or bosom. He was now looking back and forth from Athene to Vridar.

Lars Emmet, a short stubby man, was a painter. Mac bowed before him and asked gravely, "Do you have hands?"

"Of course I have," said Lars, looking at his hands.

"Then why don't you use them? Your stuff looks as if you paint with your feet."

Lars had his room hung with photographs of imbeciles, most of them, he said, suggested by those in Tredgold. Great art he believed, no matter in what form, should try to recapitulate the entire past, in its representation of the present. Vridar found the thought breath-taking. The painting of a man that did not suggest the low forehead behind the high one, the heavy lips behind the thin mouth, the untold centuries of savagery behind the mind was no work of art at all but only an exercise in deception. It should be the same in fiction, he had said; and after considering his words Vridar had said to Athene, "He's right but how can I do it? He says that most writers write as if unaware of all but the last two thousand years, and of most of that. It isn't true?"

"But how far back are you going?"

"To the cell."

She looked at him as though he were mad. "But how?"

"Intuitively. We have to feel our way into it but before that we have to develop a scheme for coming out."

What he meant, Lars had explained, was this: if an artist projected himself into a time when man was a hairy naked beast grasping a club, and succeeded in occupying the life and world of that beast, he might pass the point of no return and not come back. It was a horrifying thought. Vridar looked into the man's small green eyes, as far as he could into the complex depths of the man's soul, and thought, Here's a great artist in his reach if not in his grasp.

"It's what we must do," he said to Athene. "I must try it."

Mac had been talking to Lars and was now turning the pages of a book. With dreadful snorts of derision, with bursts of harsh laughter, he was announcing his findings. Swift and Baudelaire, Rousseau and Gogol, Hoffman and Schopenhauer and Nietzsche, Tasso and Eichhorn and Palestrina, Benda and Dussek had all been insane. Montanus had thought he was a grain of wheat and wouldn't move because of fear that a bird would swallow him. A canary chased him into a trunk . . .

Back into the past, Vridar was thinking. But how?

Mac was now looking with immense incredulity into a book called *New Backgrounds for a New Age*, highly praised by reviewers. Mac read: "Is there not something a little tragic here? Has not something beautiful disappeared with the passing of the sweet pretenses of yesterday's adolescense?" Mac looked round him at every face present. "Do I have to tell you that this author is another babilan, who looked into his mother's bosom? If there are publishers for such nonsense, why don't we all write? Is there not something a little tragic here? O my God, if Max Ohm ever reads that!" He was still looking from face to face. "A *little* tragic." He erupted with a snort that shook him. "No wonder that Lloyd ate sawdust but not for the reason that Hunter eats figs. No wonder, as Hergesheimer says, writers are caught between constipation and neurosis. Something beautiful has gone and its name isn't Coolidge. Something beautiful has come, and one of Tredgold's imbeciles named Johnny Hart says it is Communism . . . "

Listening to Mac, Vridar recalled having read that from New York City alone fourteen thousand persons were going every year to psychopathic wards. What was happening to the people of his own land? Some of these persons before him behaved as though they had drunk stimulants more powerful than gin. They acted as though they were full of obsessions and compulsions and had to keep talking and clowning or themselves go insane. Mac seized Wilma's chin as he might have a doorknob and cried, "Gather ye rosebuds while ye may, the equinox but once." With sudden fury Wilma gave him a burning slap on his sallow face. The blow left a red stain that slowly faded. He threw arms round her and together they struggled and fell to the floor and then Wilma sat on him, bouncing her big rump up and down. When Mac got to his feet, looking white and spent, he said that women seemed determined to destroy love by being frank about it.

Except when half-drunk or alone with Athene, Vridar was a morbidly shy and reticent person. At these parties he was content to sit back and listen and observe, storing his mind with memories. Black Thursday had come and gone, and a nation hellbent on a scapegoat (and what, he wondered, was the psychology of the scapegoat!) had fixed its wrath on a man named Hoover. Vridar read in the news that some persons were going into one Church or another; some were going into Communism; and some, like these before him, spurning both refuges had no place to go.

Looking into himself, looking into these persons, he felt that there was a large sickness of soul in the Western world, but he could not divine its cause or imagine its cure. Lars said that if art was to escape the fate that Spengler had foretold it would have to recover its health and vigor. He said it was becoming too egocentric and introverted, and as instances among writers he cited Kafka and Proust.

Vridar took pen and paper and began to write:

> He sits through afternoons of talk and tea.
> His ego makes a gracious overture
> from shallow chambers, while a cavalier
> bows low upon his cracker; then the spoons
> take up the converse and a kitten mews.
> He snores athwart the loges and the pews.
> He curls in bed with stomach to his knees
> as once he curled in crotches of the trees;
> and one by one he counts the ironies.
>
> Within the sophistries of an afternoon
> he smells the nakedness of jungle moon
> and then remembers how to hold a spoon . . .

Handing the verses to Athene he said, "Part of an obituary for T. S. Eliot."

Yesterday it had been the laughing red sweet mouth of wine but today it was Millay's

> Let me make it plain:
> I deem this frenzy insufficient reason
> for conversation when we meet again.

Yesterday it had been

> for thee all soft delight
> that shadowy thought can win,   ·
> a bright torch, and a casement ope at night
> to let the warm love in.

But now

> My dear, our world is sick,
> for science now shapes it in the form
> of soulless gadgets, while from its waist
> God has withdrawn his arm.

Mac, quite drunk now, was declaiming again. All great lovers of the past, he said, whether real or mythical, had been women. Women had never believed that physical love was sinful, and so could become what men called whores. The oppression of women had been emotional rather than economic. Hallucinated tutors, masquerading as lovers, had for centuries taught women to exalt the pleasures of the flesh into a sophistry called spiritual devotion. It had been men, the stupid unbathed asses, who had searched the earth over for aphrodisiacs, using in turn everything from salted crocodiles and bee-wings and the genitals of hedge-hogs to toad bones, staghorn, valerian root, the gall of children, menstrual fluid, camel hump, and the powdered teeth of dead men. Women had never sought aphrodisiacs, for the reason that they had never needed them. So men had done their best to make women feel inferior and degraded—

"Oh, shut your big wide mouth!" Carl cried. "I've heard Vridar say all that."

Mac squared off and looked at Vridar. "You're ambitious, Hunter. So was Caesar. He wanted to conquer the world and you want to get into *Who's Who*. Have you read any of the obituaries of those in that morgue? You like a lot of company when you set up as a famous man but you'll never be famous, because you're no more subtle than a Rotarian eating beans." Mac put his big feet far apart, hands on his hips, and fixed Vridar with his nastiest sneer. "Just where did I get the idea that you have intelligence? I met you among the Mormons and out there there was simply nothing to judge you by. You should take to heart Thomas Carlyle's words, that there's a great discovery to be made in literature, that of paying literary men by the quantity they don't write. In Russia you'd be paid to throw that old portable away and go back to the Antelope hills . . . "

Johnny was saying to Wilma, "Even a woman as thick as you are must realize that under capitalism the masses are exploited. They've always been under your system. They'll always be. Exploitation is the essence of it. Do you approve that?"

632

"No, nor my shape, but I can't change it."

"You big selfish woman—"

"Johnny, you're an unspeakable bore. What this country needs is a million Isadora Duncans and we wouldn't have such silly utopians as you. No, nor even any H. L. Menckens."

"That's right," said Mac, staggering up. "Bawd and pimp and harlot, brothel, whorehouse and rape, incest, politics and censorship—if the Christian way is a glory where did such words come from? From Johnny Harts with a Jesus complex. God must pull his beard when he looks at you, you hermaphroditic son of Eros and John Calvin."

He broke off and his bloodshot eyes looked round him. Again he fixed Vridar, and drew from his pocket a sheet of paper, which he had taken from Vridar's room. "Shut up, all of you friggers," he said. "Shut up, while I read you Vridar Hunter's epitaph." And when there was a moment of silence he read: "Stranger, underneath your feet lies a novelist, long since rotten. His books none now remember: sweet the grass grows on a thing forgotten."

XVI

Vridar was at the sumptuous Fifth Avenue apartment of Dr. Harrison Woolf, a psychiatrist. Woolf wanted to write and publish some articles, and to improve his English had enrolled in Vridar's evening class. He was a small dark man with a sensual mouth and restless black eyes. He made a lot of money and, he had confessed to Vridar, seduced a lot of women. He lay with all his female patients whom he found pleasing, and with the wives of all his friends—a crafty and capable man whose position as a psychiatrist gave him such power over women as only priests had had, in former times. Vridar wondered if many psychiatrists were as unscrupulous as this shyster.

This evening Woolf was playing poker with a man named Norman Mall and with two women, a Miss Arnstein and a Mrs. Jode. Miss Arnstein was a stout voluptuous young woman with a growth of fine dark hair on her upper lip, and nipples that stood out against her tight blouse. Carlyle Orcutt said that a woman was sexually excited when her nipples stood out of her breasts that way. Mrs. Jode looked cool, able, and sophisticated. Mall was a postgraduate student in business. When Vridar entered, Woolf was saying that he believed in scholarship.

"I don't," said Arnstein. "It makes me feel stuffed."

"Maybe you mix love with learning. Have yourself a drink, Professor, and pull up a chair. There are some new photographs if you're interested."

Vridar had seen some of Woolf's photographs: they were of himself alone or with different women, all of them naked. Vridar thought he had never seen anything or heard anything so shockingly crass, or known any man as contemptible as this one. He had come to the apartment several times because he was trying to understand that there was a "sophisticated" world of which he knew nothing. Besides, Woolf's whisky was smuggled in from abroad.

633

When Vridar drew a chair up, Woolf gave him a low brittle laugh and said, "Did you have a mother?" They all laughed.

Mrs. Jode turned to him with the air of one accustomed to a lorgnette. "We have naked minds."

"I'll soon have a naked body," Woolf said, "if my luck doesn't change." He stripped off his shirt and looked down over his hairy belly. "Suspenders next." ·

Arnstein hiccoughed gently and said, "Pardon."

"You're a psychiatrist," said Mall, looking over at Woolf. "Did Sappho sing because she had a withered leg or because she was a Lesbian?"

"She must have been a horribly homely woman," Woolf said.

Mrs. Jode lost consistently. She had removed rings, a necklace, both shoes and stockings, and now pulled off her blouse.

"One of my favorite theories," said Woolf, "is that the loveliest women are the best poker players."

"You reassure me," Arnstein said.

Mall turned to Vridar, who was sipping a highball and watching them. "Hunter, you write, I'm told. Do you agree with me that the best poetry is limericks?"

"I like your one on Jeffers," Mrs. Jode said.

"Have you heard it?" asked Mall, looking at Vridar.

Vridar shook his head no.

"Love used to be roses and zephyrs but now its roan stallions and heifers make such symbols of passion that we're all out of fashion. Oh shame on you, Robinson Jeffers." He glanced again at Vridar. "You like Jeffers?"

"I like the one about trigger," said Arnstein.

"Any woman would," said Woolf.

"Heard that one?" Mall asked, again glancing at Vridar.

Again Vridar said no.

"A statistical genius named Trigger loved to take any problem and figure. In covering a bawd the guy broke his rod while cubing the root of his vigor."

Arnstein gave a snort. They all looked at Vridar.

"The women love that one, all right," Woolf said, "but not the one about Daisy Lou."

Again glancing at Vridar with large rather bulging hazel eyes, Mall said, "You heard about Daisy?"

Vridar had become selfconscious. He was tired of saying no.

"Said Dallas's Daisy Lou Padgett, If I could I certainly would cadge it. What she meant down in Dallas is the masculine phallus is externally a handsomer gadget."

Again Arnstein snorted. Woolf slyly drew an ace from his lap and raked in the pot. "Does anyone agree with me that no man likes to see a woman entirely naked? Professor?"

Vridar was silent.

"What I wonder," said Mall, "is why nobody speaks of the ascendants of the apes. By the descent of man did Darwin mean getting down out of the trees? Another thing that worries me is our super-sophisticates. Will Aldous Huxley end up in the Roman Church or writing nursery rimes?"

Woolf was looking across his cards at Arnstein's white flesh. Her nipples were standing out.

"And as for our expatriates," Mall went on, "after Europe has become a province of America and Paris a suburb of New York with a moat between, where will our genius go after saying goodbye to Wisconsin?"

Miss Arnstein was now naked to her waist, and Mall was looking in a kind of meditative way at her breasts. "My father told me it's a smelly grotesquely awkward performance, attended by panting and squealy noises, and a sense of going at life at the wrong end."

Both women were looking at him. Woolf glanced at him quickly and then a sly smile lit up his face like a light. Vridar drank off his highball and said goodnight and left. Outside he looked up and down Fifth Avenue and then headed for Romany Marie's and another drink. He was annoyed with himself because he seemed unable to put Arnstein's breasts out of his thoughts.

A few days later he was in the studio apartment of Lars Emmet. Emmet's paintings troubled him. They seemed to be a kind of horrifying synthesis of dementia, idiocy, and sanity: there was a crazy wild face with broken teeth, one dead eye, the other eye frenzied under a hairless lid, the mouth that of a child calling to his mother. Lars said he had got the idea for a number of paintings from Brushfield's photographs, though every day on the streets he saw persons much like them. He was trying to portray the present *in* the background of man's heritage—all the lunacies, all the weary imbecilities, all the wealth of hope and faith, all the exploited and the exploiters—a kind of x-ray effect of souls in a semi-civilized menagerie, with all of it reaching back to the beginning, yet into the 21st century. In a way, he said, it was the transformation of men into robots before they had had time to become men. One thing man had never learned to do, that was how to ask a question. "Until we know how to ask the questions we can never get the answers; but we almost have to know the answer before the question can be asked." He thought Eliot's waste land a poor symbol: with all the provender and plunder and the fat bellies on the lunatics and the jowls on the gangsters it was more like a Bruegel scene.

Mall had come in and was staring at a painting of a hideous fellow who seemed to have got entangled in a mass of weird tendrils. "Is that Adam?" he asked.

Mac had come in. "Compare these," he said to Vridar, "with your dull words about Idahoans in the hills."

Sitting in a chair before a group of paintings, Vridar was studying them. These were a far cry—these were ages and worlds away from things he had studied in the Metropolitan—Ingress' fat self-complacent Gentleman, Pollaiuolo's vapid and vacuous Young Lady, Bruegel's Harvesters, Ruebens' monstrously fat Venus and Cupid with a stocky overmuscled Adonis—though in El Greco's Toledo there were hints of things to come and in Botticelli's Jerome a face that Brushfield might have wished to include.

Yes, these things did make his own work seem thin. Troubled by his feeling of failure, he stopped off to see his brother. He did not understand his relationship with Marion or Marion's feelings toward him. There were times when he had no doubt that Marion hated him—hated him with a deep and terrible hatred that would never forget or forgive, yet loved him too in a strange inexplicable way. It was as a child might both hate and love a mother.

Marion poured gin into glasses and asked, "What did the market do today?"

Vridar shrugged. While teaching in Utah and here, he had lived frugally and invested his savings of six thousand dollars in stocks that his broker said were recommended to orphans and widows. Marion, Athene and Carl had all invested and like Vridar had lost most of what they had. "You lose your pittance," Johnny Hart said, "and it goes right into the pockets of the Bernard Baruchs."

"Remember Annis?" Marion said. "That pot of vegetables she dumped on my plate, and the way that Swede made her moan after he got on top of her? Remember the way that bastard made us turn the grindstone? It's a wonder we have any sanity at all."

"You think we'll be able to keep what we have?" Vridar asked, sipping the gin.

"Oh, you will," Marion said with his habitual contempt for his brother.

"Got your book about done?"

Marion hated the question. It was his brother who had told him to stop getting shot at by married men and to return to school, who had urged him to go on for a doctorate, who had expressed the hope that they would both write books. When Vridar got a book published, he wanted Marion to have a book published. If Vridar were even to get in *Who's Who,* he would want Marion in *Who's Who.* He would want Marion there first, but all this he did not yet see clearly.

Marion ignored the question. He said Vridar had always taken life seriously. "You try to make me take it that way. If I ever go insane it will be your fault."

Vridar looked at him and was silent. He had been on the river home of his parents when Marion came west with his bride, and day after day Marion spent so much time embracing his wife, utterly indifferent to his mother's spying, that Prudence almost went mad. She would come to Vridar with such lunacy in her eyes as he had rarely seen there. "She's killing my son!" the mother cried. "I tell you no man can stand it!" Vridar was pained, bored, and at last disgusted. He said it was none of his business and he refused to speak to Marion about it. Prudence almost went insane that summer.

Marion was now saying, "God saw that he had blundered in making this world, so to help us endure his mistake he gave us alcohol. And then tobacco and drugs. But you can't use what he put here without a sense of guilt, as though you had broken a padlock and swiped it from a pantry. You used to be a Socialist, and as I size you up you're busting at your seams to become a Communist. You should have my job a while. I've so many psychotic patients that the whole world looks crazy to me. It's all mankind's attempt to draw attention and pity to itself, now that telescopes can't find any sign of Pa in the sky."

Was that it? Vridar wondered, or was it deeper than that?

"At every party we have," Vridar said, looking at his brother's face, so much like his own, "you tell the women that if I'm ever adulterous I'll be through as a writer. Just what in hell are you up to?"

"You will," Marion said.

636

Vridar met his eyes. They were the small-boy eyes he had seen many years ago when catching Marion in some deception. "That's crap and you know it."

"I'm the psychologist," Marion said.

"Oh, God damn it, you're the psychologist. What do you think a writer is? I want to know the nature of your treachery."

"Treachery!" Marion feigned astonishment. "To protect you, of course." He now feigned anger. Feigning anger was his commonest dodge.

"You lie and you know it. You'd be willing to let me have the renown if you may have the women. Is that it? And have you seduced Athene's cousin yet?"

"That's my business." A moment later Marion's face broke into a broad grin, for he simply had to tell someone about his conquests. "You should see her legs," he said. "She could marry a duke with legs like that."

After he had left, Vridar was sorry that he had stopped at his brother's. In the years of their manhood he had never been able to get Marion to meet him on a level of plain speaking, with their masks off. If Vridar challenged him, he feigned anger, or slipped into evasions so sly that it was impossible to follow him. He could be so sly and devious that his wife was unable to catch him at all; for even while she was trying to flush him out of one lie, she lost him in another. He was what she called cute in his deceptions, what some people might have called charming; for he was a good actor, he could play a part convincingly, he had a baffling change of pace and mood. Confused, and almost doubting her own senses, Mollie would stare at him and Marion would then put on one of his clowning acts. In her laughter she forgot what had troubled her.

On a corner of Union Square a man was haranguing a crowd. There were only two classes of people, he said, the producers and those who exploited their labor. Vridar thought again of Clemenceau's words, that any man who was not a Socialist at twenty-five had no heart, and who was still a Socialist at sixty had no brains. He entered an arcade. Along one wall men were inserting pennies into slots and peering at the photographs of nearly naked women. A short powerful man was striking blows to make a bell ring. He would deliver a blow, look at his score, and then look round him to see if persons were watching. He would then flex a biceps and look at it.

Vridar entered a burlesque show, having never been in one. A chorus of girls was dancing and singing bawdy songs. On leaving the stage, in turn they paused by a box where men were sitting and shook their breasts at them and then thrust their rumps out and slapped them. Vridar studied the men around him, noting the excitement in a pair of eyes, the drooling lust in a mouth, the movement up and down of an Adam's apple as a man swallowed hard. There were five girls on the stage now. Two men went from one to another, pinching thighs, looking with feigned astonishment at rumps, and reciting the love-history of each girl. One of them walked around Cleopatra, rolling his eyes, when suddenly in an excess of ecstasy he slapped the other man's face. Vridar wondered if only the Christians made such a vulgar thing of love.

He thought it strange that a nation should license such shows yet try to suppress *Sister Carrie* or Margaret Sanger's pamphlets.

Vridar's publisher had urged him to meet a few celebrities. He didn't want to. Serious artists of all kinds, he told Athene, were emotionally so immature that they detested one another, knowing in their souls that they were all asses. Should he go to Rosita Armstrong's tea?

"Have you read any of her books?"

"Oh, it was delicately suggested that I ought to read at least one of them. Reputations in this country are nourished by being talked about. When people cease to talk about you you're pushed off the stage and another takes your place."

"I think you should go."

He went. Rosita, he guessed, would weigh about two hundred pounds. She regarded herself, it seemed to Vridar, as one of the titans, for reviewers and her friends in high places had been praising her most recent novel to the skies. Her husband was so small that she could have held him on her lap. He deferred to her, his manner humble, or pretending to be, his gaze patient and inquiring. When out of her great bosom she delivered a platitude, he looked quickly at Vridar, as though to see a transformation in him. She talked about art, her pronouncements booming in the small room.

Two critics came in. One of them was a slender spectacled man with a round owlish face. The other was an art critic, a Jew, who wrote for the liberal weeklies. Of her most recent novel he had said in a review that it began where Dostoievsky had stopped. Now Rosita and the critics talked about art, Vridar and the husband listened. They seemed to think that art was something like a garden, that flowered and gave off fragrance and made the whole world sweet.

After a few minutes the art critic turned to Vridar. "Mr. Hunter, I believe you're spoken of as a realist. I have not," he said, his smile gracious, "read your book—you have published only one?—but I read a review or two. Just what is realism?"

The critic in spectacles murmured and fixed his nearsighted eyes on Vridar.

Why in hell, Vridar thought, did I come here!

"You tell us," said Rosita, her face open and incredulous.

Vridar wondered whether he should speak to the point or beg off. Their attitude was patronizing and it annoyed him. "The realist," he said, deciding to make an effort, "tries to see life as it presents itself to the five senses. He has no interest in standardizing human errors in observation and calling them truths, or in withdrawing because his sensibilities—"

"Then what," asked the impatient Rosita, "is romance?"

"Chiefly evasion and escape, as found in American fiction. An unwillingness to believe that the universe can get along without us. Maybe Communism is man's most romantic notion so far."

"Why do you say that?" asked the spectacled critic.

"For the reason that none of us, not even a Marcus Aurelius, can be trusted with power over our fellows. Only the child argues that we can."

"Then you don't accept the Marxist argument?"

"It reminds me of what Lamb said of Aquinas, that he reveled in cobwebs and subtleties until a man's brain spun. Have you ever looked at the emotional interior of a Communist?"

He knew at once that he had blundered. He saw it in their cold offended eyes.

638

"I'm sorry," he said, "but I must run along." He bowed a moment over the big strong hand of his hostess, then took his hat and walked out.

An hour later he was pouring a drink of gin and looking at his wife. "I shouldn't have gone," he said. "They drew me into talk, and when I talk my stock falls like the market on a black Thursday."

"You offended them?"

"That, my dear, is the general idea. They're Communists or sympathizers. Are all the so-called intellectuals going into this new illusion? John Wiggam wants me to come to his apartment and hear his classical records, but what he really has in mind is making a Communist of me."

Athene looked at him. She had no political interests.

"What I'm wondering is whether I should go on writing this novel about myself. Reading David Hawke's self-idolatrous book has almost cured me of the itch to scribble. Imagine having a babe in diapers—himself, that is—looking at people around him and thinking about them as an adult would. And not a single reviewer challenged it. How far does one have to go into self-glorification to gag one's judges?"

"Well, but you're trying to be honest."

"Ho-ho-ho. But you don't want me to put you in. Shall I tell all the shameful things about our relationship?"

"Is it necessary?"

"If I start leaving things out, where do I stop? If I protect you, shall I not protect my brother, my sister-in-law, Carl and his mistress? What, then, would the novel be worth?"

"But you don't have to portray yourself as a detestable person."

"Self-love in people is so strong, their anxieties so acute, that they find the truth detestable."

"Not all of it."

"Oh, not all of it but a lot of the most significant part."

"The masochist in you—"

"Oh yes, the masochist in me. You'll never forget my brother's words that I seek martyrdom. In this country if you don't play every card for all it'll turn up in dollars and public acclaim, you want to be a martyr, don't you?"

"You've admitted masochism. And have you asked yourself what people in Idaho will think?"

"There aren't ten people in Idaho who ever read a book."

"Your parents—"

"Yes. Dave's mother read his book and bawled her heart out. He showed me the letter, and he bawled just as hard but he's going to write another one. About the people in his home town. I worry most over Neloa's people. They don't yet know how she died, and they think she's buried. If they know I had her cremated they'd probably kill me."

"Couldn't you change the story and have her buried?"

"That wouldn't be Vridar. It all comes down to this, I think—down to what Stendhal said, that one has duties in accordance with the range of his spirit . . . . "

639

There were other celebrities whom Vridar was asked to meet. There was a literary critic named John Adgate, a dark, intense, voluble man who said he liked to meet authors. He told Vridar that he liked to get to the bottom of them, though some of them, he admitted, were a little deep. All the while he was staring intently at Vridar and Vridar was thinking, Just for the hell of it you might have a look at the bottom of yourself.

Adgate talked and Vridar listened, wondering about the man. This critic had given Vridar's novel a long and favorable review. He had sent a note saying, "Drop around to our apartment sometime." Vridar found the apartment full of cats and dogs, and Mrs. Adgate in bed with a cat in her arms. The Adgates had no children. Almost at once Adgate and his childlike wife began to talk about dogs and to play with them, as though the apartment were a nursery, as though these creatures were their daughters and sons.

"You like dogs?" Adgate asked.

Vridar's memory went to that time when he knelt at the grave of one and wept. "Not especially as pets," he said.

Adgate seemed to stiffen a little. "What kind of pets do you like?"

"I— Well, none, I guess."

"A dog," said Adgate gravely, "is a man's best friend. There's loyalty in dogs. They never betray you. Don't you agree?"

"You recall what Mark Twain said about it?"

"What was that?"

"I can't give his exact words. In effect it was that he trusted no man who was a dog-lover."

"Mark Twain said that?"

"Somewhere. What I've sometimes thought," Vridar went on hastily, "is that Americans have made too much of them. Is it a symptom of loneliness, of unfulfilled hungers? I know a man disappointed in his sons who has turned fanatically to dogs—" Ah, Lord, there it was again! Again he had blundered. Adgate looked as if he had been struck. His wife had risen to her pillow.

Adgate said coldly, "Just what do you mean?"

O God damn! Vridar thought, why do I go to these places? "I only meant," he said, trying to smooth the face of something that had no face left, "that the dog-lovers I've known have seemed to be pretty cynical toward human beings. I once knew a college teacher who devoted himself to preposterous poodles of one sort and another—" Mrs. Adgate looked as if she would scream.

"Go on," said Adgate, looking as if he had been poured full of fortitude. "Say what you have to say."

I might as well, Vridar thought, for this outraged ape will never again review a book of mine. He said: "What I mean is that people who are overly fond of dogs are rather cold in their attitude toward their own kind. As I've observed them, I mean. And certainly I don't mean you. But a man who makes a major meaning of the servile devotion of dogs very possibly would welcome that kind of devotion from men."

"Are you suggesting that I'm cynical?"

"Oh no, not you at all."

"Am I?" he asked, appealing to his wife.

"Certainly not."

"As for human beings," said Adgate, fixing Vridar with a cold stare, "they do betray and deceive, don't they? They do lie, don't they? They stoop to all kinds of meanness, don't they? Dogs give affection and ask for nothing, don't they?"

"But the point—"

"That *is* the point."

"Do dogs flatter our vanity? Do they leap to our commands and vanish without sulking when we're weary of them? Do men like to be small Napoleons among the beasts?"

"Oh, not at all. Dogs are loyal and we're loyal to them. That's the whole point."

"Dogs aren't murderers," said Mrs. Adgate. "They don't steal your purse and whore your daughter . . . . "

When Vridar reported the evening to Athene she was deeply distressed. She always was by these things. She said that wherever Vridar went he was tactless and imprudent. He made enemies.

"Oh well," he said, "I get fed up with this sick neurotic glorification of dogs. These men are Marats. I wouldn't trust them around a corner."

"But do you have to let them know it?"

"Well yes, for the reason that I was once a self-deceived self-pitying bastard who sat all night by the grave of a dog, grieving—but not over the dog. Over myself. To hell with it. The human animal is not within ten millenniums of what Shakespeare said he is, but he's about the best animal we have any knowledge of. If I can't love my own kind, I won't lead a poodle down the avenues or give my heart to a bitter London Jew named Marx. When I seek affection I don't want to go down on all fours for it, or turn to mass-murderers for it."

"But is that the point?"

"Then what in hell is the point?"

"Mr. Adgate gave your novel a nice review. You go to his home and offend him."

Vridar was stung. He admitted to himself that what she said was true, but he didn't want to admit it to her. He despised her wish to make him a conventional man. "You mean I'm to be a hypocrite to get good reviews? If an honest opinion is too big for his size, then to hell with his reviews."

"You'll to hell yourself right out of authorship."

"I'll not be surprised."

"Haven't other people as much right to their views as you have?"

"Oh God yes. But we can't build a decent world until we kick the totem poles out of the way."

"You could be discreet—"

"I've never learned how."

"You don't want to learn."

"Damn it, I'm afraid to learn. I see people going around who are bloated with discretion—with both hands clutching their purses. As for Adgate, his little world of pups and kittens is his own business but can't a literary critic, of all people, exchange views without crying, See how you've wounded me!" Now Vridar was angry, or pretended to be. He got to his feet. "Shall I be fool enough to take seriously an opinion of my book by one so ignorant that he doesn't know the psychology of dog-lovers?"

"The point," said Athene, looking pale and exhausted, "isn't that. You can't expect to get anywhere as an author if you offend your critics."

"Oh, good Christ! Stendhal offended them. He had to wait a century for recognition, but look at him now and where are his critics? Forgotten."

They were silent a few moments. They were both angry and miserable. Athene spoke at last, saying, "My guess is that Adgate will never review any more of your books."

Athene was right. There were to be many Adgates in Vridar's future.

He promised her that when again in the presence of a book reviewer or a celebrity he would keep his mouth shut. For a reason that was never to be known to him, he was invited to the home of Edward L. Massing, a famous poet. Massing was an old man with a young wife. Smiling and gracious, she met Vridar at the door and led him to a large room where, standing by the fireplace, was the poet. He did not turn. For half an hour while Mrs. Massing set dinner on and chatted pleasantly with Vridar, the poet never once looked at his guest. Was it, Vridar wondered, because he thought of himself as a superlative genius; or was it because he was old and sick and tired?

When dinner was laid, Massing came over and was introduced. He did not offer his hand. He glanced briefly at Vridar with eyes that looked halfblind and then, groaning as if in pain, eased his big belly down to the table. He opened a bottle of medicated wine and drank like a man whose thirst was extreme. For several minutes he ate in silence. Then abruptly he looked across at Vridar and began to speak. An angry shrill voice said that he was incensed at capitalists and political shysters.

"Greed!" he cried, his tired eyes taking on life. A handful of billionaire robbers were grinding other men into the earth. There was enough misery in the United States to fill a thousand worlds, yet what did the people have in Washington? A moonfaced incompetent who was a messenger boy for Morgan.

Mrs. Massing seemed to be uneasy under the diatribe. So far as Vridar could tell, she thought her husband a great man or an awful fool. Turning to Vridar she asked, "What do you think of Communism?"

Remembering Athene's admonitions Vridar said, "I really don't know."

Massing turned on him a solemn and accusing stare. "We all have to be Socialists," he said, "if we place compassion above greed, a healthy child above a yacht." Then, as if deciding that his audience was beneath his powers, the poet withdrew into brooding gloomy silence. He opened another bottle of wine and drank and returning to the fireplace stood there, hands behind his back—a big unkempt rather shapeless man looking into the flames. Vridar chatted with Mrs. Massing an hour

642

or so, then thanked her for the dinner and went home. At the door he hesitated a moment but Massing did not turn to say goodnight

Vridar did not tell Athene about Massing. He felt too much pity for the man. He had decided that a sense of himself as a great man might be a part of it, illness and old age might be a part of it; but that the heart of it was the fact that a fickle nation had once acclaimed Massing as a great and enduring poet, who was now being swiftly forgotten. Was fame all curse and no blessing?

Vridar accepted against his will another invitation, this time to the home of another novelist whose husband was a distinguished professor. Martha Jackson like Rosita Armstrong was thick and heavy, with ankles that looked swollen, with large heavy arms, and with the fat of her neck resting in a roll on her collarbone. She came almost at once to her favorite subject, the English language. She said it was a lucid instrument, marvelously rich and subtle . . .

That was too much for Vridar. In his politest voice he said that he didn't agree at all. She was astonished. "It seems to me," he said, "that language is obtuse clumsy approximations. Isn't it our tendency to exaggerate the value of things dear to us, to give ourselves more meaning and prestige?"

"Well, yes—"

"Take odors. What words do we have, if we search Roget through? How can we make any person unfamiliar with them understand the difference between heliotrope and lavender? Do you know the scent of western sage? If not, I doubt I could more than dimly suggest it to you. What words do we have to convey touch? Hard, soft, slippery, wet. Do we say velvet is soft? So are ten thousand other things. Do we have words for taste? Or emotions? Don't we merely have what a writer has called skeletons on which we hang effects? Aren't we like a Meredith character who intended her statements to be understood in a broad general way and not dissected?"

"Well," Mrs. Jackson said, looking at Vridar with interest, "maybe it's because I've been reading Jespersen. You know him?"

"I've read him. I felt that he greatly overstated his case."

"Philologists, I suppose, fall in love with their subjects. Tell me this, do writers determine what they want to say and then find the precise words to express it?"

"I don't think so. What are the precise words? I think we're all David Hawkes, though he's an extreme. So far as I can tell, words come along and fill up with meaning for me, and it's of course silly for me to imagine that they have exactly the same meaning for anyone else. It's even silly for me to imagine that I know with any exactness what they mean for me." He knew he was talking too glibly but her wine was excellent, her face was sympathetic.

"But teachers of writing tell their students to find the precise word."

"It's easier to teach that way. It puts the students in awe of their teachers."

Martha Jackson gave a little laugh. "Vridar—may I call you Vridar?"

"Of course."

"Vridar, if a critic says nice things about your book, do you write him a note of thanks, or is that in bad taste?"

"I don't," Vridar said. "If author and critic become friends, it would be a rare critic who did not tip the scales in favor of his friend, or who, sensible of that danger, did not tip them against him. I think the relationship should stand above personal exchanges, and especially in a country where the literary Sigma Chis spend so much time scratching one another's back."

"Sigma Chis?"

"In my undergraduate school the most offensive fraternity was the Sigma Chi. I think of popular novelists busy promoting one another as Sigma Chis."

Again she laughed.

"You know David Hawke? I'll tell you a thing that shocked me. In the two most important newspapers his first novel was reviewed by women. That was a prodigious break for him. One of those women wrote her review and took it to him and told him to rewrite it in any way he wished to. I know this is so—confidentially—because he showed me the review before it was printed and asked me to read it. My God! What an impertinence to call it criticism when it descends to that level."

Martha looked at him a few moments, thinking about it. Then: "I asked the question because two years ago I wrote a note of thanks to two different reviewers. Both of them ignored my next novel."

Vridar said, "A lot of reviewers have to be horribly sensitive of their honor, having so little."

Her smile spread. "You think that could be it?"

That afternoon, with Prof. Jackson tagging along, they went north up Manhattan to a great park. Vridar and Martha walked side by side talking. Jackson, behind, began to caper, and repeatedly his wife looked back at him, her brows lowered. When she saw the frail little fellow trying to chin himself from an overhanging limb, she cried, "Andrew! Stop acting like a child!" Andrew looked only a little abashed. He released the limb but he remained behind, frisking and capering; and once, looking back, Vridar thought he saw in the professor's eyes what he had seen in the eyes of monkeys. Vridar wanted to go back and caper with him—to chin himself, climb a tree, or scamper away in the undergrowth looking for nuts or old berries; to lie on dry humus and dig fingers deep into old rotted leafdepth and moist loamy earth. But Margaret Jackson, who so plainly thought of herself as an intellectual, was talking about the writer's craft. Vridar listened politely but his emotions were back with her husband.

"Don't you think so?" Martha asked.

"Oh yes, I do," Vridar said. He glanced back. Andrew, looking impish and simian, gave him a droll wink.

XVIII

It was early in January, 1929, when Vridar first laid eyes on David Hawke. He had heard about him. The chairman of the department had spoken of David as "one of my boys." Hawke, he said, had completed a novel and gone abroad but would be back for the winter quarter. Vridar was sitting at his desk when Hawke came in.

He came on enormous strides, for he was a huge man, fully six feet, six inches tall, with a great mass of bushy uncombed black hair that made him seem taller than he was. He came in as if propelled from behind or as if in desperate haste, his huge shoulders thrust forward, his long arms swinging. His desk was just across an aisle from Vridar's. When Hawke came to his desk, he dropped a pile of books and sank sprawling to his chair, his dark smoky suspicious eyes darting from face to face but not meeting the gaze of anyone. Sitting at his desk, Vridar had a full view of the man and he now studied him. He soon became aware that Hawke knew that he was being observed. He revealed it in his movements. He revealed that he hated it, that contempt for it was welling up in him. Vridar then pretended to read themes.

David Hawke, unlike most of his colleagues, spent little time at his desk. When he came to it, he would sit only a few minutes, and he sat like one who was boiling and steaming inside; who could not endure even the casual glance, much less the steady stare, of the other teachers around him; who was so utterly filled with consciousness of himself, of his destiny and meaning, his ambition, his future, his coming wealth and fame, that he had no time for his inferiors. When he knew that he was being studied, his eyes flickered with spite and after a few minutes he would rise abruptly and leave the room on his long loose-kneed stride.

His first novel had been accepted. It was published the next fall, a big amorphous chaos of words and emotions, a cyclone of power and rhetoric, a long paean to David Hawke. Its self-glorification was more extreme than any Vridar had found in literature. But for all its self-pitying rhapsodies, its incredible lack of economy and skill, it was a huge hungry thing, an American thing, and Americans were quick to claim it as their own. Vridar and David had become friends by the time the novel appeared. Almost at once Vridar had perceived that they had much in common—the same terror and distress and fear of father in childhood, the same need of loyalties, security, peace. He perceived that Hawke had a shrewd and calculating disingenuousness on a mammoth scale: this deceived all but those who looked into him; it brought sentimental women fluttering to him; it made paternal men feel protective toward him. Words poured out of Hawke as though every organ in his body was busy manufacturing and ejecting them: his manner of speaking was that of an untutored, credulous, forlorn lost soul, but the eyes were awake and watchful. The eyes missed little. They often darkened with suspicion, contempt, hate. Vridar found it strange that adults, and college professors at that, looked on this man as a big gawky overgrown boy in need of a guardian. How could they be so unaware of the dark amusement and the pitying scorn with which he dismissed their patronage!

A few times Vridar had been to Dave's room. Like his book, it was a huge and splendid chaos: manuscripts were piled on the floor, cases were laid open, letters and books and magazines and newspapers and clothes were a carpet underfoot. It was there, soon after his novel appeared, that Dave handed to Vridar three typewritten pages, saying that this was a review of his book by a woman, for one of the two most important newspapers in the city. She had given it to him to rewrite as he pleased. "My God!" Vridar murmured, appalled. He had not known that this sort of thing was ever done. He had not known that any serious writer would stoop to such deceptions on the public. Right there, sitting in Hawke's room, he resolved that rather than ever be a party to this kind of thing he would go to the other extreme, and keep whole continents, if that were possible, and in any case an unbroken silence, between him and his critics.

645

The review, written by a woman, Vridar thought effusive and fatuous. During the few moments it took Vridar to read it, David was impatient. He wanted to read it again, and he did, his hungry eyes devouring the three pages of praise. He guessed it was all right, he said, glancing quickly at Vridar and back to the pages. With a ravening hunger he read again. "Good God, it's fine, don't you think so, huh?" David never waited for replies. He wanted none.

Before they left the room, David loped from tray to tray looking at all the cigarette stubs. He crushed one after another, already dead, and at the door he stopped to look back. Had he extinguished them all? He hastened to the trays, again peering, crushing. They then went down the stairs and at the street he turned. He said he guessed he'd go back to be sure they were all out.

When they were walking along the street, he said, "Vridar, you think my book will sell ten thousand copies? Huh? You think so? Good God, I hope it does! The critics have been swell. Except that son of a bitch James Ragdon. That vermin, that little holyass of a creature, that spitheel, so God damned little he smells little. Huh? You think it might sell fifteen thousand? Good God, I hope it does. . . . . "

David told Vridar that he would be the most significant, the greatest, the most unforgettable author of his time. His childlike words recalled to Vridar Balzac's boast, "I shall rule unchallenged in the intellectual life of Europe! Another two years of work and patience—then I shall stride on over the heads of those who wanted to fetter my hands and hinder my advance! Under persecution and injustice my courage has grown hard as bronze." Vridar had done a Doctor's thesis on an author's self-pitying conviction that he had been neglected, misunderstood, persecuted. Listening to Hawke and recalling the petulant words of still other writers, and the faces and words of the writers he had met here, he thought, My God, my God! Are we nothing but children?

"Vridar, honest, you think my book will sell? Huh? Fifteen thousand, that's what Edwards hopes for; maybe twenty. If it would sell a hundred thousand, huh? That holyass of a son of a bitch Ragdon! Does he review you?"

"He—" Vridar began.

"Huh? You think it will? Did you see the window they gave me in Brentano's? God, it's a great experience having a book published! How many will I publish, I wonder. If each one is better than the last, and the first is as good as they say it is, then the last should be the greatest novel ever written. Huh? O my God, I hope it will. . . . "

On and on he talked about himself, always about himself—pouring out his hopes, his worries, his dreams—a great loping hulk of a child who prayed in his heart to be the greatest genius that ever lived. He recalled to Vridar Stendhal's words about a man who, under the illusion that he was very clever, never bothered to reason anything out. David Hawke, Vridar decided, would never be a thinking man, but only a feeling man. He could never be greater than his intuitive powers. David had recently broken with his mistress, a woman almost twice his age, and was drinking a lot. He told Vridar that when he got drunk he tried to uproot lamp posts and push buildings over.

When a bookstore window came in sight, David went loping toward it and even before Vridar came up he was talking to him—or to himself, Vridar supposed, or to the universe; he was admiring the jacket on his book, the color harmonies, the arrangement of the book in the window. He would go inside to ask how the book was selling, and Vridar, waiting, would be sunk deep in wonder: he would never have asked if a book of his was selling! He would never have risked being seen looking at it in a bookstore window. He would almost rather have died than talk about it. Why, he asked, was this so?—and then David was outside again, admiring and exclaiming. He was so completely lost in admiration of what he had done, and he struck such grotesque postures to get one view of the books and another, almost knocking down people who were passing, and causing many to look back, that Vridar, feeling that a soul was showing itself naked, wanted to slip away from him and go home.

But he walked with David and they came to another bookshop. Again David bolted inside. Was his book selling? Were people reading it? What did the readers think of it? Did those in the bookshop think it would be a best-seller? O Lord! Vridar thought, watching this child and marvelling. He would no more have talked about his own book than he would have talked about his intimate relations with Athene. Am I the ass? he wondered. He was fascinated by this huge gawky child who could think of nothing but himself. He watched closely every move David made, listened to every word he uttered, his wonder and amazement growing. David, outside, was again admiring the arrangement of his books in the window when a person came along and entered the shop. David followed him in. When it dawned on Vridar that David had gone in to see if the person was going to buy *his* book, he was simply flabbergasted. He felt shame. Again he wanted to slip away. He had never known that a man could be so completely ego-centered and be so utterly childlike about it. The person didn't buy David's book. David moved close to the man to see what book he was buying and when he was again on the street with Vridar he muttered, "Woollcott! My God, he reads Woollcott!"

Vridar was with him one evening after David had received letters from his hometown. He had hoped that the hometown people would read his book and hail him as a great writer, and now he was worried sick by what they were saying about him. Sitting on a bench with Vridar, he read a few of the letters and then wept like a heartbroken child in the form of a giant. Vridar felt such deep compassion that he wanted to put an arm round him and say, "To hell with them, don't let what they say bother you at all!" He wanted to go to David's hometown and say, "Look, you bastards, stop torturing this child, for he has in him whole worlds of which you'll never have the faintest notion!" David would glance at Vridar, and in his wet brown eyes there seemed to be no malice then, no suspicion or contempt, but only the hurt. He said he had wanted—O God how he had wanted to receive letters, lots of letters from the people he had known; but not such letters as these. Not letters that told him he had broken his old mother's heart! not letters that told him he had insulted and outraged the city of his birth. Sobbing, his great shoulders trembling, his chin trembling, he handed a letter to Vridar saying, "Read it. It says—uh-God, I did take the hide off that place, didn't I though—Huh? Vridar, read it. It leaves me empty and hollow-

647

ed out, a big vacuum down in my guts and a nightmare in my soul. Some of them—
they say they'll kill me if I go back. Can a writer ever go home again?. . . "

Vridar almost exploded with mirth. Here the ridiculous clown was, weeping, yet
looking through his tears to boast that he had taken the roofs off the city, by God,
so that people could look in! His was no far land of dear old Cockaigne, no tale of
white gentlemen appalled by a Negro's rape! God damn you, no!

"At college they all got letters but me," he said, again shaking with grief, thrusting another letter at Vridar. "Now I get letters—these! These stinking little spews
out of dark little souls. Anonymous things on a grocer's wrapping paper! How can
you have this crime upon your soul, you wicked man, writing murder stuff to kill
we good people!" He was mimicking now. He was exaggerating. No grief, no threats,
no bitterness of memory could long keep David Hawke from caricaturing people.
Even while wiping at his eyes, even while trying to see another abusive letter to
thrust at Vridar, he went on:

"By God, my novel is no cheap little comedy about the Old Tradition! It's no
romance between one of the white brethren and a high-yaller gal! It's no love
affair between a cow and an imbecile. It took their hides off, Vridar. By God
did I, huh? Here, see what this son of a bitch has to say. Did I give it to 'em, huh?
Here, look at this one . . . ."

It was all Vridar could do to keep from bursting. Later, when with Athene,
he lay back and howled. "O Lord!" he breathed, wiping tears from his eyes. "There
he sat, blubbering with grief—O God, how he was suffering, and I was suffering
with him. I was ready to go down and shoot the whole town. But under it all, under
the wet handkerchief, under the tears was a sense of triumph as big as the Tetons!
Did he give it to 'em, huh? They say if he goes home they'll dunk him in a barrel
of piss. Oh, the things they're going to do to him and it all tickled him almost to
death, for now at last he feels that he's avenged on a dull provincial town that
hadn't enough sense to recognize his genius. It's pretty terrible. All the time he
was weeping, the sly bastard was watching me and pulling out of the pile of letters
those which tickled him most, while pretending that they were the ones that were
like branding irons on his soul!"

On another occasion Vridar was not so mirthful. He had spent an evening drinking with Hawke, listening to Hawke, staring at Hawke; and when he joined Athene
he was exhausted. He said, hiding from her his dry smile, "I've learned that if a
person wants to talk about himself, but is denied, he's more exhausted than by anything else in life. For four hours I have lived nothing, breathed nothing, thought nothing, seen and heard nothing but David Hawke. I couldn't even find out if Edwards
has read my book." Edwards was David's editor.

"Why do you go see him if he wears you out?"

"Remember how Professor Dobram's odor fascinated Pyke Rowe? So this man
fascinates me. I suppose this incredible egocentricity, this fixation on self, this monstrous narcissism at a ten-year-old emotional level is typical of artists. How then
can they produce mature work?" He stared at her and said, "Can I ever?"

"Do you think you're immature?"

"Oh hell yes. I wouldn't tell anybody but you—and I'd tell you this besides, that possibly the chief reason we don't get along so well is your greater maturity. You're not very tolerant of my childlikeness. Excessive drinking, ranting, grieving—such things aren't found in the adult mind. Are they?"

"They're not found in me."

"I thought you'd be flattered. Yet if I'm such a child why don't I, like Hawke, talk about myself all the time and lope around to find out if people are reading me?"

"Nobody has to be such an extremist."

"The golden mean again! There was no golden mean for Wagner and Meredith, Dickens, Chopin, Gaugin and Van Gogh, not even for such as Thackeray and Tennyson, God knows, not for Goethe. For whom? To be great, does the artist have to be odious?"

"You always talk in extremes," she said, wearily, for they had discussed this before. "There *is* a golden mean in all things."

"Not for artists—or maybe you'd like to name one. The truth—and I will now admit it's an appalling truth—is that artists are so egocentric they're simply insufferable. They're children, of course. If they mature emotionally, are they through as artists? I suspect so. If art comes out of emotional immaturity, can it be of any worth really? Are we living in a child's world?"

"The child can be disciplined," she said impatiently. "You always forget that."

"Yes, and then you get a Henry James. Look, I don't kid myself about this. I also want to talk about myself and my work. I never will. Is that because of my mother's teaching? Will I to the day of my death be the manly little man who is to be seen and not heard but not seen too much?"

"Aren't you just negative like your father? You don't really want to be a successful writer, do you?"

He flared. "Oh God damn, of course I do!"

"Then why so angry about it? You've said that anger—"

"Oh I know. There's something holding me back—for I could," he said, and again he turned to hide his smile, "I could be as odious as any of them. But I'm afraid I'll be lost somewhere in a private dedication to modesty, while the David Hawkes, proclaiming their genius from every housetop, are taken to the nation's huge sentimental bosom."

"For most persons," said Athene, herself becoming dry, "that's the only evidence. People can understand you if you say you're great. They don't understand it if you think you're great but don't say so. You say, My book? Oh, it's nothing really— only four hundred pages about farmers and hills. Do you expect people to take *that* as evidence?"

He looked at her and considered her words. He met her eyes and saw in them the dry mirth, the smouldering impatience. Then his gaze fell to her nose, as if he were studying that; to her mouth; to her chin; to her breast, and at last to her slender freckled hands.

"What I'm afraid," he said, "is that my egocentricity is more monstrous than that of those who can utter it. It's not that I'm more sure of my powers. It's not that at all. It's something holding me back and that's something I'm afraid of."

In a newspaper Vridar saw that J. P. Morgan and Owen D. Young had dined in Paris. The luncheon had begun with Ostend oysters and Chablis 1921. Then came lobster l'Américaine and Pouilly 1919. A barbecue of venison followed, accompanied by Château Rothschild Bordeaux 1881. The bird course was served with Clos de Vougeot 1921, and the salad with Château Karem 1910. With the cheese, fruits, and coffee was cognac Napoléon 1820. Tammany had also dined: lobster cocktail Orientale, okra créole; suprême of turbotin, lamb Colbert, chicken Virginienne, endive, génoise, glacé, and demi-tasse. There had been a Kennel Club show. "Come of All Celia, a tiny Brussels Griffon no larger than a house cat, was barking and snapping and pulling at Jeannot of All Celia. Chippy Again, a Pomeranian, was yipping at first-prize winner, Rehalt Mollie of Ashburne. Lady Indo of Arr, a little Maltese, was sending piercing yips from her blue satin-lined box, draped with blue velvet. . . ." On the same page silk pajamas for poodles were advertised. On the next page was a plea for contributions to the milk fund for undernourished children.

A lot of people, Vridar reflected, seemed to be wondering if they should go into Communism. Like Robinson's Miniver, he thought and thought and thought about it, and returned by the same door wherethrough he went. He was convinced that Communism was not for him.

Two of his colleagues were determined to make a Communist of him. Vridar had not been able to learn how many Communists were in the department of English. He knew of three. One was Madge Stauffer, a large homely woman with an unpleasant voice who, many years later, would flee to the Communists in Poland. Another was John Wallace Wiggam, an effeminate over-dressed man with dainty gestures and affected speech. "How bee-utiful this morning is!" he would exclaim, rubbing his soft useless hands down over the silk of his cravat. The third was a short stocky bright-eyed Jew named Richard Hansen. Vridar supposed that he was only part Jew: he had learned that Jews, like Negroes, called themselves by their own race even if they were chiefly Swedish, British, French, or something else. Unlike the Negroes, with Jews it was a matter of choice.

One evening Vridar accepted an invitation to Dick Hansen's home. He was not surprised to find Wiggam there.

"Good evening," said Wiggam, advancing, bowing, extending his soft moist little hand.

Another man was present. He was William Homer. Homer had written such an effusive review of Woolf's *Orlando,* becoming so ecstatic over her "genius," that Vridar day after day had studied him, when they both sat in the big office. Vridar read the novel and thought it tiresome and pretentious and was not surprised later to learn that Mrs. Woolf herself had called it a joke and a freak.

Hansen had music playing softly. Like Wiggam he was devoted to the classics, particularly Mozart and Bach. Vridar had begun to suspect that he himself was tone-deaf and that all the Hunters were, for he knew of none who carry a simple tune without falling offkey. Marion's singing simply drove people from the house.

Vridar accepted a drink and then became aware that Homer was studying him with his large pale blue speculative eyes.

"Ready to join us?" Dick asked.

"I'm afraid not," Vridar said. "I rather agree with Clemenceau, that a man who's not a Socialist at twenty-five has no heart, and no brains if he's still one at sixty. I was a Socialist at twenty-five. I'm a long way from sixty but I don't think I'll be one when I get there."

Homer said, "You think the Roman Church is a tyranny?"

"Why yes, no doubt it is. Anything based on a belief in absolutes is a tyranny, isn't it?"

"You believe in tyranny?"

"Are you serious?"

"Well, look. Communism offers the only way on earth to strip the power from the Roman Church. Are you familiar with its history?"

"Yes, to some extent. I've read most of Lea, for instance."

"Vridar's principal objection, as I understand him—" Dick broke off and turned to Vridar. "You want to say it?"

"I can try," Vridar said, and for a few moments tried to organize his thoughts. "My objection is not to Communism per se but to any one-party system, under which the people have no way to recall, replace, or chastise their leaders. I object to it because I believe with Lord Acton—a Catholic, Homer—that power corrupts. I think any man—I say *any* man—placed in a position of power over his fellows will exploit them. If you argue, as you people sometimes do, the virtues of government under a benevolent dictator, I remind you that there has been only one. And what kind of son did Marcus Aurelius leave to rule? The type is Napoleon."

"Do you," asked Wiggam in his high womanly voice, "do you take the position of some of these American intellectuals, that the dignity of man—whatever in the world that can be," he said, pursing his soft womanly mouth, "that the dignity of man is meaningless unless sanctioned by God?"

"I don't know what you or anyone means by God. I don't think it necessary to bring him into this, unless you want to argue that most men feel they never had a father, and so seek one in one pope or another. I—give me just a moment, please— I didn't really have one in that sense either— a father who makes the son feel loved and cherished; but damned if I'm going wailing to the Catholic pope or the Communist pope."

"I think you're entirely off the track," Homer said, his voice rather cold. "It's pretty childish to drag in fathers and popes when the whole question is whether we're going to tolerate a system that produces such monstrous thieves as Commodore Vanderbilt, John Jacob Astor, E. I. du Pont, Daniel Drew, Jay Gould, Jim Fisk, and Rogers, Rockefeller, Carnegie, Morgan, Gates, Schwab, Insull and all the rest of them. We're in an economic crisis today because a few robbers have been allowed to seize most of the nation's wealth. Do you agree with that?"

"I think there's a lot of truth in it."

"But rather than give another system a chance, you'd go on with this one, that has brought us to the brink of disaster. Is that your position?"

651

"Vridar, don't you agree with me," said Wiggam, coming in with fluttering gestures, "that if a system has failed, we should try another, even if we can't guarantee that it will be perfect?"

"I'm not sure our system has failed."

"Hasn't failed! My God, man. Soup lines all over the country, millions out of work, and a moon-faced incompetent in the White House!"

"Has it had a fair chance? The American system was designed for the protection of minority groups and for the control of the leaders by the people. That we have had plundering on such a huge scale means that human beings—"

"It means," said Homer, cutting in, "that the natural resources belong to the people and the people have to be protected from the robbers. Have they been protected, if a few men own so much of the country that nobody can guess at the extent of their holdings?"

"No."

"Then you admit—"

"Oh yes, I admit that a few sons of bitches have got hold of much of the country's wealth. I don't admit—"

"Let's approach Vridar from this point of view," said Wiggam. "He's a writer. I've heard he got only six hundred dollars from his first novel and no publisher wants his second. Now under Communism he'd not have to go begging from door to door. He'd be among the elite—"

"Elite in a classless society? Yes, that's exactly what you'll have—industrial thieves and brigands will be replaced by bureaucratic thieves and brigands."

"Oh no. No, the ablest will rule. Only the ablest—"

"The most ruthless will rule, God damn it. They always have. You fellows are romantics."

"We're realists," said Homer. "We look straight at the facts of life. We see that in this country of fabulous resources a few are fabulously wealthy while millions don't have enough to eat. We execrate such a system. We say that man has the intelligence, yes, and the decency, to build a better system. We say—"

"Not yet."

"Why not yet?"

"Because man isn't yet civilized enough. He doesn't yet dare to free his leaders from controls. Not even the best of them. Generations, maybe centuries, of self-discipline and education must come before we can have a workable Socialist system."

"We say that men with a conscience can't afford to wait for millenniums. We can't afford to wait for perfection in human behavior. We look at the enormity of the suffering in the world today and our conscience forces us to act. How men like you can stand back, how you can refuse to join hands with us, how you can live with yourselves. . . ."

"So there it is," Vridar said, after telling Athene about it. "Over and over I ask myself, do I stand back because of selfish reasons? They have, God knows, a lot of arguments on their side. It is true that a handful of ruthless brutal greedy apes have been plundering this land, while in the White House sat such stupid bastards as Harding and Coolidge. But the fact that such men exist, and plunder when they get the power, should make us afraid of all men.

"What bothers me most," he went on, "is the nature of these intellectuals who become Communists. They seem to me to have aneurysm of the mind, and soft pus-filled tumors in their emotions. Looking at them my mind goes back to the trial of Marie Antoinette—the disgusting fanaticism and cowardice in her accusers and judges and the foul obscenities they threw at her. As for the Homers and Wiggams, are they actually grieving over the world's suffering, or over themselves? I think it's something very personal and raw in them and I'm going to try to run it down. Have you any idea?"

"I'm a woman," she said.

"There are some women becoming Communists."

"Not *women*," she said.

"Not women?" He looked at her and considered her words. "If not, then are Wiggam and Homer men? I've a feeling they're not. Are they only boys who in their unconscious minds feel they never had a father? For them, is the son of a bitch named Stalin a father surrogate? If they never had a father who is a more logical candidate than I?"

"But you're aware of the lost-son-no-father in yourself. Before you became aware of it, weren't you a Socialist?"

"Yes, but let's not rest it all on that base."

"You're the one who first said it."

"You should be a Catholic. You think that once a thing has been established it is changeless. What I meant to say, or what I say now, is that these intellectuals are giving their souls to a system over which they'll have no control at all. That's really surrender of the will, isn't it? A Catholic can get out if he wants to—"

"Not if the whole world is Catholic. How was it in the Dark Ages?"

"But in a Communist country, even if most of the world is not Communist, he can't get out. He has no freedom of movement." They were silent, looking at one another. Then he said, "Isn't this some kind of enormous surrender of the human will? And if so, what does it mean? That people have lost faith in a God who was a Papa?"

"Communism doesn't appeal to me at all."

He went on, talking to himself really: "Man has got himself in a hell of a jam between his emotions and his mind. Jeremy Bentham made such a fetish of reason that when an invention was brought to him, in which he could see no faults, he felt compelled by reason to invest in it. At the other extreme are men so much the slave of their emotions that they would surrender their wills to the Papa in Rome or the Papa in Moscow? Athene, I'm fed up with this city. Come June, we're going east or west. Would you like to ride a bicycle over Europe. If Carl and Eltie want to go with us, can you put up with them?"

"If you wish."

"All right, I'll get the reservations. We'll see what Mussolini is doing. We'll find out if the Germans hate us and if the land of Shakespeare is all fog and sleep."

XX

Early in June, 1930, the four of them sailed thirdclass on an old ship. Vridar kept a journal. He wrote:

> We've been sailing for four days out of sight of land and my simple Antelope Hills soul is still trying to realize that the world is mostly water, that we all live on islands. The continents were such big things in our geography classes! I look at a perfectly round sea and a perfectly round sky; smell the salt and the sea and the infinite centuries of time; and love it! I pace the decks, looking, breathing, feeling—troubled by the presence that haunted Wordsworth. For many besides David Hawke a journey is the nicest of all our symbols. I look at this great rolling body of water, like the sky blue with time and with all that mankind has forgotten, and make futile attempts to understand how long I lived before I was born— what a long heritage looks out of my eyes. For four days I have heard the deep water-washing sounds of a rolling sea; have felt the prodigious power of the ocean over my sleep and dreams; and am now lost in the emotion. If I were not a person of such abnormal restraint I would say Goodbye, Idaho, goodbye, country; I am going now, too far ever to come back. I am going now to that far moment when the first ape stood on his legs and realized that his hands were free. There is something here that I'm not getting into my books, nor, so far as I know, is any man.

> Sitting in a cheap London hotel room I remember: how the gray rock-bound coast of Galway gave the lie to the green legends of Ireland; how in Liverpool Carl and I were accosted by nine whores within a couple of blocks, while policemen stood back and grinned; how when our women wanted to go to the Lake country, Carl blew scornful winds out of his long nose and cried, I suppose you want to find the spot where Wordsworth wrote a violet by a mossy stone! My God, if only you find that stone!

> I have fallen a little in love with the English countryside, but as a mistress, not a wife. I shall always love most the Rocky Mountains and the semi-arid plains. Mary Borden says England's greatness has come from the passionate sense and feel and smell of its people for its lazy climate; that the United States, stripped of fog, brilliant with light, encourages ceaseless racing on the hours. So, she thinks, we produce skyscrapers, religious maniacs, and more impostors, fakers, neurotics, drunkards, tabloids, fads, cults than any other people. There's just enough truth in it to take a part of the sting from her typically British condescension. It is true that my land falls on its vulgar face to welcome such unimportant noddies as the Prince of Wales, or bankrupt dukes and earls looking for rich wives; that it spawns all sorts of adolescent cults; sends hordes of expatriates bellyaching to Paris; perjures its soul for a dollar in a testimonial to almost anything; responds to demagogues with cheers and tears; and invites into its academies of arts and letters only the spiritual fraternity brothers of William Dean Howells.

> But the British are a long chronic invalidism away from the time of Raleigh and Drake.
> If we remember with shame the abuse heaped on Dreiser, let us not forget what London said about Ibsen and Zola. Zola's English publisher,

an old sick man, was thrown into jail and driven to his death. If we are young and raw, brash and vulgar, are not the British smelling of decay here in their fogs? When Elizabeth ruled and fornicated, nationalism was the new and mighty force; adventurers sailed to the ends of the earth then and art caught the spirit. There may be fortitude against death but there seems to be no growth in the philosophic mind, that has been forced into philosophy by age. I don't know whether it's a faint odor or a sense of quiet but you know that Henry James has been here. . . .

My mood is not charitable toward expatriates today. I can smell the pus in their emotions. My country may be a vast lunacy and a monster may be emerging. Call it a Caliban but I prefer calibans to elves. My land is a vulgar barbarian so full of energy that it uses sleeping pills by the carload; England is an old grandmother in an armchair, looking back to the vital younger years when her consort was more than a houseboy. The World War rocked her but she still sits: we missed our parents and having only grandparents over here we are the world's noisiest orphan. . . .

For Spencer was the Thames actually a sweet and fragrant stream? It is a sluggish sewer now. But English ale is fine. Scotch whisky and Irish whisky are fine. Carl and I are drinking everything in sight, while our women, using some kind of osmosis, run wildly hither and yon absorbing culture. Dover I shall remember as a place where we saw six Americans drunk; Ostend as an enchanting loveliness in a dark night; Brussels as the spot where we were first descended upon by the hordes that prey on tourists. After traveling a bit you realize that internationalism is only a dream that Woodrow Wilson had at Princeton.

We've been in Paris two weeks. I'm sitting now in a cheap little hotel in the Rue Git-le-Coeur on the Left Bank. In the smallest cafes the food is good but only the cook knows what goes into it: loaves of bread as long as Lindbergh's legs are used by street gamins as dueling swords, or by cats in the cafes as beds. Carl and I have explored parts of the Louvre— I stood breathless before the simply incredible color harmony of Clouet's Francis I and the equally incredible richness in Giorgione's Pastoral Concert. Our women dragged us into the depressing dark mysticism of Notre-Dame. They rush around to gawk and gape at Institut Pasteur, Balzac's house, Hugo's, the Sorbonne. Why see such things if you've been disappointed in Yellowstone, Niagara Falls, New York's skyline and the Champs-Elysées? Why deliberately seek to be disillustioned in Atlantis, the Hebrides, Heaven? If our reach does not exceed our grasp . . . .

Carl loves to look into the dives. One evening we followed a group of students into La Source where they stole all the drinks in sight; thence to D'Harcourt where they turned the tables over; then to La Rotonde, le Dôme. This seems to be the Parisian's notion of uninhibited living. In Le Jockey the dances were about like those in a cheap Harlem cabaret. We went to Moulin Rouge which advertises "pretty women in as few garments as possible." It bored us. We went to Le Cabaret l'Enfer where damned souls make their infernal rounds: an American girl screamed, a bald man clutched his wife. In Les Folies a man, assumed to be amorously out of his wits, ran his tongue over a woman's thighs and up her belly. Judging by American faces around me that was real lovemaking. . . .

I came to Paris with a lot of illusions in my head. I thought love here was franker, more unashamed. It's true that men here drop a coin before a woman sitting on a public bench and the woman manifests her favor or disfavor by taking or rejecting it. It's true that on the subways men often woo their maids but they seemed to me to be selfconscious about it. It may be true that the Latin temper hasn't the Nordic relish for virginity and all its outlandish cults. It is true that men here are not arrested if they accost a woman, and that the woman is not fool enough to think she has been insulted. But I imagine that in the neurotic Christian world people are pretty much the same everywhere. They have been pretty well conditioned into emotional imbecility.

I also expected to find Paris a very sophisticated city. It may be. But at the sidewalk tables and in the cafes are the most tiresome adolescent posturers I've ever seen: if this is the kind of abnormality Gertrude Stein detests because it is obvious I am with her. Paris gapes. I'd think it a singularly insular mind that, unaware of its own inexplicable self, measures sophistication in terms of surface credulity for another. Fancying themselves horribly disillusioned and civilized they become specialists in a contrived ennui. Freud should have had his clinic right on the Montparnasse.

I look at Paris and realize that I'm looking at the end of a decade: *transition's* twelve propositions; Dadaism, expressionism; Stein; the expatriates, loose-lipped, eyes trying to look oh so sophisticated: the lost generation in flight from itself, coming to its sick end in Paris. . . .

We've cycled across France, eating and sleeping where no American ever ate or slept. France I shall remember as a lovely land, when my nostrils are stuffed: poppies, quaint hamlets, picturesque dwellings, rolling hills. But the hamlets have a godawful stink, and France from one point of view is little more than sewers and cemeteries. Countless millions have died and been buried here; for ages diseased bones have been washed down the watersheds. Hating French beer and unable to afford the water sold in bottles we ventured to empty a carafe; and for three days in La Charité (how we love that name!) we thought we would die of bellyache. What agonies! What vomiting as with stricken eyes we stared at a lovely land fertilized by all the graveyards of the past, and watered by foul streams with their cargoes of dysentery and the Dark Ages!

I came over to be a Roman when in Rome. I grew up believing it all right to eat hog but not worms. How deep our prejudices go! I discovered *that* when I pulled a piece of maggot from a piece of cheese; when I saw a Frenchman plopping fish eyes into his mouth; another drinking off the dead bugs in his wine; and still again when passing through the kitchen in a cheap inn, where a piece of meat was black with flies. That was the meat we had for supper and it was delicious. Only once have we balked—when we found flies in a stew as thick as raisins in raisin-cake. Worms we'll eat; fish heads and eyes; meat white with fly eggs. But flies in our soup? Not yet. . . .

We assume that Americans own the highways over here. Twice with their automobiles they've run us off the road and into ditches. All natives give us the right of way. The Americans remind us of such brigands as William E. Corey, whose wedding breakfast cost $5,000; the flowers $6,000; and who set aside $200,000 for honeymoon expenses, telling the press afterward that his wedding and month of honey cost him exactly a half a million.

Keats was right: the mirth of Provence was certainly sunburnt when we went through—a barren rocky country ablaze with sunlight. Defenseless scalded towns. The French Riviera may be lovely but not for me: orange and lemon and olive trees; pale villas, a meandering coastline, a merciless sun overhead. Every city along here has the same hard glittering quality, but what lovely names, compared to our Chicagos and Pittsburghs—St. Raphaël, Boulouris, Miramar and Théoule; La Napoule and Anthéor and Juan-les-Pins. I'm sitting in a villa in Menton, remembering that some famous persons have called this the loveliest spot on earth. I prefer shadows and depths in background. It's turquoise sea is lovely, but so is all the sea along here—the gulf of La Napoule, Nice's Bay of Angels, the sheltered perfection of Villefranche-sur-mer. But they're all as hard as jewels and I've the notion that people who live here are brittle. We've almost every drink known to France on our shelves and Carl, sipping and loving this climate, wants to stay a while. I want an open road and German beer. . . .

Bored to death, Athene and I left them and cycled across a part of Italy. Mussolini! His damned arrogant henchmen met us at every turn, demanding our passoprts, pawing through our wretched belongings scattered over the earth; gloating; winking at one another. And the roads! The Romans built some fine highways and we've shaken our guts out over what is left of some of them. Everywhere we saw small boys drilling; everywhere Mussolini's prognathous jaw on walls and trees; and everywhere we heard the songs of derision and hatred:

> *Contro Parigi noi marceremo*
> *E vittoriosi ritorneremo*
> *Al nostro Duce riporteremo*
> *La mozza testa della Marianna. . . .*

Athene's knowledge of Italian comes in handy. The Duce's braggarts, we hear, are going to march on Paris and return with the bloody severed head of France. The Christian people are civilized: ad uno ad uno li ammazzarem: one by one we will massacre them. So the boys are singing in the most Catholic country on earth. In Busalla our passports were stolen while we slept and we had a hell of a time getting them back. In Pontedecimo I got into trouble by touching what I took to be white oil-cloth: it was a sheet of spaghetti dough. In Oleggio we ate more flies than lamb. But Arona was nice; and across a lake from Pallanza we saw a city of shining light in an evening sun. But again in the hideous little town of Domo-d'Ossola bedbugs drove us from our room. It is morning, birds are singing (though Italians eat most of their songbirds), Athene is laundering our few things while I make these notes. The Latin temperament is just too effusive for me. . . .

My darling sleeps under a tree by a loveliness called Lake Neuchâtel. Our journey through Switzerland has been a joy: our room in Sierre was drenched with apple blossom smell. This land is not a graveyard; the water here we can drink to our heart's content. Its mountains remind me of the Rockies and I gaze at them, soft and flabby with nostalgia. But there's no hint anywhere of western sage, dearest to my heart of all things in the world's landscape; nor of buffalo bush; nor of the strong smoke of cotton-wood fires; nor of buckskin and huckleberry and big mountain rivers. I think I must go west again. . . .

Athene is photographing the Rhine while I catch up with note-making. Germany has overwhelmed me. Being part German I had expected to feel at home here but I had forgotten the war. The hatred of Americans has amazed and silenced us. We entered this land at noon and at midnight were still looking for a place to sleep. From Gasthof after Gasthof we were turned away. At last, exhausted, we entered a small inn and drank beer and in my poor German I asked for a room. The girl said yes but when her mother came, a woman who hadn't smiled since 1914, and learned we were Americans, pure hatred filled the place. Mother and daughter argued and at last we were allowed to stay.

We left without breakfast and cycled with the low mountains of the Black Forest on our right, with poppies and morning glory along the road. At noon we passed a man in a wagon who had lost his endgate and I overtook him and told him. He scowled and asked if I was an American. Later, while we were eating lunch under a tree, he came to reward me. He offered a coin. "Nein," I said. "Sie haben mich falsch verstanden. . . . Nein, nein, was liegt daran? Es ist nicht der Rede wert." He was offering me the equivalent of half an American cent.

Five times the second day we asked for a room in vain. Then we entered a tavern where several men were drinking. "English?" asked the barkeep. American, I said. After a while I got him to drink with us and over foaming steins of beer we cursed the war and its leaders. His father, brothers and all his uncles had been slain. He was still so bitter that after twelve years we couldn't make him laugh but he shook my hand the next morning and watched us disappear.

Our other experiences in Germany merely repeated these two. The climax of bitterness, the most hostile unwelcome, came to us west of Bad Dürkheim. We had been turned away from nine places and as we rode along, despairing of finding a place to sleep, I spoke the simple and necessary questions in German, trying to correct my accent; and I succeeded well enough to fool the daughter in the next inn we entered. But the mother came in and was not to be fooled. She said she had no rooms. I told her the daughter had said she had. Seeing that she would not yield I decided to lie. I said we were Germans, born in America, but that our fathers had been born in Germany; and watching her I saw that I had found her Achilles heel. Her next question staggered me: on which side in the war had our fathers fought? I explained that our fathers had had no choice. She saw sense in that but wanted us to go. She withdrew to a wall and looked at us. I turned to the daughter. She said her father and all her brothers had been killed. After a little the mother and daughter drew apart and talked, and suddenly the mother asked me our name. Hunter, I said. She asked me to write it down. She studied it. She asked her daughter if Hunter was a German name. Then she asked to see our passports. Next, she wanted to know in what part of Germany my father was born. I saw a map of Germany on the wall and went over to it. The first name I saw was Coblenz. "Coblenz," I said. "Coblenz?" "Ja. Coblenz, es liegt mit viel daran. Gottlasse ihm seinen Willen." The statement that God let him choose his birthplace I thought would please her. It did. She gave us a room.

But attempts to soften what war had done to her were of no use. She gave us a cold supper and her manner said she had gone as far toward friendliness as she could go. I told her that thousands of Americans had been killed too, that their mothers had been saddened by loss. She retorted that millions of Germans had been killed. In the nightmarish blackness of such insanity as war where can you find an answer to her simple statement?

The next morning we were up at daybreak and were astounded to find our door locked. We were prisoners of war. I dare say Germany had been full of stories of American soldiers raping German girls. We knocked and waited and knocked for more than an hour. Then footsteps came, a key was turned. As I write these words there are stories in American newspapers and journals of the friendliness of Germany for my land. What lies! They lie to us to get us into war and then go on lying. No doubt Germans appear to be friendly in those firstclass places where Americans spend freely. What member of Government ever traveled at my level? It is easy to imagine what such hatred as this will lead to. It's not easy to hope that the War's leaders rest in peace.

I thought it appropriate that we rode out of Germany into the desolation of Lorraine. I shall never forget the sudden bloodrush of emotion when, after leaving Metz, we came to the first barbed wire entanglements. I wanted to sit down right there and cry my heart out. I looked at the trenches, the wire, the crosses in fields of oats—all a part of that other war in which Germany was the victor. I tried to understand why men leave such grisly records of brutality and slaughter. I must try to look to the causes of war. Now, here, I can get hold of nothing but a sense of something brooding and darkening—being absorbed into the lies of legend where the truth will never be told. It was not until we reached Douaumont that we realized how deeply quiet everything is on the western front. Rain fell all during our journey through this wasteland. We climbed to France's ironically magnificent monument to the murdered, and stared a long while (or I did) at the Tranchée des Baïonnettes where men were entombed alive at the moment of charging, with their bayonets thrust up like a row of pickets. We stood there in shell-gutted land, under a dismal wet sky, trying to realize not only that 400,000 men had been slain in the small area we looked at, but that only 80,000 complete bodies had ever been found. They were digging for bones all around us. What brutal indifference to the living young man, what devotion to his bones! Those who give ten francs to this monstrous hypocrisy "will receive an artistic parchment, designed by Georges Scott and bearing Marshal Pétain's autograph." Can crassness be more complete than that? This was Thiaumont. It was lost June 23, retaken the 24th, lost during that night, retaken by the French on the 29th, lost on the 30th; and between then and July 4th it changed hands four times. "It is soaked," says the Guide before me, "with the glory of France." No human being could ever have written such words. They were written by some mindless and souless thing. We made a long journey in pouring rain to see the American cemetery of Romagne-sous-Montfaucon. Near the infamous Mort-Homme we read on a monument this insolence:

> Qui que tu sois, Francais qui passe, salue
> bien bas ceux qui sont morts ici pour toi

They had died for the infamous imbeciles who call themselves the leaders of nations.

On our way out we paused to look at the Rheims cathedral; and while staring at it I recalled the rage of certain American editors because the

Germans were shooting the stone saints off it. It takes a creature somewhere below the level of the gorilla to work up a fury over the shooting
of a building, and not over the shooting of twelve million men. Yes, a lot
of the saints on this cathedral got their heads shot off, a matter I think
quite fitting in a Christian land. They're rebuilding it now. I've no
doubt at all it will be ready for the next war between Germany and
France. . . .

In Menton for sixty francs I bought *Lady Chatterley's Lover,* with
Lawrence's preface. In the Bois de Boulogne we read it to one another.
All his life Lawrence struggled to write one book, and from the groping
Sons and Lovers to this one he made an agonizingly miscalculated pilgrimage to an idea and a vision, which it appears he had no power to come
to. Or should I say only intellectually. He understood, with his mind, what
we must all understand, that we can never be decent as long as the mind
is ashamed of the body, the body afraid of the mind. Words which
shock so much at first, he says, don't shock at all after a while. People
without minds may go on being shocked but they don't matter. Isn't there
something pretty naive there?

We are today, he says, "evolved and cultured far beyond the taboos
which are inherent in our culture." Isn't that nonsense? In my Notes
I find Tylor's statement, "To ingenous attempts at explaining by the light
of reason things which want the light of history to show their meaning,
much of the learned nonsense of the world has been due." Lawrence
made the common mistake of thinking that he could find the explanation
within himself. Well, so he might, if he had a broad enough background
to stand on. "In the past," he says, "man was too weak-minded, or crude-
minded, to contemplate his own physical functions without getting all
messed up with reactions that overwhelmed him. It is no longer so." Says
Lawrence! If he had read more and looked at his navel less he would have
learned that the lower natures didn't get messed up: the messing up came
with what he is pleased to call the higher cultures. "There has been so
much action in the past, especially sexual action, a wearying repetition
over and over, without a corresponding thought, a corresponding realization. . . . When people act in sex, nowadays they are half the time acting
up. . . . Mentally, we lag behind in our sexual thoughts, in a dimness, a
lurking, groveling fear which belongs to our raw somewhat bestial ancestors."

God-all-Friday! Why couldn't Lawrence get the self-pity out of him?
Why did he flee into the cant about somewhat bestial ancestors? Did
Lawrence never realize that the human face, which even with its nostrils
fastidious care can make acceptable to the "higher culture," and the
crotch, which not even bidets can make acceptable, are irreconcilable on
the mental plane? Certainly we must applaud his anger at the "perversion
of puritanism," the "perversion of smart licentiousness," the "perversion of
a dirty mind." "But I stick to my book and my position: life is only bearable when the mind and the body are in harmony, and there is a natural
balance between them, and each has a natural respect for the other."
But can the mind ever possibly respect the body? They occupy two worlds
millions of years apart.

Of his Lady Chatterley he says, ". . . do what she might, her spirit
seemed to look on from the top of her head. . . . Yes, this was love, this ridiculous bouncing of the buttocks. . . . After all, the moderns were right

when they felt contempt for the performance; for it was a performance. It was quite true, as some poets said, that the God who created man must have had a sinister sense of humor, creating him a reasonable being, yet forcing him to take this ridiculous posture. . . . Even a Maupassant found it a humiliating anti-climax. Men despised the intercourse act, and yet did it."

How pathetic and feeble his whole statement is! Why couldn't he leave the God-myth out of it and look at it down the long ages of Evolution, perceiving then that what he calls ridiculous bouncing and ridiculous posture is simply our inability to make a satisfying aesthetic thing of an act that served well enough, and aroused no contempt, at the "bestial" level? Can the sexual act, so primitive in its purpose and passion, ever be aesthetically acceptable to the person of sensibilities? Anyway, let's leave God and his sinister sense of humor out of it. . . .

XXI

On arriving again in Paris Vridar and Carl decided that they could smuggle in a gallon or two of whisky and rum by taping the bottles on the bodies of the four of them. If their wives would pretend to be pregnant, each woman could take a quart, possibly two, on her belly.

Athene was outraged. Angrily she cried, "Do you know what it'll mean if you get caught?"

"Vaguely," he said. "We'll all lose our jobs. But there's no reason in the world to get caught if we do it right. On the ship we'll rehearse the matter a few times, all taped up and ready."

"You actually think I'll walk in with a whole quart of whisky on my belly?"

"Two quarts," he said. "You have a lean flat belly, so we should put two there. No customs official would ever dream of feeling over a woman's belly."

"You sound insane," she said. "And you intend to take in the Lawrence novel? Don't you realize it's prohibited?"

"I'll tear it in two and put half under each typewriter."

"And if they ask you to lift the typewriter out?"

"That'll be my most embarrassing moment."

Carl and Vridar searched over the city to find bottles with unusual shapes. There was a half-pint size that was convex on one side, concave on the other: it fitted nicely around an ankle, or the inside of the upper arm. They spent hours studying the shape of their bodies, trying to fit a bottle here, a bottle there. "If they feel over us," Vridar said, "the academic world will lose three fine teachers and Tom Lewis out in Utah will be glad he got rid of us."

"We'd better put most of it on the women," Carl said.

On the boat going across they had what Vridar called full-dress rehearsals. In their cabins they undressed and taped the bottles on them, from ankles to armpits. Then three of them would sit on the deck as judges while the fourth walked back and forth. It was necessary, Vridar believed, to learn to walk naturally with all the bottles on; to move without awkwardness; to seem un-selfconscious. The women

661

detested their part in it but they had been prevailed on to do it. When taped up, each looked about six or seven months pregnant.

They had better go in separately, Vridar said. They might think it strange if two women, traveling together, had conceived at about the same time.

Vridar had written Marion to meet them at the customs house. He wrote: "We'll have booze taped all over us. To get through as soon as possible we'll pretend to be in an awful hurry: from time to time I'll look over toward you and shout, saying we'll be there as soon as we can; and if you can get close enough to be seen by the apes searching us, try to give a sense of urgency. Say you have to meet a class or have a sick child. . . ."

"But I suppose," he said, "the customs men know all the dodges."

Two hours before they were to leave the ship they carefully put on the bottles and taped over them. Again Athene protested, her face red and frightened. "A hell of a gunmen's moll you'd make," Vridar said. "Have you no nerve?" Angry and outraged she allowed him to put the bottles on her and tape them. The four of them had their luggage ready. They wanted to be among the first down the gangplank, though they had heard that American customs officials were ornery creatures whose choice of whom to examine, whom to ignore, was capricious. They had also learned that if they were cabin or firstclass they could give the ship's luggage master a handsome tip and then go right through without having their bags opened.

After they were all taped and dressed they sat in one of the cabins and waited. Athene was still for pitching the liquor through the porthole and the novel after it. She said she had never felt so degraded in all her life.

She now asked, "What if a bottle falls off?"

"How can it? Every bottle has enough tape around it to support a keg."

"It's the damned novel that worries me," Carl said. Half of it was under Carl's typewriter.

"It's worth a hundred dollars," Vridar said.

Eltie said, "You men have to carry the bags."

Vridar looked at Eltie a few moments. She was not at all like Athene. She seemed to be enjoying this, for she was a rebel at heart, she liked secrecy and mischief. And unlike Athene she really liked alcoholic drink.

Vridar stood up and seizing a typewriter and a suitcase gently lifted them. He had a small bottle taped in each armpit. When he lifted the luggage he could feel his arms pressing the cool glass in against his ribs. But these were rugged bottles, they'd never break.

They went abovedecks early to get in line and then stood, their luggage at their feet, all four of them trying to look unconcerned. Covertly watching the other three, Vridar thought Athene looked angry and smouldering; Eltie, devilish in a sly stealthy way; and Carl, nonchalant, except those moments when his black eyes surveyed himself.

The disaster came with appalling suddenness. Vridar at the moment was looking at Carl's face and saw a horrifying change in it, and at the same instant smelled the fumes of rum. With his horror growing he looked down, and saw, running from Carl's right trouser leg and bubbling up out of his shoe, the golden liquid of St.

James rum! Rigid with amazement he saw that the two women were sniffing, and Carl was staring down like a man astonished at having found himself making water. People in the line behind Carl were looking at his face and at the wetness at his feet.

"Carl, you imbecile!" Vridar breathed in his face. "What have you done?"

"It blew the cork!" Carl whispered.

Vridar was thinking fast. If they were not to be caught cold here, with all these bottles taped on them—if they were not to see their names in headlines in tomorrow's newspapers, they would have to devise a miracle in the next few minutes. Remembering that Athene had bought an ounce of expensive perfume he moved toward her, breathing at her, "Where is it?—your perfume."

"Oh no," she said.

"Don't be a fool!" To Carl Vridar said, "Come!" and seizing his bags left the line. A moment later he hastened back to tell the women to stand above the rum wetness and not move from it. Then he and Carl fled to a cabin, a sense of disaster almost bursting their skulls. Vridar swiftly found the bottle of scent and opened it. Carl had his trousers down and was peeling the empty bottle off his thigh. "Good God!" said Vridar. "You taped it on upside down!" He poured perfume over Carl's hairy leg and inside his shirt collar and down his shirt front. He drenched him with it, muttering, "My wife will divorce me for this. God, man you're going to look as if you had pissed your pants but we can't help it." He took Carl's shoe off and with a bed sheet wiped around inside it. He poured a little water into the scent bottle, sloshed it around and then dumped it into the shoe. Looking up at Carl's face he said, "Try to look like a fairy."

"A what?" asked the dazed and scented Carl.

"A homosexual. Act like one. Man, you're stinking up the whole ship."

With their luggage they went to the gangplank deck and stood at the end of the line. It seemed to Vridar that Carl's stench, a mixture of rum and Narcissus, might be smelled as far away as Hoboken or White Plains. "Act peculiar!" Vridar said. "Can't you act the way you smell?" Eltie was smirking; Athene looked as if she had been caught in a brothel.

All his life Vridar was to remember with amazement what happened next. He was ordered to open all his luggage and take the lid off his typewriter case; and as he took the lid off he thought, Here's the end of another college teacher. But the official only looked down at the typewriter as he might have looked at the first crocus, and said, "Put the cover on." He made Vridar take everything out of the big suitcase and then knelt to feel through the clothing, like one after diamonds or heroin. Carl and Eltie meanwhile had been passed! As Carl told it afterward, the customs man took a good sniff at Carl; gasped, as though he had filled his lungs with the fumes of nitric acid; had then seemed to stagger a little and roll his eyes inward; had shaken his head hard as if to clear his senses and waved them on. He opened no bags. He asked no questions.

Vridar was closely questioned. He decided afterward that possibly it was because he had shouted down the long room to Marion and Mollie, who were standing above the throng and shouting at him. This, Vridar told himself, was an old dodge. He told himself that there was no trick or deceit on earth that customs officials were

663

blind to. After pawing all through his luggage, like one of Mussolini's henchmen on the Italian highways, the man looked into his eyes and said, "What do you do? What is your job?" "I'm a college professor," Vridar said. The man's eyes seemed full of unbelief. He turned to look a few moments at Athene, his gaze at last falling to her swollen belly, and then passed them.

They were safely through, and Marion was hustling them all to a big cab, and Mollie was saying, in her southern honey-child voice, "What you-all got on you there?" She put a hand on Athene's belly. "O my God!" she said. Like one who had endured centuries of extreme thirst, Marion was demanding in anguished whispers to know how much stuff they had. He began to feel over them, his face looking like the face of a man approaching an orgasm, as he found bottles, one by one. Carl's odor filled the cab overpoweringly, even with the windows down. Vridar saw the cab driver looking at them in his rear-view mirror.

In Marion's apartment, Vridar and Athene went to one bedroom, Carl and Eltie to another, and there they undressed and stripped off the tape and the bottles. Vridar observed that Athene's tape was fairly covered with fine golden hair. Gurgling with joy Marion loped from door to door, to reach in for bottles, to rush to the dining room to stand them on the table, in rows, like priceless antiques. He kept swallowing hard, like a man in from the Death Valley deserts. It was September 6, 1930, and the experiment Herbert Hoover had called noble had produced a nation of gangsters and crime syndicates, and rotgut. Marion had not had a drink of decent whisky since coming to New York: he picked up one bottle after another, to hold it to the light, to hug it to him and make silly cooing sounds over it, and to try to smell the contents through the glass.

Then the six of them stood in the dining room and looked at the treasure on the table. There were twenty-eight bottles, in sizes from three ounces to a full pint. Marion found it impossible to keep his hands off them, and Carl and Vridar growled at him, afraid that the eager thirsty clown would break one.

"Which do we try first?" Marion asked, trying to look at all the bottles at once.

It was what those full of self-pity called the lost generation. It was what those looking under the surface recognized as the end of an era.

PART II

Heloïse

"To her master, rather to a father, to her husband,
rather to a brother, his maid or rather daughter, his
wife or rather sister, to Abelard, Heloïse."

I

Vridar remained at Manhattan College three years but teaching for him became more and more of a nightmare. It was so for David Hawke. Like David, he had learned that only a few students were educable: most of them sought only advantages over their competitors, when at last they should find themselves in a trade or profession. To fortify himself to face their ignorant cynical eyes he got the habit of drinking off a glass of gin before entering the classroom—and was astonished one day to learn that David often did the same thing. As the talk of fat vulgar merchants had had a stupefying effect on Stendhal, so their students had a paralyzing effect on David and Vridar.

A few years later Vridar was to be amused and touched by the confession of Dr. August Forel, a famous psychologist: "I was absolutely overcome with terror before my first lecture; so much so that before entering upon my martyrdom I allowed our steward, who, as a former apothecary, distilled a currant brandy after a recipe of his own, to give me a large glass of his concoction, and drank it down to give myself courage. Gudden, who had driven into town with me, suddenly declared that he meant to listen to my first lecture. At this I almost fainted, and besought him not to do so. . . ."

But Vridar went west for more reasons than pathological shyness. His sons were out there and he felt that he had neglected them, though he had employed a private tutor for them during his years in New York. His father was out there. Joe had had a large ugly cancer cut out of his throat—and the surgeon was the same dirty drunken Dr. Gunn to whom Vridar, when overcome by lunacy, had fled in Rigby.

The West was out there. He had never known until he went East how much he loved it—its magnificent mountains, its vast forests of Douglas fir, pine, and spruce; its great clean rivers, the strong pungent scent of its campfires, and above all, the boundless semi-arid landscapes smelling of sage. Theodore Roosevelt had called it "the masterful, over-bearing spirit of the West. . . ." Vridar was unable to think of its as overbearing but he was not, like Roosevelt, an extrovert.

He was sick of Manhattan's poisonous gases from thousands of automobile exhausts; of its filthy stinking street, its cynical merchants, its speakeasies, its foul rivers, its underworld of crime and heartbreak. He wanted to draw Rocky Mountain juniper through his closed palm and then smell the marvelous incense; to break open a twig of buffalo bush and then breathe of it; to see whole mountainsides of flaming maple after the second frost; to hear the deep-in-the-earth roaring of Snake River between its sheer stone walls; and at daybreak to listen breathless to the song of the meadowlark (and what other music on earth was as sweet at that!). He wanted to feel the healthy pull in his muscles as he climbed a thousand, or two or three thousand, feet up the Big Hole mountains, looking for elk or bear; to taste the wonder of a logger's breakfast after three hours in pre-daylight sub-zero cold. When he went East, he had thought he would never want to see the West again. He had not known that he was and always would be a mountain man.

He left Athene in Chicago, to complete the work for her doctorate, and after buying an old car for a hundred dollars he drove westward, alone with his thoughts. The stock market crash had left him almost penniless. He had no publisher. He had no job. It was almost two thousand miles to the ranch on Snake River: he would eat only sandwiches, he would sleep in the car by the roadside, and all the while he would be wondering what he should do.

He would rather starve than go on teaching. Teaching and creative writing did not mix: the artist or the pedant won and it was usually the pedant. Hawke had said he was quitting, too, but Hawke had a publisher. Monckton and Snafflin had agreed to publish a second novel for Vridar, if he would waive all royalties on the first two thousand copies. This he had done. But of his next offering the publisher had written, "This is too strong meat for our table." Vridar had seized the manuscript and read here and there in it. He had cried to Athene, "What in hell have these Boston people been eating all their lives?" New York publishers didn't want it either; they said it was too realistic and brutal and unromantic.

So here I am, Vridar thought, crossing the Mississippi and entering Iowa. He had a few hundred dollars; an old typewriter and an old car; a stack of unpublished novels; a Doctor's degree which had cost four years of his life and was now useless; two sons to support; and a marriage that did not strengthen with the years. Here he was, who was babilan and was still half-babilan, hoping some day to be no-babilan; with a bad hangover from Socialism, yet resolved to be damned and pushed into hell before he would accept Communism; a writer whose first book had sold twenty-eight hundred copies, his second eight hundred, and whose third nobody wanted. . . .

And what was he going home to? What could there possibly be for him out there? His parents were now renting their ranch, their domineering and unyielding ways driving tenants off almost as fast as they appeared. Vridar now thought of one who had come a few years ago, when he and Carl were teaching in Utah— a tall gandershank of a moron with the strange name of Chaste Bumbell. Chaste was still honeymooning when one Christmas Vridar and Carl drove up from Utah to shoot duck. Joe and Prudence were spending the holidays elsewhere.

Vridar took one hard look at Chaste and wondered, as he was to wonder ten thousand times, why such stupid people were allowed to propagate. Though not yet thirty, Chaste had false teeth, with most of the front ones missing because of his habit of chewing on chokeberry limbs. His speech was so thick that he was barely intelligible; his grin was enough to stop a grizzly bear; and his way of showing affection to his short thick wife, whom he called Poggie, threw Carl into gales of laughter. Their first night there was one that neither Vridar nor Carl would ever forget.

The two small bedrooms at one end of the lodgepole house were separated only by a partition of boards covered with wallpaper. A person lying in one room could hear a whisper in the bed beyond the partition. But it was not a whisper that Vridar heard. At first he simply didn't know what it was. After a few moments he thought he knew and was so astonished that for a little while he lay and listened. He then turned to Carl and clapping a hand over his mouth aroused him. In his ear he whispered, "Wake up! You've heard wondrous things but nothing like this." Carl stirred and turned over. "Listen!" Vridar whispered. "And for Christ sake don't spoil it!" What the two men now heard was a prodigious roar of laughter blown out of Chaste's wide lungs.

The two men listened, looked at one another and listened, the eyes of both filling with amazement and mirth. Laughter was building up in them with explosive force. "Don't!" Vridar whispered, admonishing Carl with a deep scowl. "O my God, don't spoil it!" Chaste let off another terrible roar. Then, in silence, his wife made an effort, and erupted with thunderous glee. The two morons, bridegroom and bride, were competing with one another to see which one of them could fart the loudest. It was with full realization of this in their eyes that Vridar and Carl stared at one another, with restrained laughter almost killing them. They could sense the silence in the other room as Chaste contracted his diaphragm and worked his belly muscles, determined to win the contest once and for all; and the moment after he broke wind with a sound like that of a rifle his broad chest exploded with a triumphant bellowing. They would then hear his thick guttural tongue saying to her, "Jist try now an beat that one!" And when they sensed how hard she was trying Vridar and Carl bent over and hugged themselves in uncontrollable joy, their mouths bawling muffled hysteria into their pillows. They then would straighten up, their faces red and strangled; they would listen; they would hear Poggie's effort, followed by laughter as joyous as a child's.

When Vridar and Carl could no longer contain their mirth, they exploded like two lunatics. They pounded one another, they drove clenched fists into the pillows and the bed, they staggered to their feet and groped for their clothes, their minds barely able to hold this new revelation of the common man. When their mirth was spent, they listened but in the room beyond everything was now as hushed as death. Vridar could picture them there, the two astonished and crestfallen honey-mooning blockheads, looking at one another with eyes full of questions, amazed to learn that their little act had been discovered: two morons who would have ten or twelve children, all morons, and all, as Carl was to say later, champion farters.

It was too much for the professors from Utah. It was too much for them when the breakfast was put on—the steaming bowl before Vridar was some kind of por-ridge but it stank. As when, lying in bed, he could not at first believe what he heard, so now he could not at first believe that this bowl of porridge had the smell of some awful decay. He looked across at Carl and saw his fastidious friend making a hideous face of disgust. Then Vridar glanced at Poggie. She had come out of the bedroom with a red face and it had been red during the whole time she prepared breakfast. She had refused to meet Vridar's eyes. Chaste had put on his stiff and stinking barnyard clothes and hustled out to milk the cows.

Carl shook his head at Vridar. He meant that he could not eat the porridge or anything else on the table. He meant that he was ready to go home. Driving past an Iowa cornfiield, Vridar became so filled with mirth recalling the experience that he had to draw over to the side of the road and let the laughter out. Two persons in a passing car, seeing him stagger around, convulsed, slowed down. He waved them on. How many times was he to be thought insane, when privately reliving some hilarious episode in the past! Now, sobering, he said aloud to the world, "How damned silly it is to put up Communism or anything else as long as hundreds of millions of morons in the world are allowed to reproduce their own kind!" The thought recalled to him the words of the Rev. Charles T. P. Grierson, a contributor to the Hastings Dictionary: "The widespread belief of the early Church in the virgin-birth can be reasonably accounted for only by the occurrence of the fact itself." Vridar had begun to keep a list of what he called especially choice stupidities and at the moment Grierson's words were his favorite. Just under them, in his file, he had the words of the Rev. A. W. F. Blunt, a Fellow of Exeter College: "The interpretation of a dream 'belongs to God'; the question whether its message is a Divine communication or not must ultimately be answered by an appeal to the religious consciousness, or in other words to the higher reason."

Day after day he drove along at thirty miles an hour, thinking of one thing and another. There was his father, whom he was only beginning to understand. The day Vridar married Neloa, he had seen Joe looking at him with something in his eyes that Vridar did not like. That evening when bedtime came, the thing that had been in Joe's eyes came down to his tongue: "Better sleep in our bed," said Joe. "Make your first baby there." It had been such a gross statement of father to son, so indelicate, yet so deeply rooted in a baby-worshiping Christianity (make the baby in the bed where he and Prudence had made Vridar!) that the son felt anger and shame, as well as astonishment. The next morning his astonishment was even greater.

The previous evening Joe had said, "We work tomorrow. Just because you marry you don't get time off around here." Joe had meant that they would be off to the harvest fields at daylight. They harnessed four horses, and the father mounted one, the son another, to ride up the mile-long dugway, where so many times as a terrified child Vridar had listened for the sound of a homing wagon. To the day of his death he was to remember the exact spot on this dugway, so great had been his amazement and pain, so deep his humiliation, where the father squared around on his horse, spat a stream of tobacco juice, and said, "Guess I otta tell you a little about sex."

O my God! *He* was going to tell *Vridar* about sex!—he who long ago had boasted to his sons, once, briefly, that he was a virgin when he married—he who had never known but one woman and that one in fumbling and shame! He's going to tell *me!* Vridar thought.

Joe was trying to choose his words with care. He said at last that he had always figured that sex was something—well, to have only once in a while, as a special treat. He knew that God wanted it that way. Vridar stared at him and waited. Joe said he had had it only every two weeks and sometimes not that often. Oftener than every two weeks simply wasn't good for a man. Vridar was not meeting his father's eyes. He could not have met them, anyway, for Joe was not looking at him, had almost never met his gaze, from childhood until now. Joe was a morbidly shy man, so introverted and shy that some people thought he was stupid.

Driving along, Vridar chuckled, remembering the experience. What would Joe think if he knew the whole sexual odyssey of his son Marion?

Bringing the thoughts to his tongue only with an effort, a supreme effort, Joe had gone on to say that when he married Prudence he had asked her how a woman felt about it. She felt, Joe now told his amazed and staring son, as though she wanted something in it. He reckoned that that must be right, because a man felt that he wanted to put it into something. Those had been his last words on the subject. Like one who had said all there was to say on the delicate and mysterious subject of sexual relations, Joe bit off another quid of Horseshoe plug, looked up a few moments at the sky, and kallated that it might rain.

From time to time during that long day of labor, Vridar recalled now, while crossing the Missouri into Nebraska, the son had looked with fresh wonder at the father. It had not occurred to him then, but it occurred to him now, that Prudence had prevailed on the father to advise his son. No doubt she had told Joe that in such matters Vridar was still pure and innocent. . . . Lord God! Could she have forgotten that when he was eleven he had persuaded his sister to show herself to him? Could she have forgotten that horrible hour when she faced him with a green chokecherry cudgel and, using the short ugly four-letter word, had demanded to know if he had done that to his sister? He hadn't, but Lord, he had wanted to! Had she forgotten all that she had learned about her sons, year after year, and for which more than once she had taken them into the bushes and laid a green whip across their bare backs?

Well, possibly she hadn't asked Joe to talk to his son. Possibly the incredible idea was born in Joe's own strange Irish-German mind. Strange, for Vridar, was the word for it: a strange father whom he had never understood and of whom he had lived in quivering terror: a brute of a man who took what seemed to be an evil sadistic delight in letting his male beasts become yearlings before he sawed off their handsome horns, cut open their pouches and tore out their stones, and pressed deep into the hide with his huge redhot branding iron. What horrible things he had done! Had he no sense of pain or agony in anything besides himself?

The father had not been a brute, Marion had said. He had only been ignorant. The sons would have to understand him now—not love him, it was too late for that, but understand why he had acted as he had. He had never been loved. That was it. Instead of loving him, his furious tyrannical black-eyed and half-demon Scotch-Irish mother had made a baby-tender and drudge of him, because he was the eldest in a large family. That was why he really didn't care for children. And Prudence had never loved him. He was a man whom nobody had ever loved, whom nobody ever would. That, Marion said, was the reason he had been brutal.

Yes, that obviously was the reason. A lot of men had been brutes for want of love. "We might have become brutes too," Vridar had said to Marion. "We got no love either." "Oh, you got some," Marion had said. "I got none." His gray eyes had darkened. "None," he said, "except from you, and I didn't want that."

In childhood Vridar had thought his father a very brave man. He *was* brave against everything in the world but men: though not an expert swimmer, or even a good one, he would venture into the most dangerous rapids in a frail leaky boat; he would stand up to any wounded big-game animal, including the grizzly; he would ride the wildest horse and single-handed would rope the most maddened bull; but he would rather die than stand up in a fist fight to a man. The source of this timidity in him Vridar did not yet understand. He was so unlike Prudence that way: Joe's wife would face any man or any person alive, with a gun or without it. . . .

Well, he was going back to the ranch now. Possibly he would understand his father better after a while—and a lot of things better, including himself. He simply had to have a fuller grasp of things or put his typewriter aside, for he had no wish to write superficial stuff-in-trade for ordinary readers. Before he began writing books about himself and the people he had known in childhood and youth, he had thought he understood them pretty well. He doubted that now. In writing about a thing the writer discovered how much he didn't know about it, and became dismayed, if he had any brains at all; became humbled, if he had any imagination; and doubled his resolve, if he had any ambition. "I've written pages and pages about my father," he said to Athene, "only to realize at last that I don't understand him. I've written pages about you and I don't understand you. Or myself. So I'd better go away somewhere and discover some point of view, some method in art, some approach, some aim—something worth my life. I've a feeling I can do this best on mountains and rivers."

He had thought he might see a light in Europe but over there it was a deeper darkness. He knew he would never see lights in the canyons of Manhattan. If he could not find himself in the mountains and rivers, the deep white snows, the full ripe summers, then possibly he was lost as Hawke was lost. Sometimes it seemed to him that illumination might come if he got down on his belly and crawled back to the beginning. He had a wish to live for a while with adult chimpanzees in their cage, for in the apes he saw human beings with their masks off. On the ranch he would again renew his study of beasts—for in them he learned more about human beings than in studying human beings. No source of irritation would become more chronic than the self-pity and the self-love in persons, including professors and writers, and O God yes, the liberals, who would ask him, down the years, "You honestly mean you learn about *human beings* by studying the *animals?*"

His mother he thought he understood pretty well. She was aggressive, extroverted, energetic; fiercely ambitious for her children, especially her sons, but contemptuous of her daughter, who by choice had been a tomboy—who had preferred the outside world with her father, and all the more in later adolescence. Prudence had only her small Mormon world, whose horizon stood visible all the way around her. She was immensely proud but there was base metal in her pride, as there was in the pride of all the English; she was inexorable, uncompromising, stern, puritanical, and rather humorless. She had married an inept, bumbling, inefficient man and had driven him with an iron will, had driven him so hard that again and again he had broken into a lumbering awkward stiff-legged lope. She had lodged in him a dream, the Branton dream, of three educated children; but if he had had to make the money to send them to school, they would never have got to the eighth grade. Joe simply had no talent for making money. If he became a herdsman over a thousand head of valley cattle, he lost so many that he ended the year almost bankrupt. If he went into the sawmill business, one helper got a hand chopped off and another a leg. And so it had been Prudence who, laboring sixteen or eighteen hours a day, had done most of the milking; had made cheese, raised chickens, and had gone, alone, on hundred-mile wagon journeys to the valley; who had trotted a mile up and back to cross lumber-haulers on the ferry; who had gathered serviceberries by the bushel to feed her hens; and who in still other ways with energy and drive unbelievable for all but those who knew her had got together the few dollars necessary to send the children out. It didn't take a lot of thinking to know a simple character like that. It took a lot of insights to plumb the darkness and bring the pain up out of Joe.

If in some ways Joe seemed to be a moron, that was because of his abysmal ignorance. He had looked solemnly at Carl, an extremely hairy man, and had said, "He's from Esau." All knowledge for him was in the Bible and the Mormon holy books. He argued with heat and anger that the Mormons would control the entire Rocky Mountain area before the year 1940, and that the world would come to its end before he reached his hundredth birthday. "Then," Vridar had said, amused, "you'll never die." Joe nodded, meaning that he would never die. It took a lot of indulgence in a son to look amiably at a father after that. Vridar had stared at him and thought of the awful terror to which Paul Cézanne's father had driven him.

Two years ago Vridar was sitting one day with his father when he became aware that Joe was eating his fingernail parings. He watched a few moments and then turned to his mother. Joe had always eaten them, Prudence said; and now, driving along, Vridar was thinking, If such a person's anxieties and sense of insecurity were only a little stronger, he would drink his own urine! A deep dark tormenting sense of insecurity, that was the clue to his father. That was the source of most of the hate and fear in this world. This night Vridar dreamed that he was sitting somewhere looking at a man. The man was Stalin. He became aware that Stalin was trimming his nails and eating the trimmings; and a little later that he was eating the scab-flakes off old sores. The dream woke him up, and he was so astounded by its revelation that he left the car and walked round and round it. Our Father in Heaven, was that also the clue to Stalin? The more he thought about it the more he had no doubt that it was so. They were so much alike, the two Joes, both of them deep, silent, brooding—and brutal! Both of them unloved and without friends. There was a door here that must open, for he felt that beyond it were whole realms of light.

Driving along he recalled Balzac's words, "I have never had a mother! My mother is the cause of all the ill that has befallen me in my life." Balzac had cried aloud to the heavens, "The most dreadful childhood that has ever fallen to the lot of any man!" But not so dreadful as his own, Vridar thought. Freud had said that a man who had been the favorite son of his mother went through life with the feeling of a conqueror. Freud, Vridar now reflected, was an ignorant ass in a lot of ways. For look! He, Vridar, had been the favorite, yet had no feeling of a conqueror, and not much confidence in his powers. Was it because he had not been breast-fed? He suspected that might be part of it, for he was, along with millions of American men, a breast erotic. He could remember vividly the envy he had felt, the rage and outrage, when he saw his sister sucking at the mother's big white breasts. But was Dr. Ernest Jones right in thinking that Freud's anxiety about catching trains was related to a symbolic breast?—that the train was the breast for him? Vridar doubted that. He had the same morbid anxiety about being late: for appointments he was always early, absurdly stupidly early; and if he had to meet a train, he was there an hour, two hours, ahead of time. Vridar decided, after fifty miles of thinking, that Jones had erred: the train was not symbolic of the breast *but of the mother.* . . .

Dimly, far away, he could see the mountains like mist. The terrain was becoming more arid. He couldn't smell the sage but it was not far ahead. The long stretch across southern Wyoming, which most people thought desolate, was the kind of country he loved: as a child and youth he had seen upon it in the black nights the dim pale yellow of a sheep-wagon light, or of a small campfire—and lights in the dark had become symbols for him. In this kind of country a man could think without being jostled and shoved by the human myriads; he could hear the silences and the sounds of his living. He would go home again. He would complete these books about himself and the people he had known, keeping in mind always what had been said of Stendhal, that his whole life had been a preparation for his books, that no man had ever brought to the task more interest and passion. Not even a Rousseau, not even a Proust, had so ransacked his memories, had so faithfully explored his mental attics and cellars, had looked so frankly into the darkness of his ego. Stendhal, with the detachment of the scientist, had tried to understand himself. Nobody who called himself a literary critic had taken him seriously. Chateaubriand, that monumental ass, had been, in the opinion of the critics, writing one deathless masterpiece after another. Of him Stendhal had said, "What would be a blasphemy to say of M. de Chateaubriand now will be a truism in 1880." How true! Stendhal, knowing that he was ahead of his time, or at least ahead of the critics, had addressed himself to posterity, predicting that he would be read in 1900. It had taken an ignorant mankind a little longer than that to discover him. My job, Vridar told himself, is to keep ahead of Stendhal, if I can . . . .

He would go back to the ranch. Life there would be like that of the Carlyles at Craigenputtock—isolation, bad roads, infrequent mail, deep winters, an outdoor privy, a lack of physical comforts; but there would be compensations. If he could find enough money for the materials, he would build a modern home for his parents, as well as other structures, such as barns, hencoops, garage, millshed—for he would like to have a small sawmill of his own, with which to produce lumber and shingles. For years he had not had the physical activity he loved and he had grown flabby and unmasculine. He recalled Nietzsche's words, "My most creative moments were always accompanied by unusual muscular activity. The body is inspired; let us waive the question of the soul." Vridar did not think of it as inspiration: he knew only that when he worked hard he felt better, slept better, thought better. He would write in the forenoons and in the afternoons he would work hard. He would eat hard, if among them they earned enough for food. He would love hard, if the estrangement between him and Athene did not continue to grow. She was a good lover, who embraced with passion and without shame.

He could smell the sage now and the dry hot scent of alkaline earth. The mountains had come into view. He pulled off the road and went out to the prairie to gather sage and rub it between his palms, and an armful to put on the seat by him. When he drove again he would from time to time raise a palm to his nostrils to sniff or with his right hand he would crush some of the gray-green foliage and rub its essence across his upper lip and chin.

II

He crossed southeastern Idaho to Pocatello, turned north past the old Fort Hall site to Idaho Falls, and then, with his heart sinking, headed east. He wondered if it would always be this way. When he saw the Antelope hills, would he be so full of Neloa that he would choke up, so conscious of the childhood terrors that he would want to flee? He tried to fight down the emotions rising in him. Presently he was in Poplar, and on his right was the old schoolhouse, on his left the canal on which he had skated with Helen. Helen, he had heard, was living here. Some day he would stop off to see her, for he was curious to learn if life had been kind to the golden-haired girl whom once he had loved. Yonder in a field was the old cottonwood-log shack where he and Marion had lived, with mice and the bitter cold and their own whimpering terrors. . . .

He was climbing now into the hills and soon Snake river was on his left, deep in its canyon; and a few minutes later, coming to the top of a hill, he looked straight ahead at Neloa's home. There by the north wall a man had lain with her when she was only fifteen and still the madonna in his heart. It didn't matter now, did it? No, he told himself, it didn't matter now. It had been six and a half years since her death; most people forgot their loved ones in far less time than that, so why did he remember? Why was the hurt in him as raw as it had been six years ago? . . .

Well, it was out of sight now. Just ahead of him in the east were the cool fragrant depths of Black Canyon, and over there on the left, of Burns, with the Bridwell place at its mouth. He was at the brink now, and then he was going down the long dugway over its hairpin turns. He honked the horn to let them know he was coming. They all stood in the front yard waiting, his parents, his sister, his two sons. He gathered his sons to him and kissed them and turned to his mother.

It was the old lodgepole house that Joe had built with such pride, after the family had moved out of the two-room cottonwood shack because the roof had fallen in. It was the same outdoor privy, the last one Vridar had built. It was the same rickety tumbled-down barn. Shanty Irish, by God, he told himself. Yes, it was all the same, but he would change all that.

The next day he looked at his father and said, "What you doing for those cancers on your face?" The one on his nose covered half of it and looked bad.

Joe grunted. He had used sheep-dip on them; lye, creosote, carbolic acid, blue vitriol, and God only knew what else. He would not go to a surgeon. He was a baby about pain *if it was not self-inflicted*. Was that because his mother used to beat the hell out of him? It was not the pain, but the indignity? Joe would hurt himself, as when he had discharged a 12-gauge shotgun across a palm, and fill the wound with tobacco and go on with his work; but the thought of a surgeon taking a cancer off his nose filled him with rumbling furies.

The next day Vridar's older son wanted to know why his books didn't make a lot of money. Didn't the books of other writers? "One per cent. The other ninety-nine per cent you never hear about."

"Why don't you belong to the one per cent?" Larry said. That question Larry was to have with him all his life. And so would Scott. They would never understand their father, for the simple reason that they would never understand why he didn't make a lot of money.

Because Athene would join him at the end of the summer, Vridar wanted to have a small one-room cabin ready for them, in which to write, in which to teach his sons; and so with the front end of a wagon to use as a logging cart, and with a team, his sons and a grub-box, he crossed the river and went up Black Canyon. He had to boat across the harness and wagon wheels, axle and bolster, doubletree and grub-box, chains, ax, crosscut saw, and then swim the horses across behind the boat. The river where he crossed it at the old ferry site was about four hundred feet wide. Horses were good fast swimmers compared to most beasts, but even so he went up the river a hundred and fifty yards to put them in, so that he could make the far landing. He went up the canyon about three miles, following the old millroad, and fording the stream more than thirty times because all the bridges had been washed away. He knew where there was an excellent stand of lodgepole pine.

It was called lodgepole because Indians had used it in their lodges. Without any limbs at all, thirty, or even forty or fifty feet up, with less taper than most trees had, and in good fertile situations as straight as a plumbline, this was by far the finest of all western timbers for the building of cabins. He put Larry on one end of a two-man crosscut saw, and one by one they felled the trees, topped them, and snaked them out to the loading site. This was work that Vridar loved. It was up this canyon that Joe had had his sawmill. It was there that Vridar had almost drowned in the flume, but he remembered with pleasure his months at the mill—the smell of great piles of fresh Douglas fir sawdust; of the cool depths in the canyon, which the sun left at four in the afternoon; of all the berry shrubs, of the elk and bear. He had loved to sleep under the roaring music of the down-rushing canyon stream; to fill his belly with its cold pure water, tasting of snows, and with luscious thimbleberry, raspberry, currant and huckleberry; to wade barefooted in damp sawdust; to listen to the chilling whine of the great saw when its teeth struck the tough fir log; to see his powerful father walk away with three hundred feet of green lumber, which meant three hundred pounds; to eat with ravenous hunger and put flesh on his skinny frame. Recalling with pleasure so many things, he even felt indulgent toward the terrible Swede who stood naked on the fir stump at daylight and neighed at the universe while daring his wife to come out and get it.

He loved to be here with his sons, sitting by a campfire and breathing all the delicious scents of burning woods, of frying mountain trout, of steaming coffee and simmering beans—to listen to the beasts contently cropping grass kneedeep, to feel under him the humus-rich clean fragrant earth without a taint of human living, to stretch out and sleep as he hadn't slept for years. This was a long way from the canyons of Manhattan. This was another life in another world. Why, he asked himself, why if I love this kind of life with all my passion and soul, why do I want to write books and be famous? Why do I give a damn what the world thinks of me!

In this cool odorous canyon filled with the music of birds and snow-waters, the two lads ate with the appetites of big men. Vridar said they would run out of food. Then what? Before his sons, should he kill a deer or an elk out of season, if one appeared?

Eating supper with the boys one night, he remembered how he and Marion had starved when away at school. "Guess I've had enough," he said, though he was not half-filled. "There's more beans, more of everything. Divide it, eat it." They divided and ate, and then with a hunk of stale bread wiped their tin dishes clean. They had eaten twice what they would have eaten at home, three times what they would have eaten if they were living in a big city. This was the life to give a man an appetite—for food, for tobacco, for women. Were the millions still sucking poisonous gases into their lungs and racing down stone streets? Shelley had said that hell was much like the city of London: memory of Manhattan made Vridar feel blighted. Stretched out by a fire that crackled and exploded with Douglas fir, he looked up at a star-filled sky and said, "All right, now I'll tell you about the big city. Twelve times as many people live in it as in all of Idaho. . . ."

They cut and snaked out sixty poles, thirty feet long and from five to six inches in diameter at the larger end, in a day and half. They took them to the river by loading the larger end on the cart and letting the smaller end drag behind, securing the load with a large log chain. They rafted them across the river, loading the raft behind the boat. It took them just four days and a half to deliver the timber to the building site.

Despairing of finding a publisher in the East, Vridar had sent a manuscript to Reuben Taylor Rhode, who had a small printing shop. Rhode had published two or three books but no novels. "It's just a shot in the dark," Vridar wrote Athene. "I think that sending manuscripts back and forth to New York is only to squander the few dollars we have. I'm beginning to imagine that I'll never get much of an income from my writing, so who or where the publisher is seems to make little difference. . . ." Rhode read the story and sent it off to Prof. Elmer T. Merrick, who edited a regional literary journal. Merrick's report, Vridar soon learned, was favorable, but qualified with the statement, "Though it is a book that should be published, I suspect you'll be run out of Idaho." Vridar wrote Athene: "Rhode says he'll publish the novel, even if he has to walk the streets barefoot. It's a rather romantic statement, but he does seem to have courage."

With his younger son driving him, Rhode came in one day, when nobody was expecting him. Joe was in his filthy work clothes, and so was Prudence. So indeed was Vridar: he had on patched overalls, a pair of shoes thrown away by a former tenant, and a tattered cap. A car came down the long dugway out of the sky and a small man got out, grinning amiably and advancing with outthrust hand. Was this, he asked, his eyes incredulous, his new author? Miserably selfconscious, Vridar said it was. Vridar then introduced Rhode and his son to his parents, his sister, his sons, all looking like Ozark hillbillies. In her stiff English way Prudence asked him if he would come in. Vridar thought he saw Rhode make a startled appraisal of the lodgepole shack. He thought he saw something in the man's eye that he did not like.

Quickly Rhode thanked her and said no, he had in mind doing a little fishing. Prudence said she would be happy to get them some dinner, and Vridar had a picture of Rhode's face if the man should ever see the kind of earthenware and forks and knives afforded by this house! But in his quick nervous way he thanked her again and said no, he had a spot in mind farther up the river; and if the Doctor (Vridar winced) had time to come along—they had a camping kit and food. They would build a fire. He bowed again and told Mrs. Hunter that he liked to get out once in a while and rough it. If the Doctor would come—?

"Oh, of course," Vridar said, not liking what he felt here but not understanding it, not yet.

He entered the car with them and they went up the mountain and across the hills, on the road to Swan Valley and the Palisades. Vridar could call him Rube, Reuben said; he was just a common homespun sort of fellow. He talked about the book, repeating what he had said in his letters, that he liked it immensely; that he had for some time been thinking of becoming a book publisher—oh, only in a small way, of course. He did not imagine that he would ever be among such big boys as Knopf. He had mentioned Knopf three or four times. Vridar thought, He admires that guy.

After about thirty miles they halted by a beautiful mountain stream. This was the place he had in mind, Rube said; he thought he might catch a fish here, and anyway they could have a bite to eat and some gab. They could get to know one another better. Rube took out his fishing tackle and put on his fishing garments; and with a bow, with the grin-smile that seemed to be constant, and a farewell gesture of his hand, he vanished into the heavy upstream growth. Vridar and Ted were alone.

Ted, several inches taller than his father and sixty pounds heavier, stripped down to his waist and flexed his biceps a few times. Vridar thought at first that he was striking the pose of the muscle-men in the body-building advertisements. Ted had a fine torso, back and front. Vridar knew good muscular development; he had spent hundreds of hours in gymnasiums with the bars and pulls and rings. Was this youth showing off? He decided after a few moments that Ted was merely stretching and sunning himself.

Reuben Taylor Rhode returned after an hour, again grinning the moment he came in sight, again making that peculiar bow in which he dipped to the right and moved his head to the right and down. He had had no luck. Well, now, by gum, they would get a fire going and have something to eat. Was Vridar hungry? Were his people real pioneers? He had understood that they were, Rhode said hastily, reading the novel, though he did not assume for a moment, oh, not at all, that the whole story was of Vridar's own life. Vridar let it pass. He said yes, his parents were real pioneers. All his people had been, on both sides for severals generations. A number of them had come west with Brigham Young. His father's father had been a member of the first colony Young sent to the Snake River country of eastern Idaho. At each statement, Rhode gave that polite little bow with his head, twitching his brows up a little and deepening his grin in a mechanical way.

With apparently no diffidence at all, Rhode stripped naked, explaining that he had fallen into the creek. Vridar pretended not to look at him. This man he thought more simian than any other he had seen—even more than Carl, though both men were extremely hairy and had abnormally short legs. They were in fact almost completely covered with hair from ankle to crotch—legs, belly, and chest, even the back and shoulders. Rhode had apelike legs. After dressing, he turned on Vridar his fixed smile, gave that quick downward gesture with his head, and went over to the fire his son had made. Ted had a coffee pot on and was frying bacon. Rube was telling Vridar how much he loved once in a while to get out and rough it—to get away from civilization and his worries and work. Vridar suspected that like so many men who expressed a wish to rough it, Rhode took most of the civilized comforts along with him.

Ted cooked a meal and filled their plates and their coffee cups, and Vridar ate and listened and tried to look into the depths of his new publisher. Did Rhode fancy himself as a man of cultivated charm and graciousness? Or was it something else? Did he think of himself as a man of destiny?

The climax came, and in Vridar an explosion almost, when Rhode looked into his eyes, his own small simian-like eyes filled with lights and mirth and with what Vridar at the moment could think of only as evil, for it was deeper than mischief, and said, his brows shooting up at the same moment, "You know, Doctor, I'll never be able to understand how such wine came from such casks."

It took Vridar a moment to grasp the meaning, though even if the words were a little cryptic, the man's grin and the look in his eyes were plain enough. When the truth of it came to Vridar, the incredible truth, the unbelievable impertinence, he stiffened with anger and hurt, and at once drew all friendliness and goodwill deep within himself. On the return to the ranch, he was polite when Rhode spoke to him; he tried not to show what he was feeling, but suspected that Rhode knew he had been affronted—had indeed been outraged in the most sensitive part of his being. Or could a man so tactless see a wound even that large?

Vridar wrote to Athene about it, concluding: "I suppose it's about time I stopped wearing my heart on my sleeve. Few authors, and least of all I, are in a position to look their publisher in his mouth. Somehow he called to mind Hardy's words: 'If people are at all peculiar in character they have to suffer from the very rules that produce comfort in others.' My family are peculiar, I suppose. All of us *did* look like Ozark hillbillies. But does this man, who wants to publish books (great books, he said), judge people by their house and their clothes? Yes, most Americans do but *does he?* If he does, I have the wrong publisher. . . ."

III

Among the things reaching back to his childhood that drew deep response from Vridar were snowstorms. He was walking in one a few months later, his father's twelve-gauge two-barrel shotgun lying across his left arm. He was on his way into the meadowland, among steaming creeks and bogs, for wild ducks and geese, or for the walk only. The water from the countless springs in the meadows steamed in cold weather because its temperature of fifty-eight degrees was constant throughout the year. It was known as cold water in warm seasons, as warm water in cold seasons. On very cold days the bottomland was filled with lovely soft fog.

This was not a bitter day, or the snow would not have been falling in such large-flaked abundance. Some of the flakes were as large as dollars. The snow underfoot was more than three feet deep, but he had been across the meadowland and river islands many times and had beaten paths. He knew every favorite spot of the mallard ducks. He knew where the geese would be if any had come in. He knew where the beaver were working, the muskrat, the mink, the otter, the bobcat; he liked to walk over their trails and into their haunts, to see what they were doing.

The beaver was a persistent cuss. Hoping to build a waterwheel to supply a hydraulic ram, Vridar had undertaken to destroy a beaver dam, to lower the level of impounded waters. He had at first merely torn apart the intricate and elaborate network of poles and sticks, mud and moss. It had been difficult and tiresome labor; only those knew what an ingenious creature this was who had torn a dam apart. The next morning the dam was repaired. Three times again he tore the dam out and three times it was restored.

He then tried dynamite. He placed a half-dozen sticks deep in the dam, banking them around solidly with mud, stones, and pieces of heavy timber. He attached a long fuse and waited until midnight, when the creatures would be busy repairing a section he had torn out. He then lit the fuse and ran. The explosion blew the dam to hell and gone. It hurled hunks of beaver flesh over an area fifty yards wide. But three days later the dam was as good as new.

Next he tore the entire dam out, clear to the bottom of the creek, and strung a wire across from bank to bank. He suspended two lighted lanterns from the wire. Right at the water's edge on one bank he made a bed for the dog and tied him there. The next morning the lanterns were still burning, the dog was there, the dam was half-built. Vridar then gave up, deciding that the only way to get rid of a beaver dam was to get rid of the beaver.

He was standing now in a marvelous world of falling snow, looking at the work of beavers. The creatures were not as smart as they were said to be in romantic writings. They didn't like cedar, but now and then they would chew halfway through a cedar tree before becoming aware that it was not the kind of tree they had thought it was. They would chew all the way through a cottonwood two feet in diameter and bring it down and never touch it again. They would with great labor take to their dam-site logs eight or ten inches through and eight or ten feet long and then never use them. Today they were busy felling trees, not for food but for dam-building, though they had impounded all the waters in the area and had no dam-sites left. The beaver had gone into folklore as a symbol of industry and ingenuity. He should also have gone in, it seemed to Vridar, as a symbol of the unspeakable nuisance, when he chose to dwell where he was not wanted. He had been a great enemy of erosion and floods; but here, Vridar reflected, looking round him, the insufferable pest would before he was done destroy every tree in a magnificent grove, and flood most of Joe's pastureland.

Vridar went on, feeling warm and snug in his heavy winter clothing. He wore rubber boots, hip-high; his army jacket, his heavy army greatcoat; and furlined mittens and cap. Athene was warm and cozy, too, sitting in the cabin he had built, writing a novel. For years Vridar had nagged her to write a novel, unaware of his motive in this. He would have said, Damn it, the woman has talent. She should write. He would have said, She is mine, I want her to be famous, too. He might have said, I had one wife with no talent; this one has talent, so let her show it. But when he read a few chapters of her book he went off alone into the white world and stood looking at the scars up and down the trunk of a large aspen. I wonder, he murmured, what it is that puts so many wounds in a tree. . . .

He was standing by the river now. The storm was so deep that he could see only a part of the water. He was recalling Joe's wish to go fishing. Fishing in wintertime for Joe meant getting up an hour before daylight in cold that went straight to a man's bones. It meant shoving off in a small boat into the black waters of a river choked with ice floes. It meant for Vridar the heavy labor of pulling his guts out on the oars, for Joe would never touch an oar when his older son was along. He had said that Vridar was a better river-man than his father, but not a better hunter, he added with pride. If there was a better hunter in the world, Joe didn't want to hear about him.

As a young man Joe had taken prizes as a marskman. His deadly accuracy had always been a riddle to his sons—for his rifle was an old forty-five ninety that looked as if it had come through a dozen wars. Vridar had seen his father kill an elk a halfmile away when the elk were on a dead run. They had been so far away that to Vridar they had looked like rabbits. This shotgun Vridar was carrying looked even worse than Joe's rifle and it kicked a man over backwards, if he didn't watch out. Vridar had a bandaged wound in his right cheek, and his right shoulder felt as though it were broken. Now he wore deep padding on his shoulder when he took the gun out.

Vridar didn't know how to shoot a gun, Joe had said, scowling at him.

"You mean it doesn't almost knock your shoulder off?"

When one of his sons addressed him in that tone of voice, Joe growled and subsided.

The stubborn old fart, Vridar thought, and turned back from the river, looking for geese. Finding no geese, he shot a half-dozen mallard ducks and took a leisurely roundabout way home. Beavertail many of the frontiersmen had thought was a delicacy, if properly cooked. Lewis and Clark and their men had been fond of it, but Prudence would not cook beaver, or porcupine, which Joe's father had told her was better than beef. Prejudice stood deep in his parents: they would eat only what they had eaten as children. As a child Joe had lived chiefly on the flesh of elk and deer, and elk and deer were still his favorite food. He had made a horrible face when Vridar persauded him to eat an olive. Rumbling with astonishment and contempt, he had spat it out as though it were a spider or a beetle. Any person, he said, who would eat olives had something wrong with him—or cheese with the stink of worms in it; or any cured meat except pork; or in fact any food that Joe had never eaten before. Prudence was so prejudiced that she still would not fry testicles or allow them to enter her house. "Son!" she would cry, and her voice could have been no more outraged if she had seen him using the Bible's paper for cigarettes. The expression on her face had been that of a person deeply and unforgivably offended. Prudence would no more have touched a testicle than a redhot stove, yet she wanted all people to marry when young. She had wanted her children to marry before graduating from college, and had grieved over Marion because he had not married until almost thirty, and over Diana because she had not been able to get a husband before she was twenty-five. Vridar had said to Athene, "Why in hell do these damned Christians want youthful marriages? I look back and realize that I'd never have married Neloa but for the urging of my mother, who wants all girls knocked up in a hurry, yet thinks that testicles are things Satan has scattered around in the Garden!"

It snowed without letup for three days and nights and on the level the snow was then fifty inches deep. A man could hardly walk in such snow. Vridar wrote in the forenoons; in the afternoons he climbed the mountain to aspen groves, to cut wood for the coming year. Once a week he made a ten-mile journey on skis or snowshoes to the mailbox out by the highway. His novel had been published, it was being reviewed, and he had a great eagerness to see what was being written about it. This, he told himself, remembering David Hawke, was all vanity and vexation of spirit, but telling himself this did no good: he would have braved any blizzard to discover what waited for him out there in the box. One day he risked his life.

The weather had been so cold that trees had snapped open. Then it had faired off, as Joe put it, and a wind had come in from the west. On the wind came a storm. He should not venture out, his mother said; in a blizzard a person got lost and just went round and round. Vridar said it was not blowing very hard. "Is it?" he asked his father.

Joe went outside and Vridar followed him. Joe looked up at the ledges high against the southwest, and there the thing was, for any man who could read it: the snow in driven mists coming over, the huge drifts on the brink. Joe glanced at his son and said nothing. His look meant that there it was and any man with brains could see it.

A little later Vridar went outside alone and looked up at the wind-spume. Returning, he said to Athene, "Don't worry if I'm longer than usual and don't be fool enough to come looking for me. I'll be back. I've been in blizzards before." He slipped into the kitchen and cut off a few ounces of cheese. Then he took skis and snowshoes and turned up the mountain.

He was clumsy with skis. Finding it impossible to climb the mountain with them, he put on the snowshoes. It was about a mile up the mountain to the rolling benchland above and the ascent was so sharp that few automobiles could climb it, even in low gear. Going up through deep soft snow was exhausting toil, and Vridar's face was drained white by the time he reached the top. He then hung the snowshoes on an aspen and put on the skis. There was a wild storm over the Antelope hills but it had not yet reached the frenzy of a blizzard. You had better go back, he

681

told himself; there's nothing out there but a few reviews by persons who are no more literary critics than you are Shakespeare. . . . But he knew he had to go on. He thought he could make it. From where he stood the distance across the hills to the mailbox was a little less than five miles. In the first two miles there would be landmarks—fences, coves of aspen and chokecherry, and one building. After that for nearly three miles there would be absolutely nothing to see but snow.

He struck out in a beeline, leaving the road to go straight across the hills. He wondered why he hadn't thought to buy a small compass. With a compass he could have gone through a blizzard so dense that a man could not see beyond arm's length. As it was now he could see a hundred feet ahead, and once in a while a hundred yards. When he came to what he knew would be the last landmark he stood a few moments to get his bearings. He looked back, but the mountains in the east were hidden. Facing the southwest he went on.

Before he reached the mailbox he knew that the storm was becoming more violent. It was now a howling frenzy all around him, and as he stood by the box, taking the mail out and stuffing it into a gunnysack slung from his shoulder, he clasped the box post to keep from being blown down. There was no sign of the highway. The mail carrier had come with a light sleigh and a fast team, and at Conant, a few miles in the southeast, another fast team would be put on to make the run to Irwin. Mail carriers on routes like this had to be hardy and resourceful fellows.

With the mail stuffed into the sack, he pointed his skis into the northeast. Such ski-tracks as he had made coming over had been instantly obliterated: where the wind swept hard there was no soft snow but only the frozen crust on three or four feet of depth. In the ravines he would come to huge drifts and his skis would sink four or five inches. He then had to walk with them, plowing along; and when he came to hard swept snow he had to take a ski off and use it as a crutch to keep from being blown down. Most of the time he could not see more than thirty or forty feet ahead of him, though now and then the storm would open, in some kind of cyclonic maneuver, to reveal the grayish white world for a hundred yards or more.

The realization that he was lost came to him little by little. He had been on the return journey more than an hour when he sensed that he was going round and round. He didn't know that he was: in a blizzard a man could never tell what he was doing. He hadn't the remotest notion which way was north. If I don't know the directions, he told himself, I am lost; and if lost I will keep going round and round. In a situation like this the worst enemy was panic: supporting himself with both skis, his eyes almost shut because of the lash and sting of the wind, he considered his predicament. He felt around to his back to see if the piece of cheese was there. He wiggled his toes and fingers to learn if they were becoming numb. Well, the thing to do was to burrow.

He now walked slowly, pausing to take soundings, seeking a spot where the snow was deep. He found one in what he took to be the head of a ravine. He knew the head of every ravine on this route and now asked himself, Which one can this be? It would be at least halfway home, for there was no cove like this between the midway point and the mailbox. He kicked the fresh snow away and with a ski heel broke through the crust. He knelt and seizing the frozen pieces of crust laid them aside, and then let himself down into the depths, kicking as he went. As soon as he could do so he knelt and with his mittened hands pushed the snow back and away, burrowing down and down until, when he stood, the crust level struck him at his chin. He made room for himself back under the crust and then set the two skis upright in the hole, so that if his tiny chamber became drifted over he would have an air vent. He hoped that nobody at the house would be foolish enough to try to find him. To Prudence's anxiety Joe would rumble, "I tell you, wife, he's all right." Joe meant that Joe would be all right in a similar situation. Joe meant that any man who would not be all right was a damned fool weakling who had no business living. . . .

Joe was the damndest man. He had recently told his son that there were two unforgivable sins. What, Vridar had asked, were they? When challenged to dispute or argue Joe could not speak without glaring and sounding very angry. He now sounded enraged when he said in a loud voice, "One is to deny Christ." Vridar stared at him and said, "And what is the other?" "To shed innocent blood." And what, Vridar asked, was that? Then, blowing the angry thundering words out of his chest, Joe had said, "To kill a man thout you know he's guilty of what you're killing him for!" This amazing statement had for a few moments left Vridar speechless. He had then exploded with laughter, and the pain in Joe's dark eyes had deepened. Vridar gave off a snort now. To kill a man thout you know he's guilty of what you're killing him for! What an inquisitor Joe would have made in the 13th century! Vridar had said, "If he's guilty, then it's all right to kill him?" It had taken patience and a pretense of humility to drag from Joe the statement that that might or might not be all right. The point, he said, scowling horribly, was this, that to kill him without knowing whether he was guilty was an unpardonable sin.

Now and then Joe said something that put his son to thinking. After Vridar was born, Joe had said one day, Prudence had wanted fish to eat, nothing but fish. Joe said he had had a hell of a time filling her up. Why, Vridar wondered, staring at his mother, had she wanted nothing but fish? Fish were a phallic symbol. They had been a symbol for the early Christians, who had called themselves the Little Fishes and Jesus the Big Fish. How inextricably mixed up in human affairs the genitals were!

After a half-hour Vridar felt into the gunnysack, trying to count the number of letters. He despised himself for this. Why should he give a damn what ignorant people had written about him? But he pulled all the letters out and striking matches found the one from the clipping service. It was stuffed and fat but he had known this at the mailbox. He pulled the reviews out and by the light of matches found the one written by a brash Yale man named John Cumberland. Holding match flame above it he hastily read what Cumberland had had to say.

What the man said kindled in Vridar a black and smouldering fury. Cumberland said he had wanted to throw the novel through a window. Vridar was so enraged that he thrust the review into a pocket and stood up, his head in the storm. God damn! He had read an article about this Cumberland fellow, now one of the most influential book-reviewers in the world; how on graduating from Yale he had looked round him, as any supercilious extrovert might have done, and decided to become a literary critic! That's all there was to it. He could not have become a doctor, without training, or an engineer; but he could become a literary critic! In the United States of America a person did not have to have the background, the learning, much less the humility of a Matthew Arnold to set up as a literary critic. All he had to be was a brash extroverted superficial jackass with enough cleverness to conceal his ignorance from the average reader. Minnie Slaughter, Chicago's arbiter of fashions in reading, had even had the gall to call herself a literary critic in *Who's Who*.

With the blizzard stinging and whipping across his face, Vridar tried to push his fury down and out. He had risked his life to find out what this callow adolescent from Yale had had to say. David Hawke was right: some of them were so God damned little that they smelled little! What had Stendhal said?—to catch the favor of men in your behalf you must use a certain kind of bait. When I want to avail myself of their good will I fish about for a good word or two, but my hand tires quickly of the fishing-rod. . . .

He ducked back under and sat, thinking. He had said to Athene, "I'll be boiled in oil and mixed into pemmican before I'll scratch the backs of the literary Sigma Chis. I don't reckon I'll get much before I die but there won't be any price tag on it." Now he asked himself if he was taking a romantic position. This novel, that a man in his mid-twenties had wanted to hurl through a window, was the one that had been too strong meat for eastern publishers. It was the one Rhode said he would publish if he had to go barefoot. One of the big New York newspapers had given it what was called a rave review, and at once both Rhode and Vridar had begun to receive telegrams from publishers in New York. Then came the letters.

Gus Hornfield, president of Snapper Brothers, had written Vridar, "I only wish you had given us a chance at it. . . ." Vridar had replied: "I took it to your editors. They returned it without even a letter of thanks. . . ." Seven other publishers wrote to ask why they had not been allowed to see the book. Every one of them had seen it and rejected it.

"The incredible asses!" Vridar muttered, shivering in the snow-depth. The wind now was absolute frenzy overhead; he thought he could feel the whole earth trembling. He began to wonder if he would have to spend a long night here, and if so, whether he could keep from freezing to death. The hole through which he had descended had been blown full and the skis stood up in the blown-in snow. He wiggled them back and forth to make an air vent. Looking inward to his stomach he decided to keep the cheese for a while. The blizzard might wear itself out before dark: its lunacies would go howling over the Big Hole mountains, into Wyoming, and then over the Yellowstone. Impatient to know what other reviewers had said about his book, he struck matches and tried to read, until his matches were all gone. Then, bringing the greatcoat tight around his neck, he thrust up through the snow that had filled the hole and looked round him.

The winds were not so frenzied now. There seemed to be a little more light. As soon as he could see a landmark, he would climb out and go. Withdrawing again under the crust he shivered and waited; thinking—thinking of the seven-year-old Stendhal kissing and fondling his mother's big white breasts. The little bastard must have been erotically precocious! And how he had hated his father! With what

684

desperate ardor he had as a man pursued women! Had it been to avenge himself? Was that what it was with Marion?

He thought next of Marion. The wonderful thing about Marion, Carl had said, was that he took them all. There was a man who played no favorites! Dolly Kurtz had come to New York—Walter's sister, a big woman who stood five feet nine or ten inches and weighed a hundred and eighty pounds. She was not fat, she was simply big. One night at a party Marion had come to Vridar and whispered, "I'm going to run up and see Dolly." He meant that he was going up to seduce her. He did, he told Vridar later. He was back within an hour. He had a brisk professional way in these things. Sometimes he didn't bother to take off his hat and coat, much less his shoes. . . .

In Chicago when he was there he had astounded Vridar again and again. Vridar supposed now that Marion liked to astound his brother. One day when they came out of Washington Park after listening at the Bug Club, Marion had fixed his gaze on a woman ahead of him. Vridar saw the gaze and then studied the woman. She was about forty and quite fat but she was well-dressed and looked clean. With Vridar at his side Marion followed her to an apartment building; followed her in; followed her to her door and turning there said to his brother, "See you later." The next day Vridar had asked, "Was she a whore?" "Oh no. Just wanted a man. You can see it in their eyes or feel it in them if you're any good as a male."

Marion knew women. It was this knowledge that astounded his brother. Vridar still was unable to put away the notion that women, being strictly monogamous, were not available to the wandering male. Oh, he knew that Neloa had been! Indeed, he had now and then wondered about her and Marion, that winter when Marion was in Salt Lake City, that summer when he was in Chicago. . . .

Was Athene like most women? There was Bones Jagger.

Six feet two and weighing over two hundred pounds, with no fat on him, Bones was a Montana cowboy as tough as bull buffalo hide. How Diana ever corralled him Vridar would never know. He would never know what it was in the man that had captured her heart, or what in her had appealed to him. Anyway, she had married him. Finding her pregnant, Bones had demanded an abortion; and there must have been, Vridar reflected, a dreadful scene. He could imagine how Mormon picty had filled her with anger and with what words she had spurned his proposal. Then he had fled. She was never to see him again.

During the few weeks when Bones was on the ranch he had thrown a lariat on a wild mule that weighed thirteen hundred pounds, and alone had held him, with nothing on the beast but the rope around its neck. It took a powerful man to do that. Even Joe was impressed. Athene, Vridar had perceived, was most impressed of all. Glancing at her he had seen the look in her eyes: she was unaware of everything in the world but this man holding the mule—and Bones at that moment was a picture of maleness that no woman could ever forget: braced, feet wide apart, his end of the rope across his two powerful thighs, he was holding the beast while it reared and plunged and all but catapulted end over end. The look in her eyes had been one of pure wonder and admiration—the look not of a woman but of a female, entranced not by a man but by a male.

685

Bones was a handy man at carving. A few days later he was looking for a piece of wood and Athene was looking with him. When Vridar came up she turned to him and said impatiently, "Can't you find the kind of wood he wants?" Her tone was that of his mother, long ago, when she had rebuked him before a man who was flattering her. Athene didn't know that she was a little infatuated with this man: she did not believe in looking to motives! Vridar had been annoyed and jealous, for he knew that the infatuation was mutual, that they were smitten by one another, and that almost like two lovers they were hunting around in the woodsheds for the kind of wood Bones liked to carve.

The day Bones deserted his pregnant wife and fled, Athene kissed him goodbye.

Vridar had said to himself, as he said now, Why should you make a fuss about it, you abysmal ass? You've been adulterous. You've kissed other women. . . . Yes, but there was a difference. He had looked at no other woman as Athene had looked at Bones. There was a deeper adultery than that of flesh to flesh. . . .

Shivering, waiting, his thoughts turned to his sister. For him she was an emotional illiterate. Vridar had seen her the morning after her bridal night, sitting in her nightgown on the edge of a bed, an expression on her face that he could never forget—of shock and wonder, and deeper than these, of shame. He had seen that look on his mother's face when she saw the mating of cow and bull or of mare and stud. After Prudence and Joe went through the Mormon temple (that was the Mormon way of saying it), Vridar had again seen on his mother's face that look of shock and shame and horror. Vridar had questioned her but she would tell nothing, for she was supposed to tell nothing. In books about the most secret Mormon rites, by impious rascals, it was said that the husband and wife acted out the scene in the Garden, as Adam and Eve; and, looking at his mother, Vridar had chuckled all over inside, as he was chuckling now, while trying to imagine her as Eve, seducing Joe-Adam! As Vridar understood it, the rite didn't lead to actual intercourse. Just the same, Eve was expected to bring against Adam all her female cunning and guile, and Adam was expected to find himself feeling pretty sinful. The things that happened to Prudence in the temple almost took the Mormonism out of her, for years and years. . . .

Vridar again thrust up and looked at the world. He could see a landmark now. He climbed out, put on the skis, fixed his direction and headed home. Darkness was moving in, and with it a more terrible cold. The river would groan in its ice-shelves tonight.

IV

Athene's time was her own, for Prudence did not want her to help cook or keep house. Prudence didn't like her daughters-in-law. Like most American women, she simply didn't like women. Athene worked on her novel, read, studied the notes for her thesis, helped teach the boys, and once in a while gave her emotions to the outside world, though she was not an outdoors woman. Vridar wrote in the forenoons; worked at hard labor in the afternoons; helped teach his sons; and during the long evenings sat with a book or wrote parodies and satirical verse, or drew up his building plans.

As soon as the snow melted he went with his father up Burns to fell lodge poles for a house. Athene went as cook. It was hard labor but Vridar loved every minute of it: they rose at daylight and worked till dark. The stand of timber was on a tableland high above the canyon's floor. They would fell a tree that was about ten inches through at its base; top it at forty feet up; drag it with a horse over to the canyon brink and slide it over the brink, butt-end first. Its flight then was a marvelous thing to watch: for a hundred yards Vridar could see it streaking like an enormous woods-gray serpent; then it vanished into thick shrub-growth and when it came in sight again, halfway down the mountain, it was completely peeled. Lubricated by its own sap, and flashing like a huge pale-yellow lance, it shot down at terrific speed, striking the canyon floor with such force that some of the logs were shattered, and some were driven eight or ten feet into the earth, with the part above the earth standing as a naked gleaming pole.

Vridar and Joe worked hard and they ate like wolves. Their food was chiefly beans because beans were cheap, and stuck, Joe said, to a man's ribs. Every morning when they ate, every evening, Joe would gaze up at the mountains roundabout, hoping to see elk or deer sign. For the western frontiersman it was not signs but sign: all of it taken together—tracks, broken twigs, leaning grasses, odors. . . . "They're higher up," Joe said. Though in almost all things fanatically honest, in a literal way, he had no time for game departments and game wardens: he got his game when he wanted it, in season or out of season, and he had said that no game warden would ever take him, if he could get his gun up first. The frontiersmen were like that. With his Uncle Ike one Fourth of July years ago Vridar had gone up Long Valley and Big Elk Creek, and over the divide into Jackson Hole country, after elk. They had killed two fat elk and were packing them out, moving day and night to keep the meat from spoiling, when in the distance behind them they saw a man, and Ike said, "There the son of a bitch is." Vridar was to take the meat and go on ahead. Ike would fall behind and ambush the game warden. It took a bold warden to come up on mountain men in those years. . . .

"A fat deer would taste awfully good," Vridar said, following Joe's gaze over the mountains. When he asked Athene if she would like some venison, she gave him the look she always wore when he proposed something that was contrary to her scruples.

"They ain't very fat yet," Joe said.

"How far you think we'd have to go for one?"

Four or five miles, Joe said. He said he could eat a hull deer right now, meaning a whole deer.

Vridar looked at Athene and winked. Of all the persons he had known Joe Hunter was the mightiest eater. One morning at breakfast Vridar had seen David Hawke eat a pile of pancakes, ten sausages, a half-dozen eggs and a pot of coffee. Joe would eat twice that much. Except the coffee, which was an outlaw among foods in the Mormon Word of Wisdom. When out on the hunt he would eat the entire hind quarter of a young deer for his supper. At a feast, such as Thanksgiving, he would eat enough for ten persons, and top it off with one-half each of two twelve-inch pies. Prudence said he had a tapeworm.

They had made their beds under the wide spreading boughs of two Douglas firs. Gathering the smaller green twigs they had spread them two feet deep to form a mattress and then had laid the blankets on them. Joe had said they could all sleep under one tree and Vridar had known what the sly rogue meant. To the mystified Athene he said, "He means there won't be any monkey business if his bed is close to ours. Envy has made a tremendous virtue of continence."

After the first night Vridar moved his bed out under the stars. He was too tired each night to think of what Americans in their evasive way called love. He wanted to be under the sky where he could look up and point out the constellations, and with awe think of the inexplicable nature of infinity. A stream ran close by, murmuring and gurgling with pure mountain music, under its tangle of berry vines. The air was saturated with the scent of mountain things. God, how he loved it all!

Clasping her hand he would say, "The Mormons say that a God with body, parts, and passions created this universe. Let's see. The distance from the star nearest to us, and our sun, which is a star, is about four and two-tenths light years. We live in a kind of crowded part of the universe—that is, in the Milky Way, which is an assemblage of stars. How many?" When she gave no reply he said, "Only three hundred million. Three hundred million suns, yet that incredible number is only one group among an immense number. Try to grasp this fact, that more than thirty million such groups are known, and the average distance between any two is two million light years!"

"Nobody can grasp that."

"Nobody. It's so much simpler to grasp Genesis."

"Three hundred million suns in each of thirty million milky ways? And every one may have planets around it?"

"So far as we know. But this little iron-ball called the earth is, of course, the center. As I multiply it, three hundred million times thirty million is nine and twelve zeroes. Nowhere around that many suns is there a creature as magnificent as this belching and farting animal called man."

"Do you have to be vulgar about it?"

"With most people no possible emphasis could drive the appalling fact home to them. Look, there is Aldebaran."

"The red one?"

"Yes, the eye of Taurus, the Bull's eye, the brightest sun in the Hyades. Over there is Altair in Aquila. Those suns are so big that if our sun were thrown into one of them it would be much like dropping a tear into the Pacific ocean."

"Oh, come now!"

"That's right. Though our sun is so large that our earth could fall into it about as a ten-pound stone might fall into Lake Michigan, it is just about the smallest sun known to us. Some of them are so immense that no human mind can possibly grasp their size. My father would say I am talking utter nonsense. He thinks that some day he will be a god ruling over a planet somewhere." He waited for a reply to that but she was silent. Remembering George Meredith's words, that his wife always returned the pressure of his hand, Vridar squeezed Athene's fingers but there was no response. So he said, "You know why my father didn't like Neloa?"

"I was not aware that he didn't."

"All dark women are for him related to the Negro, and for him the Negro lives under a curse. He prefers red hair above all. Really, though, I think his aversion to dark women comes from his mother. Though she was Irish and Scotch she had coal black hair, snapping black eyes and a swarthy skin. He hated her but of course he has never known it."

He felt Athene turn a little to look at him. She always had to look at him when his words astonished her.

"Didn't you once say she was strong for favorites?"

"Oh, very. She tranfers her love about every five or six months, and word goes out to the clan that this son is her favorite now, or that one. It is never my father. She has never forgiven him for marrying my mother."

"Isn't her favorite ever a daughter?"

"Never. Rose hates daughters-in-law most of all. Next to them, daughters. She hates my mother most because she is the most intelligent one."

"Maybe it's because she had reddish hair."

"I saw dad looking at your hair the other day after you had washed it. Maybe he'll be allowed to rule over a planet around Aldebaran."

"You shouldn't laugh at these things. The Bible reveals more and more, as we look more deeply."

Vridar made no reply. He had learned recently that Athene had never accepted his agnostic free-thinking position. He had not known that the mysticism of Plato and the Fourth Gospel had so filled her that all rationalism had been driven out. This knowledge disturbed him, for he could not see himself living with a woman who could stomach the Gospel of John.

It wearied him to think about her and people like her. "Well," he said, releasing her hand and turning away, "we'd better sleep now."

For six days they worked from daylight till dark on the tableland, felling trees, topping, piling limbs, and shooting the logs over the brink. After breakfast Joe and his son climbed the mountain, each leading a horse, each carrying a lunch pail and a pail of water. Usually during the day Athene climbed up to watch them. Vridar sensed that she was not too happy here: the urban world was her world, the academic world was her life. She had been born and until she went East to college she had lived in the mountainless Middle West. Trimming a tree or snaking a log out he would see her sitting on a stump, looking over his way; and he would think about her and wonder about the years to come. He knew now that they had not really been in love with one another on that bitter day seven and a half years ago when Neloa died. They had known so little about one another then. Like the young Shelley they had been in love with love: they had been two fatuous romantics with heads full of poetic raptures; and ever since then they had been slowly moving out of the romantic auras and mists into the cold realties of a man-woman world.

On each return from the brink he passed close to her. He paused and said,

"When they asked George Leigh-Mallory why he wanted to climb Everest he said, Because it's there. Does that mean anything to you?"

She gave him the queer look she always gave him when she felt he was trying to trap her.

"I want you to think about those down below looking far up that ridge, where for a few moments Leigh-Mallory and Andrew Irvine were limned against storm and eternity. They were never seen again."

"Why should I think about that?"

"If you're a poet how could you help it?"

"You don't want me to be a poet, but a novelist."

"Oh, hell, I want you to be many things—poet, novelist, scholar, lover, wife."

"And mother?"

That was another thing that disturbed him: Athene wanted a child. Her dreams clearly revealed it. How, he asked impatiently, could they afford a child, when they were both broke? He had told her that any woman who mated with him ran a great risk. "Ever heard of Tommy Tamel the fightun tiddo? There are a lot of morons on my father's side and nobody has yet found a way to outsmart Mendel's Law. Would you risk a feebleminded child merely to be a mother?"

"Merely to be a mother! Is motherhood so unimportant?"

"But there are so many ways to be a mother. Writing a book, for instance."

"A novel can't be a child for me."

He had looked hard at her and said, "If you ever have a child by me you'll have to be financially responsible for it. Will you? For I already have two." She had said yes and he had said, "All right, don't forget it."

He was thinking of these matters now, while snaking logs to the brink. He was such a hypochondriac, so incurably an anxiety neurotic, his sense of insecurity was so constant and inexorable, and his prospect of earnings so meager that it enraged him to have her look at him with eyes that wanted a child. So he passed close to her when returning from the brink and flung words that he hoped would disturb her: "Is the greater writer the one who stands on his generation, like Hemingway, or beyond it, like Hunter?" He chuckled and passed on. Glancing back he saw her sitting there, intent and earnest, her face offended yet in its strange way adoring him, because, full of pieties, she liked wicked men.

"I've decided," he said, again pausing, "that like Carl and his wife you have no sense of humor, save as it illuminates your amour-propre. The deepest reach in humor rests squarely on that figure nine and twelve zeroes; for how can anyone be said to have a sense of humor who believes in meaning?" He went on, her eyes following him; and while hitching to a log he was busy composing a limerick. He wanted to shock her, for when shocked, she had so much the appearance of an adorable imbecile.

He paused again, and making his face as deadpan as Max Ohm's, said, "Though a decade this side of pubescence she was haloed with saintly quiescence: while her boy friend's ardor grew longer and harder, she showed not a sign of tumescence." To hide a grin he hastened on: the trouble with my wife, he told himself, is that she has no more wit than a robin.

690

He made a half-dozen journeys past her before again pausing. Then he said, "A psychologist has told us that the more strongly man feels his freedom and independence, the more intensely he is conscious of guilt. It's a profound statement. Is it true because under the Judean-Christian systems nearly all adults are children? Do you find it pretty fantastic that we have the gall to call it a civilization, in which the children write the poetry? And do you agree with me that as long as we have these systems we'll have father-hating tyrants of various sorts who will exploit the emotionally immature?"

He gave her no time for reply but she didn't want to reply anyway. She watched him, fascinated, as she might have watched any evil thing that wore a heavenly radiance. On his next journey past her he said, "What worries the beans out of me is that most of the big book reviewers are now Communists or their pals. If I write a novel in which I come out against this new tyranny, which has borrowed the methods of the Roman Church, will I get reviewed at all? If not, can I possibly make it? Should I ask them what Horace asked in his Satires, Why should the worthy be in want while you have wealth? Why should an author have to starve his guts out merely because you emotional illiterates hold the whip-hand over him?" He looked at her but she said nothing. "Very well," he said, "I don't think the Gospel of John has the answer either."

Her face reddened.

After they had cut a hundred and fifty trees and shot the logs down the mountain they labored in the canyon below to pile the logs. They had to be piled so that they would air-dry. Those that had been driven into the earth they sawed off at earth-level. Later, perhaps next fall, Vridar would come up the canyon with a team and cart and haul them to the river; raft by raft he would pull them across the river behind a boat; and with the cart he would haul them from the river across the islands and up to the building site.

When the logs were piled, Joe headed down the canyon, riding one horse and leading the other, packed with the camp things. Vridar and Athene walked side by side. Pausing to sniff odors or to point out fresh bear sign by a rotted log he told her again that he loved these deep cool canyons. He would like to build a house in one and live there, with his bedroom spanning the rushing stream. "A bear," he said, pointing to the scratchings six feet high on a tree. "A deer," he said, showing where rotted wood had been freshly disturbed by an animal stepping over a fallen fir tree.

When they came to the river they unharnessed the beasts. The end of a rope was tied round the neck of each horse, Vridar took his seat in the boat, with the two ropes clasped between his legs; and after he had shoved off, Joe smote the horses with a cudgel and drove them into the river. They were strong and fat and they swam high, though their bulging eyes looked wild and anxious. The river was still running spring flood water, and though Vridar pulled on the oars until his eyes stood out like those of the beasts he was carried down almost half a mile. Leaping out, he seized the boat-rope, yanked the front end of the boat up on a gravel bar, and then ran down the bank, feeding rope out to the horses as they came in. They emerged like river-beasts, with water pouring from their sleek hides. He tethered

691

them where they could graze and then pulled the boat upstream, wading ahead of it.

Vridar saw Adolph Buck coming down from his shack on the old Bridwell place. Adolph owned the place now. He had seduced Beth Bridwell and old Charley had forced him to marry her. Beth had died long ago and Adolph had got himself a squaw, by whom he now had a child. No man liked Adolph Buck: he was sneaking and treacherous; he would steal your traps or the food out of your house if you were gone; and he might kill you if he felt he could get away with it. But Vridar felt pity for the man. For many years now Adolph had had piles; a part of his intestines fell out of him when he walked along. When he was out in the fields gathering his few acres of hay, his right hand kept reaching down or back to push the guts up into his body.

Bringing the boat in, Vridar said to Adolph, "Hy-ya."

"Huh," Adolph said. The man had cunning green eyes and the look of one who would stand for no nonsense, though as a deputy game warden he had never dared to try to take Joe Hunter. The past winter he hadn't dared to try to take Vridar, either, though he could have walked right in on him skinning a deer. Adolph himself took game when he wanted it, and trapped out of season.

"How's everything?" Vridar asked, loading the boat with harness and bedding.

"Finearee, I guess."

"Didn't see you here when we went up."

"Yeh."

Vridar took the equipment across and returned. Joe and Athene climbed in. "You in the front," he said to his wife. The three of them sank the boat within six inches of its top. "We'll be seeing you!" Vridar called to Adolph.

"Yeh," he said, sitting there like an Indian. Fifty yards away his fat squaw stood, looking, her child at her side.

"Why didn't he marry a white woman?" Athene asked.

"They're not married."

"No white womern would have him," Joe said.

After the beasts were again packed, Vridar left with his father and went ahead to get his mail. Among the letters was one from Prof. Merrick of Montana College in Missoula, inviting him to teach there the summer quarter. The offer was a thousand dollars.

"A thousand dollars," he said. "I'd forgotten there's that much money in the world." He read the letter again. "I guess I'd better accept or we'll be eating rose hips. What do you think?"

"I'd accept it," she said.

V

Vridar had heard of Danny McGivern, a teacher at the College and a writer of short-stories. Sitting in a big room while helping to register students, Vridar became aware that a pair of eyes was studying him, and he looked over and met the gaze of a man with an uncombed bush of dark wavy Irish hair. At once the man got up and came over.

"You're Vridar Hunter, aren't you? I'm Danny McGivern. Let's leave this morgue and find a drink."

This sort of thing was contrary to Vridar's scruples, but he followed Danny to an automobile. They slipped inside and Danny drew forth a bottle of whisky from under the seat. He pulled the cork and handed it to Vridar.

"Drink," he said. "You're out west now where men don't use glasses."

Vridar tipped it up and drank a little, thinking, This jackass is drunk now. Danny's eyes were a little bloodshot. They looked Irish, all right: they were brown and full of mischief and sly humor. Behind the humor was bitter unhappiness. Danny drank deep and long, wiped his mouth and said, "Now we have to go back to the morgue where the corpses sit up."

Before the day was over, Danny came again to Vridar. He said he and his wife wanted Vridar and Athene over as soon as possible—this evening?—and if not, why not? Vridar distrusted this man. He tried to put him off, saying he would have to speak to Athene about it; but then he saw the doubt and suspicion, the hurt, in Danny's eyes and said quickly, "I think maybe we can come this evening. What time?"

"Any time," Danny said.

Later, Vridar said to Athene, "You'll say, as you always do, that I'm impulsive, I move too fast, I like a person too soon and size him up too late. I can call and beg off."

"What's he like?"

"What's any Irish drunkard like? A child. About thirty-five; bloated and flabby with a big hanging gut. His jowls sag to his collar, the muscles of his face are flaccid, he has alcohol darkness under his eyes. He looks like a man who hasn't been sober for ten years. He's witty, charming, warm, impulsive, lonely, frustrated, malicious. You feel that a knife is hidden in his warmth. His dress is sloppy, his tie half-off, his trousers baggy and soiled, his fingernails unclean (like mine), his hair mussed up."

"I don't think I'll like him."

"Oh, of course not. You like Calvinists who read Ezekiel, Jews who read the Fourth Gospel, Sunday school deacons—"

"That will do."

"I mean you like them religiously starched and manicured."

"What's his wife like?"

"Like the kind of woman who would love that kind of man. Shall we call it off?"

Her slight shrug was a rebuke. She knew that he liked the outlandish anti-social half-crazed drunken bums. She might have said, with justice, "As long as I live with you our friends will be the kind of people you like, never the kind I like. . . ."

They were at the McGivern door at eight o'clock. A woman opened it. Vridar's first impression of her was never to change: he saw a large grossly fat woman, with a large square face; eyes that looked red from weeping; a loose irresolute mouth; a flabby double chin. He did not like her smile: it was put on. She said she was Genevieve McGivern. Would they come in?

Irish too, Vridar was thinking, and followed Athene inside. The house was like its occupants: clothes, books, newspapers and magazines, empty beer bottles, manuscripts—everything was scattered, everything suggested that these people never sobered up. Danny now came from the bathroom, his face smiling through lather, his undershirt pushed out by the heavy growth of hair on his chest. He would be only a moment, he said, and vanished.

"Call me Gen," Genevieve McGivern said. Her smile was almost a simper. She seemed pretty drunk.

Looking at her, Vridar saw again that she was a large woman—at least five feet seven inches tall, and large-boned. Like her man she looked as though she hadn't been sober for years. Her hands trembled when she took a cigarette and struck a match.

She swung a big fat arm in a contemptuous gesture at the littered house and said, "How you want your drink?" At once she went to the kitchen. She brought straight whisky to Vridar and Athene and took fully four ounces in a glass to the bathroom. Danny came staggering out. He had slipped into a shirt but had not buttoned it. He had not combed his hair.

"So glad you came," he said, his smile warm and Irish, his eyes Irish and dancing. "I have some things to say to you."

That, thought Vridar, sounded a little ominous. "Beautiful country up here," he said. "Lewis went close to this spot on the return."

"Louis who?" asked Danny, his face hard for a moment. He came over and stood before Vridar and Vridar looked up to a pair of accusing eyes. Danny said, "I've things to say to you."

"You said that before."

"I'm saying it again. I want you to understand it."

Vridar felt annoyance. "Understand what?" he asked, looking into the malicious unhappy eyes. He realized now that Danny was quite drunk.

"How it is when a man comes to Missoula. If I tell you how it is then maybe you won't get in trouble. First now—first, I'm a Catholic but so is the president, so the bastards can't fire me. You get that?"

Vridar glanced over at Athene and saw that she was looking unhappy. He glanced at Gen and was startled by the way she was looking at him. Doubting his senses, he glanced at her a second time and then met Danny's drunken gaze.

"It's my wife Genevieve," Danny said. "I saw you look at her just then. Twice. All the men look at her that way. I observe things, for I'm a writer, too. You knew, didn't you?"

There was a world of malice and hate and murder in those soft words, You knew, didn't you? Resenting the man, Vridar said to himself, I should get up and kick his flabby Irish ass.

Danny was saying, "Merrick has writers' conferences, you know. I'll tell you first the kind of man he is. He's never seen his wife naked. Do you need to know more than that?"

694

"No," Vridar said.

Danny's eyes were now fairly dancing with malicious humor. "I knew it because he told me so. He's John Calvin's oldest son. He has never got over the shock of discovering that there were two things he could do with his john. Until he was twenty-one he had thought it was only to make water through. Merrick, I mean— and stop looking at my wife. Merrick never drinks anything stronger than mint tea; and if he were to say out loud the Anglo-Saxon word for covering a woman his heart would stop. But like all people with a squatter's right in heaven, he finds wicked people fascinating and just loves to invite them to the campus.

"He invited Lloyd Bell," Danny went on, then seemed to lose control of his thoughts. "Where in hell is my drink?" he said. Gen rose awkwardly and hastened to the kitchen. She brought a bottle and set it on a table by Danny's right hand. "Thank you, darling," he said and there was that world of murder again. "Bell— Bell arrived drunk, as any decent author should when coming to a graveyard like this. Merrick expected you to. He'll never forgive you. He'll blackmail you—he'll destroy you. To try to save you I asked you right over to my home—for he'll learn that you were here. In dark nights I can feel him out there staring at my house and forcing his Calvinistic mind to try to imagine what orgies take place here. I can feel him out there, straining through all his virtues. As for you, he fully expects to have to fire you because of outrageous conduct. So I wanted to talk to you about it and tell you what to do."

Swaying a little, then gesturing with his glass, drinking and wiping his loose lips, Danny turned with comical deliberateness to look at Athene. Vridar saw self-consciousness and color fill her face. Before Danny took his gaze away, color had drenched her throat. Horror of him had filled her eyes.

"First," said Danny, turning back to Vridar and leaning unsteadily forward, "first I should tell you a little about me. I'm the campus drunkard and everybody talks about me. Ask Laura Mayfield, that creaking spinster with steel slats down her belly. The whole campus is devoted to me because I'm wicked. They would all hate me if I ever became as virtuous and two-faced as they are. If I were an atheist it wouldn't be like this. I'd be fired. But I'm a Catholic. The bishop defends me to the president—to the—to the—

"Vridar," he said, his eyes mocking the amused man before him, "this campus is an eddy full of monkish fish. When a wild thing comes in from the stream and dashes around like something actually alive, all the monkish fish are horribly shocked. They draw their embalming shrouds closer around them but they're pleased too. They just have to have scandal the way some people have to have patent medicines. Me they try to pity because I'm human."

He tossed his drink off and went weaving and staggering to the kitchen. After a moment he thrust his head out. "Want another?"

"Thank you, no," Vridar said.

"You will before you've heard all my story." Danny came out with what looked to Vridar like straight whisky, almost a glassful. He again stood before Vridar, the shirt back off his hairy chest and belly, his fat naked feet spread far apart. "It's my wife I have to tell you about." He looked at Gen. Vridar couldn't see Danny's eyes

695

but he could see Athene's and Gen's eyes. In Athene's eyes he saw horror; in Gen's, what he took to be ecstatic self-approval.

"Men," said Danny, "find my wife irresistible. They all fall for her. All of them," he said in a tone that would accept no denials. Astonished, Vridar started to his feet but Danny shoved him back, spilling whisky over him. "You listen to me!" he said. "Don't be silly or you'll bore me. I tell you all men fall for Gen. She's the siren who waylaid Ulysses. She's Aspasia and Sappho and—" He licked his lips and turned drunkenly toward his wife. His gaze fell on Athene.

"Your wife there, I can see she's cold because she's virtuous. Gen is all fire. I don't blame the men. After all," he said with charming self-contempt that was not self-contempt at all, "look at me: I'm her slave. She reaches out to men who come here—Hunter, I won't blame you. Understand that. It would be ridiculous," he said, trying to drink from the glass and spilling his whiskey. He smiled. It was a mechanical smile but it was charming because there was so much warmth in this man.

"To hell," Vridar said, "with all this Irish blarney."

"Shut up!" Danny roared. "I've told you I'll explain it. But by God you should decide right now whether you're going to be my friend or my wife's lover."

Amazed, Vridar could only stare up at him.

"You decide—"

"Oh, in God's name I've had enough of this. You—"

"Sit down," Danny said. "If you can't resist her—"

"Look, McGivern—"

"Call me Danny. Everybody does. I want you for a friend but if you can't resist her," he said, with a gesture elaborately comic, "why— I'll tell you how it is: no man ever has. She is the siren—"

With Danny trying to keep him down, Vridar got to his feet. He backed away from him and turned to Athene. Then, glancing at Gen, Vridar was astounded: she was looking at him as any siren might who was fat and flabbly and drunk, yet sure of her powers. My God! Vridar thought. Until this moment he had thought that Danny was putting on an act. He now realized that Gen actually believed herself to be a siren, and was confident that he could not resist her.

"Shall we go?" Vridar said.

Athene started to rise but Danny rushed at Vridar, shouting, "Oh no, you don't go now! You'll hear what I have to say."

"I've heard it." Vridar tried to go around him, but Danny faced him at every turn. Vridar then seized the man's shoulders to thrust him aside. Danny looked at him with a whipped foolish smile but his eyes still shone with mockery and suspicion.

"Don't be brutal with me," he said. "It's enough to seduce my wife—"

"Shut up or I'll knock your head off."

"The first law of psychology," Danny said, his smile sly and artful. "Seeking to seduce his friend's wife the man feigns anger when found out."

"Look, I care nothing about seducing your wife. Where's my hat?"

"Sit down," Danny said.

"I don't want to sit down. I want my hat."

"Hunter," said Danny with comic dignity, "you sit down. You'll be like a worm trying to swim in honey and pretty soon the honey will be in the worm."

"The worm in the honey," Gen said.

"What?" asked Danny, turning to peer at her.

"That's the way you said it the last time, the worm in the honey."

"The worm in the honey," Danny said. "That's what you'll be."

Vridar turned to Athene. "Get my hat if you know where it is."

"Oh no you don't," Danny said. He put his glass down. He staggered over to Vridar and seizing him tried to drag him to a chair. Vridar looked into the man's eyes and then he saw it. Then he understood. Danny's eyes had darkened with hate and grief. Danny *had to believe* that men found his wife irresistible and he had to hate them if they did not. Vridar allowed himself to be shoved down to a chair.

"You have to listen to his story," Gen said. "He has written the world's greatest short-story."

"That's right," said Danny, staggering off toward the kitchen.

"We should be going," said Vridar, looking at Athene.

"Not till you hear the story," Gen said.

Vridar refused to meet her eyes. Her eyes said that he was a fool to try to resist her.

She struggled up from her chair and went barefooted off to another room. Vridar looked for a moment at her broad bottom. In a low voice he said to Athene, "I guess we're stuck with it but as soon as it's read let's get out of here."

"I heard you," said Danny, coming in with another glass of whisky. "I'm not offended. I expect guests to talk that way, no matter how much I do for them. This story won a prize and it's greater than any you've ever written or ever will; but if you don't want to hear it— You're not the only great writer in the world, you know. Besides you and me there's Shaw."

"This belongs to his rose period," said Gen, coming with a magazine.

"I've had three periods," said Danny, turning on Vridar a grimacing face. "My blue, my rose, and my Ewig-Weibliche. My rose period was my greatest."

"This story won a prize," Gen said, easing herself down.

"I've told them that," Danny said.

"It's called The Little Girl in Blue," Gen said. She looked round her and her look called for silence. Clutching his glass Danny sank to a chair, his gaze on Vridar.

In a rather harsh voice that was too loud Gen began to read. By the end of the first few paragraphs Vridar was feeling pain: the story was filled with cliches and maudlin sentiment. After a few more paragraphs he looked over at Danny and was again astonished. The man was weeping. He was not making any sound but the sobs were shaking him; when he put the glass to his mouth he uttered a kind of moaning belch and dragged forth a handkerchief. He dabbed at his eyes. Then, for an instant, Vridar saw one of the brown eyes regarding him, a brown crafty eye that did not want to be seen.

697

Vridar was startled by a new sound and looked quickly at Gen. She was weeping, too. As though grief had come on her suddenly and with overwhelming force, she raised her head, like one short of breath, and then let off a gurgling wail that ran through the whole house. Vridar glanced at Athene. She was embarrassed, he supposed, for she was looking down at her hands.

For Vridar the scene became more and more incredible. The little girl in blue was an orphan who was adopted by an old derelict who happened to see her in a park. The old man and the little girl in blue were talking, and their talk, Vridar concluded, was intended to be the substance and soul of pathos. But he thought it silly. It was the author talking through a couple of puppets. "I never knew my mother," the little girl said; and the old bum replied, "I—I knew mine and broke her heart." These words brought from Danny a moan and a shudder and a frenzied blowing of his nose, and from Gen an unabashed wail of woe.

Knowing that Danny's crafty brown eye was watching him for signs of grief, Vridar tried to look sad. Now and then he glanced at his wife, furtively, for he did not want Danny to think that he was exchanging intimacies; but Athene never met his eyes, she seemed all the while to be studying her hands. The old man had taken the child to the garret where he lived and was rummaging through his few things to find something nice for her. Gen was now so overcome that she was barely intelligible. The words, "My darling child, you see—you see this poor old tramp has nothing" broke Danny down to tortured sobbing, and left Gen so undone that for a few moments she laid the story aside, to give both hands to her grief. Danny then got up and went weaving over to where Gen sat. He picked up the story and tried with tear-filled eyes to see the words. With a supreme effort he said, "But you —you have me—" and broke again.

The story fell from his hand. His big Irish body was convulsed by sobs, through and through. His face now looked twice as flaccid: his jowls, wet with tears, hung down to his collarbone; his mouth was loose and wet, his lips hanging; and from both eyes the tears ran. The crafty brown eye was no longer watching Vridar: it was plain that Danny McGivern was shattered by grief. And so was Gen. They were both sobbing and blubbering like children, Danny standing where the story had fallen, Gen bending forward in the chair, big moans pouring from her lips. "O God O God!" she was whispering, with dreadful anguish in her voice.

Breathing gently, his gaze on the floor, Vridar waited, his mind busy speculating. He was a little moved now. The story was so maudlin that he thought it disgusting, but there was something genuine in the grief of these two people. There could never be such perfect dissembling of grief. Had they lost a child? Danny with glass in hand had gone back to his chair but had put the glass aside and now just sat there, shaking with grief, with tears spilling in huge drops to the hair on his chest. Gen moaned as though tortured.

Thinking that perhaps this was the moment to go, Vridar stood up and looked round for his hat. He found it and went softly to the door, with Athene following him. Softly they let themselves out. Neither Danny nor Gen seemed aware of their going, but Vridar suspected that Danny was aware.

After they had walked a block or two in silence Vridar said, "What do you make of that?"

It was hard to tell, Athene said. The story held some special meaning for them. Had they both been orphans?

Or was it that they felt so helpless and defeated? Athene said she thought they should not see too much of them. She had in times past said this about other people and Vridar had always been annoyed. She would have preferred not to have met the McGiverns but he would not for the world have missed this evening. Where in a few hours could any novelist learn more?

Looking back to the scene he concluded that with them self-pity had become a luxurious habit. They had so obviously enjoyed it. "You think I can resist Gen?" When Athene gave no reply, Vridar said, "She recalls Stendhal's words—I could foretell every one of the woman's gestures and the most fleeting nuances of her thought. It is that which makes me often perfer low company, where one finds more of the unexpected. And of course we do find more of the unexpected, for it doesn't dissemble so well."

Athene gave no reply. He could not tell whether she had been deeply moved or deeply bored. He dropped the subject.

VI

"If you don't like lowbrows," he had said, "we'll find some highbrows." The highbrows turned out to be Ernest Hellyer and his wife Nora Nolana. Though Ernest stuttered, and sometimes when confused or blocked in his emotions could barely speak at all, he was a professor of economics—a tall cadaverous man, almost a spectral man, with a huge skull completely bald but for a low fringe of sandy hair; large bulging blue eyes that were spectacular when turning from face to face they deliberately rolled in their sockets; a sallow sickly-looking skin and a large mouth that grinned far back across its dentures. His laugh was a kind of triumphant gloating cawing deep in his chest.

Nora Nolana—she always used both names and would have thought a person impertinent who used only the first—was under five feet in height and looked like a child walking at the side of her man. She had a thick body and poor posture; a thin neck with scar tissue; and a childlike face if you did not look at her eyes. Her mouth was a small thin little-girl mouth; her chin, her cheeks, her forehead were those of a girl; but her bright intelligent eyes were those of a woman who had striven and suffered and lost. They lived in a handsome apartment and kept a poodle, with which they bored their friends to death. If, indeed, Vridar decided after meeting them and hearing the campus gossip about them it could be said that they had friends. Other faculty members distrusted them. One asked, in a whisper behind his hand, "Are they Communists?" It hardly mattered, because in 1932 in the United States, and for years afterward, Communism was a popular cult. Whether Communists or not it was well known that the Hellyers took immense glee in stirring things up.

"Of course we d-d-do," Ernest said to Vridar and Athene, and his laugh was the most diabolic Vridar had ever heard. Or possibly the laugh seemed more satanic than it was because of the way the man rolled his huge bulging blue eyes, filled with wicked mirth.

Indeed, they did, said Nora Nolana. Her voice was thin and rather shrill—an unpleasant voice that became twice as unpleasant when she became excited.

For all her professed sympathy with the downtrodden, the undernourished and exploited; for all her devotion to Franklin D. Roosevelt, at that moment campaigning against the nation's scapegoat, Nora Nolana took breakfast in bed and gave herself the airs of a blase and fashionably-ailing duchess. The snobbery, Vridar thought, was plain all over her, when she walked the scrubbed and scented poodle. It was plain when the Hellyers had him and Athene to dinner—for the service was of the finest sterling and linen, and most of the food Roosevelt's common man had never heard of. A woman had been hired to act as butler, and Nora Nolana had a small encrusted bell close to her right hand. Vridar could hardly restrain a snort when he observed with what hauteur she summoned the servant, with what coldness her voice spoke to her. It was this snobbishness in the intellectual liberals, all of them professing to grieve over the common people, that Vridar was determined to see to the bottom of.

The chief interests of the Hellyers were politics, music, and the poodle. They were two dedicated people. Danny McGivern had looked forward to Vridar's coming but had wished only to share whisky and sentiment. The Hellyers had looked forward too, for different reasons: they had hoped to find him a radical who loathed Herbert Hoover and capitalism—and who bowed, at least a little, in homage to Eugene Debs and Norman Thomas and (Vridar suspected) Stalin. They had hoped that he would be devoted to classical music. "It beats all hell," he said to Athene, "how many of these Stalinists are crazy about Mozart and Bach."

The first evening Vridar and Athene were with them Ernest told his favorite story. He was teaching in a college back east when by chance he happened to see Nora Nolana in the library stacks. He marched right over to her and said, "Do you believe in God?" Nora Nolana had looked up at him and said, "Of course I don't believe in God." Ernest had then asked, "Are you an atheist?" and she had said "Of course I'm an atheist."

"I n-n-nknew right then d-d-dthat this was the woman for me." Ernest was staring (it could not be said that he gazed, his eyes bulged so) at Vridar or rolling his blue protuberant eyes over at Athene; and deep in his chest was the gloating laugh that was not offensive being too ingenuous and boyish for that.

In her small shrill voice Nora Nolana said, "None of the intellectuals today believe in God. I hadn't since I was a child."

The funny thing, Vridar thought, looking at her, is that you still believe in the God-Father but don't know it. He restrained himself from saying to her, "Stalin in his youth had a drunken father who beat the daylights out of him. At seven he had smallpox that left him disfigured for life. He had an arm broken by school bullies and it was never properly mended. He was hooted at and pushed over because of a malformed foot. He was dismissed from the Church school. Later he was exiled six times to Siberia. Even if you can no longer stomach the Old Testament god, is this any decent substitute?"

Even though he stuttered Ernest loved to talk. He was saying, "k-k-kconstipation is a b-b-bigger peril to k-k-kChristians than Communism. For centuries they've tried d-d-desperately to repress their natural fuh-fuh-functions out of existence. Like me," he concluded, rolling his eyes in turn from Vridar to Athene. Ernest said that sometimes he did not defecate for six, eight or even ten days.

Vridar said, "Communism seems to me a hell of a poor substitute for laxatives."

At once, swiftly, the big blue eyes looked at Nora Nolana and something passed between them. With the blandest kind of innocence, Ernest rolled his eyes over to Vridar and said, "You know Percival Wren?"

"Christopher's brother," Nora Nolana said.

"He lost one of his t-t-t-testicles," Ernest said. Ernest had a manner: he would utter a statement and then look from person to person as though expecting them to fall off their chairs. He was looking that way now, his eyes rolling but the remainder of his countenance as expressionless as concrete. "He had the mum-mum-mumps."

Ernest was so sidesplitting that it was only with an extreme effort that Vridar held his snorts in. "The mumps," he said.

"The sad thing is his wife Muh-muh-Mary. She won't fuh-fuh-fuh him any more."

Vridar could no longer withhold it: he let off a snort of laughter and reached for his handkerchief. "She doesn't know one's as good as two?"

Before replying, Ernest rolled his eyes at Athene, back to Vridar, and over to Athene. You could see the man *feeling* inside, I'm not going to fall into this trap! "Is it?" he said and rolled at his wife. "Did you know I'm a ho-ho-ho-homo?"

Vridar stared. Was the man jesting? He then saw that Nora Nolana was distressed. She looked angry. She got up and left the room. Ernest looked after her until she vanished, then rolled his big blue marbles over to Vridar.

Vridar and Athene did not want to become friends with the Hellyers, but they persisted. Nora Nolana registered as a visitor in a class Vridar was giving on the contemporary novel, and Ernest waylaid him in hallways and on the campus to ask if he had read this book or that. Vridar and Athene were invited to breakfasts, to dinners, to parties: the Hellyers acted like two lonely souls who were socially ostracized and desperately in need of fellowship. Ernest also acted like one compelled to confession.

Vridar tried to hide the fact that he had lost half his teeth and had bridgework in his mouth, but Ernest, with no embarrassment at all, said his teeth were false. When a youth he fell off a house and the fall knocked out most of his teeth. With no embarrassment at all he said he was a homosexual; and when Vridar asked him in what way, Ernest said, "The kuh-kuh-kcornhole way." He said he was intimate with his wife only two or three times a year, and then without passion and almost against his will.

Listening to the man Vridar would wonder if he actually was a Communist or only sounded like one. He asked himself, What is the common denominator in intellectuals who become Communists? Was it that they all subconsciously felt themselves to be orphans? Were they looking for Parents with a capital letter? Were

701

they all emotionally immature—for how childish it was for anyone to glow with pride over the statement that he was an atheist! They couldn't be atheists if they were still looking for Mama and Papa.

"People who believe in a God the Father," Vridar said to them, "seem to me to fall into two groups: those who felt as children that they had no parents or who, failing to mature emotionally, never adjusted to the separation from their parents; and those who profess to believe merely because their parents professed to believe. Which group do you two belong to?"

Ernest rolled his eyes over to his wife. Shrill and intense, Nora Nolana took up the challenge. "Do you call people immature who are sick of the exploitation of the weak by the strong?—who—"

"Wait a minute!"

"—don't think that the lords of Wall Street are necessarily the last word in civilization, or that immensely wealthy churches with their parasitic priesthoods—"

"Just a minute!"

"Let him speak," Ernest said and for a moment fixed his big blue orbs on Athene.

"You damned phony liberals all rant about exploitation, yet have servants bring breakfast to your bed. You rant about the world's undernourished, yet feed your poodle delicacies that ninety-five per cent of the world's people have never heard of."

"You—"

"One minute, please. I have at the moment a publisher's editor who confesses that it costs him nine dollars a month just to keep his poodle sheared. Most of the families in the world don't have that much in a year. This man talks the way you do; he loathes Hoover and capitalism. All his phony professions of compassion—"

"Whether I feed a Siamese baby or a poodle is a trivial matter. The thing is to change the system—"

"Oh God, yes, so that the bureaucrats will be the elite, instead of the lords of Wall Street! I tell you it comes down to Ma and Pa. What makes you so goaded and unhappy?"

"She was raped," Ernest said.

"Raped?" Vridar looked at Ernest. "By you?"

Ernest's eyes opened wider, his head went up, and he looked at Vridar down a long sallow nose. "By me?" he said.

It was true, damned true, Nora Nolana said, speaking with bitterness, that she had been raped but that had nothing to do with it. A stinking son of a bitch of a dentist raped her in his office when she was only eight. Vridar looked at her, recalling now a strange matter. He had gone over one morning about nine to say that they could not come that evening to dinner; and when there was no response to the doorbell he had tried the door and found it unlocked. He had opened it and entered and called their names. When there was still no response he went to the stairway and looked up. Then there came the terrible scream. It was Nora Nolana's voice. "It is Vridar!" he had called; and her voice came again, shrill with terror, "You get out of here! Don't you dare come up!" Astounded, he had left the building. Now he thought, Yes, she was raped all right and the terror of it is still in her.

A few days later the bitter argument was resumed. "I don't know," Vridar said, "if you are Stalinists or not, but what kind of father is he?—an illiterate runt of a man covered with poxmarks, limping on a clubfoot and trying to hide a withered arm."

Nora Nolana asked sharply, "Where did you pick up such rot?"

"From a Communist in New York City."

"He lied."

"Why should you care so intensely? As a child did you have a warm relationship with your parents?"

"Did you?"

"No, but I'll be damned before I'll go round in a self-pity looking for parent substitutes. I'll not loathe Herbert Hoover because he doesn't look like an ideal father, or idolize Franklin D. Roosevelt because he does."

"All that has nothing to do with it."

"I'm beginning to suspect that it has everything to do with it."

"You ought to know the reasons," she said angrily, her voice becoming shriller. "You lived them. The novels you're writing about yourself give the answers—the poverty of your childhood, the rags, the earth hut, the hunger, the long hours of toil—"

"That's all nonsense: If a child is made to feel loved and wanted, he can go naked and live on rose hips. The economic base is a myth. What about these sons of American millionaires who are staring wide-eyed at Stalin's face? I'm going to begin to keep a file of you Hoover-haters and Stalin-lovers, to find out what you have in common. I think you're all orphans, in a manner of speaking. In saying you're atheists you mean only a parentless condition. Having lost God—"

"Oh, what absolute shshshslop!" Ernest cried.

"Reductio ad absurdum," said Nora Nolana. "The last feeble rationalizings of the capitalists. One doesn't have to be parentless to see how childish it is to put a God-Father out there in space. You papists—"

"I'm no papist. I say that having lost God—"

"By the b-b-b-balls of a priest!" cried Ernest. "An atheist from infancy I had no G-G-God to lose."

"All right, having lost father and mother—"

"Do you really believe such dismal absurdities?" asked Nora Nolana, fixing him with a withering stare. "Do you face the appalling breakdown of capitalism in the Western world with no more than feeble generalizing about father and mother?"

"He's rationalizing exploitation behind p-p-p-pa and m-m-m-ma." Ernest rolled his big orbs over to Athene to see what she thought of that.

Looking accusingly at Vridar, Nora Nolana said, "Do you agree with Nietzsche that the basis of the Christian religion is a slave morality?—meekness, humility, poverty of spirit? Do you agree that Luther came along and made it democratic?"

From Ernest's chest came the deep diabolic laughter. He said, "I have a p-p-poem I want Vridar to hear."

"Just a minute," his wife said. "Do you agree?"

"There's truth in it."

"Seneca said, All men will admit that we have a soul, and a jackass with a reputation as a scholar says, All we know of it is its existence, not its nature. Do you think both statements foolish?"

"I do."

"All right. Edward Carpenter—have you read him?"

"A couple of books."

"Carpenter has said that the promise of something better than paganism and better than Christianity is a precious thing in man's hope, and that it is past time it should be fulfilled."

"But not in Stalinism. Not in Norman Thomasism. Let me give you a point. A person who was analyzed has said that in many instances an overly severe conscience is softened during the analysis. This then happens, that one has a greatly diminished anxiety about death. He said to the analyst, If I didn't respect my old man so much I'd have killed him long ago. There's a lot of repressed murder in the hearts of you so-called liberals—and a lot of anxiety related to your own dying. You've killed your old man, that's your tragedy. As children—"

"Oh, what utter rot!"

"Wuh-wuh-wait!" said Ernest, raising a long bony arm. He rolled his eyes in turn at the three persons before him. Then he said: "A man went into a shuh-shuh-shithouse and after he was duh-duh-done he wrote, I do not like this place at all, the seat is too high and the hole is too small. Then another Kuk-kuk-Kinglish-man came along and wrote under it, You lay yourself open to the obvious retort, your bottom's too big and your legs are too short." Ernest shook with wicked sunken laughter, his eyes fixing them in turn.

"I guess I'll have to give you a limerick," Vridar said.

To stop him, Vridar suspected, Nora Nolana opened a door and let the poodle in. It was a large fat poodle of boundless energy and it now raced slipping and sprawling all over the floor and then looked under shaggy forelocks at its master, waiting for orders. Ernest told it to stand on its hind legs, to lie down, to roll over; and after each performance he laughed loud with parental pride. Vridar was annoyed because his limerick had been side-tracked, and vexed with himself because he was vain enough to be annoyed. The Hellyers, he told himself, bored him but he knew that actually they outraged him. Ernest would have his dog perform until all his guests were ready to murder both dog and master. Watching him now, listening to his explosions of laughter, seeing the pride and joy like small sunbursts in his eyes, Vridar speculated again on the buried nature of the rabid dog-lover. He distrusted such men. He felt in them the ruthless tyrant.

After enduring dog and master for an hour, he said to Athene, "We'd better go."

Ernest interrupted his pleasure to say, "You don't have to teach tomorrow. And whu-whu-where is that limerick?"

Vridar thought, He deserves it. He said, "I know that the thing sounds absurd but a man named McTavish McTurd was born in a gutter and there heard to utter a fantastically unprintable word."

Ernest let off a burst of laughter but sobered almost at once. He gave Vridar a hard stare and looked over at his wife.

On his way home with Athene Vridar became aware that she was glancing at him now and again. More than once in times past he had become aware of her sitting back and looking at him, mirth in her eyes, a little smile on her face: she would listen to him argue, or drop a witticism, or rise to eloquence, her expression one of mingled pride and superior tolerance. She had told him that he was simply invincible in argument, for if he was routed from one position he quickly took another; if exposed in specious logic he fled with redoubled nimbleness into logic still more specious; and all in all ran the gamut of every position she had ever known persons to take. Her words had offended him. He had said that she made him sound both stupid and dishonest; and she had said, "I don't think you really care about winning an argument, for the reason that you're a Hamlet, with no deep convictions except the conviction that deep convictions are childish. You like to confuse and perplex your opponent, obscure and derange the subject, and drive everything before you."

He had turned from her to hide a grin, knowing that there was truth in what she said. A Hamlet? Well, maybe; but a chameleon, surely: he always took on the coloring of the people he was around. He had been stuttering since meeting Ernest. He had picked up several of Danny's mannerisms.

He came to see more and more that Athene was like his mother—not only in appearance (Prudence had been called a redhead as a girl: they had the same abnormally strong chins, a tendency to freckles, a steady direct gaze)—but also in their traits; the same inflexible wills, the same stern moral codes, the same—Damn it, there was no Irish in them, no Celt, no Latin: they were all pure stiffnecked English. Somehow they had entered into a partnership with God, and God, he was sure, found their selfrighteous inner purity a little tiresome.

In bed he reached over to clasp her hand. He fell asleep thinking that if he had never lost to her the Irish ardor buried in his soul, he had given to her what she valued more, complete faith in her integrity, an abiding admiration for the quality of her mind and the indomitable strength of her spirit.

VII

The Merricks asked Vridar and Athene over for an evening and a duller evening Vridar had never spent. Merrick was a sandy man: his hair, his brows, his eyelashes, his skin and even his clothes were a pale reddish brown. Vridar sensed that one darkness in him was the fact that he did not have a doctorate: college teachers developed ulcers and psychoses because of that lack! He sensed that another darkness was his relationship with his wife. Mrs. Merrick was sandy too, like her man: they looked like brother and sister, not only in complexion but in the same angular frames and lack of grace in movement. The husband's unhappiness, Vridar supposed, was related not to her appearance but to the quality of her mind: she was not intellectual at all, and so could not share her husband's interests or even grasp the nature of them. She would sit and look at him when he talked, rather stupidly adoring, her mouth open a little, her mind obviously a blank.

Elmer T. Merrick loved to talk. He fancied himself a brilliant talker and a brilliant man. He had never used tobacco; he never served alcoholic drinks in his home. What he liked to do, and what he did for nearly three hours when Vridar and Athene were there, was to take up a popular play by a New York hack and read it through, in turn trying to project himself into each part. The man had large squirrel teeth: because he had been a Rhodes scholar and took inordinate pride in his enunciation, his lips were manipulated with amazing vigor over his teeth, his teeth appearing and disappearing, and becoming, it seemed to Vridar, a little larger with each appearance. Merrick never doubted that he enthralled his auditors: his eyes would flash at them under his sandy brows, seeing nothing in their faces but what he imagined he would see, and seeing least of all their dreadful weariness. The reading went on for almost three hours with no break, no refreshments. . . .

As he grew older, the egregious egoism of persons, their crass self-adulation, their obtuse sensibilities, drove Vridar deeper into reticence. There was Don Mitchens, whom he met at a party. In his middle or late twenties, Mitchens was a slender man of average height and fair complexion, with no outstanding feature. He was boyish and ebullient and immensely taken by himself. He looked to Vridar like the spoiled and pampered favorite of some doting mother, as indeed he was: his mother, called The Duchess behind her back, was thick and short like a bag of grain, with peering eager eyes and a smart coiffure of white hair. She was the custodian of the city's morals and its most tireless gossip. Because her husband had died with snakes in his boots she was a fanatic on the subject of alcohol, but she admitted the Devil into her cosmos nevertheless; and though she did not love him—he had been too much her husband's counsellor for that—she admired him in her way and deferred to him with droll comment. She knew, as her grimaces declared, that he was inextricably mixed in the affairs of men and gave flavor to experience, even to gossip. But she wanted him to stay away from her son.

Her son had only a feeble capacity for devil-worship. When he drank at a party he let it be known that nobody was to say a word about it. "His mother," Ernest said, rolling his big eyes. Though a native of Montana, Mitchens had been living in Manhattan and had returned to his old haunts as a sophisticate. He was eager to be off to Capri, where he was going to write a great novel, possibly the great American novel. Only think, Nora Nolana said to Vridar, of all the genius that had gone to that rockpile and never returned! That was what Vridar was thinking: his friend Jake, the Jew, had gone there to write the great American play—and where was Jake now?

Having no wit of his own, Mitchens recited the wit of others—such as the Field mot about an actor who played the king as if at any moment he expected to be trumped by the ace. Vridar would sit back in shadow and study the man. He asked Athene, "Does this brash extrovert really think that he will go to Capri and write an important novel? How in the world can he imagine that he has anything to say? I suspect he'll end up as a literary critic. . . ."

Vridar studied all these people, and thought about Communism, Socialism, Capitalism, Fascism: on coming west he had determined to see his way through these things. He would think of Jeremy Bentham who, on the one hand, had advocated universal suffrage, the vote by ballot and annual parliaments; yet who, on the other, had cynically accepted from Parliament twenty-three thousand pounds for an

706

idea that was never used; had his own private mansion and deer park; and a piano in every room. Bentham had advocated political democracy, yet had practically no faith at all in mankind, having looked deep into himself, "It may be just that," Vridar said to Athene. "It may be that faith in mankind is exactly in proportion to the depth at which we look at mankind. If so, I expect to have no faith left. Have I told you what William Graham Sumner said?—that the yearning for equality comes from envy and covetousness. Have we nothing on which to rest our faith but our ideals, and nothing to support our ideals but our vices?"

He thought of what Theodore Roosevelt's malefactors of great wealth had done with their money: of all the vulgar mansions built along Fifth Avenue; of the ostentation and competition in the size and luxuriousness of yachts—the Mellons, the Fricks, the Stewarts, the Vanderbilts, the Astors, the Morgans; of weddings or balls that cost a quarter or a half a million dollars at a time when half the people in the nation were hungry. There was, he supposed, a little of Ward McAllister in every person.

The vulgar extravagance had alarmed a few of the barons of wealth. They had turned in their chairs of gilt and brocade to read the handwriting on the wall—the smouldering resentment and hostility of the people they exploited. The astounding Fete of the Bradley Martins had precipitated it: there had been such rumblings of anger and amazement that the stupid vulgarians had fled to Europe. No wonder Veblen had written about the theory of the leisure class, or another Martin, about the passing of the idle rich. For the idle rich *were* passing. The nation was in a deeper economic crisis than it had ever known, and thoughtful people were looking hard at the American system.

When talking about the matter Vridar would say to Athene, "It seems more and more obvious to me that no system can solve the thing, for any system can be corrupted. The American system may be the greatest yet devised, yet it allowed a few greedy pirates to get possession of vast areas of the nation's wealth. The only possible answer I can think of is self-discipline but the logical end of self-discipline is suicide."

Athene would look at him and say nothing.

"Look at the Hellyers: they just love to have breakfast in bed. They love the idea of servants. So does Carl Noyce, who's getting the I'm-breaking-my-heart-over-the-common-man look in his eyes. Aren't such people phonies? What do you think?"

"I feel that their trouble is spiritual poverty."

He looked at her and considered her words. "What do you mean by that? Were Christians in the Dark Ages spiritually impoverished?"

"You asked what I thought. I told you."

"Thank you, darling. How sweet you are. Am I spiritually impoverished?"

She gave him a faint smile touched with pity. "I wouldn't say you are well-nourished."

"Are you telling me that these so-called intellectuals who turn to Communism are spiritually undernourished?"

"What do you think?"

"I think they're emotionally immature."

"You've said they're seeking parents. Wouldn't that mean spiritual hunger?"

After a long moment of silence he said, "Yes, that would be in it. But do you propose their return to some Church?"

A little sharply she said, "Oh, not necessarily. Thoreau was deeply religious. So was Wordsworth. Let's not confuse religion with theology."

"You don't think self-discipline is the chief thing needed?"

"I think the chief thing needed is a more radiant spirit."

"But how do we get it? By seeing Pa in F.D.Roosevelt?"

"I think any person's way to the radiant spirit must be private."

"For unusual persons, yes. But the undisciplined person feeding himself is not a pleasant sight, is he?"

She smiled. He could invariably make her smile with a witticism.

"How about Danny?" he said. "A Catholic—goes to Mass, confesses his sins, prays his head off. Why isn't he spiritually nourished? What's the fault there? Are the Irish religious or only superstitious?"

Danny had lost the path, she said; he was going round and round in a darkness.

"And the Hellyers were never on the path?"

"Never."

"You're on it but I'm not?"

"I was once on it but you've been getting me off."

He was shocked. "*I* have been getting *you* off? I've never heard that from your lips before."

Suddenly he felt something that was close to panic. Was this marriage also going on the rocks? What did she mean?

"Just exactly what do you mean?"

"I don't want to talk about it," she said.

He thought about this problem (that was also his problem) and these Missoula people (who were also his people) on the way home, while driving in his old Hupmobile through the mountains where the bold Meriwether Lewis once rode with nine men. He thought about it when he boated a cart across the river and swam a team, and went up Burns Canyon to drag the great pile of logs to the river. I'm the world's worst God damned bore! he told himself, over and over. Why didn't he do what he had to do to make money, dine in sumptuous places, go to Europe first-class, and wear monogrammed linen? He had a deep feeling that he was no good, that David Hawke was no good, that all artists were no good. He had a deep feeling that the novels he was writing about his life and his people were no good. On rising, on lying down to sleep, he would ask the stars and the sky, How in hell can I write a book that is worth a damn if I can't look any deeper into life than hunger!

One day while he was laboring there came a thought. In bed with Athene he said, "The novels I'm writing are no good. We can't explain the man in terms of his childhood. We have to go to his past, and his past is the whole life on this planet. I'm going back to hell and gone."

She was silent a few moments. Then: "How far?"

"To the ape, to the cell, to the stone. Could I project myself into the ape-man, pull the horizons in, see no farther than he saw, feel no higher than he felt?"

"Why should you?"

"To discover why you ask such damned stupid questions. Could you project yourself into different periods of history? Could you get inside the radiant lunatic who wrote the Fourth Gospel?"

He wrote his brother, laying his project before him and asking what he thought about it. Marion replied: "I don't know what you can do with that ego of yours. The present isn't big enough to hold it, so you are going into the past to find room. I expect to hear that you are off in space somewhere, filling up the universe. You're insane, but I no longer suppose that it matters. . . ."

Vridar tossed the letter to Athene. "What a wonderful brother I have! But he does have the decency to recognize that there is no meaning and nothing matters."

Athene read the letter and turned on Vridar a dry smile.

When out felling aspen trees for the next summer's woodpile Vridar would try to feel himself into the ape-man of long ago, in turn with each of his senses, and then with all his senses together: he would look, listen, sniff, grasp a heavy club; he would go walking off, the club dragging from his hand; he would try to shrink the world to the world the ape-man knew—the small dark world of enemies, mating, food and drink—the dreams of terror in the black night—the puny frightened effort to understand the nature of the sun, the moon, and stars. In his play-acting he early discovered a truth that was to stand at the core of his life: there was a point of no return. When one day he realized this, he trembled with horror: a man could go back, yes, if he were intuitive enough, but if he went too far he would not come home again. It was like going against the gravitational pull and going too far. How could he ever know when he was close to the point where the hold on him of the present would be less than the hold on him of the past? If a man didn't come back, what would he be then? A lunatic, he supposed. . . .

The project seemed to open to him immense possibilities. Could he, for instance, go into the dungeon and be Roger Bacon?—feel that great and brave man's anguish of soul and mind? Could he come out of the dungeon if he went into it?—or would he have to say, You go now, back to the living, and I'll suffer here? How silly it was to speak of the artist as a person! He was the sum of all his projections. There was no himself in a great actor: he had no personality of his own, or if, like John Barrymore, he had, he was not an actor but a clown. . . .

He got to the point where Athene no longer expected him to be the man she had first known: she would find him rolling his eyes and stuttering; lifting his brows and manipulating his lips across his teeth, as he declaimed the dullest lines he could think of; or affecting the shrill umbrage of Nora Nolana—for it made no difference to him whether he was male or female. "I'm the paronomastic," he would say to Athene, grinning, "using emotions instead of words." If his mother saw him when he thought himself unobserved, she thought him inspired. His father thought he was stupid or insane.

Pereceiving, then, the pain in Joe's eyes, Vridar would look away to the mountains and say, "Where are the elk now?" If Joe gave no reply Vridar would say,

"Fishing through the ice ought to be good now." Joe said he kallated they could catch some dandies, for the ice was thick enough now, the moon was right. Across the river. . . .

It was always across the river! If Joe had lived on the other side he would have thought the best fishing was on the side where he now lived.

"Oh, sure, across the river," Vridar said. "About ten miles up or down?"

Joe's eyes then darkened, he sank back into his silence. He hated his sons and his sons hated him.

VIII

Vridar thought that nothing in the world was as cold as an alarm clock ringing in subzero weather an hour before daylight; and nothing so cozy as warm deep bedding when the clock rang. He raised his head a little to look through a window at the gray night-gloom of a winter world. Out of deep bedding he brought an arm and thrust a hand out to silence the clock. There then was no sound but he knew that in a small cold bedroom in the house Joe would be thrusting his legs over the edge of the bed, encased in heavy woolen Mormon underwear; he would be leaning forward, groping in darkness for his socks, trousers, and shirt. Why, Vridar asked himself, did he go on these bone-chilling forays with his father? Was it a sort of father-rivalry?—a wish to prove himself a man of pioneer hardihood like William Clark or Jedediah Smith? Or was it just kindliness? No matter how bitter the weather Joe at the drop of a hat would leave his snug bed long before daylight, to wade through deep snow and cross frozen rivers, or to climb tall mountains for a shot at an elk.

Athene was awake, he supposed, but had made no sound. She was lying there thinking—thinking no doubt what a strange man Joe was, to go traipsing off in dreadful cold and darkness, in snow to his crotch, to risk his life in a frail boat on a black river filled with ice-floes. But that was Joe. Joe wasn't a learned man or a college teacher or a writer of books, but he could still teach his sons a few tricks. . . .

With a sudden move Vridar left the bed. He drew his shirt from under a pillow and slipped his arms into it, and almost at once he was chilled and trembling. In the night gloom through the window he could see no stars. He seized a cap and put it on, drawing the fur flaps down over his ears and pulling the visor low. Quickly he put on heavy socks, then his trousers, then his shoes, and stood up, shaking all over. It was so cold that a man had to keep moving or he would soon die. It was so cold that when he walked his legs felt paralyzed. Without speaking he left the cabin, his footfalls sounding heavy and frozen on the floor boards. The door creaked like a door of ice when he closed it behind him. He went down the hill to the kitchen and found Joe there, setting a fire in the wood stove. Nothing was said. On the table were two fishlines about six feet long, with a hook attached. Wrapped in a heavy piece of old blanket were two small cans of bait—of what Joe called muckets, a fat grublike worm which they found in gravel in shallow water. Vridar put one can and one line into a pocket of his army greatcoat, and into the other

710

pocket a hatchet. When Joe thought the fire no longer needed his attention, he took the other line and can of bait, put on his cap and his big mittens, bit off a quid of tobacco and went outside. Vridar followed him. The air of the outside world stung like fire, even though there was no wind. In this kind of cold a man could lay a steel nail across his tongue and it would burn a furrow.

It was almost a mile to the riverbank and the boat. The snow was about three and a half feet deep, but on the previous day Vridar had beaten a path through it, and he now took the lead, stepping into the frozen holes he had made. The aspen trees around him were burdened with snow and sheathed with gleaming frost. Frost on the snow roundabout was like fields of diamonds. Vridar's breath went before him in heavy clouds; his feet, on which he had overshoes as well as shoes, made loud crunching sounds. He had gone no more than a hundred yards when his face felt frozen. The cold had entered through all his clothes. His hands were freezing in heavy fur-lined mittens, and as he stumbled along over the deep frozen footholes he swung his arms around his body to warm his hands. They trudged along in single file, stumbling, half-falling, and then suddenly the broad black river came in view. Only it was not black: it looked like an almost solid expanse of floating ice: that's what happened when a brief thaw released the ice on the river bottom, so that it could come to the surface. Vridar knew from experience how difficult it was to put a boat around the floes or across them; it would be an ordeal this morning that would demand all his strength. He ought to have eaten some breakfast. He had not known that the river would be so choked. He would be the one to row, for long ago Joe had said this his older son was a better oarsman than he.

The mush-ice was sure thick, Joe said.

Vridar gave no reply. They were now within sight of their boat, a light thing of wood that leaked in a half-dozen places. How many men, Vridar wondered, would have ventured in such a boat into such a river, gorged with drifting ice? A number of times in the past Joe had capsized his boat in this river and had been plunged into its waters, usually clutching his big rifle. Once, as he told the story, he had had two or three grouse in the other hand. Lord! He swore to heaven that once he had swum halfway across the river with a rifle in either hand. You never knew what to believe in Joe's stories; the fable-making Irish in him simply raised unholy hell with facts.

There were big eddies on the side of the river next to them, frozen over, where they might have fished; but Joe was always partial to the spots that were hardest to get to. Not for anything would Vridar have suggested that they ought to fish on their own side. Rather than have his father think he might be afraid he would have waded in and drowned. He *had* almost drowned a number of times, back in childhood. Though a poor swimmer he was not afraid of this river. It was pretty silly to think of swimming in this kind of weather: if a man were thrown into those waters he would soon be dead.

They both took the rope to drag the boat out to the edge of the ice shelf. When they had it there, they stood for a moment looking at the river. It was about four hundred feet across at this point and was flowing at about two miles an hour. The water looked as black as ink where it was visible among the floes.

It was hard to tell, Vridar said, how far down they would go. He meant that if the boat got lodged on floes many times they might be carried to hell and gone downstream. Joe said quietly that they would land somewhere.

They shoved the boat off the ice shelf and into the black water. Vridar then stepped in and sat and grasped the oars. Joe knelt on the ice and pulling the back end of the boat toward him crawled in. He was a big man, in his winter garments he weighed well over two hundred pounds, and he sank the rear end of the boat about half its depth. Vridar was looking out at the river and watching the floes. Sometimes a path would open for twenty or more yards. He was waiting for one. He had never seen so much ice in the river. He knew that the long struggle with the oars would pull the guts out of him. Well, when Joe conceded to a man a superiority in anything, he made him pay for it!

Vridar waited until a black path opened and then bent to the oars. If he had been alone in the boat he could have moved it with ease, but Joe's inert weight on the back seat made it feel as though he were pulling against an anchor. The boat was leaking in a number of places, and Joe with a gallon can was bailing; but instead of sitting in the center of the seat he would move to one side, to make it easier to scoop up the water. Then the rowing was twice as difficult, with one oar too deep, the other up in the sky, as the boat tipped so far it almost dipped water. All the while as Vridar labored he had to crane his head to watch the floes, as he strove to take advantage of the larger paths. When a path opened, he would row with all his strength the length of it. Then his boat would be imprisoned by the surrounding islands of drifting ice, and for a few moments he would have to drift with them, while waiting for another break. If one was too long coming, he would then try to drive the boat through a floe.

A third of the way across the river he got the boat on a huge floe and was unable to dislodge it. So there they were, in a helpless boat on a great block of ice, moving downstream. Desperately he tried to row the boat off or with oars to shove it off. Then with an oar he thrust at the ice all around him, trying to break it up and shove it away.

"I guess we're stuck," he said, panting and resting.

Joe looked downstream. There would soon be a riffle, he said. He meant that the main flow of the river was approaching a kind of shelf where the waters would break and cascade. Then the boat would be freed because the floe under it would be shattered.

Now he could get off, Joe said.

With all his might Vridar struggled again. Then the floe was torn and broken by swifter water, and the boat was free and bobbing like a cork. Joe said to keep the nose upstream. Vridar felt a moment of anger. He knew that if he let the boat turn sideways in this swift-water current, it would be turned over in a flash. He kept the nose upstream and down they went, tossed from great wave to great wave, until the river leveled out in leisurely movement. So much of the ice had been disintegrated that there was now a clear path to the farther bank. Vridar swung the boat and bent to the oars and felt that he was pulling the whole inside of him loose from his bones.

Joe said he guessed they wouldn't fish in the eddy he had in mind. That un over there, he said, looked pretty good. Vridar eased the boat in to a broad ice-shelf, struck it several blows with an oar to learn if it would support him, and then crawled out over it, taking the boat-rope with him. He stood up and drew the boat close. Joe crawled the length of it and on to the ice. They then grasped the rope and dragged the boat out of water and back a hundred feet on the ice ledge. The first signs of daylight had appeared.

Vridar wanted to be alone a few minutes. He felt spent and sick and disgusted. He was such a dolt and blockhead that if given a job beyond his physical strength he would do it if it killed him. What a miserable ass he was! He looked out at the river, knowing that he would be the one to row back.

Joe had taken the hatchet and was hacking a hole in the ice. He was kneeling. He would chop a few moments, then scoop the big ice chips out of the hole and chop again. When at last he broke through to water, he took his mittens off and lying on his belly reached down the hole, to shove a larger piece of ice back under the shelf, so that the hole would be black and clear. The ice was thicker than he had thought it was, Joe said, standing up and rubbing ice and water off his hands.

Putting a mucket on his hook, he let the hook sink into the black water. He had about six inches of stick to which the line was attached, and now moved the stick up an down, to agitate the bait down in the river.

Vridar had been looking round him for dry wood to make a fire. He had lost his interest in fishing. Walking across the wide eddy on its ice to trees and brush, he found dead willows and broke them across his knee. He carried kindling and fagots over close to Joe's hole. He had paper and matches and in a few minutes had a fire. Joe said that fire built on ice near holes attracted fish but no fires were needed on an eddy so broad and deep. Already a half-dozen trout were flopping round-about, bending and leaping in the snow and frost, and becoming frost-sheathed as they suffocated and died. They were cutthroat and rainbow. The largest, Vridar thought, would weigh three pounds. After a while the fish were so encased with snow and frost that they were hardly distinguishable save when they moved.

Vridar stood by the fire, warming his hands, watching for smoke from the Adolf Buck shack. Joe made a fetish of honesty in most things but had never bought a fishing or hunting license and never would. He scorned all laws that had not existed when he was a young man. As for Adolph, Joe had such contempt for the man that never once, it seemed to Vridar, did he ever cast a glance the deputy game warden's way.

Suddenly Joe dropped to his knees. Vridar knew that he had a big one. Joe shook his mittens off, sprawled down on his belly, and with both hands seized the line. The trout was racing back and forth under the ice, and Joe was trying to bring its head to the hole. This at last he did, as Vridar moved over to watch him. Joe got his fingers in the trout's throat and slowly pulled it out. Then he looked up at his son. It was a beautiful fat five-pound cutthroat.

"Ain't you gonna fish?" asked Joe.

"You're doing all right," Vridar said.

He went to the bank and cut a green forked branch to string the fish on. He took the smallest fish and gutted it, and without letting Joe suspect what he was doing he impaled the trout on a green stick and roasted it in the fire. He knew that he would have to have food in his stomach, before he could row across that terrible river. Out of sight of Joe he gulped the fish and felt grim humor. Last summer he had pitched hay against a young giant who was so nimble and powerful that he could walk up to a twelve-hundred-pound horse, slap his palms down to its spine, and in the next moment be astride. Neither Vridar nor his opponent walked from haycock to haycock: they ran, they buried Joe, who was loading; and before the noon-hour came Vridar was famished and almost spent. When out of sight of both Joe and the young giant across from him, he stuffed his mouth full of alfalfa leaves, and chewed and choked them down as he labored. He thought he must have eaten at least a pound of leaves. When noon came he was suffering from cramps because he had eaten so much hay, but he was still neck and neck in the hay-pitching race.

Now, with a half-cooked fish, Vridar went over for more wood, and while hidden gulped the fish down. He then felt a little better. It was daylight now; the mountainous world around him was gray with morning dusk. Farther out toward the river Joe chopped another hole and there caught another large trout. He was a happy man when he caught a big fish or shot a two-point buck or a fat elk cow. While moving his line up and down he now scanned the eastern mountains, looking for elk trails in the snow.

"There," he said at last.

Vridar gazed up for a full minute but could see no path.

They were going that way, Joe said, bending his head a little to the south.

Vridar had no doubt that his father was right. You could fool him about human beings, but you couldn't fool him about a game trail. "How many?"

Joe looked at the trail, which was more than a mile distant and about fifteen hundred feet above him. More than two, he said.

Vridar counted the fish and said they had enough. Joe said he was about ready to go. He would go home and eat enough breakfast for five men, and then fill his old pipe and sit back and puff and belch while digesting. Vridar roasted another small fish and slipped away to eat it. He thought he was strong enough to make the return journey.

Joe drew his line up and wound it around the short stick. He looked at the high mountains in the eastern sky. Again he studied the elk trail.

"How many we got?" asked Joe.

"Twenty-three."

Joe turned, looking round him. He said he thought he had counted twenty-five. Vridar looked with him, kicking in the snow and bending now and then to examine something. He said maybe two of them had flopped back into a hole.

He put the fish in the boat and with his father dragged the boat to open water. It was no longer black but it looked even colder than it had looked in darkness. Joe crawled in and back through the boat to the rear seat. Glancing across the broad expanse of flowing water, Vridar drew a deep breath and stepped into the boat. He sat and grasped the oars. It should be easier this time, for there was light and there was not so much ice below the riffle. He swung the boat, waited for a pathway among the floes, and shot it out. Joe bent forward and began to bail water. After pulling desperately a few minutes, Vridar again felt spent and rested on the oars, drifting downstream.

When Joe became aware of this he looked all around him and said, "You best row, son, or we won't make it."

Joe meant that between a quarter and a half mile below them were dangerous rapids. Again Vridar rowed, his mirth bitter inside him, for both his father and himself. Dodging floes . . . then rowing swiftly a few moments . . . thrusting with an oar to push floes away . . . resting just a moment and rowing again—until he was white and his senses were swimming. The sun was up now. The world was white and cold.

"I don't know if we'll make it," Joe said, looking round him.

Vridar felt grim humor. He knew that they had to make it. He knew as well as his father that this frail craft would be knocked to pieces or flipped over if it hit the rapids, where, against the stone mountain, the ice was piled up like huge glaciers. He was measuring the distance, his strength, the speed of the current. He could now hear the plunging and foaming of the river below him: instead of striking the mountain and recoiling upon itself, it was now striking the vast accumulation of ice. Yes, he knew that if he were borne down into these convulsed whirlpools it would be the end of him and Joe—and with all the grim and desperate will he had, he kept rowing, though his strength was practically gone. The current was increasing in speed now. Vridar thought, I'll have to miss every floe from here on if I make it! He thought, If I hit against one, and am delayed for just three seconds, it will be too late then. "Sit in the center!" he cried at his father. "Don't bail now, or you'll slow me up." Joe moved to the center and sat straight. He glanced down the river, then at the bank they were approaching, then at his son's white face.

Vridar had luck. He knew it. He missed every floe in the last desperate forty yards. When he came to the bank he was so close to the rapids and the current was moving so fast that he cried to his father to seize willows and he grasped willows and hung on, and the boat was swung and almost overturned, as broadside it struck the bank. Clutching a stout willow, Vridar bent forward over his lap, utterly spent, feeling as if he had been gutted, as if he might faint. Joe cutched willows and crawled out. Then it was easier because the boat rode higher. Joe reached into the prow and got the fish. He looked at his son.

"Ain't you comun?"

Vridar gasped, "In a minute."

Carrying the fish, Joe turned home. He had mighty legs: he plowed forward, breasting the snow, shoving, thrusting a leg forward and down. "Let him break it!" Vridar thought, now angry because his father had gone on and left him. Fifteen or twenty minutes passed before Vridar could manage to stand up. Another five minutes passed before he could summon the strength to leave the boat. He managed to claw his way up the bank and then sat in deep snow, with snow all around him up to his neck. I should just sit here and freeze to death! he thought—for he felt that he was no good—that he was a worthless stupid neurotic who would some day wrench the heart out of him or spill all his guts in a big hernia rather than accept

715

defeat. Oh, it was more than that: he would not accept the thought that he was a physical weakling. Possibly nobody in the world but himself thought he was, and his mighty father least of all; but nobody else knew how much of what he did was done on grit. . . .

Possibly a half-hour passed before he tried to rise. He was unable to. So he pitched forward and began to crawl, following Joe's path. It was about as easy to crawl, he decided, as to walk; he had heavy garments on and big mittens. After a bit he rather liked it, for he began to fancy himself as some dim-witted animal far back in the past, on the trail of Joe and determined to eat him. He was almost home and still crawling when he heard Athene's amazed voice.

"What on earth are you doing?"

Vridar looked up, and saw her there in the path Joe had made. He uttered a growl and shook his shoulders up and down. Then he went right on, and clawing a path around her in the deep snow went on up Joe's path, never once looking back at his wife. A hundred yards from the house he rose to his feet, tired of the acting and the folly, and after kicking his overshoes off on the porch went staggering in. He was not surprised to see Joe sitting at the kitchen table, with a quart of oatmeal before him and a mound of sour dough cakes six inches high.

IX

That was not the only time that Vridar came close to death with his father. For rafters for the house he intended to build, and for partitions, he wanted dry lodge poles, four to six inches in diameter. The easiest place to get such timber, for him, was southeast just across the Wyoming line, at a place called Alpine. He asked Joe if they could raft them down and Joe said he thought they could, though as a river-man years ago Joe had never brought a raft past Calamity Point. Joe thought it might be a little difficult there.

Loading Vridar's old Hupmobile with tools, wire, a lot of rope, grubbox, and bedding, Vridar climbed in, with his father and wife, and set off—over the Antelope Hills, through Conant Valley, through Swan Valley, past the Palisades, where Rhode had gone fishing. . . . At Calamity Point he drew off the road and stopped.

He got out and went to the edge of the precipice to look down. It was called Calamity Point because a man—or heaven alone knew how many men—had died there in the terrible maelstroms that boiled between the stone walls. It looked to Vridar like a fearsome spot. He asked his father to come look, and Joe came, grumbling, and Athene, and then the three of them stood on the brink looking down.

It looked tough for a raft, Vridar said. It would be tough if a man got thrown off, for only a seal could swim in that water.

"Just don't get throwed off," Joe said.

"See the way it sucks the water back under over there. What if it sucked our raft back under? The stone ceiling doesn't look two feet above the water."

They wouldn't get sucked under, Joe said.

The river here came plunging straight against a sheer wall of stone and recoiled in immense boiling downsucking maelstroms that poured round and round in their funnels. The released water swung to the right at a right-angle turn, and then to the left. Vridar was not at all sure that they could make the raft hug the safe side, the side where they stood. It seemed to him, looking down from a hundred feet above the water, that the whole river at this spot was plunged into powerful whirling currents that poured over against and under the south wall. It seemed to him that almost any raft would be torn to pieces in such waters.

He looked at his father as both sons had always looked at him. "If you say we can do it, I guess we can do it. What do you say?" he asked Athene.

Athene had nothing to say. Her way of life had always been urban. She admired Joe and his son as resourceful mountain- and river-men and had only a vague sense of the dangers in what they did. She had gone elk-hunting with them and had thought little of it when Vridar handed his rifle to her and then went bounding and leaping down a steep mountain covered with slide rock, where if he had once missed his nimble footing he would surely have broken bones and might easily have knocked his brains out.

This river before him, Vridar recalled while looking down, was *the* dangerous river, the South Fork of the Snake, down which some early explorers had tried to go in boats. On this fork, and below the junction, on the main stream, a number of them had lost their lives. Between the most remote source, to hell and gone up in Wyoming, against Yellowstone Park, and the junction of the two forks, this spot before him was one of the two or three most dangerous. Across the line was another bad spot, where the water rushed through a gorge as if hell had kicked it in its end.

They went on up to Alpine, cut their dry poles, hired a local farmer to snake them to the river, and built their raft. They had a hundred poles twenty-five feet long. Joe said they would build it in two sections, for in one it would sink too deep and might get lodged on a gravel bar. Now and then while laboring with poles and wire Vridar would glance at Athene, sitting on the bank, watching them. She always had the same expression on her face when she watched her man toil—of wonder about him; of matronly amusement tinged with concern; and of admiration—the kind she had had for Bones Jagger. The pale goaded creature she had known in Chicago was not this man before her. That's what her look said. The teacher in Manhattan who got drunk every weekend, and burst into sweating in the classroom, was not this man. This man was ten or fifteen pounds heavier, and getting to be as tough as nails. He hadn't had a drink since he was in Missoula, with McGivern and Hellyer, both of whom together hadn't the strength of a small mountain boy.

Sitting around the campfire after supper, he had told her about Joe as a river-man during those years when he ran great rafts of lumber from his own mill, or other mills, down the South Fork to valley towns. Charley Bridwell was usually the man on the rear sweep. At the foot of the Antelope Hills, to divert water into a canal a low dam of stones had been flung across the river; and over this dam the great river poured in an arc and down. The drop to the waters below was about twelve feet. Joe and his assistant took the rafts over it, and twice Prudence and her children had watched from the bank. "It was quite a sight," Vridar told Athene, while Joe listened but pretended not to listen. "We looked upstream and there they came. Dad was maneuvering the front sweep to put the raft across where the water was deepest. Both men had a stout rope with one end tied to the raft. As they drew close to the plunge they picked up their ropes, for the ropes were the only thing between them and death."

Vridar paused to roll and light a cigarette.

"The most spectacular part was when the raft went out over the break. The front end of the raft seemed to drop or to plunge—I could never tell which—and then the whole raft disappeared and the two men with it. We knew they were under the water holding their breath and clinging to their ropes. We knew they'd come up but we never knew where. It seems to me now that it was at least a hundred yards down the river and that they were under a long time but I suppose they were under less than a minute." He looked at his father. "How long was it?"

"Long as we could hold our breath."

Athene was looking at Joe the way she had looked at Bones Jagger. She said to Vridar, "You mean they held to the ropes."

"If they hadn't they might have got their brains knocked out."

For the sweeps of their Alpine raft they used two twenty-five foot poles and spiked to the larger end of each a piece of plank. At each end of the raft the pole was bound with wire and rope across a fulcrum. To handle the sweep a man took the small end of the pole and walked back and forth across the raft, with the piece of plank serving as an oar blade in the water. Athene would drive the car. Vridar told her to go straight home but she said no, she would watch them at every vantage point along the way. He could tell that she was worried.

He was worried, too, and all the more when Joe asked him to take the front sweep. "Oh no," Vridar said. "You're the expert."

"You won't never learn no younger," Joe said.

"But you'll handle the front sweep past the Point?"

"You take it all the way home."

Vridar looked at his father, thinking, Fifty miles down this wild river, and I've never handled a sweep in my life! Down a river that most of the distance ran in its own deep gorge, often between sheer stone walls several hundred feet high. Past Calamity Point, where, he had heard, no man but a fool had ever tried to take a raft; and under a bridge set on piers only thirty or forty feet apart; and around right-angle bends, where the waters turned white in plunging over immense stones that had fallen from the ledges. Joe himself had never taken a raft past the Point, yet now expected his son to.

Vridar turned to Athene and blew a kiss. "Don't worry," he said.

Athene came over and walked out to him on the raft. She put her arms round him and kissed him and held him tight, with her gorgeous hair under his chin. A man knew what it meant when a woman did that. Vridar was embarrassed, though, for no woman was saying goodbye to his father, and his father looked hurt. Vridar kissed her and sent her away.

The river was broad and lazy here: after its wild plunge through Wyoming mountains, it relaxed through Long Valley. They shoved the raft off. The sun was just coming up. It would take them till dark, Joe had said. It would be at least twelve hours of hard labor, but Vridar had his pockets full of cheese, his belly full of beans;

and there was lunch wired to a pole. He waved goodbye to his wife, standing on the bank, but Joe paid no attention to her. No woman had ever kissed Joe goodbye.

They had not gone far when, looking ahead, Vridar saw that the river's waters separated into three channels. He turned to his father. "Which?" he said.

Joe studied them a few moments. The middle one, he said.

Vridar walked back and forth with the sweep, pushing it against the water in one direction, raising it above the water in the other. The raft was three poles deep and seventeen poles wide, in two sections, coupled together with wire. He knew that if they went too sharply round a bend the wire would break and the sections would separate, leaving him on one and Joe on the other. He knew that if he took the wrong channel, where the river ran in several, he would strand the raft on a shallow bottom. But most of his worries were fixed on the point.

At the lower end of the valley, where the mountains came in, the road was close by the river. He saw Athene, parked and waiting. As soon as they left the valley, the river was swifter and would be dangerous until they came to Swan Valley, where it would again be broad and lazy for eight or ten miles.

When Vridar saw that they were about to leave Long Valley, he looked the raft over to see if everything was all right. He thought it would be well to take his heavy workshoes off and lash them to a pole, for with them on his feet he might drown in swift water; but if he took them off, what would Joe think? He kept them on. He did take all the cheese from his pockets and put it inside his coat, which lay across the fulcrum. He did tie an end of a rope to a pole. Joe saw him tying the rope and he knew what it meant, but he did not tie one for himself. Vridar thought, Damn it, if he wants to drown let him drown!

A mile or so after they had left the valley, they saw Athene on a high bank. She was waving to them. Vridar waved. Joe looked at her but he did not wave: to show affection or even friendliness was for him a third unpardonable sin. A half-mile farther down she was again on the brink; and then again. Vridar knew she was worried.

"How far to the Point?" he asked.

Joe studied the mountain walls on both sides. As a young man he had hunted elk all over this country. It was not much farther, he said; and after a few moments, "There it is."

Vridar looked down the river at a great wall of stone. He thought it about a mile distant. The river was running faster here, but it was still too muddy with the spring floods for Vridar to see its bottom. He was telling himself to keep the raft as far to the right as possible, without hitting the right bank. He knew that he was using his sweep too much: he would imagine that he was too far out, and sweep a few strokes, and then imagine that he was too far in. He was annoyed by his nervousness.

Then, suddenly, there it was, straight ahead of him. He glanced up once and saw Athene on the brink, looking down. He then fixed his gaze on the horribly con-vulsed waters, but repeatedly glanced round him, to take in his whole position; and on dipping his sweep discovered to his amazement that it was tossed up and down like a cork, touching the water and then missing it, for the whole raft now was being tossed from crest to crest, as they went plunging over the huge boulders deep down in the river. He saw next that the downsucking power of the whirlpools was drawing him to the left, and with all his might he strove, but in vain, to sink a sweep and pull with it. Next he saw, with his hair rising, what he had not known was there, and what Joe had never known was there: the river waters went boiling back under the stone wall for what seemed to be a considerable distance; and between the churning waters and the stone ceiling above, at least as far back as he could see, there was a space of not more than two feet! My God, had Joe seen in! If the raft were sucked back or driven back under that overhanging stone, back into that black vault, out of which the waters came roaring at both ends, they would be stripped off as the raft went under; or if they remained on the raft they would be crushed. All this he saw and understood in a fraction of a second. They would be sucked down and under and churned round and round, until they, and poles broken like toothpicks, and the whole mess of them and their raft was vomited forth. He understood it all in an instant—in a moment when he hated his father for not having examined this spot, and for having put him on the front sweep, a greenhorn in the middle of a disaster! In that one instant these thoughts raced horrifyingly through his senses, while, desperate, with gooseflesh over his whole back, he was trying not to be pitched off the raft, and at the same time was striving to get the sweep in firm water. But there was no firm water, he could not put it down: they were being churned with such violence, the raft was being tossed with such fury from the funnel-crest of a maelstrom to the valley of a downsucking void, and they and the whole thing were being spun round and round with such infernal speed, that it was all he could do to keep his wits, as white waters poured boiling across the frail craft, as deep as his knees, sweeping away his jacket and food. In one instant he saw Joe's lips move and knew that he was shouting, but no voice could be heard in this inferno. Vridar roared, "Shout, you stubborn jackass, and keep your heavy shoes on!" Then in another flash he saw Joe's spume-drenched face and knew that his sanguine indifference to this river's power had been shaken. Joe was alarmed. Joe was now clinging helpless to his sweep, that was as useless as a toothpick would have been between his teeth. "Keep your God damned shoes on!" Vridar shrieked at him, knowing that he could not hear. In fact, in this hideous roaring in water and stone he could not hear his own words. But still he fought with all the strength he had, and still he sought a way to save them, his mind clear and speeding. . . .

In these few seconds they had been moving closer to the wall and the awful hellhole under it, as their raft spun and turned, dipped down, half-stood on end, like a terrified thing trying to get out of there. Vridar heard a sound like that of a gun and in a flash saw a pole rear as if thrown, and then snap in two; saw in the drenched halfblind world that a part of it had fallen at his feet, and straddled it, clasping it with his ankles, as a thought opened like a light—he let go of his sweep, seized the five feet of broken pole and jammed one end against the fulcrum, as in the same instant he came down hard with the other end against the stone wall—knowing that a part of the raft had gone back under and that his father was standing at one corner, with barely enough of the raft left to cling to; knowing that it was death for both of them if that piece of pole broke. . . .

But it held. The front end of the raft shuddered and was transfixed; again buckled in the middle, and more poles were shattered to splinters; and then sank as a vast surge of water came in a torrent of power from under the ledge, driving the raft back and out and then half-spinning it—driving it with one blow into the only current that was flowing away from the ledge. Almost before Vridar knew it they were past the Point and bobbing up and down on breakers. . . .

He was drenched, white, exhausted, and furious. He wanted to clutch his safety rope and sprawl on his back and breathe hard, but he had work to do. He pulled the end of his sweep down and tied it, to hold the blade above the water; and on hands and knees he moved back and forth over the raft, drawing poles into place where he could and repairing broken wires. It was a sorry-looking raft now; it had been torn almost to pieces. Perhaps they would have to anchor somewhere and rebuild it.

Joe had also dropped to his knees and was laboring. Together they worked, father and son, combining their strength to force poles into place. Now and then they scanned the river ahead. At last they rose to their feet. Not once did their gaze meet, not a word was said. Not a word was ever said by either of them about this harrowing experience, for in the mountain- and river-man code you did not talk about such things.

Three times on down the river they almost lost their raft and once again Vridar thought they would lose their lives. Around a bend that in half a mile completed three-fourths of a circle, the river in the whole distance breaking in fantastic violence over immense stones spilled from the ledges above, their raft caught on a huge boulder, like the emerging back of a river monster, and was spun round and round until it began to disintegrate. The two men fought desperately to get it off. The moment they got it loose from the stone, the raft began to break apart and they both drove their sweeps hard, trying to get closer to the shore. Tying one end of a hundred-foot rope to the raft, Vridar seized the other end and plunged into the river, swimming until his feet struck bottom and then wading frantically toward the bank. Around the roots of a huge cottonwood tree that had been beached he got the rope looped twice before it tightened. If the rope would hold. . . .

It held. The raft was spun and swung in toward the bank. All their poles but about a dozen were saved.

X

There came another invitation to teach in the Montana college, and Vridar eagerly accepted it because he was almost out of funds. He did not foresee that his return to the school would lead to one of the most humiliating experiences of his life.

He and Athene had found a tiny apartment and were unpacking their bags when the smiling malicious face of Danny McGivern appeared in the doorway. Would they come to dinner this evening?

"Look, Danny, we just got here. We have to settle down."

"Don't," said Danny. "That's one of the worst human habits. At eight o'clock, then, but come early for drinks."

All the sense Vridar had told him not to go but he went. When they arrived at seven-thirty Danny was drunk, and full of spite and the unholy old devil. Before Vridar had time to sip his first drink, Danny was standing before him, saying: "You're a fool to trust me. I'll get a knife into you some day."

"You'll do what?" asked Vridar, looking up.

"Do you know the Irish? They're meaner than a wolverine with his tail in a sausage grinder. In the College they think I'm an angel. I'd like to knife the whole outfit. . . ."

Vridar was feeling anger. What a fool he had been to come!

"I could almost predict what I'm going to do to you."

"What?"

"I mean I'll destroy you here."

"Look, Danny, I guess we'd better go."

"Oh no you don't. You're having dinner with us. I'm warning you because I love you." Slopping his drink Danny moved in and sank to the couch by Vridar. He put a hand on Vridar's shoulder. "Mind if I put a hand there?"

"Danny really likes you," Gen said.

"I'm beginning to understand that."

"Don't try to be ironic," Danny said. "Irony is for priests." With his hand on the shoulder Danny was looking into Vridar's eyes, his own full of hurt and loneliness. He said he had to tell someone these things. He was telling Vridar because he was a writer and would understand. "Will you listen?"

"Do I have a choice?"

"I wish you wouldn't try to be clever. It doesn't become you." Danny's fingers on Vridar's shoulder pinched hard. "Vridar, will you flog me?"

"With a good hame-strap. You have one?"

Danny's fingers pinched again. "You should," he said. "You should knock me down and kick me until all my bones are soft. For I'm a sneaking rat, Vridar. I'm the most sneaking son of a bitch you ever looked at. Shall I tell you how I mean?"

Vridar was looking into the man's eyes and wondering about the things he saw there.

Danny said, his fingers pinching, "I'd like to kill you before you leave tonight."

Feeling disgust, Vridar stood up and moved away.

Still grinning his tortured lost grin, Danny said, "That was a mistake, Hunter—to cast me off like that. I was struggling against the Devil in your favor and you let the Devil in. Now I'll tell you something else." Danny staggered to the kitchen, filled his glass with straight whisky, and returned.

"Once upon a time," he said. "Did you ever begin a story Once upon a time? Once upon a time I became infatuated with one of my students. I took her out to the country. I kissed her and held the kiss as we sank slowly to the earth. Do you like the simple unadorned monotonous Gertrude Stein way of writing? I mounted her. The woman was wide open to me and I couldn't do it. A studhorse like you wouldn't understand that. If your wife and I were to leave this room, you'd rush right over to my wife."

"In God's name!" Vridar cried. "Isn't there something else you can talk about?"

"What else is there? That's the meaning of the Adam and Eve story. Adam couldn't and God booted him out. Now as to your downfall here and how it will come about. . . ."

Athene thought Danny was insane. Vridar said he was another babilan whose over-submissive traits were driving him to thoughts of murder.

A few days later Ernest Hellyer came to Vridar, rolling his bulging blue eyes. He said with a snort and a chortle that Danny had disappeared. Now and then, he said, Danny got completely fed up with the academic life and vanished into some whorehouse hotel. Unless he was back by next Monday, he would lose his job, for even the Catholic president had about enough of him. Ernest said Vridar was the only person on earth who could persuade Danny to return to his job.

"I?" said Vridar. "You must be crazy."

Danny loved Vridar, Ernest said. That was why he wanted to kill him. Danny so loathed himself that he wanted to kill anybody who liked him. But it was on the shoulder of the one he wanted to kill that he would weep hardest.

"Yes, I know you're right. How do I find him?"

That, Ernest said, was a problem for Sherlock Holmes. Find him he must, because the campus needed Danny a hundred times more than it needed another lecture by Will Durant. Danny was its Flammonde. He would be in a city hotel, a jug of whisky between his knees, and a fascinated whore listening to his ranting.

Vridar went with Athene to the city and from one hotel desk to another looking at the registers, studying the handwriting and asking questions. Ernest said Danny would not register under his own name but would betray himself somehow in the name he used. Ernest had given Vridar a list of Danny's and Gen's family names. Or he might betray himself with some obscenity.

In a wretched hotel with the reception desk in a dark hallway on an upper floor, Vridar was studying the register when he grunted. "Look," he said to Athene. The name was Baldwin Cunter. They looked wonderingly at one another. "That must be Danny," Vridar said.

It was, in room 436. At the door Vridar paused and listened. He could hear two voices. He knocked, and the voices fell silent. No one came to the door. He knocked again. Then slowly the door was opened about an inch and one of Danny's malicious brown eyes looked out. Danny staggered back, cursing.

"You son of a bitch," he roared, "get out of here! You seduce my wife and then you come to tell me about it!"

Vridar entered, drawing Athene in behind him, and closed the door.

"Just what do you want?" Danny asked. He looked terribly drunk.

"A drink. An introduction to your girl friend."

"That's Bobby and she's a whore in your world, but she's worth a whole heavenful of frauds like you. Now get out."

Vridar had been looking around him. He saw several empty whisky bottles, and a quart, nearly full. The girl was looking at him with frightened whimpering hate.

"We want you to come back," Vridar said.

"To hell with all of you," Danny said, falling to a chair. "Bobby, pour me a drink." Bobby poured a glass full of whisky and Danny took it and gulped, spilling whisky over his unshaven chin and down his filthy shirt. "I try to get away from you God-damned hypocrites and the morgue you call a college and you come sneaking after me, you studhorse. He's just a studhorse, Bobby. He spends most of his time trying to seduce the wives of his friends and thinks he's respectable compared to you. He's just a piece of bogus, nickel-plated and badly tarnished over his moral surfaces—a medicine man of culture with books standing round him like rows of totems. Bobby here's as genuine as a keg of nails but you're a straw-filled mattress with a silk cover. And don't think I'm going to sit here long looking at the tinsel of your mug. . . ."

Vridar was smiling. "You're in good form today. Talk it out of you and then we'll go."

Danny was looking at Vridar, at Athene, back and forth, his eyes almost yellow with loathing. "This redhead's not so bad, Bobby. It's the thing she married." Bobby also was looking back and forth, her thin pallid face twitching, her eyes expressing fear and contempt. "What a pile of sham you are," said Danny. "Bobby, he's like a dead pimp in a cheap coffin. If one honest generous impulse could penetrate his cold hedonistic heart he'd fall to pieces like a pile of potato chips." Danny emptied his glass and handed it to Bobby. Without taking her gaze off Vridar's face, she filled it.

"If you go now," said Danny, glaring at Vridar, "you have a chance to save your sawdust. Otherwise I'll call one of my friends and he'll flush you down the toilet."

"Has he slept any?" Vridar asked Bobby.

"Don't you speak to me!" she cried, her voice shrill.

"That's right, Bobby. He's one of these sham sophisticates who has sucked around a medicine man named Freud. You know more about life in one night than he has learned, yet he thinks of himself as a writer. He doesn't know what a big-breasted wench life is. He has never seen its huge thighs and belly and its hungry mouth."

Staring at Vridar he gulped whisky. "Your novels, Hunter, will never be any good until you take off the brocade and lace. You haven't learned that life has dirt in its ears and all the beauty of earth in the lines of its face and all the deep odors in the smell of its genital area. Life is a wind breathing, a tide moving, a sound of deep waters. Men like you bind up a few sophistries and call them books; build a wall around them and call it a library. You get a bunch of fornicating casuists into a building and call it a university. And I get so sick of your well-bred quibbles and your cultured lispings that I run away to hear again the clean dredging beat of the life-heart. Then here you come with your dismal longnosed Freudian face—"

"Get out!" Bobby cried at Vridar.

Vridar had been looking around to see if there was more whisky than the part of a bottle that Bobby held. He supposed he would have to let Danny drink until he was in a stupor and then take him home and he was wondering if there was enough whisky here. Like any good Irishman, Danny could drink an awful lot of it.

The phonies in colleges, Danny was saying, his eyes moving in and out of focus, didn't accept a whore as a human being. Bobby's feelings ran as deep as wombs and womanhood, but Vridar's were limp wet things that stammered and raised eyebrows. Lord God, how he despised the paralysis of good breeding! "When Bobby farts she doesn't say I beg your pawdon, but you're a hypocrite trying to walk in the right places. Now get out of here."

"We want you to go with us, Danny. You've missed your classes for three days—"

"Don't lecture me. Tell Merrick to fire me. That pedant is stiff in the wrong places." Danny had to smile a little at that one. "He wants to save Danny McGivern for the middle class. He wants to be able to say, There he was, sinking right down into the proletariat—"

"Danny, you better come along now."

Bobby leapt to her feet, hands clenched, moist lips curling. "Get out!"

"Come on, Danny, or I'll carry you." Vridar picked the man up, with Danny's legs across his right arm, and was astonished a moment later to see the flabby Irish face smiling up at him with heavenly innocence. Vridar almost dropped him. Why, this man wants love! he thought. This man is an orphan. He carried him like a child out into the hallway, down the stairs and to the car; and after he had pushed Danny into the car, he turned and saw Bobby on the sidewalk, staring at him.

"Goodbye, Bobby."

"What will you do with him?"

"Take him back to his job and the middle class. If he doesn't teach, what'll he buy whisky with?" Athene had got into the back of the car with Danny and he had fallen over, face down in her lap. Vridar slipped under the wheel and drove to Danny's home. He put him to bed and called a doctor.

About midnight Vridar was routed out of bed by a telephone call. The voice was Gen's. "Can you come right over?"

"I'm in bed. What's the trouble?"

"I need you bad. Please come."

"The siren," he said to Athene, after hanging up. He began to dress. "You want to go along?"

"I think you better go alone."

He made the mistake of going alone. Gen met him at the door in a light silken robe, a glass in her hand, tear stains on her alcoholic face. In her preposterously coquettish way she tried to dimple and look alluring, and boredom as heavy as lead went down into Vridar. He stepped inside. "You in trouble? You said you were. Is it Danny?"

"He's asleep."

"Asleep?" Vridar was looking for a place to lay his hat, but he now turned to her. She was still trying to be girlish and flirtatious, the big awkward cow!

"You want a drink?"

"Look, God damn it, you got me out of bed. What's the trouble?"

"I told you he's asleep now." Her voice was sharp. That was what astonished him most in this woman: in a flash she could turn from siren to bitch, from bitch to siren. She went to a couch and sank, her big rump spreading. She said, "Sit by me, I want to talk to you."

"If you have no trouble I'm going."

"Please come and sit."

He went over and sat at a little distance from her, and at once she began to move toward him, her eyes looking into his eyes. What under heaven, he asked himself, was so pathetic as a woman striving to be seductive who was no longer attractive? There had been several of the middle-aged creatures in Salt Lake City, who had taken his evening class in literary criticism. Two of them had practically thrown themselves into his arms, saying, "Please take me!"

Gen now clutched one of his hands and looked at it. He had a small hand, she said, and stubby fingers but it was a strong manly hand. He took his hand away. Looking up at his eyes, she asked, "Have you guessed our secret?" Vridar was silent. She moved closer, whispering, "Danny hasn't been my lover for years."

Vridar suppressed a yawn. "For years," he said.

"Ten years. Vridar, why do all men find me attractive?"

He was not astonished or shocked. The McGiverns no longer had power to shock him. He glanced over at his hat.

She was now trying to snuggle up to him. She was saying, "Why don't you look into my eyes? Are you afraid to?"

Was this what the wise guys called nymphomania?—or only pathetic emotional imbecility?

Gen's flimsy robe had fallen away, exposing the upper parts of two sagging breasts. "You afraid to? Are you like Danny?"

He looked into her eyes and was distressed by what he saw there—all the loneliness, the waste, the venom—and the record of years of striving to be an irresistible siren. He felt deep pity. He got up and went over to his hat. Like a huge female tiger she was at his heels. Then she faced him, her eyes wicked, her painted lips breathing at him, "You're afraid of me!" Her mouth was ugly with lipstick and slobber. Her cheeks were daubed as with barn paint, and below the paint the skin had a waxlike whiteness. She opened and closed her eyes with languorous abandon, whispering, "Kiss me!" He backed away. With violence in her movements, she followed him. She followed him to a wall by the front door and then moved in close, thrusting her breasts against him, and her thighs. Breathing up at him she hissed, "God damn you, you love me!"

"I'm going now," he said.

With a hideous cry she ran to the couch and sank. She seized a cigarette and with trembling hands struck one match after another, her lidded eyes watching him. He had not picked up his hat and wondered whether if he moved toward it she would scream. He felt that something dreadful was about to happen. When at last he moved toward his hat, she did scream, and with energy and violence that amazed him. Then she was shouting words. She was calling to her husband. She was telling Danny that Vridar had tried to rape her. With the incredible treachery of it ringing in his ears, Vridar got his hat and bolted, and went rapidly along the dark empty street, feeling utterly stupid. Without waking Athene he crawled into bed.

The next morning Danny walked in. He did not bother to knock but just walked in and sinking to a chair said to Athene, "A cup for me, too." Then he turned to

726

Vridar and smiled. "I knew it would happen," he said. "It always does. None of the men can resist her but you're the only fool who ever tried to rape her. You—"

"Just a minute, McGivern!"

"Oh, don't try to explain it. It always happens, I tell you. Sugar, Athene, if you please. When a man comes to my home—"

Trembling with rage, Vridar had risen. His hands clenched, he walked over to Danny, and Danny looked up, smiling. Vridar said, "Don't tell me I tried to rape your wife or I'll knock your brains out!"

"You wouldn't. You would no more strike me than you would strike your own wife. What is your brother's name?—the one with the bad eye or bad foot or whatever he has? The one you took care of so devotedly as a child. Marion? I'm another Marion for you. The world is full of Marions for you and every God damned one of them hates you. For they don't want to be taken care of. They want to be able to take care of themselves. And because we all hate you, we'll destroy you. Now sit down."

Vridar backed off and sank to a chair.

Danny turned to Athene, supplicating her with both hands. He said she could see how it was: all men fell for Gen, so why should he blame his friend Vridar? He didn't, he said, making a gesture of infinite tolerance. His tone said that denials would be foolish, that denials would weary him. She was the siren who haunted Ulysses. . . . Then with charming self-contempt that was not self-contempt at all he said, "Look at me, I've been her slave for twenty years."

Vridar and Athene were both looking at Danny. Vridar said, "You poor damned clown. Your wife isn't attractive to any man and you know it."

If Danny had been propelled from behind, he could not have come up from his chair any faster. He came up with his arms flailing and rushing over to Vridar struck at him in a wild childish tantrum, his voice shrieking, "How dare you say that? How dare you?"

Vridar folded the man in his arms and held him till he was quiet. Then he forced him back to a chair and looked into Danny's eyes, thinking, Yes, there he is, the bitter hurt lonely unloved child! "Poor Danny," he said, running a hand through Danny's mop of Irish hair. "I'd better take you home again." Meekly Danny went along and at the door Vridar left him, neither of them having said a word.

A few days later the whole campus was agog with the story: while Danny Mc-Givern was drunk in a hotel, Vridar Hunter, a hyprocrite who had pretended to be his friend, had tried to seduce his wife. The mother of Don Mitchens, the little old woman called The Duchess, gave wings to the story and soon it filled the town. People on the campus who had spoken to Vridar now snubbed him.

"That stinking Judas," he said. He was talking to the Hellyers. "He said he'd destroy me here and he has."

In her shrill voice Nora Nolana said, "I don't see it that way. Nobody can destroy you anywhere. This campus is conferring on you the only honor and distinction it has power to confer."

"Just what do you mean?"

"Envy." She looked at Ernest and he nodded. "If you can afford to be a scapegoat—if you are willing to accept fellowship with Satan, then do nothing about this. It's a dirty story, but taking it away from them would be like taking Will Rogers and Elbert Hubbard away from the middle class. For weeks they'll talk about you. Think how much that will mean to them."

That was all true, Ernest said. "After that they will sssssink back into the morgue. All corpses and all uhuhuhlike."

"Accept the distinction," Nora Nolana said.

Vridar had been studying the Hellyer faces. He knew that these two persons could be venomous in their malice. They could kill. "But what you think so good for me you'd not accept for yourselves."

"We're not novelists," Nora Nolana said. "These people have to have scandals or go mad. If you prove the story false they'll hate you. Weren't you telling us the other evening that men invented a God so perfect that, discovering they couldn't love him, they had to invent Satan, whom they could love. You were telling us that virtues have never been lovable, only admirable; vices never admirable, only lovable."

"But I have to make a living. Merrick will never ask me back again, or recommend me to any other school."

"We're both glad of it. You've been in danger of again sinking into the academic rut. This, Vridar, might be the most priceless thing that will ever happen to you. . . ."

He and Athene were again journeying east past the ugliness of Anaconda; then south into Idaho and up the South Fork. Not long after they arrived home, a letter came from Elmer T. Merrick, chairman of the department of English at the College. It was brief and to the point. It said that because of lack of funds there would be no position there for Vridar in the autumn quarter.

He tossed the letter to Athene and went outside.

XI

He did not know it now, not yet—he hardly dared think of it yet—but Nora Nolana was right: Vridar Hunter who had spent four hard years in postgraduate work to prepare himself for it was now through with the academic world. He turned furiously to his writing and to his labor outside. During his four years at the home of his parents, he built for them two large chicken houses, two granaries, two barns, a garage, a millshed, a woodshed, and a modern three-bedroom house. To provide water for the house, he built a dam and a waterwheel and installed a hydraulic ram, that forced the water a horizontal distance of five hundred feet, and a vertical distance of eighty feet. For the first time in her life his mother not only had running water in her house, but hot water in a tank and a modern bathrooom. While laboring he wrote and rewrote scenes for books he had in mind, or in such ways as were open to him here tried to add to his education. He had undertaken to memorize an unabridged dictionary, but by the time he came to L he perceived that he was being stupid and abandoned the project. He despaired of his ignorance in the pronunciation of names. He could never decide whether Mohave or Mysore was pronounced in two or in three syllables; he would forget wether the c in Seleucia was hard or soft; whether the second syllable in Tangier was pronounced jeer or jer. He had not been able to break himself of pronouncing Tubingen on the second instead of on the first syllable, and to the day of his death he would pronounce Wellesley with three. He had fairly mastered Giotto, Malesherbes, Puccini, Debussy, Avicenna, and Turgenev; but he could never remember how to pronounce Hammurabi, Torquemada, Savonarola, Zoroaster, and Velasquez.

He was also trying to see more clearly his relationship with Athene. He had known that she was not happy here, though she had never complained; she had taught his younger son, had read many books, had written a novel, and had tried to adapt herself to a life that she found uncouth and strange. She liked the mountains and the river, and all the seasons here, but this was not her kind of life. Vridar knew that she was waiting patiently for him to make another move.

What move, he asked himself, could he make? His royalties had averaged only six hundred dollars per book. Worse than that, he had decided to speak, through a protagonist, in unequivocal terms against Communism, and well knew that this might mean the end of him as a published author. He had sensed in New York and in his reading since leaving there that most, possibly all, the book judges in high places were Communists or sympathetic to the Communist cause. Their fanatical devotion to Roosevelt was not all for Roosevelt.

He had talked to Athene about the matter, and she had asked why he had to write, least of all to publish, a book that would turn the book-reviewers against him. He had replied, "Because I can't forget Roger Bacon in the dungeon and Bruno at the stake. If I'm not worthy of the freedom the lives of such men bought for me, then I'd better take my place with all the whores who sell themselves for a price."

One day Athene staggered him with a statement. "I'm pregnant," she said.

For perhaps a full minute he could only look at her. Then he said caustically, "By a serpent, I suppose. Are you aware that the moon can cause lunacy, else why call them lunar months? Did you know that the tolling of bells at a funeral drives evil spirits away?—or that charivari is all we have left of the former custom that allowed the groom's friends to share the bride? Did you—"

"Oh, let's not try to be learned about it."

"You're sure you're pregnant?"

"I'm sure." She had been vomiting, she said. She had all the symptoms.

He took her to a valley doctor. After the examination the doctor looked at them, back and forth, before asking, "Do you expect to have children?"

Vridar said, "Not on six hundred a year."

"Your wife isn't pregnant."

"Isn't pregnant?" cried Vridar. "Isn't—" He felt frightfully silly. Blood dyed Athene's throat and face. Vridar seized her hand, saying, "We'd better get out of here." On the way home he said, "There's no hope for me. I drove my first wife to her death, my second to hysterical pregnancy."

"Let's not talk about it." Her voice was sharp.

"You halfwit, we have to talk about it. When a woman gets hysterically pregnant, she's in trouble. I've never known that you want a child that bad."

"Any woman wants a child."

"But that a woman as intelligent as you can actually make her belly swell when there's nothing in it! That she can vomit every morning when she's not sick! That she can suspend her menses!"

Athene flew into a fury and he said no more until they came to Poplar. Then: "There's somebody here I must see a moment." He did not tell her that as a lad he had found and memorized Poe's lyric, Helen, thy beauty is to me. . . . He did not tell her that it was Helen, the golden-haired lass with whom he had skated on the canal. He had heard that Helen was back in her old home with her mother and he was curious to see what she looked like.

He passed first the old schoolhouse, on his right; next, the old Stauffer place, which long ago had been an inn for tired travelers; and then came to the big stone house where Helen had lived. He would be only a moment, he said. As he approached the house, he looked at it curiously, because for him in childhood it had been a great mansion. He recalled Helen's birthday party there, and his insane fight afterward with Alvin because of what Alvin had said about Marion's eyes. Helen had married when only fifteen. She had married a railroad man, her mother had said: Vridar had learned later, with shock, that the railroad man had been only an illiterate section-hand. Was he dead now or had he left her?

He knocked softly on the door. It was opened by a little old man with screwed-up eyes. Vridar entered the parlor—how well he remembered it!—and saw on the far side a woman lying in a bed. He went over and saw that it was Helen's mother. She seemed to have changed hardly at all.

"I'm Vridar Hunter," he said.

At once she came up to an elbow. "Helen!" she cried. "Helen, it's Veedah!" In spite of fifty years in the United States, she still had a Danish accent.

Vridar looked round him, wondering where Helen was. He again saw the little old man with the screwed-up eyes and wizened face—a tiny creature in overalls and a man's ragged shirt. The man seemed to be losing his hair, to have lost most of his teeth. Vridar looked at him, then at Helen's mother, and said, "Where is Helen?"

O God! The pain of it was so sudden, the shock of it so terrible, that he could only stand like a man of stone, numbed all over. So this was Helen! God, I hate you now! That you could let Neloa go into the dark, doubting my love—that you could let this radiant golden-haired child become such a shriveled thing as this, when still only thirty-seven! Was it for this that I read your holy book five times as a child? Was it for this—

"Helen?" he said, and his voice sounded strange to him.

"Yes!" said the little old thing. It had come up, it was looking up at his face. Yes, it had lost part of its hair and the other part was turning white. Yes, it had lost nearly all its front teeth. It was less than five feet tall now, it would surely not weigh more than eighty pounds; but it was smiling up at him, the eyes searching his face. The eyes seemed pitiably small in their frame of wrinkles, compared to the eyes he remembered. Were these little old bloodless lips the lips he had wanted to kiss? Were these the cheeks that had had such bloom after skating in the winter air? Was this—

"You're famous now," a little old voice said.

"Not so very," he said, trying to choke down the grief. Was she remembering those hours of magic on the canal?

"You write books," she said, as she might have said, You have gone to heaven!

"Yes, I write books," he said, staring, doubting, as the pain went into him deeper and deeper. How horribly the lips fell in when she spoke!

"I'd like to read your books," she said.

"You're in one of them," he said, fighting to keep the hot emotion down, and the tears. "Remember how we used to skate on the canal?" She nodded. "How you mocked me because I was so shy?" She nodded. "And your birthday party?"

She nodded and said, "You licked Alvin because of me." She giggled, and put a small wrinkled hand to her fallen-in mouth. "It was him made you jealous."

Perceiving that she was stupid as well as hideous—that in their childhood relationship that had been pure heaven for him there had been no heaven for her—he could no longer stand the pain of it. He told himself it was not her illiterate speech; it was not her look of a little old witch out of a dry forest—it was his realization that she was stupid and had always been stupid, this girl whom he had idealized. He turned to say goodbye to her mother. He told Helen he would send her a book, knowing that she probably had never read a book in her life. Then he went to the door, his senses darkened, and the moment he was outside the tears burst.

He got into the car, trying to hide from Athene his tears, and the pain that was all through him. He glanced north to the alfalfa field where he and Marion had lived in a shack, with mice; and down at the canal, where he had skated with her. Then he drove home, without once speaking.

A year ago he had seen Hankie, the boy with whom he had played and fought; the lad who had caught magpies and cut their tongues out and spread-eagled squirrels and cut open their chests to watch their hearts beat; Hankie, who had initiated him into the sexual mysteries; Hankie, who in so many ways had seemed to Vridar to be far above him in intelligence and daring. Helen was only about thirty-seven now. Hankie when Vridar saw him was only forty or forty-one, but he looked old, shockingly old; and small and sick. The lids had fallen away from both eyes and were inflamed and moist with pus. He was several inches shorter than Vridar and walked with an old-man stoop. He had stared at Vridar, his eyes full of a moron's questions. Was he writing another book? Yes. It had taken Hankie half a minute to think of another question: Was he married again? Yes. Did his books make a lot of money? No. . . .

Vridar had seen a number of his childhood classmates. Most of them looked like morons and talked like morons: no wonder they had made life such a nightmare for him—for they were only animals, these louts that he had thought were human. One by one to the number of twenty he passed them in review, the men he had seen in the past four years who had been boys with him in school; and one by one the girls. The disillusionment had left him confused and depressed, but no disillusionment had gone into him so deep as this with Helen. None, but that with Neloa.

He had sworn as a child to avenge himself; he had solemnly written down a list of those who had tyrannized over him, whose brains he would knock out when he was grown. For years he had practiced with boxing-gloves, with that one thought in mind; he had spent thousands of hours putting on muscle in gymnasiums; but now when he saw these boys, who now were men, he could feel only pity. Looking into Hankie's stupid diseased eyes, he had recalled Prudence's outraged cry to Hankie's father, "Let's see whose children amount to most!" As a child, after he had begun to write, Vridar had dreamed of going to Nephi and saying, "Some day I'll publish books and your son Hankie won't even be able to understand them."

But there was only pity now.

He went on with his work, thinking about Helen, about Athene. He knew that a woman who could develop hysterical pregnancy was horribly unhappy. What could he do about it? The stupid, who wanted nothing so much as an earth choked with people, would have told him to give her a child—O Lord, to give her ten! He had studied the wives of some of his friends and it had seemed to him that having a child did nothing to solve the problems for American middleclass neurotic women. Having a child was like drink or drugs. He had told Athene that she would never be happy until she had fulfilled her talent, but she appeared to be too fogged-up or indolent ever to fulfill it. She had given indications of wishing to escape into Christian Science or into the platonic lunacies of the Gospel of John. He sometimes wondered if she had a buried wish to escape from him.

Well, he was not easy to live with, he admitted that, while putting on the final coat of paint. No magic had ever been found that would let a man see himself. If those persons who were most decent were to see themselves as they actually were, he thought they would all crawl away and pray to die. Had he been neglecting Athene, while putting up all these structures for his parents? An artist should never marry. He knew that now.

How was he to earn a living? He had decided that he could never write at the popular level of taste and would be a fool to try to. To write for the common people you had to shut your eyes to the realities: his eyes opened wider all the time. What were they to do? he asked Athene, facing her in the little cabin he had built for them. He would be a coward to return to the academic world, even if he could. She had gone to Chicago a year ago to take her doctorate and she could teach; but how could she teach and have babies? "I suppose," he said, "I misjudged you: you want me to build you a home and let you have three or four kids, and how I earn a living is secondary, as long as I earn it. . . ." His words were cruel: they hurt her and he was sorry. But he felt angry and frustrated, and all the more so when remembering that at a time in his life when he was broke and couldn't decently support the two children he had, his wife's subconscious mind developed a hysterical pregnancy. He could hardly argue from that that she was greatly concerned about him.

And then out of the blue there came a messenger from the telegraph office twenty miles distant. He bore a telegram, which said,

THE WORKS PROGRESS ADMINISTRATION IS ESTABLISHING WRITERS PROJECTS IN ALL THE FORTY EIGHT STATES EACH UNDER A STATE DIRECTOR STOP WILL YOU ACCEPT THE POSITION AS DIRECTOR FOR IDAHO STOP CAN OFFER SAL-

ARY OF TWENTY SIX HUNDRED STOP PLEASE WIRE COLLECT
STOP DATA AND LETTER FOLLOW
ASSOCIATE NATIONAL DIRECTOR
ROBERT BINGHAM

He read it twice and handed it to Athene. When she met his eyes, he said, "A project for writers! Have they all gone insane back there? There aren't three writers in Idaho and the other two don't need jobs. And who in hell is Robert Bingham?"

"Associate national director," she said.

"What they should do is invite me back to show them how to save money for the taxpayers. Forty-six words," he said, counting the telegram, "and they could easily have cut out ten. A straight wire, and it might just as well have been a night-letter."

"It's a job," she said. "I think you should take it."

"Can I, with honor?—or are we so desperate that we no longer consider that?"

He decided not to reply at once. He would look into himself. He would face the question whether he was going to give his best to his writing, or to his duty to wife and sons. While he waited and pondered, there came another straight wire, by special messenger (whose fee in each instance was five dollars), which with profuse apologies said that it was impossible to offer a salary of more than twenty-three hundred. Would he accept that?

Vridar handed the telegram to Athene, saying, "I may as well wait. Tomorrow there will be a third wire, still longer, saying that the salary offer is two thousand. I begin to understand that one of the best places to observe a man is in a telegraph office when he is spending someone else's money."

"That's not even two hundred a month," she said.

"Oh well, this is Idaho. In New York the director will get twelve thousand; in California, twenty."

"Are you going to accept?"

He looked at her until she met his eyes. Then he looked into her eyes a long moment, thinking, there can't be much of the artist in you, if an empty purse can make you so oblivious of conscience. He said he would have to give it further thought and he went away to the river to be alone. He could see three advantages in accepting: (1) he would make some sort of living while the job lasted; (2) he would get to know his own State well; and (3), the most important of all, he would discover for himself, by studying the inner workings of Federal and State government, whether any form of Socialism could be successful at this stage in human evolution. This reason had great cogency for him. On the other hand, the artist in him might wither and die while he labored to provide for children and wife. For forty-eight hours he thought about it, he dreamed about it: he felt so frustrated and depressed and defeated that he might have killed himself now, if he had had a large insurance benefit, with the latest premium paid. He thought of his older son's question, "Why don't your books make more money? Why don't people read them?" He thought of the look in Athene's eyes when she said, "Are you going to accept?"

733

and that look became, for him, one of the unforgettable memories when a month later in Boise she said, "Let's have a nice apartment, we have had so little for four years." The rental on the apartment she wanted was exactly half his salary.

He drove to the telegraph office and sent two words collect:

I ACCEPT
VRIDAR HUNTER

XII

Early in November he went with Athene to Pocatello, and there, in the District WPA office, presented himself as the Idaho director of the Federal Writers' Project. A tall cynical drooping man looked him up and down.

"You're what?" he said. Vridar told him again and offered the telegrams. "These don't mean a damn thing to me," the man said. "Look, Bud, I'm the director of this whole damn district and I've been here almost a year and I still don't know a God damn thing about what I'm supposed to do. So how in hell can I tell you what you're supposed to do?"

"The wire says to report to you."

"Hell yes, I saw that. Look, Bud, I've got hundreds of wires. I have whole damn stacks of them. Look," he said, gesturing at the vast litter of his office. "Whole bales of stuff from Washington and I just set around and read it like some people read the funnies. I tell you, you better go to Boise and see the boss."

So Vridar and Athene went to Boise. The Idaho director of WPA was a tall dark handsome man named Roger Wood. Vridar went to Wood's suite of offices in one of the handsomest buildings and gave Wood's secretary his name and his reason for being there. Like the man in Pocatello, she looked him up and down. She was a large sandy-blond woman with a brusque manner. He was to know her well before many months passed.

"We've never heard of this," she said.

"Neither has the district director in Pocatello."

"I'll see what Mr. Wood says."

Roger Wood came out and offered Vridar his hand. He invited Vridar into his office and asked him to take a chair. When they were seated, Wood said, "I've heard of you, of course, but I don't know a thing about this new project. You'll just have to wait around a few days. . . ."

And so Vridar waited around, becoming more impatient and disgusted. While he waited there came from Elmer T. Merrick a long telegram:

CONGRATULATIONS ON YOUR NEW POSITION STOP DONT TAKE IT SERIOUSLY STOP IT IS NOT INTENDED THAT WE SHOULD ACHIEVE ANYTHING BUT ONLY THAT WE SHOULD PUT THE JOBLESS TO WORK SO THEY WILL VOTE FOR ROOSEVELT STOP TAKE IT PHILOSOPHICALLY AND IF THEY SEND YOU A TELEGRAM FROM WASHINGTON A HUNDRED AND FIFTY WORDS LONG SEND THEM ONE THREE HUNDRED

WORDS LONG STOP OR CALL THEM LONG DISTANCE
COLLECT

ELMER T MERRICK
STATE DIRECTOR
FEDERAL WRITERS PROJECT FOR MONTANA

Vridar read the telegram with a feeling of shock. "Why, the God damn stinker!" he said to Athene. "Is he that cynical or am I still the world's most ingenuous man? Am I stupid to imagine that we have some responsibility to the tax payers?"

When Vridar asked how he was to get an office of some sort, he was referred to Archie J. Reese, assistant-director of the division of labor. Reese also looked him up and down. Vridar knew that he would not like this man and that this man would not like him. Reese was a small nervous fellow who acted keyed-up by a sense of destiny. He said he would see what he could do, though the man to see about an office was Johnny Huston, who was in charge of procurement.

"They sent me here," Vridar said.

Two days later he was told he had an office: he discovered it in one of the old ram-shackle buildings, a kind of alcove off a hallway, with one small grimy window and no furniture at all. The room was only about eight feet by fourteen and looked as though it had been used for storage. Vridar sought out the janitor and persuaded him to bring up a few old packing-crates and a small rickety table; and with a gesture at these things he said to Athene, "Behold my office."

He didn't care what kind of office he had, as long as it had space, typewriters, a few chairs and tables. He wanted to get on with his work, for he intended, privately, to be the first of the forty-eight directors to get a book published, or break his neck. For one thing, that was his way. For another thing, he had been stung by the patronizing advice of Reuben Taylor Rhode. He and Athene had gone to Rhode's home for dinner; and after dinner Rhode had brought a hand down over his thin deeply-lined face, in a way he had—he would put the palm on his coarse graying hair and bring it slowly down over his narrow forehead; over his coarse bushy brows and his small restless unhappy dark eyes; over his huge beak of a nose and down to his small chin. Then, after glancing swiftly at Vridar and away, he had said, "I just hate to see you take this job. You writers are not administrators, you know. You just don't know how these things are done. And besides, you should be giving all your time to your work instead of boondoggling for that man in the White House."

Vridar had said, "There'll be no boondoggling on my project."

It was then that Rhode's foxy dark eyes had swept him with incredulity and pity. It was all boondoggling, he said; the whole Socialist mess was nothing but boondoggles and no honest man could do a decent job.

"Then I'll get out," Vridar had said.

"I'm awfully sorry to see you squandering your great talent for that man in the White House. . . ."

Later to Athene Vridar had said, "I'll show him! I'll show all of them, and if that damned puttering Archie J. Reese gets in my way I'll belt him right in his silly nose."

735

The obstacles to his progress multiplied. Wood's sandy-blond secretary called him over. Her name was Jane Essig. She summoned Vridar into her own office and sat behind her big desk and looked at him. Then, carefully choosing her words, speaking with almost comical deliberation, she said:

"Mr. Hunter, no doubt you realize that all these projects are established primarily for one reason—to give jobs to the jobless. That must always be our first thought. To that one thing everything else must be if not incidental at least subordinate. Of course, if we are able to accomplish things, so much the better; but remember that giving jobs to people is the chief reason you are here. Another thing—"

"May I interrupt a moment? It has been explicitly understood between me and the national director of the Federal Writers' Project that my primary objective is results, and that making jobs for people is secondary. He has agreed that making jobs is never to interfere with my work."

Her eyes, he thought, turned cold. They were green intelligent steady eyes and they were looking as deep into him as her powers of insight would let her look. She said, "Are you going to cooperate with us?"

"Miss Essig, I don't know what you mean. I'm going to do the best I can with what I have to work with. I've no sympathy with boondoggling."

With an obvious effort to keep her voice quiet, she said, "Do you charge us in Idaho with boondoggling?"

"I'm not familiar with what you're doing in Idaho, but the charge of boondoggling has been brought against the WPA over most of the nation. On this little project I've been assigned to, I think it is my duty to justify every dollar to the taxpayer."

"You don't sound cooperative," she said, still looking into his eyes. "Now there's another thing: these projects are established primarily for jobless Democrats. If all jobless Democrats are assigned, then of course Republicans and others can be given jobs. I don't know what party you belong to."

"None," he said. "I voted for LaFollette, Al Smith, and Roosevelt, but politically I'm an independent. The national office did not inquire into my politics. As for giving jobs only to Democrats until all Democrats are employed—well, Miss Essig, if that is what you said, I'll have none of it. My job is to get out books about Idaho and with no unemployed writers here—what *is* an unemployed writer?—I suspect I'll have to do most of the work myself. I can't be bothered riding herd on a lot of incompetents."

She looked into his eyes a long moment. Then she said, her voice level and cool, "You simply refuse to understand the nature of these projects. This country is in a terrible depression. There are millions jobless—"

"But doesn't hunger bite as deep into a Republican as into a Democrat?"

Her cool precise voice said, "It's a Democratic administration in Washington."

Vridar looked at her, anger rising in him. Trying to control his voice, he said, "Miss Essig, I didn't seek this job. Mr. Wood may now have my undated resignation on his desk; or he may take the matter up with the national director in Washington—even with Mr. Harry Hopkins. But as long as I'm on the job I'll do the most I can with the money we have to spend. Would it mean nothing to you and Mr. Wood if Idaho happened to be first among the states to get a book published?"

Her faint smile was as cold as her eyes. "Aren't you counting a lot of eggs?"

"She's a cold bitch," Vridar said to Athene. "I'll count a lot of eggs if the bastards will keep out of my way."

He lay awake nights thinking about his problem. The national office had decided that every state should compile a state guide, and Vridar was determined that Idaho's guide would be published first. He imagined that forty-seven other directors had much the same thought.

He went to see the governor, Don B. Long, and told him what he wanted to do; and Gov. Long, a large illiterate hell-for-leather man, looked at him with eager gray eyes and said, "Did you know I'm a champion cow-puncher?" Without waiting for a reply, he opened a desk drawer and dragged forth a pile of photographs. He thrust one at Vridar. It was a 16x16 view of the Governor in cowboy garb, a lariat in his hand. Vridar was still looking at it when his Excellency thrust another photograph at him: in this one the Governor, again in cowboy clothes, was astride a horse. "That was at the Pendleton roundup," he said.

Vridar lifted his gaze from the photograph to the Governor's face; and that man, beaming with pride in himself, presented another photograph, saying, "At the Cheyenne roundup." He offered still another, saying, "At the Calgary roundup. . . ."

"He must have shown me a hundred photos," Vridar told Athene, "and every one was of himself. Like a wasp he stung me with the first one, and there I sat, paralyzed and helpless, while he fed on me, by showing me the wonder of himself, riding, roping, sitting on a corral pole, branding a calf, earmarking a bull, dehorning a steer—"

"Come, now!"

"It's true. Or just looking as big and important as he could for the camera— two hundred pounds of Don B. Long, the greatest governor, they say, since this state crept into the Union—a man without the slightest capacity to think of anything but Don B. Long."

"What did he think of your project?"

"I couldn't make him conscious of it. Go see him. He will show you hundreds of photographs of himself. He'll start at the top righthand drawer of his huge desk and go right down the right side; and then he'll go down the left side. I think his filing cabinets must all be full of his photographs, and over in a corner I saw several unpacked crates—"

"Oh come now," said Athene, who knew her husband's flair for elaboration. "Did he say nothing about the project at all?"

"Go see him. I tell you he showed me a thousand photographs of himself. He hovered over me, his eyes watching me as though expecting me to break into cheers. And what I wondered was what he's like in the sexual embrace."

"You say he never finished grade school?"

"Oh, I know what you're thinking. He's scared to death of writers, yes. He was trying to convince me that he's my equal. So far as he knows I've never been on a horse." Vridar grinned. "He followed me to the door with an armful of photographs. He followed me down the hallway—"

Vridar next asked a woman's club, the Columbian, for permission to speak at their

737

next meeting, and was dismayed when the president of the club wrote him: "Though I haven't read your books myself, the things I have heard about them don't make you seem a suitable speaker for our group of ladies but I will reserve ten minutes for you. . . ."

After the ten minutes were over, he again mopped his brow and looked at his wife. "If the hundred women looking at me had been born in igloos and nourished on icicles, they couldn't have been colder. There wasn't the slightest expression of sympathy in the whole group; and when I had concluded, they spoke not a word but let me go slinking out like a thief who had been caught at their till."

"But they surely would approve books about Idaho."

"No, they were thinking that they'll all be filled with profanity and masturbation. I tell you they just sat there, looking frozen with horror because their chairman had allowed me into their hall—one hundred Christians and mothers whose husbands detest them. The president in glacial tones said, This is Mr. Vridar Hunter—and at that point she turned to take a fresh view of the horror—who wishes to speak to us about something. You should have heard her pronounce that word something. She said I would talk ten minutes. I talked for exactly ten minutes, for their big clock was straight ahead of me, and I don't think they understood a word I said. All they could do was feel and they were feeling, Here is that horrible Idaho writer who is called a realist. They were thinking that they would take romance but to know how funny that is you would have to see them. . . ."

For months nobody with whom he talked manifested the slightest interest in his project. Republicans said it was only another shameful waste of taxpayer money. Democrats, he could tell, wondered if he actually was a Democrat, or a shyster who with some dishonest trick had got himself into a position that belonged to one of the faithful.

He knew that it was good experience. He began to understand, deep in him, that the capacity to view objectively was the greatest of the human virtues. Next to that and inseparable from it was compassion.

He was told after several months that he could have a secretary, whose salary would be eighty-five dollars a month. One day he dropped in at a Federal project where a hundred women were sitting at tables. One caught his eye. Unobserved by her, he studied her a few minutes. Then he went over to her and said he was looking for a secretary. Would she take lunch with him? So it was that he met Kate Mann.

She was about twenty-four years old. She had a large strong and rather bony face and a rather ungainly body, but she had superb skill in the use of make-up, and faultless taste in her choice of clothes. Much later Vridar was to hear her story, that as a child she had been so ugly that her mother, despairing of her, had forced her always to wear only the loveliest things. At the luncheon she told Vridar that she had been married but having caught her husband in bed with another woman had left him. She was extroverted, calculating, intelligent, able. She had tact and charm.

She accepted the position, saying, "I won't be satisfied with eighty-five a month very long." In the old building she looked at what he called his office and was horrified. "Why in the world did you accept this thing?"

738

"It's what they gave me."

"Didn't you know they were trying to humiliate you?"

"I hadn't thought of it that way."

"You know Walter Spear?"

"I think he's the head of procurement, isn't he?"

Kate was looking at him with lidded calculating eyes. "The girl he's trying to put to bed is my close friend. You'll have a decent office in a week."

"Fine secretary," Vridar said.

In less than a week, Walter Spear, who had treated Vridar with undisguised contempt, called Vridar to his office and beaming at him asked him how he was getting along. He had not realized, Spear said, that Vridar had been given that ugly storage room as an office. It had all been a stupid mistake. He said he had arranged for a suite of three rooms—not very nice but the best he could find now; and Vridar's secretary—what a charming person Miss Mann was!—would requisition everything needed—desks, typewriters, filing cabinets. . . . He begged Vridar to understand that he had had no part in that hole-in-a-wall thing. Vridar was to realize that after this his secretary had only to come to him for anything that was needed. . . .

Vridar stared at the man and said not a word. He marveled at the graciousness blackmail could buy overnight, but he saw that the contempt was still there, behind the smile and the soft words.

Late one night Vridar happened to be walking along a third-floor corridor in Boise's most sumptuous hotel, when suddenly a door was thrown open and a girl almost naked came wildly out. Right behind her was a man stark naked but for shoes and socks. It was Walter Spear and he seemed to be pretty drunk. The girl ran down the corridor with Spear hot on her heels, both of them soon vanishing into another room. Vridar knew that Spear had recognized him in the moment of passing. He wondered whether having been seen naked chasing a woman would make Spear more or less friendly toward him. He decided not to tell his secretary about it.

One day, looking off at the sky speculatively with her heavily-mascaraed, gray-blue eyes, Kate said, "Spear is awfully friendly lately. I think something happened that I don't know about."

Concealing his emotions and thoughts, Vridar said quietly, "I'm beginning to get a better idea of the inner workings of the bureaucratic elite. It would really be something to look into the private lives of the guys in the Kremlin."

"In the Kremlin?" she said, turning to look at him. "Why don't you say in Washington? In fact, why don't you say in Boise?"

XIII

Athene's aunt, who in Athene's childhood had been the only mother she had known, became ill in her California home and Athene thought she ought to be with her. Vridar encouraged her to go. He was not interested in any other woman, but he knew that his marriage was not a happy one and he felt that a separation of a few months might do them both good. She had said to him one day, "I want a child," and he had blown up a great storm. He had said that he had two children now whom

739

he was trying to put in school. She had nothing decent to wear, and his own clothes were so shabby that his secretary was openly ashamed of him. How would he support another child?

She had said, "I want something to show for our relationship."

The words had filled him with pain and shock. He had clasped her arms and looked into her eyes, his thoughts going back across their terrible years together. "You think we're through?"

"I feel that you're turning away from me."

"You aren't turning?" he asked gently. "You well know what distaste you have for my free-drinking and free-thinking ways. You know that you don't like my way of life."

"Some things about it I don't like."

It was decided that she would go to California for a while. He said he would be busy sixteen or eighteen hours a day. He had to log all the Idaho highways, run down all the points of interest, and write a guide of a hundred and fifty thousand words, all in the next five or six months. "I had hoped that you could do the flora and fauna for me. Kate will do the Indians."

"Do you call her Kate already?"

"Well, yes, I do, and she calls me Mister Hunter. Look, dear, I don't belong to the tribe who sleep with their secretary—not that I have scruples that would override it, but because it's bad for a business relationship. Besides, she has a lover."

Vridar saw her off on the train and for days was haunted by the way she had looked at him. There had been hurt in those wonderfully clear steady eyes; anguish in her lips when he touched them. He had held her close and had whispered, "Don't worry. I'll be working hard. I don't say no to the child but let's wait a little. . . ."

He put all his own work aside and plunged in. The most maddening and frustrating thing about the project was not Reese or Essig, or the contempt of Republicans and chambers of commerce and of women's clubs, or the incompetence of the workers available to him. It was the incredible confusion and mind-changing and inefficiency in the national director and his staff in Washington.

The quantity of bulletins, directives, instructions, long letters, and long telegrams sent almost daily to his office simply staggered him. If he had devoted ten hours a day to it he could not have read it all. The stuff piled up in his small office until there was a hundred pounds of it; then several hundred pounds; and finally, he wrote Athene, about fifty or sixty tons. So this was bureaucracy!

Kate found him a stenographer, a short-legged plump moon-faced blond girl who in three years with Vridar was never to get off her face the look of astonishment because of the speed at which he worked. He could dictate two letters at a time as easily as one; or while dictating a long letter to the national director, he could go through a pile of papers on his desk, discarding, approving, signing. Lillian Loring, his stenographer, was able, even though on "relief"; she could take dictation at a hundred and fifty words a minute, and her typed letters were nearly always without error. "She's getting only forty-five a month? Try to get the top for her, the sixty-nine."

"That reminds me," said Kate, with her almost calculating look. "Of all the secretaries on these projects I'm the lowest-paid."

"I'm probably the lowest-paid director in the nation. All right, you know how to get a raise, don't you?"

Vridar's idea of a good administrator was one who himself was efficient and fast; who could quickly size a person up and place him where he could serve most ably; who could delegate power and not wish like Franklin D. Roosevelt, to keep his hands on everything; and above all, who could win and keep the loyalty of his staff. He would say to Kate, "Try to find some relief persons with some college training who can do research in the libraries. Give them ten items to check, which you have already checked. If they get them all right, they'll do." He would say, "Try to find a typist or two who can spell two-syllable words. Send Miss Brown to the library and tell her to gather facts on the grizzly bear. Keep her out of the office." He would say, "Encourage Bill. He has some stuff in him but is schizoid. Mother him a little. . . ."

Then he was gone again, five hundred or a thousand miles, logging the roads with a car he had bought for the purpose; running down old-timers to discover lore, legend, and points of interest; hunting out data on ghost towns and remote areas; and returning for a few days to look at the piles of stuff from Washington and to write furiously far into the night. Again and again he thought he should resign. The staff in Washington would decide in solemn council that the tours should be written one way; decide a day or two later that they ought to be written another way; and decide a week later that a third way was best. To directors all over the nation the bulletins went out by the tons, saying, "Please note that we have decided on these changes. . . ." Vridar would pick up a tour he had written, and, according to their instructions, rewritten and rewritten, and hurl it against a wall, crying, "God damn them to hell anyway! Only imbeciles or tyrants can possibly believe in a one-party system!" He excited, astonished, and sometimes alarmed members of his staff but he kept them keyed-up: the ten, then the twenty, then the thirty who filled the three small rooms or overflowed to the libraries became with a single exception dedicated persons who were determined with him that Idaho would be first. Those on relief—that is, those accredited as destitute, and eligible to WPA projects—were not supposed to work overtime but some of them did.

Then he was gone again, driving alone fifteen hundred or two thousand miles; stopping at every crossroad or sideroad to set down the speedometer mileage; wondering endlessly about the national directors—for they had written: "It will amaze all of you to learn that in an Atlantic coast state is a primitive area larger than Rhode Island. . . ." Vridar had written back: "You should come west of the Mississippi some time. We have in Idaho a primitive area into which you could throw the one you mention, and it would take you two weeks to find it. . . ." They would write Vridar: "You are proceeding too fast. You're going to embarrass us with the other states. . . ." Thinking of their efforts to slow him down, he would snort with scorn. "Harry Hopkins!" he would say to Kate. "He has a huge empire of boon-doggling and feather-bedding, and a philosophy of taxing, spending, electing. That sallow little fellow looking with one eye at the votes of the common

741

man and with the other at the social ladders is not going to slow us up. Try to spot all their ways."

Once she said, "I think I've found something. They're sending us all the psychopaths."

Vridar had wondered about that. When he entered the offices, he went straight to his own little room and his typewriter, but now and then, in passing through, he saw a strange staff-member whose appearance he did not like. Kate, like other secretaries, was supposed to staff the project to the limit of the assigned personnel, as long as persons on relief were available.

One girl was such a thief that she was stealing the typewriter and carbon paper, the ribbons, the ink, the airmail stamps. Another, a tall blond skinny creature, had reported for work one morning, and standing in the middle of the main office had done what babies do, right down her legs. That was the way Kate had put it to him. The staff members roundabout, she said, had just stared horrified at the puddle on the floor.

There were Roberta Dillon and Angus Smith. Roberta swore that Angus had raped her and that she not only was pregnant but had gonorrhea. She said the Federal government would be held responsible for it.

Kate said, "Her father is a lawyer in Pocatello."

"Then why is she on relief?"

"I don't know. She threatens to bring her father over."

Vridar had taken a hard look at Angus and Roberta when they first came on the project. Angus was a small dark sullen man; Roberta was a gawky flatchested blonde whose smile was like the innocence of heaven, but whose scowl, after the smile had fled, was pure schizoid.

"You're convinced they're deliberately sending these people to us?"

"Look, Mr. Hunter, every project secretary in Boise is my personal friend. The other projects aren't getting such people."

"Have you asked why they send all the queers to us?"

"We know, don't we?"

"It might be well to let Reese know that we know. What does this Roberta girl do?"

She just raised hell, Kate said. She had passed her on the street the other day and had seen her, as she approached, bend low and seem to scoop up something. When she passed Kate, she threw a handful of sand into her face.

"Schizoid," Vridar said. "Well, take the puddle-girl and the sand-girl off the project."

"You know what Reese will do then? He won't send us anybody at all."

Vridar said drily, "It's too bad for us that his private life is so irreproachable. Is Daisy Merck any good?" Daisy, a former highschool teacher, was non-relief.

"Slow," Kate said. "She has man-trouble."

"Project man?"

"A high state official, Daniel John Lange."

Vridar had met Lange. For a long time he had published a newspaper in another city. When Lange took the Boise job, Kate said, he persuaded Daisy to give up her teaching job, because she had been his mistress for years. Now Lange was trying to seduce his secretary, a devout Mormon girl.

"The boss and his secretary," Vridar said. "What would American marriage do without that fine old relationship?"

After the sand-girl was removed from the project, she came storming up the stairway and hurled a four-pound brick through the hallway window of Vridar's office. Kate called a policeman, who had to take Roberta away by force, dragging her screaming and clawing down the stairway. Vridar paid for the window out of his own pocket. The puddle-girl, another pathetic schizoid, threw herself under a Union Pacific train.

The obstacles placed in Vridar's path only made him drive on with greater vigor. The bulletins came in increasing quantity from Washington: having no time to look at most of them, Vridar had the janitor carry them to the basement furnace. The telegrams or letters begging him to proceed at a more moderate pace he hung on his office wall. Washington learned that he did this, for Reese came snooping in now and then to see what he was doing. He reported to Harry Hopkins; Hopkins wrote to the national director, who would then write Vridar: "What in the world are you doing out there? You have come to be known as the project's bad boy. . . ."

In May Athene came up from California to get herself pregnant. "You old Brigham Young," she said, when at the bus station she left him. Her words had annoyed him. In a novel he had published, the protagonist (whom readers took to be the author himself) had confessed to a number of adulteries; and one day Rhode had turned to Vridar at the dinner table, his face contorted, his small eyes wicked with what Vridar took to be envy, and said, right before his wife and other guests, "You old studhorse." The words had shocked Vridar as deeply as Rhode's other statement about the wine and the casks. He wrote Athene, "This from a man who pinches the bottom of his daughter-in-law!"

In June, Maxwell Cahan, the national director, summoned all the western directors to a conference in Salt Lake City. It was to last a week. It was to be immensely fruitful. There would be, said the letters and telegrams, a meeting of minds, an exchange of views. Vridar took all this seriously. . . .

"What a damned innocent naive thickwitted hillbilly I am!" he wrote Athene. "I traveled by the cheapest means; ate sandwiches on the train; checked in at a secondrate hotel, all to save public funds; and though I was not able to verify this I was told (1) that the California directors (two short fat fellows built like barrels) came by special plane; (2) that after two or three days of it they quit in disgust and chartered a plane to fly home (I'd like to see their offices down there!); (3) that most of the directors, some with entourage, demanded only the best in accommodations (I can say this, that I was invited to one of the parties and saw some of the directors so stinking drunk that they didn't know whether they were in Zion or Stalin's Utopia). A rumor went around that our boss himself got bored with Mormon food and took off for San Francisco. I know this, that he vanished; that a full-dress meeting was called for ten one morning and the boss was not there, nor did any of us see him again before the conference adjourned. I guess I was the only one in the whole damned outfit who misunderstood the purpose of Mr. Harry Hopkins.

"Thousands of dollars were absolutely squandered, while so-called public servants drank and wenched and raised hell. Not a single iota of good was accomplished— and at last I have got it into my simple Antelope Hills head that accomplishment was no part of the purpose. The boys and girls just got together at public expense —and I stood around and watched them, who only three or four years ago actually wondered if Communism might be a good thing! How clearly I now perceive that the only political system that can protect people against those who would exploit them is our own, with two or more parties, and checks and balances. The thing that saves us is the independent vote, which switches from party to party, as each in turn becomes corrupt. . . ."

Filled with disgust, shame, and anger he returned to Idaho, believing that his disillusionment was now complete. Those who founded the American system, he told himself, had not been foolish idealists like him, but wise men, not cynical but knowing; not without faith in the future of mankind, but without faith in any man when given too much power. They had known, even more than Lord Acton was to know later, that power corrupted. Looking back across the empires that had risen and fallen, they had known that the power to tax was the power to destroy. They had known that restless itch in most people to manage the affairs of other people—and their inordinate vanity—their incredible capacity for self-deception. These things he told himself, riding back on the bus.

Should he vote for Roosevelt again? He was being steadily disillusioned in the man: he could not study photographs of the Roosevelt face and doubt that here was a man of colossal vanity, who, with great power, would be dangerous; a man who was at heart an orphan, never having been weaned from his mother; a man who, never having had to earn a dollar, would never have any sense of a balanced budget, and so would spend in fantastic ways, having discovered that people, losing God-Father in remoteness, and their spiritual messiah, were now ready to flee, and all over the world were fleeing, to the political messiahs. In Russia it was a barbarian and a brute named Stalin; in Italy, another, named Mussolini; in Germany, another, named Hitler—orphans all and brutal butchers all.

He wrote Athene: "I'll get the guide out and then resign, for I can't long endure this daily revelation of small cynical souls in positions of power, struggling for more power, more prestige and salary, with never a thought indeed, with no realization, of their solemn duties and obligations to the people, above whom they sit as petty tyrants in one way and another. What a simple self-deceived lackwit I was when I was a Socialist! . . ."

Rhode said he would publish the Idaho guide if he could be assured of a sale of three thousand copies. Vridar took the problem to Roger Wood. He said he was sure that three thousand copies could be sold, if a prospectus of the book could be put before the people. He proposed the mailing of fifty thousand circulars under the frank. He would need fifty thousand envelopes.

Wood looked appalled. That was a lot of envelopes, he said. How were the other states going to do it?

744

"The Washington office doesn't know. They hope some big publisher will want all the guides, and he may want such as New York's and California's, but not Idaho's. Even if he did, Idaho would have to wait on other states. I want ours out first."

"Is there some special advantage in being first?"

"I think so. I think the first guide will get the most review space, which means the most publicity. The guides will be old stuff after a while, and if Idaho, a state of little importance politically, is on the tail end our guide may never be reviewed at all. What publisher would want it then?"

"I see your point. Rhode will publish it?"

"If we can mail fifty thousand circulars."

"How will you choose the names?"

"Go right through the principal telephone directories."

Wood continued to look at him. "Well, all right," he said at last. "Requisition the envelopes and the printing."

Within a few days after Vridar talked to Wood, ten typists were addressing and filling envelopes. Nine months and ten days after Vridar accepted the job as Idaho director he delivered the manuscript of the Idaho guide to the printer. Then suddenly there came a long distance call from Washington.

XIV

"Hello," Vridar said. "Hello, this is Vridar Hunter, Idaho Writers' Project."

"Hello," said a drawling voice, and at once Vridar had a picture of an urbane easy-going man who seemed never able to make up his mind. "Is this Vridar Hun-tuh? This is Maxwell Cahan speaking."

"Yes, Mr. Cahan." Vridar glanced at his secretary and in a few minutes his entire staff had gathered around him.

"Mr. Hun-tuh, I have been advised . . . that you uh are going ahead uh publishing the Idaho guide. Of course back he-uh we haav great admiration for your industry and zeal; but Mr. Hun-tuh, I haav written you agayn and agayn that we cawn't allow a small state like Idaho to—"

"Why not?"

"Mr. Hun-tuh, I haav explained all that. There is a political aspect of life, ya know. We haav forty-eight states in a political union. There are bound to be rivalries and jealousies . . . as well as a sense of uh appropri-utness . . . in these things." Kate and several others had put their faces close to listen. She was looking at staff-members and winking. "It is going to be in the utmost degree embarrassing uh, not only to me and the national office but also uh . . . to Mr. Hopkins and the entire Roosevelt administration. You see—"

"How long do you want us to wait?"

"Uhhh—a reasonable time. We'd not want you to be the laast, by any means, but nyther the first. You see—"

"We want to be the first."

"Waal now—"

"We've worked hard. If the other damned lazy boondogglers—"

"Waal now, ya know. Not all problems are as simple as yours—"

"Nor budgets as small."

"We had thought, Mr. Hun-tuh, it would be appropriate for the Washington D.C. guide to be furst. As the nation's capital—"

"Do you have it about ready?"

"Oh, good heavens no! As a maater of fact, I doubt that we haav even a paragraph ready yet. Other problems—"

"And you want us to wait a year, two years, three years?"

"Mr. Hun-tuh, you can be busy with other things. We have plans—"

"We're proceeding now to an encyclopedia."

"Oh, good heavens no! An encyclopedia, did you say? We haav nevuh thought of anything like that. As to your guide—"

"Mr. Cahan, can you hear me?"

"Yes, Mr. Hun-tuh, I he-uh you."

"We're going ahead."

"You're going to do what?"

"We're going ahead and publish the guide. I don't think we should be penalized because your other states aren't working as hard. We've worked hard here. I've averaged sixteen hours a day seven days a week. I took this assignment seriously. I took you seriously when you summoned me to Salt Lake but nothing was accomplished there and you walked out on us. You may have my resignation any time you want it but as long as I'm on this job I'm here to get things done and I won't be a scapegoat for the shameful loafing states that are only squandering public funds. Is all that clear?"

"Yes, Mr. Hun-tuh, you've always managed to make yourself clear. As I say, we do admire your zeal but we cawn't let you go ahead and embarrass—"

"We're going ahead."

"I'm telling you, Mr. Hun-tuh, you're not going ahead. Do you he-uh me? You will not publish the Idaho guide until we tell you to."

"How will you stop us?"

"I'll send Robert Bingham out and he'll stop you."

Vridar covered the mouthpiece and turned to his staff. "He's almost lost his drawl. He's going to send Bingham out to stop us." Into the mouthpiece he said, "All right, send Mr. Bingham out. When will he be here?"

He would come at once, Cahan said. Meanwhile, Vridar was to do nothing at all. He was sweating a little when he hung up. Leaving the office he went downstairs for a cup of coffee, wondering what he could do. Returning he said to his secretary, "Get Mr. Rhode." When Rhode came on the line Vridar told him what had happened, and Rhode said, "That's the way the bureaucrats always talk. It takes only a little power to go to their heads and then they get drunk with power. Was he angry?"

"Toward the last."

"What did you tell him?"

"That we're going ahead."

"I think perhaps we should. I've seen my lawyer and he feels there is nothing they can do. If they give us much trouble I can call on Senator Borah."

"He's sending Robert Dingham out. You know, an associate director. I think they must have a whole building full of associate directors."

"Oh, they always do. A bureaucracy is a parasite, and like any parasite it keeps growing on the host."

"I don't think I should tell Roger Wood."

"I'd not tell him. He would try to stop us. He might get that man in the White House on our necks."

"As for Bingham, I happen to know that he's a heavy drinker. Why don't we get him drunk and put him on the train and send him back?"

Rhode chuckled. "That sounds like a good idea. Where'll we see him?"

"In your home?"

"Why yes, sure."

"Have on hand plenty of the best."

"Whisky, you mean. Why yes, of course I will." Rhode chuckled again. "You call me the moment he arrives. And don't drink anything before you get here. If you should be picked up—"

"We'll both arrive sober."

Vridar had talked to Rhode in his own small office, with the door closed. He now opened the door and asked his secretary in. He told her that when Bingham came they would try to get him drunk and while he was in a stupor send him back. "How's the addressing coming?"

"Fine."

"You know all the secretaries. Heard anything new?"

"Yes, Dr. Hunter."

"Never mind the doctor. What?"

"They intend to plant a spy in our office."

Vridar looked into her eyes a long moment and then sank to a chair. "A spy? What for?"

"To catch you in something. Adultery, for instance."

"Then they fire me. You know who the spy will be?"

"His name is Wilford Pogue."

Again Vridar stared at her, his mind busy. "Well, let's play it dumb. When Pogue comes introduce him just as you do all the others."

Wilford Pogue was a powerful young man, about six feet tall, and weighing about two hundred pounds. His handsome wavy hair was a very deep yellow; his eyes were blue; his smile, revealing perfect teeth, never left his face. Vridar wondered if he smiled when he slept.

Vridar had been looking at his data-sheet. "How long were you a high school teacher?"

"Until they fired me," said Pogue, smiling.

"Why did they fire you?"

"I molested the girls."

In that moment Vridar was looking at the man: the smiling blue eyes were the

747

same, and the smiling lips drawn back from the handsome teeth. I must be groggy with fatigue, Vridar thought, for surely my ears failed me. "You did what with the girls?"

"I molested them," said Pogue, smiling. He looked as if he might have just said, It's a fine day.

Vridar studied him several moments. "You mean you seduced your high school students?"

"I tried to," Pogue said, still smiling. "Most of the time I didn't succeed."

I must be losing my mind, Vridar thought. He tried again. "You actually tried to seduce girls only fourteen or fifteen?"

"Most of them were older. In our rural areas most of the seniors are eighteen or more."

Vridar glanced at the data-card. "You're married?"

"I was. My wife left me."

"Because you were seducing students?"

"No. Because I was too ardent."

Vridar decided to take a walk. There was something in this man that shocked and frightened Kate. All the women in the office were afraid of him. That, Vridar reflected, was strange, because Wilford was a quiet gentle person, who always spoke in the same low tone, always smiled, always seemed eager to please.

A day or two after Wilford came to the project, Vridar had to make a journey to an eastern Idaho city. He asked Pogue if he wanted to go along. "Oh yes," said Pogue, smiling, eager. "If you'll just make a little detour so I can see my wife."

After Vridar had driven a hundred miles, he became aware that Pogue was looking off into a rural area and showing intense excitement. He said his wife was over there in a farmhouse. Would Vridar drive over? A hundred yards from the house Pogue asked him to stop, and at once got out and walked swiftly away. Vridar had supposed that he would go to the door but instead he slipped around among trees and softly approached a window. Vridar saw him peering in. In heaven's name, what sort of man was this? For there he stood half an hour or longer, peering up over the sill into what appeared to be a bedroom. Then just as softly he turned and came back. His face was red, as though from intense heat.

Vridar said, "What in hell were you doing?"

"I wanted to see if he was screwing her," Pogue said.

Vridar thought, I have a lunatic with me. Had he ever been a high school teacher, or had he escaped from an asylum? On the return to Boise, hours later, Vridar drew the man into talk, and marveled at his bland candor. Pogue said—nothing that he said ever seemed to have the color and emotion of confession—that he loved more than anything else to get an erection and show it to his wife. At any time of day or night he would do it, if the impulse took him: it made no difference what she was doing: he would interrupt her and ask her to look. This went on for years, he said. Then one day she exploded. She shattered a big earthen platter over his skull and screamed into his ears, "I can't look at it all the time, you God damn fool! I have work to do!"

Some of Pogue's statements Vridar found so astonishing that, turning to look at the man, he now and then almost ran off the highway.

Pogue said he had wanted to be intimate with his wife three or four times a day and she had got so she could hardly stand him. So he began to molest the girls. He had to do that, he said, or masturbate, smiling at Vridar. He said he had read all of Freud and Jung and was ambitious to write a great work on philosophy. Plato was his favorite. Plato had said that the universe had its origin in time: if that idea could be integrated with Einstein's simple formula, men would have the key to the riddle.

"They might," Vridar said. He had no notion at all of what Pogue was talking about.

The World-Soul, Plato had said, was made up in part of not-Being: Wilford felt that a profound thought was there, but its exact nature eluded him; and he wished he knew whether for Plato the thing had been wholly impersonal. Since Nature was Becoming rather than Being, only the study of Nature could lead to truth, and, above all, to the secret of religion and the spiritual life.

When the lights of Boise came in view, Vridar felt better. He said, "Well, was the new husband doing it?"

"Oh no," said Wilford, smiling. "She was scrubbing the kitchen floor. Her bottom is bigger than it was."

The next day Vridar said to Kate, "Is Pogue of any use to us?"

Not much, Kate said. He spent most of the time typing out his dreams or reading them to those who would listen. They were so erotic that they made most of the girls red all over. He even used the four-letter words and spoke them right out loud in mixed company.

"Don't let him read his dreams to anyone. Tell him they're Federal property and file them away. And try to put up with him and learn all you can."

"Here," she said, and handed Vridar a telegram. It said that Robert Bingham would arrive at the Union station the next day at noon.

XV

Robert Bingham was a sandy rather florid man of middle age, who looked fat with rich living. Vridar clasped a feeble slightly moist hand and said, "Mr. Bingham, welcome to the land of primitive areas."

"Cahan's bad boy, I assume," said Bingham, grinning. "So this is Idaho." He was standing by the handsome Union Pacific station and looking north across Boise to the great mountains behind it. "What a revelation of our country this project's books will be!"

"Should be anyway," Vridar said.

"Will be," Bingham said. "Don't imagine that only Idaho will have a guide."

"Oh, I suppose they'll all have guides some day. I hate to think how much per word some of them will cost."

"You're obsessed with that," Bingham said, and waved a hand toward the northern mountains. "Just where is this immense primitive area you wrote us about?"

749

"Straight north to hell and gone, beyond where you're looking."

"You know," said Bingham, still looking, "this is the first time I've ever been west of Chicago. None of us in the national office had ever been west."

"Whole bales of stuff you sent us revealed that."

"If you've lived all your life in New England, you just can't believe it when you see the West for the first time."

"No doubt," said Vridar acidly. He wanted to say, That imbecile Harry Hopkins would staff the Washington office from New England!

Vridar picked up Bingham's bag. "Where do we go?" Bingham said.

"To the Idaho office first."

When they entered the three shabby rooms, Bingham paid no attention to crumbling plaster and warped floor boards, as Kate had hoped he would; he went from one desk to another, from desk to table, seizing papers to look at them. Turning at last to Vridar he said, "Where's your manuscript?"

Vridar said, "One copy is in your Washington office; one copy is with Mr. Rhode; and a third copy is locked away in a vault."

His voice became rather sharp as Bingham said, "Where are your photographs?"

"With Rhode."

"Do we have to go there? Are you ready?"

Vridar turned to Kate. "Call Mr. Rhode and tell him we're on our way."

On the drive to Oldtown and Rhode's home, Vridar tried to put Bingham in a less officious mood. The man had been human at the station but after entering the office he became the bureaucrat who remembered that, cloaked with authority and powers, he was on a mission. While driving through beautiful countryside Vridar told him that he now wanted to compile an encyclopedia of the state, and then a volume of folklore. Before Bingham could raise objections, Vridar asked if he did not think such projects would be worthwhile. "You've heard of the time Paul Bunyan drank nine kegs of rum in Idaho Falls and on his blue ox headed for Seattle. It was a black wet night full of rain—"

"I care nothing about Paul Bunyan stories. They bore me."

"All right, Arkansas is not the only state with a slow train. When Harry Hopkins was out here, he rode the branch line to Twin Falls. When the train stopped, with no station near, Hopkins wanted to know why, and the conductor said there was a cow on the track. He would have to chase her off. Again the train stopped and Hopkins said, Now what in hell is wrong? Oh, the conductor said, they had just caught up with the cow." Vridar turned for a moment to look at Bingham's eyes.

"We have a lot of stories about Idaho potatoes. When a CCC camp moved into the Shelley area—that's where the largest ones are grown—the boss of the camp went to a potato grower and said he wanted a hundred pounds. Only a hundred pounds? asked the potato man. That was all. God amighty, feller, I wouldn't cut a spud in two for no one."

Again for a moment Vridar met Bingham's eyes. Bingham said, "Is that story supposed to be funny? Never mind your spuds. Maine has better potatoes."

"Maine!" Vridar cried, as though shocked. "Mr. Bingham, if you go around Idaho saying that, we'll have to send you back in a coffin."

"You Idahoans should stop boasting about your potatoes. Your primitive area is more important. How large did you say it is?"

"One million eighty-seven thousand seven hundred and forty-four acres. It is bounded on the north by Salmon river, on the east by the Bighorn Crags, the Yellowjacket range and Sleeping Deer Mountain; on the south and west by rivers, creeks, mountains—"

"Can you drive to it in a car?"

"O God no."

"Have you been in it?"

"In it and I've flown over it. Come along and we'll have sour dough hotcakes and chokecherry jam. . . . Well, there's Oldtown."

Rhode saw them coming and met them at the door. He thought of himself as a gracious host; he would bow to a guest, extending his hand, his deeply-lined face smiling, his small brown eyes vividly watchful. "Mr. Bingham," he said, taking Bingham's hand, "this is a most unexpected pleasure."

Vridar restrained a snort. Rhode hated Roosevelt and his New Deal with such intensity that his face became purple when he talked about them.

Vridar and Rhode had agreed to drink water of the color of whisky, with just enough whisky to give it a whisky odor. Bingham took bourbon and soda. Rhode raised his glass and bowing to Bingham said, "Here's to the success of your great project." He and Vridar drank their water off.

Looking from one to the other Bingham said, "You take your whisky neat?"

"It's an old western custom," Rhode said.

Mrs. Rhode came with an Old Taylor bottle nearly full of whisky-flavored colored water and filled her husband's and Vridar's glasses. The two men drank again. Bingham then seemed to feel a great thirst, for he emptied his own glass and accepted another. He was a little drunk by the time they all sat down to dinner. The main course was pheasant, which Mrs. Rhode cooked superbly. Bingham was hungry. Rhode pressed on him both food and drink. After dinner, Rhode said he and Vridar would switch to brandy.

Staring at them Bingham asked, "Do you westerners go right on drinking after dinner?"

Rhode said, "Mr. Bingham, for a real westerner a meal is only an interruption."

"A very pleasant one," said Bingham, with a little bow to Mrs. Rhode. He accepted a tall bourbon and soda and looking around him said, "Now I'll see the photographs."

Rhode entered his library and returned with two hundred photographs, which Vridar had gathered from many sources, including national forests and Federal departments. Rhode piled them on a table at Bingham's elbow.

Bingham said, "You're aware, of course, that the photographs used will have to have our approval?"

"Yes, Mr. Bingham," said Rhode, bowing his head and smiling.

What Bingham now did was so incredible that Vridar wondered if his senses were deceiving him. The man didn't merely lay a rejected photograph aside. He would take one from the pile, glance at it, and saying, "No!" in a voice that was loud and sounded angry he would send the photograph sailing across the room. To the second, the third, the fourth, the fifth his response was exactly the same: he said no, took the pasteboard by a corner and sent it after the first. Glancing at Mrs. Rhode, Vridar saw that she was gaping with amazement. He looked over at Rhode and caught a quick wink from a brown eye.

The sixth photograph was of a magnificent field of potatoes, the potatoes sacked and the sacks standing row on row. Bingham studied it a few moments and said, "No photographs of potatoes" and sent it after the others.

"No photographs of potatoes, Mr. Bingham?" asked Rhode with deadly politeness.

"No photograph of potatoes, Mr. Rhode."

"But potatoes are Idaho's most famous agricultural product. Wouldn't it be a strange guide—"

"Every state, Mr. Rhode, has things it has over-advertised. We're not a chamber of commerce. There will be no hyperbole in these guides. Idaho has boasted so much of its potatoes that Idaho potatoes have become, to put it simply, a frightful bore."

"But the fact remains, Mr. Bingham—"

"I said no photograph of potatoes."

"Yes, Mr. Bingham. May I uh fill your glass?"

Bingham was gazing at a photograph. "What is this supposed to be?"

Rhode leaned forward to look. "Onions, Mr. Bingham. Idaho produces some of the finest onions—"

"No onions," said Bingham, and the photograph of a field of onions went sailing across the room. Then Bingham looked round for his glass. It was full, and right at his side. He took a deep swig and seemed to have a little difficulty putting the glass down. He was getting drunk, and more arrogant. Hardly glancing at them any longer, he would send photographs flying, one after another. He said, "We'll choose the photographs for you in Washington."

That was too much for Vridar. He knew that he was supposed to remain silent and let Rhode handle this, for Rhode fancied himself as an accomplished politician; but he was so angry that he spoke up. "Mr. Bingham, who is better qualified to choose the photographs, we who live here and know the state, or you in Washington who have never been west of the Potomac?"

Rhode said quickly, "We are eager to do just what Mr. Bingham wants us to do."

Bingham had been looking at Vridar. He now turned to Rhode. "Thank you," he said. "What is this?" His tongue was getting thick.

Rhode bent forward, scowling and peering. "That's Hell Roaring Lake, one of Idaho's finest."

"Who ever heard of a roaring lake? Anyway, Idaho's lakes are nothing compared to those in some states."

"Yes, Mr. Bingham."

"We can't let you use that," he said and the photograph left his hand. "There is nothing unusual about your Idaho lakes."

"Yes, Mr. Bingham. It's interesting to get an easterner's view of these things. Will you join us in another drink, Mr. Bingham?"

752

Bingham looked round at his glass, picked it up and emptied it. "Thank you," he said.

Rhode now and then glanced at a clock. After he had flung the last photograph from him Bingham said, "Have you any more?"

"Only those, Mr. Bingham."

"We'll choose the photographs in Washington," Bingham said.

"Yes, Mr. Bingham."

"You won't go ahead with the guide—I mean you're not to publish it until we in Washington—"

"We understand that, Mr. Bingham."

Bingham was looking more jovial. Staring at him, Vridar was thinking, You fatuous bureaucrat! You spend hundreds of dollars of public funds to take a five-thousand mile journey to throw two hundred photographs across a room!

The man now seemed to sense that he had been pretty highhanded. He looked at the scattered litter of photographs and at last, making an effort to rise, said, "I guess I'd better gather them up."

"Don't bother," Rhode said. "Our maid will do it."

Bingham sat back and looked at his glass. Again Rhode filled it. Then Rhode looked at the clock and said, "I understand Mr. Bingham has to leave on the midnight train. You haven't much time."

Vridar stood up. Bingham went to his hostess and bowed and thanked her. He turned to his host.

"It has been a great pleasure," Rhode said, smiling at him, wicked lights in his eyes. "Do come out some time and go hunting with us. And uh maybe you'd like to take a little drink along on your drive."

"Why of course," Vridar said.

With drinks in their hands, Vridar and Bingham bowed their way out. Rhode went with them to the car. He again bowed to Bingham, with that little movement of his head to one side. He waved goodbye.

They had gone only a few miles when Vridar heard an explosion. "God damn!" he said.

"What is it?" asked Bingham anxiously.

"A flat." Moving fast, Vridar left the car and opened the trunk. He had no flashlight, he had to work by feeling. Bingham came staggering out, highball in hand. "The roads out west are horrible," he said. Vridar said, "We have big states, few people, little money, and we have to support a Washington choked with bureaucrats."

"Can I help you?"

"Just take it easy. I'll soon have it."

When they were ready to go, Vridar struck a match and looked at Bingham's watch. He had twenty miles to go, and exactly twenty minutes. He pressed the lever clear down and was driving at seventy-five when he heard a siren.

"Hold on tight," he said.

The anxious voice asked, "What does that mean?"

"The cops are after us but I think I can ditch them."

"We'd better let them arrest us," Bingham said, peering back.

"Just pray that we don't have another flat." He was now driving at eighty and the car behind him was sounding its siren. "Eighty is as fast as this car will go," he said, "but I doubt theirs will go any faster."

"I think we should stop," Bingham said.

Vridar said he knew a tricky sideroad a couple of miles ahead. He would lose them there.

Bingham said, "I'd rather be arrested than die in Idaho."

"It's a good place to die," Vridar said. "We'll bury you in a potato cellar and pile onions on top of you."

"They're gaining on you," Bingham said.

"I know it. I'm slowing to make a turn." He made the turn on little more than two wheels, throwing Bingham over against him and spilling the last of his whisky. The police car, unable to turn, had gone on; and now Vridar dashed from one dark street to another. He could hear the train coming.

"That's your train," he said.

"We'll never make it," Bingham said. "I'll have to stay in Boise. Does it have a good hotel?"

"We'll make it. Hang on." Vridar figured that he was about two miles from the station. He had time. He heard the train's whistle and judged that it was four or five miles distant. . . .

And then they were there, just as the train pulled in, and he had Bingham's bag out and Bingham by the arm, hustling him along, saying in his ear, "It has been nice meeting you. I hope you have a good sleep. The club car is the tail one. . . . There's a porter. . . ."

A few minutes later he was in his small shabby room, washing the grease from his hands. He undressed, poured himself a tall drink of straight whisky, and sat in thought. What a creature the human male was! Roosevelt had been in office less than four years, yet how rapidly his cult was growing! It reminded Vridar of things he had thought about but had not known the meaning of: a professor's fanatical devotion, for instance, to some writer—to Chaucer or Milton or another, whom he had taught for many years; whom in teaching he had come to regard as the greatest of all writers, for the reason that such regard elevated the professor in his own esteem. . . .

He took from a file of notes a card and read what a psychologist had written: "A Goethe philologist is a man who not only thinks but acts, breathes, and lives in the mental atmosphere of Goethe. His entire and only interest in the world is the worshiped poet, to such an extent that everything he does and everything that has happened to him is seen through Goethe's eyes. His own life and that of others is understandable only in terms of Goethe's sayings. All things and events of the past and the present are tested according to Goethe's views. Everything concerning the divine figure is of vital importance to him. The weather of the day on which a certain line in a poem was written or whether Goethe liked Teltower carrots is a question of life and death to him. . . ."

What could this mean except that a frightened "orphan" was seeking a father? What horrible enslavement of the human spirit!

Capitalism had been a pretty safe institution for the simple reason that nobody had been able to make it divine. Let me see, he thought, struggling to bring fully into consciousness an elusive meaning—yes, he had it now: under any form of Socialism, discipline was imposed from without; under capitalism, it had been imposed from within, when, under this form, there had been discipline. It was the parent-child relationship, or the lack of it. The rub was that apparently only a very few persons were civilized enough to discipline themselves. There was Honest Harold Ickes, a demigod for the so-called liberals; yet Honest Harold had a huge office suite, with costly woods in the floors; with private dining room, baths, conference rooms all adjacent—all because Honest Harold felt himself to be so important and so privileged. . . .

There were the Hellyers: Ernest had been fired from his job and the Hellyers had come through Boise, Nora Nolana walking like a duchess who had mislaid her jewels, the ridiculous poodle at her heels; Ernest stuttering out words of reverence for Roosevelt. Roosevelt and Henry A. Wallace had become for these two, Ernest and Nora Nolana, demigods or gods. Of those whom they called conservative or reactionary they could not say or think evil enough. Herbert Hoover they spoke of in such venomous terms, and Roosevelt with such maudlin idolatry, that Vridar was sickened. . . .

Remembering them now, he drank the whisky, turned out his light and went to bed.

XVI

Rhodc had not had the slightest idea of submitting the decisions to Washington. He called Vridar the morning after Bingham's departure and said they ought to strike the iron while it was hot. If they waited, they would have a thousand bureaucrats on their necks. "You choose the photographs, for you know Idaho better than any other person alive."

Vridar's staff was agog with curiosity. Kate came softly into his small office, closing the door behind her. Her eyes werc shining under long lashes that were waxed into spears. What had happened?

"We got him drunk and sent him back."

"Oh no! Mr. Hunter, you surely didn't do *that!*"

"We certainly did do that, on the midnight train."

"What'll he think when he sobers up?"

"He may decide he's not quite the man of destiny he thought he was."

"What'll Harry Hopkins do?"

"He's too busy trying to make the Social Register to do anything."

Vridar expected an angry letter from Maxwell Cahan. For weeks there was only silence. Then one day Kate said, "I've bad news for you. The Post Office here has been mad at us ever since we paralyzed it with that fifty-thousand mailing. They have sent you a bill for a thousand dollars."

"What for?" asked Vridar, looking at her.

"Postage on the fifty thousand circulars."

Vridar was enraged. He wrote Rhode:

> It's all right for these parasitic congressional gasbags to choke the mails with all the junk they send under the frank; but it's not all right to use the frank to acquaint the people with the nature of the state they live in. I'll go to jail before I'll pay it. . . .

Rhode replied:

> I'd not worry about it. It's the way the bureaucratic mind works. I'll take the matter up with Sen. Borah and I expect he'll knock some sense into their heads back there. . . .

Early in 1937 the Idaho *Guide* was published, and all the reviews that Vridar saw were favorable. An American historian wrote in *The Saturday Review of Literature* "The publication is momentous, since the first guide will be used as typical of the whole enterprise. In the main, the first volume succeeds overwhelmingly, far better than we had any right or reason to expect. Whatever the difficulties caused by the extemporized and necessarily haphazard method of producing the guide . . . the final result is an almost unalloyed triumph."

The Associated Press wrote: "Mr. Hunter and his aides not only have published their book first; they have brought to life a state less known east of the Mississippi than any other in the west. It is a first-rate solution to a difficult problem." In the New York *Times* the reviewer said, "The word guide is far too modest a term to describe a book with such readable text, such broadly illustrative pictures." And in *The New Republic* "This book, so far as good writing and sensitive observation of detail can carry, is an achievement some states may think themselves fortunate to equal. . . ."

The response over the nation was so enthusiastic that Maxwell Cahan wrote Vridar:

> We are so pleased with the reception given the Idaho Guide that you are invited to come to Washington as our guest, all expenses paid. You need a little vacation. . . .

"I'll be damned!" Vridar cried to Kate. "They plant spies on me. They did their best to stop the book. Then, finding it has added luster to their lousy boondoggling, they give me a pat."

"Quite a pat," Kate said. "Are you going?"

"I suppose so. I'd like to see what they're doing back there."

Maxwell Cahan, a worldly drawling lazy sophisticated soft-spoken man, took Vridar from office to office, saying, "Here is Cahan's bad boy." They gave him a sumptuous party (at which a half-dozen members of the Washington staff got staggering-drunk) that was paid for, Vridar supposed, out of public funds. He went to the offices of other national projects and everywhere saw evidence of lavish spending, and in most of the Federal officials a sense of themselves as privileged managers, set apart. Whence had come the idea of the public servant? He perceived now—he had suspected it a long time—that under Communism or any one-party system the elite would be not an industrial aristocracy but a bureaucratic aristocracy. He despised the one as much as the other.

When he went into Bingham's office, Bingham came forward, grinning, hand outstretched. "Well, you used those damned lousy photographs after all."

"The critics liked them," Vridar said.

"I know they did. It's astonishing."

"When will the next state guide be out?"

"Only God knows."

"Some of them must be about ready, aren't they? Don't tell me that Idaho, with the second-smallest budget in the nation, can get a guide ready for the printer in nine months, yet states like New York, spending five hundred times as much, can't have a guide ready in eighteen months?"

"Let's talk about something pleasant," Bingham said. "You not only put in the damned potatoes and onions but you put in Hell Roaring Lake."

"You remember that? I'd thought you'd be too drunk."

"You got me drunk, all right," Bingham said. With a sly suspicious grin and a twinkle in his eyes, he added, "Were you and Rhode really drinking it neat?"

"Let's talk about something pleasant," Vridar said. "The other guides, for instance."

Vridar had a picture of forty-seven other state directors, every one eager to be the second one out with a guide. It would take two more years to complete his disillusionment.

XVII

It was in April, 1937, that he went to Washington. His staff was now busy gathering data for an encyclopedia, for a volume of Idaho lore, for a study of the state's industrial resources. Most of those who worked with him had been deeply pleased by their participation in the first guide to be published, and by what was being written about it. Wood was pleased but there had been no unbending in Jane Essig and Archie J. Reese. The spy was left on the project but that did not matter now: Wilford Pogue had confessed the plot to Vridar and switched his loyalty. "Don't let them know about your change of mind and heart," Vridar said. "Go on as usual." After this, Pogue said, he would give Vridar a carbon of all his secret reports.

One day there walked into the office a young woman who was to change the course of Vridar's life. She was about twenty-two. She was petite, chic, over-rouged, and had a chip on her shoulder. When she sat at Vridar's desk and crossed her legs, her short skirt exposed both lovely knees. He saw in her eyes intelligence, spirit, and something sly and concealed; and on looking her over he perceived that she had what Americans called a fine figure. She said she had read some of his poems and for years had wanted to meet him. This made him shudder, for he had given up the idea that he was a poet.

A small insistent voice deep inside him said, Leave this woman alone! It said, You have a wife in California and another child now: are you going to be a damned fool clear to the end? He recalled one of Athene's letters, written years ago in Chicago: "I have never loved anyone to the point of great sacrifice. I ask, If Vridar were to die, would I return to the herd? Every step of the way I have refused to decide anything until you forced me. I have wished I had the courage to renounce you. . . . Ever since we met you've been holding me up and leading me and giving me courage. . . ."

All that, he supposed, had been true. Did he love her? Had he ever loved her? He felt that he loved her deeply, and would, to the day of his death. What had David Hawke written?—

To lose the earth you know, for greater knowing; to lose the life you have, for greater life; to leave the friends you loved, for greater loving; to find a land more kind than home, more large than earth—Whereon the pillars of this earth are founded, toward which the conscience of the world is tending—a wind is rising and the rivers flow.

He doubted that Athene could understand such words: only the poet, the artist, the creator could. To lose the life you have for greater life! Yes, he loved Athene but it was not a simple matter of love. It was chiefly a matter of daring to grow. Two days after the strange woman came to his office, he called her. "How about a ride this evening?"

"If you'd like to," she said.

"I'll pick you up at eight."

While bathing and dressing he thought, Should I turn back? and despised himself for his need to ask the question. Should he call her and say, I'm sorry, I've changed my mind; for you see I have a wife and child. . . . Should he call her and say, Look, you fool, run from me and run fast if you know what is good for you. . . . Oh, she would discover that for herself, soon enough.

He rode with her up the mountains to a great tableland of stone that overlooked the city, and there, sitting on a precipice wall, with their legs hanging over, they looked at the lights below. Like him, she was shy and introverted; they did not find it easy to talk.

He said, "You know, of course, that I'm married. I like to have all such things understood at the start. I think—"

"Have there been so many starts?"

"Angele, let's not fool ourselves in this. Something draws us together. I don't yet know what it is but it's there, and we must decide early whether to surrender to it, or flee."

"Let's flee," she said. "I don't want to ever love anyone."

He learned that her father had abandoned her mother soon after she was born, that her first twelve years had been spent with her maternal grandparents. She was half-English, half-French, but looked more French than English. She had never married; she had never been in love. She was afraid of both. She had observed the marriages of her friends, none of which seemed to be happy; so she thought she would die an old maid, after traveling a lot, if she could manage to. She wanted to spend a deep winter far back in the mountains.

"In a forest lookout?"

"That would be nice."

"With me?"

He said he had to go to the Packer John Lookout. Would she like to go along? She said yes. He said he would like to build his own home somewhere in the mountains; four years in Chicago and three in New York had taught him that he was a mountain man. He said he was crazy about trees and would far rather live in a house built of wood, than of brick or stone.

During one of their many silences, he looked into himself and thought, You dismal blockhead! Take this woman home and say goodnight and forget her! What he really wanted to do was to put her to bed (for she was half-sick tonight) and tuck her in snugly; give her a hot bracing drink; and then sit in a comfortable chair by her and hold her hand. Lord, was there ever such a romantic as this!

"Ever seen your father?"

"No."

When she said he lived in Los Angeles, Vridar said he had to go down that way soon, for he had a wife and child in Long Beach. Should he look her father up?

"If you want to."

After three hours he drove her to her front door, folded her close against him a moment, kissed her beautiful hair and left her. He went to his room and sinking to a chair with a glass of whisky tried to shrug away his feeling of contemptible guilt. He felt that he would fall in love with this woman, and this woman with him. He did not want that. He felt that falling in love at his age (he had passed forty) would be a stupid thing. So he drank and brooded, and wondered what in hell drew him so powerfully to this girl, and her to him—for he knew that he could have gone to bed with her tonight and he knew that going to bed with men was not one of her habits. She was not beautiful. She was pretty. She had spirit, vivacity, charm, wit, and, above all, sharp insights. He suspected that she was perhaps the sharpest woman he had ever known, in looking into human depths.

He drank himself into a stupor and the next day went on thinking about her. It was not her fine body, he told himself, though fully aware of his interest in it—for Neloa had had a beautiful body, too, and Athene's was good. No, it was nothing in her physical appearance. It was something that appealed overpoweringly to the pity and compassion in him—to that meaning in the core of him, that need to protect and cherish. Time and again he came close to the words for it, and the image in it, while the emotion of it filled him.

Why, he wondered, did he appeal to her? Because he was a writer and in a small way distinguished? No, not that. It was not, he told himself, because he was handsome: he was so weary of his own face that he found shaving an ordeal: invariably he was astonished when he met a woman who thought him handsome—as astonished as he always was on finding a man who liked to look at himself. Sight of his balding head filled him with distaste; sight of his thin mouth, in which half the teeth were now missing; sight of his large brown eyes that looked at the world with such confounded hurt and sadness. His agent, a woman, had written after meeting him, "What an ageless mouth you have—what small-lost-boy eyes!" He was tired of his nose, which a news magazine liked to call hawked, though it was not as hawked as

759

the nose of a distant relative, Douglas MacArthur, whose nose the same magazine never thought it pertinent to remark on.

This girl Angele was a child. Though twenty-two, and wise in the ways of men and women, she was the most completely childlike adult person he had ever known. Marion had come west and had seen her one night at a party. She had got terribly drunk and after screaming at those who had tried to restrain her and telling them all to go to hell, she had fled to the bedroom where Vridar had gone to bed and had crawled in with him. The meaning was plain then, if only he could have seen it!— for she sighed like a child that had never known love and fell asleep, and he lay with an arm round her, feeling as he might have felt if he had been sheltering a wounded bird. The next day Marion had angrily faced his brother and said, "You unspeakable cad, get back to your wife! This woman will be asylumed in two years. . . ."

Again Vridar came close to the deep meaning but it still eluded him.

As she more fully possessed his consciousness, he became curious about her parents. Her mother was a lovely woman, still in her thirties, for she had married when very young. She had blue eyes misty with motherhood and tenderness, and a great heart that reached out to men who needed a woman's care. As he got to know her better, Vridar thought of her as the Mother: the capital letter stood for nothing divine, but only for female virtues magnified. It was her daughter and her only child who said to Vridar, "She's a godawful fool. She's an absolute sucker for men."

After Angele's father abandoned her, Leatrice Lee had married again, taking as husband this time a fast-talking booze-running outlaw of an Irishman, who would so degrade and shame her that at last she would draw on all her pride and run from him. Had she, Angele asked, learned her lesson with two sons of bitches? Oh, no! Leatrice had then taken to her compassionate bosom a lonely lost wastrel, who soon afterward was killed in an accident. Angele had decided that the world was indeed made up of murderers and murderees, and that her mother was of all murderees the one with the least gumption.

What was her father like? She shrugged. She showed Vridar a photograph, and he concluded that her father was a fop and a dandy—a very slender graceful man, who dawdled for an hour, Angele said, over shaving and primping—brushing his dark wavy hair into the exact position he fancied; tidying the small patch of hair on his upper lip; smiling to show off his handsome white teeth. He had married a woman more than twenty years older, a stout iron-willed tyrant who lorded it over him, babied him, dosed him with physics, piled hot water bottles around him if he coughed, slapped him down if he looked at another woman, and got all his property in her name.

"What kind of people are yours anyway? Your father marries a woman a lot older; his daughter is now interested in a man almost twice her age. Your mother married a man a lot older, then took up with one a little more than half her age."

Angele said, "I prefer older men."

"Oh, of course," he said. "Your grandfather was the only father you ever knew.

I dare say your interest in me is that of a girl for a father. Think of all the incest there's going to be in it!"

"You think of it," she said.

Vridar went to California to see his wife and child, sending word ahead to Angele's father to meet him at the railway station. He was there, looking just like his photograph—a very slender man, almost frail, who looked sickly and horribly neurotic. Vridar soon perceived that like his daughter he had sharp insights, for it was plain in the eyes of Wilmoth James that he was thinking of Vridar as his daughter's lover.

Having hated his father with hatred that knew no bounds, he had legally changed his name. After suggesting a cup of coffee and leading Vridar to a table, he sat and began to talk about his daughter; the tears came welling to his eyes and rolled down his cheeks. He wiped them away with what looked to Vridar like very fine linen. He was telling Vridar how deeply he loved his little girl, his darling, his beloved adorable one, when a waitress passed; and with his eyes lighting up James said, "Hi, darling, how are you this evening?" Then he went on talking about his precious and adorable Angele.

"My great dream," he said, his lips trembling, tears rolling down his face, "is to have my baby girl with me, to love and cherish. For over twenty years I've not seen my little baby girl. . . ."

No, Vridar thought, staring at him, or ever tried to; or ever sent her a Christmas present, or even a thin dime!

He wanted to tell Vridar, he said, how deep his love for her was, and always had been. He had tried to tell her this but she had never believed him. Would Vridar do it for him?

"I'll tell her anything you ask me to say," Vridar said, looking into the man's wet eyes. They were brown alert unhappy eyes, at which he daubed with the linen.

He said to tell her that all these years her father had worshipped her. There was nobody else in the world whom he loved half as much, and no father in all of history who had loved a daughter more. The waitress came by, and James reached out to pinch her buttock. "Darling, how are you?" he said. When another waitress brought a second cup of coffee he said, "Honey girl, how are you tonight?" Vridar doubted that this man was a genuine libertine. He thought it more likely that he was starved for love.

After coffee they sat on a waiting-room bench and James went on talking about his baby. He looked like a man who would burst into tears at any moment. He asked over and over how his baby girl was and if she loved him and if she would ever come to see him. He begged Vridar to make her understand the depth of his affection, and how much he had suffered, being away from her.

Vridar looked at the man, thinking, This is her father. At first he had thought James was an unblushing fraud. After an hour he was not sure. The man was an actor and loved to act but there was something very pathetic under it all. Wasn't there? Angele had said he had always been this way—a no-good fastidious little dandy whose great dream had been to be a famous baseball player! Vridar continued to look at him, thinking, He deserted his wife and child, changed his name, and married a woman old enough to be his mother. What sort of man was that?

When he rose to go, James offered a small soft hand. "Will you tell her, Vridar?" He was calling him Vridar now.

"I'll tell her but why don't you write it to her?"

James was weeping again. He said he couldn't bring himself to write it. He took out the expensive handkerchief and delicately wiped at his eyes, as a woman might who was conscious of her make-up. He wiped delicately down across his pale cheeks and at his nostrils and over the Hitler patch of hair. He shook Vridar's hand again.

Vridar picked up his bag and crossed the street. On the far side he turned to look back. James was standing there, a woebegone smile on his face. He waved a delicate hand. The man had so deeply disturbed Vridar that he took the wrong bus and rode for half an hour in the wrong direction. Then, in a fury with himself, he walked in a mental fog, saying, You miserable tinhorn ten-cent fool! Like Angele's mother you're a sucker for impostors. Just the same he couldn't put away the feeling that James was a poor unhappy lost soul who had never found love and would never find it.

It was about nine that evening when Vridar walked in on his wife. She was nursing the baby. He had not known that she intended to nurse it. He now had a vision of her down the years with sagging breasts and big ugly nipples. She rose to meet his brief kiss and then sat again to lift a full white breast to the babe's face. Vridar looked down at the child: it was reddish like its mother, with reddish hair, a reddish face, and even, it seemed to him, reddish eyes. He could see none of himself in it, nor wanted to. Out of the blue he said, "A Boise doctor told me that the last thing a man wants to lose is his testicles, a woman, her breasts." Then he sat and looked at mother and child.

He had always felt a little resentful toward human mothers. The foolish things got a babe in their arms and pulled out a large dug, and seemed then to think that the whole world gathered round in reverence. As possibly it did, one concluded, after studying scores of paintings of the Madonna and Child, all but two or three of which wearied him, because the babe was so fat and looked so complacently stupid. Pa had become a butcher, a war-maker, a murderer with his mouth full of platitudes: Diana-Ma above the good rich earth, Jeremiah shaking his fist at Pa.

The small apartment was full of baby-smell and he hated baby-smell. He had always hated it. He had always found it so nauseating that he had wanted to puke, as he wanted to puke now. That all came, he knew, from taking care of his sister when she was a babe: he had had to hold her, at his mother's command, just after she had been taken from the breast, and she had smelled of the sweetish odor of woman's milk and had rolled her stupid eyes at him and belched milk all over his lap. He had watched her toddle around with her diaper full and had sickened at the stink of her. Athene smelled of baby, the whole damned place smelled of baby.

When standing by the mother, looking down, he had for a moment seen the nipple before it was sucked into a greedy little mouth. It had looked monstrously enlarged. Athene had had nice nipples but now they were sucked out of shape and would be like big tough red fruits fastened to her udders. What horrible things life did to people! What a hell of a husband and father he was, according to all the mother-

762

judges: damn it, he was supposed to kneel and adore his child, and simper with protective ardor over the mother. He knew what the Judean-Christian world expected him to be but he couldn't be it. He had never liked small children and he would never like them; so now, sitting slouched down, detesting himself, he knew that he could never like them because as a child he had had to take care of two of them—to change the diapers on one and fight the battles of the other. Joe didn't like them either, and for the same reasons. Why did parents blight the life of a child with a sister who stunk you out of the house, and a brother who was the victim of every bully in school! He could remember how, when his mother was away peddling cheese, he had walked away from his sister to get away from her smell; how she had then toddled after him; how Marion had looked up at him, his eyes out of shape and his little mind full of wonder. He hated it all, he hated it all.

He searched round him now and found an army cot hidden away in a closet. He set it up in the kitchen and then went to Athene and said, "It's late, I'm tired, we can talk in the morning." Her aunt had come out of a small bedroom, and he had tried to be pleasant to her, though knowing that from the beginning she had despised him. During the few times when she had seen him drinking, she had fallen over with what doctors had diagnosed as heart attacks, but Vridar had known that they were faked. She so detested him for his drinking that she would utter a shriek and begin to flutter, but she always quickly recovered the moment he left the house.

Closing the kitchen door he stretched out on the cot, thinking. Athene would soon be in bed, cuddling her little one, holding it close as a mother should. Yes, a mother should. No mother had ever held him close. He had been a detestable sickly screaming thing that had convulsions, then was white and still, as though dead. He had been a fleshless little nightmare with big spooky eyes. He had been scared to death all the years of his childhood and no mother had ever held him close to hush his fears, no father had ever spoken gently. To hell with parenthood. To hell with it all.

The next morning while he was outside looking around, Athene laid a simple breakfast; and he sat at a table with her and met her steady eyes.

"You're pretty smart," he said. "You already know."

"It's another woman?" Her voice was low and quiet.

"Isn't it always?" He saw the pain in her eyes and he wanted to take it away from her and endure it himself. Her next question astonished him.

"How old is she?"

"Twenty-two."

"So young? She's hardly more than a child."

"Both child and woman—a very old woman, a very small child."

"In Boise?"

"Yes."

The hurt in her deepened. She was now unable to eat. She has pride, he thought: only her eyes will tell me, never her tongue.

"Are you sure? Could this be only a passing fancy?"

It would have been so easy, and so cowardly, to have said, Maybe! "I'm not the kind, Athene, who has passing fancies. I'm the kind of damned stupid adolescent

763

who falls in head over heels because he never had a mother. The physician is crazy and the prescription is wrong, but that's the only kind of medicine the patient will take."

"Did you fall that way for me?"

"You have only to ask how much it cost me."

"Or Shelley?"

"Or Shelley. Possibly the stupidest thing about me is that I don't stop loving one woman when I love another. The part of me that belongs to Neloa nothing can ever take from her. So it will be with you. I marvel at people who love and turn away to love again, as they eat and turn away to eat again. I'm the kind who must go on eating. With me each new love enriches those before, and they in turn enrich it. Don't think it a crass thing when I say that you will have me all the more securely for letting me go."

"You mean this won't be the last woman?"

"For how many artists has the third one been last?" Drily he said, "She asks that question, too."

"You remember what Neloa said? That day—"

"She said a number of things but I know what you mean. You mean the time she said in a fury, All right, she can have you. You'll leave *her* too, and that will be her punishment for taking you away from me."

"Well, I've seen this coming. Even before I left Boise I knew it was coming."

"I suppose we both sensed it. An estrangement had been growing between us. If a husband and wife grow closer as the years pass, it means that one to some considerable degree is assimilated to the other. We're both too strong for that. My unconventional way of life, the blight on my parental affections, my unappeasable restlessness, my free-thinking, my belief that the greatest quest is the intellectual—all these things have found no welcome in your heart. Your devotion to the mystical, to St. John and Plato; your extreme concern about what other people think of you; your strong tendency to conform to the herd, and do the right things in the right places—all these are no less distasteful to me than certain things in me are to you. Believe me, I find your fondness for St. John just as much of a vice as you find my drinking. So even if there were no other woman, should we remain together merely to widen the estrangement?"

"I knew it was coming," she said, her steady eyes looking at him. "That's why I wanted a child. We suffered so much together that I wanted something to show for it."

"My books—"

"*I* wanted something."

"Yes. Well, let us hope that he will be for you a prayer and a blessing. As you know, I was afraid. There's so much taint in my background, yes, and so much insanity in yours, that you'll need luck. Not for years can you know if you have a child worthy of your devotion."

"If I do have?"

"I'll be as proud as you." He took a cigarette. "You'll have the sole custody.

764

If you are now turning back to God—because, poor dear, you never had a father—I hope you will not make that a blight on his development."

"I expect to give him religious training."

"Do you mean theological? Nobody can give religious training." He smoked a few moments while looking at her, and said: "I suppose it doesn't matter what you do. If he has talent you can't blight that. If he hasn't, it doesn't matter."

"I want him circumcised. Do you approve that?"

"I don't think it matters one way or the other. Do as you please." He arose and went to her chair to tilt her face up and kiss her. "Just so you let him grow up to be a great man. Will you do that?"

"I'll try," she said.

Knowing that she was not as fully in command of herself as she seemed to be, that she might break and go to pieces if he lingered, or allowed her to talk longer about it, he took a bus to Los Angeles, and before noon was on a train headed home.

XVIII

He did not have much time to spend with Angele. Ten hours a day he gave to the project, and six hours to his own reading and writing. He was so busy that he had to decline nearly every invitation to dinner that came his way, but he made an exception of Dr. Julian Horne.

Physician and surgeon, aviator, baritone, gourmet. Horne was one of the most remarkable men Vridar was ever to know. His love of life, his zest, his energy were simply superhuman: it was not uncommon for him to eat four, and sometimes five, top sirloin steaks in twenty-four hours, washing them down with mugs of beer or pots of coffee. More than once Vridar was to see him drink two full quarts of whisky in a day and a night. He drank and ate and flew with amazing enthusiam. Now and then he wanted a woman, but women were not one of his passions and he knew nothing about them. If he slipped away from his wife to take a nurse out to the desert, he would say to Vridar the next day, "It was a poem, a perfect poem."

Julian was fat but he never moved like a fat man. Two inches under six feet in height, he weighed two hundred and twenty pounds. He was bald over most of his huge skull. He had blue eyes that usually were warm with good will and fellowship, but that could look terribly cruel; strong perfect teeth; a full sensual mouth that was not repulsive; and ruddy fat jowls that puffed out when he sang. He would sing, whether invited to or not. He would sit at a piano and sing and drink all night. He said he was as good as any other baritone alive, and there were music lovers who agreed with him.

His great passion was flying. For a few hundred dollars he had bought a small two-seater that he called The Crate. Almost every day he left his office and went to the airport to fly an hour or two, and usually begged Vridar to come along. Vridar went as often as he could find time for it. They would take a quart of whisky and squeeze themselves into the tiny craft, an attendant would flip the propeller, and they would be off. Again and again Julian headed in his tiny plane for a medical convention in San Francisco, Seattle, or Chicago. He never got there. Always he was forced down en route, at one time landing in an alfalfa field, at another, far out in a sagebrush desert. Once he came down in a treetop. His friends expected him to be killed: when in War II he was the only one testing a new plane who did not take a parachute with him, and was found dead, his head a hundred feet from his body, nobody who knew him was surprised.

People told Vridar he would be killed if he kept on flying with that lunatic. Vridar told himself it did not matter. If he were killed he would be done with his wretched life and two women could find a better man. Besides, he loved flying. He responded to the spirit of reckless adventure in Julian. They would swig from the bottle back and forth and sometimes Julian would sing like a madman in the roar of the engine, while banking steeply round and round, until for Vridar the sky was in the earth, the earth in the sky. Julian would take off for McCall, a hundred miles distant. Instead of flying over valleys, where he might have found a place to land if he had needed one, he would go up the backbone of a mountain range; and with a long bamboo fishing-pole Vridar now and then could have touched the pine trees. In McCall Julian would have three or four drinks and a huge steak, before flying home.

What, Vridar wondered, drove this man? Was it because all his children were girls? Horne slept only four or five hours a night. He would eat a huge breakfast, spend an hour or two in surgery, make his hospital calls, and then be off to fly or ride a horse or drive a car out to the desert. One day he prevailed on Vridar to go with him over Idaho's Primitive Area, in a cabin plane, with a pilot called Cyclone. When Vridar went to Angele to say goodbye, she held him close and wept, for she expected him to be killed any day, and Julian with him.

They took with them several bottles of whisky and a photographer. Removing a door from the plane, Julian persuaded the photographer to sit in the doorway, with his legs hanging down, and with his body secured by ropes around it that were made fast to the metal structure of the plane. With a drink in his hand Vridar rushed back and forth, trying to recognize landmarks and give instructions to the photographer, never suspecting that he was a pest and a menace. In Chamberlain Basin the angry pilot took the plane down and said he would not take it up until the whisky was gone and his passengers were sober. Julian hustled Vridar over a hill to the cabin of two strange brothers, where Julian said there would be such pork chops as Vridar had never eaten. He meant venison.

The next morning they were off again. Sober now, Vridar was never to forget the descent into the Middle Fork of the Salmon river. The canyon was about five thousand feet deep, and though the walls were not sheer, it was not a great distance from wall to wall. Around and around they went as they descended. On landing, Cyclone was worried about the take-off. The runway was too short, and at the take-off end there was a sheer drop of a hundred feet to the river. He and Julian paced the field to measure its length and then stood apart to talk. The photographer offered to remain in the canyon but the pilot thought he could take them all out. He was one of the "peak-jumpers": he flew supplies into lonely lookouts, or to fire fighters and hunters, and from inaccessible places he flew sick people out to hospitals. He was known beyond Idaho as a mountain pilot of great courage and skill. Vridar was not worried.

Cyclone carefully seated them, to balance the plane. He even clasped Vridar's arm and leg to guess his weight. He told them to remain just as he had placed them and not move an inch. Bringing the engine to full throttle before he released the brakes, he took off down the short field, and Vridar found himself holding his breath, found himself saying in a voice inside him, "Angele. . . ." It was a rough field of plain earth: the three men sitting on the cabin floor were thrown against one another and flattened. Then the journey was smooth and Vridar knew they must be airborne. Not until the pilot landed two hours later did they learn the dreadful truth: by the time the plane reached the end of the field it had not left the earth, and he had thought it would plunge down. He supposed that at the moment of leaving the precipice the plane was at the point of rising, for instead of nosing down, as he had expected it to, it had leveled out, after losing only a little altitude. It had been his closest call in fifteen years as a pilot.

A popular picture magazine asked Vridar to serve as guide to a photographer who was being sent in. Wallace Howser brought his wife with him. Her name was Jane. Wallace was a large blond man, fat and flabby, who looked like one who made it a principle to detest all forms of exercise. His wife the moment Vridar was presented to her moved close and fixed him with burning eyes; and when, a little embarrassed, he turned to Wallace, the man shrugged as though to say, If she appeals to you it's quite all right with me.

Vridar wanted some views from the air but Wallace said he hated flying. Jane said she just adored flying, and looked at Vridar the way Danny McGivern's wife had looked at him. Wallace agreed at last to take one flight ("Understand, I mean *one*") over the Sawtooth range. Vridar briefed the pilot: he would fly the entire length of the spires, and then veer to the Middle Fork. From there they would head for the deepest gorge in North America, the Seven Devils.

Vridar was so eager to see the magnificent Sawtooth peaks from above that for a little while he paid no attention to Howser. He had heard that high in the misty basins of these granite peaks were many small lakes, each like a jewel in an incomparable setting. He now saw that this was so. Going at last to Wallace, he whispered in his ear, "It's like this for almost two hundred miles in every direction." Wallace's response astonished him. The man made a horrible sound and lurched forward, and out of his mouth poured the contents of his stomach, while his hands sought round him for paper bags. He buried his face in a large bag and heaved and choked, and for half an hour he never took his face out. Then he staggered up, deathly white and smeared over with slobber, and told Vridar that the pilot had to take him down.

"In this country? Man, look out the window."

"Down!" Wallace croaked, and pointed a thumb down.

Vridar went to the pilot and cried in his ear, "Man very sick, says must land!"

The pilot looked round him. "Warren!" he said.

Warren was a mining town high in the mountains. On its field Wallace Howser staggered out of the plane and stood trembling, like a man chilled. He said he

767

would get to Boise somehow. Jane said she and Vridar would continue the journey, for she was as good a photographer as her husband. So they flew across a vast area of peaks and rivers and forests and suddenly were over the Seven Devils gorge, the depth of which at He Devil Peak was 7,900 feet. Vridar told the pilot to bank steeply, so that Jane could get some good views. Looking down, he saw Snake River like a narrow band of silver, eight thousand feet below; and as the plane banked and went round and round, Vridar knelt, looking out, and had never been so deeply thrilled in all his life.

On the return to Boise Jane again fixed him with hot challenging eyes but he refused to meet them; and to keep her from speaking to him, he pretended all the way home to be making notes. The pilot took them in his car from the airport to town. When at last he stood alone with her, she boldly faced Vridar and asked him to take her somewhere for a drink. He begged off. The next day she called to ask if he would go with them to dinner. Had her husband returned?

"Oh yes," she said, her voice high and airy. "It cost the magazine only sixty dollars to bring him in."

At dinner in the hotel Wallace looked ill. He picked at his food and smoked one cigarette after another. At last, turning to Vridar, he said, "Don't you think most Americans make too much of sex?"

Vridar said drily, "Some have thought they make too little."

"Just what do you mean?"

Vridar stuck a tiny fork into a piece of shrimp and was trying to formulate a tactful reply when Jane said: "My husband doesn't understand you."

For a moment Vridar met her eyes. They still looked at him in a bright hot rather insane way. Was her man a babilan? He was not, Angele said later, after she had met them. Wallace Howser simply didn't like women.

"A lot of men don't, for different reasons. What's his?"

She reminded him that the other day he was reading a Talmudic scholar, who had said that if after two years of married life a husband knew what his wife looked like he had never been in love with her. "Wallace Howser has always known exactly what his wife looks like."

Vridar looked at Angele and considered her words. It was Angele, not Howser, about whom he was wondering now.

XIX

She spelled her name Angele because she was half French but everyone pronounced it Angela. Her middle name was Marilyn. "Angele Marilyn Lee," he had said. "It's as lovely a name as Edna St. Vincent Millay. What my lips have kissed and where and why I have forgotten—"

". . . and what arms have lain under my head till morning."

Angele cast light for him on the things people were, when he could draw her out of her schizoid silence. One day he said to her, "According to Stendhal, the truest flattery lies in being a good listener. No one has ever flattered me so."

768

She looked at him with amusement in the sagebrush green of her eyes. "Who was Stendhal?"

"A novelist born in 1783, died in 1842. The greatest psychological novelist of his century but no one thought so in his time. No one but Stendhal. It was he who said, How many young girls die before reaching the age of twenty-three, and then what good are all the pleasures they denied themselves, to win the good opinion of ten old women who form the high society of the village."

"He must have been fond of young girls."

"Immensely. Nobody ever worked harder at falling in love."

One Sunday Vridar picked up a case of iced beer and drove Angele out to the desert. It was not desert really, but only semi-arid region overgrown with sage. They both loved the scent of sage and the ways of lizards. After following an old sheep-wagon trail for many miles, they spread a blanket on the sands and drank beer and talked.

Angele asked if he knew the Odes. William Ode, she said, had been a prominent Boise business man. He had driven his secretary out to a place like this, and had died of a heart attack while on top of her. In the black of night she had had to walk four miles on high heels in desert sand, to get back to town. The story shocked Vridar. He was looking at Angele when he became aware that she was feeling pity for the girl: so many times since he had met her, her response had been different from his, and more nearly right!

Vridar said, "I wonder how many people die of heart attacks in the sexual embrace. I had never thought of it. I'll die without having thought of any but a few of the things I should have thought of."

Angele said she wondered how many girls had experienced such horror. Imagine the poor thing's fright and anxiety, as she waded mile after mile in the deep sand, she was a girl with pride and spirit; she had called the sheriff's office and told them where to find him, and she had given her name. For being so brave about it, they kept her name hidden.

"That took real character," Vridar said. "Well, I suppose the moral is to see a heart specialist before you take your secretary out." He crushed sage between a thumb and finger and rubbed it across his upper lip. Then he opened two bottles of beer, thinking all the while of this woman whom he sometimes called Angele Lorelei Lee: she was a strange person, so much the little lost child, so much the old-old woman. After they were first together, he had found her at daylight, sitting by a river, bathing, and had known in a flash that the act for her was pure ritualistic cleansing.

She now asked him if he knew the Langweisses. By name only, he said. Mrs. Henry Langweiss was a social boss on Boise's most fashionable avenue. When she had her first baby, Angele said, it took her five hours, and during that time she ate three full meals.

"Oh come now!"

"That's what the doctor says. You know Mrs. June Plover?"

"Yes."

"She tells the story."

Yes, he knew June. He had been a guest at her table and had listened to a number of tales about Boiseans. There had been, June said, tremendous excitement along the avenue when a certain count came to the city; the matrons with the largest jewels and the most sumptuous summer homes on Payette Lake vied with one another for the honor of entertaining him. An old dowager named Janice Mae Hickenberry had won. After the count retired, Janice Mae, still agog at the size of her good fortune, had been looking the house over to see if everything was all right, when, with horror, she saw the count's shoes just outside his door. In a panic she had seized them and fled to her own chamber. What on earth could she do? Like most of the dowagers she had no servants that stayed the night, and she had no husband. Desperately she called a cab and hastened downtown with the shoes but all the shining parlors were closed. At a late newstand she bought polish and rode the cab back home, and there in her own kitchen she shined the shoes herself. She would never have told the story if the count hadn't turned out to be bogus: his father was a barber, and he himself had never got beyond high school.

Beer loosened Lorelei's tongue. "Have you ever heard about the man and the Mountain Home whorehouse?"

Now and then he was flabbergasted by the way this woman said things. "I'd think there must be a lot of men associated with any whorehouse."

"The one who climbed the ladder."

"All right, the one who climbed the ladder. What about him?"

Well, she said, when this man visited the house of love, he took with him a ladder and set it against a second-story window. He then climbed it and for a few moments peered in; then tapped softly on a pane; then raised the window—for he had known that it would be unlatched. It had to be, or he would have had to climb the ladder all night. He would raise the window and crawl in, but if at this point he did not feel as manly as he wished to feel he would go back down and come up again. Now and then he had to descend and climb the ladder a number of times, before he felt as virile as he wished to feel.

"You mean the imbecile had to climb the ladder before he could do it?"

"Yes, but why?"

Vridar set his beer beyond reach and lay back on the blanket and laughed. He laughed until his cheeks were wet. Then he struggled up, crying, "What a beautiful story!"

"Cookie, another beer, please."

Her endearing names for him also astonished him. He had decided that they were the kind of names children would use.

The meaning? It was simple. This dullwitted lubber had lain with his first woman after climbing a ladder. Maybe he was only a youngster at the time. Maybe this affair with a woman had endured for years; anyway, he had climbed a ladder to get to her room, and so had formed a strong association of the act and his manner of approaching it. This was much like another Mountain Home story she had told him—of the woman who always hung up with her wash a nightgown or two that were three or four feet longer than ordinary nightgowns. Her man had to have a lot of nightgown when he started up under with his hands. Both stories reminded

770

him of Moses McGuire who had sworn to heaven that because twice he had tried as a boy to seduce a girl in an outdoor privy he would always have to embrace his wife in one, if he were fool enough ever to marry. It was all a form of fetishism.

"Lemon sugar, what is that?"

"Associating sexual ardor or the act with an object to which it isn't normally related. When done in childhhood it carries over to adulthood. Common fetishes for men are handkerchiefs, perfumes, shoes, women's underwear, gloves, hair. The commonest in this country—you have only to look at the piles of magazines on newsstands—is breasts. The only possible conclusion is that most American men have never been weaned."

She was silent, thinking of what he had said. "When this man marries, he will have to have a two-story house and a ladder?"

Vridar snorted. "Either that or a psychiatrist."

"All his life he'll be climbing ladders? Is that what Jacob in the Bible was doing?"

Vridar turned away to hide a grin. On turning back he said, "My mother has always believed that a man can have his way with a woman if he'll rub under her nose the moisture from his armpits."

Angele made a sound of distaste. She was abnormally sensitive to unpleasant odors, for reasons that he had not yet looked to. She said, "Could a man conquer your mother that way?"

"God in heaven, no. No man could conquer my mother any way. I mean it's a superstition that my reading tells me is found in many parts of the world."

They sat on the blanket all afternoon and until midnight, drinking the case of beer and talking. Then they drove back to the city.

Marion had come out from New York for a long vacation, and to learn if he would like to establish a practice in Boise. Within a few months he was looking at skeletons in the closets of some of Idaho's most prominent families. It was not professionally ethical for him to tell his brother about them, but he did tell him, after pledging him to secrecy. One day he asked Vridar if he was acquainted with a certain ex-governor, two of whose abandoned mistresses were now on his hands. One of them was cracking up. Vridar had seen her, a scrawny neurotic middle-aged woman who lived in a Boise hotel. One midnight, Marion's wife called Vridar to say that she was worried about her husband, and to ask him to go with her to find him. Vridar drove with her up and down the city's streets, looking at every club and tavern entrance; and at last she said that maybe he was in a certain hotel, for he had a patient there in room 621.

While Mollie waited, Vridar entered the hotel and went to room 621. He was about to knock when he saw that the door was slightly ajar, and so he pushed it open an inch or two and looked in. He could have been no more amazed if he had looked at a room full of dead people. The head of the bed in this room was against the hallway wall, close by the door; and on looking in Vridar had found himself looking at the bed. On it was a woman with bony scrawny legs, naked as far up as Vridar could see them and on the woman was a man who not only had not bothered to take off his shoes or overcoat—he had not even taken off his hat!

Like one who at last had seen all in human beings that any man could ever see,

771

Vridar softly drew the door almost shut and hastened to the ground floor. At the car he said as casually as he could, "He's with a patient but will be down in a moment." In three or four minutes Marion came, briefcase in hand, a tall broad professional-looking man who in a professional voice said, "Waiting for me?"

"Mollie thought it would be nice to pick you up."

A few days later when having a drink with his brother Vridar said, "Don't you usually bother to take your coat and hat off?"

Marion's shrewd gray eyes narrowed and studied him. Marion drew deep on a cigarette and emptied his glass. "Not always," he said. "It depends on whether I'm in a hurry to get to the next patient."

"Do you give all the women the same kind of therapy?"

"Is it any of your damned business?" He said—he had told Vridar this a number of times—that the sexual embrace could be an important part of therapy, with certain patients. Hadn't priests known that for ages? Would Vridar give them sleeping pills or one of his damned novels to read? "You're not fool enough to think I enjoy it, are you?"

Vridar stared at his brother, wondering what to make of him. Was this the little boy whose battles he had fought in three public schools? "You charge for it?"

"You stupid blockhead! It's a part of the therapy, I tell you."

"I suppose the ones who need such therapy are always the homeliest?"

"Always," Marion said. "Always."

Vridar went away, thinking, What a world this Christian world is! He was thinking, After you've looked so deep into human beings you know that only a few of them are worth writing about, but that not enough readers want to read about the few worth writing about to give a writer a living at it. . . .

There was a State official who had become a Boise legend: two or three times he had been seen in his office on a table with his secretary. The fool had not even bothered to draw the shades, as Marion had not bothered to lock the door. At a party Vridar had seen this libertine, when drunk, suddenly run his hand up under the dress of his host's daughter, a child only about twelve or thirteen. Another State official had come to Vridar one day with a bottle of whisky, to say that the next time Vridar went to eastern Idaho he wanted to ride with him. Vridar was surprised on picking the man up to find that he was taking his secretary along. A devout Mormon girl who looked frightened, she sat on the back seat, and from time to time her boss turned to look at her. He was a man three times her age, with a mop of gray hair like Einstein's. On the way, he would lean over, like a naughty lad, to whisper in Vridar's ear, confessing that this time he hoped to seduce her. He felt that among her own Mormon people she might be more vulnerable than in Boise, where, so far, he had not been able to kiss her. He also confessed that he would receive an expense allowance for both of them and pocket all of it.

When Vridar told Angele about such things she merely shrugged. Her stepfather had been a bootlegger and booze-runner; she had heard a lot of stories about Idaho people. Both she and Marion were more disillusioned than Vridar. Having spent many years as a psychoanalyst, Marion now looked in vain, he said, for motives without taint. Conscience, he said, was a function not of the emotions but solely of the mind, being a perceptive faculty. It was found developed only in highly intelligent people whose minds were not the whores of their emotions. "Sheridan once said that the Prince of Wales, son of the mad George, was too much every lady's man to be the man of any lady. You're the exact opposite, so get back to your wife."

"You're a fine one to give advice."

"I'm the only kind accredited to give it."

Vridar had dwelt on those words: he liked his brother's subtle wit, he wished they could be friends, but he knew that they never would be friends. Marion would never have it that way. When Marion came to him it was only because he had to talk to someone about his patients. . . .

Ansel Macatee was a short round fat man, in business, who was working his way into the slot machine and other rackets. His bored wife, whom Vridar had seen at parties, had a huge nose, full red lips, and an indiscreet infatuation with a Boise newspaperman. Macatee, Marion said, had discovered her infidelity and had gone completely impotent. Marion thought he would become one of the worst crooks in Idaho, for the reason that the impotent crook was one of the most deadly. "When you were swiping all those groceries in Salt Lake City, I foresaw a brilliant future for you—and you turned out to be nothing but a writer!"

"In my babilan period I was quite a guy," Vridar said, grinning.

Gary Ward was another business man. He too had gone impotent. Instead of making a gangster of him, impotence was forcing him to bawl like a child and beg Marion to save him. Unable to think of anything else to do, for one with so little mind, Marion had sent him back to his Church. "The churches," Marion said, "are a kind of home for the foundlings whom the psychologist can do nothing for. It's better for them to be mindless and praying daily to an imaginary father than to be in asylums."

John Boyd Tatem was one of Idaho's most powerful politicians—a man who spent much time in Washington, always working behind the scenes, for a handsome fee. Vridar had sat one day in a hotel lobby and covertly watched Tatem for half an hour: the man's stare had been fixed with chilling sexual greed on every pair of trim female ankles that passed, and his lips, now old, had actually drooled. He had not come to Marion but two of his castoff mistresses had. Vridar had seen Marie Le Seuer at a party—a strikingly lovely French girl who was now venomously bitter. She wanted to kill. She said that Tatem had got her diseased first, then pregnant, and had hustled her off to a quack doctor who had taken out her baby and womb and almost killed her. *"John Boyd Tatem!"* she would say, grinding her teeth on each word. "How I hate the son of a bitch!" He had promised to leave his wife and marry her, but that, along with the mink stole and the flowers, had been only to seduce her. Marion said he had found a nice man for Marie, who knew all about her past and would cherish her. The man looked to Vridar like a neurotic mother-bound simpleton who needed a psychologist more than a wife.

Jonah Houck Shaw was a wealthy business man and another powerful Republican politician. One day Vridar had seen in Marion's waiting-room a tall handsome brunette. Later, Marion had said, "You saw the girl? She's trying to crack up

773

because of another of your God damned Republican friends. Jonah Houck Shaw. He promised to leave his wife and marry her, and instead of suing the rat and exposing him she comes running to me. Did it ever occur to you that in this happy Christian country, abandoned mistresses, and all their abortions and bastards, are one of this country's major problems? I looked at my files the other day and found that exactly sixty per cent of all my patients in this city are abandoned mistresses, and every one of the men has a reputation as pure as a jar of honey." Marion was silent a few moments, looking at his brother; Vridar knew that something was coming that he would not like. It came only after Marion had brought to his face his most twisted sardonic grin. "I could tell you things about your dear friend Rhode that would make your eyes fall right down on your cheekbones."

Marion would talk as long as Vridar had time to listen about the skeletons in prominent Idaho closets. He hadn't been in practice here a month before he knew about the girl who had to walk in from the desert on high heels; about the Mountain Home woman with the long nightgowns; and the socially prominent woman who did a little whoring on the side for money; and what had been done in a dark night when a socially prominent girl got pregnant by a Negro. . . . In a year or two, he said, he would have all the skeletons tagged. Did Vridar realize that he, Marion, could go up to the first hundred well-dressed men he might meet any day on Boise streets, and say, "I know all about it but for a hundred bucks will keep my mouth shut," and ninety-five of them would hand over the hundred, and the other five would run to their lawyers?

"And how many women?"

"More than you realize, including a couple you know. There are two compartments in life: people as they are and what they do, and the ideals they think they should live by. Those who crack up are those who can't abandon the ideals."

One day Marion strode into Vridar's office and shut the door and said, "The spy on your staff is now one of my patients. He has written a statement that you should read, but keep your damned mouth shut."

Taking from Marion a sheet of paper Vridar looked at it a few moments and then read these words:

> When I came to Boise, I did so with the conviction that I had two bosses over me, each of whom had to be humored. I already knew that they were not on good terms, and was in the unenviable position of having to be diplomatic with both and of keeping my self-respect.
>
> It soon became evident that Mr. Reese was trying to use me as an informer. Sometimes he telephoned me, sometimes he came over to the office, and occasionally we met on the street. On every occasion, he asked me questions in an effort to cast discredit on Mr. Hunter. I called it "pumping me," and as a matter of duty reported Mr. Reese's tendencies to Mr. Hunter, though for diplomacy's sake I concealed much. Mr. Hunter happened in and found us there, and afterward kept running in every few minutes during the rest of the visit. I was extremely embarrassed. I had no quarrel with either of the two men, and was anxious to remain the friend of both, which was an impossibility.
>
> Then Mr. Hunter went away somewhere on a trip.
>
> During his absence, Mr. Reese telephoned me to come at once to his

office, as he had something important to talk over with me. It was a rainy spring day, and I wore my overcoat. When I entered the door, he closed it for privacy, which surprised me. I sat down, and he started talking about the project and Mr. Hunter. He was again trying to pump me for information, and would make such remarks as, "Mr. Hunter spends all his time on the writers' project doesn't he, and takes no interest in the survey of historical records" and then try to get me to agree that he was right. I hedged and cross-examined, or better, like a prisoner on trial. Presently Mr. Reese informed me that Mr. Hunter was on his way out, as *they* had him over a barrel, so to speak. All it required was to push the matter a little with Washington. He then propositioned me, offering to give me Mr. Hunter's job, if I would join with them in ousting him. I at once protested that I wouldn't be a party to anything of that kind. I had gotten the impression that they intended to remove him entirely. I was flattered at the offer and the apparent confidence Mr. Reese had that I would not run and carry tales. At the same time, I was insulted that he would ask me to become a stool-pigeon. I also felt guilty, knowing that my attempts to be friendly had encouraged him to make the proposition.

Vridar read the statement and met his brother's eyes. Marion's whole face wore an expression of cynical doubt. "They got anything on you?"

"No."

"I expected a fool answer like that. Don't you suppose that they know about you and Angcle? Don't you realize that she can destroy you in this set-up?"

"I suppose she could," Vridar said.

"Why in hell do you get involved with women? Can't you screw them and let them go, or do you feel that you have to marry them to make them pure again? All that summer in Chicago I watched you with Athene; and now, by God, it's another one."

"Look. Remember the Italian in New York who came to your office and poked the gun in your belly? He said you'd knocked his sister up."

"He lied. She was a hysteric."

"Remember the husband whose bullet plowed a furrow across your skull? Remember the one who chased you with a butcher kinfe down Charles Street in Baltimore?"

"Those were both too close," Marion said, grinning broadly. "But you have a public position and have to be like Caesar's wife. You have to be the virtuous one for the two of us, for you have always been and you have loved the job. As for Reese, why don't you go over and knock his nose back into his throat?"

"I'm thinking of it."

"Why do they want you out?"

"To understand that you'd have to know what a stinking feuding conniving thing a bureaucracy is."

"Why don't you get out of it?"

"And make a living how?"

"Go back to teaching."

"I can't. I'm supposed to have tried to rape a faculty member's wife in Montana."

"Did you? Of course you didn't but you should have. Most women love to be raped if a man knows how to do it properly."

After thinking the matter over, Vridar decided to write the national director. He said he was sick and tired of Reese's attempts to force him out, by putting on his staff a spy, and all the psychotics in the city. He concluded with the words: "If he doesn't leave me alone I'm going over and belt his nose right back into his throat."

A week later the telephone rang. The voice was that of Archie J. Reese. "I hear you're coming over to bust me in the nose. Is that right?"

For a moment Vridar was speechless. Then: "Who told you that?"

"The district director in Denver. I want to know if you said it."

"I said it and I'm ready to come over and do it right now."

The telephone at the other end went dead. Vridar picked up his hat, stopped at a liquor store for a pint of whisky, and went for a long walk.

XX

At my age, he thought, I'm learning those things about human beings which any graduate of a decent public school system would know at twenty. Angele knows better than I what persons are like behind their faces. She knows that men and women are dominated by their deepest hungers, that only now and then does one rise to the level that can be called human. She knows that most people are far closer to the animal than to the human level, and she knew without being told that any government is made up for the most part of greedy selfish prestige-and-salary seeking irresponsible sons of bitches. Why haven't I known it? Why did I have to take this infernal job to learn that most of the so-called public servants are a particularly unattractive kind of whore? One day Angele had said out of the blue, "What happened to Prince Albert? He was a pretty good Bertie. He had a lot of good ideas for improving the British, but the more power he got the more he wanted; and at last he wanted to manage the lives of everybody."

"Another Roosevelt," Vridar had said.

Today he drove north to the hills and the mountains, and leaving the car walked a half-mile away from it and the end of the road, to be alone. He felt as sad and unnecessary as Titian's man with the glove. What he wanted to feel like was the Chopin by Delacroix, of whom an art critic had said that the face was agonized, rebellious, and burning with the fever of genius. Vridar had looked at it in the Louvre and had thought this Chopin a petulant neurotic brat who needed a good kick in his ass. Much closer to his mood had been the woman in "The Glass of Absinthe" by Degas.

Sitting on a grassy mound he took a swig from his bottle, rolled a cigarette, and looking out over Boise told himself that he was a romantic jackass and not a realist at all. Why had the book-reviewers thought he was? Thinking about himself, he began to think about the Idahoans whom he had met in the past three years, who had astonished him most. There was Johnny Wingard, who wrote books for boys. Johnny would get a woman alone and take his erect organ out and show it; Vridar

776

had heard him say, with smirking self-complacency, that eighty per cent of the wo
men in the world, or in the Christian world at least, would surrender to the male
organ, if it was as handsome as his own. He had made the statement at one of Dr.
Horn's parties, and a chorus of shrill women had cried, "Oh, Johnny, let us see it!"

There was Dr. J. D. Waltrough. Over in Oregon a man had kidnaped his wife and
fled with her, after having been driven almost insane by inlaws; and when out in an
Idaho desert the posses had closed in he had shot her. He was caught and sentenced
to hang, but slipping away from prison guards had climbed to a wall and plunged,
breaking his neck. Vridar sat one evening in the Waltrough home and listened to a
group of men talk about him. They all felt cheated, they all felt murderous. They
hated the man for having taken his own life. It was Dr. Waltrough, a small gray man
married to a huge and politically ambitious woman, who was most violent. He became so furious that he rose from his chair, hands clenched, the veins swollen in his
throat, his face looking strangled; and shaking his fists in the direction of the
penitentiary, he cried out that it would have been a pleasure to have choked this man
to death. Another doctor, two lawyers, and two business men had agreed, with
varying degrees of passion. Not a one of them had been interested in what had
driven the poor devil to desperation, or in the indignities he had suffered from his
wife's people, or in the unhappiness in his own childhood. Vridar had been too
shocked and amazed to utter a word. Recalling now the brutal enraged faces, he
thought, Who in hell wants to write novels for people like that! Then he laughed,
for there came to him the words in Athene's divorce complaint:

> That during their married life, the defendant was guilty of cruel and inhuman
> treatment towards this plaintiff in the following particulars: that the defendant
> was of a highly nervous and impatient temperament, and repeatedly nagged and
> harassed this plaintiff with unwarranted criticism; that defendant consistently
> felt and showed his disapproval of and contempt for the friends and acquain-
> tances of this plaintiff, and refused to be pleasant to them, so that the plaintiff
> could not feel free to invite them to their home; that the defendant frequently
> used violent and abusive language towards this plaintiff in fits of temper; that the
> defendant on a number of occasions humiliated this plaintiff in front of her
> friends; that the defendant was emotionally unstable; that the defendant was
> unjust in his demands for accomplishment by the plaintiff, expecting the plain-
> tiff to do twice the amount of work she accomplished in any given time. That
> on account of the treatment of plaintiff by defendant, plaintiff's health was
> seriously impaired and she was made nervous and caused to suffer from
> insomnia, and her peace and happiness of mind were destroyed. That the
> defendant is not a fit or proper person to have the care and custody of their
> child...

A few of the allegations Vridar recognized as the foolish stereotypes that lawyers
used, but in the remainder of the document he saw Athene's hand. Some of the
allegations were such outrageous lies that Vridar had been staggered, for he had
lived with this woman twelve years without having known whole areas of her
character. He had written her, "Sue on adultery; that's the truth and it's the easiest."

Why had she rejected the simple truth? Because, he suspected, she had wanted to make a record of her bitterness toward him, and pour a warm self-pitying salve over her wounds. He *had* been unjust in his demands on her talent, he *had* driven her to write a novel, he *had* nagged her to return to Chicago and take her doctorate. He had used abusive language, but he had never shown contempt for her friends for the reason that they had no friends who were not the friends of both. Why had she allowed such untruths to stand?

Well, to hell with it.

There was James Pope, senator from Idaho, running for re-election. Kate had entered Vridar's office one day and softly closed the door. She had told him that a man had come from Wood's office with a whole sack of Pope buttons. The man said that Vridar and his staff had to wear them. Vridar had said to his secretary, "Tell him we'll do nothing of the sort."

"They're going to wear them on all the other projects." In a low voice she added: "Did you know all your top staff members are Republicans?"

"I didn't know it," he said. He had never inquired into political beliefs. He had not cared about them.

It had been more than Jim Pope buttons. Roosevelt or Harry Hopkins, or one of their cynical underlings, had ordered the distribution of thousands of hams and food parcels in Idaho, to the poorer families, during the October before election day. So far as Vridar knew the human record had always been this way. It had always been dictators, corn, and circuses. What was needed was to strip away the accretions of myth, legend, superstition, and the self-protective assumptions, and feel the size and shape of the primitive man. He was determined to do this or throw his typewriter away.

Rolling one cigarette after another and swigging from the bottle, he thought of still other persons who had astonished him, and of his naivete in being astonished, a novelist at his age, with half a shelf of books behind him! There was Betty Brown. He and Athene had met her in Montana, and her tall handsome husband, a professor. Betty, a lovely blonde with cheeks like apple blossoms, had confessed that she could get an orgasm only from a man's finger. This she had said, with no shame at all, while her husband, red with embarrassment, had sat back sucking at his pipe. Looking at her, Vridar had thought, Because of fear of pregnancy, as a girl you let boys use their fingers, as so many girls do, and the habit stuck.

Betty had come to Boise to become one of Marion's patients, and had asked Vridar for a job. At the moment a top position was open and he gave it to her. That very evening she showed up at one of Dr. Horne's parties, and within a few minutes was holding hands with a tough-looking pock-marked aviator, who carried a walking-stick on which he had notched his many seductions. Virdar counted thirty-seven notches and said to the aviator, "My brother is whole leagues of women ahead of you." When by noon the next day Betty had not appeared Vridar went to the hotel where she was staying. Finding her door open a little he looked in, and saw on the bed Betty and the aviator, both stark naked.

No wonder the Christian world didn't like Freud!

There was Bill Moeller and his wife Peggy. Bill was bald over nearly his whole skull, but over the top of it had a wirelike furze half an inch long. His scalp when he talked about sex became the color of flame, and Vridar was then fascinated by the luminous underlightings in the furze. Peggy had eyes so small that they were grotesque, and when she smiled they seemed to close completely. Bill had confessed to Vridar and Marion that for years he had been trying to find a mistress, whom he would be perfectly willing to establish in a nice apartment and support.

Vridar accepted dinner in their home and during the long evening the Moellers told and elaborated and embellished one story. They had a maid. One evening the maid had a rendezvous with her lover, not far from the Moeller bedroom window. Whether Bill or Peggy first heard the ecstatic sighs and gaspings was a matter of rather angry dispute between them; but in any case Bill had knelt on the floor and peered out to see what was being done out there. He liked so well what he saw that he invited his wife to join him. So they had knelt together and watched the two lovers, until, no longer able to endure it, Bill had drawn his wife back to the bed.

They told this story, talking in turn, or sometimes together. Not only Bill's face and throat but his whole skull became red. Peggy twittered, closed her eyes, and clasped and unclasped hands in her lap. Then with eyes no larger than peas she would peer at Vridar through thick lenses, or at her husband; and because she was the intellectual member of the family, and proud of it, she would say sharply, "No, that's not quite the way of it. Why *can't* you get such a simple matter right?" Bill would then sit like a thing preternaturally alert, expectant, eager, his big agate eyes on his wife. Vridar listened to them all evening, saying within, What a thing is man!

Yes, yes, no wonder the Christian world hated Freud!

And there was always, as a matter for astonishment, his incorrigible and incredible brother. All through high school the girls had looked at Marion with a touch of horror, and Marion had suffered only Marion knew what torture. For years he had been taking his vengeance, if it could be called vengeance to lie with so many women who were willing. The plain truth, Vridar wryly admitted to himself, was that Marion was a realist, while he was a romantic, stuffed to his hair roots with ideals, most of them infantile: Marion said any woman could be seduced, if the man caught her at the right point in her curve. "I mean," he had said, "that she's like a stock market chart: if you manage things right, her interest in you climbs steadily, until it reaches its highest point---let us," he said, with a leer, "call it the bull market point. Then it begins to descend. If you let her begin the descent, if you let her go beyond the point at which she is ready to surrender, she will never again be ready for you and she will never forgive you." Marion had said that no person, man or woman, had ever regretted a sexual embrace that had been pleasurable and had not led to unpleasant things. This was true, he said, no matter how adulterous or shameful the act. "Wouldn't it be well for you, a novelist, to know these things?"

Vridar now groaned and blew his nose, remembering.

One of Marion's Boise secretaries was a young attractive woman who was married to a good-looking boyish but rather ineffectual man. One day Marion's wife blew up in a fury and fled to a distant city. Vridar was then living in Marion's house. She would return soon, Marion had said to his brother, and had poured himself four ounces of whisky. "I'm invited out to dinner tonight. Want to come along?"

779

Driving out Harrison Boulevard that evening, Marion said to his brother, "I'll tell you something if you'll keep your damned mouth shut." Marion always sounded angry when pledging his brother to silence. It was not because Vridar didn't keep his mouth shut. It was because Marion felt that he had no right to tell, and so feigned anger to pour ice on his sense of guilt. This woman, he said, had a baby. Her husband thought it was his baby. It was Marion's. "A damn cute kid and he's crazy about it."

On arriving, Marion at once marched over to the crib and looked down at the child. Vridar went over. It was a cunning baby, all right--dimpled, cooing, slapping around with its fat hands. Covertly, Vridar observed the mother, the husband, his brother. It was true: the husband was simply daft when he looked at the child. So far as Vridar could tell there was in the wife not a trace of self-consciousness or shame, now that both husband and lover were looking at the infant.

To the husband Marion said, "Fine boy. Bet you're proud of him."

"I sure am," the husband said.

"Looks like you," Marion said.

"That's what my mother thinks."

Marion then turned to the mother and said, "Don't you think he looks like his father?" Such an incredible double-entendre left Vridar gasping.

Marion turned away to see what was being laid for dinner. He met Vridar's eyes a moment, and in his brother's eyes Vridar saw so many things---the little hurt lost boy, the amusement, scorn, contempt, cynicism. Halfway through the dinner the telephone rang. It was for Marion. Almost at once he lost his bland poise. His wife had come home unexpectedly, he said, and he would have to run along; and run along he did, without finishing his dinner, with Vridar at his heels. The moment he entered the car he said, "God damn. I left my mistress in the house and I hope she had sense enough to get out the back door." After a few moments he said, "It's a wise child that knows its own father in the Jewish and Christian worlds; and if this hypocritical nation knew how many millions haven't known their own father, besides the millions of Indian and Negro halfbreeds, it would erupt in one great belch of self-pity. Compared to women, men know nothing about double-dealing. We're only males eternally rutting, on whom Nature placed a mandate to see that no female goes empty. Bulls, studs, boars, and rams all accept that as an honorable burden. And so do I," he said, turning to grin at his brother.

"We, of course, know our father. That's because our parents were so busy working eighteen hours a day on a frontier that they had no time for what Christians and Jews quaintly call adultery—doesn't it come from the Latin ad and alter? I can tell you this after all these years of seeing hundreds of patients, that if the full extent of bastardy were known in this nation, everybody would look with pity at everybody but himself."

When Marion talked about these matters, Vridar was content to look at him and listen.

"I suppose your conscience is killing you today," Marion went on, casting another cynical glance at his brother. "You could never be made to understand why this woman wanted a child by me instead of by the nice curly-haired boy she married.

All women worthy of motherhood want a child by a man greater than their husband. This man will never know it is not his. The child will never know. We all live in one way or another with things that we don't know." Marion was silent a few moments, as though to let his cogent remark sink in. Then: "If this son is smarter than any of his own sons, both he and the child are fortunate, aren't they?"

"Unless you push Mendel out of the way, isn't that a pretty big if?"

Marion seemed to brood over that a few moments. "Look, Athene's child is actually yours, yet you leave the child and mother. Your conscience got around that like a greased pig around a poke. I give this couple a child they'll both be devoted to, and that probably will be more intelligent than any of their own, yet you think me the worse stinker."

"I haven't said so."

Back in New York, Carl Noyce and Mollie had been a little infatuated with one another. One day Carl came to Boise on his vacation, as immaculate as ever, his nose twitching to lift the patch of hair on his lip, his black eyes flashing round him. Marion turned on him a cynical face, and said later to Vridar, "I know why he's here, but I think the woman long ago passed the top of the curve." One evening Marion picked up a woman for himself and drove with her and Carl and Mollie out to the desert. Afterward he told Vridar what had happened.

"My woman and I left the car and walked off into the night. We were gone an hour. When we returned, by God there they sat, and the stupid bastard hadn't even got his hand inside her blouse! Most of the geniuses in times past have been illegitimate. If all men were Carl Noyces, the human race would soon be one enormous Jukes family. And did you know that women have contempt for such men?"

O Lord, yes he had learned that! Nothing made him feel more the fool than to recall the contempt in the half-dozen women who had lain for him, whom he had failed. He was thinking now that he had read hundreds of novels, including all those that had been thought the greatest: how many of them had looked deep? It did not seem to him that he had, or that any American novelist had, except in an occasional passage by Anderson, or Cabell, or Nathan. In New York City he had taught the contemporary American novel to a class of about fifty students, most of them Jews; and he still felt self-conscious when he remembered what some of the students had said about certain novels, or had done to them. Rachel Steinberg, for instance, had savagely smeared with heavy black pencil every love scene in *A Farewell to Arms* and then presented her copy to Vridar with the words, "This childish author knows nothing about love, but only about eff-ing, and not much about that." Most of his students had liked *Ethan Frome, Something About Eve,* and *The Silver Stallion* (after he had pointed out their meanings to them), and *Winesburg, Ohio;* and a few had liked *The Time of Man.* Almost none of them liked Hemingway.

Sitting on the hilltop overlooking Boise he felt that a new approach to the novel was needed: *Ulysses,* and some of its imitations, he had found exciting, but choked, like a babe strangled in its umbilical cord. Some of the painters had been striving for years to evolve a new form: most of them, Vridar felt, like Picasso, Chagall, and Dali, would eventually be remembered, if at all, as experimenters rather than

781

artists: Picasso's "First Steps" he liked to look at, Orozco's "Victims" and Chagall's "I and the Village"; but he had not been able to put away the feeling that looking into depths not yet seen was far more important in art, than fluid and versatile art-forms that strove to represent a world that had become nightmarishly complex. He wished that he could achieve both but had decided years ago that insights rather than inventiveness were his strength, if he had any....

He wished he were not a wage-slave—that he had been born to some kind of substance, as so many writers had been, so that he could abandon this job, which he now found tedious and unprofitable, and give all his best energy to his own work. He and his staff had compiled an encylopedia of the state, and a volume of lore. Both had been published. So far as Vridar knew, not another state in the nation, nor any large city, had its guide ready; many of them, the national director had told Vridar by letter, seemed to be hopelessly mired in confusion or lost in loafing. A few years ago he would have been shocked by such news---by such shameful squandering of public funds, such betrayal of public confidence; but now he did not care a great deal about it, because three years on this project had forced him to look at men for what they were. Oh, there was a lot of good in mankind---there was in its highest members some pity and compassion, and a sense of honor; but its overriding passions were greed, vanity, and cruelty. Or were they? He would find out...

Darkness came to him on the hill and at midnight he was still there. He had smoked two cans of Velvet and drunk a pint of whisky; and he had decided that the time had again come, as it had come in New York, when he must choose between a meager economic security, and greater devotion to his own creative powers. He knew what the choice should be, but he had two sons in school; and conscience, as his brother loved to tell him, was the chains that bound him. Conscience, Marion had said one day, would make him second rate; and Vridar had said, "Very well, let me be that kind of irony, and put me in plain view of all men." Then Marion had cried, "Haven't you learned, you idiot, that those who fill most of the pages in history books had no conscience?"

Vridar walked back to the car and drove to his room. It was one o'clock. He took a bottle of whisky from the clothes closet and sat with it and drank and smoked; and when daylight came he was still drinking and brooding. For the life of him he hadn't been able to force the matter to a clean irrevocable decision. He bathed and shaved, and after pausing at an all-night stand for a cup of coffee he went to his office and stood, sleeply and tired and halfsick, looking at a desk that he hated.

XXI

On that desk lay an unfolded letter, and after a few moments he became conscious of it. He picked it up. It was from the national director. It said:

> Will you accept the position as Regional Editor of the Rocky Mountain States? The salary unfortunately will have to remain the same but you will receive actual expenses when outside Idaho. Most of the States seem to be doing nothing; I hope you can find out what the trouble is. . . .

Vridar read the letter several times and then in dismay sank to a chair; for he knew that he would accept, that again he would dodge the return to his own work. To try to rationalize the thing he told himself that he was being honored in a special way; that he would now assume larger responsibilities; that there was a lot of good to be done here.... O God, yes he would be eternally thinking about that! The good! The pure God damned righteous holy good! Conscience, his brother had said, would make him secondrate---the brilliant cynical son of a bitch! So here I am, he thought, an evasive cowardly fool, just about to assume larger responsibilities! Jesus, I'll be president some day! Some of those states don't have a single paragraph ready at the end of three years and they expect me to pull them out of the mire! Washington, I mean! As though it matters whether a second guide is ever published, or if the whole shittaree called mankind goes back to the slime!

This day there came another letter from Cahan, begging him to accept the assignment, and suggesting that possibly Vridar would like to drive the highways in a few of these states and write up the tours, and describe the national parks and monuments. "The fool," Vridar said to his secretary, "sounds as if the project is to go on forever, like syphilis and lunacy and Roosevelt!"

He had nobody to talk it over with. Athene had called him another Brigham Young and gone back to her people---and why think of her anyway?---for she would advise him to stick to the job. She hadn't liked the kind of books he wrote, and the time would come when she would refuse to read them at all. Angele, who wished to be a dancer and an actress, had gone to the Playhouse, in Pasadena. Marion had left the city.

Stupidly he said to his secretary, "Should I accept?"

"Yes, Dr Hunter. It's a great honor."

"An honor to make enemies in every state I enter?"

"Oh, but you won't, if you're tactful."

Vridar said wearily, "I'm afraid I'll never learn how to be tactful with boondoggling bastards who squander public funds."

He accepted the position, as he had known he would, and wanted to get drunk, or fly with Julian to the Primitive Area and eat venison pork chops in midsummer. But there was his conscience---O Marion, my brother! He went first to State Number One and unannounced he walked into the office of the Writers' Project. A group of ten persons was sitting on the floor, cutting patterns out of newspapers.

Vridar said, "Is the secretary present?"

A tall dark girl rose to her feet. "Are you Mr. Hunter?"

"Yes. Where's Mr. Shelton?" Vridar saw two of the women lean against one another and snicker. The secretary said he had not come in yet. An hour later at lunch Vridar looked at her across the table and decided that she was a Basque. He liked the Basques; they were self-reliant and high-spirited.

When he asked her if the project had any copy ready, she shook her head no and looked unhappy. It was this way, she said: the state director was a chronic alcoholic. He was drunk all the time and seldom came to his office. Nobody could do anything with him, nobody dared try, for the reason that he had been in politics all his life and had plenty of dirt on the others, from the governor clear down.

"So you just sit around cutting things out of papers?"

She tried to keep the staff busy, she said. There was nothing else to do.

Vridar sent the facts to Cahan by air, and concluded: "Shelton is a drunkard and a disgrace to the Project and the nation. I urge you to fire him at once." Instead of firing the man, Cahan sent a long telegram, asking Vridar if he would travel the principal highways and write up the tours. Vridar knew that he was a fool even to think of it; but now, in the prime of his writing life, he drove thousands of miles over the highways of this state and wrote every night until midnight, all because politicians in Washington didn't have the guts to fire a drunkard. Seven days a week he was up at daylight; gulped a hasty breakfast; ate a sandwich for lunch as he drove; ate a hasty dinner, and then for hours wrote copy. With what bitter mirth he was to learn two years later that when at last a new director was put on the job, he pitched into the furnace every word Vridar had written, crying, "Who is this bum from Idaho who stuck his nose in our affairs?"

State Number Two was Utah: the director there had been such a well-oiled politician that Harry Hopkins had taken him to Washington, to a fatter job, leaving the project in the hands of two youngsters, whom Vridar found cruising over the state and having the time of their lives. Here, again, he labored more than sixteen hours a day, seven days a week, visiting and writing copy on the state's magnificent parks and monuments. He never dreamed (this man who thought himself disillusioned) that a year later a new director would toss into a waste basket every word of the copy, to which Vridar gave his best talent, and four hundred hours of devotion.

The moment he was done in Utah he was sent to State Three: matters there, the national office had advised him, were in one hell of a mess. Vridar was met at the station by the director of Women's and Professional Projects, a large woman with gray hair, piercing eyes, and a chilling dignity. Margaret McHugh invited Vridar to luncheon in her handsome home, and he found there several other women, as stiff and formally proper as Miss McHugh. He nearly fell off his chair when she said, "Dr. Hunter, I suppose you already know that the director of our writers' project here is a drunkard."

Recovering his poise Vridar said, "I've just been in a state where the director is a drunkard."

"But surely not such a man as ours. Ours has corrupted the whole staff. Made drunkards of them, I mean. Most of them have bottles now right in their desks."

"Does your director here have dirt on the governor?"

"Oh, I suppose so. It's a most shameful situation that we have here. I've heard that some other states have their guides almost ready, yet after three years and a half we don't have a single paragraph. Did you know that?"

"They don't put such things in letters and telegrams."

"Have you time to write our guide?"

"No, Miss McHugh. I've written over a hundred thousand words the past three months for two other states but I can't give the remainder of my life to this."

"But perhaps you can rewrite a few chapters for us."

And so again Vridar allowed his will to be broken. What am I, he asked himself,

784

but a poor thing without self-confidence, and a pitiable wish to be loved! All my life it has been my way to do what people have asked me to do. Darling Mother!

Miss McHugh brought to his desk piles of manuscript, and all day long and late into every night he sweated over it, wondering when he would get back to his own work. It was past midnight one night, and he was typing, when the screen was removed from his open bedroom window and a woman's face looked in. It was a big fat round face and it was smiling. "May I come in?" she said. "My husband is behind me." Thrusting a huge leg across the window sill she said, "I own a book shop here. Would you like to meet Hoater Toater?"

Vridar just stared at her, his hands resting on the keys.

Having got a leg across she plunged forward, as though propelled from behind, as in fact she was; for now her husband's face appeared. He was pushing against the great hulk of his wife and grinning at Vridar. He patted his wife's enormous rump and said, "All that meat and no potatoes."

Struggling like a creature in a morass, the woman at last got through the window, and her husband followed her in. She extended a hand to Vridar and said, "I'm Bess Finnian. With a name like that you know of course that my husband is a Finn."

With prodigious enthusiasm Bess and her man dragged him away to a party, where he was presented to Toater, a dark handsome man who had brought his "girl." Bess had told Vridar that this writer was a homosexual. Toater's companion was a small delicate man who never said a word, but who looked adoringly at the garrulous Toater. Vridar thought Toater an awful bore: he talked about himself without ever once pausing, now and then squeezing the hand of the little man at his side.

One day Bess asked Vridar if he would like to see Frieda Lawrence. She was only a few hundred miles distant, she said. "Did you know Lawrence was not a modern man at all, but a bearded monk out of the Middle Ages?"

It was a long drive to the New Mexican spot where the restless and tubercular D. H. Lawrence had looked into the west to a magnificent skyline. Rass Finnian had a dry, sometimes a droll wit that delighted Vridar. Indicating a puddle of water in an almost empty riverbed, he asked his wife, "Is that the Colorado?" He looked at a highway map. "It was," he said, "the last time we came this way but they're moving rivers all the time."

"Don't try to be cute," his wife said.

To Vridar Rass said, "I'll give any man a thousand dollars who can think of one plausible reason why I married her."

Bess said brightly, "On my wedding day I was almost this fat. There's something special about a man who loves a fat woman. The painters of most of the madonnas did."

"And the little Jesuses," said Rass. "What soup most of them would make."

All the way it was incessant banter between the two, but Vridar perceived that they were fond of one another in a wonderful way. Rass was a handsome man, in both body and face. Bess was simply monstrously fat, but she moved, save when stuck in a window, with graceful nimbleness.

785

There would be visitors at the Lawrence place. There always were. There had been a Lawrence cult, Bess said, and now there was a Lawrence shrine. It stood on a hill above the house. "If you can say that a shrine stands, or has a geographical position."

Rass said, "Shrines are just about the worst thing that happens to famous men. Vridar will have one in the Antelope hills among the badgers."

Turning to Vridar, Bess said, "Have you ever figured out what was wrong with Lawrence?"

"It was more than bouncing buttocks," Rass said.

About twenty visitors were at the Lawrence place when they arrived, including Lillian Gish and a British poet named Angus Boden. Frieda came out to welcome the Finnians, whom she had met many times. Vridar saw a stout and rather dowdy woman, who looked, he thought, like a typical peasant out of the German hills. She took them into the parlor, where on walls Vridar saw a number of Lawrence's paintings; and she introduced a dark Latin-type man who came up and bowed stiffly. "Veesiters!" Frieda was exclaiming with disgust. "Always veesiters!"

"Is the shrine still up there?" Rass asked her.

"Vy, uv curse. Vut you mean?"

"The shrine of so restless a man ought to move around."

Frieda gave him an incredulous look, clucked a time or two, and went clomping away to see who else had come. Vridar and the Finnians went up the hill to the shrine, a tiny chamber, around the walls of which hung fresh boughs of evergreen. Rass said, "Would you rather have a shrine or an honorary degree? My wife thinks fame is something you pursue, but if you have real talent it is something you evade. For instance, there's Boden."

Boden fascinated Vridar. A tall homely man who looked arrogant in the English way, Boden was walking around with the air of a bird-watcher, and following him were five giddy middle-aged women, each with a copy of his poems. Each of them had her book open and was imploring him to unfold the sense of this line or that. Boden walked slowly, and five women yearning, according to Rass, to be knocked up by culture, twittered at his heels and the moment he paused they surrounded him. Vridar sat on a bench fifty yards distant. Not once did he see Boden look at the women. The poet looked above their heads at the sky; over at the skyline; at the trees; and now and then he looked past them but never at them, with an air of bland weariness, as a person of infinite self-discipline and tolerance might have looked at parasites embedded in his skin.

Earlier Vridar had been introduced to Boden. Bess had said, "Vridar Hunter is one of our most promising novelists" and Boden had given him one glance, a brief glance that was not even faintly curious; and Vridar thought, In Boden's world novelists are of little importance, and American novelists of none. Boden was a poet of whom it had been written that his adoring disciples took down and preserved in little magazines every word that fell from the master's lips. He was the one of whom the entranced book editor of a news journal had written, "He can write to order, in satirical vein, more brilliantly than anyone since Byron." As evidence the editor had offered to his readers these lines:

Thou shalt not do as the dean pleases,
Thou shalt not write thy doctor's thesis
  On education,
Thou shalt not worship projects nor
Shalt thou or thine bow down before
  Administration.

Vridar had read the verses doubting his senses. He had reread them. He had looked at the magazine's cover, at the name of the book editor, and then had gone to the bathroom and washed his face with cold water, thinking, When sound asleep I can write cleverer verse than that.

Well, there he was, Vridar now reflected, the most brilliant satirist since Byron. The poet was now looking up at a tree, but whether there were birds in the tree Vridar could not tell from where he sat. The five women, momentarily checkmated, seemed to be disputing with one another; then they were reading from their books, pointing, and their voices became shrill. Boden walked around the tree, still looking up. Then, like one watching butterfles in the sky, he came back up the hill toward Frieda's house, and the five giddy fat middle-aged women panted along after him.

Bess came over and sank to the bench, her large rosy fat face smiling. "Poor Dufferin, what did he know about Dufferin? What does Vridar know about Vridar or Boden about Boden? Are you ready to go?"

The three of them went to the house to thank Frieda and tell her goodbye. She said to wait, there would be food soon. Vridar saw that a dozen eggs had been broken into a blue bowl, and that the rim of the bowl was black with flies. Frieda was bustling around like an angry hen that had been lifted off its nest, her feathers fluffed out, her tongue exclaiming about veesiters. Watching her closely, Vridar saw that she was relieved when Bess told her that they would not stay for food and a few moments later when he took her hastily put-out hand, he knew that she was only dimly aware of him. Something had upset her.

The three of them stood a little while looking into the west. Lawrence had said that this was the world's greatest skyline. Bess asked Vridar if he liked it.

"It's the finest I've ever seen," he said.

It was too fine, Rass said; not even a poet could live with it, not even a woman who had lived with a poet.

"We'd better go," Bess said. "Around persons like you he strains so hard to be witty that he upsets his ulcer."

XXII

Vridar headed for State Number Four with a letter from Cahan which said, "Be extremely prudent. Our director there plays golf with the governor." The Colorado director refused to admit Vridar to his offices, much less to let him examine the materials. Firmly, coldly he met him at the door and said his presence was not needed and it was not wanted. The director in State Number Five also met him at the door and told him to go home. In State Number Six—

But he had had enough of it and more than enough. Sick and tired of the whole stupid dishonest thing, he returned to Boise, wondering if Norman Thomas was feebleminded. What kind of simpleton was a Socialist anyway? Only a child could argue for a one-party system, whereunder the people would have no control of their leaders, no power to remove them, no right to ask for an accounting of the stewardship. Who could be more the child than the Socialist, and who more dangerous?

God, yes, he had seen enough! Everywhere he had found the same cynical indifference to public funds, the public welfare, and the solemn duties of public office. Hundreds of millions of dollars were being squandered, but that, it seemed to him, was by no means the most evil part of it. The wickedest part was the steady and relentless corruption of character and principle under a government becoming more and more paternal. He wondered if F. D. Roosevelt would not eventually be remembered chiefly for that.

He wanted to leave it all and get back to his own work.

On returning to Boise he learned that another spy had been put on his staff, a short moon-faced little man, who sat at a typewriter pretending to be busy. After a couple of weeks the man came to Vridar's office and said he wanted to make a confession. He was a spy, he said. He had been assigned to this project and given one task: "I was told to get something on you."

"Have you?"

"Oh, I know about the woman named Angele Lee."

"Tell the man who put you here that he can relax. I'm about to resign. I'm fed up from my balls to my roof with these stinking two-faced bureaucratic sons of bitches who are squandering public funds, and you may quote me exactly. I've been working more than sixteen hours a day writing copy for three other states, on a salary of twenty-three hundred a year; and during my absence they put another spy on my project. That's my answer to all the infantile emotionally-immature self-idolatrous Socialists in the world. From now on I'm going to give a part of my talent and my energy to the effort to preserve the two-party system in this nation, in spite of all the Roosevelts. Tell Reese I said these things, and shall be gone soon, so that he can put an incompetent like himself on this job and run it into the ground."

The astonished little spy rose from his chair and bowed and left the room.

Vridar had a new publisher and a new editor, Jonathan Langfeld, who came west on his vacation and stopped in Boise to see Vridar. Angele was back from Pasadena. Vridar rented a small apartment, so that she could cook a dinner, for she was a superb cook. "I want to give the Langfelds the works," he said. "The best food and drink in this part of the world."

Langfeld was a shrewd, affable, able man with an itch to be wealthy and a bad tic in his right eye. Vridar took him for a drive and told him about a project he had in mind for a series of novels, that would try to go under the surface. Langfeld did not like it. He said that Vridar ought to write only American historical novels, like one he had written, that had been given a prize; and that if he would write such novels, delivering a book at least every two years, Langfeld would guarantee him an income of not less than ten thousand dollars a year. "It probably would be a lot more than that. Why bother about the past? Nobody cares about father and mother symbols, and Adam and Eve."

Vridar thought, If you weren't afraid to look at the Adam in you, you wouldn't have that tic in your eye. He said, "I'll think about it." During this hour he had got a chilling sense of his future: in this nation of children, would any publisher want such books? Vridar went to see Rhode.

"Go right ahead, old man, go right ahead. It's a magnificent project. These will be the greatest books of your entire career, and if no eastern publisher wants them I'll see you through."

Vridar was so delighted that he almost kissed the man. "But if they don't sell? They will be reviewed, you know, by barnyard roosters who, interrupting their chasing of hens, write essays about hawks and eagles."

"I don't publish books to make money. We take fantastic losses, simply fantastic. On your books which we published our losses were simply incredible."

Vridar didn't believe a word of it. A few days later he lost a part of his new affectionate interest in Rhode when a letter from that man said that because of his incredible fantastic losses on Vridar's books Vridar ought to assign to him a part of the monies from his new novel. Astounded, Vridar went to find Angele.

"Good God, why should I? He's a wealthy man. Look, I've given Athene every dollar I have, all I saved in four years by living in a cheap room, eating cheap food, wearing the same suit three years, and letting Julian buy most of my whiskey."

"You certainly need a new suit," she said.

He looked down over his coat, frayed at the cuffs and lapels, and burned with cigarette ash. "I've always needed a new suit. That's my trademark. Marion has fifteen and some day will be among the ten best-dressed men and I'll be in a nudist colony." He rose and paced, glass in hand. "You've never heard about this thing I want to do. I want to go back a half a million years and open all my senses wide and get down on hands and knees and feel my way to my feet, as that ape did a long time ago; and come bent over and dragging a club down the centuries, to find out what makes Vridar run. I've no doubt my brother would say I'm a masochist. I am. He would say my ego is so big I can't control it, except when I lie on my belly looking at the dust. But I think I can feel my way into a few things back there—into things that need feeling into, on that long dark bloody path leading up to the ape-man of today. Novels, I think, get thinner and thinner. After all, what *did* make Sammy run? Not what his author thought. What sent David Hawke a dozen times to Europe? I don't think the answers are in the present. I've read a hell of a lot and I haven't found them; and when I look into myself it's too dark. There must be a lantern somewhere."

He emptied his glass and filled it. "I know, of course, that the job is too big for my talent but I can try. I may be only a damned mediocre writer—"

"How dare you!" she cried, rising to face him, her eyes flashing. "How *dare* you say that?"

He sank to a chair and looked at her. Lord, what a ball of fire she was! During the three years they had known one another, they had more than once fought with such fury and madness that both of them had gone off in disgust and prayed to die. She had hit him so hard that she had knocked blood from his mouth and nose, and broken two of his ribs. In shaking her and trying to silence her, he had torn hair from her head, he had struck her, he had flung her head over heels. Their violent quarrels had reminded him of what a biographer had written of Stendhal: "After but a few months of intimacy these two vehement natures flared up in furious quarrels." In all the arts hadn't it been that way with a man and his woman?

But why? If he couldn't answer that question, some day, he would have to think of himself as a fraud and an impostor. He could not answer it now, not yet; nor could she, with her marvelous insights. They loved but they hated; and why the hate? he asked over and over, knowing that hate was based in fear. What was the source of the fear? Once she had plunged into a lake saying that she would drown herself, and he had dragged her out and then shaken her until she moaned with pain; once she had gone shrieking into the night to find a policeman; once she had had Vridar thrown into jail. Was it because they were both schizoids?

Still looking at her, he said, "I know you don't want to marry me and I don't blame you for that. You wonder if you'll be only wife number three. Let me give you a picture of what I see, all the way down the years." He saw her look of amusement, and forced himself to become aware of what he was doing: he had copied Langfeld's tic and his right eye had been grimacing as he talked.

Grinning at her, he said, "Angele Lorelei Lee, another world war is just around the corner. Why? There will be another brutal senseless slaughter of millions of men. Why? Now I don't believe that the adult male, if intelligent and educated, goes to war, unless forced to. What motivates such colossal slaughter? Freud didn't have the answer. Vridar is going to try to find it. If that is presumption, let the Yale and Princeton sophomores who review books make the most of it. I see my project, Angele dear, as an adventure in self-discovery which the intelligence of man owes to his spirit. It is my thesis that man must free himself of a vast burden of superstitions, attitudes, and cults inherited from his dark primitive past, before he can proceed to the next stage of civilization. I think that freedom from fear can never be achieved with social and economic securities and guarantees, but only by liberating the spirit of man from its ancient bondage. On that frontier of the mind I intend to be one of the first novelists—to be, if only I have the talent for it, its Meriwether Lewis. There are lights to kindle, and hills to set them on. Just what the Jeffers tower beyond tragedy is I don't know, but there may be in us something big enough to engulf cynicism. We don't have to write apostrophes to the navel, while striving in vain to cut the cord; neither do we have to reduce life to the bull-ring, the saloon, and the bedroom. It would be infantile to rhapsodize on the summit of our inheritance, as one critic hopes I may some day do; but it's an especially ripe chump who says that having come so far through ages of terror and darkness we can go no farther."

He poured whisky into their glasses, and kissed Angele in the burnished lights of her hair. "In a novel I wrote some years ago I said, Persons everywhere sought the simple and eternal things and struggled meanwhile with a social organism so intricate that they could no longer see its outline and form. That is part of our problem but it's not, I think, what is making such fools of us. Whatever it is, it has come from the past. I'm going back to find it. I still have two or three thousand books to read, and most of them are big fat books. What a feast it's going to be! What an intellectual adventure!

"I want a piece of waste land—of utterly worthless waste land, with plenty of water on it. Is that more masochism? I want the two projects to go hand in hand— our development of this waste into something beautiful, and of the past into a light on a hill. Are you going to like it?"

She did not reply at once. She looked at him steadily for a full minute before she said, "I think so."

"You're very brave or very foolish—for I'm talking about a project that would scare any sensible man into the cellar. Are you insane?"

"About half," she said. "The other half is drunk."

"Good bourbon," he said. "We won't be able to afford that kind, or possibly any kind."

He drank again and went on talking. He said he would have to read his eyes out and take tens of thousands of notes, and classify and file, and brood over the project endlessly, like a hen full of paranoia. From libraries all over the nation books would be sent to his mailbox, and he would find the joy in reading them that some men found in killing defenseless things in Africa, that others found in power over their fellows. He would want a few thousand trees, for he was a fool about trees: in his childhood they had been strong lovely things that stood firm against wind and storm and all the terrors.

It would all be a labor of love. There would be countless hours of talk: they would marvel at the fact that the ancients worshipped the sky as a god (people still invoked its protection); at the fact that the horseshoe above the door, and most church doors and windows, were a symbol of the female genital; at the fact that the bishop's mitre was a modified form of the fish-head and mouth, plum pudding a survival of the festival cakes made to honor the sun, and bonfires and the lights on Christmas trees a part of what remained of ancient sun-worship. They would learn why the woman received presents prior to her wedding, why the man went to the bride's house to be married; why the bridegroom had a best man; why he placed a ring on the bride's finger; why they hastened away on a journey. If Christians only knew the meaning of that one!

They would cast an inquiring eye at the origin of the priest's stole, his vestment, his cross, and the golden rays; and at the walking-stick which Rhode loved to carry. They would know why serpents until recent times had been burned in the Pyrenees on the Eve of St. John; why there were church houses in Ireland above whose doors was a sculptured woman pointing to her genitals. They would learn how saturated human habits and thinking were with the superstitions of the ancients. They would know why a person covered his yawn with a hand; why all the men present got to kiss the bride—a long time ago they had copulated with her, and the best man today, poor fellow, was only the pale ineffectual survival of the god-phallus. They would know the origin of elopement, of lifting the bride across the threshold (ah, that menstrual blood!), of woman's fear of the serpent, of the childish story of the Garden. . . .

He would be a difficult thing to live with, he said: there was his unbreakable habit of projecting himself into the emotions and senses of the persons he met, such as Langfeld's tic, Wilford Pogue's grin, Julian's bouncy walk—the Langfeld tic had got so bad that Kate had asked what was wrong with his eye.

Angele said, "I wish you'd stop picking at your nose. What does that mean?"

"Probably only that the damned thing is hard to keep clean. Marion also does."

"It's a repulsive habit."

"Abominable. It's a habit with people who think a lot."

"Do you learn anything imitating people?"

"Oh hell yes. I don't know what Langfeld's compulsion is, but I learn a lot by projecting."

"What?"

"Well, take the way people walk. If you'll imitate the walk a while, it will help you get inside the person and tell how he's feeling. Take you. You have a small foot and you're proud of your shoe size. You have what people call a dainty walk. Either you feel dainty or you want to. You have a great urge to feel physically clean and that is related to your walk. When I walk daintily as you, I want to take a bath or I feel as if I had just had one."

For a few moments he studied the incredulity in her face. "Yes, you'll find me difficult at times, and not only when I'm picking at my nose and thinking, unaware that some important person is watching me. I mean when I go hellbent projecting into the past—for how did the ape-man feel? Will I knock you senseless with a club? Will I rape you?"

"I hope so," she said.

He went over to kiss her and then resumed his talking. Mankind's job, as he now saw it, was to grow up and stand on its feet, without wailing to Papa. "That means without Aquinas or Joseph Smith, Stalin, Hitler, or Roosevelt, Isaiah or Paul or the Pope. Religion is a private and sensitive matter, for anyone sensitive enough to be religious. The rest of it is theology and the orphanage.

"Lorelei, as children we stagger through life, carrying the dreadful burden of misinformation and superstition from our parents—their prejudices, phobias, compulsions, illusions, and all their myths and legends; and we never get out of it. Scores of writers have called this nation adolescent. I'll find a better word for it. I haven't been able to see much adultness in the Judean-Christian world. There's a reason for it.

"Faust's sin was love of knowledge. In all the stories about Faust the Devil is defeated because of the treachery of man. As Mark Twain said, Satan's side has never been told. I'm going to tell it. It's not the popular side. I may not have many readers—can hardly expect to have in a nation of breast-worshipers who have cast knowledge out and glorified ignorance. This country is incurably anti-intellectual."

He drank again. Wavering a little he stood with a full glass and looked at her. "In fact," he said, "Christians have made knowledge and mind such shameful things that you have to get drunk to have the nerve to talk about it. To dare to use your mind, I mean. To give me cheer and courage, in those moments when the Jewish god or my mother yells at me, I'm going to make a panel to hang on the wall by my desk." He took a three-by-five card from a pocket. "Such as this," he said, handing it to Angele.

She took the card and read:

> There can be no true objective criticism until a man stands more or less indifferent to the result, and frees himself as far as possible from all subjective relations to the object of criticism—Baur

"That's Baur, a great scholar, the kind of father I should have had. What he says is so deep and true that nine-tenths of the book reviewers in this country could not possibly understand it, even if they could be got to read it. Hatred, says Inman, is generally to be measured by the mental incapacity of those who indulge in it. Not hatred: that's not the word he should have used. Maybe the word is fear.

"I know," he went on, pacing, "that I presume. But I tell you an era has ended, and it needs a Dante to bring it into synthesis and lock the door. I'm no Dante, nor is this age as simple as the one he closed but I'd like to do a little pioneering toward the task. Somewhere in his monstrous encyclopedia Vincent of Beauvais says that of making books there is no end: if only he could see the libraries now! In Klinger's novel about Faust's compact with the Devil it is predicted that the art of printing will turn out to be mankind's greatest enemy. Look at the newsstands and tell me if he was right."

He kissed her hair and then bent over to look at her scalp. "You have dandruff," he said.

"To hell with you!" she cried and pushed him away.

"Well, I can think of nothing else on which to spend such intelligence as I have. And I must spend it. In this world much is said about the waste of natural resources, but the greatest waste is of intelligence. Our public schools don't develop minds; they merely give diplomas to lazy habits. The ablest of all my teachers told me that I should learn one thing that very few people are able to learn, before I could call myself an educated man—to respect the integrity of a fact, and the privileged position of a probability. That light has been shining on me ever since that day.

"We have come through what self-pity has called the lost generation. Hitler has taken the world to war again. This kind of madness will go on until people are forced to get off their bellyaching ten-year-old asses and stand up. There can be no salvation through the Roman or any other Church; nor through any form of Socialism as long as emotionally immature butchers like Stalin are allowed to rule, or Roosevelt, whose umbilical cord reaches clear to his mother in Hyde Park. No man knows through what wild centuries roves back the rose and I am going back to have a look at it. Life at the human level is a challenge to be conscious. A high degree of consciousness leads to an examination of motives. An examination of motives leads back to their ancient sources. All that we are begins away back there."

A little unsteady on his feet, he paused awkwardly now and then to drink from his glass. He saw that Angele was getting drunk, too. They had been drunk together a number of times.

793

He said, "Like a submarine I'll submerge. I'll go as deep under the surface as I can but I'll have to surface from time to time. Or go mad. D'Annunzio begged Duse to promise that if he cracked up she would hide him from the world. Then he asked, But how will you know that I am crazy?"

"You're half-crazy now," Angele said, looking at him.

"I've always been. Or is it what Strindberg had in mind? He said he lived the lives of all the people he put in his writings—that he was happy with the happy ones, evil with the evil ones, good with the good. He abandoned his own personality and spoke with the tongues of children, women, old men. Any artist must do that. Shaw said he was fond of women, or of one in a thousand, but earnest about some other things. For most women, he said, one man and one lifetime make a world; but he required whole populations and historical epochs to make the writing machine that was Shaw. Love for him was only a diversion. The historical epochs were his life. Would Marion say that another colossal ego ran wild?

"Goethe said that all his writings were confession. For an intelligent sensitive person, what is living itself but confession?—as it is with you and me at every turn; for we both know that these insane impulses to destroy one another and ourselves are frustrations in the tree shut away from the sun. And that reminds me that I must begin to jot down clues—must carry a pad with me. Heaven help me if I'm found in an accident and the police carry the pad to a newspaper!"

He sat and drew her to his lap but at once he was up, his mind full and over-flowing, his emotions because of whisky flowing across his mind. Would she like this kind of life?—he wanted to know. Did she agree with her favorite, Duse, that she has the greatest riches who is not compelled to want them?

"Are you going to be like d'Annunzio, who drove himself crazy worrying about growing old?"

"I expect I will. It's a horror I shudder to think of. Upon the breast that gives the rose shall I with shuddering fall? asked Meredith. I suspect maybe he did. As for me, yes, yes! I'll fall shrieking and they'll have to put me in irons. In all serious-ness though we must face the fact that Marion and I may both be institutional cases before we die. We had the parents for it."

He sat on the floor by her and enfolded her knees. She put a tender palm over his bald spot. "What a person you are!" he murmured against her. For she actually did not mind his baldness, or the fact that most of his teeth were gone. He knew that this was so because the closest and dearest man in her life had been her grand-father, who had taught her to be a friend to all helpless things.

"Cookie," she said, "I like to hear you talk as you have tonight, but I wonder if you want to be a successful writer. If so, why did you weep when you got the prize?"

If she had stung him with flame, he would not have moved more swiftly to his feet. He stood, looking down at her, and she looked up, her eyes troubled. He turned to the table to pour himself another drink. Yes, it was the shameful truth! He had gone absolutely hell-roaring mad. He had poured bitter grief out of him like a stupid blubbering lubber, moaning out of anguish that he would never be worth a hill of terds. He had wept himself into complete exhaustion and slept where he had fallen.

But this! Her words had stirred something hiding deep within him, some evil furtive thing down there in the dark of his nature.

"But why?" he said, turning to her. "How stupid that would be!"

"Yes."

He put the glass away and sank to the floor, putting his face to her knees. "I don't know," he said, "I don't know but I will know some day." Then, in spite of all he could do, his controls and restraints failed him; and he turned weeping to the floor and buried his face in his arms.

PART III

THE ORPHANS

"When mankind desires to create something big, it must reach down deep into the reservoir of its past"—Stekel

I

Vridar had played with the thought of living in Austria, Majorca or Mexico, where costs were low, but a wealthy industrialist from San Francisco gave him a party in a Boise hotel and begged him to remain in the state where he was born. "Idaho needs you," he said; and Vridar replied, "Idaho detests me." He looked for a piece of waste land on which to build a house, in which he could read a few thousand books, and write a few of his own. He chose a spot in Cold Water valley, because of its many springs and waterfalls.

He and Angele were still exploring it when one morning he hustled her into the car and headed for town. She was alarmed. She turned on him in fright and suspicion, and demanded to know what he had in mind.

"We're going to be married," he said.

"Like hell we are!"

He was in slacks and open shirt; she was in shorts, with shoes of different colors, her long hair piled in a big loose topknot on her head, a short fur jacket hanging from her shoulders. For twenty miles she angrily protested, while he tried to silence her by thrusting at her a bottle of whisky. She did drink with him and they were both a little drunk when they arrived. Seizing her arm, he dragged her, protesting, out of the car and into an office; and to the astonished justice of the peace he said, "Make us man and wife but cut out the fancy stuff, no honor and obey, none of that." With eyes as big as duck eggs and an open mouth looking like a lamphrey's, the justice looked at Angele's shoes, one brown and one white; at her naked legs; at the ridiculous piece of fur around her shoulders. He saw that she was sullen and unwilling, but jovially he said, "Do you take this man as your husband?" When Angele gave no response Vridar poked her in the ribs and hissed, "Say yes, you idiot!" In a barely audible voice Angele said yes. His eyes still bugged out, the justice asked Vridar, "Do you take this woman as your wife?" "Yes." "I now pronounce you man and wife. Kiss your wife and give me ten dollars." Angele cried. "Ten dollars! Is this little farce costing ten dollars? We should have bought a mule." The justice seemed to think her remark terribly funny: he doubled over with loud cynical laughter, while from behind a curtain a woman, who had served, Vridar was to learn later, as the witness, peered out, her small white face as round as the moon. Vridar took his wife's arm and hustled her back to the car, saying, "Always remember that if you didn't marry the right man it is not only your bad luck but also his." He looked at the distaste in her face and added: "Taking a woman off me is like taking her off narcotics: she hates the habit but has surrendered to it." Angele made a face, as if suddenly she had felt nausea.

A few days later Vridar received a letter from his mother. Joe had a wild six-year-old stud that he was trying to break to the harness. Would Vridar come help him? Before Vridar and Angele arrived at the South Fork ranch, they heard the bad news: Joe had gone into the stable where he had the beast tied, and the stallion had reared and fallen on him, breaking seven ribs. "I'll teach the son of a bitch," Vridar said.

Angele's temper flared. "Why call him that? You men call any animal a son of a bitch that doesn't come crawling to you like a dog."

Startled, Vridar looked at her. Day after day out in countryside he had learned how deep was her sense of fellowship with the animal world.

With the help of his mother and wife, Vridar got the stallion harnessed and in his place against a wagon tongue, with a large gentle horse across the tongue. He thought he had them both securely snubbed to a fence, but when he moved to lift the neckyoke the stud came up in a flash, striking blows with his front feet as swift as lightning. One stone hoof struck Vridar's forehead and knocked him rolling. He was rushed to a hospital where it was found that he had a multiple fracture; and though he was told that he ought to remain in the hospital a week or two he left it at once and went with Angele to a motel. There they got drunk. There they quarreled. They quarreled about animals—like Albert Schweitzer she thought that nothing should be killed, not even scorpions, rattlesnakes, and black widow spiders. While he shouted at her, she shrieked at him. He knew that he was acting like an incredible idiot—knew that he was getting drunk and violently angry, and might die at any moment because of his broken skull. In such moods he did not care. In such moods he felt that he had thrown his life away on women, and Angele felt that she had been sentenced to purgatory when she married him. On her wedding day she had said, "I'd rather be the mistress of twenty men than be hurt by one." Now, roaring out of self-pity, he shouted, "I could fall before you with a brain hemorrhage and you'd not care a damn!" With rage as violent she replied, "You said you were going to shoot that poor horse, you criminal! Do you care about him?" Exhausted, at three in the morning, they fell into bed.

For two weeks he had splitting headaches and was afraid of a blood clot. But his luck still held. A dozen times in his life, it seemed to him, he should have died, for the odds had been long against him. Angele said he must take better care of himself. She was contrite after the quarrel, as she always was—penitent, humble, lonely, and lost: she then had to have his arms around her, his lips on her skin. Holding her and knowing how alone and lost she was, he again came close to the truth he sought, but still missed it.

Minor truths were leaving his subconscious mind and coming to the surface. In thirty days the two of them, rising at daylight and working till dark, built a small cabin, with parlor, bedroom, bath, kitchen, and closet. They would live in this while building a larger house. Sun-tanned, healthy, and ravenous in all their hungers, they drew spiritually closer, working as man and wife: few memories for either of them would be more pleasant than their memories of this summer. They had chosen a spot with a small natural lake against a mountain wall, from which white waters burst and came foaming down. At noontime they took bread and a can of beans, lettuce, radishes, and pickles, and sat by a waterfall to eat. This, Vridar said, looking round him, was the life he loved. He guessed it was the Joe in him. "You get more like Joe all the time," his brother said contemptuously.

One day when looking round him he was astounded. He began to mutter. What was he doing here anyway!—digging out of the bowl of his childhood home, or out of his mother? For look! Good God, look! He had chosen a spot that in most ways was a small image of his childhood homeplace; the river was on three sides of one, a large creek on two sides here; a great lava rimrock rose above both; a road descended to each. On the homeplace were thousands of evergreen trees; here he planned to have hundreds!

He hungered so mightily for the sight of green and growing things on his patch of alkali waste that from a neighbor he got a few square feet of grass sod and set it in the earth by the cabin door. He was so ignorant of horticulture, of the nature and composition of soils, that he bought an azalea, a heather, and a rhododendron and planted them in clay so fine and heavy that it was perfect for making pots. He was heartsick as he watched his plants die. For years he would toil like a slave here, he would plant hundreds of lovely trees and shrubs, and whole orchards of apple, apricot, pear, peach, plum, and cherry, before discovering that his soil was a part of the ancient Bonneville lake bed. The fine silt had been laid down in strata: digging into it he found the shells or skeletons of small creatures that had lived a million years ago.

He bought two hundred lodge pole logs, peeled but still green. He put up what he called a shop, a garage, a barn; with mattock he labored long hours uprooting the huge greasewood and sagebrush; and one day when he sank the blade beneath a root and heaved upward on the handle he felt a pain like flowing fire across his belly. On hands and knees he crawled to the cabin, and then lay on the bed in such agony that sweat poured from his whole body. Angele hastened to a doctor friend and returned to tell Vridar that he had a bad sacroiliac sprain and that his days of hard labor were done. He rumbled with fury. "The imbecile! What damn fools doctors are!" He knocked sweat from his brow and rubbed it out of his eyes, and muttered that he had lancinating pains all through him.

For a week he lay on the bed, hating this that had happened to him—hating it with such fury that hate and fury made him ill. The agony when he moved was so sharp and terrible that it sucked at his breath and took it away. But he forced himself to move. God Almighty, he was not going to lie here the rest of his life! Moving, he sought desperately for some miracle, some magic, that would restore him to his strength and his work. He was not one who would ever be an invalid; he would move around normally or he would die. Angele begged him to go to a doctor. There was a chiropractor in Boise— He exploded with scorn. Would she have Mormon elders laying hands on him next?

But at last, with sweat bursting from all his pores, he bathed and got his clothes on, and walking doubled over headed for the car. Trying to enter the car, he fainted. After he was in it, sitting was unbearable torture as the machine jolted over rough roads. He had no more faith in chiropractors than he had in astrologers, dowsers, and exorcists, yet consented to see this man in whom Angele's mother had great faith. Dr. Hernander asked a few questions. Saying then that he would give Vridar a blood-test, he swabbed with alcohol the third finger on the left hand. picked up a needle, and thrust into the second finger, which he had not cleansed at all. Vridar's eyes popped out, as he looked at one finger and the other and at the man's sunless sallow face. Vridar was next sent to a nurse, who had him pull off his trousers and shorts; and with cool professional hands she placed a pad around his genitals. Ready to explode with fury, Vridar asked as quietly as he could, "May I ask what that thing is for?" His prostate, she said, in a voice as cool as her uniform, was in a terrible condition. The doctor said it was ulcerated, and possibly cancerous. He looked at her, his fury mounting. "Damn it, he never even examined it!" The nurse went away from him and he lay on a hard table, seething with pain and rage. A half-hour later the nurse removed the pad. She did not meet his eyes. He thought she looked at him as she might have looked at a corpse.

Feeling like a fool, he returned the next day and was ushered into a tiny office. There the chiropractor gravely regarded him a few moments. Then, clearing his voice, he began to talk. He said Vridar had a very bad prostate gland. It was seventy-two point four. "It's what?" asked Vridar. The man wrote it down for him. His vitality, the grave voice went on, was dangerously low—66.3. His blood condition was 81.6. His energy was 73.9. The man was mumbling words that Vridar did not catch and had never heard before. Eleven sets of figures were written on a sheet of paper, all these percentages determined from three or four drops of blood! The doctor said it would take a year to cure him, at least; he would have to come to Boise, for treatments, three or four times a week. Incredulous and astounded, Vridar stared at the pale grave man, recalling with grim mirth that the bungling jackass had not even punctured the finger he had cleansed. The pain through his whole torso was so intense, while sitting on a hard chair and listening to infernal nonsense, that suddenly Vridar put hands on his knees, and almost fainting rose to his feet and left the office. He told Angele he would have an ulcerous brain before he would ever again go to a quack. He showed her the eleven figures, each with its fraction, and muttered in a voice as low and sinister as he could make it, "I should have decorticated the man!"

Dr. Julian Horne was not in the city. Vridar went next to Dr. Harold Rascall, of whom Horne had said that he was the best internal man in the State. Rascall examined Vridar's prostate and said it was all right—possibly slightly enlarged, but nearly all prostates were in men of his age. He should go up and see Dr. Stoat. And so Vridar made his tortured humped-over way upstairs to Stoat, whose specialty was bones. An assistant took large x-rays of Vridar's front, back, and both sides and said briskly, "Come tomorrow at ten." At ten the next day Dr. Stoat, a large extroverted thick-looking man, took Vridar into his office and said, "You have a bad sacro all right. You need a back support." Stoat wrote on a prescription pad. The support, he said, would cost twenty-six dollars. After Vridar had put it on, he must go home and make a hard bed on the floor and stay in it. He was not to leave it, even to go to the bathroom. Vridar wondered if the man was pulling his leg. How long, he asked, was he to remain in bed? Six weeks, the doctor said; then Vridar was to come see him.

That was all. It was so comical, so unlike his notion of the *physician,* that Vridar told Angele what Voltaire had said: "Doctors are men who prescribe medicine of which they know little, to cure diseases of which they know less, in human beings of which they know nothing." Within the hour he learned that Dr. Stoat owned the shop to which he had sent him, and that a back support of the same quality could be had in a Sears store for $6.50. Rumbling with fury, Vridar said he was not yet old enough for back supports, hearing aids, dentures, crutches and canes, wheel chairs, bed pull-ups, hernia harness, cod pods—

"Come now!"

"No wonder you see cemeteries and dead people everywhere. Take me home."

He had a plan. When life drove him back to his own resources, he became very quiet, and strove intuitively to feel his way into what should be done. He was convinced that if he lay on his back for six weeks, he would never rise again. He would be as stiff as a poker; he would move around like a man in a corset of steel. That was no good. The way to do it was to get out and work—to put heavy pressure on his lumbar bones, as he might if he knelt to a huge stone and tried to roll it over. That was exactly what he intended to do.

He suffered and seethed and cursed on the long ride home, and went bent over to the cabin and his bed. He felt so useless and depressed that he wanted to die: he was not one who took adversity cheerfully, much less graciously, but went roaring into its face, beating at it with his hands and kicking at earth and heaven. Neither was he one who would stay in bed if he could possibly move. The next morning he put on his working clothes and made his way slowly to a field of lava boulders, with an anxious Angele following him. By a stone which he thought would weight four hundred pounds he lowered himself to his knees, and clasping it with both hands put his chest against it. Then, carefully, he tensed his muscles, until every part of his body was challenged and ready; and then applied his strength to roll the stone over, all the while looking inside himself to measure the effect on the bone-structure in his lower back. There was no effect from only moderate pressure; but when, after a little, he heaved with all the power he had, he could feel an easing of the pain, as though a warm salve were flowing across the aching bones. He knew it was good for them. The doctors might have bugged their eyes out with astonished unbelief, but he knew that the pressure was good for the bones. After a while he heaved until his face turned beet-red and his lower eyelids sagged, rolling stones over, his senses fixed on his back and what was happening there. He put himself in different positions, so that with each new effort the force would be applied to bones from a different angle. When at last he stood up his back felt so good that he could draw a full breath without pain.

He was not fool enough to imagine that a few hours of such labor would do much for him. Indeed, soon after he returned to the cabin, the pain became so severe that sweat ran down his face. It would take time, but he wouldn't be lying in bed like a stupid lubber with a heating pad on his balls. To Angele he said, "Most people, like the beasts, are barely conscious of any sort of world around them, and not at all of themselves. It is this low level of awareness that saves the world from madness. In pain we see so much farther." He grimaced, wiped sweat from his brow, and said: "I used to think the endorsement racket was a recent thing, but Henry Ward Beecher, the hypocrite, endorsed patent medicines, and so did several of the presidents; and in the 'Nineties more than half the members of the U. S. Senate endorsed ivory soap. Sarah Bernhardt, as big a fraud as ever lived, endorsed anything she was paid for."

When in severe pain or sickness, he liked to hear the thoughts of great minds.

He now asked Angele to read to him from his notes, and quite by chance she picked up Leon Gautier on the history of French epic poetry. She read: "Represent to yourselves the first man at the moment when he issues from the hand of God, when his vision rests for the first time upon his new empire. Imagine, if it be possible, the exceeding vividness of his impressions when the magnificence of the world is reflected in the mirror of his soul. Intoxicated, almost mad with admiration, gratitude, and love, he raises his eyes to heaven, not satisfied with the spectacle of the earth; then discovering God in the heavens, and attributing to him all the honor of this magnificence and of the harmonies of creation, he opens his mouth, the first stammerings of speech escape his lips—he speaks; ah, no, he sings, and the first song of the lord of creation will be a hymn to God his creator."

Vridar said, "Write Athene's name on that bathos. I'll send it to her. Pa. The son praising Pa. I'll get to the bottom of that."

Angele was looking through cards. She read, " 'Tis not in the high stars alone, nor in the redbreast's mellow tone, but in the mud and scum of things, there always, always something sings."

He was looking at her. "Sometimes," he said, "I suspect you of a special order of cunning. When I'm on my back and dying you read Emerson to me."

"Cookie, you said the other day you'd keep those words before you as you come down the centuries on hands and knees."

He was ashamed then. One side of her was so sweet and innocent and without guile, so completely the child, that he could only shelter and cherish it.

Two or three times a day he forced himself out of bed, sweating all over and almost fainting, and took his way to the hillside, where for an hour he would put all his strength against stones, his mind meanwhile ranging over a multitude of topics. He would talk aloud to himself, saying, "What is egoism. A vegetarian, Hitler says he loves beasts so much that he detests hunting, yet thinks nothing of slaughtering millions of people. Did he hate his father? And Schweitzer down in Africa, who won't swat a mosquito or cut down a tree! Well, my mother put such a sense of guilt in me that my conscience sweats if a day passes in which I don't try to achieve something. So it is that I abhor loafers and loafing. . . ." He would grunt and heave, all the while speaking out of his thoughts. "No analysis on earth can make the neurosis disappear. Marion says no form of compensation ever cured a feeling of inferiority, for the reason that compensation cloaks instead of exposing. I feel more and more normal," he said, glancing at his amused wife. "On my knees I try to push something out of the way. I see now that's all Roosevelt is trying to do—push old Joe Stalin out of the way." He crawled to a larger stone and heaved against it; he liked the way his back felt when he gave all he had. He supposed that he had deposits of calcium and was dislodging them and hustling them along; but if that was so, why had Stoat prescribed absolute rest. Poor Stoat, what did he know about Stoat!

As the days passed and Vridar limbered his back, driving out the stiffness, he came to like digging his toes into the earth, bracing himself, and lifting for all he was worth. It was when he lifted until he looked like one about to have hemorrhages that he felt best. For he had always felt best when he worked hard. He had asked doctor friends why this was so, and they had all thought him queer. He was to learn from his own self-explorations that it was because he had low blood pressure, low metabolism, and a sluggish heart.

He told his wife that it was good to push an object and turn it over to a new place in the world. But would Roosevelt turn Stalin over? He thought it more likely that Stalin would turn Roosevelt over. The war was something that he and Angele did not talk about. With imaginations abnormally active, they found it too horrifying, too utterly brutal and senseless: Vridar had dreams of the millions of young men clutching their torn guts on battlefields, turning their stricken faces to an empty sky; and recalling the horrors of his dreams, he would hate the obtuse ruthless men like Roosevelt who while millions of young men were dying were proudly conscious of their place in history; and women like Mrs. Roosevelt, who after going through a ghastly hospital for amputees, went to lunch and overate, and then publicly confessed it. Rousset had said, "Misery that goes too deep arouses not compassion but repugnance and hatred." No man could keep his sanity who looked hard and long at the worldwide struggle between two forms of tyranny, the Communist-Fascist and the Judean-Christian. "Kyber Pass!" Vridar would mutter. "Mankind's symbol is there."

He felt so enraged and sickened, thinking of the butchering of millions and all the patriotic rant and cant, that he crawled to a ledge of stone and was butting his skull against it and smelling old pigeon nests and spider lairs and lizard caves when the shrill voice of his wife asked, "Now what in the world are you doing?" He turned and said, "Pushing this mountain over."

"You're crazy."

"No crazier than Roosevelt, who think's he's pushing Hitler over. My Ma told me we develop character by tackling things too big for ourselves." She asked him to come, and he went with her down the mountain and lay on his bed. She sat by him and looked at him, as a woman might who wondered if her man was stupid or insane. He said, "I've been thinking up there. Now that I'm going to give my remaining years to reading my eyes out and emptying my soul out, leaving only a few bones for the undertaker, I need a panel of wisdom to inspire and arouse and guide me. Bring my wisdom cards." She laid a pile at his side and holding one above him he read, "Love, proclaim to every wind: pure humanity atones for the frailty of mankind. What did Goethe know about Goethe? Rank says the Freudian content disguises itself under the occidental religious morality, from which we still suffer, and in his failure to solve his individual problem the modern man has shattered in terms of the neurosis. A lot of writers are trying to define the problem, and some of the shortest of them are entering the Anglican or Roman Church. Well, here's a question by Henry Osborn Taylor: who can draw the line between reality and conviction? Ask the first hundred people you meet and they'll say they can. Who, asks Taylor, does not believe what his reason labors in vain to justify? Ask the first thousand and you won't find one laboring in vain. What they believe *is* reason for them. Wonderful tomnoddies!"

Angele said she had not been able to believe that human nature had improved at all. Was it any better in any respect than in the time of Greece and Rome? When it was proposed to slaughter beasts and men in arenas in Greece hadn't a great man said, You'll first have to throw down the altar of Pity? Had anyone said it better, to the modern bullfighters, and the lovers of bullfighting, and all the lovers of the lovers of bullfighting? Thinking about her words Vridar said, "Ingersoll asked why we don't throw the superstitions away and take the higher and nobler ground. Three thousand years ago no man would have asked that, so mankind must improve a little."

"Oh, I don't know, man-love. Who has taken the higher and nobler ground?"

"I'm trying to but I need ropes and ladders and steeplejacks to help me." He picked up another card. "Leuba: the higher the state of intellectual progress, the less is there a belief in a god. Vaughan: there is in God a deep and dazzling darkness. Lecky: the number of persons who have a rational basis for their belief is probably infinitesimal. Gilbert Murray: we should walk gently in a world where the lights are dim and the very stars wander. In such words as all those, child-woman, we have the human animal at his best."

He lay back, thinking of Murray's words. Angele was looking through his cards. "I like this one," she said. "Deep wells take a long time to realize what has fallen into their depths."

"Nietzsche. It's fine. Well, mankind's a deep well, and we don't yet know much about what has fallen into it. I'm going into the well as deep as I can." She read from another card, "In probably no region of the personality do we find so many residues of childhood as in the religious attitudes of adults." He said, "That's Allport but I doubt that they're adult: I sense something here, some big discovery." He was leaning forward to catch a glimpse of the next card, for he fed on words from brilliant minds as some men fed on women or praise. "Arnold? That old schoolmaster!"

She read: "The mere endeavor to see and learn the truth for our own personal satisfaction is indeed a commencement for making it prevail."

"That's good, yes. He looked like the Dean of Canterbury but no dean ever uttered such words. They go in the panel." He was leaning forward, like one being spoon-fed. "Who's that?"

"Maitland. He says, We study the day before yesterday, in order that yesterday may not paralyze today, and today may not paralyze tomorrow."

"It would be a nice thing if we did, but few persons care anything about the past---including Carl Noyce, a college professor, who told me it is of no importance." Vridar reached behind him for a card; he had slipped it out of the file and had been hiding it. "Here, I think, is the one you'll like best---an old Jewish proverb: What a blessing that not only the hunted but also the hunters get tired."

She took the card and read the words, and after a few moments left the room. When at last she looked in, her eyes were wet, her lips trembling. "Did Jesus ever say anything as fine as that?"

"If you mean *that* Jesus, he said nothing that his worshipers think he said."

"You think Hitler will get tired!"

He called her to the bed and putting arms around her drew her down. He had not known before they came to the country that her compassion embraced the whole animal world---she would fight to protect even a wasp or a black widow spider. One day she had seen two hunters approaching, shotguns at the ready; they were after pheasants and they were intending to pass through her front yard. She ran toward them, screaming, "You get out of here, you horrible nasty killers!" Astounded, they had looked at her a moment and fled. Kissing her wet cheeks, he murmured, " What a blessing that not only the hunted but also the hunters get tired. That one, woman-child, I'll put at the head of my panel, with your name on it."

Like a child she murmured against him, "Thanks."

"Deep wells take a long time to realize what has fallen into their depths. That will be second. Third will be Baur---you see, I know them all by heart, for they're my bible—There can be no true objective criticism until a man stands more or less indifferent to the result, and frees himself as far as possible from all subjective relations to the object of criticism. Not one person in fifty thousand could be made to understand what he means. Fourth---"

She was softly weeping. He enfolded her, and while she wept against him he looked up at the ceiling, thinking---thinking of Jessie Taft's words, "the evolution of man's will with its inexhaustible creativity, its dynamic of projection and denial and its ever increasing burden of fear and guilt."

II

On awaking the next morning he said to his wife, "Ratiocination is a sensuous pleasure, for me and those like me; but there's another level, so let's find it." She said a little sharply that a male should never so abruptly approach a sensitive female; but as an act of forgiveness, she reached out and patted him. While clasping her hand he realized that he had not yet put in his panel the statement which, of them all, had revealed the most to him. It was by the great scholar Franz Cumont: "If the torrent of actions and reactions that carries us along were turned out of its course, what imagination could describe the unknown regions through which it would flow?" What fields of light those words disclosed! What words for conjecture! Surely in nothing were human beings so obstinately and unmovably stupid as in their self-flattering assumption that what had happened had been, in every instance, better for mankind than what would have happened if another direction had been taken. It reminded him of Marion's statement, that no woman ever regretted a seduction, if it was pleasurable. Mankind did not regret even its wars!

If (to take only one instance of a dozen that came swarming over his senses) if the Maccabeans had lost in their struggle against Syria, the force called Christianity could never have developed. It took a person as blind as a bat and as ignorant as a warthog to say that would have been a loss, without knowing what would have taken its place. This, he said to Angele, was what he meant by ratiocination: the sheer sensuous pleasure in exploring the Cumont statement thrilled him like a physical orgasm.

Angele squeezed his hand. She had told him that living with him kept her in a state of almost continuous excitement. There was his clowning. Sometimes he would wake up in the morning, throw the covers back, and seizing his penis swear by God and Heaven that he was going to lift himself off the bed with it. The first time he did this, he had been astonished by her alarm. She had given outraged cries of remonstrance. With mighty huffing and grunting, all his muscles flexed and rigid, his face turning red from exertion, he would heave upward, this way and that, muttering, "Out, damned thing!" She would cry at him, "Stop it, you idiot, stop it!" When at last he lay back, panting, she would say, "O my God! Sometimes I think you have a mind and sometimes I don't know."

"If I'd started yanking and pulling that way as a child, I'd now have a longer one."

"You fool."

"All American men want a longer one, who've been brought up on farms. Does Kinsey know that?"

"You preposterous ass."

Gravely pretending, he would look over at her and say, "Then how do some men get longer ones?"

"O good Lord!"

"I'll have to do a lot of that when I get down to the time of Christian asceticism--- the time when those imbeciles fled to the desert by the thousands and stood for miles across the sands, each with fifty pounds of rock hanging from his scrotum."

"Stop it."

"But they did. Testicles fell off by the millions, and the untesticled men walked away to sainthood."

He had learned that clowning often concealed deep dark meanings. One day he was sitting in the sun with sprigs of mint stuck up each nostril. Coming up and regarding him with astonishment, Angele had said, "Now what in hell are you doing?" He had forgotten the mint. Well, what *was* he doing? It had been easy to go to the source of that one: Angele could not stand untidy nostrils, and Vridar's, like those of most men, were not always tidy. When Angele caught him in an untidiness, he would blow up a great fury, largely feigned. One day she paid him a supreme compliment: she had got the habit of typing things on cards and putting a card on his typewriter, to be found when he went to his machine. One day he found these words:

> Cookie, Bunsen wrote to Lady Houghton: "In dealing with her husband's paradoxes and humorous leaps in the dark, she transferred into daily practice the inimitable apophthegm that *'tout comprendre c'est tout pardonner.'* For behind every jest of her ever youthful, often frolicsome, lord she distinguished ---and she inwardly prayed that everybody would duly distinguish---the meditative mood, the continuity of thought and of mental elevation, and the well-tutored wisdom of experience not lightly bought."

After reading the words twice, Vridar had kissed the card and given it a place among the hundreds on his wall. Yes, but he was not sure of the source of his penis-wrestling: how deep in him was the castration-complex? He kept on a wall above his typewriter these things from Jung:

Persona---person's mask---a vice when it dominates the personality under it
amima---female principle in man---pettiness, rage, gentleness, appreciation
of finer things, compassion
animus---male characteristics in women
old wise man---king, hero, savior, magician
earth-mother
self----embodies elements from the conscious, unconscious and above
archetypes

Why had Jung included rage under *anima?* On another card he had typed a few
things from Herbert Silberer's *Problems of Mysticism and Its Symbolism*

Retrograde aspect
Anagogic aspect
killing of the father
killing of the old Adam
desire for the mother
introversion
     (laziness)
incest
love toward an ideal
auto-eroticism
Siddhi
copulation with mother
spiritual regeneration
improvement
re-creation
death wish
attainment of the ideal

Every day he would look at the card, hoping that his explorations would throw
some light on the words. All of them, Silberer said, "take place in each and every
one of us, otherwise we should be mere beasts." Vridar would let off a snort and
a shout, thinking, If the self-lovers only knew what it is that makes them different
from the beasts! On still another card he had typed:

Freud is of the opinion that the original inquisitiveness about the sexual
secret is abnormally transformed into morbid over-subtlety; and yet can still
furnish an impulsive power for legitimate thirst for knowledge.

"That's me!" he would think, grimly amused. On still another:

Jung especially has of late strongly insisted upon the dangerous role of
indolence. According to him the libido possesses a monstrous laziness which
is unwilling to let go of any object of the past....Laziness is actually a passion
as La Rochefoucauld brilliantly remarks, "Of all the passions the least understood by us is laziness; it is the most indefatigable and the most malign of
them, although its outrages are imperceptible." It is the most perilous
passion affecting the primitive man.

Or the modern either, Vridar reflected, recalling his four years on W.P.A. What would happen to people if the Socialists achieved their dream of only a little labor, or none at all? Where was there a more hideous nightmare than the Christian idea of Heaven?

Attached to the walls around him were many cards that he looked at almost daily: they contained the thoughts that he wanted to keep at the surface of consciousness. One panel he called CLUES.

HOMOSEXUALITY

A lot of married men and women whose husbands and wives are insanely jealous, now and then kiss or otherwise manifest what is or seems to be erotic interest in the same sex. This is also true of some of the lower mammals. Strange that psychologists haven't discovered this simple fact!

At a party a willowy fluttery woman had come up to Vridar and exclaimed, "I just now felt an urge to kiss a woman on her bare shoulders. Is that Lesbianism?"

FATHER-SON RELATIONSHIP

I am aware now that throughout childhood I deeply hated my father. I think often of Leonardo da Vinci's words to a friend who had a son, that he was to be congratulated on "having provided yourself with an active enemy whose one desire will be for the freedom that cannot be his until you are dead." I ask myself if I would feel any release of courage and powers if my father were to die.

"Would I?" he asked Angele. She said she thought he would have to look pretty deep into that one. He gave it a few moments and said, "It's my brother, I think, who is at the heart of my problem." In regard to incestuous yearnings, he had come only to the conclusion that as a child he had wanted to be intimate with his sister, and would have been if she had been willing. As for his mother, he had yearned toward her breasts, but now understood that: standing with Marion, he had watched Diana suckle, and both lads had felt a bond of love between mother and daughter that they had never felt between themselves and their mother. The breast had become for both of them, not as with so many men a carnally voluptuous symbol of the erotic, but a symbol of nourishment, of love, of mother.....

DUNG

I had a dream: looking out after dark I saw my father coming in such a posture that I realized he had filled his pants; behind him came a woman in similar distress. They went into a shack and seemed to sit together in some sort of outdoor privy shed. On waking I thought the dream out. I had just read John Fante's story of his embarrassment on the train because of his father's uncouthness. The shack was one I saw a farmer moving two days ago. The woman was a mother-symbol.

After telling Angele the dream he said, "To put it bluntly, my childhood was a nightmare of shit. There was the horrible corral after heavy rains, knee-deep in cow dung; and how vivid is the memory of bending over in downpour squeezing milk from teats covered with dung!—and dung dropping into milk pails—yes, of my father reaching a foul hand with manure-juices running from every finger into the milk to pull a hunk of terd out. What a filthy bugbear it all was! Nor did we ever have a privy until I built one. Until then it was the old decomposing accumulations behind bushes, with the small child staring, with the child having to wonder, even as God touched his eyes and closed them, which was the father's, which the mother's."

"The poor little boys!" she said.

"And it was a sister toddling around with her diaper full. It was Hunter women coming now and then to visit, bringing their babes, changing them while sitting there gabbling their heads off. God, how I remember the way they wiped the child with the cleaner parts of the diaper, rolled the mess up and tossed it into a corner. Standing back in shadows, I could see the rolled-up diapers over there---I can see them now, the wet saggy brown contours; I can smell them, I can smell them. It was hogs in pens belly-deep with their own filth, their bodies so completely encased that their eyes could barely look out. It was mice droppings all over the house, in the food, in jars, in the beds. It was chicken dung tracked in, and not even cat dung is so foul to smell. When Athene and I cycled down the Mediterranean in Italy we stopped twenty or more times and went off the road to find a place where we could sit and eat lunch. Human filth everywhere. Sometimes when I hear the word Europe, I think of a place where people have just shit themselves out of house and home."

"You're making me sick."

"The hen houses I had to clean—a long big stinking roll of it under every roost; or a barn with ten inches of drowned-in-its-acids horse manure."

"Most farm boys don't feel that way about it."

"Most farm boys are about as sensitive as a manure-spreader."

One day he read a story about Calamity Jane and felt so deeply the pathos of her, as her kind of world went away from her, leaving her alone and lost, that he dreamed he was back in childhood, going across the hills in twilight, looking for cows and listening for the sound of a cowbell. He was almost rigid with fear, for at any moment he expected to meet a mountain lion. On waking, he wondered if fear had not shaped him more than any other force, and mankind. He was coming aware, as he read about the remote past, as he thrust himself back into it, as he sank deeper into primitive man, that fear had been the most powerful of all human emotions. With that door opened, he looked far. A psychologist had written, "The original fear for the safety of one's self is usually a psychic reaction to repressed hatreds which the ego cannot accept because the hate contradicts one's moral demands." Oh, yes, yes with modern man, but that was not the way of it in fear long ago.

DRINKING

I understand at last that as a child I felt horribly weak and inadequate and afraid around my father; getting drunk has been to some (possibly to a large) extent a compulsive wish to assert myself as an individual, to establish myself as a not-contemptible thing.

809

Away back there where his story was beginning had there ever been a sense of fear and inadequacy, in the son when around the father? Yes! All the records proclaimed it. But he would study the beasts to see how it was there he would look deeper.

Some of his clues he followed quickly to their meanings. There was his imitativeness, which so amused Angele: he had a friend who limped, and after visiting the friend Vridar limped for days, and then dreamed a dream: he was somewhere in a pasture, back in childhood land, among wounded yearling bulls, which Joe had just mutilated by sawing off their large handsome horns, burning almost through their hides with his huge branding iron, cutting off about half of each ear, and cutting open the pouch and tearing out the testicles. Vridar in the dream went among them, imitating their stiff-legged walk, the droop of their bloody heads, the infinite sadness in their eyes. Compassion, he said, was the cross he bore.

Now and then a meaning came to the surface when he was conscious. He had never liked to drink anything out of bottles. One day in a tavern he had asked for a glass, saying, "I don't like to drink out of a bottle. I was a bottle baby." There it was! How neatly it had slipped by the Censor!

Now and then he got a clue to Angele's baffling personality. "Do something about that damned internecine nature," he would say when her inner struggles wearied him. He was reading one day in a book by his brother about suicidal tendencies and the reason for them, when in a flash it came to him that, being schizoid, Angele was psychically unintegrated. She was in some ways a wise old woman ("No mother really loves her children if they become so mature they no longer need her"); in some ways a poet (after one friend had died, and then a second and a third, she had said, "Think of all the doors closing behind us"); in some ways the psychologist who looked deep into their friends: when Vridar wondered aloud why a certain literary critic had married a fat Dutch woman, Angele had said, "For that kind of child, all Dutch women are mothers with rosy cheeks and broad bottoms." But in most ways she was a child, with a small girl's motivations and interests. She was a little mother, and the world was peopled with her children, including hornets, spiders, toads, snakes, and mice---and, of course, all the birds everywhere.

He wondered if his fantastically morbid consciousness of death came from having seen so many creatures die brutally (a neighbor's sons had bolted to an iron haft the triangular dull rusted section of a mowing machine knife, and with it thrust at the bodies of stray cats until they drove the weapon in, saying to Vridar with an innocent smile, "A cat's hide is tough"). In his dreams he saw, endlessly, the eyes of the dead. Sometimes he was so madly in love with life that he wanted to seize it with wild frenzied arms and clutch and hold it, remembering his brother's statement, that deep down in the affective make-up of every person there was an implicit assumption of immortality: ideas of life's finiteness were wholly of the mind and not at all of the emotions. But again, viewing the whole thing rationally, and despairing, as he sensed the inexorable crawl of time and the slow dissolution in his own system, he felt compelled to surrender, to shriek out to the vast insensate that it would be a mercy and a blessing to die. As far back as he could remember he

810

had been tortured between these extremes. The chronic wish for death, his brother said, most likely came from a mad desire to preserve a part of the ego—to stop its steady erosion by life. Vridar felt pain and pity when his friend Reuben Rhode looked at him with eyes emptied of hope and heaven, and said, "In all your reading haven't you yet found any evidence that we live again?"

There was his intolerance, which (he had no doubt) would become more offensive as he grew older. As a child he had been so desperately in need of affection and security, but had got almost none; had been forced to be the manly little man, shouldering responsibilities far beyond his age, and hiding from his parents his quakings and terrors. He had been forced to wear a fraudulent face to conceal the inner chaos. He had become what psychologists called a person of low affective tolerance. He knew this, and he knew that to enlarge his tolerance he would not so much have to accept the things that offended him, as to reduce the loftiness of his ideals, the magnitude of his aspirations. He looked forward with pleasure to death, that would destroy both.

He was sensing, on hands and knees back there in the remote past, that not arrogance but submissiveness was in him the stronger force—indeed, that the former was a gross vulgar monster sucking at the twelve teats of the latter. When he understood this, there unfolded in a brilliant page of meaning the riddle of the Jews: the most arrogant people on earth because in the tenderest and least-defended part of their souls, where they hid from Father, they were the most submissive. How simple it all was!—the prophets, wailing walls, priests to all nations—the whole dark compost of it! For a long time Vridar had detested himself for what he had taken to be his arrogance—and all arrogant people: the pushing popular idols, everlastingly calling attention to themselves with their cheap vain strutting filled him with an emotion close to nausea. He had been taught by his unbending mother to be seen and not heard; to give more than half and the better half; to submit his will rather than stand and fight: in protest against all this he had developed an austerity that was mistaken for arrogance. To Angele he said, "What an effort it has cost me to grow to even half the height I had in me!"

What was arrogance? Angele asked. He reached for a dictionary. "Haughtiness, hauteur, assumption, lordliness, presumption, disdain, insolence . . . making exorbitant claims of rank, estimation or importance." His tendency, she said, was to the other extreme.

"Then why do people think me arrogant?"

It was his impatience, she said. "It drives us all crazy. You expect everybody to think as fast, walk as fast, know as much, be as ambitious as you. It's what Marion said to me—Tell him to stop trying to hold me up to his level."

"Yes," he said, feeling the shame of it. "I look like Paul Blanshard and Paul Blanshard looks to me like a minister full of dyspepsia, ulcerous cysts, hemorrhoids, sexual impotence, castration complexes, crusading zeal, Jeremiah—"

"Oh, come!" She went to a card file, where she kept his sayings which she thought ought to be preserved. She read, "It's one of the tragedies of mankind that so few persons can accept moral responsibility, without being coerced with threat of punishment, or bribed with promise of reward. Is that what I wanted?" she asked, looking at him like a bird. She read again: "The power to which people should surrender themselves is neither God nor Ceasar but their own talent. Oh, here's a nice one: The highest compliment an artist can pay another artist is to feel infuriated by his existence."

"Not bad," he said.

She read another: "For a lot of women sexual intercourse is no more than changing a diaper, and indeed is much the same sort of experience."

"Read on," he said, trying to look like a man enormously pleased with himself.

"Well, let's see. You said, The most depressing fact I know about people is that nearly all of them like what they see in a mirror. That alone is enough to prove that they have no future."

"You say some nice things," he said.

She turned dubious: she had so little faith in her powers that one stinging rebuke could strike her down. "What?" she said.

"You said, Call any woman a whore and she'll not be half as mad as if you call her a fat-ass."

"That's no joke," she said.

III

He wondered through how many channels he could understand the ape-man. There were the zoos: he had spent many hours in them, studying the great apes, seeing in them himself and friends, and them in his friends and himself. Some of his friends were so simian that they shocked him when he saw them naked: Rhode with his abnormally short and rather bowed legs was clothed with coarse black hair all over his body; his dark darting eyes were like a chimpanzee's; and to top it all, his face was apelike in its mouth and forehead. Carl Noyce's body was much like Rhode's.

For many years Vridar had found delight in watching people manifest apelike facial expressions, emotions, and traits. He had studied his own face in the mirror of the zoo until he could no longer think of it as human. All the while he was reading, from Aristotle to Zell. Such studies as Köhler's fascinated him: he hadn't known that if a human and a chimpanzee child were given identical care and situations, the latter would outstrip the former in the first two or three years, not only in development of physical traits but of mental faculties as well. Do animals reason? Camacho asked. Angele said cats did. Besides Köhler, Grünbaum, Keith, Lankester, Milne-Edwards, Mitchell, Sayers, Mead and others, there was the monumental volume under the editorship of Yerkes, with its magnificent photographs of ape faces—such as the one of Utan on page 146, the adult chimpanzee on page 198, the orang-outan on 183, and the gorilla on 422: he spent hours over these and others, and Angele with him. What kind of fool was it, she asked, who said these were not his cousins? She could see her father in a number of photographs.

Besides such books as these there were many related to them, in the fields of ethnology, anthropology, and natural history, a few of which he bought but most of which he had sent from out-of-state libraries. Hungrily he read them all, and some of them two or three times, striving all the while to get down to the level whereon the ape-men went furtively over the earth, dragging clubs. He so completely fell in the habit of imitating the bow-legged bent-legged posture of walking, with head sunk down in shoulders and prognathous jaw thrust out, that he had one embarrassing experience after another, when people happened to be watching him.

There drove in one day a man and wife who said they had read his books and wanted to meet him. Vridar didn't like the man: he was short and thick with a mean ugly look full of suspicion and hostility. But the four of them sat on the floor of the house Vridar was building and drank claret and whisky and talked. When Vridar got up he forgot to walk in his normal way (his normal way!) but slouched along in bent-legged fashion like a gorilla; and he supposed afterward that the man thought he was being mocked. Whatever the reason, when Vridar at last lay on the hard earth outside, drunk with whisky and primitive man and fatigue, the stranger suddenly hurled himself out of darkness and began to smite Vridar with furious blows all over his face. It took him a few moments to shake the fog out of his wits and realize what was happening. Then all the primitive man came up in him, furious and murderous and determined to kill. His thought was to get his hands on the man's throat and choke him to death, and this he would have done if he could have found the throat. For the life of him he couldn't find it, or much of anything. The hard firsts were knocking the blood out of him and over his face, and all the reason out of his skull. The man might have killed him, there and then, if Angele, suddenly becoming aware of the situation, had not seized a club and come running, her voice screaming with madness as she laid the club over the man's skull and almost knocked him out. He struggled off on hands and knees and then got to his feet and ran. Vridar found his bed and the next morning looked at himself in a mirror: he had seen men who had been beaten but not more than once or twice had he seen a bloodier and more contused face than his own. Angele told him the man and his wife had run down the lane to their car but that the man had sneaked back and stolen their bottle of whisky. "That's about average of a writer's fans," Vridar said.

His task at this time was to stand forth, not in the way of Gautier's simpleton, trying to make his peace with Pa, but as an elemental organism that at last had risen to its hind legs and released its front legs to become hands; but he soon perceived, through all the overflooded channels of feeling, that his great burden while coming down through the eons would be one of accretions, and that these would thicken and dull him far more than they would enrich and enlighten. No discovery that he was to make, save one, would more astound him than this: he now saw the human animal as a creature within accumulated sheaths, and his task as one of sheath-stripping-away, until he got underneath the first layers of the Judiac, the Islamic, the Christian—yes, and if possible under the layers, the folds on folds, of superstititon, prejudice, and habit, that had insulated man from the world, long before one tribe of Arabs became Hebrews and made fear of Pa a religion. He went around looking at his hands, now freed, and doing things with them that only ape-men would do, until Angele despaired of him and her marriage.

To feel his way into the ape-man he sought out as well as he could the ape-man's natural lairs. There were many caves in the walls of mountains and river gorges roundabout and many mining tunnels: Vridar often went back into these dark places, during the months when he was writing the first novel: he would take a big club in with him, dragging it from one hand, looking back across his shoulder; he would go in, sniffing at the odors of his enemies, of bear, jackal, and other beasts that housed in caves; he would prowl back in the gloom and nightdamp, among the bats, owls, scorpions, smelling their body-smells, their nests, the bones, feathers, and fur of their victims; breathing these ancient wild scents; putting his nose to cold stone that had never known the sun, to sniff the owl droppings, the dung of pack-rats; finding at last a shelf of stone above a water-flow and sitting there on his haunches, the club between his legs, his eyes looking far out at an irregular patch of wan daylight, across which he saw a hawk come upwind, its wings spread wider than the club in his grasp. . . .

It was so hard to think his way into the small dark preadamite preglacial ante-mundane world and its small dark mind—to feel and see and sense *only* what filled that world—not the stars as stars nor the sun as sun: not the sky as a sky even but only as a color that changed; not the clouds as rainborne but only as a patch, an area, a place of floating or drifting color; not the horizon as the down-dip of a sphere but only as the farthest point he could see to, the end of things: it was a small world!—for there was nothing beyond what he could see, nothing that he could imagine beyond this plane upon which he fixed the intimacy and the immediacy of his five fierce senses; his gaze brooding, his ears straining to the sounds, his sensitive nostrils flaring and full of twitching interest and anxiety. . . .

In every way he could think of, Vridar went back and down, far back and down deep; insinuating (no, it was blunter than that)—feeling (but it was more powerful than that)—pushing, thrusting his own sentient sensuous peeled-to-the-quick being back into what it had come out of; possessing it, filling it; encompassing its small taprooted breeding-place—and at night before sleeping, thinking about it; in sleep dreaming about it, striving all the while to nose around its actual emotional boundaries and feel through the simple lines of its few primitive meanings—for these had been his, long ago, they were still his: he could feel them within him, deeper than most of the emotions he used because deeply tap-rooted—infinitely deeper in him than logic and faith and belief—ages and eons deeper than compassion and pity. . . .

One day the sky opened and light flooded and he was so shocked that he sank to the earth, amazed; trying to grasp the full revelation of it and hold it in the mirrors of his emotions and mind, while at its flood-height: the primitive ape-man's chief emotion had been fear! He had thought (in how many ways was he deceived?) that it must have been some lust—for food or the female, and he had been lusting, at a more primitive level, upon both the table and his woman (saying to Angele that the embrace anciently and normally had had little body contact: front legs around flanks as with dogs: face to face must have brought psychic changes); or if not some lust, then some rage because his will and supremacy were disputed; or possibly some small feebly glowing but intensely hot ambition to be a little bigger, see a little farther. Fear. It was fear. This realization came not out of his childhood nightmare but out of his intuitive usurpation of the faces in Yerkes: in acting and feeling his way through the whole part—the hunting with a club, the hiding in a cave to peer out, the sleeping curled up in a dense thicket, the looking at sun, moon, stars, earth, and water, the covering of the female—yes, it had been fear, fear had been his guide, his light, and at last his curse—fear in the hand that dragged the club, in the small bright opaque eyes that kept looking around or back; in the sniffing as with slow deliberate stepping and peering and smelling he pushed deeper into lairs that did not belong to him alone: it was fear in this earth-man, so mighty yet so feeble, for he had enemies that could fell him with one blow, gut him from chin to scrotum with one talon.

Fear, and what else? Hope, faith, belief, not these; or love, not even for his own children—for he did not recognize his children as children, but only as moving things with his smell on them; nor his woman as a wife, nor even as a mate, save in the moments when they mated. O Universe! here was the vision to lift a man's gaze to the dim immense eternities, and his guts to his heartbeat: this!—not the child-like fable of a man and a woman in a garden; not the torpid stupidity of original sin!—no, but this vast deep all-encompassing capacity for faith and belief, that opened to the eyes that would see, when a man sensed how far he had come from the little dark world of the small black fear-laden eyes; how far he had risen even in centuries of wars, above the brutal ugly need to seize a handhold somewhere on life, hoping merely to endure; expecting momentarily to have the hold broken! The soul—and this difference *was* the soul— could sing on that.

"Or can it?" he asked Angele, looking at her with eyes past-filled.

He had made her afraid. One day he had come howling and cursing out of a cave, clutching his belly. He had seen the enemy—a scorpion an inch longer than the biggest scorpion he had ever known had plunged its dagger in his belly. Cursing his small simian luck and shouting to his wife to get the car out, he had come lumbering down a mountain and Angele had come running to him with a bottle of whisky. At reckless speed she headed for the nearest city; and Vridar, gulping whisky, looked in the car mirror and saw that his lips were turning purple. "How appropriate if I die!" he muttered. "Vridar-Ape-Man goes prowling in caves, gets stung by scorpion as ape-man got stung; dies." His doctor-friend was enraptured. He had never had a case of rattlesnake bite, scorpion sting, or Rocky Mountain fever. He had prayed to have all three. With Angele at his elbow urging him on, he thumbed through medical books. Then he hustled Vridar to a hospital; gave him a shot and asked how he felt, gave him a second, of a different potion; and then a third, of a third. With his senses pouring and his brain ready to explode, Vridar was driven home.

A few days later he was trying to maneuver in a primitive way when he fell back-ward on the tines of a common garden rake. One blunt curved rusted tine was driven so deep into him along his coccyx that when he got to his feet the rake came up with him. He reached around to take careful hold of it and draw the tine out. He then felt blood washing against his trousers. Feeling unspeakably silly for being so clumsy (for he was an extremely agile man), and for having driven such an absurd thing into his tailbone, of all places, he hoped to hide the accident from Angele. He examined the tines and found them all covered with rust. In his barnyard one day he had driven a rusted upthrust nail through one of his feet, and had then rushed off for an anti-tetanus shot. He had had a cousin with lockjaw whose mouth for months had been held wide open.

But Angele discovered his wound. A garden rake? she asked, unbelieving. Into his tailbone? "Let me see."

"No," he said. All his mother's precepts came up hot and chiding inside him: in her world it was better for a child to die and return to his heavenly home than expose his rump. But Angele's angry hands were undressing him. He bent over for her to look and then heard her cry of astonishment. "Come!" she said, and they were off to the doctor again, with Vridar murmuring, "Primitive man, you know, had a very short life-span."

During this time he was also building a house, a workman so careless that Angele was convinced he would break his neck. Once he was ten feet above earth on one of his flimsy scaffolds when it collapsed under him: he had seen it coming, and in the moment of falling had brought his arms in tight, his legs up, and hurled himself in a rolling movement and at the moment of striking the earth had rolled over and over at lightning speed and so was not hurt. When painting shingles on a steep roof he slipped because he had got paint on his rubber soles, and went thudding and skidding down the roof, a bucket of paint in one hand, a brush in the other, his voice crying for Angele. At the roof's edge he paused a bare moment like a big hawk trying to settle himself; and then plunged the ten feet down. Again he was not hurt. Angele had come running. "I fell off again," he said looking foolish.

A rickety scaffold collapsed under him one day when he was only three feet above the earth. He felt a sharp pain in an ankle and falling to the earth rolled over and over down a hill, drawing the ankle up against him. He got to his feet and went off, limping. The ankle swelled and turned purple but he went on with his work, walking on it most of the day. The next morning it looked so bad that Angele took him to a doctor, who found that he had a double fracture. Vridar was furious and depressed by turns: now for weeks he would be half-immobilized while using crutches and an iron heel. He hated these invasions of his work by the useless and senseless, as when he smashed the nail off a thumb and for a month found it difficult to trip the space-bar on his typewriter; as when he sliced open the big finger of his left hand and had to type with only the forefinger.

Angele said one day, "When you get down to the Jesus book, what will you be? A Jeremiah nailed on a cross? As your brother says, you've always wanted to wear a hair shirt."

Quoting his brother annoyed him for he knew that his brother detested him.

"And when you get down to Christian asceticism, will you go to the desert and hang a boulder to your scrotum?" He said he supposed he would, and she said the neighbors would love it.

The neighbors already thought him a queer one. It had long been a habit with him to develop scenes in his books while laboring, even while walking along city streets: when writing dialog he would talk it out, he would make gestures; and during the months when he was writing about primitive people it was his way to pull his face into ape-like appearances. Some of his grimacing was pretty ferocious and all of it was startling to those who beheld it. He was walking on a city street one day when he was brought to his senses by the look of amazement on the face of a woman approaching him. He then realized that he had been acting the ape. It annoyed and humiliated him to have people think him queer. He tried to put his writing out of his mind when he was not alone but found that as impossible as when he slept. And he tried not to be caught turning an inner ear to the condition of his health.

Having seen him more than once timing his pulse, Angele bought a stethoscope for his birthday. Like a lad with a new toy he put the prongs in his ears and the sounding disc over his heart, and then listened, with astonishment growing in his face. When he moved the disc down to his belly the astonishment in his face grew to amazement, for he now heard gurglings, rumblings, small explosions, and sounds as of water being poured from spouts and funnels. "My God," he said, looking over at Angele. "No wonder man believes in a spirit. There's nothing else but gas to believe in."

Angele told him that she had read an article about the marvelous sounds to be heard inside various small creatures, including insects and snakes; and thereafter she saw him now and then out in the woods, stealthily creeping along on hands and knees and pausing to take a sound-reading of a spider, a snake, a turtle, a toad. He listened to the heartbeat and the explosive rending sounds of digestion in the cat, in his calves and sheep, and in his more intimate friends. Looking at a grave countenance staring at him he would say, "Our five senses detect so little of all that goes on around us that it takes a lot of presumption to come to any conclusions at all."

To Angele he said one day, "As you know, my brother's principal approach to a woman he hoped to seduce was by way of her knee-jerk. How many times at parties have I seen him kneeling, his lewd face watching the response in the face above him! If he had thought of a stethoscope can you see him there, slipping it under the blouse and looking into startled fascinated eyes, while gently moving the disc over the left breast! Poor Eve, listening and looking, with a berry half-way to her lips!"

Now and then Vridar did something that supported the belief held by certain persons that he was insane. There was Johnny Bacon. Johnny was a dwarf of a man; he was no larger than a boy but he looked old. He looked like a little old monkey. On first moving to the valley Vridar had to go to a post office for his mail, and always in the post office he saw Johnny, waiting for mail, too. Johnny chewed tobacco and stood back by a radiator, so that he could spit behind it; and every few moments he went to his box and peered through its window. It took Vridar some time to realize that Johnny never received any mail. Just the same, the queer little man came every week day and waited with the other people. When Johnny saw a person take mail from a box, he would look at the mail and then up at the person's face.

One day Vridar spoke of the matter to a neighbor. Him! God Almighty, Johnny couldn't even read. He was as dumb as a dead steer, but for years his father had rented a box for him and Johnny had gone six days a week to look into it, though there was never anything in the box. Vridar told Angele about Johnny and saw her eyes mist over. He said he was going to have Johnny's name put on a lot of mailing lists.

The first time mail came to Johnny's box Vridar was watching the little man. Johnny went over, peered in, and saw the mail. He then acted like one who simply didn't believe his senses: he turned around and fixed his strange rattlebrained eyes on one face and another, looking in turn at every person in the room. He looked again at the box. Someone shouted, "Don't believe it but Johnny's got some mail today!" Johnny stared a few moments at the person who had spoken. He looked again in the box. The person who had spoken looked in Johnny's box and said, "Holy Jesus, it's almost full!" He opened the unlocked door and pulling the mail out handed it to Johnny. Johnny hugged it tight against him and looked from face to face. When he left the building, Vridar followed him for two or three blocks. Johnny stepped along briskly, like a man who had important affairs in the world. When it became known that Vridar had had the mail sent to the little man, the only response people made, so far as Vridar was ever to know, was to think that another author had lost his mind. One of them said to Vridar, "You must be off your nut to send mail to a jerk who can't even read. Think of all the postage wasted."

IV

The lower animals, Vridar said one day, and Angele challenged him. Lower in what? He then thought of birds in cages. Angele had a friend who kept a canary. When Angele went to the friend's home, she would slip to the bedroom to see how the canary was. It was never all right. She told Vridar the poor tortured little thing still had on its leg the heavy band, and was still starved. "Does she ever talk to it? No wonder it never sings!" Angele wanted to take the band off and buy feed for the bird, but knew that if she did her friend would be offended. Angele had said to her one day, "When you go on your vacation I'd love to take care of the canary for you." She told Vridar about it and said, "She looked at me for maybe half a minute and her look got foxier and foxier. She knew why I wanted it and will never let me take it now."

In nothing else did Angele so astonish and educate Vridar as in her attitude toward beasts and birds---indeed, toward all living things. Like all ranch or farm boys, he had known birds and animals; he had in fact made a study of them a part of his education, but not the kind of systematic study which he was to undertake here. It was Angele's great sheltering compassion for all dumb things, and her amazing fellowship with birds, that made him sense how much he had missed and how much he could learn. A professor-friend, one John E. North, had said with a polite sneer, "You actually mean that you can learn about human beings by studying animals?" The question was so pathetic with self-love and so laden with dark ignorance that Vridar had given no response.

Did the so-called lower animals kill for sport? Angele asked Vridar. Did they torture living things and call it religion? Did thousands of them gather and cry their mean brutal hearts out while watching men torment bulls? She reminded him that Spinoza---yeah, the *gentle* Spinoza!---had loved to amuse himself by

818

putting live flies in spider webs. She read to him from one of his books: "At one time a bear and a bull, chained together, rolled in fierce contest along the sand; at another, criminals dressed in the skins of wild beasts were thrown to bulls, which were maddened by redhot irons, or by darts that were dipped with burning pitch. Four hundred bears were killed on a single day under Caligula, three hundred on another day under Claudius." She paused to look at him and say, "The lower animals! Lower than what?" And went on reading: "Under Nero, four hundred tigers fought with bulls and elephants; four hundred bears and three hundred lions were slaughtered by his soldiers. In a single day, at the dedication of the Colosseum by Titus, five thousand animals perished. Under Trajan, the games continued for one hundred and twenty-five successive days. Lions, tigers, elephants, rhinoceroses, hippopotami, giraffes, bulls, stags, even crocodiles and serpents, were employed to give novelty to the spectacle. Nor was any form of human suffering wanting. The first Gordian, when edile, gave twelve spectacles, in each of which from one hundred and fifty to five hundred pair of gladiators appeared. Eight hundred pair fought at the triumph of Aurelian. Ten thousand men---"

"That's enough," he said.

"Oh no it isn't!" She ran to a shelf to return with Lea's three volumes on the Inquisition and lay them on his lap; and on those she piled two histories of human torture; and on those, a book about the instruments of torture, and another about sadism. He took the book she had been reading, thumbed through its pages, and then read: "It has been observed that a very large proportion of the men who during the French Revolution proved themselves most absolutely indifferent to human suffering, were deeply attached to animals. Fournier was devoted to a squirrel, Couthon to a spaniel, Panis to two gold pheasants, Chaumette to an aviary, Marat kept doves." Vridar closed the book. "There's a deep truth here and I'm on the trail of it: this much I know now, that those who torture animals, or people, hate some one, or several or many---hate some one, deeply, terribly, and in the case of men and boys it's likely to be father or mother or both. I'll get to the bottom of it. Meanwhile, I'll try not to call them lower animals any more, not any more."

She picked up another Lecky book and read, "It is one of the most subtle, and, at the same time, most profoundly just, criticisms of Winckelmann, that it was the custom of the Greeks to enhance the perfection of their ideal faces by transfusing into them some of the higher forms of animal beauty." She closed the book. "Brutal men who gaze fondly at themselves in mirrors can't see any beauty in the so-called lower animals, unless in a dog that crawls and creeps to them. I can show you a cow with a more beautiful face than any woman in this valley and what man among your friends wouldn't our cat put to shame?"

All his life he had hated the brutal and the cruel. He had hated his father because of his ways with beasts. Angele was now giving him a fuller view of the thing; and when she first looked upon the ruins of the Colosseum, Vridar was to stand back and watch her, wondering if she would remember that five thousand animals perished in its dedication.

She loved what Jane Welsh Carlyle had written after losing her dog: "Is *it* to be extinguished, abolished, annihilated in an instant; while the brutalized, two-legged, so-called *human* creature who dies in a ditch, after having outraged all duties, and caused nothing but pain and disgust to all concerned with him, is to live forever!" She loved what a biographer had written about Mrs. Richard Francis Burton: "The fact was that Isabel's passion for animals, beginning normally enough in her country girlhood, was assuming the proportions of major eccentricity in a childless woman of thirty-eight." Angele said she saw nothing eccentric in it.

She wouldn't, Vridar reflected, until in her it had reached monstrous extremes. Had there been nothing eccentric in her keeping a black widow spider in their parlor window for six months? "Nothing. It has as much right to live as we have." So many persons had cried out with horror on seeing the spider that Angele at last had told Vridar to take it away. Their house was to become so full of spiders of all kinds that windows, walls, and ceilings would be festooned with webs, and little spider feet would run across their faces when they slept. Their house would become full of wasps, which Angele would protect until visitors ran screaming outside with dismay and fright. Vridar would then gather them up in a vacuum sweeper and take them away and shake them out in a tangle of spider webs. They wouldn't bother him, Angele said, if he didn't bother them. She recalled to him Ellen Glasgow's statement about Thomas Hardy, that "he also suffered all his life over the inarticulate agony of the animal world;" and of Ellen Glasgow's strong distaste for "barbarians who go to Africa to kill animals."

Nothing aroused Angele to wilder passion than the fate of sheep under the blow-fly. One of their ewes lambed in August, and two or three weeks later Angele happened to be passing the barn when she heard the baby's low plaintive cries. She found it hiding in a patch of weeds and after one look at it came crying to Vridar. The rear part of the poor thing was a swarm of maggots that had worked through its wool and hide and into its flesh. Vridar wrapped it in burlap and they drove pellmell to a veterinarian; but it was too late: the doctor opened the anus for Vridar, and the vagina, to show that maggots by the thousands swarmed inside. On the way home Angele sobbed out her grief and horror. Some people, she said, thought there was a God, a merciful Father, who watched over all things. So, then, did he create the blow-fly! The same day she was reading in a yearbook of agriculture and came to the words, "Among all the insect pests there are on this earth, those that raise their maggots in the living flesh of animals are peculiarly loathsome." She learned that the screwworm destroyed untold thousands of animals all the way from South Carolina to California.

When they were driving along the highways, Angele would cry out if she saw a beast that seemed to be in distress, or even underfed. "Stop!" she would say, looking out at a bony old nag, that seemed to be propped on its four legs, and asleep. "Now what?" Vridar would ask impatiently. "That horse! I'm going to report this man." He would cry at her, "In the name of whatever god presides over snoopy children you'll do nothing of the kind!" One day she startled him by saying, "Did you see that nasty little boy? He went up to that nice cat and instead of petting it he kicked it in the belly." And Vridar would say, "Nasty little boys are kicking nice cats in the belly all over the world."

Her fury became uncontrollable when she saw boys shooting songbirds. "You nasty little monster!" she would shriek. Setting out on a deadrun for the nasty little monster, she would go on screaming, "Hey you, you fiendish little killer!..." If Vridar tried to calm her, she would turn her fury on him. He would say, "Look, God damn it, in your nice Catholic country Italy did you see any songbirds? Only in butcher shops." She always gave the same reply: "I can do nothing about all the things I don't see, but something about what I do see." And he would say, "If you shriek at boys that way, you'll make enemies." He did not tell her, he had not dared to tell her, what some of the neighbors' boys did with cats.

She caught two lads in her lane one day. They had treed a cat with a dog and were shooting at it with an air rifle, when Angele ran screaming down the lane. The boys fled, with her imprecations following them. He tried to make her understand that small boys were brutal little monsters; he offered to tell her what he had seen them do, as a child.

But she cried, "I don't want to hear it! I know what the little fiends do and I hate all of them!" She would never have invited to her home, nor would Vridar, any person who went to bull fights for the pleasure of it. When in Spain, as she was to be again and again, she always sent to her friends postcards of bull-fights in which the bull had the man down and was goring him.

If a mouse trap sprang in the night, it would wake her up and she would say, "The poor little thing!" These were invariably her words for any hurt creature. She would take the mouse outside and set it free, saying to Vridar that a mouse was only what life had made it. He would say, "So is a blow-fly. If the world were to follow your philosophy, everything might as well be turned over to the insects." She would retort, "Absolutely." He detested mice because during his childhood, when he and Marion lived alone in shacks to go to school, he had found it impossible to keep mice droppings out of the food. He loathed their smell. Angele astonished him one day by saying that mice were beautiful things.

"Your damned loyalties are all mixed up," Vridar told her, after she found her cat with feathers and blood on its whiskers. The cat had just eaten the bird with which she had talked most—the bird that had so learned to trust her that it had come into the house. Bursting with grief, she said, "I didn't make the damned world! If I had made it, cats and birds would like one another." The poignancy of her words sent him away, to be alone: there was, it seemed to him, so little evidence of the God-Father, so much of the Goddess-Mother, no matter where a man looked, except on battlefields.

In her furies Angele was now and then quite insane. She had a nest of robins in a flowering plum tree, and every day she talked to the mother and watched the little ones grow. One morning he heard her give an awful shriek, and left the house and ran. A huge blowsnake had climbed the tree and partially engorged a nestling. In a dreadful rage Angele seized the snake and ran to the shop with it; and laying it across a block of wood she took pruning shears and cut its head off. An hour later, subdued and chastened, she spoke sadly of the astonishment in the serpent's face. "It was only getting its dinner," she said.

So many times she startled him with what she said. Vridar one day shot a magpie, and a score of magpies gathered around it for a powwow. Angele said. "I went out to console them but they so reproached and scolded me that I felt shame and came back." She would gather a whole handful of spiders and gently take them outside, softly saying as she went, "You know you're not supposed to come in the house, you naughty little fellows. You upset Cookie." In the barn one day Vridar heard a strange clacking sound and on looking up saw four perched owls, staring down at him. Knowing that Angele loved owls, he called her and she came running to the barn. Vridar was fascinated by the resemblance the owls bore to certain persons he knew, and by the way they turned their heads when he moved around them. Angele persuaded him to go away, for she wanted to talk to them. "You'd never understand them," she said.

Angele had one pet cat after another. One was caught in a beaver trap and drowned; another was shot by a boy out with his first gun. After the death of a pet, Angele wept and felt dejected for days or weeks. Her favorite of all her cats was a spayed female which she called Suzy, after a famous dress-shop she had seen in Paris. Taking the sexual urge out of Suzy had, it seemed to Vridar, improved her mind, and he wondered if this was true of eunuchs in general. Suzy was such an intelligent cat that she rarely did what she was not supposed to do: if she sat on the window ledge and tried her best to open the door of the refrigerator, or stood on hind legs outside and reached up, trying to turn the door latch, or came with a mouse and loudly demanded attention, it was because Angele indulged her in these things. Angele swore that because the cat annoyed Vridar she had taught it to whisper. Now and then he would see them talking softly together, Angele whispering, the cat looking up at her.

It became a habit with Suzy to come in the early morning with a mouse. Her crying woke Vridar and annoyed him, and he would yell at her through the open window to shut up; whereupon Angele would reproach him, saying, "Shame on you! She has a fine mouse and she wants me to praise it." For a long time Vridar didn't believe this; he thought Angele was playing one of her small-girl games. But at last, curious, he left the bed and went with her to see what the cat had; and sure enough, there she was with a huge fat mouse and she was looking up at Angele's face and talking to her. Angele was praising her for having caught such a big fine mouse, though she turned to Vridar and said, "Look, it has large Disney eyes." Again he was struck by the aptness of her observation. He did learn that the cat actually came seeking praise, or at least kind words from Angele, and that after it had got the praise it went serenely away to eat its breakfast. Never in the morning after catching a mouse did she fail to demand Angele's presence (never his!) and her words of wonder and astonishment; and always she went away and said no more after the praise was given. Never did she make the demand when she had no mouse. One day when Angele and Vridar were studying Rembrandt's "Night Watch" the cat squawked horribly and he shouted, "Shut up, damn it!" Angele said, "Why speak that way to her? She was only commenting. She thinks that if great artists had had much sense they would have done a few paintings of beef liver." Vridar would then have to turn away to hide a smile.

Now and then she charged him with hating the cat. One day he was in his den writing, when Angele came in, with the cat trailing her. The cat looked up at her and began to squawk. Blandly Angele said, "She's upset by your housekeeping. She thinks your den is an awful mess." A few moments later, after the cat had walked sedately out of the room, Angele said reproachfully, "Now you've offended her." One day at dinner the cat was looking up at Angele and complaining, when Vridar commanded it to be still. Angele said, "She's only human, you know. Maybe she doesn't feel very well today." One morning Suzy brought a mouse to the door and called, and Angele went out; and a second time the cat called, and a third; and on returning from the third call Angele said, "She's hungry and she's just dying to eat but she loves praise so much."

Angele invariably called the forelegs of a cat its arms, its front feet its hands. Her way of looking at the world of animals was so strange to Vridar, so unlike anything he had known, that he made mixed responses to it. Sometimes he was annoyed and thought her silly. Sometimes he suspected her of a form of self-pity. But as the months and years passed he came to understand that she was right, that most people were wrong: there was not much difference between the animal and the human world. Bitterly one day she said to him, after he had shot a grebe that was busy eating fish in his lake, "He doesn't know why you do that—he's only trying to get his dinner. I didn't grow up with your values. Cats, dogs, spiders, mice, owls— they're all my fellows and they all love me." A poet named Dwight Hand came one time and after observing Angele's way with birds, insects and cats he returned home and sent her a few lines:

> Because of her smile, the lichen forms
> on certain rocks that I remember;
> her laughter is an all-day matter for the
> astonishment of the blue-jays;
> and it is in her eyes that it is possible
> for certain streams to go on forever flowing

One day she read a statement by a writer named Robert Penn Warren: "If we take even the extreme case of the idiot Snopes and his fixation on the cow in The Hamlet, a scene which shows a human being as close as possible to the 'natural level,' we find that the scene is the most lyrical in Faulkner's work: even the idiot is human and not animal, for only human desires, not animal, clothe themselves in poetry." After reading the words a half-dozen times, Angele came to Vridar, her lips curling. "Who is this guy?" she said. Vridar looked at the name and said Warren was a college teacher, a novelist, a poet. "A poet! What's the mental age of an idiot?" "Under three years." "Even the idiot is human and not animal, and clothes himself in poetry! Is this the kind of man they let teach young people?" "Look—" Vridar began but she cut him off. "Has the simpleton ever seen a thousand redwing blackbirds singing above their mating? Has he ever watched a robin mother feed her young? Does he know the incomparable rhythms of the barn swallow when building its nest? The idiot is human and not animal, is he?—the drooling brainless hulk of nothing! A human being as close as possible to the natural level? Doesn't this man know that most people are under it?.."

John Harold Rober, another professor-writer, came to see Vridar—a man so small and frail that he reminded Vridar of Leopardi's witticism, "My organism hasn't enough strength left to contract a mortal illness." John had a large ragged mustache on his small pale boyish face; a crown of bushy hair which, Angele said, he blue rinsed; and bony long-fingered hands too large for his small almost fleshless frame. "Rober," Vridar said alone to Angele, "has never thought much of me as a writer, and this belief he finds comfortable, like his belief that tomorrow he will be able to make water." After an evening's discussion, Rober turned his quiet sad boyish eyes on Vridar and asked if he actually thought that a person could learn about human beings by studying the beasts. For Vridar, who had been studying the beasts ever since his earliest years, the question was so obtuse, so deeply rooted in diseased self-regard, that he wanted to say, "Edward Carpenter has asked, Which of us has ever really seen a tree?" He wanted to say, "You remind me of a professor-friend who once asked me how it was possible for a man to get it all in a fat mistress. When I asked why he didn't try another position, he exclaimed, Hunter, you think I'm an animal?" He said, speaking quietly, studying the growing astonishment in the man's face, "I have learned that the mammalian male will kill quicker if denied the female in heat than for any reason, and will attack practically any combination of enemies. I have seen a ram cover a ewe thirty-seven times in a little over an hour, and then for some time continue to mount her, without effecting penetration. When I was a child there was a notoriously amorous man who in the lambing season ate quarts of lamb testicles, with the notion that they gave him superhuman potency: after a night with a mistress, he was at daylight walking the footpole bridge across a wide deep canal when he fell off and drowned. Nobody had any doubt that he fell off because of weakness; his potency became a legend; women sighed and yearned toward the eternities when thinking of him." Vridar paused to fill his pipe. Then:

"Take the cat here: though spayed she just loves to have me gently massage her dugs, pressing my fingers into her belly and almost getting rough with her: does she feel intimations of nursing?—or some sort of amorous pleasure?—or is there chronic distress in her dugs that massaging relieves? Have you ever asked yourself why a boar, to name one, spends so much time covering a sow, whereas a bull's embrace is, as Gourmont says, only a thunderclap?—is it because long ago the milk givers that chewed the cud spent only a few moments mating, for the reason that they had deadly enemies all around them?—whereas those more invulnerable to enemies took a longer time? And if this is so, what was man's position then? If his mating-time was brief, does it go against the deep grain nowadays when men prolong it to an hour or two hours?..."

When he talked to an absurd simpleton, who cherished the notion that in spite of his farting and belching and bad odors he was a different order of creation from the stud or the boar, Vridar found it impossible to talk straight, without ironies or sly intimations; and after a bit his auditors became suspicious, then hostile, then outraged. The Robers left in a huff and never came again.

Angele's great compassion for the whole world of the living was revealed almost daily. She might be reading in a journal about another bull-fighter who had been gored, and suddenly cry, "Goody! I hope the sadistic bastard dies!" She might be walking along the Lido beach looking for shells and see a hideous rack-and-bones of a horse drawing a cart: looking round her, she had said, "I suppose hay here costs a small fortune per munch." In a Paris shop window she saw several turtles on their backs, kicking desperately with their small legs; and she not only went inside and asked the shopkeeper to turn them over, but then stood by the window half an hour to see if they were all right. In Tangier she went out into a black wet night with a paper sack in her hand: on her return Vridar drew from her the confession that she had taken the supper's leavings where "some poor starving person will find it." Gently she gathered to her hands big cockroaches in the bathtub of an Istanbul hotel room and bore them away to freedom and safety.

She also had such compassion for human beings that malice was as alien to her nature as deliberate meanness. In Klagenfurt she bought a piece of salami and watched the girl wrap it in an old soiled newspaper. Suddenly, looking hard at Angele, the girl took the meat out of the newspaper and reaching around behind her brought forth a *used* paper bag and put the salami in it. Angele had tears in her eyes when she left the shop. She had tears in her eyes in Salamanca when she stood looking at an old blind woman, sitting in rags in a cold drizzling rain at the entrance to a tavern, trying to sell the few trinkets in her lap. Vridar would never forget how she chased around in a downpour at the zoo in Vienna, looking at the starved gaunt beasts and cursing the Russians because they had left a people so destitute that the whole land was hungry. She liked the words that a friend sent her, "How lovely animal people are! Folks like your cat and my cat do not spy on one another, do not yowl and bark their nasty responses. When they do clash over food or sex they do it openly, cleanly, and their grappling is to the death. . . ."

It was not true, Vridar reflected, that they did not yowl and bark nasty responses: they were much like their human cousins. Suzy, who presumably had no interest in males or mating, would scare the living daylights out of another cat if it appeared in her domain. When Angele heard furious battle outside, she would rush forth crying, "Shame on you! Isn't the world big enough for both of you?"

But nothing that she did so astonished and enlightened him as her way with birds. She would talk to them. She told Vridar that they talked to her. Some of them did: she and a catbird, or she and other birds, would utter sounds for the other to imitate; and time and again Vridar listened, his wonder growing. If Angele happened to be sitting in the house and leapt up with a cry, he knew at last what it meant: a bird from former years had returned and was calling to her! She would rush outside and find it perched in a honey locust and they would talk and sing to one another. It was commonplace for her to lure birds into the house; and she even brought owls to the tree close by the door, a thing Vridar would have thought no person could do. "See," she said one day, "he brought his little wife." Vridar said he would be damned, for on looking up he saw two solemn faces, and four round solemn eyes staring down at him. When after a week or two they no longer came, Angele said, "They're off now having their babies." She said birds had memories. It seemed to him they had, else why would they return year after year and call to her? Studying her way with birds, he thought of what Colette had written about one of her characters, that "he belonged to a class which forbade itself to recognize and even to have any conception of its kinship of animals." Poor John Harold Rober, what did he know about Rober!

Angele had insisted from the beginning that their few acres of land and water should be a game refuge. And they were. Vridar now and then had to exterminate magpies and crows---and the bittern, the heron, and fish-eating ducks that came to their lake; and the beaver. The beaver had an insatiable lust to fell trees, even when there was no need to. The raccoon in spite of his efforts to rid his place of it managed to eat the thousands of crayfish which Angele had numbered among her pets. All creatures but these, including fish-eating snakes, had freedom of life on their acres, and most of all the pheasants, which during the hunting season came in by the hundreds.

In his beast and bird sanctuary he had for his study, beaver, otter, muskrat, raccoon, porcupine, bobcat, and domestic cats gone wild; a dozen or more species of duck; the redwing; yellowwing, and common blackbird, sometimes in such numbers that he could hardly believe what he saw: passing from their night-haunts to their feeding grounds they filled the sky for half an hour, and their number, he thought, was hundreds of thousands, possibly millions. He had wrens, robins, warblers, flickers, catbirds, swifts, swallows, hawks, and now and then a meadowlark, whose song for him was the finest in the birdworld, possibly because it had gone into him so deep when a child. Angele convinced him that two swallows building a nest under an eave had actually lured or pressed into service a third swallow, that acted as a feather-and-mud-carrier but did none of the actual building. He had quail and dove, partridge, pheasant, tern, and gull; turtles and frogs and lizards, toads and snakes. The black racers and blowsnakes would sun themselves on the stone walks approaching the house: if Vridar and Angele heard screams, they knew that women had seen the snakes and were beside themselves with fright.

What had he learned? Rober asked. Enough to fill a book. He had learned as a child, and here on his own place, that some mothers, such as the hen, the sow, the bitch, would fight to the death to protect her brood, when it was so young as to be defenseless; but later, when it was old enough to be adult, would starve it to death at the same feed trough. In fury at a half-grown daughter gobbling mash with her, a mother hen chased her child into a corner and would have killed it if Vridar had not intervened. Only four weeks earlier that mother would have fought to the death to protect her child. In varying degrees of intensity it was that way with all barnyard mothers. A sow would fight any foe to save her babies, and the next day eat them alive.

What light did all these things throw on human behavior? None for the blind. Had Rober known mothers who would have fought hell and wildcats to protect their daughters when they were small, yet turned on them when they were grown? And if most mothers were still devoted to their sons, or to some of them, after they *looked* like adults, how deep did he want to look into that dark night? "If bull-man or stud-man is still devoted to his daughter, flash on the screen for us his attitude toward his son-in-law—and never mind Freud, who never got away from his Ma, in spite of fifty years of effort. The way parents hang onto children after the children want to leave them and build nests of their own is the most shameful perversion in the world. My own mother has never been willing to let her sons go (her daughter, yes!); nor any mothers I have known, except two. Isn't this dark monstrous perversion especially true of Judaism and Christianity?..."

The Robers denied it all and begged off and fled. Then Vridar would say to Angele, "When such stupid men, with their dull stupid eyes, and their souls rotten with their own hidden diseases and smelly evasions and sneaky self-righteousness, put their boy-faces up at you and pretend to be thinking, it's enough to turn any stomach. Being more conscious and intelligent than their animal cousins, cow-ma and bull-pa should continue to have a relationship with their offspring; but not the one we see everywhere. Let them go not to the ant to be wise, but to the beasts. In the Jewish-Christian world no generation is ever allowed to grow up and be adult: none ever has been: the parents pull it down, as they were pulled down, with the result that the Western world has never got out of adolescence. But don't expect the Robers ever to understand that: the preposterous ass is no more adult than his ten-year-old son."

Vridar learned—this he had not known as a child, this he could not have known then—that fear was the strongest of the constant emotions in bird and beast. In some, as in the quail and the rabbit, it was the emotion that dominated their lives. ("And is it not so with man?") In none did he find it absent, not even in the hawk. It seemed to him that the strongest emotion in the male was fear, with possibly food-hunger second and sex-hunger third; in the female, fear, food-hunger, mother-hunger, and sex-hunger. Always, in all the creatures he studied, fear was present.

He bought a three-hundred-pound calf and hauled it home in a trailer. When he moved to unload the beast, it became so terrified that it struggled and bawled like a mad thing, putting up such violent fight to be free that by the time he got it to the pasture Vridar was exhausted. He turned it free and the terrified creature ran back and forth along the fences for hours. It never became gentle. During the year Vridar kept it, never once would it enter the barn for food, no matter how extreme its hunger, if it could see Vridar anywhere; and if Vridar approached it the beast would run at top speed for a hundred yards, then turn, its head up and all its senses wide open, as he had seen deer and elk. What astonished him most was the wide variation in creatures that had been brought up in identical situations: in the strength of their hungers, the violence of their passions: one cow, hungering for a mate, would let off no more than a gentle moo now and then; another, her sister, with the same mother and father, would become so loud in her calling and so impetuous in her eagerness that no fence would hold her—she would plunge through five strands of barbed wire and rush frantically from neighbor to neighbor, pausing now and then to look, listen and call. In sex hunger there seemed to be much wider variation in the females than in the males, among all barnyard beasts: there were cows, ewes, mares, hens that would let the male cover them repeatedly; others that once covered, would resist and try to escape. And so it was, Vridar reflected, with women. The differences seemed to be born in them: he could find no reasons in health, food, or environment.

Wide variations existed in mood and temperament. Two steer calves which he raised from birth, in identical situations, had different attitudes toward him: one would kick his heels and invite Vridar to play; come up to get his itching hide rubbed, his face nuzzled, his horn stubs dug at; would come to Vridar when he was lying on his back in the pasture and by cavorting around him, kicking and bawling, would urge Vridar to rise and play; but the other calf would never come close enough to be touched, or put aside his fear.

His discoveries (all of them to be found, he supposed, in books but he liked to make them himself) delighted him: he had imagined that beasts recognized people with their sense of sight: this, he found, was not true of barnyard animals and he wondered if it was true of beasts anywhere: that recognition came through their sense of smell he proved again and again. With his old yard coat on Angele could go up to any beast to which he could go: with some of her garments around him, he could not go up to them, but could go up to them naked. Farmers with whom he talked added to his knowledge of these things. He had known that an orphan lamb could be put on a ewe that was not its mother, if the skin of her own dead baby covered it; or if, a sheepman told him, he rubbed the smell of the dead lamb's anus on the other lamb's anus. Most animal mothers seemed to recognize their offspring most easily and naturally by smelling its dung: his thoughts went back to his father's crude earthy sisters, changing diapers, slapping their babies' rumps, shrieking. . . .

One autumn day he saw a number of pheasant hens feeding under a black locust tree, and a male pheasant in the tree. It seemed to him that the cock was shaking the seedpods loose for the hens below. Doubting this, he got his high-powered glasses and with Angele slipped as close as he dared to the feeding birds. There could be no doubt of it!—with wings and feet and beak the male was actually dislodging seedpods, which fell to the hens, scurrying around under him.

One day with a strand of wire he suspended from a rafter in his shop a pail with two quarts of wheat in it. A few days later he looked in and saw mouse droppings. It had been a law of life with his parents that if an article was hung at the end of three or four feet of wire, mice could not get to it. How were the mice getting into the pail? How were they getting out of the pail and down to the floor, five feet below it? Hiding, he waited to see what they did: from the rafter the cunning little fellows slid down the wire to the pail; and after filling their stomachs, they balanced a moment on the edge of the pail and then dropped lightly to the floor.

The bittern one naturalist called the bog-thumper, because of its cry when nesting. The cry, he said, was like the sound of a wooden stake being driven into a bog. All night in the tule marshlands below Vridar's bedroom window the females uttered their cry, in a series of three, four, or five, with a time interval between every two series of about a minute. The noise so disturbed him that he would take his shotgun and wade into the marsh. He never found the nesting birds: day and night the blackbirds acted as sentinels: three or four redwings would cling to the tule stems and give off their little cry of distress and warning; and the moment the blackbird spoke the bittern fell silent. So many creatures had signals and sentinels in other creatures, with which they had no conceivable fellowship, and no bond in common but the bond of fear!

"Fear," he said to Angele. "What a different perspective it puts on the entire world! What a light it sheds on war! . . ."

V

He would have butchered his own animals in any case, for he had said to Angele, on coming here, "The person who will eat meat, yet will not kill his own, is a specially odious kind of coward." He had another and larger reason: he wanted to project himself into the primitive man, standing above his prey. He wanted to learn why the only animal making claims to compassion was the worst killer of them all.

It filled him with deepest woe to raise a calf from birth, and then shoot the trusting creature in the spot on its forehead, no larger than a silver dollar, that covered its brain; to gash its throat open and then jostle it around to make it bleed freely. But he built a slaughter scaffold, and for years he raised his own lamb and beef and did all his own killing.

He found that it was not easy to project himself into his primitive forbear in the act of slaughter. How did the man do it? Grasping club or stone axe he went skulking around, trying to sneak up on unwary creatures; and when (how rare the occasions must have been!) he was able to bring his weapon crushingly on the head of deer or gazelle, did he then drink the blood (running from nostrils?) and with ravenous eagerness open the belly to reach in for the quivering mass of liver? Vridar, a sentimental and rather melancholy fellow, maneuvered his fat glossy cornfed steer into position, and then fought an impulse to turn him back to pasture: the large ox-eyes were so full of friendliness—so expectant, as though wondering if it would be cornmeal, or carrots doused with syrup, or alfalfa meal sprinkled with honey. Then the twenty-two pistol spat flame, the whole beast stiffened with shock, and dropped; and a moment later Vridar was slashing deep into the throat, and moving away from the red bloodgush that poured over the earth. Angele, knowing how he felt about it, and with sensibilities even more delicate, refused to come out, but knew that the worst of it was over when he came to the house with a panful of heart, tongue, liver, and kidneys.

Vridar would cut the head off and after removing the tongue take it away, so that he would not by chance look again at the eyes. His farmer neighbors thought no more of killing a beast than of rolling a cigarette or eating an apple. Vridar wondered how they could open the warm wet depth of its heart and cut the heart from its moorings and lift it out, without becoming strangely, breathlessly, aware of the incredible miracle of their own heart! He struggled time and again to put himself in the primitive man's emotions, standing above his prey. But the act of killing actually filled him with horror: kinship of animals had gone too deep in him, in childhood.

He was amused by the response of city people, who now and then asked to watch him. The man would peer curiously into the beast, to learn how the organs were situated. Both man and woman were more interested in the sexual parts than in any other. The Lunds came from Boise, Sunny and Bill; and Sunny gave off a shriek when she saw the length of the penis. "Holy surreptitious!" she gasped, bending forward to peer. "Did he use all that?" she asked, her blue eyes as big as eggs. Her husband said, "Do I use all mine? Half of it is back in my body." "In your baw-dy?" she said, turning to him. "It runs clear back to the anus. Didn't you know it?" Sunny turned impulsively to Vridar. "I want it," she said. "I've give a party and show it to all my friends."

Her party, Vridar heard later, was a sensation in Boise. She brought the penis from the refrigerator and laying it before a dozen women asked them to guess what it was. She swore that when she told them, three of them fainted dead away and one ran from the house screaming. Vridar hardly knew what to make of the Lunds, after Angele told him that Sunny gave Bill an enema, when he asked for one, and talked about his sexual vagaries as calmly as about the antics of her children.

Vridar had known from childhood that many men on ranches thought the eating of testicles increased their sexual potency. A neighbor boasted of what such eating did for him: after a few lamb-fries in the spring, with about two quarts at a sitting, he embraced his wife three times every night, and once every day at noon, for a week. His wife blushed and cried, "Shame on you to tell such things!" Later, Vridar had said to Angele, "What power of mind over balls!"

The man who astonished him most was Homer Richards, a short fat moonfaced sheepman. Lambs were castrated by cutting off the lower third of the pouch and then seizing the testicles and pulling them out, cord and all. Sheepmen had learned that the work could be done faster if the castrator used his teeth: kneeling, he would dive with his head, close his lips and cheeks over both balls, at the same moment setting his teeth in them, and with a swift movement tearing them out. Homer, a social snob, who belonged to country clubs, played golf, and boasted of his English ancestry; who said, "Between you and I" very distinctly, to impress people with the college quality of his English; and who would kneel all day tearing the testicles out of lambs, rising at night bloody from head to feet, would no more have eaten fried testicles than he would have broken wind before his mother. He thought those who ate them were an inferior order of being.

Mountain oysters, men called them, with a lewd wink. Mountain oyster fries were annual events. The testicles, only as large as the end of a man's thumb, were brought to kitchens by the pailful, slipped out of their sheath, and gently simmered in butter and seasoning. Angele and Vridar thought them delicious. Most of the men who ate them had the notion that they were adding to their potency: they would wink at the women, tell dirty stories, and laugh loud. One who had spent a year in college took pride in fancy words: "Ever hear of the man with the fixation on women's underwear? They sent him to jail. The prosecuting attorney called the wife in and said is your man oversexed? Why no, hell no, she said, he ain't good for more than two or three times a day." There were lewd snorts and shrill howls all around the big table, at which sat a score of husbands and wives, eating nothing but mountain oysters and hot cream biscuits.

"Well, I guess you heard of the mother who went to the doctor," the story-teller went on, his whole face suffused with lewdness. "The doc, he took out the big bouncing twins and told the mother in pretty fancy language it was wonderful to have twins. Why, Doc, she said, that ain't nothun, nothun at all. I already have four sets of twins. The good old doc, he was trumped. Holy mountain oysters, he said, don't tell me you get twins every time. O Doc, she said, how can you be so silly? Thousands of times we don't get nothun a-tall."

The snorts were louder this time, the howls shriller. Looking at the man who had told the story, Vridar recalled what he had once said about a hostess in a night-club. "Jeez, she just sidled up and rubbed me with one of them big tits and I like to have fainted." Sometimes the lewd men of the valley stirred Vridar to laughter that left him undone. There was Dick Littlefield, whose boss had a high nasal voice that Dick imitated exactly, his thin sensitive face all the while simply glowing with malice. "Have you heard what that sneaky old bastard's wife said to him? She said, After this when you fart you have to leave the bed and the house. That upset his stomach and made his Parkinson twice as bad. He said to me," Dick said, imitating the man's thin nasal complaining voice, "he said, By God, Littlefield, what's marriage coming to in this country anyway, if a man can't fart in his own house?"

Vridar exploded with joy.

There was Lars Jorgensen, who had the curiosity of a woman and twice a woman's skill in ferreting out the more odorous secrets, and in telling about them. One day Vridar wondered aloud why a certain beautiful woman had married a certain man. Lars erupted; in his ordinary normal voice he was loud enough to blow a man down. "You, a writer, can't see through things so simple? You'd better trade that type-writer in on a sewing machine. Now the first thing this guy done was to put on his fancy cowboy outfit. That always knocks them eastern dames silly. Then he goes up to Sun Valley and there she was, loaded with jack and jewels and looking for a man with rape in his eyes. What did she do, Hunter? Why, when she saw this guy with all his war paint on and smelled the buckskin in his chaps, she just pissed down both legs and took right in after him."

Then Lars would smile. He had the sweetest, the most absolutely innocent, smile that either Vridar or Angele had ever seen. But his smile could vanish in an instant, his face turn grave. Then in a loud voice that sounded angry he would demand, "What did the guy do, Hunter? Why, with all his teeth showing and with half his ass out, just like a traveling salesman, he piled right on to her." And there was that incredible smile again.

One day Lars told Vridar about John Gibbs, a farmer, who late in life developed a furiously ardent interest in a woman who was not his wife. "Why did he?" Lars demanded, fixing Vridar with accusing eyes. "Because Ma Gibbs spent all her time chasing dollars. So John, he goes to her and he says, Look, Ma, this dollar-chasing is interfering with my screwing. You'll have to cut it out. But Ma wouldn't, and so John takes after this other hen, though God knows why, for she's built just like a little brick shithouse." Again Vridar exploded; and Lars, hugely pleased with himself, turned on him a smile so sweet that it made women want to kiss him.

Vridar had long wondered if erotic hunger in excess was not chiefly ego hunger. The woman who had felt the impulse to kiss the naked shoulder had often said O my God how starved she had been in earlier years, when her husband lay ill. After she had gone home, Vridar would say to Angele, "All the women in the world would be in jeopardy if that woman had the trinity she wants." Dick Littlefield was a queer one, too: he confessed with the candor habitual to him that he felt most like a male when his wife's belly was swelling. Vridar had heard two or three other men make the same confession. Soon after Dick married, his wife caught him winking at himself in a mirror while copulating with her.

Vridar was still charged with prurient and obsessive interest in sexual matters by a person now and then who had read some of his books. He had learned long ago that those who brought such charges had the dirtiest minds. There was an evil-looking neurotic fellow who said, "That's about all you think about, ain't it?" When at a later time the man, in the presence of his wife, boasted of his erotic powers and passions, Vridar said to him, "You have the most sex in your mind and the least in your scrotum of any man I know." At once the wife had swept her arms high above her head and brought them down, hands clenched, her voice shrieking, "How right you are!"

Vridar had a distinguished friend who was what in the Unted States was called a fanny-pincher: his wanton behavior recalled to Vridar Stendhal's account of General de Lafayette in his dotage—of a repulsive old libertine who at parties pinched all the loveliest women and looked down into full bosoms. Vridar had never seen his friend let his daughter-in-law pass without reaching out, with a shrill studhorse whinny, to pinch her; and after he sponsored a girls' softball team, Vridar saw him, while watching them play, fairly drool with the overflow from his lecherous yearnings. Striving during these years to see the dark things in man-animal, Vridar wondered if it was frustration that forced the American people to an obsession with sex that astounded the world. And then one day he knew what it was: all but a few of them were children: he decided to make a study of popular magazines, such as *Time* and *Life* and the women's and men's favorite journals; of the comic strips; of radio and television programs; of popular fiction, to arrive, if he could, at the approximate emotional age of the mass of the American people. When he spoke of their incredibly obsessive interest in sexual matters to Angele, she said, "Amelia?"

"Whose Amelia?" She put before him a card on which she had written Jane Welsh Carlyle's words: ". . . a dreadful bore—one prays to Heaven that the poor woman could but once and for all get herself *seduced* and so let us have done with her alarms and precautions, on any terms! Upon my honour, I do not see the slightest sense in spending one's whole existence thro'out three volumes in taking care of one's *virtue!*" He read the words and said, "A smart woman, our Jane, but she doesn't state it well: Amelia was a symbol of virtue in an age of depravity, as Satan five hundred years earlier was a symbol of depravity in what had the gall to call itself an age of virtue. Strange, by the way, that nobody has figured Jane and

Carlyle out. Did they have lovers?" Angele said she was sure they had; and he retorted, "Isn't it your tendency to think that way?"

"And isn't it your tendency to be stupid in these things? How many women have you defended, only to find out that they were what I said they were?"

"Too many," he said wearily. "Let's not talk about it."

"Why not?"

In such moments, when she forced him to the vomit of his excessive idealism, his stupid adolescent romantic faith in mankind, he wanted to boot her hard. In these moods it was the other person in her schizoid nature who came up---the cynical old witch-woman, knocking credulity's face off with a broomstick. "All right," he said, willing to let her have her triumph. "I'm an over-believing ass, particularly in regard to women---though the Almighty God knows I've no reason to be. But you go too far in suspicion."

"When?" He shrugged. "All right," she said, with sharp anger, "give me an instance! Did I see what your damned sweet virtuous—"

"Enough, enough!"

Now and then she affected the mood of a wanton, of a world-weary debauched woman who knew it all. He then wanted to seize her as he might a wet towel and wring the impurities out of her. It was simply impossible, he told himself, for a woman to be objective: her uterus and breasts would not allow it. Baur's words were not for her. He was trying to take a detached position, in his study of beasts and men; he was reading night and day in the works of hundreds of great minds, to establish (if he could) a picture of himself and of mankind that would be valid for at least a generation. But a woman brought everything down to the level of uterus and mammary glands! A woman was an organism, in which mind was superfluous, yet he was forever defending women—not the masculine strivers who loathed men because they themselves had no penis—not the shoulder-kisser who one day said, "Why did the Lord make us squat to do it?—yet let the man stand up in lordly fashion to do his pissing!" If ever, Vridar reflected, the mind became master, all passions and instincts would then be abashed into moderation; but could a woman be got to understand that? "The human mind," he said, striding away and talking to himself, "will eventually encompass its restricted sphere on this planet, and perish for want of more to do: since what we call life must have happened billions of trillions of times in the Universe, yet has left no record known to us, only a paranoiac can believe that mankind can leave a record. Try to interest a woman in *that!*..."

Oh, he knew what it was. In his old dreams of Neloa appearing as a whore he had come close to the deepest truth of his nature, and missed it; all night, night after night, in those years, he had sensed the truth, and missed it. The truth was this, that his bossing caretaking nature had wanted to care for her and cherish her, but Neloa had been too mature a person to need it. He had thought of her as a weak one, as the whoresort—and so she was, because so normal! He wanted to cherish and protect Angele: she allowed him to most of the time, for she was an orphan and a child. Yes, he wanted to boss, direct, take care of, manage, in part because his mother had put this chore on him, but in greater part because of his nightmarish sense of insecurity as a child. The need to feel secure, and the compelling desire to reshape the world to the need, he now recognized as the chief motivation in all the political liberals known to him. How simple was the psychology of a Stalin, for those who looked deep into the well!

Neloa, he reflected, must have hated him, for the same reasons that his brother hated him—for the reason that most of the free world hated the United States, with its infernal old-woman bossing and managing! He took a pail of carrots and headed for the barnyard. Where in life was there a vision more comforting than a cow blinking over a feeding of carrots, turnips, or potatoes, the teeth crunching and the mouth drooling? He watched her eat and then lay outside on his back, to study the superb flight of a hawk, riding the air currents and never once flapping a wing. Nowhere else, not even in Faulkner's idiot, was the rhythm of poetry so perfect. Why had he and Angele quarreled again? Getting to his feet he made up a bouquet of lovely gray sage, thornpods, cattail flags, sunflower, and goldenrod, and went to the house to make his peace with her. As always, she was ready, and met him, eyes misty, at the door.

VI

Well, then, insufferable God-Pa, the basic emotion was not sex at all; it was not hunger for food; it was not even hunger for position and power, prestige and acclaim. It was fear. Projecting himself into ancient man and feeling his way through one situation after another, he always came to the hot blind core of the thing, and the core was fear. He had thought that race prejudice rested in self-love, but found that it rested chiefly in the *perception of difference*. The recognition of difference aroused fear. *That* he discovered when he brought two ancient peoples together in war. Indeed, he now understood that it was not on ideals, or struggle for resources and markets, that most wars had rested. It was on fear. He now suspected that the Jews had been a father-image for Hitler.

Having found that in the very heart of things fear was the deepest emotion, he then strove to feel his way into the patterns and evolutions that fear engendered. The discovery of fire was a great and wonderful thing: he quickly felt at home there, because for so many times in the past he had built his own fire, when hunting, fishing, or camping in the mountains. So many times he had sat alone by a fire in dark night, or looked through darkness at the pale yellow far-distant light of a sheep-wagon. He knew what a golden comfort fire had been to ancient man---the fire by the river or on the plains, or in the golden rooms of the caves. But it had been a terror, too, almost the most paralyzing of all; and this he had known, for he had seen prairies and hills swept by flame, and immense forest fires; and he had smelled all the burned carcasses of the dead.

It had been a great thing when the first wolf became a dog. Vridar was not a dog-bosser. His friend Rhode bored him stiff by saying every time Vridar entered his home, "You don't care much for dogs, do you?" Vridar had told him what Mark Twain had written about dog-lovers, but Rhode was able, simply and with no bother at all, to forget anything that crossed his way of life. He always admitted his huge bird-dog to the parlor, where it ran around like a small moose, thrusting its face up against Vridar and pawing over him, while Rhode smiled indulgently. A score of times while Rhode was telling Vridar what a wonderful thing a dog was, the beast had begun to masturbate by licking its moist red penis. Mrs. Rhode then became wholly intent on her knitting, and Rhode, after bringing a palm down over his nose and sunken cheeks, hastily stated again the reasons why the nation and the world were headed for catastrophe. After three stray dogs had cornered one of Vridar's sheep and eaten the flesh off the top of the neck and a part of a shoulder and after Angele found the poor thing still alive and ran screaming like a demented person, Vridar was never able to look at a dog without seeing the wolf in it.

Yes, the dog had a part in the human story but not the dominant part that Rhode would have given it. "The man and his dog!" Rhode would cry; and Vridar would say, "The man and his ghost." Rhode would not talk about such things as ghosts and graveyards. He did not want to know the meaning of the tolling of bells; the horseshoe-yoni above the door; the heraldic crests, mascots, fasting, and baptism. He didn't want to be told that the Nutka of British Columbia gained rebirth and immortal life by ingesting hunks of stone crystal: like most people he refused to think about the past and his lowly origin: he wanted to be told that his ego, his personality (his meaning!), his name would live again and be perpetuated through an eternity of time. One evening Vridar had said, "There's no evidence at all, simply none at all, to support your notion that incestuous offspring are degenerate." The man had thrown his hands up, his face gray with horror. "Poor Rhode!" Vridar had said to Angele. "What does he know about Rhode?"

It was the grave and its ghost that opened another world to Vridar: not an ancient world but the world of his time: he had only to go to a funeral to find people saying good things of the one who had gone—"He was a great man....He was a good man....He was generous to the poor....He was kind to the sick....He was a legal and devoted husband....He was an exemplary father....All people loved him."

"He was a faithful servant of his God."

"A great man----"

"Noble----"

"Wise----"

"Generous----"

"Kind----"

Hearing these pious lies from every tongue, the ghost was flattered and pleased, and hovered near the body, watching the movements of the people. Though flattery might win the good will of the ghost, you dared not depend on it; and so, to be safe from its angers and whims, you hid from it, by putting on mourning garments. These were black, as an emblem of the night. Though he detested funerals he went to two, and found nobody who was not breathing words of praise about the one in the coffin---and it was the handsomest coffin the family could afford; and it was banked deep with flowers; and for months or years, relatives would go to the cemetery to put flowers on the grave. They pretended that these were flowers of love.

835

Yes, it was still the primitive world in the modern: should he feel shame for a people so deeply sunk in superstitions? Weren't they the kind the Caesars gave corn to? They were the kind who looked at him as though he were a lunatic when he said, "If I couldn't feel the pain of having a child, if I couldn't project myself into a matter as simple as that, I'd not have the gall to write books; nor would I ever wish to read a book by a woman author who was not able to feel herself in possession of a penis, at least for the purpose of writing about it." They were the kind who looked at one another when he said, "The only person who can be honest is the actor; all others have to be true to themselves." They were the kind who thought it time to go home if he said, "All truth has begun as heresy and ended as superstition." If he said, "Truth isn't some ideal thing without error, but an assumption upon which we may act without fear," they were the kind who would say, "You ought to read the Bible and get this crap out of your mind."

The world he was trying to understand was the world of fear, the only world of which mankind had any knowledge. On a card he had written the words of a scholar, "The most astonishing logical paradox ever to be cherished by man is presented in the circumstance that the theologists, convinced that God in his omnipotence had predetermined the fate of every man, and in his omniscience had from the beginning of time foreseen that fate, should yet hold to the belief that he nevertheless holds man responsible for his action, rewarding him either with eternal beatitude or eternal punishment." Such statements made Vridar groan aloud: why should any scholar turn a grave concern on the childish beliefs at the subhuman level! Why did most of them refuse to face up to the simple meaning of the word God? How could they look at a Universe measured in trillions of light-years and then solemnly put down in cold words, as matters still to be settled, the pathetically feeble conjectures from the dark dimwitted cranium of primitive man?

For weeks he lived as fully as he could with a ghost, as an ancient man, feeling haunted by the spirit that had survived (Alexis Carrel believed that a spirit actually survived the body!), seeking ways to placate or imprison it. He knew, as ancient man had known, that it was not imprisoned by the stones piled on the grave: the fear that most people felt in a graveyard made that plain. Vridar would go to a cemetery and sit for two or three hours among the headstones, looking round him, *looking back*. How incredibly childish it all was! For there could be no doubt of it: the horror with which most Christians looked on cremation revealed their old ghost-fear: they would put the body away in an expensive casket, smother it with flowers, and speak only good of the one who was gone! If they were to burn the body, what would the ghost do? Vridar thought it a peculiar irony that a Catholic, with his great burden of superstition and mummery, should write a supercilious novel about a cemetery. . . .

What deep black terrors people had felt in that long-ago time, who had no knowledge of natural causes or of the reasons for misfortunes and ills; who thought that the dreadful thunder and lightning were flung out by the Moon-Woman; who had not even a vague notion of what the stars were or the sulphur smell from the earth---well, then, the poor terrified creatures had conceived of the spirit, the ghost, as a source of evil, and had searched their feeble darkened wits for ways to circumvent its malice and its vengeance. What terrors then, what terrors still, with no man knowing in the age of his most diabolic ingenuity what terrors were still to come! What a profound mind it was that talked so glibly of freedom from fear!

He spent weeks as a primitive man fleeing from the ghost that haunted him. Had the Mother been born of such fear? Had the matriarchy evolved from desperate need of a higher and nobler shelter? Oh, not alone from that---nothing came from single causes: it had taken millions of years to produce Eve: in scores of books, in many dreams, he felt the intimations of her coming, with Adam somewhere far behind, a club in his hand and the tiny foetus of a thought in his dim brain. Thinking of Eve, he would murmur over and over Ralph Hodgson's poem, and then say to Angele, "It's just about the sweetest damned thing I ever read. Wondering, listening, listening, wondering, Eve with a berry half-way to her lips. Oh, what a clatter when titmouse and jenny wren saw him successful! Picture her crying outside in the lane, haunting the gate of the orchard in vain! Picture the lewd delight under the hill tonight---'Eva!' the toast goes round, 'Eva!' again!"

What a huge advantage over the male the simple fact of the menses had given the female! For she then by right and by logic claimed the moon as her own. Completing their cycle every time the moon completed a cycle, from youth to age, women knew that the moon was a woman, and was like all women, save only that *she* had discovered the secret of youth and was immortal. "Come!" he would cry to Angele. "Come look at Her, and put your insights with mine." Angele would lie on the earth with him and they would look at the moon. "Having discovered the secret, Woman now lived above the earth, eternally in her own special home, fertilizing the earth's women or making them barren; and controlling, in ways dark and unpredictable to her children, the whole pattern of human life. If their house fell down on them or caught fire and burned; if they were sickened by overeating or poisoned by plants; or even if they were wounded when moving carelessly, they never thought their craftsmanship poor, their appetite abnormal, their choice of food ill-advised, or their movements clumsy. Nothing was ever their fault."

"Most people are that way still," Angele said. "They've changed less than you think. How much difference is there between the ancient who stared at the moon, and the modern who stares at an icon of Mary?"

Not much, he said. Well, it was plain even to superficial reflection that the woman's sphere was more limited, but sharper and clearer; the man's larger but more obscure. A woman spent most of her time within the periphery of fixed habits and customary chores; the man felt a deep urge to alter and shape his environment. It was this that led him to persistent and usually foolhardy efforts to shape the Universe to his will. The Old Woman had magic--- "Haven't all the people today that you call subhuman?"

Well, yes, he said: for most Americans, F. D. Roosevelt was some sort of magician: the political messiah was replacing the theological messiah: the "economic emergency" was replacing Hell. "But what I need to know," he said, sprawled on his back with his mind open to the sky, "is not that Adam until recent times was unaware of his essential part in procreation: I need to know what the unawareness did to him. Think of the tens of thousands of years during which Joe-Adam did not know that he was necessary to the making of an infant. What star-bursts invaded his psyche? The matter was all in the keeping of the Old Woman up there---of the women on earth with their magical menstrual blood. Poor miserable Whelp-Joe got to embrace them now and then, but only because their body-hunger allowed it: the embrace, so far as he knew, and certainly for her, was a piece of sensuous folly. His task was to club the enemies and bring in the meat. I ask you, what did all that make of him?"

"Joe," she said.

"Yes, Joe, the schizoid brute. No wonder so many Joes ran to the desert wailing to Heaven about the wickedness of Eve, and cut off their testicles! Because for so long he was a pathetic rabbit hiding in a canebrake: a sneaky dimwitted scared-to-death simpleton who jumped out of his ego when the Old Woman yelled at him."

"But look at him now!'

"It's enough to unseat any mind to look at him now. For man the male had been housed in a great hunger that for ages had no windows and could find no doors. That hunger in time produced, in ways not yet clear, the orphan before the wailing-wall, out of which came the poet. If only we had a picture of all the things that took place in the fear-ridden ego-throttled psyche of man! For such a long time, at least with certain peoples and in certain areas, he had not been a participant in the miracle of new life, but only a superfluous man unable to write his memoirs."

"You think that's the way Albert J. Nock felt?---in the Christian world?"

"Absolutely, but always think of it as the two inseparable worlds of Christian and Jew: it took both peoples to perfect the nightmare. But tell me, can you imagine how it was then, before the domestication of animals forced on Joe the realization that he was necessary, too? Did man find his part in the act too trivial? Denied the womb, the sensations of nine months of life-growing right under his heart, and the unbelievable fresh new wonder of baby-lips on nipples, with still no capacity to be the poet, and denied the sphere within which to be the tyrant and brute, did Joe just sulk and look forward to the time when he could torture and destroy millions of his fellows? Oh, I know there is more in it and I am reaching to that, too...."

He would go back to man's new idea of the ghost and of the invisible world, and then try to feel, intuitively, as though he were an octopus-core with nothing but tentacles, his way down to magic, when all the ills of life and all the terrifying manifestations of nature were the work of ghosts. He would go back to the grave and its ghost and then come down---back and down, to the terrible shuddering haunted time when the spirits of the dead, malicious, malevolent, malignant, evil, skulked invisibly, lurked in crevices and holes, under rocks, in hollow trees, in whispering reeds and agitated seedpods; when day and night they tried to creep into people, through their mouth, ears, nostrils, anus, and genitals. All this he could feel. He could easily and simply sense the development of all the amulets to ward off the evils, including those (yes, these most easily, because of the miracle of birth) in phallic form---the form of the female in its time, for why should an amulet take the shape of testes or penis when these were of no worth? Oh, they would have their worth later; they would be enthroned in trinities and godhood.

Images of them would be worshiped by millions of women, and set above church doors, fondled, kissed, prayed to. That time would come with Adam-Joe but he was not yet....

Vridar brought books by the score and had them sent in by the hundreds, feverishly hoping all the while for lights in his subconscious mind, insights in his dreams. He read such books as *Man and Woman* over and over: "...confirms the opinion of the bad influence which has been exerted by mother in this matter of promoting the menstrual invalidism of their daughters...." But *that* was only a gesture out of angry frustration from women in Adam's, not in Eve's, world! The breasts, a sculptor told Brucke as reported in *The Human Form,* "should always live at enmity; the right should look to the right, the left to the left." That was only driveling *childness* from male artists. "This obliquity of the legs is the most conspicuous aesthetic defect of the feminine form in the erect posture, while it unfits women for attitudes of energy, and compels them to run by alternate semi-circular rotation of the hips...." "Adam-Joe speaking," he said, laying the book down. "In a time of almost complete patriarchy who else speaks, except a few women who want to be Adam-Joes? Imagine what Eve would write, in a matriarchy, about Adam's conspicuous aesthetic defects! It's too bad," he said, turning grave, "that a scholar as great as Havelock Ellis had to be so adulterated with prejudices."

Men, said the Adams, in patriarchy, had more delicacy of perception in their sense of smell. Yes, said Vridar with a snort, "Yes, good God, such a fine sense of smell that not one in a hundred can recognize the human female in heat, with his sense of smell alone!" Men, said the Adams, had more delicate discrimination in foods and liquors. "Yes? Most of those known to me prefer hamburger drenched with catsup, and whisky mixed with ginger ale!"

"A woman instinctively hides her defects, her disorders, if necessary her age—anything which injures her in the eyes of men, including even her best qualities, if she thinks that these may call out ridicule or dislike....in a woman any demonstration of love which has not been invited by a man is regarded as immodest, whence a training in deception which in the excitable nervous systems of women is particularly severe; again, in women the exercise of the natural functions of urination and defection have been regarded as immodest so that any natural call of this kind must either be repressed, or some ingenious ruse must be invented...."

To Angele he said, "Of six hundred religious sects in the world only seven have been founded by women: there is a clue: men have been driven to found innumerable religious orders. Why? And of all the peoples on earth the Jews---their forbears were Arabs who came in from the desert---enthroned the Father, that is, the Male, in the most absolute power and splendor. For these people there was never a Mother (there might have been if Solomon had had his way), there is none yet. The Father was childless. Why? We have a dark well here that nobody seems yet to have dared look into: these people who more than all others put together shaped the Western world, enthroned the male in majesty and splendor and cast the female down. It's long past time we were looking at that and daring to say what it is.

839

"On the psychic side, it says in the book there, women are more inclined than men to preserve ancient customs and ancient methods of thought. Isn't that because of the nest? In males generally, we are told, there's an organic variational tendency to diverge from the average, in females generally a tendency to stability and conservatism. The nest. Women had to protect the nest with its young. Men, bless our Adam's apple, were left free to become queers, freaks, outlaws, beatniks, griffons, unicorns, hermaphrodites, black swans, exotics, novelists, mystics, prophets, monks, and popes."

He searched in hundreds of books but found few clues to what he sought--he found no conjectures, by great minds, on the evolutionary directions the male had been *compelled* to take, by his unconscious mind, because for so long he had no role in the making of life, and found it so trivial when at last it came to him. He rejected with snorts of derision the analysis by certain popular novelists of the struggle between the sexes. He read histories of contraception, of prostitution, of pimping, and of what people liked to call sexual perversions. What had driven the male to tyranny, enslavement, torture, *organized* war? Was love of evil inherent in him? What an irony---O Universe, what an irony!---that man, who formerly had mated with woman only when she accepted him, and never when she was pregnant or nursing, had made a whore of her when she came to power! That the psychologists he talked to, hiding deep in the velvet of their self-protective male assumptions, refused to perceive so obvious a fact was a greater irony still. Fear was the parent of cruelty, Froude had said: yes, but there were more parents than that.

He was irrigating his trees one day and thinking of the ancient rites of rain-making, the fertility rites with water, the reverence for water as a life-giver; thinking that out of the waterless desert came the Hebrews, to establish a Father but no Mother, and bequeath to the whole Western world their extreme form of patriarchy ---he was thinking of these things when suddenly there occurred to him the question, What essentially is woman anyhow? He thought of Janice Mott, whose contempt for her sex took the form of wishing to be smothered and almost destroyed in the sexual embrace. Vridar had observed her one day, sitting with a leg over the other knee, revealing every beat of the heart in the slight lifting of the leg by the pulse in the calf. With her customary grimace of distaste she had said to him, "You don't know women, except the mother." "I'd rather have a woman tell me that," he had said. "Anyway, what other kind is there?" She had cried, half-rising, "You don't call me a woman?"

"No. Anatole France, we're told, was haunted all his life by a vision of Dido in the Fields of Sorrow, half-surmised and half-seen. I know only the mother?" He was thinking, You sly stupid bitch, you say I don't know women because you thought you'd get to bed with me and didn't. After Janice had gone he said to Angele, "Are you a woman?"

"You've said there can be no women in a patriarchy, but only the things that men have made of women."

"It works both ways: we're only the things that women have made of men. What was the primal Adam, the Eve? It accurs to me that possibly we can never know more about religion than its dogmas, until we've submerged ourselves in choas and come to a great healing. What is woman, what is man? The prigs who have asked the question have meant not man but mankind. What is man? asked Pepin. The slave of death, the guest of an inn, a wayfarer passing. What is man? asked David Hawke. For the most part a foul wretched abominable creature, a cheater, a scorner, a mocker, full of brag when surrounded by his fellows, without the courage of a rat when alone. What is man? asked Thoreau. A creature so degraded that he cannot speak of his necessary functions without shame. After all its eons and ages of travail, said Balfour, the human race has enough conscience to know it is vile, enough intelligence to know it is insignificant. The joker there is that significance is a concept only in the tiny dim human mind, and exists nowhere else."

"Woman?" Angele would say, looking at him soberly. She liked to define things by giving instances: she now called to his mind his sister-in-law Mollie, a vain woman who had said (ah, many times!) that after she became bethrothed to Marion, various young men in her hometown area had come to tragic ends: had one killed himself, had another gone insane? What was her fantastic story anyway? Or Prudence's! After Joe died, Prudence one day had told Vridar a yarn that made his eyes bug. What had happened to the young men who had been wooing her? After she married Joe what had they done? Why bless your soul, one in a frenzy of grief had left the country and nobody had ever heard of him again; another, named George, had married a stupid wench named Julie, who died giving birth to her second child, where-upon George, broken with grief and terror, had come weeping to Prudence, his first and only love; and a third had become a drunkard, a pitiable sot who went to the dogs. Speechless with amazement, Vridar had stared at his mother, for never had he suspected that in her depths was such childish vanity as this. The thing that chilled him when he heard women tell such stories was their utter lack of pity and compassion for the other women. Angele agreed with Vridar that Prudence was not a woman, not a female, not an Eve, but the terrible half-sexed neither-male-nor-female thing that men had made of women in the Judaic-Christian world: it was so plain that her telling of what these abandoned forlorn suitors did was compensatory: with what cunning rationalizing women strove to avenge themselves on the whore-makers in whose scheme of things they were an inferior order of being!

"Harriet Gosmer," Angele said. Harriet had a daughter who, assisted by a conniving mother and grandmother, had got herself a West Point man. "I ask God for just one thing," Harriet told Angele, "to let me live until my daughter is married." The man had kissed the daughter on Flirtation Walk, and when telling about it Harriet's eyes had shone like stars. This was a thing that always gave Vridar wonder, that although Harriet had been married four times and had found no happiness with men, her eyes would glow, her lips would turn tremulous like a bride's, when she told of a woman being kissed in a "romantic" spot.

"Jenny Bogan?" Jenny was the phenomenally energetic busybody kind: a snoopy hen who had to keep busy or go mad. She had to participate in everything that interested her. When within one month in her area there were three lovely weddings, Jenny was fit to be tied. She then couldn't rest day or night until she had prevailed on her eighteen-year-old-son to find a girl and get married. Angele said, "She's so full of joy that with just a little push she would fly. A wedding all her own! She'll be the sole boss." What she wanted, Vridar said, was babies: she had no more interest in men than cows had in bulls. Angele said, "But is the modern American woman really interested in her children?"

"Are men who climb mountains interested in mountains? The beast-mother is not interested in her children when they no longer need her."

"That's it," Angele said. She laid a card before him, on which she had typed: No person wants to live if the need to struggle for it is taken away.

With a slight smile he said, "Is that one of my deeper insights?"

"Yes, man-love."

"Well, woman-child, then it follows that the human mother must resent her children when they no longer need her. The vacuum in her casts a shadow to the end of their lives."

"Yes."

"What a shadow my mother casts! What a shadow David Hawke's mother cast! Even when he was in Europe the night of it still enveloped him. What a shadow Dick Littlefield's casts---Ronald Teague's---Hector McTavis's---Reuben Rhode's ---in fact, of all my men friends who amount to anything, by Who's Who's standards ---what standards!---there's not a one who doesn't stand in the shadow of father and mother. Marion and I, possibly, most of all. It is extremely important, in the scheme of my project, to understand Adam and Eve...."

VII

After months of striving in every possible way to project himself in Eve, Vridar became alarmed. He felt that he was losing his sanity, or such shreds and tatters of it as he had left. He understood that in this, as in some other matters, there was a point of no return. He got so that he chronically felt the wide abdominal hip-spreading heaviness of one who had given birth after birth; the long empty sagging breasts, with swollen ugly nipples brushing across his belly as he worked, or touching the back of his neck like eels, when, in the way of ancient women, he flung the breasts back over his shoulders and tied them together to keep them out of the way; and in all hours the pressing need to look and feel inward. When he entered Adam he began to run, for there was then a looking and feeling outward, and a need of freedom; but his genitals flapped back and forth in their nest of hair and became, even for a primitive man, ridiculous. Nowhere were they more ridiculous than in Greek statuary. . . .

In the jargon of the day Vridar was an anxiety neurotic, a neurasthenic, a hypochondriac, and a good bit of a schizoid, for there was a cleavage if not a split in his personality. He was a person who could never relax, but lived intensely from the moment of waking, until, exhausted by fatigue poisons, he slept again. Tensions built up in him with explosive force. The only way he had found to relieve them, and to relax his aching bones, was in the comradeship of alcohol. Occasional drunkenness with him was a form of therapy.

Angele would look at him and say, "Carlyle complained endlessly all his life, yet lived to be eighty-six. Was there ever an hour when he didn't think he was about to die?"

"As big an ass as I am," Vridar said. "But bear in mind Jane's statement, that there's nothing like a bit of pain for taking the conceit out of one. Arthritis, for instance." One day he said, grinning, "I think my bowels will eventually triumph over my mother." When the Japanese struck at Pearl Harbor, Vridar first cursed Roosevelt, "Another man of destiny winning his place in history with war!" and then hustled around to buy all the brown psyllium seed he could find. Shortly he discovered that all he needed was whole bran: some people had their blue and gold periods, he said; he had had his fig, his yogurt, his lemon juice, his psyllium; and in his later years entered his bran period, which promised to be his last. "I hope my critics, if I'm cursed with any, will have the gumption to separate my books, and get the yogurt, the psyllium, and the bran novels where they belong. As Freud said —I think he must have been as constipated as hell—as soon as the soul attains peace the body begins to give trouble. But I'll never win peace: for me as for Stendhal it is *la crise des quarantaines*."

"Poor quarantained Cookie."

His furiously persevering effort to project himself into the dim past laid him prostrate with neuritis. His doctor told him to take elephant doses of vitamin B-one. "How big?" Fifteen milligrams anyway. Vridar learned by increasing the dosage that he had to take at least a hundred, to feel it—"That's expensive for an author whose books no publisher wants." He also learned that he was allergic to a number of foods, including all fresh fruits, except the citrus family. In the peach season he would eat four or five large luscious tree-ripened peaches, and then itch and scratch and groan all night. He loved pears, apples, raisins, dates but could not eat them without chronic itching. When all the pressures bore him down, he would get drunk.

He had no symptoms, so far as he could tell, of the chronic alcoholic. Marion had become one and was contemplating a study of alcoholism, in a nation of drunkards. He asked Vridar to write down the reasons why he got drunk, and Vridar gave the matter a great deal of thought. Alcoholism, various journals told him, had become a national problem.

"Why do I get drunk?" he asked Angele, and tried to talk out the reasons. "How much ego-frustration is there? Some, though I hold it in contempt and see the folly of it. I mean," he said, with a wicked grin, "the folly of wanting to be a man of distinction and sell my name to Calvert whisky. Then there's the morbid shyness: alcohol scares the Censor off and let's me talk. And don't forget the taste of whisky: I like it, though nothing sold nowadays tastes half as good as those few drops I used to find in the bottles Charley Bridwell threw away. Then there is father-fear. . . ."

He thought of Adam and Eve as the archetypes of his parents, and asked over and over the question, *What and how much has happened to them?* All of Adam was in Joe perhaps but Joe was wider and taller than Adam—more brutal, crazier, and possibly more afraid. For thirty years he had been fighting off cancer, and his doctor, shaking his old gray head, had told Vridar, "He should have been dead twenty years ago." A will to live kept Joe alive: he said he would live to be a hundred, and to support his will he brought forth an astounding rationalization: he had convinced himself that before he reached his hundredth year, the world would end with the return of Jesus, and therefore he would never die!

His cancers were on the surface but they had eaten ugly holes in his head, and the stink of him was more than anyone but his wife could stand. There was a pus-wet deep hole back of one ear; a hole in the bridge of his nose; a hole in his cheek close to his right eye. His whole face was a cancerous blotch but only twice had he submitted to surgery. He preferred to suffer pain and be his own doctor; he put on his sores practically everything he could think of, including lye, nitric and carbolic acids, blue vitriol, various astringent juices, urine, and only God knew what else. His deepest grief in his last years came from the fact that he was not allowed to do his temple work: the sight and smell of him were too much, the Mormon officials shut him out. He was also troubled by a fear that he might not get above the third heaven, where, in his belief, no women would be: having only one wife, and three children, had been a great woe to him, who with many wives and children might some day have become a god. Prudence had said to him, her voice harsh with scorn, "You don't think you'll ever be a god, do you?" He had made it a habit never to reply to such questions. He had looked at her as he had looked ten thousand times—"Not," Vridar said to Angele, "as you'd expect a man to look at a woman with whom he expects to live twenty billion trillion years." Vridar had come to feel deep compassion for him, though it was not easy to feel sorry for Joe, after hearing his rumbling angry tones say that Catholics would be lucky if they got to the first heaven; after hearing him say with his scowling obstinate Judean-Christian dogmatism that only Mormons would go to the top heaven, where God dwelt. Or after hearing him talk about ears. Joe was utterly devoted to a whole galaxy of superstitions, among which was his belief that persons with ears high on their skulls would die early. Vridar one day had seen him looking at Angele, and, amused, had said, "She won't live long, will she?" Gruffly his father had replied, "Don't you think I know?" Joe believed that in another ten years the Mormons would completely control the Rocky Mountains area, and eventually the United States. When drunk, Marion would stare at his father and say, "Your trouble is you're stupid. Is it impossible for you to understand that Mormonism is for small dull children?" Vridar never liked to hear Marion talk that way to his father. He could see the dark awful pain in Joe then—in this man who, never understanding his sons at all, had hated them, and his wife. Joe had a bitch named Kitty. When she gave birth to pups, Prudence had Joe put the pups in a sack and go away to drown them. This happened year after year, until the time came when Kitty abandoned her babies the moment they were born. In the dry way she sometimes had Prudence said, "She just figured there's no use to bring children into the world." His mother's words reminded him of the time he was sitting at breakfast with Angele, on the ranch, when a mouse came out of hiding. A cat sat watching it, tail moving from side to side. Angele had said, "Poor little mouse, he thinks he has a future."

The thing in Joe that most amazed his skeptical and unbelieving sons was his appetite. Angele cooked the dinner for his eighty-third birthday. Joe ate three pounds of prime porterhouse steak, including every morsel of its fat; three large helpings of mashed potatoes, drowned in rich gravy; and an entire half of two ten-inch pies. He said the only thing he had ever found that was too rich for his stomach was swans. His appetite did begin to fail a little at this time: for his next birthday dinner he could manage only half a chicken and one large helping of dessert. This, Vridar reflected, looking at him, was not the Joe who came down out of the deep white mountains to bring food to his sons, and then ate half the food he had brought, while his famished skinny sons sat back and hated him. This Joe was a sick man, though he would not admit it. His bladder had become a tyrant, and so he never went to bed any more. His heart was bad. Though his property was more than enough for the comfort of him and his wife, he walked half a mile daily to buy a loaf of stale bread and save a dime. Vridar understood now that as a child Joe had lived in such a nightmarish sense of insecurity (because of his wild Irish mother, who hated him) that his fear of being destitute (of being abandoned, of course, and lost) had become his master. That was the simple psychology of the miser: what a brilliant light it cast over such persons as John D. Rockefeller Senior! "It's deep and dark in me too," he said to Angele. "Encourage me just a little and I could squeeze Lincoln's face off the penny."

It filled Vridar with darkest woe to look at his father and think of what old age did to persons who once were strong and self-reliant. Here was a man who had picked up three hundred pounds of green lumber and walked off with it; who year after year had driven a huge grubbing-hoe into the roots of serviceberry, chokecherry, and aspen, to make a place for himself in the world; who so far as Vridar could remember had never been sick a day in his life, before they almost cut off his head to tear a cancer out of his throat. There he sat, a shrunken pathetic old man—see an old unhappy bull, sick in soul and body both, banished from the herd he led, bulls and cows a thousand head! He always thought of Hodgson's poem when looking at his stricken father: there they left him, every one, left him for the birds to pick . . . . half the bull he was before, bones and leather, nothing more. There he sat, with hideous sores eating his face away. There he sat in his stink, his eyes rheumy and wet, that years ago had glanced along a rifle barrel and dropped an elk on a dead-run at half a mile. Dreaming, this old bull forlorn, surely dreaming of the hour: pity him, this dupe of dream, leader of the herd again only in his daft old brain! Father, my father!

Then one day he was stricken, and taken in a coma to a hospital, one side paralyzed. They strapped his free hand to the bed, so that he could not dig at his cancers. Vridar looked at the agony in his father's face, squeezed his strapped hand, and said softly, "You are in a horsepital for the last time, Dad." That was his word for it. He was old and sick and tired now, they should let him die. Even now the swarm of flies blackening his bloodshot eyes. . . . Yes, they should let him die but doctors were not like that: they were pumping him full of drugs to keep his weary old heart beating, and saying with infuriating cheerfulness, "We can keep him alive for some time." This old bull in a coma! "Why should you?" Vridar asked angrily. "Let him die." He went to his room and wrote a letter:

You tell me that you cannot possibly keep him alive more than a month; that he will never regain consciousness; that if you take the drugs off him he will die in a few hours. You are hereby instructed to take them off. . . .

The next morning Joe was dead—all his splendor, all his strength, all his beauty's breadth and length dwindled down with shame and grief. . . . To please his mother Vridar had to go listen to the dull pious sermon; he had to stand around and hear Joe's relatives brightly saying, "How natural he looks!" He had to go to the cemetery and be a witness to the primitive barbarous custom of trying to bury the ghost deep in the earth. He had heard a two-faced shyster murmuring to his mother, the widow, "For your loved one you should have only the finest: see how beautifully this one is furnished—and of course you will want a copper vault to keep the dampness out. . . ." On returning home Vridar had gone to an undertaker to make arrangements for his own cremation; and had been astonished to learn that under the law of the land he would have to be burned in a casket. "But I want only a wooden box," he said; and later to Angele he had cried in a fury, "Of all the God damned stinking rackets! People are so stupid and venal that they actually enact laws to make it necessary to destroy valuable materials with their corpses!" Undertakers, monument-peddlers, burial-plot vendors—how many trades preyed on nothing but grief and fear?

It all reminded Vridar of one of his favorite stories. At a party he had said to a group, "You all know Jake Gobels." Hell yes, they all knew Jake. They thought Jake was just about the most worthless thing alive—a lazy loafing drunkard and wife-beater. Not a one of those who knew him would have given him a meal or raised a finger to save his life. Yet when Jake, drunk, fell in a river and drowned, the very people who had detested him most had turned out and spent four days and a part of four nights searching the river waters for the corpse. "The grave and its ghost!" Vridar said. "What a task we have, to tear the primitive past out of us, so that we can breathe."

Joe was gone. His passing filled Vridar with dark grief. "I had no father," he said. "All my life, until recent years, I've looked for a father-image, but found none big enough to win my soul: I can only think them very thick and ignorant, who could make one of a Stalin or even a Roosevelt." Yet look, he said, how many sons had turned to him: he meant young men who came seeking him out, as a father-image—the fatherless, the orphans. The Judean-Christian world was full of them. When possible, Vridar turned the father-seekers away, and said to those strong enough to bear the words, "Look, understand the hunger in you." He would tell the man how he saw it, how it had been with him, too, and usually then they became friends, and, in a way, brothers.

No, he and Marion had had no father, Joe had had no sons: the Judean-Christian blight had almost destroyed all three, and millions of others, hundreds of millions of others. He was digging it out and seeing it all more and more clearly, as he came in spasms of furiously persevering projection down through the eons.

Looking at his stricken father, Vridar had recalled the words of a biographer of Pierre Radisson: ". . . probably no English-bred boy could quite understand the tug at his father's heart, when the old man, sitting in the chimney corner, thought of the mad rapids and clear lakes of Canada, with the fish leaping in the water and the dark forest ranged along the lonely beach. Radisson could never have made them know how he felt about the dancing campfire by the river's edge, the smell of the woods as a man lay under an overturned canoe. . . ." Joe would have understood all that, as he understood the hunger in his stomach. On Joe's last living birthday Vridar had led him out, knowing that there was only one subject under the sun and the moon that Joe really liked to talk about—of his adventures when hunting: of the time he followed a wounded bull elk, and stepping around a stone ledge saw in an instant that he was cornered and that the bull was charging. Joe had barely had time, he said, to yank his rifle up and fire. The beast had dropped almost at his feet. Of the time when he found a huge female black bear in one of his traps: the bear had gone away from him, slowly backing to the length of the chain; and Joe, a greenhorn lad in bear country, had followed. When the bear charged and the chain sang with taut and strain the bear's talons missed him only by inches. He would tell a story, and then sit as though run-down and empty until his son tactfully and gently led him out; and then he would tell another. But he never put aside his distrust, his hurt. The Old Woman really went deep into him, Vridar thought, looking at the gray watchful eyes.

The day his father was buried Vridar had a dream. He saw Joe in a stockade with palisades. There were several courts and in one of them was a huge male African lion. Vridar was afraid of it but his father seemed not to be. Angrily Vridar had said to Joe, "I'll get books and prove to you that it's dangerous. One of these days it'll take your arm off." His father had then prevailed on him to approach the beast where it lay at the far end of the inmost stockade, its eyes green and wicked, its tail moving in the cat way. Vridar then rushed across the stockade and climbed far up a ladder. He saw Marion there. Joe seemed to be sitting out in the court, indifferent to the lion, even after it got up and growled at him and tried to leap up the palisades. Vridar was out of its reach but still frightened.

When he awoke he thought about the dream and at last said to Angele, "I can find no clue to it." Angele asked if the lion was not a death-symbol. Then in a flash of insight like a burst of lightning it all came to him: throughout his historical novels, in which he had been looking for himself and for parents and brothers and sisters, there had been an omnipresent pervasive sense of death. He had thought that death became less dreadful to people as they grew older. His father had been telling him in the dream that death was not so dreadful after all, as the voice told the girl in the Millay poem that hell was not. He recalled Reik's words, that only the young are afraid of death, only the old of dying. But he had not been able to accept Reik's view that preoccupation with death was always a reaction to secret and murderous impulses. He preferred Marion's view, that it might well be fear of ego-erosion: a person could become so afraid of losing his identity, of becoming depersonalized, that in a desperate effort to save what was left of himself he would wish to die. How well he understood that now! Because on the death of his father and his brother, his wish was to die and get it over with.

"Who has come closest to a father-image for you?" Angele asked one day.

He looked steadily at her violet-green eyes for perhaps a full minute, thinking;

847

and then said, quietly, "You'll perhaps be astonished to know. One came close to it, the brilliant Chaucer scholar, to whom I fled for advice after Neloa's death; but in classes under him I had seen too much vanity in him, too little awareness on his part that he was vain. Not Rhode: the demon in him is too huge, tyrannical, unsleeping, and ruthless. Meriwether Lewis."

"Meriwether Lewis! Of the Lewis and Clark——"

"Yes. There was a man in some ways like my father—Joe would have been a dandy on that long dangerous journey. I want to write a novel about Lewis some day, and if I live for it, a book about his death."

Angele thought that Vridar's mind was not always lucid during these months of grief. She told stories with which she tried to amuse and arouse him. "Your mother had a dream. She died and went to heaven. She looked all around her, she says."

"I can see her standing there, looking the thing over."

"Yes, she looked the whole thing over. While telling me her blue eyes looked right into mine, and she said, You know, Angele, there didn't seem to be much to it."

"That's Prudence," Vridar said. "Joe's pieties and Bible-mumbling never took root in her. But then, women are not theological, having no need to be."

After Joe's death a friend wrote Vridar, "Joe Hunter's boy has fixed it so he isn't entirely gone. The old chap is now one with Gant and that ilk. He will be alive and kicking with pioneer vigor as long as people read. It's bearable if it is remembered that Joe fully expected to go on ranching after his last long leap—and with A-1 equipment!"

The Federal Government was going to build a dam now, and bury deep under water those acres that Joe had cleared with back-breaking toil. He had been spared knowledge of that. He had been taken before the machines came to destroy what it had cost him fifty years to build. Thinking of this, Vridar stood alone one evening by his father's grave, looking at the stone tablet with Joe's name on it. "Dad, farewell," he said. "We were never father and son and it's too late now. Farewell. . . ."

VIII

In spite of his approach in every possible way he could think of—in spite of his reading, his thinking, his dreaming, he was not able to untangle the two skeins that Adam and Eve had become, that Male and Female had become—the modern Man and Woman. He wondered if it were not all inextricable and inseparable, to the inquiring mind. Oh, he could see the Old Woman in Prudence and in a few other women—the Old Woman of the Matriarchy, when the female and her values were dominant; and in Joe and Rhode and a few others he could see the Old Man. But they were so much of one another now that it was absurd to call the one Female, the other Male, or to think of them as the primal Eve and Adam. He would study the faces in newspapers and journals; in the back of the Oscar Williams *A Little Treasury of Modern Poetry* he studied the faces, and of the men saw not a man among them. There was in them indeed so much of the Female that he found it embarrassing to look at them. In a mirror he saw so much of Prudence in his own face that he detested it. He came closest to the Female and Eve, to Adam and the Male, when he went far out and back and mingled with the peasants: the skeins there were not yet so mixed, the things that belonged primarily to the one or the other were plainer.

His efforts to untangle this matter sank him deep in dreams. In one he stood facing a remarkably lovely young woman, whose order of beauty was that of Elizabeth Taylor, but with less prominence of bone in nose and lower jaw. With the tip of his tongue he touched her lower lip here and there, and found it marvelously like flower-petals; and the flawless perfection of throat, cheek, or forehead, and found it like pressing his tongue or fingertip to warm lilies. Her dark Latin eyes (French or Italian) were the kind of pools in which a man could surrender his will and drown—for the eyes were like flowers, too, and the nose, from which nobody in his right mind could think mucus was ever blown. He smelled the wondrously beautiful hair: it was as if it had been washed in purest rain, and dried by warm winds blowing across flower-masses. . . .

With what billions of money, he thought, on awaking; with what fantastic ingenuity; with what sleepless perseverance the American man has devoted himself to the task of representing the American woman as a creature that never blows her nose, belches, farts, urinates, or defecates: there was some great dark meaning behind all that devotion, that he was trying to reach to. Was this a modern and colossally oversize representation of the virgin birth? Anyway, the female was not in it. The female was no longer in the hideous things that stared at you from the pages of the so-called glamor magazines. She was still out there in the sweating peasant: yes, in that peasant, if you had the nose for it and the sense for it, you could still now and then, in the healthy ones, catch the ravishing odor of the female in heat—but never in these deodorized, scrubbed, sandpapered, plucked, scent-and-lotion-saturated creatures that were indeed American women, but not females any more! Nor were the creatures males who had built up this multi-billion-dollar industry dedicated to the task of destroying all the femaleness in the daughters of Eve. Vridar also studied the photographs of the men, in magazines for women, and shuddered, as he shuddered when looking at six fingers on a hand or five legs on a calf.

In Boise he knew a woman whose pride and joy was her fingernails: the first time Vridar saw them he would have been no more astonished if he had perceived that she had no fingers at all. Her nails were an inch long, beyond the fingertips, and were painted a barn paint red. When drinking, the woman held up both hands, so that she could show off her nails. Her whole face said that she was conscious of them and damned proud of them. Nail by nail she broke them off until she had only one nail left; and she then folded nine fingers and thumbs inside, exposing to view only the one long nail.

In contrast to her was Dick Littlefield's wife Bertha, a Slav. Sometimes Vridar and Angele went to the Littlefield home, taking a jug of wine or a bottle of whisky. One evening just as they drove up, the Littlefield car came in at high speed behind them, and Bertha at once rushed into the house. Dick's thin sensitive face was covered from chin dimple to hairline with a sly sardonic grin. He confessed to Vridar that they had been in a friend's house when Bertha saw the Hunter car pass, and had jumped up, exclaiming, "We'd better go home or they'll use all our vaginal jelly!" The words were so incredible that Vridar could only stare. He told Angele about it later, and said, "I know there are idiots in this area who think we spend most of our time in bed; but Bertha, as level-headed as a theorem! What can you make of it?"

Angele said quietly, "Haven't you been looking for the female?—and don't know her when you find her? Bertha is about as far away as you can get from *Vogue* and *Glamour*."

Yes, that was it: he saw it now: at one pole, the woman with the fingernails, at the other, Bertha.

He read, now and then, with amazement, a letter that Thomas Wolfe had written his mother: "I couldn't stand Booneville now—I couldn't stand the silly little grins on the silly little drugstore faces. I couldn't stand the silly little questions of 'What're you doing now?'—and the silly little 'oh' and the silly little silence that follows when you say you are writing—as if they could know—stupid little vermin as they are—the tragedy, and the heartbreak, and the travail of mind and spirit— that has kept me ragged. And for what—a dream—a poem. And what do they care, in their mean little hearts for a dream or a poem? Oh I know them—know them—know them to the bottom of their base, greedy, money-loving little souls— I know how the vapid sneer will change to the fawning smile once they hear you have prospered and that it has gone well with you. If such people ask news of me, be silent or say that I am dead. Let me be dead to them as they are dead to me."

It was so painfully infantile, so mawkishly full of self-pity, so much the cry of an adolescent orphan before the wailing-wall, that Vridar would say to Angele, "Some think he's the greatest American writer of our time. If he is, then we have a riddle indeed; for do children write great books?"

"Maybe for children. Haven't you said we have a nation of children?"

"A world. There's possibly not a real adult in it. But are we so infantile that a writer at the age of twenty-three can be acclaimed for his ten-year-old tantrums? And as a child was he as tormented as I? Did the big bullies throw him down and pour syrup on his genitals, and then hunt round for spiders and ants to bring to the syrup? Did they pull his thing up taut and actually put a knife against it, vowing to cut it off? Why should he expect truck drivers and hog gelders to be interested in his writing? After all, he's not particularly interested in hog gelding either."

Oh, he knew what Wolfe had meant by the vapid sneer, the tiresome questions, the fawning smile. He knew it all, he knew it all. It was not the questions that annoyed Vridar; it was the taunts and jeers from some of his friends. There was Ronald Teague, a pharmacist: "If you'd write a book like this," Ronald would say, in the presence of a dozen persons, and snatch from a reprint stand a book read by millions. "I tried to read your latest but went to sleep in the second chapter." There were snorts and laughter. "You got to get him to bed with her," Ronald said. "There isn't a decent screwing in all the books you've written. There," he said, pointing to *Peyton Place*. "That author doesn't miss a trick or a wiggle. Even Hemingway has a lot of screwing in his books and that's why they sell. Why is *God's Little Acre* such a seller? Because in it somebody is screwing somebody all the time."

Vridar had to smile in spite of himself. Ronald was fond of Vridar, but he was baffled: Vridar knew that he was thinking. This man my friend is smart or he isn't. If he's smart why is he driving a car fifteen years old?—for he could write books that sell just as easy as books that don't sell. It was worse than silly to argue with a person like Ronald, or with anyone who lived in his world. "For his world," Vridar said to Angele, "is not my world."

"The trouble," said Angele slyly, "is there aren't many readers of novels in your world."

"True. Reminds me of Edmund Yates of the New York *World*. He invited contributions from bluebloods, promising that all spelling and grammar would be corrected, and the manuscripts buried at midnight in a thunderstorm, so that the capital sin of possessing brains might never be brought home to anybody. Have I any friends with enough mind to care about what I'm doing?"

He would be lucky, she said, if he found a thousand persons in the whole world who really cared. For what had Robinson Jeffers said?—Truly men hate the truth, they'd liefer meet a tiger on the road.

"You're the tiger," she said.

"And the road? I see nobody on it."

IX

He had typed Sumner's words and hung them high:

> It may well be believed that the change from the
> mother family to the father family is the greatest
> and most revolutionary in the history of civilization

Who, Vridar asked, could doubt that? It had become the fashion with certain ethnologists and anthropologists to say that there had never been a matriarchy. He had learned during his many years as a college student that most professors sought a thesis or a theory with which to elevate themselves to solitary splendor, or with which to knock a colleague's theory on the head. Some of the theorists developed cults, and both theorist and cult faded away with the theory. His friend Carl Noyce seemed to believe that his school of psychology was actually defining human personalities in terms of mathematical formulas. Carl's wife said to Vridar, "He can't talk to you about it because you couldn't understand him. I can't. Only a half-dozen persons in the whole world can." Vridar had looked at Carl a moment and then, grinning, had said, "You and Einstein, what splendid bastards you are!" To Angele he had said later, "How funny it is! Carl and I used to be close friends. Now we're estranged because we can't understand one another. What folly, then, to expect understanding between this country and Russia!"

"How far are men going to carry this? And when they've developed such horrible weapons they won't dare go to war, what will they do?"

It was Carl who wrote Vridar that he ought to read Roehm, Margaret Mead, and Ruth Benedict. He had read them all. He would open a Benedict and read to Angele, "The importance of the study of the whole configuration as over against the continued analysis of its parts is stressed in field after field of modern science." Again: ". . . history is by no means a set of facts that can be discovered by introspection. Therefore these explanations of custom which derive our economic scheme from human competitiveness, modern war from human combativeness, and all the rest of the ready explanations that we meet in every magazine and modern volume, have for the anthropologist a hollow ring." Again: "Now for the first time the comparative study of religions is free to pursue any point at issue." Vridar closed the book and said, "That may be true, but I can show Miss Benedict scholar after scholar, internationally known, who are good in the Old Testament field, but fall flat on their pious faces when they deal with the New. She says the matter is one of honest-dishonest situations, not of honest-dishonest persons. She's as wrong as hell there."

He did not for a moment think that any of the professional anthropologists, ethnologists, or psychologists would find him valid at any important point, if they were to read his books; but he had no doubt that if he tried to choose among their many and conflicting theories, instead of reading all of them and following his own insights, he would take a shortcut to the literary graveyard. He found it significant that Benedict quoted in her notes almost as many women as men. Well, in a world that was sneering at both Freud and Frazer, he would have to move warily, leaving dogmatism to such extroverts as the Meads and Benedicts.

Was it easier to divine the origin of the soul-concept by accumulating piles of data, or by sinking as deep as a man could into the primitive life, and then surrendering the will to dreams? With no notion of natural causes, what could primitive man conclude but that a part of him had wandered while he slept? How else could he explain the dream in which he killed the boar or caught the fish? On perceiving that various things renewed themselves, such as the moon, the serpent, the earth in springtime, how inevitable that the dull ignorant mind should decide that there was some animating and indwelling principle or part that survived death!

How much easier and simpler to understand how the god-concept came to be, if you accepted the matriarchy as prior to the male's dominance: not knowing that he was an agency in procreation, and smarting under the tyranny of a triumphant womanhood, man must have racked his brains endlessly for a way to equalize his position, or elevate it above the woman's. As standing on two legs had released his front paws to become hands, as the development of his hands had enormously stimulated his mind, so, in a later time, a degraded and insupportable position had driven him to phenomenal progress in the formulation of concepts. With father-hatred giving him a boost at every turn!

Woman had taken possession of the moon, when forced to observe the analogy of its phases to her own. Man took possession of the sun. What a colossal disaster when the female, so warm and fruitful, was abandoned to a frozen satellite, while the male seized for himself the source of light and heat! What an irony it was! An irony almost as appalling was still to come—when the Arabs (who became the

Hebrews) would toss the Mother out completely, and consummate the union of the Sun and the Desert in a batch of angry thundering precepts that would do more than anything else to shape the Western world!

Adam and his serpent! Vridar had read everything he could find about the serpent, and had come to nothing. Concluding that the analogy was based on more than the obvious similarity in shape and appearance, he went off to conceal himself and to study his penis. It was then, using a mirror, that he discovered, on holding his organ up and looking at it in the glass, that the head when held up and back, and seen from the front, had an unmistakable resemblance to the serpent's face. It also had something of the serpent's odor. The ancients would have known these things: some of the biblical prophets must have looked closely at the female human genitals, or they could not have applied to them the descriptive terms they used.

The penis as the serpent!

He strove to get inside the father-son hostility and rivalry, and see the relationship in terms subtler and deeper than the simple values of the bull and the stud. An existentialist psychoanalyst had concluded that cutting out his eyes instead of cutting off his sex organs meant that the tragedy of Oedipus was self-consciousness. Life was not the riddle, for there was no life, or everything was life: the riddle was consciousness. Because man became conscious of his existence he then had to become conscious of non-existence. The early anxieties from Kierkegaard's non-existence and Sartre's nothingness. "Nonsense," he said to Angele. "There is neither non-existence nor nothingness: those preposterous orphans at the wailing wall really got lost in the dark night of self-pity."

What was Satan? he asked, going round and round with this concept—reading about it, thinking and dreaming about it. Where, Angele asked, had the idea come from. "It seems to have entered the records with the Persians, and went from there to the Jews. For the Persians it was the evil principle. For the first Christians woman was the evil principle. By the Middle Ages Satan for most Christians had become a loveable rascal." He picked up Rudwin's *The Devil in Legend and Literature* and read: "According to the Talmud, Satan's sin lay not in his rivalry with God but in his envy of man. When Adam was created, so say the rabbis, all the angels had to bow to the new king of the earth, but Satan refused. That," Vridar said, "seems to me a most reasonable thing to do."

Angele said, "Have people ever loved God?"

"The Jews tried to. They drove themselves crazy trying to. I know of no other people who ever tried to. The uniqueness of the Jews is this, that the son made one hell of an effort to love his father."

"Which is the principle of love, God or Satan?"

"Neither. The Orphan is. The God-Satan thing is chiefly the father-son relationship. A famous monk of the Middle Ages cried, My Holy Satan! and a scholar has called that a lightning flash of genius. But the son doesn't become holy merely because he hates his father: if that were true, this would be a nation of holy men."

Vridar was not down to the time of Satan: he was still wrestling with Adam and Eve and the Castrate. He spent hours in different postures, sometimes with his head down and his feet up; and in different situations, while thinking, no, while *feeling* (that was more the way of it) into the various symbols and meanings that had come out of fear and ignorance. Some of them seemed to yield their sense almost instantly, like the cross, so obviously the union of male and female; or like the word *sacred,* which had meant ownership. It was easy to feel his way into the meanings clustered around the word *atonement*—at-onement, or oneness; and it was in such things as this that he began to sense the vast lonely figure of the orphan, against the background of human history. It was easy to see why out of the struggle for oneness the blood-rites had developed, since blood had held such magical properties. It was not difficult to sense with what ease a patriarchy had overthrown the Moon and enthroned the Sun. For how much more splendid the Sun than the Moon! Full of the wonder of it, he said to Angele, "Imagine what the world would be today if just one thing had been different—if there had been no similarity between the moon's phases and woman's. What an immense realm that opens to speculation!"

He spent hours trying to sense how it was that Woman, for Man, became the house of the evil principle; that Man was innocent and godlike until Woman debauched him! The male horror of menstrual blood could not alone explain it, nor all such horrors put together. Why had Man conceived and nourished such a preposterous notion? Was it all a prodigious act of rationalization, because the male had so small a part in the making of the child? Even Goethe had written that When towards the Devil's house we tread, Woman's a thousand steps ahead. Goethe had been infantile in his relations with women. Nearly all great men had been. And now, in his own time, the infantilism was more than a man could stand to think of.

After putting himself in different postures, he saw faces. It got so that he saw faces everywhere, no matter whether his eyes were open or shut: when his eyes were open, he saw the faces in window curtains, drapes, over the walls, in the waving of poplars, in the scrub growth on mountainsides; and he speculated endlessly on what kind of lives these people were leading. He told Angele that he was the Great Anthropomorph, and that anthropophuism, solely a lunacy of the male, was in itself proof of man's infantilism down through the ages. When his eyes were closed, he saw faces but never the face of anyone he had known: these were the faces of strangers from the past: not the faces of the Apes in Yerkes but the faces of people of long-ago times, about whom he thought when awake, and dreamed when asleep. Many of these faces became those of characters in his novels. In his dreams he went back into the past to talk to people, though not so much in the earlier books, for people then had few words and little to say. He wanted to ask them by what magic or miracle they had moved from propitiation of the gods to the compelling of them, by invoking their names, or even by ranting and shaking clenched hands at them. . . .

This in the childlike primitive mind so amused him that he told Angele a story he had read. It concerned the Scottish Covenanter John Scrimgeour, minister of Kinghorn, who, having a dear child sick to death of the crewels, went expostulating to his Maker with angry impatience—indeed, with such bitter complaint, that at length the Creator said to him that he would be heard this time, but was never to approach so boldly again

In such as that, too, he saw the Orphan plain.

When he went outside to labor, he took with him some statement, from a free and enlightened mind, such as Edward Carpenter's, "Which of us has ever really seen a tree?" Vridar's reading had told him that for primitive peoples a tree was many things—a house of God, a phallic symbol, a miracle standing in the earth-womb, an act of divine creation, a living breathing thing with speech, powers, and spirit. Some plants had been phallic symbols of the male, some, of the female: ancient man had invested everything with symbolic meaning. Modern man had become incredibly obtuse. Vridar would look at dense growth, such as a patch of lilac or honeysuckle or buffalo bush, thinking, In these they saw the female's pubic hair. One day, seeing a remarkable triangle, he had Angele strip her clothes off and stand by it. "Why," he asked, "don't people see it any more?"

He liked to stretch out on the earth, sink his hands to his wrists in leafmold, and look into the blue, just feeling. He was a mountain man and an earth man. Stanley Vestal had written, "No man, even the most polished and civilized, who has once savored the sweet liberty of the plains and mountains, ever went back to the monotony of the settlements without regrets and everlasting determination to return." Vridar knew the statement was childish, but he liked it. His eastern publisher, passing through, had spent a night with him and Angele, foaming white water all around him, a wealth of plant and animal life, pure air and a clean blue sky; and on returning to the bedlam called Manhattan had written in a journal that Vridar's life was "lonely, on a lonely ranch out West." "The poor guy!" Vridar had cried. "He must be considerably less than half-alive."

In a deep lovely evening he would lie outside, looking at a gibbous moon, at the stars and a blue-violet sky, at the lights on the waters, at the thousands of trees standing around him, like scented shadows, at the battleship gray of the lava rimrock. . . . He would suck in the bloom-scents of locust and olive, spruce, pine, fir, juniper, sage, and tumbling snow-waters. Angele would come out with a bottle of whisky or wine, and they would sit in the deep dusk and clasp hands and drink, and listen to the frogs and cicadas singing their hearts out.

"What other thing in the world is as happy as frogs?"

"What makes you think so?"

"They sing all night."

"We don't know that they are singing. They may be hollering their heads off." She ran fingertips up and down the back of his neck. "I'm tickling you with bug-walks."

Bugwalks! Drawing a bath for him one day she had cried, "Lordy, this is hot! It will cook your hootenanny." After watching a mother change diapers on a babe and roll it over and fondly slap its hindend, she had said to Vridar, "If I did that I'd be afraid its legs would fall off." She was forever asking him what day of the week it was, until, losing his temper, he had cried, "What in hell will you do when I'm dead? You'll never know what day it is." Quickly she had replied, "It

855

won't matter then." Touched, he had taken her in his arms and whispered in her ear, "If I live a thousand years, I'll never have a finer compliment than that."

But not always were her words so sweet. One day, looking at him sharply, she had said, "Do you realize you were fifty years old before you knew you were supposed to wash behind your ears?" She had said, "Oh hell, I know it, I know it all: the chief reason you go on with me is it's just too much bother to break a new wife in." Now and then she teased him by putting on his typewriter things which she knew would make him explode, such as clippings from the book department of a journal that called itself a news magazine:

> Also, Novelist Golding makes clear a subtle philosophical notion—
> that one can change the past by what one thinks about it.

On the card she had written: "I'm going to tell the book editor to start thinking about Hitler." From another department she put before him the words: "One of the most profound questions that scientists can ask is: How did the universe begin?" And again: "Did the Virgin Mary die?" Vridar found such things incredible, for the reason that he refused to perceive how childlike, how emotionally immature, mankind was. But he was on the track of it, he would run it down. He already understood that he himself was not an adult but only a child, with an emotional age, he thought, somewhere between ten and fourteen. Of all his friends there was none who seemed to him to be adult.

Sitting with him in the deep dusk, sipping her drink and looking round her at the scented night, Angele said, "If there's a supreme being, the Jewish and Christian religions must be an awful affront to him."

"Wonderful!" Vridar cried. "Nobody ever said it better."

He sat up and looked at the giant poplars, then at the sky, to get an after-image of the trees as pale lovely blue forms, too delicate to be real. After-images were one of his joys: he had discovered that he could get them in the most unlikely places and of the most unlikely things. His mind turned next to one of his heroes, Leigh Mallory, who had said that he wanted to climb Everest because it was there: to have gone with Mallory up the rim against the sky!—or with Meriwether Lewis to the ocean!

In ancient times, religion had not existed for the saving of souls (what a base and vulgar notion of it that was!) but for the welfare and preservation of the social organism. War then had been a sacred matter, and the gods had fought side by side with their people (as parents would with their children, wouldn't they?), sometimes dropping stones from the sky or hurling thunderbolts. It had been necessary to flatter and praise the gods (with such subterfuges children still sought to win advantages over their parents), and the people had quaked with fear lest their gods be offended (and what child had not?).

It was so easy, he reflected, rising now and then to take a swig of whisky, to understand why the penis had been the staff of life; the vulva, the door of life; the womb, the house of life. It was easy to understand that, having for ages believed that their sungod fought a dreadful struggle each winter, and though surviving was pale and wan when spring came, the people's beliefs *had overdramatized their lives,* turning them to drunkenness, or to organized cruelties socially approved; begetting in them neuroses and anxieties; forcing them to foist ideals upon their timid quaking spirits, and to build pompous philosophic systems. . . .

All these things, for good but mostly for ill, the modern world had inherited.

Some things he did not grasp so easily, and so had to put his mind to them, month after month: from what had come the barbarous custom of sacrificing the firstborn son? Was it only because it was a part of the firstfruits? It was easy to see why the people felt that the gods were entitled to the firstfruits—the parents, that is, to the choicest of the things that lived because of them. But was there not more in it? Was it not a part of the terribly evil father-son relationship, that had been of such incalculable influence in shaping human customs, institutions, and values? Long before he read deep in the pathetic Jesus legend he was pondering Freud's belief that the essence of Christianity was the submission of the son to the father. Why hadn't Freud been able to dig the motes out of his eyes and perceive that, even more, it was the essence of Judaism?

Sometimes a matter so stirred his ironic sense of things that he would go around chuckling for an hour, like a fool; or he would take different postures back in a thicket and peer out at various aspects of sky and earth. There was the ancient fact of the woman's being embraced by the god in his house, which was a temple, through his agent, who was a priest: had this come about because of fear of menstrual blood, or of virginity? What things the hymen had wrought in the psyche of men! What a multitude of fears had been covered over by the thing called religion! What whores had been made of women in the temples of the gods! He said to Angele, "Joseph Smith, after all, was in the main line of patriarchal evolution, when he copied the polygamists of the Bible."

Matters that seemed obvious to him were rejected, sometimes with anger, by other people. Carl Noyce now and then wrote to rebuke Vridar, or to instruct him: "You continue to propagate the falsity that any male, from squirrel to man, yearns to impregnate every female he encounters. You restate the falsity that the female's breasts are the chief object of the male's erotic interest. . . ." Carl and his wife were what in the United States were called political liberals: none sneered with blacker contempt at Whittaker Chambers, or nourished a more stubborn belief in the innocence of Alger Hiss. Vridar was making a study of this kind of liberal, having sensed that he was one of the things that discovery was leading him to. After reading Carl's letter he said, "What can be more vicious than this deliberate distortion of one's words to change one's meaning? I never said in the novel that man yearns to impregnate every female he encounters; I said that Nature laid on the male a mandate to see that no female goes empty. I never said that the female's breasts are the chief object of man's erotic interest. I said they are the most obvious sign of femaleness. These so-called liberals can't get anything straight, for the reason that they are father-hating lads with nothing straight in them. He reminds me of Stendhal's saying that one of the women he wooed had neither wit nor tits, two great lacks. Carl seems to be allergic to both."

Angele had been studying his face. She now abandoned her study and resumed her crocheting. Vridar turned to look at her. In their early relationship he had been astonished when he first heard her call her breasts lungs. It had taken him some

857

time to probe to the reason of it. Angele had become nubile when very young: she had been small, her breasts had been large: it had been in the time when flat chests in the United States were the fashion for women, and so with every possible subterfuge Angele had tried to hide her breasts. She had confessed to him that she had so detested them that she had tried to crush them back into her body; and to show her contempt for them, or to hide from herself the fact that she had them, she had got the habit of calling them lungs. Vridar had put a question to his brother: "This is a country of breast-erotics: the mammary gland, whose only function is to produce milk, now ranks in public esteem with the dollar. Why are most American men so crazy about breasts?" Marion had said, "They're the most obvious sign of femaleness." Vridar knew there was more to it than that: hadn't the breast-erotics felt unloved as small boys? Weren't these the orphans?

Angele said to him, "You often use the word irony. Isn't it a hell of an irony that I have more breasts than I want, and some women have only buttons?"

"American men look at bosom and bottom, though most men seem to look first at your breasts."

"My mind," she said, arching her brows. "Or my button."

Button was her word for her nose.

X

Whether the intellectual quest would be satisfying Vridar had not known when he set his heart on it. Its joys proved to be deeper and livelier than he had hoped for. Now and then, it is true, he felt with Faust, that "the hot struggle of eternal study" was leaving him no wiser than before. He would mutter, "And now to feel that nothing can be known, this is a thought that burns into my heart." To know that in his lifetime the riddle of consciousness would not be solved, and perhaps never; to know that soon he would return to the unconscious and the unknowing, with all that he had stored in his mind of no use then—it was this that made a jest of all striving.

But there was with him, day and night, the fellowship of great minds. He entered many fields—religions, music, art, medicine, archaeology, architecture, war; he studied the history of costumes, beverages, torture, prostitution, superstitions; and in all these things he read the ablest scholars he could find. He averaged well over a hundred books a year, most of them big fat books; and some of them—*Religion of the Semites, The Historical Geography of the Holy Land, The Mystic Gospel of Hellenistic Judaism*—he read three or four times. On cards he took tens of thousands of notes, that eventually would add to hundreds of thousands of words. The note-taking was an irksome chore that he did not like, especially when, as so often happened, he had to fill two or three hundred cards from just one book. He knew that he was taking down a great deal more than he would ever use, but the books had to be returned to libraries, far away; and to save time and postage he copied everything that he thought it likely he might need.

The moments Angele loved best were those when a new packet of books arrived. Vridar would bring them in from the mailbox; and with her eyes shining on them she would pick them up and say, "What does the scholar-artist have this time?" Unwrapping the books, he would hold them up for her to see. Then he would open them and hungrily thumb through them, sampling, tasting, marveling. When evening came, Angele would place the pillows for him, the light, pencils and note paper; and Vridar would stretch out to hours of pleasure more satisfying than any other he had ever known. This was the case anyway if the book in his hands had been written by a scholar of the first rank. He was astonished, from year to year, to learn how few were the scholars without discernible prejudice and prepossession: these few were the ones he hugged to his heart or when feeling lonely and defeated he pressed to his cheek.

The more he read, the deeper he was driven into loneliness and silence, except when drunk. He had no friends in Idaho who shared these interests, or could discuss these matters with him. He had friends who wished to. Vridar was often startled, not by the ignorance of persons but by their presumption: most of them would give opinions on matters about which they knew nothing at all. This was particularly so of religion: persons everywhere were willing to tell him all about Jesus, without the vaguest notion of what Jesus actually was; all about how the Christian religion was put together—Rhode had amazed him by angrily saying that all religions without exception had been founded by great and worthy men. Now and then, when pompous arrogance became extreme, Vridar would tease his visitor with a question or a statement. He might say, "It's said of Terpander that he was choked to death by a fig which someone threw at him when his mouth was open." He might say, "The American people want to be average: they work pretty hard at it, don't you think?" He liked to ask questions. "The Whethams in *Heredity and Society* say that most persons assume that the acquirements of one generation form part of the inborn heritage of the next, and that the present social and educational systems are founded in part on this false assumption? Do you agree?" Usually, without pausing to reflect at all, the person would say, "No, I can't agree with that." Now and then one revealed his deep conservatism, *based on fear,* by saying, "No, I can't agree but just what was the question?"

Or Vridar would say, "I'm going to write a novel about a person and would like to know what you think of him. He's the father of most of the children of the wives of his friends. He likes children. He's fond of all his own; he remembers their birthdays, takes them to the circus, the fair, the theater; all that. From about any point of view he's a fine father and man, except that he lay with his friends' wives. Do you agree that he *could* be a fine man?" Nobody thought it possible. Vridar would look at such people and speculate on the depth and darkness of their ignorance. In one of his novels he had a scene of intense religious frenzy: a girl and a youth, both beside themselves, and for a few minutes alone in a thicket near by, fell into a violently passionate sexual embrace. Never thereafter was the girl able to recall it, or to believe that she had done it. Rhode told Vridar the whole thing was fantastic and incredible; he simply would not believe that the girl could forget it.

Vridar would say to a visitor, "Lippert, a great sociologist, says that all punishment of sexual transgressions within marriage is based on the original conception of the property right of the husband. Does that seem likely to you?" Invariably the answer was no. He would say, "According to Reville, it is the property of religious customs, which have become traditional, to perpetuate themselves even when they no longer answer to contemporaneous ideas. Does that seem reasonable?" Nobody thought it seemed reasonable—not of Christianity anyway. The time came when Vridar said to Angele, "Either all the people but a few are too stupid to learn after the eighth or tenth grades, or our system of public education is a colossal farce."

Vridar became aware that for him, the greatest books from the greatest minds were, in a way, father-symbols. He told himself that the thing to do was to accept the symbol at its most sublime mortal reach, since the orphan in need of a father could not be put away. "Henry Lea, dead long ago, and as a scholar as great as they come, is a kind of father to me. So is Frazer, though when he deals with the New Testament he's not always a scholar. So is Loisy, who had so much mind and courage the Church threw him out."

"Just how many such fathers do you have?" Angele asked.

"It's how many I need. Of the hundreds of scholars I've read, I have only eight or ten." He then explained what he meant. He could accept not even Mommsen, who had been called the prince of scholars of the nineteenth century: for one thing, Mommsen showed an almost infantile prejudice when writing of such persons as Caesar. Vridar could not put among the precious few, living by Baur's words, any scholar in whom he felt prejudice or bias at all. Turning on her a foolish grin he said, "I so strongly identified with the human race, I'm such a romantic creature of reveries, trances, frenzies, extravaganzas, fantasies, illusions, chimeras, deliriums— I'm so lost in Kubla Khan, Atlantis, Cockagne, Lubberland—yes, above all, in Lubberland—but wait till I bring a drink."

He returned with two drinks, and said: "It shames me to find those stupidly prejudiced whom I so wish to admire. Look, here's Flinders Petrie, one of the greatest of the archaeologists, who when he was busy with a staff near Cairo put in the tea of the others the same number of lumps of sugar that he took, whether they wanted it or not."

"Why?"

"Either because he was an archaeologist or was English: it might be either, for here is Weigall, another famous archaeologist. Listen: 'At the present day the scientist will tell you that God is the ultimate source of life, that where natural explanation fails, there God is to be found.' Can you imagine worse God damned gall than that? He speaks for all the thousands of scientists, whose names the blockhead doesn't even know, much less their opinions—and speaks without even bothering to define the word God. No person can make such a statement and be a firstrate scholar."

"Isn't he the kind you call the orphan?"

"Oh yes, he may be, but that doesn't excuse him: before he sets up shop as a scholar let him stop bawling for Pa. Well, here's another of the orphans who never got up from the wailing wall. Lecky. Famous historian. And this, with irony that will freeze your marrow, is from his *History of Rationalism*. He goes into raptures —rational raptures, of course—over the so-called Virgin Mother; then says, '. . . the moral charm and beauty of female excellence was for the first time felt.' Has a more monstrous calumny ever got into type? For the first time felt! I give you another Leckyism, this from his *History of European Morals*: 'Nature, by making the number of males and females nearly equal, indicates that monogamy is "natural." ' Someone should tell that to all the weaklings among the roosters and bulls and studs."

"The strong ones," said Angele. "They've always been taking a lot more than their share."

"Anyway, something went wrong somewhere, because Lecky says they're all supposed to be monogamous. I used to think such utter imbecilities came from self-love. I know now that they come from fear. The difference between a firstrate scholar (there are very few) and a secondrate scholar is not necessarily one of mind. It's more likely to be one of courage.

"Well, in the publisher's list of books at the end of Lecky's second volume I find *The Physical Cause of the Death of Christ*, by William Stroud, M.D.; with a letter on the subject by Sir James Y. Simpson, M.D. These two frightened orphans say death was caused by a rupture of the heart. In the first place, Jesus and Christ are two totally different things, in spite of Paul. In the second place, there isn't a single shred of trustworthy evidence that there ever was a Jesus of the Gospels. In the third place, even if there was we don't know how he died—a lot of early Christians thought he died in bed. Yet these two sad-asses with the minds of turtles and the courage of college deans—"

"Come now! Read something nice."

"But our lesson today is the imbecilities of the scared orphan." He had filed away hundreds of cards under the category STUPID and now had a pile of them before him. He drew one, looked at it and said, "Jackson and Lake are two titans in the New Testament field, one at Harvard, one at Union. They have an essay called 'Public Teaching of Jesus.' There isn't a single word attributed to Jesus that can be proved to have been said by him. Let your astonishment dwell on this one: 'The sinlessness of our Savior is, after all, perhaps a more complete proof of His Divine nature than miracle could be.' Who uttered those words? A full professor at Harvard. He says, I'll choose the major premise, and you try to get around the minor premise and the conclusion! Major premise: Our Savior was sinless—"

"Granted that it's the sophistry of a frightened child, what else do you have?"

"Plenty of whisky," he said and filled their glasses. "All right, take Josiah Royce, who was another full professor at Harvard: I quote from his *The Problem of Christianity*: 'The individual cannot bear this burden. His tinted nature forbids; his guilt weighs him down. If by salvation one means the winning of the true goal of life, the individual, unaided, cannot be saved. And the help that he needs for bearing his burden must come from some source entirely above his own level,—from a source which is, in some genuine sense, divine.' A famous philosopher canting about taint, salvation, guilt, divine!"

She looked across her glass at him and said, "More sophistries—but men have been awfully good at them, haven't they?"

"Awfully. Even Loisy and it hurts me to put him in such company; for he was a great scholar, and so luminous and right most of the time—so right that the Pope booted him out. But listen: 'Of Peter's coming to the city we know nothing. The chief argument in support of the Roman tradition that Peter came to Rome and perished there is that no other tradition and no evidence of any kind in Christian antiquity can be found to contradict it.' So! Jonah was swallowed by the whale: since in all Hebrew and Jewish writings there's nothing to contradict it, Jonah was swallowed by a whale. With the same halfwitted reasoning we can easily prove that Delilah cut Samson's hair, Joshua stopped the sun, and God rolled the Red Sea back."

"How do you explain it that great minds should be so childish?"

"Fear. Here's another professor, Archibald Duff: how beautiful, he says, the faith that God 'is of like nature with men. He means to eat with them; he has needs and wants just like theirs. He is to have food. What beauty of intimacy with him! This was the origin of our Lord's Supper.' That wasn't even remotely the origin of the Supper: how could a man have been professor of the Old Testament for forty years and not have found it out? As for a God who sat to eat with his people and showed his hindend to them—well, he's the one who created a universe in which the Milky Way has three hundred million suns, which is only one of thirty million galaxies known to us, the average distance between any two being two million light years."

"How can men be so childish?"

"I don't like the word childish: it means puerile and trifling. I've had to coin a word: I call it childness. Madness is a state of being mad; childness is the state of childhood. Few people grow up. Few are allowed to. Two million light years! One light year is more than the greatest mind can grasp: it is senseless to say that an adult could seriously say to his readers that the God who sat and ate lamb stew with Abraham created the universe."

"I think childish is maybe the word for that."

"Childness. These men are children and they are children because their parents never let them grow up. Look at Rhode: he managed at last to get his secretary on one side of his house; a son and a daughter just across the street; a mother at the end of a short block—"

"Wait a minute. You're the cookie-dream who wanted to build on the ranch right next to your parents."

"I admit it. I turn scarlet all over and tremble when I remember it. Past the age of forty, I was going right back to Ma and Pa—and so I'm the one to write about childness in the orphans, for I'm one of the most self-pitying, lost, lonely, frightened—"

"Oh come! Not all people are what you call orphans."

"Only the important ones," he said. "Study the faces in your journals and when you find one that looks really matured and adult put it on my desk. After all, why did the Father and Mother concepts evolve?—for they're only the human parents idealized. Why should religion have been tied to them?—for it has nothing to do with them. A scholar as great as Cheyne says the author of Ecclesiastes had a religion—'he is neither practically nor theoretically an atheist'—as though religion and atheism are opposites! You can find such silly notions only in children.

"Children!" he said, staring at a card. "I see here Jacob Bondoff, a Jew, and a famous editor—I think he was one of Mencken's friends. He says, quote, 'all that is true, good and beautiful in Christianity is basically Jewish.' All Christians, he says, know that but—I quote, 'most of them still haven't it in their heart to question the concept of the divinity and divine mission of Christ.' Imagine a Jew confusing the Jesus and the Christ! Imagine any man printing a falsehood that would have choked even Stalin. To call such statements puerile, childish, silly, won't do: we have to look deeper: we have to look at childness ensepulchered in fear. Here's a Jew book-editor saying that Moses with his ten commandments marked out the entire history of the Western world. Poor ignorant self-loving child!—for he doesn't know that if there was a Moses (some of the greatest scholars have doubted it), and if he had ten commandments, they were *not* at all the ten commandments we have today. Is ignorance sufficient excuse for these monstrous perversions of history and fact? How much ignorance are we going to excuse in our professors and philosophers? For here, I see, is Sidney Hook, a philosopher—isn't he a Jew?—who speaks of the 'Christian dogma—Sartre rightly calls it a legend—that the Jews killed Christ.' He wouldn't for a moment speak of the *legend* of Moses or Solomon. Of course the Jews didn't kill Christ! How in hell could they have, when the Christ is pure myth. Neither did they kill Jesus. This man defies maturity as the possession of rational expectations. Then are we to call Woodrow Wilson mature when he expected to make the world safe for democracy? Or the editors of the *New Republic* who solemnly wrote that at Yalta Roosevelt made the world safe from war for generations to come? Woman-child, after a lot of reading in the right things nothing becomes more obvious than this, that Christians won't face the historical facts of Christian and Judaic relationships; and Jews won't either."

"They won't review your novels."

"They wouldn't Stendhal's either. He said he might have a few readers a hundred years after his death. I expect no more. Children try to kill things that make them afraid and all but a few book reviewers are children.

"But to hell with the stupid. Let's take Frazer. These are the words a teacher gave me in high school and they have been the light in my mind ever since: 'It is indeed a melancholy and in some respects thankless task to strike at the foundations of belief in which, as in a strong tower, the hopes and aspirations of humanity through long ages have sought refuge from the storms and stress of life. Yet sooner or later it is inevitable that the battery of the comparative method should breach these venerable walls, mantled over with the ivy and moss and wild flowers of a thousand tender and sacred associations. At present we are only dragging the guns into position; they have hardly yet begun to speak. The task of building up into fairer and more enduring forms the old structures so rudely shattered is reserved for other hands, perhaps for other and happier ages. We cannot forsee, we can hardly even guess, the new forms into which thought and society will run in the future. Yet this uncertainty ought not to induce us, from any consideration of expediency or regard for antiquity, to spare the ancient moulds, however beautiful, when these are proven to be outworn. Whatever comes of it, wherever it leads, we must follow the truth alone'."

He read the noble words and was then quiet. Angele slipped over to him and knelt, her cheek to his knee. She knew that these words, typed on a card and hung above his desk, had faced him every morning when he wrote, for all these many years. He knew by heart several passages in Frazer: now, with his hands on her hair, he murmured, " 'We can only say that something, we know not what, drives us to attack the great enemy Ignorance wherever we see him, and that if we fail, as we probably shall, in our attack on his entrenchments, it may be useless but it is not inglorious to fall in leading a Forlorn Hope'."

She patted him and said, "You won't fail, all you other hands."

"I like to think I'm one of them. If it is some day found that I was, it won't matter that certain book-reviewers, defending intrenched ignorance, tried to destroy me. All my reading tells me that those authors wear best who write best for the future, and those who write for the present perish with it. Who was Jules Jarin? A famous and powerful critic a hundred years ago who said Stendhal spent his time dissecting moral leprosy.

"I suspect that the parent of fear is a sense of insecurity, and that a sense of insecurity, if too strong, makes normal emotional development impossible. If emotionally arrested, does the person seek a substitute for adultness? Is art one of them? There is no artist known to me whose life could possibly be called adult. Our great, and it may be our impossible, task is to orientate ourselves to a new attitude to the universe. An adult attitude, I hope it will be.

"Well, let's see some more of these in the category I call stupid. *Saints for Now,* edited by a new Catholic convert named Luce. She holds up triumphantly Rebecca West's words on Augustine, 'His works are the foundation of modern western thought.' If they are, that may be what is wrong with it. Augustine—"

"We've had enough of that," said Angele, rising to her feet. She picked up a pile of cards. "Here's one on Sartre. Let's see what he says." After a few moments she read from the card: " ' The Existentialist thinks it very distressing that God does not exist, because all possibility of finding values in a heaven of ideas disappears along with him; there can no longer be an *a priori* Good, since there is no infinite and perfect consciousness to think it'." Angele was silent, pondering the words. "Why does he use such words as infinite and perfect? Aren't those concepts man has dug out of his microscopic little bugmind? He says Dostoievsky said that if God didn't exist, everything would be possible. That, he says, is the starting point of Existentialism. He says because God doesn't exist, man is forlorn, because neither within nor without can he find anything to cling to."

"The Existentialists are just about the loudest wailers among the orphans today. Man wouldn't be dashing tears from his eyes and trying to find something to cling to if he'd cut the umbilical cord and take the nipple out of his mouth. Somewhere in that stack in your hands you'll find Niebuhr saying that because of original sin man is anxious, and because he is anxious he sins. That's one of my favorite child-orphan statements: an adult, a real adult, would give it one incredulous reading and file it away with Tillich's—which says that man is estranged from the ground

864

of his being. Man, the immature man, which is nearly all of us, is merely a self-pitying frightened child, who has never had to learn how to be adult, because first the parents and then the priests told him what to do. Funny the Neibuhrs and Tilliches can't see what is under their nose, for it has a terrible odor and surely they smell it."

"Cookie?" she said, searching through the cards.

"Yes? Now Tillich—"

"Oh, to hell with Tillich. Let's give the bearded boys a rest. I have found a card on Jane Welsh Carlyle. Listen: 'Maggie, of all people in the world, told me a small specimen of *french sentiment* which she had read somewhere—worth repeating even to *you*—'" Angele paused to glance at him.

He said, "Go on. She means Carlyle and you mean me."

"'—who have not all the sympathy with french sentiment that could be wished. An injured husband rushed in upon his wife and her lover, in an illfated moment, and was proceeding as in duty bound to kill the lover—whereupon the wife threw herself frantically between them and passionately remonstrated, Would you kill the father of your children?'"

Vridar grimaced. "Send it to Marion," he said. "He'll appreciate it."

"O goodie! Here's another one by Jane." She looked at him; he knew by her face that he was not going to like it. From the card she read: "Let no woman who values peace of soul ever dream of marrying an author. That is to say if he is an honest one, who makes a conscience of doing the thing he pretends to do."

"Carlyle gave her a rough time, I give you a rough time. You give me a rough time, she gave him a rough time. The moral: never get married. You knew that, I didn't."

"You want to hear more from Jane?"

"I've heard it but I can stand it again. Is it—"

"It's the one on devoted husbands. She says, People who are so dreadfully *devoted* (she underlined that) to their wives are so apt, from mere habit, to get devoted to other people's wives as well."

"From mere habit: she put the sting in that. The moral now is for me to love you only a little, if you would have me love other women less."

"I'll read you one more. After Jeffrey—"

"You know I can't stand that pompous extroverted epispastic—"

"Why don't you *first* listen and then explode? After Jeffrey visited Carlyle and Jane at—what a word!—Craigenputtock he wrote to Carlyle, as follows: 'You have no *mission* upon earth, whatever you may fancy, half so important as to be innocently happy, and all that is good for you of poetic feeling and sympathy with majestic nature, will come of its own accord, without your straining after it . . . you mystics will not be contented with kindness of heart and reasonable notions in anybody—but you must have gifts and tasks and duties—and relations with the universe, and strugglings to utter forth the truth—God help you and your vainglorious jargon'."

"Yeh-yeh," Vridar said, "another Jules Janin. The most powerful English literary critic of his time, who tried his best to silence and destroy Wordsworth.

Why did Carlyle ever invite such a prehistoric crustacean?" Angele had fixed him with half-smiling eyes full of shrewd knowledge of him: yes, yes, *she* was the kind who could be innocently happy among her birds and bees, spiders, toads, cats, turtles and frogs: she did not strive for relations with the universe, or struggle to utter forth truth. He said, "I've observed that those who love every minute of living work pretty damned hard at it. As for that horse's ass who gave loud and continuous advice to his superiors—"

"Oh, come, come!"

He settled back and smiled. He said, "You know, most of the time I'm as solemn as a mother looking at the vents of her child, wondering if they need attention. My need to believe is as deep as Fanny Brice's, my bowl is just as empty, but my mind— had you observed my mind? Let's have another drink. Poor Jeffrey, what did he know of Jeffrey!"

All night they drank and read notes and talked, as they did so many nights, consuming a quart of whisky between late afternoon and morning.

XI

Before settling down to his project, he had read many books about the past, and knew that the worst ordeals ahead of him would be facing up to the cruelty of man to man, the hatred of the father for his son, and the tragic immolation of the son in his emotionally eunuchized capitulation to the father. He would not be surprised, he said, if he developed a hell of a case of orchitis, and wens and warts all over his john.

The first of these tasks was to understand, if this was possible, the castrate: this he thought ought to be easy for him, who had what in psychological jargon was called a castration complex; but he decided to talk the matter over with some of his medical friends. Dr. Craig MacKnight was a man whose emotions boiled all the time, whose mental processes never rested. He had the handsomest blue eyes Vridar was ever to see, for there was not the slightest hint in them, ever, of cruelty or malice. Angele asked him and his wife to dinner, though she and Vridar well knew that when drunk MacKnight was no more manageable than a bull moose: he would fall crashing over furniture, break mirrors, roll downstairs, a man so monstrously fat that he couldn't tie his shoes. He came staggering in with two fifths of fine Scotch and began at once to argue that in all normal copulation the penis entered the uterus. At first Vridar could only look at the man and think, He's drunker than hell. Craig was a graduate of one of the world's greatest medical schools.

"I know it," Craig said, his blue wide-open eyes begging Vridar not to be such an obstinate fool. He turned to his wife. "Gracie, am I right?" Gracie looked a little embarrassed. "Don't ask me, that's what you say." Craig staggered off to the kitchen to refill his glass.

When he returned, Vridar said, "I suppose you also believe in vagina dentata."

"What's that?" asked Craig. "I know both words but don't know what they mean."

Vridar went to his den and returned with that issue of the journal *Neurotica* which dealt with the castration complex. "Look, it says that American boys and men are forever telling of cases of penis captivus. These blockheads argue that the vagina tightens in a spasm because of sudden fear, caused by a policeman's flashlight in the girl's face, or a sudden train whistle. When I was in school in Rigby the town was thrown into an unholy uproar over the story that a white woman and a Negro had been taken off the train, in penis captivus."

"Well," said Dr. MacKnight, furrowing his brow, "how do you know they weren't?"

"The astounding thing for me is that my brother actually believes in penis captivus. By God, he does. He argued me black and blue all one night. Which of you two, I wonder, is more foolish."

"Don't call me foolish. I know."

"Conceivably it could happen, if the uterus were in the right position, with an abnormally large neck, and the penis were abnormally small—and how are you in that respect?"

Craig burst with laughter and when he laughed he was a sight for sad people: with jowls plumped down on his collar his fat face was a great red roundness, his bulging blue eyes drowned in joy. He turned to Angele. "Am I right."

"Not in our case."

Craig exploded again. "You're not worthy of your wife," he said, beaming on Vridar, his eyes bathed with tears. "You better let me have her for a while."

When midnight came the two men were half-drunk and still arguing. Picking up the journal, Vridar read a story about a farmer who got his thing caught in a milking machine, whereupon his desperate wife called the dealer; but the dealer only said, "Relax, lady. It's set for only two quarts, so just keep pouring water into him." Craig's face looked tortured; it twitched all over.

"That's a real case of vagina dentata," he said. He took the journal, opened it, and began to read aloud: "A man in a public toilet urinates on another man. 'Aren't you from Cleveland?' 'How did you know?' 'Rabbi Bernstein there circumcises on the bias.' " Craig considered the story a moment and then exploded with laughter that shook the house.

"My God," he said, "listen to this. It says circumcision has a supreme advantage —men circumcised are immune from cancer of the penis. They didn't teach me that in school," he said, scowling at the page. "It says women who have intercourse only with men circumcised in infancy never have cancer of the cervix. The Jews seem to have a big advantage over us. . . . My God, here's a lot of circumcision jokes—anti-Semitic novelty cards—Abie getting his first ten per cent cut. Gracie, listen: it says surgeons have been known to suggest circumcision as a premium with tonsillectomy." With a roar he sank back to a chair, almost crushing it. "You know, I should subscribe to this damn thing."

"You should have it in your waiting-room," Vridar said.

"Sure. Gracie," he said, turning to his amused wife, "listen to this. A butcher puts a cow's udder inside his pants, allowing one teat to protrude from his fly. The lady customers complain. He says, Is that thing hanging out again? and chops it off. The ladies all faint and he runs to the next butcher shop; and then to another

867

and another. The fifth time he faints. He didn't know cows have only four teats."

Vridar said, "Some have five but that guy was in the wrong herd."

Craig took a deep drink and blew off another snort. "Listen to this," he said, appealing to his wife. "A Miss Juliet Lowell has been collecting actual letters. One says, Dere Mr. President, I ain't had no relief since my husband's project was cut off. Then here's a wife who poured explosive cleaning fluid in the toilet bowl. Her husband tossed in a cigarette while urinating. Then he shouts to his wife, 'To hell with my right ear! Find my right hand—it—has—got—my—'" But Craig couldn't complete the sentence. He staggered up, pouring thunder out of his great chest and spilling his whisky. His eyes blind with tears, he looked at the cover of the journal and read aloud the words, The Castration Complex. He opened the journal and pointing said, "I don't dare read that one."

Angele was telling Gracie how Marion handled bores. Marion would tell a story —and all his stories were dirty—and then a male guest would tell one. Looking at the man gravely Marion would say, "I don't get it." So the man would tell the story all over again. Trying to look both shamed and stupid, Marion would shrug and say, "I guess I'm thick, for I simply don't get it." A little angrily the man would say, "You don't get it! You mean you don't understand it?" With another shrug Marion would say, "Does it have a point? I just didn't get it." And so with all the patience he had left, the guest would tell the story a third time. Marion would shake his head, his face solemn, blank, lifeless; and the man leaping to his feet would cry in a rage, "Where's my hat? I'm pissed off you, Hunter! I don't think I like you at all!"

Craig was exploding again. He had found a joke on a fat man. "Listen," he said to his ever-listening wife. "It says that even impotence is modified down to the problem of fat—that is, eunuchoid—men who must use a long shoe-horn. 'Why don't you diet?' 'Dye it! What color is it now?'"

Vridar took the journal. "Just the same there's a lot in all this. How about the Samson story? How about Harpo Marx in nightclubs cutting off neckties and handing them to the men—or is it to their women? How about the story in *Collier's* of Jews fascinated by the slicing of kosher bacon. On the equivalence of food and sex it says here see Dagwood. You can see castration symbols all over the nation. What I need to know, if you will now be serious, is why men have so long been obsessed with it. What is it in a man that makes him castrate himself?"

"I don't know," said Craig, trying to look thoughtful but looking only charmingly drunk.

"We have here the story of a doctor who excuses himself for being late at a banquet by saying that he had to amputate a man's penis. 'Did you have to saw through the bone?' his wife asks; and all the guests stand up and gravely bow to the husband."

Again Craig erupted. "I'll be damned," he said.

The Son and the Castrate! Vridar strove so long and faithfully to project himself into the emotions of the self-mutilated male that he felt castrated, almost, and enfeebled; and went around talking, when Angele did not catch and hush him, in a squeaky voice. He became during these months such a ridiculous figure of a man

868

that his friends wondered about him, and his wife said, "I'll be glad when you get this Son out of the way and done with."

"We'll never get him out of the way until we dredge the stuff out of the unconscious and face it. In Jewish literature there's a story about Noah which says that he castrated the whole human race, including his sons, before he took them into the Ark. Sometimes I think it would have been a hell of a good thing if he had."

"All right, but stop squeaking at me."

"I have to squeak. My thing got caught in my zipper. Did you know that's a popular ballad with men since *Esquire* made the zipper-fly as fashionable as the mammary gland made of cotton? Thousands of men have had their things caught in zippers."

"Vridar! In God's name stop that squeaking!"

"The eunuchoid squeak," he said, squeaking. "Le homme impuissant: behold me!" Indicating a copy of *Neurotica* he said, "Read Friedman on Struwwelpeter. Read Scott Fitzgerald's 'The Boy Who Killed His Mother.' Why do you suppose boys shoot their mothers? Read Otto Fenishel, 'Castration Anxiety in Boys'. Fear of Pa—and so they flee to the wailing walls. Is Rhode a castration neurotic? Is he another homme impuissant?"

"If you don't stop that damned squeaking I'll leave the house."

"All right, leave!" he howled, squeaking at her.

He was sitting with a distinguished elderly friend one day when in an extremely grave tone the man said, "I'm afraid for the general."

Vridar looked at him, wondering what general he had in mind. Was it MacArthur, who had Truman like a bulldog on his neck? He waited.

"The general has a pimple on him."

Vridar still waited. He looked at the anxiety in the narrow deeply-lined face. What general had a pimple on him and why was it a matter for concern?

Then the man astounded Vridar by opening his trousers and exposing the head of his penis. Unbelieving, Vridar sat stunned. Then all that he had read about penis-length, fear of castration, shrunken or atrophic or malformed testicles, came upon him, and he was silent with wonder and pity. What a thing man was! How naive and superficial, how anile and fatuous and foolish, were most of the novels that tried to tell his story!

The divine passion! No, no, he said, replying to Angele's question: the divine passion in the ancient world was *not* mother-love, it was *not* father-love, it was not love of justice, honor or right. It was *not* love of God. The divine passion had been the erotic, the sex, passion. He added drily, "It still is, isn't it? Is there anything in which Americans are half as interested as in screwing? What beats the hell out of me is how people in the throes of the divine passion could conceive of the Father but not the Mother."

"You mean it was the divine passion for Jews?"

"I think it must have been. The scrawny insane old prophets were forever ranting against it."

It was during his months with the Castrate and the Divine Passion that Vridar had a dream in which he plainly saw three words, Fear estranges truth. On waking,

869

he thought about the words all day long, and for days, wondering why his subconscious mind had chosen the word estrange. Fear did not estrange truth; it denied it. Resistance to obvious truths and facts was getting mankind nothing but the will for stronger denial. Wasn't that the chief lesson of history? Hadn't truth always been an outcast for the reason that people were afraid of it? You had to realize how precarious they felt their hold on life to be. . . . No, damn it: not on *life*—on *consciousness*—their hold on consciousness.

A few nights later he saw more words in a dream, as though hung on a wall:

Fear begat the Father and the Father begat the Orphan

The next morning he typed them off and hung them above his desk. He liked the way his unconscious mind was organizing the materials of his reading and thinking.

XII

He was reading about Lawrence of Arabia: "Occasionally he would stretch out his fast periods for three days to see how long he could go without food and still remain master of his physical and mental faculties; and invariably he fasted at Christmas to show his disapproval of the more vulgar custom of feasting. . . . Now I am tired, too tired to strive or smile; I sit alone, my mouth is in the dust: Look thou upon me, Lord, for I am vile. . . ."

Fasting was one of the many things that he had to try to understand. He went without food for ten days, except radishes, lettuce, alfalfa and clover leaves, and rose hips, keeping in mind that now and then in the old American west a man had lived for days or weeks on nothing but rose hips, the reddish seed pod of the wild rose, which for all its richness in vitamin C he found as tasteless and unnourishing as wood. He would think, As a damned masochist whose curse is over-submissive tendencies; as a wretched sad-eyed babilan; as an organism with fears and anxieties crawling all through it and making horrors of its dreams; as an absurd adolescent ass imagining personal relations with the universe and trying to stutter forth truths, I'm an especially choice candidate for the rigors of fasting, castration and monasticism. What a monk I would have made!

He was on the threshold of recorded history now. Through a thousand books and a thousand projections he had been trying for years to feel his way intuitively up through the darkness and the ages; up and across the primitive emotional and intellectual planes, whence came the ghost, the soul, the spirit; the serpent and the bower and the cross; Eve and Adam. After reading so many books, he became aware that people had lived in and by and for symbol and myth. He rushed, fascinated, through such works as Bayley's *The Lost Language of Symbolism,* and perceived how deep was the truth that the languages of his own time were no more than dictionaries of faded metaphors. He would read, "The Kafirs of Indian say of the stones they worship, This stands for God but we know not his shape; the Maoris of New Zealand represent their tribal deities by stones set up in the ground. . . . According to Deuteronomy, the God of Israel 'is a rock' . . ." Except a few with restless inquiring minds, did anyone want to know that Peter was also a rock—or what the rock meant? Did the painting of a woman with apples as breasts mean a thing to his New York publisher? Did he or anyone like him care a hang about Anwyl's words, "Nothing is clearer than the marvelous persistence of traditional and immemorial modes of thought"? Had they the power of mind and courage to grasp the meaning in the words of a famous semanticist?—that "Our problem is, in large degree, one of unraveling this net of symbolism in which our human destiny has become entangled." Would they have agreed with Prof. Caird?—"The intellectual grasp of truth as self-evident—because inseparably bound up with the consciousness of self—can only be won by a long discipline of self-abnegation, in which the individual gives up his own opinions, his own prejudices and desires." Would they see the light in Lippert's words?—"If to the savage in his intellectual isolation a soul seems to be the cause behind every phenomenon, then, in the natural development of thought, to a philosopher, whose intellectual horizon has expanded to comprehend the idea of a universe, the cause of all causes behind this universe must seem to be a universal soul. From this idea, so evidently derived from the domain of the cult, philosophizing humanity has never since been able to extricate itself." Well, there was God overboard, and an end of him!

Would they agree with Dr. Victor Robinson of the Temple University School of Medicine?—"Intellectually, we are but a stone's throw from the stone age; emotionally, we are still there." What had Frazer said?—that we cannot foresee, we can hardly even guess, the new forms in which thought and society will run in the future. Well, the old forms had to give way, and for all their brutalities and slave-camps and monstrous lies the "Communist" leaders were forcing some of the old forms to give, while Americans, scared to death, dug deeper into them. There was Reuben Rhode, who actually believed that the free world's (and where was *it*?) greatest bulwark against "Communism" was the Roman Church! Prejudices, falsehoods, distortions and perversions, forgeries and lies, buttressed, enshrined and elevated down through the ages, were now being defended by powerful individuals and forces, on the radio, in popular journals, in the public forums; and by denying forums to those who would speak out with Frazer, they were silencing them.

He had come to the stage where he had to face the fact of human cruelty, and he drove himself almost to the point of no return trying to feel his way into the attitudes and emotions of men who skinned other men alive. It was not enough to say that it was primitive: Hitler and Stalin, unspeakable monsters both, had committed horrors as great as any in the ancient world. It was not enough to call it madness: Caesar had dragged a brave Gaul, a more courageous man than himself, through the streets of Rome and then had killed him, who earlier had given his word of honor not to. Caesar was not mad. The Syrians in the time of Solomon had not been mad who hung shrieking captives up by their wrists and then skinned them alive, beginning at the scalp, coming down over face and neck, and going clear to the toes. They were not mad who cut open the bellies of captives and dragged the guts out foot by foot with a winch; who opened the anus and filled the bowels with hot lead; who threaded rope through lips or cheeks and led the bleeding creatures in triumphal marches. Were the Romans mad who ran a hot pike into a man's anus and up through him and out at his mouth? Were people all over the Roman world mad for whom men screaming with agony on crosses were a commonplace? Were

871

Solomon, David, and other ancient Hebrew leaders mad?—for they had tortured and killed as wantonly as any.

At the histories of corporal punishment and of torture Angele refused to look; she would not even touch one of these books, or listen to him read from them. She would shriek at him, "Man, the pompous self-lover, has the gall to call the beasts cruel!" If Vridar spoke of the subject of ancient torture to any of his male friends, they would turn smug faces to him and say, yes, maybe long ago, but not now. He wanted to say to them, and to make his words seethe with acid and fury, "You lubberly imbeciles, we must face these things, for they are in you, in me, in us all!" Yes, all that was long ago, yet in the valley here, during the war, men hurled water-melons at the head of a Japanese citizen who came through and chased him out of the county; and when Vridar published an article condemning America's bar-barous treatment of its Japanese citizens, he received anonymous letters from persons who threatened to lynch him, and from friends who in a whisper told him he was guilty of sedition. He would roar at anybody who reproached him or tried to silence him, "I tell you, God damn it, we must struggle against these horrible things that men do to men, and struggle in anger, or let the whole damned shittaree go back to the slime!"

Angele knew that his reading of books in this field—Scott's *The History of Torture Throughout the Ages* and *The History of Corporal Punishment;* Evan's *The Criminal Prosecution and Capital Punishment of Animals;* Lea's *Superstition and Force;* Ive's *A History of Penal Methods;* Parry's *The History of Torture in England;* Rowley's *Slaughter-House Reform in the United States and the Opposing Forces;* Stekel's *Sadism and Masochism;* Timperley's *What War Means; The Japanese Terror in China;* Berg's *The Sadist;* Clarkson's *An Essay on the Slavery and Commerce of the Human Species*—she knew that his reading of these and of other books like them was almost unhinging his mind.

He would come up from his small chamber, sweat on his forehead, his eyes full of flayed bodies and gutted bellies, and say to her, "At least you should read this and learn for yourself what people and forces opposed more humane slaughter of animals."

"No! I see enough of it without reading about it."

"Are you aware that there has been prosecution and capital punishment of animals?"

"I'm aware that the human male has done about everything he could think of. Is there anything evil he hasn't thought of?"

"Well, tell the half-assed reviewers to stop saying I'm morbid. Do they know the mountains of evidence of their brutality and shame? Do the fools even know the evidence exists?"

"They don't know that they are brutes."

"No, they don't. Down through the ages people have established metaphysical systems to obscure or conceal the facts of their existence—its pain, suffering, brevity, insignificance, extinction. Only fear, I think, could compel them to do that. Once we understand that much, it's not easy to despise the human animal, no matter what he does. For we all live in terror of one day losing consciousness. All down the ages, on hands and knees, or bent-legged, I've followed the path of fear. To find what? The schizophrenic society, which fear produced. I see now that the heart of the schizoid is fear—and I've fine examples of it before me for study— my father, my brother, you, myself. For me it was a light over a large dark part of the world when I first realized that fear, and not much else, had made a brute of two Joes—the one in my childhood and the one in Moscow."

One day there came from a news magazine's correspondent a questionnaire: Was it true that Vridar Hunter fainted at the sight of blood? Was it true that he hated women who wore fur coats? Was it true that once on a time he gave up eating meat? Was it true—Gray with rage, Vridar sat at his machine and began a letter to the correspondent: Tell the venomous overpaid sadist with the title of book editor to shove these questions up his ass! If this seems to you severe punishment for one who probably has hemorrhoids of his anus as well as his mind

But he broke it off here and destroyed it. What, he wondered, would such an ugly little monster think of Albert Schweitzer for his confession that it took him weeks to get over the experience of seeing two men, one pulling at a limping horse, the other flogging it from behind, on their way to the slaughter-house? Would he merely sneer in his father-hating depths if he were to read Lea's words about Arnaldo de Vilanova?—"To a man of his lofty spiritual tendencies and tender compassion for his fellows, the wickedness and cruelty of mankind were appalling." To Angele Vridar said, "That book editor should have been not a victim but a guard in Buchenwald or Belsen."

Stekel dwelt on the opportunities for cruelty inherent in medicine and surgery. "Once in visiting a torture chamber I was struck with the similarity between instruments of torture and various medical apparatuses. . . . During the war tortures were made use of by over-patriotic physicians to extort admissions of health!" He had known, Stekel said, a doctor who got an ejaculation when he sutured a wound. It made Vridar ill to think of a man sunk so far below the human level.

Among what human beings were pleased to call the lower, but which Angele called the higher, animals there was, she said, no cruelty at all. Turning to the word in the dictionary she said, "It says inhuman treatment. *Inhuman!* Unhuman! What gall! It says it is Old French and means disposed to inflict suffering."

"That includes cats," he said.

"Oh no. It says taking pleasure in the pain of others. Cats don't know they cause pain."

"That may be."

"It takes an intelligent animal to realize that its actions cause pain to others, and a depraved animal to do it after realizing."

"Not depraved, just scared to death. Let's realize once and for all that fear was the disease in Hitler." He picked up a study of life in the Sudan and read to her: "But the end of life of such splendid beasts is really very sad. Be they killed by lion, leopard or man, when in their full prime, the death is not so bad. They struggle for existence with their full force; their end is quick. But when they grow old their end is slow. Teeth begin to fail; then the beasts get thin and poor . . . . at the last, struggling feebly, he is torn to pieces by wild dogs or hyaenas. Even the aged lion

873

comes to this ignoble end. . .. What the end of the elephant is, when old age takes him by the heels—that no one knows. Most likely, it seems to me, he slowly wades into some deep swamp and, unable in his weakness of age to struggle clear, is miserably drowned in the muddy water."

Vridar looked up and said: "It's something else I intended to read: Nature is terribly, desperately cruel. But without suffering there would be no fear; without fear the alertness and splendid quick movement, the wariness and wildness of the wild things, would in time be lost. All the glory of the beasts of the forest would then be gone; they would become as beasts of a park. They would become as the slow-moving dullards bred in menageries—as fatted steers. But nature is frightfully cruel. The cruelties of man to beasts, which make our blood boil sometimes, are kind in comparison to the cruelty of beasts to each other. The coyotes tear a grown deer to pieces; but they eat a fawn alive. The stoat eats the rabbit alive. Blow-flies—"

"He's a damned stinking liar!"

"Just a minute, I'm almost through. Blow-flies eat a sheep until it breathes with its ribs standing out as bare bones—the maggots crawling in its bowels. Hornets catch the great 'leather-jacket' flies of Northern Canada, and I have watched them saw the buzzing wings off with their teeth, and bite off the struggling legs—"

"Oh no!" she gasped, her eyes furious. She seized the book and hurled it. "What a self-loving rationalizing bastard! Do the hornets go to church? Do the blow-flies cant about God? Does the stoat fold pious hands across a fat belly and say My God, there's Mamie Moak with a new hat, it must be her third this month! Does the coyote preach sermons about the chosen people who will be saved and about the infidels who'll be tormented? Does the leopard—"

"Yes, yes, I agree with you. I wanted you to see what a fatuous ass this author is, who says the beasts are more cruel. Apparently he has never heard that the human animal eats other animals alive—he should stand in the market-place in Venice where we stood and watch the men swallow alive the creeping wriggling sea-beasts that look like monstrous spiders. In ancient times when people ate the god-surrogates, such as the lamb, they ate it alive, as well as they were able, to partake more fully of the god's attributes."

"In the name of religion!"

"Belief in gods has nothing to do with religion."

She opened the dictionary. "It says religion, the outward act or form by which men indicate a recognition of a god or gods to whom obedience and honor are due."

"That's parent-worship, not religion."

"Well, if animals are to become sluggards if they lose their fear, what about Roosevelt's freedom from fear?"

"That was political malarkey from an ignorant man."

"Why are the beasts in menageries dull sluggards? Because people catch them and pen them up for their cruel little brats to look at!"

The question that troubled Vridar was, What part had fear had in the development of mind? What had forced mind to develop before self-consciousness came?

For a few months he put the problem of cruelty aside, knowing that he would have to face it fully in his novel about the Middle Ages. There were plenty of other problems. There were the Hebrews and the Jews. Certain facts about them were clear enough: the Hebrews (it was not their own name for themselves) were Arabs when they entered the stage of history; they came in from the desert to wrest cultivated lands from their owners, and at the time were like nearly all the people around them, polytheists. They got their concept of monotheism from another people at a later time. There seemed to be evidence to support the thesis that after a nomadic people became a settled people they tried to develop a Mother but the prophets cried the Mother down: so the Jews came forward to the threshhold of the modern world without a Mother, thereby giving to Christians a problem they found it impossible to solve, until they assimilated Mary to Isis. Some of the scholars called Judaism a tribal religion.

Vridar would go away to a desertlike area, where the sun was hot on stunted sage and only lizards moved over the sands; and he would lie on his back in the heat with the sun full in his face, trying to understand more fully the feeling toward the sun of a desert people; toward water and rain and the moon; or thinking about the words on a card.

> There is a fundamental difference in outlook between
> the Semitic and the Indo-European mind . . . . the
> latter has invariably tended to become pantheistic. . . .
> The Semitic mind laid intense stress on personality.

That was from Oesterley and Robinson, two of the Higher Critics; he spent hours thinking about it. The few words said so much that so few people were aware of, much less likely to accept. He had to keep in mind, always, the fact that the Hebrews were Orientals, whose culture and religion were simply saturated with the atmosphere, attitudes, loneliness, and moral values of desert-dwellers: he thought it one of the major ironies of history that those people whom they would influence most would be from agricultural valleys and colder climes. There were other ironies: that a people occupying lush northern Israel should never have developed a Mother; that so much of the world should have had thrust upon it by the accidents of history a severe patriarchy in which the male was all-dominant until Mary-Isis-Mother led to the enthronement of the female; that of the hundreds of scholars Vridar had read, only one had pointed out any of these obvious matters.

He looked at another card:

> Though possessed with instincts of self-preservation and
> adaptability almost unique in humanity, the Jew is essen-
> tially an idealist, cherishing dreams of happiness and peace
> in a future age of righteousness.

Those words were by Jackson and Lake, another pair of distinguished Higher Critics: they must have had the modern, not the ancient, Jew in mind, for the adaptability came largely as a result of the dispersion. He read for the twentieth time the words by Dean Inge:

> These two streams, the Semitic and the European, the
> Jewish and the Greek, still mingle their waters in the
> turbid flood which constitutes the institutional religion of
> civilized humanity; but to this day the waters flow side by
> side in the same bed, perfectly recognizable—so alien are
> the two types to each other.

Robert Nathan, a Jew, in a fine little novel called *Jonah,* had also said it; and this idea would be the heart and soul of his own novel about the most crucial of all struggles for the Western world. Would the waters ever mingle? Not if all Jews were like Klausner: in a book of six hundred and ten pages called *From Jesus to Paul* he had written:

> And when in those days the mystical and un-Jewish quality
> of important parts of Paul's teaching shall be done away
> with, and Judaism in the form of ethico-prophetic mono-
> theism shall spread over all the world—then shall this
> refined Judaism know how to appreciate the great merit of
> Paul: that through him the pagan world accepted, along
> with many strange and unnatural superstitions, the Jewish
> Bible as the foundation and basis of a religion for the
> Gentiles. In this sense—and only in this great and deep
> sense—was Paul also what Maimonides so beautifully
> called Jesus:

> *A preparer of the way for the King-Messiah.*

The Catholics also hugged to them the illusion of their specially chosen apartness; and the Mormons also; and still others. Yes, it was long past time the guns were brought up and the old moulds shot all to pieces.

Putting the cards aside, Vridar reached out and brought handfuls of sand to his nostrils. It smelled of sage, lizards, and stone-heat. He recalled what a scholar had written about Islam, that its doctrines compelled "its followers to surrender utterly to the will of God, a faith peculiarly suited to the desert which gave it birth." In a later time Vridar would wander over parts of the Moroccan and Egyptian deserts; he would fly over the appalling desolation across which, in legend, Moses led his people, and over the Dead Sea and its environs; but all this would only make more obvious the truths obvious to him now. All around him today he could see no sign of life, except the lizards, nor sign of anything to eat or drink. *Of course* the Arabs had to surrender to the will of the Father: their dependence on him was absolute, for a little water and a little food to keep their lives going. It was only in the deserts that you could understand the Prophets and the wailing walls.

Breathing in the desert odors he looked down at the words by Erich Fromm:

> [Man] projects the best he has onto God and improverishes
> himself. . . . The more he praises God the emptier he

> becomes. The emptier he becomes the more sinful he feels
> The more sinful he feels the more he praises God—and
> the less he is able to regain himself.

When he first read those words Vridar's thoughts raced back to that time in his youth when he went insane, and was saved only by Turner's laughter: how clear it all was now! Horrible fear of father and Father had driven him to a lunacy of prayer and tears and pleading; and he *did* become emptier and feel more sinful; and the more sinful he felt the harder he prayed! How simple it all was! Man projects the best he has onto God (that is, an idealized image of his father) and impoverishes himself (that is, feels all the baser the more he elevates the other to splendor). The more he praises the idealized image the emptier he becomes, the more sinful he feels. The more sinful he feels (that is, unworthy as a son, of such a father) the more he praises the idealized image. What people could be compared to the Jews in the chanting of praise to that image?—what other had so lost themselves in a colossal act of submission and projection, until they were all stricken orphans going into the gethsemanes to pray! They were the world's most pathetic orphans, the poor wailing fatherless sons. You had only to read the Jewish Bible, with Fromm's words in mind, to see how those words were borne out in every part, almost on every page. Had Fromm read Briffault's words, that it was Judaism "which ultimately imposed itself upon the Western world" and that this fact "is perhaps not unconnected with the natural tendency to obliterate the last traces of matriarchal society"? How little those understood this vast and complex problem, who wrote glibly and superficially about the "war between the sexes"! The Jewish idea, his next card said, appears over and over in their literature as "The pious sit, their crowns upon their heads, delighting in the splendor of the Divine Presence." How completely the Western world, including all but a handful of the Jews in it, had failed to understand the origin and essence of Judaism!

Where else on earth had the sons so completely capitulated to the fathers?

What, Vridar wondered, besides the desert, had driven them to elevate the father-image to transcendent splendor—to spend so much of their lives supplicating, praising, and adoring him? What had given them such a deep sense of sin? Had it in deep part been a subconscious wish to destroy the father because, having projected onto him so much of self, the sons felt impoverished and empty? In any case, a sense of sin meant a sense of separation, of separateness; and so it was that the Jews, even long before the time of Jesus, had demanded for themselves a life apart from all other people. What irony and what pathos in the fact that, having lost themselves in their fathers, the sons felt so sinful and empty that they felt compelled to demand a place apart and then set themselves up as a chosen and elect people, the priests to all nations, in an effort to regain what they had lost! The lost and wailing intellectual Marxists were doing the same thing: they were spending so much of themselves in idolatry of a monster, of whom they had made a father-image, that they had lost their conscience, their sense of decency, and almost their minds, yet thought of themselves as the elite of the earth. Vridar thought it not at all surprising (indeed, inevitable) that more intellectual Jews had become Communists, in proportion to their number in the population, than any other people in the United

States. Immolation in the father was a habit with them, that reached clear back to the desert.

He opened the Bible (a Jewish, not a Christian, copy) and after thumbing through it put it down with a shudder: he had read it so many times that he knew it, he knew it all, he knew it so well that he could smell the fears and furies in it, and its insane unreasons. He knew deeply now that this most famous of all books in praise of the father-image, together with his own father, who had lived in it and sworn by it, had driven him so far into insanity that he had never fully got out. . . .

He now looked to another profound truth. When he taught in Manhattan he had again and again heard non-Jews say that the Jews were the most arrogant people on earth. Vridar had admitted to himself that they seemed to be: so many of them were brash and pushing and full of self-praise. But all this, he understood now, was over-compensation: the Jews were, in fact, by nature the most submissive people on earth. How could they be otherwise?—for look at their record, look at their record! While lying here in the sands he suddenly sat up crying, "Holy Joe and Adam!" For now he saw another thing. He knew now why the Jews had never had a Mother. Their men, at least their phophets and similar teachers, had been so female-identified that they couldn't stand the thought of femaleness, and so had enthroned the Male in solitary wifeless childless splendor! They had got such an abnormal female-identification because they had enthroned the family-unit, and the Christian world had copied them exactly in that. The Virgin-Mother, he saw now, was so utterly non-Jewish, and by derivation and logic, non-Christian, that her survival was a miracle of history.

Frazer, he now recalled, looking at the desert around him, had said that the national genius which produced the Bible had degenerated to the task of producing the Talmud. Well, many of the Hebrews had intermarried with other people, and all of them had forsaken the desert. Hannay had said that a small minority of ancient Levites "had left a terrible legacy to Europe." Professor Case had written that a "dualistic world-view necessarily enthrones the supernatural, and by rendering it philosophically respectable only makes it the more truly tyrannical." But was Judaism the principal villain? On a card Vridar had written:

> The Romans bequeathed to us the idea that we must live
> in an orderly society under law; the Greeks, that the
> creative powers in man must be free to express themselves;
> the Jews, the concept of the dignity of man, and moral
> responsibility. Paul left us the monstrous notions of moral
> depravity and original sin, which produced unspeakable
> brutalities and horrors, and the schizoid Western world.

He saw no reason to change a word of it. It seemed, in the present stage of his reading, that the chief villains were Paul, and the fanatics who made his views a part of the Christian dogmas. . . .

But his problem at the moment was the Arab-Hebrews, and Solomon. What had this king actually been like? All the ablest scholars, without a single exception, agreed that Jewish writers of later centuries had created a legend and embellished it, making of their ancient king a paragon of enterprise and wisdom. No scholar, among the firstrate ones, thought he had written more than a few, but more likely none at all, of the noble words attributed to him. It was probable that he had not been able to read. After all, this people had only recently come in from the desert, to seize lands belonging to others. Solomon had built a temple that must have been, in actual fact, a pretty mean edifice, compared to the great temples around Israel. Among his wives he had an Egyptian princess. For his capital he took a mud-baked sun-scalded village that had been there for centuries. After reading a great many scholars, and then looking at the whole broad picture of the thing, Vridar decided that for the purpose of limning certain major truths against the sky he would have to make Solomon a greater king than the scholars thought he had been. He would give him a great vision: opposing the wild fanatical sons-lost-in-their-fathers prophets, Solomon would try to take his people into the fellowship of nations, and into the verdant valleys and to the Mother, as well as to the Father: Astarte was only a three-day journey away.

"If Solomon—the Solomon of my story—had won," Vridar said one day to Angele, "we'd not now have so stifling a triumph of patriarchy, a wifeless and son-less Father; nor the shameful down-the-centuries degradation of women, under both Judaism and Christianity; nor the kind of world we have now. But Solomon lost. The real Solomon, I suppose, wouldn't have had a gnat's notion of what I'm talking about. I hate like hell to depart so far from historical facts in this book."

Angele sat looking at him, while he studied a handful of cards. She then spoke words that were to grow in size with the years, until they became a chronic headache. She said, "Not many people are going to like it."

"No? They won't like my novel?"

"Few reviewers, I expect. Have you asked yourself what the Jews will think?"

No, he hadn't: he still cherished the romantic notion that people would accept the truth, if it was pointed out to them: if he could come to healing through it, and peace with his father, wouldn't they want to also, if they knew it?

"I suppose you're right," he said at last. He was deeply worried. He had reason to be. His New York publisher wrote him that he didn't want his novel about Solomon—at least not as it was written: that publisher was one of the gentlest, most compassionate, most enlightened men in the world. Vridar's mind then turned to Rhode, who had solemny promised to see him through; but before turning to Rhode, Angele thought he should go to New York, to see if he could find a publisher there.

XIII

Vridar's agent was not happy to see him: Vridar's novels had made no money for him either, and he was pretty tired of them. Vridar then suspected that none of the publishers would want to see him, but he found them gracious: Vridar Hunter was no author to ask to lunch or dinner, but a sad-eyed half-cracked melancholy fellow to be polite to and get rid of.

There was John Fuller. When Vridar called him, John said, "Oh, fine, fine! Let's have dinner at the Harvard Club." John was a fat flabby sandy near-sighted man who breathed hard, even when sitting still. While they were having cocktails, he put his hand on Vridar's thigh. He seemed about to weep. Ten minutes later he had tears in his eyes. John's yearning to help underpaid neglected authors filled his fat frame—but it was something else that had filled his purse, for it was well known that this man was a multimillionaire. He would clasp Vridar's thigh and lean forward, his eyes misty, his thick pallid lips murmuring, "See what I mean? Vridar, you see what I mean?"

Just what, Vridar wondered, *did* he mean? To discover if he could what John meant, Vridar mentioned a once-famous author whom John used to publish, but had abandoned. Now John was really deeply moved: a tear or two fell to his overfed cheek. He dragged forth a monogrammed handkerchief. He hustled his chair a little nearer, and in a voice trembling with woe blurted out the dreadful truth: this author, poor man, was not what he had been. He had become a tyrant. O Lord, it was impossible to deal with him at all. "Vridar, you see what I mean? You see, don't you?" John said he'd be happy—he'd be simply delighted—to read Vridar's novel. He would get over it in the next day or two. "I'm sure we want you on our list."

Three days later a brief note came from John. It said he was sorry—oh, he was so terribly sorry; but their lists were already crowded, he had not found it possible to make a place for Vridar's book. He begged Vridar to believe that he wished him well. The manuscript was being returned to him by messenger. Vridar wrote Angele, "He didn't have the simple decency to face me again. Angele, you see what I mean? . . ."

He went next to Jonas Hancock, a big man who stood well above six feet, with a huge nose, and a way of lifting his head up and back, as though looking down at you from a height. A professor and a scholar, Jonas, a Jew, was an editor for a Jewish house. He read the novel and said he liked it, but he doubted that Max Teufel would like it. As it turned out, Teufel hated it: never in his life, Hancock said, had he seen an angrier man. "He says it's nothing but a diatribe against his people. He thinks Solomon said all the things the Bible has him say. Has it occurred to you that when you get down to the Christian era you are going to be in real trouble?"

"I suppose," said Vridar, feeling dispirited and weary. He wrote Angele, "Truly men hate the truth, they'd liefer meet a tiger on the road. Poor scared children . . ." He didn't know whether to get drunk or go to the Metropolitan. While smoking a cigarette and trying to make up his mind he thought of Bruegel's "The Harvesters" and felt a great nostalgia for it. He went to the Museum. He stood for half an hour looking at the Bruegel and wished again that he had become a painter; and then studied some curious details in Veronese's "Mars and Venus," whose rich opulent colors he liked. He was looking at a Renoir and recalling the furor of abuse and outrage its hanging had caused, when he thought of Vermeer. He went over to have another look at "Young Woman with a Water Jug." For more than a hundred years Vermeer's paintings, even his very name, had been forgotten.

This evening he wrote to Angele, "Let them not publish me at all, for I'd rather be unknown, or if known then quickly forgotten, than be (or for money and fame pretend to be) one with the small souls who pervert history and whore its truths, to elevate themselves in the esteem of cowards like them. Hancock confided in me that he doesn't think I can find a publisher here. I'm beginning to feel that Rhode won't want me either. . . ."

He turned next to William Janssen, whose boss was Ezra Waife, another Jew. Janssen took Vridar to the Ambassador for lunch and laid it on the line: he had thumbed through the novel and was convinced that it would be a waste of time to lay it before Waife. When Vridar returned to the office with Janssen, Waife was there, and advanced with outthrust hand, saying, "Haven't we met before?" Vridar realized that the question was one that Waife put to all writers—that it was a part of the American pattern of getting ahead and keeping a purse well-filled. "I didn't want him anyhow," he wrote to Angele. "Where in hell did I get the idea that Jewish publishers have more courage? They run twice as fast and ten times as far. . . .

"Janssen told me some stories that will delight you. One of his writers, a very small man, physically, was at a Waife party, when at midnight Edna Ferber saw him; and thinking him a child of the house she said, 'Boy, isn't it your bedtime?' His stories about Sinclair Lewis and Dorothy Thompson will have to wait till I see you. . . ."

The next morning Vridar thought of Chris Teaker, book critic, editor, wit, bon vivant, boozer—and the gentlest man among intellectuals Vridar had ever known. Chris one time had come to Vridar's home with Roger Bostwick, a writer, and another gentle man; and both men had looked to Vridar so frail and pale that he had hustled them into the house, lest a wind blow them down. Nearly all night he drank with them and talked. Roger had a favorite story about his wife: he had wanted more children, his wife had wanted a fur coat. They gave up smoking with the agreement that if she resumed the habit first, he was to win another child; if he were first, she would win a fur coat. Roger had won. "And there he sat," Vridar said later to Angele, "looking as happy as a moron with eighty grandchildren." Vridar took a fancy to both Chris and Roger and gave them the best he had.

Chris was about six feet tall and very thin, with handsome bushy graying hair, small dark brown eyes, a turned-up nose, and a sensitive mouth almost hidden under a huge mustache. He looked unhappy when grave, but when he laughed he looked merry in a puckish innocent way. He said things now and then that tickled Vridar all the way through. Making a gesture at Europe with a long thin arm he cried, "The fine thing about the nineteenth century is there were so many things to rebel against!"

About three in the morning he asked, "Would you rather have a woman or dream about one?" and answered his own question: "Dream, for I'd have a higher class of woman." He said he had been a failure because the world was wrong. He said he had to have a can of beer for breakfast, but hid it during the previous day, though his wife knew where it was all the time. Exploding suddenly, like a man bursting with fury, he flung his long arm out and demanded, "How could we manage financially if we both drank?"

Chris had been an editor in a number of large publishing houses. For a while he had been book editor of a news magazine: "They had me sitting on the floor with a quart of hootch. When I had all my pages made up along came the word, Cut out the last paragraph. Cut this, cut that, to make way for more advertising." About four in the morning Chris was making a frantic effort to work up a rage, when Vridar said to him, "Cut it out. You have no talent for hate." Chris had then flung both arms wide, and staggering up from his chair had glowered round him and said, "I certainly ought to hate something." He brooded a moment and added: "It isn't that people like me; they just won't hate me and you can't imagine how insulting it is."

Vridar let the two men sleep a couple of hours, and then in his shorts went barefooted to the guest cabin, a glass of whisky in each hand. Chris took one look at him out of bloodshot eyes and came from the bedroom, muttering, "The trouble with this man's hospitality is there's too damn much of it." After breakfast Vridar drove them to the cool mountains, stopping every fifty miles or so to let the gentle Roger kneel by the car and puke.

Yes, he would go see Chris, for Chris was now book editor for an immensely wealthy Jew who had decided to add book publishing to his many enterprises. After searching for hours Vridar at last found Chris, in a gloomy old building, his office barely larger than a clothes closet. Vridar sensed at once that Chris was ashamed to be seen in this place, who in his time had had sumptuous offices and the right of command. So he said quickly, "Let's go have a drink."

Chris had been looking up at him with unhappy brown eyes. His whole manner had been saying, I gave you my home address, not this, so how did you find me? How crass it is of you to come here to see my shame!

"Let's go have a drink."

Chris said something about having to see the boss first, and went off through a warehouse of packing-cases and bales of paper, to a small office looking out on a dirty street. There Vridar met Ben Cohen, a man so fat that in his clothes he looked exactly like a barrel. He had a round fat face, bright intelligent eyes, a heavy lower lip like Winston Churchill's, and expensive garments. He put out a short pudgy hand and there was no more pressure in it than in a dead hand. Over a drink a little later Chris told Vridar that Ben had made millions in business that had no social patina: his wife now wanted to sidle up to some big culture, and Cohen had thought book publishing would be the ticket. Oh yes, Cohen would want Vridar on his list.

Vridar was not sure that he wanted to be on Cohen's list. This evening he went with him and Chris to dinner, and in an expansive mood Ben told him that he would show the stuffed shirts how to sell books. Sure, he wanted Vridar on his list: what was good enough for Chris was good enough for him. Vridar wanted to ask for a day or two to think it over but decided that this would be unwise: perhaps it was a pretty scrawny bird in the hand but there was none visible in the bushes. "I'd rather work with Chris than with any other editor I know," Vridar said. He meant it. Chris was a poet. He had imagination, whimsy, irony, depth; and he had range. He loved the delicate, like Robert Nathan's fables; but he loved the rough and strong, too. He was the most catholic book critic Vridar was ever to meet.

After dinner Cohen took Vridar a little way down the street and under a dirty yellow street lamp touched his arm and said to him, "Don't worry about nothing. I'll show the stuffed shirts how to sell books. I'll sell a hell of a pile of your next one. . . ."

It was after midnight when Vridar wrote to Angele: "I feel in my bones that Cohen will throw Chris out in a year or two, because Chris is so fine an editor, and has such sureness of literary taste, and is so devoted to the fine instead of the popular things, that in a publisher's office he's about as welcome as a boil on a cheekbone at a fashion show. I'll have the damned search to make all over again. Cohen is giving his authors a party at the Statler and I guess I'll go because most of these authors are like me—orphans in a storm who are crawling into their last coal-shed. . . ."

The party was dominated by a loud sandy Englishman who was a famous womens-clubs historian. His name was Hogan. It was clear that Hogan fancied himself as a wit; he laughed immoderately at what he said, no matter what he said. Around him were a half-dozen women in attitudes of adoration, but the eyes of all of them were watching the door, for the women were ready to switch their mechanical smiles and empty cries to a bigger lion, if one were to come. Standing by a wall with a glass in hand was an author whose bored face said plainly that in his opinion he was the biggest lion in the room. Over in a corner, alone with a drink, sat a ghost-writer named Dick Smith. After accepting Ben Cohen's weak handclasp, Vridar stood back and looked at the guests. Deciding that Dick looked the most interesting he went over.

"Chris says you're a ghost-writer. I guess you're the first I've seen."

Dick turned on him a cool cynical stare. After a few moments he said, "Do you agree with me that all Englishmen are a pain in the ass?" He looked again at Hogan. Eager to learn about ghost-writing, Vridar tried to lead Dick out. Dick said all writers would be ghost-writers before much longer. That was because there were two kinds of people: those with nothing to say but with a talent for writing; and those with something to say who had no talent. How much did Vridar know about the subject?

"Practically nothing."

Within the past year, Dick said, there had been a dozen books published by nationally known people, not a word of which had been written by the names on the title-pages. If various famous persons (did he have anyone in mind, such as Mrs. Roosevelt or the Duchess?) decided to write his or her memoirs, the only question was, Who should do the actual writing? Ghosting was a lucrative job, unless you were dealing with one like the Duchess, who was as tight as a fiddle string under high C. If any of the popular idols, with no talent for anything except making noise—if a Bob Hope or Sinatra or Godfrey decided to write a book, who would do it for him? "Me, quite possibly. I've just finished the autobiography of Congressman Boom. I'll send you a copy."

Vridar said, "Am I to assume that book reviewers know about all this and play along with it?"

Book reviewers, Dick said, were no brighter and no more honorable than

883

anybody else. This had become a nation of rackets, all of which in time would be respectable, if they continued to make money. You never could be sure any more that any book was written by the name on the title-page. "I assume," he said, turning the cool cynical look on Vridar, "that you actually write the books published under your name. That may be the reason they don't sell any better. But I've no doubt there are books in your library written by ghosts. When you pick up the *Post* or *McCall's* or any other big slick and see an article by a name you recognize, do you assume that person wrote it?"

Vridar hedged. He said he had no interest in such magazines.

"O, maybe," said Dick, "if the name on the story is William Faulkner or Henry Miller, Faulkner or Miller wrote it; but even the fools who insist on writing their own stuff get a lot of help the public knows nothing about. How about Thomas Wolfe?"

"Why do you do it?" Vridar said.

Dick knocked his ashes off to the rug. "What a hell of a question. I like good food. It takes money to eat in New York and I've no taste for the automats. The story is the thing: does it matter who tells it? Does it matter at all whether Shakespeare wrote Shakespeare? There was a time when I didn't eat very well and nobody gave a God damn whether I ate at all. I lived in an unheated rat-cell in the Village and drank cheap sweet wine. I was thinking of going back to school to take a higher degree when I learned that I could buy one. Did you know you can buy even a Doctor's thesis nowadays?"

Vridar stared, unbelieving.

"How long have you been out in Idaho? I'll buy you anything you want, from a Doctor's thesis to a scientific article in a learned journal. You want to be famous as a scientist?—or a wit? All you need is the money. For twenty thousand I'll deliver a novel to you and guarantee it to outsell anything you've published in the last ten years. All I'll do is rewrite some best-seller that has already been rewritten a hundred times."

Vridar still stared. The forepart of Dick's skull was bald; he had deep brooding-lines between his eyes.

"How much do your novels average you?"

Vridar took a swig from his glass before replying. "Five or six hundred."

"How in hell do you make a living? . . . But forgive me, it's none of my business. Remember what Chesterfield said?—that frequent loud laughter is the way the mob expresses their silly joy at silly things. Since, he said, I've had the full use of my reason, nobody has ever heard me laugh. If you're not going to give the mob corn, as the Caesars did, then you'll have to give them Bob Hope and Arthur Godfrey and ghost-writers. If there were any brains and taste in this country, could Europeans come here by the hundreds to talk their empty patronizing talk, and take more dollars home in six weeks than they can earn over there in ten years?" Dick looked at Vridar again and said, "Let's get away from this English eunuchoid and find a drink." They went a block or two to a small place that had luxurious chairs. When Vridar moved to pay for the drinks, Dick restrained him, saying, "On six hundred per book you've no right to buy a drink." Even twenty thousand a year, he said, was petty graft, in a nation where gangsterism was triumphant—where a famous historian could be made out of a hack (it had been done); a famous author out of a woman who couldn't write a correct sentence ten words long (it had been done); and a wit out of a gigolo who couldn't tell a bon mot from the Zeitgeist. Dick said he had read two or three of Vridar's books: they were too intellectual to sell, for the intellectuals of the country seldom read novels. As for that lardass, Ben Cohen, he wouldn't have looked at Vridar if Chris hadn't bewitched him. "It's going to cost Cohen a lot of money to find out that Chris thinks unsaleable books should be published."

Dick bought more drinks and went on talking. If Ph.D. theses could actually be bought; if persons opened popular magazines and never knew who wrote the contents; if a wealthy man could get a reputation as a writer, while the real writer starved; if a man spent a year or two on a book and got only six hundred dollars, while for moaning while breathing through his nose a popular singer was paid millions, then obviously Henry Wallace need no longer worry, for the century of the common man was here, and the uncommon man was either going to starve, or whore his talents to keep the common brother entertained. . . .

Vridar arrived at his hotel room at four in the morning, wishing that he had never written a book, or ever read a book. On the way east he had ridden the coach and sat up two nights, eating only the sandwiches that Angele had packed for him. On the way home he would sit up again, while the thinly-talented idols of the common people rode in private planes. Unable to sleep, he recalled, with gloomy rumbling furies, that he and Angele were living on less than three thousand dollars a year, while women who were not actresses really, but only narcissists with straight legs and full breasts, were paid eight million dollars for four pictures. During War II—which he had always called the War to save Stalin—he had pitched hay nine hours a day for three dollars, while the popular idols. . . .

But to hell with it, to hell with it!

Freud had said, Vridar told himself, turning to look at daylight on the window, that conscience was a taking over of the burden that the father had not assumed. If that was true, then for thirty years he had punished himself doing for Joe what Joe had never done. When drunk he had once shaken an impotent fist at the universe and cried out of alcoholic belches, "Why shouldn't I throw my conscience away, in a world that has no need of it, and accept a fat Hollywood offer, sell my name in the market for whores, endorse cigarettes, ale, whisky, and dictionaries for money?" He invariably detested himself for such talk, knowing that in such moments he had sunk to the level of bitterness and self-pity: in the first order of greatness, he told Angele, bitterness had never found a home. He knew that was a lie. He knew of almost no great man in the past who had not felt bitterness, and some of the very greatest had been eaten alive by it. He would observe that a popular novelist, with an income in six figures, would say pompously for a news magazine, "Whores find their own level," and a few weeks later sell his name to an ale or a fountain pen. He wondered about the inner nature of the uncommon people who, to keep their purses filled and their faces before the public, endorsed almost any product that was aimed at the common people. He thought all this a shameless form of exploitation of ignorance and credulity, and noted that it was commonest with those known as liberals, from Eleanor Roosevelt down to a cynical journalist named Saul Toadiman.

He began to dress, while muttering, "To hell with it!" What did Roger Bacon have during all the years he rotted in a cold foul dungeon of rats and darkness? Did he ever complain? He drank his filthy water and ate his crust of hard filthy bread; and in that dank lonely darkness into which a venal Pope had thrust him, he sat year after year, because of his belief that truth was stronger than tyranny. How dared he whine, remembering such men!

On the long way home he tried to think rationally of his problem. He did not for a moment believe that mankind had much of a future: some day it would all end, leaving no record. What, then, was he striving for? A hair shirt and martydom? What was the nature of the conflict in him? Because he had no father, was he trying to set himself up as a kind of universal father-image? Because conscience and honor seemed to be dying in the world, was he trying to stuff himself with them, as though by doing this he could preserve them to a happier time? . . .

Oh, he knew what the problem was. It was that of any artist, struggling against odds that were almost too much for him. His thoughts turned to such as Balzac, Wagner, Meredith—giants all—whose complaints had filled the world, no matter how large their earnings. . . .

He left the train at two in the morning and Angele was there in the dark, waiting. He folded her in his arms and felt against him the beating of her heart. She was overjoyed because again he had a publisher; and seeing how happy she was, he decided on silence. He would not tell her of his own premonitions of a darker time again—oh, not alone because of his brother, an alcoholic who was going insane, but for himself, too, with his burden of frustration and despair.

"Is he a nice man?" she asked against him.

"A nice fat man, worth fifteen millions."

"Does he know you're a great writer?"

Vridar hid a wry grin in her hair. "I don't think great writers are a part of his consciousness."

"How is Chris?"

"Still searching round him for something to hate."

They went to the car and he took from its compartment a bottle opener. In the gloom she was trying to look into his eyes.

"Now you'll be happier?"

"Of course," he said, and opened the beer.

XIV

Vridar was to say later "If I had the sense God gave little geese, I'd have seen it coming, all of it!" For the signs had been plain enough. There had been Reuben Taylor Rhode's words after he read the novel about King Solomon, "You're a great scholar, old man, and I'm just a small country publisher. I haven't read all the books you have, but I just don't believe you've told the truth. As I read the Bible. . . ."

Vridar had groaned to Angele, "Christ O God, as he and other ignoramuses read the Bible! I tell them what the greatest scholars in that field have concluded, and they say, yes, but as we read the Bible! As *he* heads the Bible! As Billy Graham reads the Bible! As Bishop Sheen reads the Bible!—and Barth and Tillich and Niebuhr! Not even with shock therapy could you make them understand that the only persons who *can* read the Bible are the Higher Critics!"

"Shshsh, Cookie. They'll all be saying it. You've brought up one of the guns."

"I'd not mind if I could have the few thousand readers who belong to me, but those are precisely the ones who have never heard of me. My books are at the mercy of numskulls who know what the Bible says!"

Again she tried to quiet him. He had always been a violent man; now, in deep frustration, he was more violent then before. He would sit in a deep dark funk thinking about Rhode, whom all the scholars under heaven could never budge an iota from his convictions and prejudices: for him it was *right* for Solomon to have said the things which the Old Testament put on his tongue; and because for him it *seemed* right it was historically true!

Ben Cohen published the novel, and a Jewish book-editor in a journal with almost worldwide coverage tried to destroy it. "A prurient diatribe," he wrote, his malice and venom so plain that Vridar went for a walk, telling himself, What a fool I am to have thought that truth has a home in any but a few minds! To have imagined that if he rested his books on the greatest scholarship he could expect at least a detached appraisal from the top book-editors! When he returned hours later he found on his typewriter a note from Angele. It said:

> Cookie darling, what else could you expect that reviewer to say? Teufel called it a diatribe. They don't want your vision of a great king. They want a guy in cloth of gold who built a gold temple and wrote Proverbs! But can you blame them: you have said so many times that fear is the disease in such people but you seem to forget it. . . .

There came a note from Dwight Hand, a poet in Los Angeles:

> Balls and little babies, Hunter! This review sickens me. If they thought it only prurient diatribe, why did they bother with it at all? I feel that they are horribly afraid of you, and horrible liars. Don't bother to read them; get on with your work.

From Chris came a note:

> The members of that book department are not bold and brave. They believe in God and are against the man-eating shark—that's about as far as they go, except to flog dead horses and discover where the wind lies. And they have an uncanny instinct as to what George F. Babbitt will think. . . .

There was not a word from such old friends as Carl Noyce—nothing from

Reuben Taylor Rhode. From Angele came two items, which she pinned on his wall: one was an effusively flattering review of a book called *The Birthday of Little Jesus,* by Golden West, one of the nation's most influential book editors. The other was a sneering contemptuous review of a Bertrand Russell book, by the one who had called Vridar's novel pruient: Russell, he said, was an "atheist" whose ideas were "as outmoded as bloomers." Under the words Angele had written:

> Bring up more guns, Cookie, and keep firing! Here is what E. W. Scripps wrote: "When you find many people applauding you for what you do, and a few condemning, you can be certain that you are on the wrong course because you're doing the things that fools approve."

Yes, he thought, reading the words: he tried to keep before him what Aurelius had said, that "there is but one thing of real value—to cultivate truth and justice, and to live without anger in the midst of lying and unjust men." Lying men? Dwight Hand sent on to Vridar the note in response to his protest of the "prurient" review:

> Mr. Hunter's novel was carefully read, and we assure you that we had no reason at all to write about Author Hunter's work with prejudice.

It was so fantastically dishonest and cynical that a man had to wonder about the country he lived in, professing to be the world's moral leader, when serious authors were helpless before the sadists on its most powerful journals. Pouring himself a glass of bourbon and drinking it off, Vridar would say, "When all the so-called critics were praising Howells to the sky, where was Melville? Not even mentioned in a footnote in books about American literature! I think of what Goethe said, If a higher mentality would become common possession, the poet could have a good time; he could always be straightforward and true and need not shy away from saying the best. But then I recall what Carlyle said about *The Origin of Species,* Wonderful to me, as indicating the capricious stupidity of mankind; never could read a *page* of it, or waste the least thought upon it. So what? The most influential literary critic of his time, in England, called Carlyle himself a strenuous blockhead and failure. But did that teach him any tolerance?" Vridar asked rhetorically, feeling the whisky like a strong sun over his pain. "Shall I keep in mind that while Janin and Sandeau and de Kock were praised to the sky as great writers, by such as this sadist who finds Russell's belief in worldwide birth control as outmoded as bloomers, a Stendhal novel sold only twenty-one copies, and *Le rouge et le noir,* which Taine says he read eighty-four times, never went into a second printing in Stendhal's lifetime?"

"Ernest Hemingway says he read his own *Across the River* two hundred and six times."

"You're really filled up with childness when you can do that. Well, one more statement and I'll get off the subject. A long time ago I published a book in which I said to hell with Communism and I was dropped cold from such citadels of the intellect as the so-called liberal journals. Remember the prodigal son story? It's the heart of the Christian system. Two sons accepted each his part of the patrimony:

one son settled down as a dependable hardworking citizen, living a frugal honest life and adding to what he had been given. The other son went away and blew his part on drinking and whores and riotous living, until, broke and in the gutter, he thought again of Pa. So he came home, and they gave him the fatted calf and wept with joy. A few of us saw Stalin and his system for what they were, and were almost destroyed by the reviewers; others, who played with that whore and eventually said I'm sorry, have been welcomed back and given the front pages. John Humberlin, who said he threw one of my books through a window or into a fireplace, has recently said Mea culpa and held his nose against the Soviet system; and all the other little Sigma Chis who also played with that whore, then changed their minds, welcomed him home. Now the ex-Communists eat the fatted calf and get love and fondness in the high places, while we who saw the conspiracy from the beginning do damned well if we get reviewed at all. It's no longer popular to acclaim the Hisses and Lattimores and Whites; but it is freely admitted that the Smedleys and Lauterbachs and Bissons could make or break a book on China, and often did. Lattimore's *Ordeal by Slander* was given the front page in what is called the good gray newspaper, and one of his partisans was called in to do the job; but when a nationally known figure reviews one of my books in the same newspaper, the review is gutted of every favorable sentence but one. I'd like to kick—"

"Cookie—"

"—the illiterate dishonest bastards in their scrotums so hard that their balls would fly like marbles out into an orbit, and like tiny frozen moons go round and round."

"Cookie," she said, "if they're either stupid or dishonest, why should you care about them?"

"Where is Chateaubriand?"

"Who is he?"

"Who is *he* ! Good God, Angele Lorelei! He was the champion of the Roman Church and dominated literature in France for decades. Would he have got the Nobel award, if there had been one then? O Lord yes. We have a lot of Chateaubriands today—but wait; I have another thing in mind. The other day I lay for half an hour watching a small bird chasing a hawk. I guess the hawk had been robbing its nest. The hawk couldn't possibly turn to attack, because its turning-curve was so large, the bird's so small. All that tiny thing needed was a strong sharp bill to have done him in."

"Is that a fable?"

"Let's fill them up," he said and they went to the kitchen. Sometimes after drinking a fifth of whisky, they would go to a tavern and drink beer and play pool. The aristocrats of the valley, who played bridge, gathered funds for charities, and said between you and I would not enter a tavern. The next social level was the hard-drinking lower middle class, who danced all night and fell into basements. The third level comprised those who had not been born on the second level, and spent their lives trying to get there. The fourth and bottom level were the unskilled. Vridar had been astonished to learn how difficult it was to rise to the next level above, how many were the rivalries, how complex the patterns of feuding. Certain women gave an unbelievable amount of time and energy to efforts to conspire against, discredit and destroy rivals.

With their drinks they returned to a window and looked out at blue lake and white water. Thinking of the four social levels, he recalled the words of an architect named Cram, who had said that most people did not behave like human beings for the reason that they weren't. He had said that only now and then did a human being emerge from the sub-human mass. All this seemed to Vridar to be as plain as day. Matthew Arnold had said, One must be struck more and more the longer one lives, to find how much in our present society a man's life of each day depends for its solidity and value upon whether he reads during that day, and far more still on what he reads. Albert Jay Nock had written, I do not mean that the great majority are unable to read intelligently; I mean that they are unable to read at all—unable, that is, to carry away from a piece of printed matter anything like a correct idea of its contents. What a spectacle it was, he had written, when colleges every year turned out thousands of bachelors in the liberal arts who could no more read their diplomas than they could decipher the Minoan linear script.

Sitting by the window with Angele, Vridar picked up a book and said, "Here is Nock on liberals. 'But one never knew what liberals would do, and their power of self-persuasion is such that only God knows what they would not do. As casuists they make Gury and St. Alfonso dei Liguori look like bush-leaguers.' They are great fellows, Nock says, for the Larger Good, and it would have to be pretty large to compel them to alienate your wife's affections or steal your watch. 'But on any point of intellectual integrity, there is not one of them whom I would trust for ten minutes alone in a room with a red-hot stove.' The Larger Good fellows: I used to be one, but that was when I hated my father."

"Oh? That's it?"

"That's part of it and possibly the larger part."

"Did Whittaker Chambers?"

"Well, I'll tell you something." He looked at one of her ears, thinking of her forty pairs of earrings. "You know why you wear earrings?" Suspecting one of his traps, she looked at him with distrust. He said: "Symbolically calling attention to your genitals."

"Really! And how do men do it?"

"With pipes, walking-sticks and—"

"Mustaches?"

"No, that's the female in them: feminine-identified men may wear mustaches and some of them manage to make their mouths strongly resemble a vulva. Dwight Hand asked me if I had observed that in Carl. As for Chambers, he confesses in his book, or somewhere, that he came to believe in a Great Design while looking at his daughter's ear."

"You once told me your father used to want to bite your sister's ears."

"All the time. It got to be a family disgrace. I see vividly before me the guilty emotion in his eyes and over his face when he struggled with her; and the cold look of distaste on my mother's face. She didn't quite know what it all meant but she sensed it."

"Well, a human being: is Eleanor Roosevelt?"

"She once went through one of our hospitals for men back from the war, and saw the blind, the armless and legless who would never leave their beds—poor pathetic things, where are they now, who helped to give Roosevelt his place in history! Then she went to lunch, and afterward in her column she blandly confessed that she overate."

Angele was looking at him. "But wait," she said at last, her voice low. "Haven't you told me that some females eat their placenta?"

He swung, to look at her, and stared; then slipped to the floor and kneeling embraced her knees. "I don't know why I didn't see that," he said, mumbling against her. "My God, how did I miss that insight!" He got to his feet, framed her face and kissed her. "Thanks," he said.

She was deeply pleased. She always looked like a happy child when one of her insights evoked a cry from him. "Margaret Sanger?" she said.

"Oh, of course."

She went to her files and returned with photographs of some of Nehru's people dying hideously of famine; a Catholic journal's sneers at Mrs. Sanger; and the magazine *Time's* smear of a book on population control.

Vridar looked at them a few moments and then kicked the two journals across the room. They didn't need any evidence, he said: any person who didn't recognize Margaret Sanger as a human being wasn't himself one. He looked round him. "Have we drunk that whole bottle?" He went staggering off to the basement to find another bottle; and on his return she gave him a card on which she had typed:

> *Time* says, "Of all the universities in Poland, none is held in higher esteem among true scholars than the Catholic University of Lublin."

He read the words, considered them a few moments, and said: "That possibly is the most damning thing yet said about Communism." He set a full bottle on the table. "Let's have a drink."

XV

Angele had told him that the happiest occasions in her life were those when she sat with him to drink and talk. They often drank and talked, now that he was in the depths of the problem of the son's immolation in the father—of the problem of the orphan—"Of such as I," he would say, "—emotionally immature; a child now in middle age; a lost lonely sad feminine-identified father-hating bald-headed arthritic creature full of childness!" Sometimes, on awaking, they would lie in bed and pass their friends in review, trying to find an adult among them.

There was Gary Colwell, a large handsome man who stood an inch above six feet, without shoes. He was nationally known in his field. Vridar liked him for his wit, his whimsy, his searching mind, his compassionate heart. Whenever he and Angele saw Gary they found him always jovial, smiling, wide awake, curious, though not curious about what was buried in Gary. He would tell stories with a sexual core, such as that of the country boy in Tennessee who was late for school one morning: when he clomped into the one-room schoolhouse the teacher, annoyed, demanded to know why he was late. The boy picked at his nose and looked round at his classmates. "Wall, yuh see," he said at last, and paused to look at the finger he had used in his nose. "Wall, I tell yuh. I tuk our cow over to be serviced." All the farm boys and girls in the room twittered. Red with embarrassment, the teacher looked sternly at the lad and said, "Couldn't your father have done it?" The boy looked thoughtful and picked again at his nose. He said he reckoned as how his father could have done it all right, but he wasn't pedigreed.

It was an old story but Gary told it superbly, and then was helpless with twitters and shrieks, all the while going through his act of trying to subdue and restrain his mirth. As a matter of fact, it was Gary's appearance, more than his stories, that convulsed Vridar: one day Vridar said to him, when they were all drinking, "You never can tell the reason for the look on a man's face: the poor devil may be sitting on a bunch of hemorrhoids." Gary let off a twitter and a snort; then seemed to be trying out his vocal apparatus, experimentally, for larger sound effects; and, finding these adequate, threw out his arms, as his distorted face turned a deeper red, and exploded with an assortment of shrill whinnies and neighings, nasal snufflings and snortings, his stricken eyes looking bathed and strangled, yet dancing merrily in their humorous lights. Now and then Gary was such a spectacle of joy restrained and shriekings confined that Vridar would have to fall to the floor and roll and bellow. When half-drunk, Gary as likely as not would begin to talk, as though dictating to a secretary: "Next to that there is nothing we wouldn't do for you. We observe that your forwarding address is Terre Haute. We will reorder immediately and let you know. There has been an increased demand but on the other hand there is a poor turnover. Word has come in recently. There is seldom more to the report than can be easily underestimated but all things being equal we'll keep you in mind. Je vis en espoir. Sheep, livestock, automobiles, and allow nothing to interfere, for the birthrate must keep climbing or there'll be a diminished demand for foreign aid. Please read the fine print. And even that we will not do unless absolutely necessary, though there are our competitors. Exempla sunt odiosa: this is a long-established policy. We shall hold until notified and are having illustrations made. Please notify your postmaster of change of address and don't forget your blood bank and your contribution to the National Quota of Pocket Vetoes. . . ."

Gary could spontaneously generate nonsense for hours on end. When he thought he had hit on something particularly funny, he would break off and twitter and choke, his dancing eyes wet with tears. If Vridar responded with a roar, Gary would then snort and shriek, his eyes looking strangled and horrified. He wrote excellent limericks and planned, he said, to write a book on the limerick as a philosophy of life. . . .

There were a lot of Garys teaching on American campuses. Timid, fearful, restless, uprooted, these orphans moved from one fad to another, one of their most recent having been what they called laws. Some of them, like Carl Noyce, sent to Vridar laws which he picked up on one campus or another; and after a while Vridar began to mumble nonsensical verse when he was outside, working, or when past

892

midnight unable to sleep he lay awake. Angele, hearing him, would ask, "What are you muttering now?"

"Carl Noyce, a professor not yet emeritus, who long ago played with taws now plays with laws; and like a muchly sated Addison sends posthaste from Madison not only those which he has evolved from travel and travail but those with which his friends make efforts, sometimes witty and sometimes Walter Mitty, to unravel the circumstance that they live gallantly but without much chance. Your first law, Angele says, what is your first? and I opine that it is (in its gruesome finalities) the worst: post obitum no more coitum; and like unto it is, in medias res most of us are glad to settle for second place. A professor says music critics are necessary because music is always better or worse than it sounds, which from de profundis profounds. Other things being equal we are all sucking at the same udder, eyether fawder or mudder. The best way—"

"Come, come!" she cried, poking him.

"The best way to grow old, says Gary Colwell, is to stay weak enough so you will never be able to do anything that takes too much puff. Still, our modus operandi comes in pretty handy. Trust, Angele gives as her first law, but take care whom, and never the groom. A man's magnum opus, says she, may delight his mother, confuse his wife, and enrage his father, yet in the final sum of things be no Canopus. Your third law? asks Angele, and I leap to the task: de profundis emeritus to the last eternal and tiresome veritas. And a furor loquendi sums up our endi. Other times, other mommies; and of sons a weird assortment of commies. Each of us has a law that we are a genius loci but for our self-loving we are hopelessly out of foci. Maximus in minimis is a law only in coitus; on the lesser planes of pleasure and striving our erections defeat us. My fourth law is that if he gives twice who gives quickly, he thinks longest who thinks thickly."

"O great Scott! Now go to sleep."

It was the postwar letdown and the disintegration of morals: Vridar undertook in his spare time to make a study of the deepening cynicism. He thought that any rational person must be staggered, even appalled, when he contemplated the outlandish farce of the Christian world: again and again it had engaged in monstrous and unspeakably brutal slaughter, with no more excuse than a headful of childish illusions, and fear. When the illusions exploded in its face it took to the bottle, or to evangelism, or to a cynical whoring of its innate decency for dollars, or to gangsterism. Incurable insanities, a steep increase in major crimes, alcoholism, juvenile delinquency, corruption of the public school system, the elevation of gangsters to the plane of public idols—it was all there in overwhelming measure; and various professors, and others, in whom honor was not yet dead, were in a way trying to hide from it, or mitigate its horrors, with one nonsense after another.

He told Angele there was some deep dark reason why, after so many civilizations and so many centuries of consciousness, mankind behaved, not like an adult humanity, but like a people who emotionally had never developed beyond the age of eight or ten. A Russian tyrant shouted across the distance, "We will bury you!" and the American president retorted, "Oh yeah?" to the applause of the nation. It was so childish that it was simply incredible. That only a small minority of the world's people ever developed, emotionally, beyond early childhood, was, Vridar thought, one of the most obvious facts of life. *But why?* He also thought it obvious that the emotional level was most retarded in Christians and observing Jews. Was it—was it because of the emotional sicknesses inherent in a too-close family relationship? "God in heaven!" he cried and came up out of his chair. Had he at last found what he sought?—the key to the riddle! Had all this developed because of a patriarchy so rigid and tyrannical that the female—well, it had come out, for those with the gumption to see it, in a book called *The Second Sex*—a book so penetrating that it brought from Margaret Mead, an anthropologist, a statement that exactly summed up one of Vridar's beliefs—that the virtues found in greater strength in women than in men had not been employed in the development of the Western world's institutions and values. How could they have been—for the Christians had taken over the holy books of a people who did not even have a Mother! Vridar walked around chuckling with sardonic wicked laughter when he saw with what disgusting obeisance various men capitulated to Simone de Beauvoir's thesis—men who had published books in abuse of the human female!

One night in a dream there came back to him the first law of Gary Colwell's wife —Go no straighter than the road is straight. How well that summed up the Christian peoples for whom rationalizing the facts and truths away had become the first law of living. Thinking of all the persons he had known or read about, he wondered who stood most completely as a symbol of all these things in a deteriorating Western world. Not the industrial brigand or the corrupt leader of organized labor; not the popular idols who appealed to a repressed frustrated sadistic people with their infantile interests in war, killing, bull-fighting, and copulation; not a thick president who had called a notorious gangster an honorable man and said he was glad to call him friend; not the spy and traitor eager to betray his country to one of the worst tyrannies the earth had ever known; not the callow evangelist journeying over the world to preach ancient superstitions. . . . Was it Evan Vaughn? He was not big enough. Was it—yes, possibly it was Ezra Pound.

XVI

For many years Vridar had received letters from other Vridars, some of them so long that they were actually short autobiographies. They had come from many states of the Union and a few foreign countries—these confessions and supplications from the sad lonely lost orphans, seeking a father-image. For many years he had known what they were seeking, for he had found the loss and the seeking in himself. The orphans, the unloved *as small children,* the wretched self-pitying emotionally arrested anxiety neurotics, striving for a place in the sun: the poor sad fatherless sons, kneeling to the immolation in the Christian and Judaic gethsemanes! More than two score of these men had come to see him, and a few, like Evan Vaughn, came again and again: from Seattle, Taos, Carmel, and other points east and west. Evan was about six feet tall, broad, rugged, and handsome but for the scared look in his eyes, the orphan-look; he had dark wavy hair as fine as silk, a good strong nose, mouth, chin. He came to the door one day, snuffling and clucking, and when

Vridar first saw him he thought the man was talking to himself. In fact, he was: he was trying to talk the pain out of an old wrong, or if not a wrong, an imagined injury to his pride and manhood. He said he had read some of Vridar's books: mightn't he stay a little while? Down in the car he had a bottle: should he bring it up?

"If you'd like to," Vridar said.

Evan returned with the bottle. He didn't walk well. He shuffled along like a man who had sat all his life in a chair. When he came with the bottle, he was again muttering to himself and hugging the bottle against him with both arms, as a man might who many times when drunk had dropped bottles. Vridar took him into the house. Evan sank heavily to a chair.

He came at once to the point, or to one of the points anyway. His wife had left him. The God damn bitch had run off with another poet. Had Vridar heard of Jon McVane? He was the villain, Evan said, brooding deep, for his pride had been outraged, his world overturned. "He's not as good a poet as I am," Evan said, "but he must be a better man in some ways." Then, as though completely oblivious of Vridar, he was again muttering, again reliving old scenes. Vridar fetched glasses from the kitchen, and became aware after a while that Evan was not conscious of the glass at his side. Vridar thought, It has gone pretty deep in that poor orphan.

Talking to himself or to the world or to nobody at all, Evan managed in his incoherent muttering distraught fashion to get a part of the confession out of him. Vridar perceived that in his strange mad way the man seemed to be laughing: now and then he made gurgling noises in his throat that sounded mirthful; or his face lit up suddenly, as if a light had been turned on behind it. Then for a few moments Evan would seem to be looking for someone, or to be listening for footsteps.

Vridar thought, This bastard is as crazy as a coot.

He learned that Evan when wooing the girl who became his wife had been such a romantic goof, such a damned stupid poop-ass, as Evan put it, that if, while strolling with her in moonlight, he tripped over a stick, he then wanted to take it along as a memento. Everything that had touched their relationship had been precious to him. Grimly amused, Vridar looked back to his golden idyl with Neloa. If the girl passed under a branch and a leaf touched her, Evan had to kiss the leaf and take it along. Sometimes, he said, he had a whole pocketful of leaves.

Vridar was thinking, This orphan as a child had no love!

There was no coherence in the way Evan talked: within the horrors where he now lived and remembered he seemed to be directed only by free associations. After telling of kissing the leaf he asked, "Why are women's thighs so short?" After telling of studying the lights in her eyes he said, "Why do some women have so much hair?" The only reason, Evan said, that Hollywood's darlings didn't show their unmentionables was that they were too utterly *animal* for any man ever to look at twice, except obstetricians. The next moment he was back to short thighs. He said he knew how short they were for he had measured them by his forearm. "And see how short it is," he said, holding his arm up.

Did Vridar know what kind of man Jon McVane was? The kind who did it to every woman he met, if he could, preferring above all others the wives of his friends. He had been known to embrace as many as five women in one night.

"Sounds like my brother. Sure his name is McVane?"

"Huh?" said Evan, listening only to his own voice. He said he was no such man as Jon. Jon could take a woman five or six times in one night—

"Stop believing his lies." When Evan went on talking, Vridar shouted at him, "Don't let the liars fool you!"

"Huh?"

"Listen. Sometimes such men withdraw without an orgasm and the women never know it. Sometimes they have only partial orgasms. I've a friend whose eyes stick out past the end of his nose when he talks enviously of these super-studs. I've tricked them into the truth."

"How?"

"This way. The ejaculation, you know, is by spurts. Ask these studs how many they have. Oh, they always know—they copulate chiefly for the pleasure of observing themselves. They've confessed to two, three, never more than four. How many a man has depends on how much he has to spend and how much his passion compels him to give. Some men have as many as seven, eight, or nine. So don't take these Casanovas so seriously: most of them are male whores, and as cold as Stalin's conscience."

"I didn't know that," Evan said, but his tone said that he didn't care much about it either. "You know what my wife is like? Uggh!" he said, and Vridar thought he was going to spit. She was the kind, he said, who delighted in kissing the genitals of baby boys. She was the kind who had curiously examined her own son, and then had demanded to examine the father. The man she ran off with was the kind who held a mirror under his rump and looked in the mirror. He was the kind who said at a party, "You put your thing in the sheath and wonder what all the dewlaps are for." She was the kind who knew what the Bible meant by the deep ditch. He was the kind who said, "Imagine squeezing a woman's breast and feeling all the milk canals inside." She was the kind who said, "My husband can't do it except when he calls me obscene names."

Now and then Evan gave off a terrible moan. Vridar supposed that he was fighting a whole pack of devils down deep in him; that he was held back by his Censor from saying all that he wanted to say. Suddenly three words came out, wild and bitter—three words flung from him, three shameful words that told more than he had yet told: "It is true!" He got up snuffling and muttering and clutching the bottle to him and went off to his car.

He came again and again, a gentle man with murder in him, a man feeding on himself. He said his wife was still with McVane. They were in Taos. He wanted to go down and murder them but didn't think he had any murder in him. He hated blood, torture, and the raw ugly pictures of men as raw ugly beasts. He could not listen even to the cries torn from a woman's throat in birth pains, or of a beast or a bird in the clutch of a thing that was going to eat it. Then suddenly out of the blue he said, "You say some men have nine spurts?"

It took Vridar a few moments to grasp what Evan had in mind. Then he chuckled and said, "Or ten or twenty, for all I know. Damn it, the thing to get in your head is that an orgasm like a potato can be very large or very small. And the ego. This my self within my heart is tinier than a rice-corn, or a barley-corn, or a mustard-seed, or a canary-seed, or the pulp of a canary-seed. This my self within my heart is greater than sky, greater than heaven. This my self within my heart, this is Brahma."

Evan stared at him a moment and then growled, "Who cares a tinker's botch about Brahma? Does your wife have catarrh? Mine has. It's in her nose. It's no fun kissing deep in a woman's mouth if you have in your mind a picture of the nose above it. I tell you, Hunter, that trying to make beauty of what nature gave us to work with is hopeless. This country has billion-dollar industries trying to do something about it, but after you peel off all their scents and lotions and mud-baths you have the same old Eve under it and she doesn't smell good. Hunter, did you ever cover what you thought was a lovely thing only to find out she had leucorrhea?"

"You've got it bad," Vridar said.

"I didn't come here to listen to pious inanities. You sound the way you look and you look like one who sampled all the fruits in the Garden and found they were all lemons."

Vridar said genially, "That's about the way I look, all right."

"Were you ever tortured by psychic impotence?"

"You've told me nothing yet that I haven't found in mself—except using obscene words when you embrace your wife. Excuse me a moment." Vridar went down-stairs and returned with a book. "This is what Theodor Reik has to say—it's about men who don't function well sexually in bed with women they idealize. Quote: I understand in my own analysis how deep the roots of this division, between tender-ness and sexuality, reach into the area of childhood- and puberty-impressions. Later on, when I treated neurotic patients, I understood why many men need a kind of degradation in their fantasy or in their action with women they highly appreciate or love. They have to degrade them, in order to bring them down from the elevated level which forbids the intimate physical approach. There. He's now talking about his patients: one was potent with his wife, he says, only if he called her dirty names, used extremely vulgar language before and during sexual intercourse."

Evan said, "I used it only before. She might still be with me if I had used it during." He looked at the cover of the Reik book and said: "Does this colossal mind tell us how we got this way?"

"Such men, Vaughn, are products of the Judean-Christian system: people who accept this system seem to think that copulation is animal, not human, and that they are human. I'll tell you one of my favorite stories. I was in the office of the Idaho governor one day when a delegation of club-women was ushered in—oh, about a dozen of them. All standing close to a big window and facing it, they were talking to the great man when two birds came fluttering through the open window and did what was necessary to get themselves some babies. I expected those women to shriek and then faint, and almost swoon, some of them did, while warm red blood made amazing things of their faces. Reik here tells an Anatole France anecdote, of the Italian girl who prayed to the Virgin, O thou who have conceived

897

without sinning, give me the grace to sin without conceiving. Has it ever occurred to you that these billion-dollar industries you mentioned are only trying to do in their own way what some man like you and me did when he conceived of the virgin birth?"

Evan was staring at Vridar, brooding, and breathing hard.

Hoping to shake the man out of himself, Vridar opened Reik at another page. "Here's an anecdote you may like: having prayed vainly for rain a Sicilian peasant at the end of his wits returned to the chapel with its image of the Madonna and Child and said, I don't speak to you, you son of a bitch, but to your Holy Mother."

"He should have used the word bastard instead," said Evan.

Vridar turned away to hide a grin. Turning back, he read from the book: "It cannot be denied that almost all the greatest men, whose life story we know, never reached psycho-sexual maturity. Get a load of that, Vaughn, and let it sink deep: almost all our greatest men never reached psycho-sexual maturity: is it any wonder we have the kind of world we have? Imagine, if you can, the degree of infantilism in that respect in such as Stalin, Hitler, and even Roosevelt. Well, I read again: Goethe never possessed one of the women he so passionately adored. Beethoven could not sexually approach any of the beautiful aristocratic ladies of Vienna." Vridar laid the book aside. "Reik, of course, doesn't have to get egghead and call it psycho-sexual—it is simple emotional immaturity, just that. Such men are no more mature in other respects: when Einstein opens his trap about anything besides physics, he's so childish that his friends want to hustle him off to bed.

"Evan, I have been thinking of it this way: most of us are orphans—or I should say, perhaps, most of the influential people. Any man who so idealizes women that he can't be intimate with them is not necessarily a man who had incestuous feelings for his mother—the Freudians haven't come out of the dark wood there: he's more likely to be a man who never had a mother's love in those early years when such love is necessary. He's a man who as a child never had love from the other sex, and probably no love at all. He is likely to be a child who feared and hated his father. You and I are two of them, the Judean-Christian world is full of them. Other psychologists go off half-cocked after the homosexual specter. They can't tell me anything about it, not any more: I've gone to the bottom. I hated my father because I was scared to death of him. I hated my mother because she forced me to be her brave manly little man. As a child I really had no father, no mother.

"Where in the Western world is there a more prodigous irony than this, that our artists and writers (and throw in all the book reviewers) have so vast an influence, yet emotionally are only children? As for the so-called liberals, who are now managing this country in so many ways, open and concealed, few of them have minds sufficiently disciplined to develop their potential into character; and so it remains all their lives diffused and often dissipated in hatred and self-pity. Being father-haters, practically all of them, they have to have father-images to hate, and these take the form of the Republican Party, Corporations, Barons of Privilege, Economic Royalists, Fascists—put that in quotes, for they are the real fascists. One of their contemporary gods—that is, an enlarged idealized image of self—has been Roosevelt, who would have pursued any course to win for himself a secure place in history —for he was aware," said Vridar, with a faint smile, "that the Devil had that."

He went below to his den and returned with what he called The Panel of Five Orphans—the faces of Dylan Thomas, Ezra Pound, Robert Graves, W. H. Auden, and T. S. Eliot. He handed the panel to Vaughn and said, "I want you to look at those five faces, close and hard, and try to see what is there to be seen. Study them while I talk: you have there five famous poets in the English-speaking world, about whose faces the most obvious thing is what? Intelligence?—sensitiveness—tenderness—sensibility—sentimentality? Isn't it plain to you that you have there five harassed, conflict-ridden, tortured children? Isn't it plain that they are all emotionally immature? Could you possibly pass them as adults? No more than you could pass you and me. Is it any wonder that of such people, some drink themselves to death, some flee into old moribund churches, some go insane?"

Vaughn looked from the five faces to Vridar and said, "You haven't fled into a Church? Are you an alcoholic?—or are you insane?"

"Quite a lot of both. Now let me finish. Freud said the essence of Christianity is the submission of the son to the father. He was never righter: that's the essence of the New Testament story. Shall we then assume that these child-adults fleeing back to the churches are surrendering their wills to the father?—that they have become so lost and terrified that they can no longer even make a pretense of being adult? What did Edith Sitwell say?—that she doesn't accept the dogmas but is weary and must surrender her will. How many people realized what a ghastly confession that was, what a shattering indictment of the Judean-Christian system, with all-dominant father glorified as Father! I may die drunk or I may die insane but I won't surrender.

"The whole of recorded history," Vridar went on, while Vaughn studied the five faces, "reveals to us the tyranny of fathers over sons, the fear and hatred of sons for fathers. Myth and legend are full of it—the slaughter of the male infants, the flight into Egypt—these are only a copying of myths common to all the Mediterranean peoples. Isn't it time we were growing up? Shouldn't it be a natural process to mature emotionally and accept adult responsibilities? Do you find it pathetic— well, possibly pretty damned funny—that so many of our intellectuals are fleeing back to Pa?—which means that they're again content to be children."

"You think I idealized my mother?"

"How in hell should I know what you did with your mother? Did I? To some extent. She never gave me love and tenderness: in the fearful wild world I occupied as a child, a mother was necessary. My mother had no time for it. She's not that kind of person. Because she was the dominant one in the family, three times as fast as her man and ten times as efficient, it was inevitable (if I was not a stupid child) that I should admire some of her virtues. Abnormally afraid, nightmarish, schizoid, lonely, guilty, half-insane, I set up various ideals. One was the female —oh, I had observed the mothers among beasts. My childhood and youth were madness from the first years to the last; but go read the life of Goethe—it was all madness there, too.

"Mankind's great problem, Vaughn, as I see it, is to preserve the sources of love and compassion, while at the same time allowing children to mature. I don't know how that is to be done."

"Your first wife, was she a mother-substitute?"

"Hell no, my second."

"Did you feel that sexual intercourse degraded your first wife?"

Vridar studied the Vaughn face a long moment and said at last, drily, "With any man but me."

"Did she feel contempt for you?"

"Oh yes, inevitably. Have you read Kinsey? But a part of her loved me. Of course in the sex act she had known only the peasant studs—you know, the ram-bull-rooster type that knows what Nature has in mind for him, and does it. Passion convulses them—doesn't it?—bugs their eyes out, drools from their lips, turns their ears purple. I think I'm a fair lover, but hardly the stud type that mounts with an explosion of flatulence."

"My wife is like that," Evan said. "She's the kind that at a party will kiss men in dark corners, or steal out to a car after I've passed out cold. Don't you think we both need fathers?"

"No, that's what we don't need. You mean what Thomas Wolfe said? Father-seeking runs through his letters. Wait." Vridar hastened downstairs and returned with a book. "This is the way Wolfe puts it: 'The deepest search in life, it seemed to me, the thing that in one way or another was central to all living, was man's search to find a father, not merely the father of his flesh, nor merely the lost father of his youth, but the image of a strength and wisdom external to his need and superior to his hunger, to which the belief and power of his life could be united.' But in that case what do fathers have? Obviously what we have is a world of frightened male children clinging to what they call God."

Evan was digging into a pocket. "You read Kirk?"

"I've studied his face. He's full of what I call childness. He's about to bawl."

"This *Time* review says, 'Can he mean it when he writes that "for the Christian, freedom is submission to the will of God"? Kirk does mean it, and this is no paradox.' "

"Not for a Luce editor probably—"

"He's a conservative, not a liberal."

"They're the same thing—merely the two sides of the same coin, Jackson on one side, Lincoln on the other. Damn it, Vaughn, you should understand at your age that the liberal and conservative—the extremes, for we don't call them that unless they're extreme—are both obsessed with a sense of insecurity. The liberal would make himself secure by changing the social order and, preferably, becoming one of its managers. The conservative, also motivated by fear and a sense of insecurity, doesn't want the order disturbed. I once had a friend who spent two terms in the Idaho legislature. He refused to stand a third time, for, he said to me, he was afraid of a growing lust in him for power over men. What he wanted without knowing it was power over father."

"Then you don't agree with Wolfe and Kirk?"

"Hell, no. They've never been weaned from the family relationship. The image

900

of strength and wisdom can be found in the greatest of our books: would Wolfe have called that father? Would Kirk call it God? I doubt that either would. If Kirk means that freedom is submission to the circumstance of facts and laws—but do you think he does? Wait." Again Vridar hastened downstairs, to return with a handful of papers. "Here's a photograph of Kirk. Look at it hard, if you can. I can't stand much looking at such faces, or at my own: I see in them too much lost-son self-pitying yearning for the monstrous vice called togetherness—the emotional immaturity (none of us even reached adolescence); the lack of an adult viewpoint, wholesome and whole. Look, here's something by Eliot: he says, 'I'm just beginning to grow up, to get maturity. In the last few years, everything I've done up to sixty or so has seemed very childish.' Good Jesus! At the age of seventy he's beginning to grow up!"

Vaughn said, " 'The Waste Land' was childish."

"Of course. Well, so he's had seventy years of chilhood, and you can see the whole picture of it in his face. Look at him again. As for Dylan Thomas, like so many who died young—Poe, Byron, Shelley, Keats, Hart Crane, Scott Fitzgerald— he was even more immature than Eliot. Look at his face. Ezra Pound they locked up. They may have to lock me up. Look at the Auden face—doesn't it touch your paternal heart the way the scared lonely child looks out of that photograph? Or do I see these things because I'm over protective? Still, Angele there sees them just as plain as I do."

Vaughn looked at Angele for a moment. "Then you don't think we need God?"

"All small children need God in the sense that they need a father or mother or both. What do you mean by God? If you mean the Father, the answer is that adults don't need a father. And where is he anyway? Or what is he? And why give him-it the male sex? Continents of talent have gone into the painting of Ma and the Son. Where is the Daughter? Tell me, Vaughn, where *is* the daughter? I'm probably the first person ever to ask the question. In the patriarchal society she simply doesn't exist, except as an inferior order of being. How many millions of hours of talent, how many oceans of sentiment, have been devoted to the idealized son?

"Have you studied the thing in this country called togetherness? The editor of a slick journal aimed at the century of the common man coined the word—togetherness: it means a fearful people huddled together in the sick ingrown emotionally inbred family relationship of the Judean-Christian systems. When I taught in Manhattan I must have had in three years six or seven Jewish girls who confessed to me that they hadn't been able to break away from their fathers. Some of them, then in college, were still sleeping with their fathers. Every Manhattan psychiatrist knows the situation. My brother had a score of instances. The same sort of thing, Pa or Ma, is found in most Christian homes."

"You think it's peculiar to our country?"

"Our time. Of course incest with Christians was an accepted thing in the Middle Ages. I think that Europeans in these matters are much like us. I like to go over now and then to study the people in cheap hotels, cafes, bistros, bodegas, coffee shops; in parks, trams, railway stations, at the zoos—have you ever watched their

901

faces when they look at the flaming red hindend of certain apes? The Italians and Spanish have more of what I call childness. I doubt there's an adult in either country."

"Unbuttoned. Kirk calls it unbuttoned."

"I know, *Time's* book editor seems to think the word original with Kirk. It was a Brownell mot in Manhattan—not emancipated but merely unbuttoned—when I taught there in 1930. The Russian intellectuals are only unbuttoned, Kirk says. Well, though I abhor any one-party system, I imagine that the Russian intellectuals are a hell of a lot more unbuttoned than Kirk or you or I. No, Vaughn, I won't accept El Pope, either in Rome or Moscow, nor in the White House; nor the Pa-image that ancient fear put in the sky. Adults don't need it. I'm not adult, and so I simply refuse to have it. I'll go on as an orphan. What the world needs is to grow up but that is going to take a lot of doing. I don't think it can possibly be done until the Jewish and Christian mythologies are kicked—Frazer would say shot or blown—into the limbo, where the Greek and the Roman and nearly all the others lie in their ruins. If I can bring up any guns against these outworn terror-systems born of fear I'll do it.

"Well, I see it's three o'clock and long past our bedtime. We've talked my poor wife to sleep."

XVII

Astonished time and again by his enthusiasm for the intellectual quest, Angele told Vridar that surely he had one of the most probing and one of the toughest minds in the world, but with it, the soul of a child. He had known that. "Orphans," he said. Yes, she said; but how amazingly the two were mixed. "But not integrated. What you mean, most likely, is the strange lights the soul casts on the mental processes—and the weird twisted distortions, like the thousand-year-old olive trees we saw in Majorca, that the mind casts on the soul."

Together they searched the faces in journals and newspapers, looking for an adult. Of American presidents in the 20th century they decided that the two most adult were possibly Taft and Hoover, and for that reason the least loved. In regard to artists in all fields, they gave up: there simply was none. Again and again they studied the faces in the back of the Williams' *Treasury of Modern Poetry*: most of the faces were not only of children but of small children, such as Emily Dickinson's frail petal-like innocence, the small-child pride and impertinence of Elinor Wylie, the tantrum-misery in Hart Crane. Across the top of two pages were Frost—Jeffers—Thomas—Auden: thrusting a finger at them Angele said, "There are four orphans whose mama never loved them. Look at those faces!" She turned a few pages and said, "O Lord!" She was looking at Edwin Muir, Dunstan Thompson, Delmore Schwartz, C. Day Lewis, Kenneth Fearing, Stephen Spender, and Ezra Pound. She almost shrieked with amazement when, on coming to the last page, she saw the face of Oscar Williams. "My God," she said, "he looks like a woman!"

"He's at least half-woman," Vridar said. "They all are, including the women."

Orphans! There came to their door one day, his hand thrust out, his forty-years-old childface smiling, a man who said his name was Ollie Winkle. His huge skull was completely bald but for a fringe at ear height; his big face was as round as a full moon. He had a long ski-nose, a wide mooselike upper lip; and blue eyes without guile. His shoulders were large and rounded, and his gait was shuffling, so that he resembled a bear when he walked.

Ollie was, as Angele and Vridar were to discover, an extraordinary person. He had barely completed the third grade—he could not spell even the simplest words, such as awful and steak, but somehow, somewhere he had studied photography and now journeyed over the nation with a Speed Graphic, an f: 2.8 Rolleiflex, a Leica M3, as well as several hundred pounds of other equipment which Vridar was never to see, but in which, he learned, was a record-player and a pile of classical records. Ollie had a car in which he could make a bed; he loved to go far out in the desert, with the coyotes and the stars, roll into his bed, and go to sleep while listening to Bach or Mozart.

He never talked about his people, or said much about his past. He had so little knowledge of Vridar's world that Vridar despaired of ever seeing Ollie's world as Ollie saw it. So far as Vridar could tell, Ollie saw the world as color and form, or as political scoundrels and graft. His notions of politics, of industry and of many other things were the delightfully false and irrational notions of a small child. The people Ollie had grown up among had thought him queer and had snickered at him behind his back; and the hurt had gone so deep in the man that he would never get it out. What bitter lonely years he had lived! He had hidden his pain and fright, he had persevered; and though for a long time he had starved and despaired and wept he was now a photographer of note, with childlike dreams of vengeance.

They were childlike—or at least they were not adult—for the reason that there was no meanness, no guilt, in this man. He wanted to buy the biggest car money could buy and drive among those who had sneered, or buy ice cream sodas for them all and tip ten dollars. Such were the limits of vengeance, with such eyes as Ollie had.

Having concluded that there was magic in learning, and that people in general thought of him as a droll illiterate, Ollie took to the dictionary like a duck to water. He used big words without any self-consciousness at all. He would be talking, his whole posture intent and earnest—for when he talked he talked with all his soul—when suddenly, without warning, he would astound his listeners with some huge word, which as likely as not they had never heard of; as when he said of the Negro problem, "It's not no easy thing to solve, this miscegenation, and the American people will know it some day"; as when he said of birth control, "Having lots of children causes labefaction of the spine, and I think women should be told that"; as when, talking about the growing rate of traffic accidents, he said, "The trouble with lots of car drivers is they are nomothetical, they just figger the laws is all inside themselves." One day in the desert Vridar lost for a few moments his power of speech when Ollie began to talk about saxifragaceous plants and correctly pronounced the word. When talking in a group, he used one of his big words, and heard gasps of surprise, or saw astonishment in faces, Ollie's grave mien would vanish, and with his blue eyes dancing he would look round him, his smile as innocent as the face of a baby lamb.

He said to Vridar one day, "You use words I don't have no exact hold on." Ollie's misuse of words Vridar called winkles. He was with the man one day at a hospital when the dead and wounded from two colliding automobiles were brought in. Ollie looked the scene over in his grave way, his eyes expressing gentle concern, and said, "You figger it was a head-on collusion?" He grew red and angry when he talked about the foul pollution of mountain streams, for he loved nature, this man, as he loved nothing else—a clean beautiful river, a mountain range, a vast expanse of scented desert were for him in the same category of values as Mozart or Rubens (as an expert photographer he found much in the painters to delight his innocent but strangely sophisticated soul).

His elemental childlike quality reminded Vridar of David Hawke, and of the tall emaciated filthy man in Chicago's Washington Park who founded a Church of his own.

Ollie had a simply unappeasable passion for candy and ice cream: having been denied these things as a child, he now could not get enough of them. Vridar and Angele saw him eat a pound of hard candy in half an hour, or three or four milk shakes, or several heapings of ice cream with marshmallow or chocolate. Vridar told him one day that he would ruin his stomach and his health. Ollie then turned to him, and as he munched the mouthful of hard candy, his face turned very grave, for he was getting ready to say something that for him had solemn meaning. He said, " 'Cause I never had none when I was little all these-here things is a roborant for me." Vridar was staggered, for he had never seen or heard of the roborant and had no idea what it meant. Having explained why he made a glutton of himself with sweets, Ollie filled his mouth and went on eating. Turning at last to Vridar, his whole face aglow with the innocence of his smile, his gentle blue eyes fairly dancing with anticipation, Ollie said, "Let's all drive out this evening." He meant to the desert or the mountains. He shared Vridar's and Angele's love of high elk country, high clean skylines, white soft deep snowstorms, blizzards full of wild winds. . . .

Yes, Ollie as an orphan could stand as the archetype of the whole clan. Orphans, too, were Vridar's own sons. Scott had gone through War II and like so many other young men had come home a wild one: he had been one of those sitting, drunk, in Pearl Harbor that Sunday when the Japanese struck. Scott laughed in a kind of weeping wild-goose honking way when he told his tales. How did he lose half his front teeth? It was this way. He was a petty officer and had given an order to a huge Norwegian, sitting on deck. "That hombre," said Scott, dashing tears from his eyes and strangling on his mirth, "that son of a bitch he looks up at me and he says, You speakun to me? I says to him, Look round you, bud, who else would I be talkun to? I says to him, You get up offen that big Scandinavian butt and do what I tell you, for I'm your superior officer, see? Well, that mountainman, he gets up offen his hindend all right, but real slow; he just come up little by little like his bones hurt, and all the time his red eyes fixed on me. He come up and straightened, and holy God all-Moses, that was the last I knew until half past four the next day.

904

He knocked me clear into the ocean, and the only part of me he left on the deck was six teeth. . . ."

That must have been a giant, Vridar was thinking; Scott stood six feet one and weighed two hundred and ten pounds. One of his comrades in the service had told Vridar that when Scott got drunk in a tavern, he would seize the first man in sight and pin him against the wall, with the man's feet off the floor. It took a lot of man to do that. Scott loved to tell about the whorehouses in Hawaii and other places. The privates, he said, were all mad enough to kill, because officers had special privileges in womaning. Their whores were kept clean. Officers didn't have to rush through in three minutes flat; they didn't have to stand in line and be plumb ready the moment they entered the door, and exactly three minutes later be out of the way for the guy behind them. When he told these tales, Scott was such a tortured strangled man, somewhere between tears and uncontrolled laughter, that Vridar and Angele choked just to hear him.

One day he came in with an ex-paratrooper pal, a giant even bigger than he, and tougher. The pal's name was Jack. Jack said Scott was no good, that by God he had better straighten up and be a man or he would knock all the shit out of him. Jack said he himself had been an orphan, he hadn't had it good either; and unlike Scott he had never had a chance to go to college, he had been too busy scratching and digging for something to eat. Now that he was out of the Service he was going to make something of himself, and Scott was, too, or he would knock the living hell out of him. Did Vridar know that Scott not only had deserted his wife and children but never even sent them a Christmas card, much less a buck? Did he know that when Scott wrote his father for money he didn't intend to buy furniture with it, or pay the doctor bill, as he had said he would: no, he blew the whole two or three hundred bucks in a tavern in one night. No, Vridar had not known that: he looked at Scott's foolish red face, and then at Jack's. He looked from one to the other thinking of what a nation had done to them: it had spent years and thousands of dollars training them to kill, and then had turned them back to civilian life, expecting them to be gentlemen. Before this night was over Jack got so wrought up because of Scott's sneering responses that with the flat of his hand he struck him such a terrific blow on his cheek that blood spattered the wall. He then bolted into the night, crying out that he would never see him again.

Larry, the oldest son, was a different breed of man. He stood over six feet, too, and was broad and deep, but he was self-indulgent and fat. Scott would put a half-pint of whisky to his mouth and drain it in four or five gulps. Larry drank only a little. Scott was a chain-smoker. Larry puffed at cigars. For all his anxieties and ulcers, Larry most of the time was a jolly even-tempered man whose handsome blue eyes seldom revealed anger, and never hate or malice. His two passions were gambling and fishing. But like Scott he was an orphan—lonely, bedeviled, and lost: they had not had the sheltering love in early childhood that every child needed; emotionally they had never matured.

Vridar's son Paul, by Athene, put him a little in awe. Paul had grown up with a professor-mother in a houseful of very old people (Athene's destitute relatives)

905

who had died around him, one by one. Paul's little-old-man letters delighted Vridar, but pained him. Typical of them was one Paul wrote at the age of thirteen:

> Dear dad,
>
> The school semester is almost over and summer vacation will soon be here. My mother and I are both fine, and I hope that things are going as well with you and Angele.
>
> I would first like to thank you, a little tardily, for the book on duck hunting which you sent me. I enjoyed the pictures of ducks, and also the stories and advice in the book. It will come in handy whenever I decide to take up the sport.
>
> If you are wondering about my activities, I can assure you that my time is well filled up. I have had no trouble in keeping up my grades, but the subjects are becoming more difficult and require more study.
>
> This winter I went out for wrestling, rather than basketball, because it required less time. I am now planning to try baseball, and, if unsuccessful, will probably take a crack at track.
>
> Oh yes, I have also entered the State algebra contest and won the preliminary round. I will go to the finals a little later this month.
>
> I will try to write again as soon as I have something interesting to tell. Give Angele my love.
>
> Love,
Paul

He won the finals that year and every year. On completing high school, he asked for fellowships in a number of the top colleges and was accepted by all of them. The school he chose had twelve hundred applicants, of whom three hundred were accepted. In his freshman year Paul was first, and he was first in the three years that followed. The child's extraordinary success in school troubled Vridar; but Angele said, "You needn't worry about him. He may be a quiz-kid but under that solemn manner is a wonderful sense of humor." Angele was so proud of him that Vridar would twit her about it; and she would say sharply, "If those on the covers of magazines had a son like that, he'd be world-famous. You won't even tell your own family about him."

From Larry and Scott the mother was taken; from Paul the father. There were millions like them. But the most tragic orphans, as Vridar had observed them, were many of those whose physical parents remained with them. Typical of them were Ronald and Lucy Teague. They had two intelligent attractive children who were worth the devotion of parents who knew how to be parents. Ron and Lucy, yapping and bickering from the time they got up till they again fell exhausted into bed, had made their children unhappy and neurotic, and their own ulcers incurable. It was all so plain: Lucy and Ron didn't want to be parents, for the reason that they were not adults. Their own parents they detested, both of them, yet if they found themselves removed from them by a hundred miles they couldn't stand the separation either!

The fact of the orphan, so clear to him at last, and so shocking in its implications, he found supported everywhere. There was Al Kaplan, a Chicago Jew, who bought parts of Broadway shows: he said he had buried all his relatives in a fine cemetery, and then had got himself a burial plot and gone out and pissed on it, because he had known that some son of a bitch would and he had wanted to be the first one. Vridar stood with Al one night at the entrance to the St. Regis in New York, in zero weather, when women in evening gowns were trying desperately to summon cabs. Al had pushed to the front and had taken the cabs one by one for the members of his own party, palming large bills to the doorman and turning each time to Vridar with a dry wink. As he helped Angele and Vridar into a cab, he whispered in Vridar's ear, "You know what I want more than anything else in the world? Forty chocolate sodas."

In the cab Vridar told Angele what Al had said. "Remember the answer the Jews gave us in Tel Aviv when we asked them what they missed most in the eastern half of Jerusalem? The wailing wall."

There was Jim Schwartz, Al's multimillionaire friend, who had passed the half-century mark unwedded, and was grimly certain that neither wife nor children were for him. He became one of Vridar's close friends and an object for endless study. The man's loneliness was the plainest thing about him. He was the father, the care-taker, the patriarch of the whole Schwartz clan, and the most pathetic child in the whole lot of them.

Encouraged by his mistress, Jim built a sumptuous home at his hunting and fishing lodge: the rugs in it were especially made, in designs to match the fantas-tically expensive wallpaper and drapes. A fortune was spent on furnishings, includ-ing tons of antiques. When Vridar asked how much one of the rugs cost, Jim said, "You know what J. P. Morgan said when they asked him about his yacht: if you have to ask what it cost, you can't afford it." For years, Jim said, he had lived in a shack, while all his relatives lived in mansions which he had bought for them (his sister had three)—though the house Jim called a shack had ten rooms and would have been thought a mansion by most people. Jim liked old clothes, dogs, guns, the simple ways of life. Knowing that he was worth millions, some people tried to prey on him: it was then that a wicked light would come to the man's eyes, but it would fade and go out, and then there was only the small-boy hurt. Hopelessly entangled in family, some of whom, it seemed plain to Vridar, were waiting for him to die, Jim had refused to marry or to have children of his own. Like so many father-images, he had as many children as his patience could endure.

At dinner one evening he brought out a bottle of domestic champagne, and on opening it found it dead. His niece, a skinny neurotic young woman who had fled her husband, spoke up to say that he ought to serve only imported champagne, and the very best. Jim rolled his full expressive eyes from guest to guest and said at last, "My sister serves this kind, only first she washes the labels off." His lady, sitting on Vridar's left murmured, "What an unkind thing to say!"

Jim looked over at Vridar. "Ever hear of the Jew who tried to change his name to Cabot? Boston, the home of the bean and the cod, where the Lowells speak only to Cabots, and the Cabots speak Yiddish, by God."

The mistress, whose name was Rose, was embarrassed by such sallies. She and

Angele became friends, but Vridar called her the Duchess, an allusion to the Duchess of Windsor, whom he abhorred. He liked Rose, though her social airs wearied him: her English was bad, her manners were not always gracious, but she was determined to play the fasionable lady in the home of a man who didn't give a damn about fasionable ladies. When she first came with Jim to call on Vridar and Angele, it was so plain that she thought their little cottage pathetic, and them naive and unknowledgeable, that Vridar said, after she had gone, "Does she have any social credentials besides those from Toots Shor's?" Angele looked at him several moments before she spoke. Then with some emotion she said, "I endured torments as a mistress—*your* mistress—from malicious bitches who missed no chance to burn me to the ground. I resolved then that no mistress would ever suffer that way in my home; I'll ask anyone to leave who tries to make her suffer. She had two strikes on her when she came to our home, and no matter what she thinks of me I'm going to be nice to her."

Hastening over to his wife, Vridar framed her face and kissed her. "Wonderful!" he cried, and kissed her again. On returning to his seat he said, "Just the same, I hardly know what to make of a woman who looks me straight in the eye and says Have you ever been to New York?"

Rose was forever getting under Vridar's sensitive hide. The night he and Angele were with Al at the St. Regis, Rose was a member of the party. In her Duchess of Windsor way she had looked at Angele and asked if she was having fun in New York. Angele said she was. Only that afternoon, she said, she and Vridar had gone through the Fulton fish market, eating oysters and shrimps at stand-up counters. With a lift of her penciled brows, dyed an outlandish purple (Rose would have shaved her head and painted it yellow, if this had been the fashion), Rose had said, "Oh, you mean the aquarium." Angele said, "No, I mean we went through the Fulton market eating oysters and shrimps." After that, Rose looked at Angele from time to time, her upper eyelids, painted purple, drooping, her mind wondering about her friend. But Vridar felt deep compassion for her when Al put her on the spot, as when he said one day, "What in hell are you getting out of this? Ask him for diamonds. He'll bounce you one of these days and there you'll be." Then into Rose's eyes would come the scared look of a woman forty years old, who had to face the fact that she wasn't a wife, but only a mistress, who could be kicked out at any moment.

Yes, Jim Schwartz was an orphan, and a perfect instance of the crass American illusion that money could buy happiness. He spent more on a month's vacation than Vridar and Angele spent for all things in three years, and then said, like a man about to gag, "It wasn't worth a dime." If a hotel gave him trouble because he was a Jew, he would say to Vridar, "I should have bought the damned thing and thrown him out." Love was the thing Jim hungered for, yet was afraid to look for, because he never could tell whether it was love, or a cynical wish to get a hand on his purse. Vridar took pains to give Jim more than he was given—more in understanding, and more in material things, such as books and evergreens. Like Vridar, Jim had "sons" everywhere, this man to whom orphans were drawn; and like Vridar he detested the sight of them, while feeling compelled to offer them his purse and his heart.

The lost children, wailing in their gethsemanes! There was Dennis McNamara, a novelist, who had a way of looking at people sidewise, like a mischievous child who had hidden a firecracker under their heels. Dennis fancied himself as a wit. Vridar and Angele spent an evening with him at the home of his publisher. Dennis's wife started the evening off by confessing—boasting, really—that with a clenched fist she had struck a blond woman a haymaker blow on her chin, knocking her silly. Dennis glanced round him in his sly boyish impish way and admitted that the woman had been wooing him and that he had liked it. It then developed from the talk that Dennis thought of himself as a man whom women (or most women anyway) found more than a little irresistible—though he was a flabby man who slouched, or moved by fits and starts, as though his major impulses came from things trying to push up from his subconscious mind.

Like nearly all the writers Vridar had known, or was to know, Dennis was an exhibitionistic showoff of a child, who took the stage and kept it. His attitude made it plain that he intended to keep it, for now and then he turned on Vridar a curious momentarily questioning stare, as though wondering when this competitor would thrust in. That any author anywhere would not compete for the attention and applause of the audience would have been unthinkable to this Irish child. So for a long evening Dennis held the floor, with his publisher and the publisher's wife beaming on him. "Abie's Irish pose!" Vridar thought, watching Dennis. Dennis would string out three, four, sometimes five or six adjectives, and ride a thought to the ground. When convinced that he had said something witty, he would smile all over his big Irish face, and glance swiftly from person to person to see if his quip was appreciated; and if it seemed not to be, his smile would vanish instantly, revealing that Dennis himself had not known whether it was good or bad, but decided such matters by the gloom or light in other faces. He made huge sweeping gestures up over his brows, across his big mop of uncombed hair, and toward the fireplace and the ceiling and the universe. His eyebrows would shoot up with startling suddenness, in the way of Chris Teaker's. Now and then with a slyness that was not at all offensive, being so childlike, almost wistful, he would name an author and ask Vridar what he thought of him; but he never waited for a reply, for what Dennis was interested in was what Dennis thought of the author. He did not like Thomas Wolfe's stuff. He did not like William Faulkner's stuff—it was too indirect, oblique, devious, gyred, whorled and involuted, Dennis said, making prodigious gestures at destiny, while looking from face to face to see if anyone present liked Faulkner. Vridar, watching him, studying him, was thinking, You sly childlike Irish bastard, you simply don't like any authors but Dennis McNamara! After Dennis and his wife had returned with Vridar and Angele to Manhattan, they sought out a late tavern for a drink, but Dennis took tomato juice, confessing in Vridar's ear that his ulcers were killing him. Then, like a man who had confessed to having only one testicle, he made up for his lack by saying that his earnings were twenty-five thousand a year and had to be, because he spent that much. Dennis for an hour shuttled between boasts and confessions in such a childlike way—between things

909

that sustained his sensitive insecure ego and things that bore it down—that Vridar wanted to put an arm round him, as he always wanted to with this kind of Marion-type orphan, and say, To hell with it, it doesn't matter. . . .

There was his old friend Carl Noyce, who came with his wife now and then for a visit. Vridar knew little about Carl's early life, but somewhere had got the notion that Carl's father had been a wenching Mormon polygamist, who had been such a brute with Carl's mother that she had died young. That Carl hated the memory of his father, and was an orphan, actually and spiritually, was as plain to Vridar as the silly patch of mustache on the man's upper lip. "Vulva-mouth Noyce," Dwight Hand had called him, adding, "If he'd only let some hair grow along his lower lip!" Because of his own loneliness and the painful erosion of his self-esteem, Carl had for a while taken a desperate clutch on the bottle, and had begun to tell lewd stories, this man who in Vridar's early years with him had eschewed anything that spoke to the knowledgeable of sexual frustration. He would slop up Angele's house (though the soul of fastidiousness in his own), spilling coffee on tables and knocking glasses over (though in his own house he would howl the roof off if a glass was broken). Like a stuck phonograph needle he would shout or mutter some obscene word over and over, while staggering around, drunk, or sitting slumped and staring out from under lowered lids, or from one black eye while the other was tightly closed. Now and then, affecting superhuman rage, he would tell in a voice that shook utensils in kitchen cupboards, stories about professors—about Algernon Aloysius Overbent, chairman of the department of psychology in a large university—a nervous brisk little man who became furious at almost anyone who called him by his first full name; and who, when playing poker with Carl and his wife, would suddenly erupt in outpourings of venom and malice and smiting the table, and rising to his full five feet and four inches (in shoes) would shout, "I'm pissed off you, Noyce! I'm simply pissed off you and I intend never to see you again!" Seizing his hat he would stride to the door; pause there, glaring; return and clutch his wife and hustle her along with him; and the next morning call the Noyces to ask them to breakfast.

When, one time, Vridar spoke bitterly of the immense and senseless slaughter of War II, Carl had shocked and amazed him by crying, "We'll trample over millions of young men to build a better world!" To Angele Vridar said later, "There you have the father-hating orphan-liberal stripped right down to the outrage in his quivering testicles. Does he have any grasp at all of what Norman Cousins wrote?" Cousins had written: ". . . the accounts of medical experimentation on human beings by the Nazi doctors produced revulsion in me but not hate . . . . my feeling was not so much one of loathing for the Germans . . . as it was a feeling of sickness and shame for being a member of the human race. . . . It was too easy to seek catharsis by hating the Germans; the big problem was to make peace with oneself for belonging to the same species." Vridar had read the words to Angele and said, "It's impossible for these orphan-liberals to make peace, as long as they are beating the bushes for scapegoats and father-images, for their anger to crucify and their fear to hate—for such father-images as the Republican party or John Foster Dulles, such scapegoats as Senator McCarthy—they've got to get the gyves and

910

thumbscrews, boots and treadmills and pillories out of their system—and the small dark Hitler who lurks there." Carl was a delightful companion when he told stories, for he told them well; but when he got on the subject of his father-images, and snarled with rancorous hate or shouted with furious intolerance, Vridar could only look at him with astonishment and pity. When in his laboratory with pure science the man was almost adult; when in the realm of national and international affairs, he was a child, for he still believed in heroes and villains. He actually believed that if the management of human affairs were entrusted to men like him the world would soon be a much better world.

There was a period in his life when Vridar told himself that he preferred as friends medical doctors: he had imagined that their years of training in the sciences must have disciplined both their emotions and mind. He was to learn better than that. One doctor-friend lost his head in reckless flying; another became an alcoholic and shot himself; a third went insane. During the same postwar years a banker friend cut his throat so deep that he almost severed his head; a business man and a sheriff lay down by their automobiles and blew their brains out. His sister had confessed to Marion that she lived in fear of being asylumed; and Marion himself was no longer sane.

Persons came to Vridar seeking help but he turned them away, for he was neither psychiatrist nor professional psychologist; and besides, he did not want to gather a large family of orphans, as his brother had done. He knew that the last thing on earth any emotionally ill person (which meant any non-adult grown person) wanted to do was to face the realities and facts of life. Now and then there came one so pitiable that he was tempted to try to help—a mother with seven children who could not control her compulsion to steal; a man whose alcoholic wife tried to kill him when she got drunk; a woman with the conviction she had cancer, who had gone from quack to quack, suffering hideous mutilations of her face; a youth who could not put away the feeling that he ought to be dead. In all of those who came to him Vridar perceived the orphan-situation.

That situation came under brilliant illumination one night at a party. Jane Kitchen Vridar had first seen in the Rhode home; she was so fleshless that Rhode had said he could spit through her, so morbidly self-conscious that her presence was painful. Later the girl was in Boise and both Vridar and Marion saw her there. Dick Littlefield, the sensitive sardonic Dick with the crippled hand, had also seen her there and had been her boy friend for a while. When her name came up at the party, Dick confessed, with self-damning grimaces, that he had not seduced the girl, or even tried to—"By God, Hunter, that girl had no meat on her! Her thighs were no larger than a baseball bat, her arms no larger than broomsticks. What man in the world could cover a woman like that?" "Marion," Vridar said. Without foreseeing what response Dick would make, Vridar went on to say, "He took her to the desert one night and told me about it. He said, Self-righteous monsters like you never would, would you? It may be the only time that poor emaciated little schizoid will ever get it but she got it once, she'll have that memory to take with her. But in your dry ministerial world, where even adultery has to be well-fleshed,

911

such a woman would never get a memory, would she? That's what he said, Dick, and I guess he was right."

Dick went away to the kitchen and confessed to Angele that he had hated Marion, because at a party one night Marion had kissed his wife. Now he admired the man. By God, he did. Thinking of the pathos of it he began to weep; and said to Angele, "I wasn't that big! God damn it, I *was* self-righteous! He *did* give her one memory, but I wasn't decent enough to do that much. Did you know that her father killed himself, and her mother died in an asylum? I'm a stinker!" he said, staring fiercely through his tears.

Dick was another orphan: his father had deserted his mother, who then completely poured her life into another son, by a second marriage, whose father had also deserted her. The second son by the age of thirty had never been allowed to woo a maid: he had been forced to give his whole life and devotion to the octopus who had closed around him.

Vridar had another friend with a deep red birthmark over his eyes and nose. One night at a party Vridar got drunk and kissed the friend's wife on her cheek. Hours later, just at daylight, the friend caught Vridar alone in a bedroom, and slipping up behind him drove a fist with all his power into Vridar's lower ribs. Knowing that he was hurt, yet too drunk to do anything about it, Vridar crawled to a bed and rolled in. Two hours later he went to the barn to do his chores, bent over like an old broken man; and a little later he set out to find a doctor. It was New Year's day. The doctor said he had three fractured ribs. He taped him. On the way home, white with pain and hangover, Vridar said to Angele, "I should have had my head broken." When men so handicapped could make a decent life, and find a woman decent enough to marry them, possibly there was still reason to have faith in mankind's striving.

In any case, all these orphans helped him understand the Jesus myth, to which he had now come.

For many years he had had the habit of talking scenes out, aloud, when busy at hard labor. While digging a ditch with pick and shovel he would pause, look up at the sun's patina on a United Airlines plane, flying above another of Robinson Jeffers's haunted valleys, and say, "Hear ye, now! A son of Hellas believed that you could not step in the same river twice, that all appearances were continuously changing; but the son of Israel believed in the unalterable, immutable, changeless. For the Greek it was the mutable, the inconstant, the vacillating, the transient, the ever-changing kaleidoscope. For the Jew it was the steadfast, the firm, the stable, the permanent, the deep-rooted equilibrium. For the one, the chameleon, for the other, the stereotype. I suspect, O Universe, that the one was adult, the other a child. Can there ever be a common ground, a meeting-place, for the two?"

When Angele came out to bring him a cold drink, he would gesture at the sky and say, "Enelow says religion belongs to the Jewish substance; all the rest is accident. M. Lazarus says, Every house a temple, every heart an altar, every human being a priest. Good old Pa! The essential character of Hellenism, says Bevan, is that it broke free from the old rule of stereotyped custom and applied reason to the facts of life. In other words, it was on its way to being adult. Greek philosophy, says Dill, was the solvent of faith. Jew and Greek! The stereotype: that's father-fear. The rational solvent: it's obvious that Greek children, far more than the Jewish, were allowed to grow up."

"You'd better come in now."

"Aroynt, woman! Busk and boun ye!"

Angele touched her lips lightly to his sweat-drenched forehead and went away.

When, in his long ascent from the apeman with the club, he came to the Jesus story he felt at home. In Salt Lake City, in 1927, he had recognized the Jesus myth as possibly the most significant myth for the Western world, and at the time had read all the scholars in this field, in that city's libraries. Before sitting to write his novel he had read most of the greatest scholars, including the German, in the New Testament.

What *was* Jesus? There had been more than one named Jesus, in Palestine, who because of his fanatical teachings had been hanged. There wasn't an iota of trust-worthy evidence that the Jesus of the Gospels had lived in human flesh: this, he had come to see, did not matter at all. There was not a scrap of evidence that a Jesus in Palestine ever uttered a single word of all the words attributed to him by the gospel stories: this did not matter either: indeed, the great thing about the story was that the early leaders had sense enough to have him say the things he ought to have said—just as, earlier, Jewish writers had had sense enough to make Solomon say what he should have said, if he was to be a great king. In both cases the child was kneeling to an idealized father-image. Paul had been wise enough to say, "Yea, though I had known Christ after the flesh, yet now would I know such a Christ no more!" Paul had been wise enough to know that if a Jewish figure, either real or mythical, were to be assimilated to the Christ, that is, to the non-Jewish savior myth, the mortal man would have to be got rid of. Nothing aston-ished Vridar more, in this field, than the fact that even the greatest scholars (with only now and then an exception) wrote of Jesus and the Christ as though they were the same thing. "Aha!" he would say to Angele, thrusting a scornful finger at Oesterley, "when will the sons dare to stand up to their fathers?" It pained him to the point of fury when he found philosophers as eminent as Bertrand Russell saying "Jesus Christ," or using the word Christ when they meant Jesus. They knew (for how could they be so ignorant!) that Christ was not a surname, but meant the anointed one, the king.

The meaning of the Christ symbol was plain: it was the old-old rebirth of the sun, after it had almost perished at the winter solstice. What was the Jesus symbol? The son, the orphan. It had been in the cluster of meanings around at-one-ment that he had begun to see the large lonely figure of the orphan, at a projection of self-consciousness; and one day the words came to him, suddenly, out of his depths, and he uttered them aloud: "So there, for the Western world, was the Orphan, who would stand for all orphans, and who would pass into myth as Jesus of Nazareth!" Freud had said that the essence of Christianity was the submission of the son to the father: well, a lot of distinguished people, including some poets and writers, were submitting! The Jesus myth was the submission of the son: that much, it seemed to Vridar, must be plain to all but blind men and fools: the idea that he died to save people from eternal death was only a clumsy rationalization of it.

He spent many hours thinking about this myth and trying to arrive at its deeper and darker meanings. He had many dreams about it, and sometimes in his dreams he went back nearly two thousand years to talk to people; but for them the matter was as strange and elusive as for him: that, too, he understood at last, was as it should be: the myth had been corrupted and almost destroyed when foolish literal minds had the Father send the Son to die for the sins of mankind. The scapegoat, the goat for Azazel, was an old myth, too: O Father, why have you forsaken me? That was the heart of the myth. That was the cry of the orphan. Among American writers none had cried the words so long and loud as Thomas Wolfe.

Father, why have you forsaken me! Vridar was to stand on the mean barren rocky eastern hill of Jerusalem and gaze at what had come to be known as Gethsemane: it was there, the theologians said (who could never be made to understand a myth, nor even their own fear and loneliness), that Jesus had knelt alone to pray: not *there,* but in all the gethsemanes in myth and legend, where all the father-fearing and father-hating Jewish and Christian sons had knelt in supplication, and were still kneeling, and would kneel, as long as the Desert-Yahweh was driven into their child-souls.

What did the word father really mean? He turned to the dictionary: Father, one who had begot a child, a male parent. Yes, but in Judaism there had not been that kind of father, for there was no mother. Throughout history there had been the male parent who had sold his sons, or killed them, and invariably had hated them— the race's mythology was full of the fear of the older male for the younger, and his hatred of him. It was Age and Youth in fable. In the myths of practically all peoples the mother of the god-child fled from the father's horrible destroying wrath. And then see: the son was caught and stoned and hung on a cross! The pathetic wretched lonely orphan, going off alone into his gethsemane (gath shēmānī, the oil press) to pray, knowing it to be the will of his father that he should die! In his death he would appease the father's wrath, who was on the point of killing all his children! How inconsistent, in their fantastic ignorance, the Christians had been, to say that the Jews killed the son and to hate them for it—the son whom an omnipotent father had sent down to be killed! The dogma that the Jews killed him was merely the vilest of all the Christian calumnies.

G. Stanley Hall called it the consummate artistic creation of the folk-soul. Prof. Guignebert had written, "We must not confound the Nazarene with the ideal which he has come to represent . . . ." O. Müller had said, "If one who invents the myth is only obeying the impulse which acts upon the minds of his hearers, he is but the mouth through which all speak . . . ." Thousands of books had been published about "Jesus." Thousands of minds, among them some of the ablest, had tried to determine what the myth meant. For Otto Rank the core of all myth in religion was the "nobility and tragic fall of the hero who comes to grief through his own presumption and the guilt arising therefrom. That is the myth of humanity, ever recurring in the various levels of development." For Albert Schweitzer "He comes to us as one unknown, without a name, as of old, by the lakeside, he came to

914

those who knew him not. He speaks to us the same word, 'Follow me,' and sets us to the tasks which he has to fulfill for our time . . . . to those who obey him, whether they be wise or simple, he will reveal himself in the toils, the conflicts, the sufferings which they shall pass through in his fellowship, and, as an ineffable mystery, they shall learn in their own experience who he is."

"They are moving words," Vridar said to Angele, "but they don't come within lightyears of the truth of the myth: they are only the son's loneliness that has been set like a halo upon it. And the fall of the hero is indeed a principal myth, but not this myth."

In his tireless effort to discover the full meaning of the myth, he turned at last to some of the paintings of Jesus, to learn what artists had thought he was. The image of him in their minds he found even more astonishing than that in the minds of scholars and philosophers. So few of the faces showed any love and compassion —as in Rembrandt's "Christ at Emmaus," which he had once studied in the Louvre. Most of the paintings made Jesus look like a brigand or a halfwit. The Jesus-babe brought from him snorts of incredulity—such as Masaccio's "Madonna and Child with St. Anne," in which the child was the very image of a muscular and dim-witted gorilla-babe; or Michelangelo's "Holy Family," where he looked fat, petulant, and sullen; or Raphael's "The Madonna of the Goldfinch," where the child looked hydrocephalic and stupid. He recalled the time he had stared at Raphael's "Madonna and Child Enthroned" in the Metropolitan, and resolved never to look at another painting of the Babe. But he now studied forty or fifty of them, until he came to Bellini's "Madonna Adoring the Sleeping Child," when in disgust he turned away; this babe was so monstrously fat, and looked so thick and dull, that he decided he was wasting time exploring the souls of painters. Obviously Jesus was not there.

In the Western world during these years, with its horrible weapons that no man dared use, its ceaseless childish propaganda, its shrill news commentators hysterically sounding their daily alarms, there were tremendous anxieties and fears. The Church leaders, it seemed to Vridar, were all morally bankrupt. Some of the magazines tried to make popular heroes of such as Sheen, Niebuhr, Barth, and a few others; but for Vridar they were so empty of spiritual substance and insights, so full of dogmas and decayings and dead ways of looking at things, that it fatigued him merely to think about them. Gazing at a face he would wonder how any man in an age of science and rationalism could still believe the Orphic nonsense of original sin. For such a man, what was conscience anyway?

What was it for him? he asked, lying back under a spreading juniper and looking out at the sky. The dictionary said it came from a Latin word meaning to be conscious and defined it as consciousness of moral goodness or badness. He thought it a foolish definition. The semanticists seemed to be the only people on earth who were concerned about "this net of symbolism in which our human destiny has become entangled." Vridar would take a word like conscience to bed with him and spend half the night trying to define it. So many words baffled and denied him that he got the habit of saying to any intelligent person who came to see him, "What is conscience? Besides the Censor, I mean." "Stripped of all the theological accretions, what is Jesus?" A university professor replied, "Jesus? He was a Jew who died on a cross, wasn't he?"

His effort to understand the Jesus-myth had long ago led him to a study of the first two centuries after Julius Caesar. He had learned, to his astonishment, that the early Christian leaders had been the most tireless liars and forgers in history: still, it was an abuse of words to call them forgers and liars: they had been instruments of the folk-soul, and that soul in contriving its myths had never had any regard for facts. The early Christians had corrupted or mistranslated the Hebrew writings, and others, when this served their purpose; had forged whole correspondences, a great many books, and miracles by the hundreds. All over the Roman world they took an idea and built a theology upon it. Paul had had the sense to understand that if the pagan world were to accept the new faith it would have to shed its Jewish elements, or most of them, and assimilate Jesus to the magnificent pagan savior-sun-god. With what zeal and industry they had labored!—yet with so many misunderstandings among themselves that within a hundred years a hundred sects had developed, and gospel accounts by the dozens. As the dramatic picture of it unrolled before him, Vridar, wonderstruck, was lost in admiration of what the folk-soul could do.

He had been surprised to learn that if there actually had been in Israel the Jesus of the gospels, he probably never said a single thing of all the things which the gospels would have him say. For how could he have? The folk-soul was shaping an ideal out of the materials at hand—the customs, beliefs, sayings of all the peoples from India to Spain. The folk-soul was choosing, not from words that Jesus had uttered, for none were known, but from the wisest and most beautiful words in the human record! The yearning folk-soul would have him say what he ought to have said! Why, of course—and how wonderful it all was! He could see the early Christians searching the records, and pausing to say, "He said this!" Or to think it. No, to *feel* it. It was too bad that in trying to make their tale plausible they had been so clumsy and inept: for any rational mind coldly viewing their labors, the historical errors, the childish contraditions, the wonder-legends, the miracles—well, it was all too childlike. But no more childlike than the millions of hours of labor and thousands of books that would be given to an effort to reconcile or explain away the absurdities!

Vridar spent hours talking aloud to himself about "Jesus," or to Angele, saying, "He was the immolated son—this is the myth of the complete submission of the son to the father—with the son-symbol standing for all Christians who submit. He was the orphan: this is the myth of the one who had no love, and went alone into his gethsemane to pray, and prepare to die, because his father willed it. This is the myth of the lonely lost man naked before the universe, and before death and time and all his enemies. This is the myth of the tiny will-toward-good in people, that is called conscience. Or is it? . . ."

His voice resonant with impatience he would say, "How can I represent the myth so that it will be acceptable to taste and intelligence, at this time? As the recurring figure that now and then rises from the subhuman to the human level? The light of a conscience that now and then shines for a moment in the dark?"

Angele said, "You're not writing for the present—you're writing for the future.

People won't dare think of what Jesus means until they've lost a part of their fear."

He looked at her and considered her words. "Tell me: after it is all over and the poor pathetic son has died to please the father; after the lonely unloved orphan has knelt in his gethsemane and prayed out of his terror; after he has been killed then shall I say, Don't you see? Don't you see it now? He has come in the only way he has ever come—as he came a hundred or a thousand years ago; as he will come again next year, or a hundred years from now, or a thousand years hence. Don't you see? He has come, he will come again, he will keep coming, until in this world there are no more Hitlers and Stalins—no more Katyn Forests, no more Oswiecims and Majdaneks . . . . But will anyone believe it?"

"There will always be a few, as there are today, if the book comes to their hands."

"Can I find a publisher for it?—or will the world go on seeing this stupendous myth in such childish stories about it as those by Asch and Faulkner? If Cohen says no, will Rhode say yes?"

Angele looked out at the sky a full minute and Vridar waited. She said at last, "I expect not."

Cohen returned the novel without a word. Vridar's agent had one of his assistants, a Jewess, read it, and she reported that it was "silly." Vridar struck a match to his agent's letter and held it to a cigarette; and then on a card typed these words:

> It may possibly be that it is not separation, as Carpenter so eloquently argues, that has produced the concept of sin and all its expiation rites; nor so much self-consciousness that has produced the need of at-one-ment, as the sense of incompleteness in each sex, because it is only a part of the whole. May not assimilation and immolation rites be an effort to achieve that sense of completeness, which was lost somewhere in the past? Which, in ancient myth, the gods had. Is it not significant that the Jews of all people have been most separate, who have been most deeply troubled by a sense of sin? Is their Motherless condition not part of it? How inevitable that the most eloquent and pathetic of all the orphan-symbols should have originated in *them*!

He hung the card among two hundred other cards on his walls, and read again the words by G. Stanley Hall: "The state of the real knowledge of and feeling for Christianity on the part of the world of modern culture, and the complacency of the Church in antiquated conceptions, constitute today the one great blemish and the one great danger of our civilization." He wondered if Rhode could be made to understand those words, written in 1917. He doubted it, Angele doubted it.

Well, they would soon see.

VIII

For fifteen years Reuben Taylor Rhode had encouraged Vridar to get on with his historical series, and had promised to publish the books if nobody else would. Ben Cohen would not; he had fired Chris and had struck Vridar from his list. Vridar's agent had given up: he said it was a waste of time any longer to look for a publisher in New York. Well, there was Rhode.

After dinner Vridar raised the matter and almost at once Rhode became angry.

917

His deeply lined face expressed unspeakable distaste; his eyes turned almost yellow with wrath. Going straight to what he took to be the heart of the matter, Rhode charged Vridar with a wish to destroy Christianity.

At first Vridar thought he had misunderstood the words. When his doubt was removed he looked over at Angele; then at Mrs. Rhode, who was knitting; and then at Rhode. A feeling of nausea filled him: he had devoted a large part of his life to a pursuit of pure truth, on that high plane where Frazer had defined the goals; he had kept close to his mind and soul the words of Arnold, that the mere endeavor to see and learn the truth was a commencement for making it prevail. And now— now he was charged with a deliberate effort to destroy the Christian churches!

When he was able to speak, he said in a low quiet voice, "On what do you base that?"

On a number of things, Rhode said. For instance, he himself didn't for a moment believe that early Christian leaders were liars and forgers, or that they corrupted Jewish writings merely to win proselytes. He thought that all the religions had been founded by great and worthy men. He thought—

"Have you read the ablest scholars and historians?" Rhode said he had not. "Don't you think their conclusions would be more valid than those of anyone else? Surely you don't take the position that you can know the truth without first going to find it."

"I know that the early Christian leaders—"

"Even if the highest authorities say you're wrong?"

"Maybe you misread the authorities. Anyway, I've no doubt of this, that our greatest bulwark against the incredible tyranny of Communism is Christianity. I simply can't publish any book that in any way might weaken the Churches, or discourage people from being Christians. The little that I may be able to do—"

"You mean that if you publish these novels I must first repudiate the findings of the greatest scholars?"

"I think you can present the facts in such a way—"

"Oh, but I can't. Facts contrary to Christian dogmas? I don't myself think we are going to get anywhere if we use falsehoods as a weapon against the Soviet tyranny. Even while we were in the Korean war, even while still more thousands of young men were getting their guts shot out, because of the mess men have made of this world, the Pope called a consistory—I quote—'to make belief in the bodily assumption of the Virgin Mary into heaven a dogma of the Catholic Church.' End of quote. I ask you in all seriousness if you think we can successfully oppose Communism, or any other ism, with such childish nonsense as that."

Rhode fetched a palm down over his face. He still looked tense with anger, but in a quiet voice he said, "I just can't publish anything that even in the slightest way will weaken the Christian religion. If you'll let some great Catholic scholar read these novels and tell you where you are wrong—"

Whelmed by amazement and anger, Vridar stood up and looked for his hat. He stared at Rhode. He thought, I understand now that this man has thought that he could make me one of his sons—I, fighting all these years to be free of tyranny! Trying to control his voice he said, "A Catholic *scholar*? There is no such thing in

918

matters relating to his Church. He can no more be objective and detached than a Communist can: they are both bound, mind and soul, by the dogmas of their faith. Do you actually mean to tell me that I must submit the findings and conclusions of a hundred or two hundred of the greatest scholars to the judgment of a small closed mind—"

"Otherwise I simply can't publish them."

Sick with frustration and despair Vridar let Angele drive the long way home, and sat with a bottle between his legs, his voice muttering in the ruins of his disillusionment. He was not a Christian, he said, nor an anti-Christian either: he had no thesis: his only wish had been to sink deep and write out of the darkest and obscurest parts of mankind's mind and emotions. Streeter, one of the giants among scholars, had written of those Christians to whom it was no satisfaction to be right unless they could thereby put others in the wrong. But that was not Rhode: that harassed goaded mother-eaten man had a perfect right to reject any book he pleased; but he had no right to encourage an author for fifteen or twenty years, to live on less than a sheepherder's wages and read and write his life away, all the while solemnly promising to see him through, to confront him at the last with a professor of apologetics in whom he saw a great scholar! Cheyne, another of the giants, paused in his book on the Psalter to extend the olive branch to entrenched bigotry. "Let us, he said, have the courage to read the Bible as truth must read it. That refrain runs through some of the greatest of the scholars: what a pity and what a shame that men whose only concern is truth have to pause in their labors to try to hush the enraged cries of small-souled bigots to whom truth will always be a stranger! Does Rhode have a ghost of a notion of what Jefferson meant when he swore eternal enmity to every form of tyranny over the minds of men?"

"I doubt it."

They were driving through sagebrush country. He had her stop and then went off the highway, returning after a few minutes with a handful of sage foliage, smelling it and breathing it. The fragrance of it filled the car.

"Was it Belloc?—yes, who said, I fear I shall be all alone when I get towards the end. Who will be there to comfort me and who will be my friend?"

She put her right hand over to touch him. "Do you realize that you're the only person who has ever stood up to him?—except possibly his mother."

He thought about it a few moments. "I suppose you're right. His children never dared to, nor his wife or secretary. He has been El Papa. Well, we're going to have in this country what Melville called an insincere unanimous mediocrity."

Abruptly Angele drew over to the curb. Peering through the car window Vridar recognized the house of his sister. He asked why she had stopped here; Angele said she had seen the light and had thought it well to stop a moment. Besides, she wanted to use the bathroom.

Inside the front door his mother, a shrunken old woman in her eighties, was sitting on a couch in a faded blue bathrobe, her hair in pins and curlers. She rose when he entered and turned on him her steady searching blue eyes; and then said, "Well, if it isn't my son! What are you doing here at this time of night?"

"Just stopped to see you a moment."

Her aggressive chin thrust out, her mouth set, as though for time and eternities, she studied his face a few moments before she spoke. She then asked him when he was going to return to the Mormon Church. He was head of the family, now that his father was dead; he ought to take his responsibilities more seriously. Vridar was thinking, Yes, she's just like Rhode: she has no interest in what I write or in what anybody writes, if it doesn't conform to her views. This woman, his mother, was so much like Rhode that he imagined that she could pass as his identical twin. Good God, they even looked alike! Some of their mannerisms were the same—as when, stooped, they walked with a stick. He said, "What inquisitors you two would have made eight or ten centuries ago!"

"Son, what are you talking about? I tell you I know. I know our Church is the only true Church and I want you back in it." She turned to Angele and said, "You don't believe in our Church, do you? What do you know about it anyway?"

Marion's way of managing his mother had filled Angele with astonishment. He had lived in the same city with her a number of years and she had got the habit of calling Marion by telephone each morning. One time he was a little more than half-drunk when the telephone rang; he took the mouthpiece off its cradle and said into it, "Yes, Mother," and let the piece fall. His wife, and Vridar and Angele, could hear the voice at the other end of the line. It went on talking, and Marion went on smoking and drinking. After half a minute, or perhaps a full minute, he would pick up the mouthpiece and say into it, "Yes, Mother. Oh yes, I'm sure I agree with you but you'd better explain it more fully. Just begin at the beginning and go all through it again." Then he would let the piece hang by its cord, and go on smoking and drinking. He would move around the house, go to the bathroom, look at papers on his desk; and after two or three minutes pick up the phone and say, "Well now, Mother, you have made it all a lot plainer than it was and I'm aware that Dad has read the Bible a lot. Ask him about Jacob's ladder and then tell me. I've for-gotten that part." Again he would drop the piece and walk to the corner grocer's and back, or go to the basement out of utter boredom. Vridar watched his brother and wondered about him.

Yes, Prudence and Reuben were much alike. It was said in Rhode's hometown that he was taken ill to a hospital and at once put the nurses half out of their minds: he would not take his medicines, he would not let them bathe him or change his sheets, until a large muscular nurse entered the room and marched over to his bed and looked at him. When he made a move to protest, she cried, "Look, God damn it, Butch, lie down and shut up! You're not the Queen's Consort. You're not running the universe, you're not running this hospital, so pipe down, kid, and take your pills." The one who told Vridar and Angele about it said, "After that he was as gentle as a lamb."

Drunk one night, Marion had said, "As a child I felt completely rejected by my mother." Many times Vridar had thought about it: in his barnyard folk he in-variably found in the whole animals a wish to destroy the cripples: it was a deep and ancient biological law that the aberrant members must perish. As a matter of fact, Prudence hadn't cared much for her older son either—Vridar had had con-vulsions as a babe—he had been a sick squally child, skinny, pale, with large nightmarish eyes; and Marion's eyes had been crossed. Marion had avenged himself on both parents with the most exquisite cruelty but Vridar had had no wish to. he understood now that Rhode and his mother had never loved, or been loved. The human animal was a terrible thing, not only in its lack of capacity to change itself, but in its bland contentedness with what it was.

To Angele, who was now driving, he said: "If I believed in reincarnation or anything like it I'd have to think that in a previous life my mother and Rhode were identical chimpanzee twins, but for the fact that she is long-legged and he is short-legged. One reason I can't stand either any more is that I am so much like them. We're the kind of high-powered people who keep the world going but we're not the kind the world loves. Didn't my father once say that God had decided he'd have to cut his world short, or he'd not be able to save anybody."

"That was cute," Angele said. "Your dad said some darn cute things."

"You know how my mother feels about children?—that they belong to her because they came out of her body. Millions of mothers feel that way. They feel— I've sensed it in my mother so many times—that because they came out of her body, and she saw their organs and wiped their hindends, there exists between mothers and their children a kind of privilege not to be so careful about exposing themselves, as when around strangers. That constitutes a vast oppressive ill-smelling atmosphere over the whole Christian-Judaic world."

"You make it sound awful."

"It is. You know, I've known a long time that if you want to understand human nature the best objects for study are the apes and the other mammals. I now add a third group, the very old. And another thing occurred to me while I studied the anger and outrage in Rhode's face. Mankind has developed a conscience to be able to see how imperfect this world is, and then to detest itself for exploiting the imperfections instead of changing them."

"That sounds about right," she said.

It was two o'clock when they arrived home but Vridar went on drinking and talking. He recalled to her, as he had once already since leaving Rhode's, for he was quite drunk, what Lord Alfred Douglas had said in his book on Wilde, "I am sick and tired of being told that a man who is kind and generous and genial and mixes without pose or awkwardness with all classes is a good democrat. Good democrats are not a bit like that. The qualities I have enumerated are typical not of the democrat but of his opposite, the aristocrat. Stalin is a typical democrat and so was Lenin. Hitler is another. Both Bolshevism and Hitlerism are the fruits of democracy." After reading the words to her from a card (he had taken it and a number of others along to read to Rhode, but had not) he felt bewildered. He said, "What was I saying?" The old dreadful fear was closing around him, and with it the haunted nightmarish sense of being depersonalized: he always felt that he was being sucked off into limbo in fragments of an emotional castrate when he came to a dead end and could see no way out. He stood, weaving a little, shuffling the cards, and came to Jeffers, and read, "Truly men hate the truth, they'd liefer meet a tiger on the road. Thou shalt not suffer a witch to live. As *he* reads the Bible—"

"Man-love, I need some beer."

921

They would get some; they would spend what money they had and die. He asked her to drive, knowing better than to drive when drinking, for he had run off bridges or got buried in snowbanks, or driven a hundred miles in the wrong direction. In an all night inn they bought a dozen bottles of beer but missed the road home and got lost. Vridar climbed out to have a look around him, and thinking that he saw his house only two hundred yards away he headed for it and tumbled face downward into a canal. Angele came screaming from the car and in pitch blackness heard him stroking furiously and cursing. He swam to the edge and crawled up out of the water like a drenched river-beast; and from hands and knees he spoke up to her: "Edith Sitwell said I've taken this step because I want the discipline of the Church. What a terrified orphan that babe was! She did all right with her loneliness for a while, and so did Eliot and some others; but suddenly these scared children came running in from play and said, Where is Pa?"

"Get up," she said, trying to assist him. She was rather drunk too and they staggered together.

He said, looking away at a black sky, "Isn't that our house?"

"You idiot!" Angele cried. "That's a mountain." Drenched with canal water, mud, and mosses, he climbed into the car, and on the opposite side she took the wheel. It was daylight when they reached their house. While fumbling with the key in the lock he muttered, "The waste land Eliot wrote about wasn't half as dreary as the one he returned to." Angele hustled him inside and put a warm blanket around him. "Now get your clothes off."

"I'll never surrender," he said, forlorn and shivering.

"Yes! Now get your clothes off." With her help he got out of his garments, and then sat shivering in a heavy blanket, a hot toddy at his side. He felt that he would vomit or weep, and decided that weeping and puking were much the same experience. He was telling her that Meredeth had written about a faint thin line upon the shore—but was it really there? Roger Bacon must have thought it was: for fifteen or twenty years he had existed in a dank black cell with rats and his own filth. Bruno must have thought it was there: he had died in flames rather than say what the dullwitted subhuman bigots wanted him to say. But was it there? He drank and talked, and at last looked at her and said, "The man of mind and courage cannot surrender today, for the reason that there's nothing big enough to surrender to."

Quickly she came to his side and kissed his cheek. "There, at last, after a day and a night you've said it. Now come to bed."

XIX

But for two days he refused to eat or sleep. He went on drinking. Now and then he looked with appalled eyes at the hopelessness of his situation, thumbed his nose in the direction of Rhode, and filled his glass. Weeks passed, and months. Every day he would go down to his book-lined den, where for years and years he had labored with the utmost devotion; and thinking of Rhode's words, "But as *I* read the Bible . . . ." he would turn to his notes. Harvard's G. F. Moore, one of the

922

giants among the Higher Critics, had written of the distaste and weariness that "a trained Old Testament scholar today feels about a man who, ignoring all the learning of the past embodied in an exegetical, historical, and theological tradition that fills hundreds of volumes, and ignorant of the methods of what is called biblical science, or ignoring its worth and rejecting its authority, undertakes to interpret the Scriptures out of his own head." In 1914 Prof. Peters, another Higher Critic, had written that the scholarship about the Old Testament was "so vast that it is impossible for any man to know it or to have read it all." Hundreds of volumes and thousands of articles had been published since then. Korzybski had written, "I cannot write just to please the orthodoxy of uninformed or misinformed people who do not read, yet 'know better'." "As *I* read the Bible!" Vridar muttered, and groaned and blew his nose.

From a file he drew some of the letters Rhode had written him. November 9th, 1940: "I really believe I shall urge you to start in on the series. You are now at the peak of your power, and the series should command your attention." What kind of books had Rhode thought he would write?—diatribes against Communism or the New Deal, or hosannahs to Catholicism? Twelve years later he had written: "We will be very happy to take over the series and do the best we can for your books. I think they are the most significant achievements in the field of letters in my day and generation . . . ." "Nice old father!" Vridar muttered, patting the letter. "What happened to you?"

He swung in his chair to look at the walls. There was a large panel which Angele had prepared, with the hope that it would divert him. On one side was a page from the leading picture magazine, on which a Catholic author named Greene solemnly told the journal's millions of readers that Mary actually went to heaven without dying! How could such a thing be in the middle of the 20th century? If he had explained her as a mother-image, or had told how she had been assimilated to Isis . . . . Next to this childishness from the same journal was lavish praise of Reinhold Niebuhr, for his belief in original sin; and in an editorial these words: "Our Lenten age is not over, but Lent is. Now we celebrate God's 'incredible' pledge, through the suffering of His son, that He cares for the human race." If such stuff were to come from a nursery, from the brain of a small child, it might be thought precocious and a little queer; but that in the Atom Age it should come from the brains of people who called themselves adults! Looking sharply he saw that Angele had written at the bottom of the page these words: The Caesars gave them corn; America's Caesars give them this stuff and it's still corn.

Vridar next pulled open a file of correspondence. He and Rhode had been exchanging letters ever since the angry scene in the man's house. It was clear at last that there would be no yielding on Rhode's side. In his infuriatingly bland way, he suggested that if Vridar would give the matter a little thought he would agree with him. Rhode had in mind, he said, a Roman Catholic in Europe, a "great scholar," a young man named Hans von Wetstein. Vridar had got hold of one of Wetstein's books and had read it—a smug arrogant attack on Protestantism and the American system of government. Vridar opened the book and began a letter to Rhode:

You believe in parliamentary government but Wetstein says, "It is virtually certain that the Catholic nations will never in their hearts accept democracy . . . . The party system must be abolished because of its inherent drive and tendencies toward totalitarianism . . . . Compromise is the heart of a parliamentary system . . . . It is precisely the contempt Catholic cultures have for the concept of compromise . . . ."

Wetstein says, "A recent contribution to American nihilism and relativism in legal thinking can be found in Chief Justice Vinson's opinion upholding the conviction of 11 Communist leaders. 'Nothing is more certain in modern societies than the principle that there are no absolutes . . . all concepts are relative'."

You believe in the middle class. Wetstein says: "It is evident that Catholicism does not harmonize with the bourgeois spirit and the whole mentality of the middle class." You like republics. He says: "The loss of religious fervor among the masses synchronized with the rise of republicanism." You believe in capitalism. Wetstein says: "The Calvinistic and Old Testament notion of taking earthly success as a sign of divine favor and next-worldly promise is absent in Catholic nations, where the beggar is a useful member of society."

Throughout his book he holds Protestantism in contempt: "Protestantism is essentially medieval . . . . we find no religious culture in Protestant countries after the Reformation." He says that except for the gas chambers, Luther laid out the complete plan for Hitler.

You have crusaded for free societies, but Wetstein says proudly that you can find none in "Catholic and Greek orthodox nations." He says that in the Roman Church in the Middle Ages "corruption had not been prevalent or conspicuous." That is a lie so monstrous that it would choke Stalin, yet this is the man you ask me to accept as a judge of my books!

He paused in his writing and looked up at his books, taking at last from a shelf a Cumont, a Lea, a Loisy, and pressing them to his cheeks, murmuring, "I'll not submit you to such indignity and insult, even if I am never published again!"

The next day he tried again to write to Rhode:

I have your letter in which you say you will publish my novels if "you feel you can properly cooperate with us in the matter of editorial changes which we feel are imperative to safeguard our joint interests." If this implies that I will in any respect go contrary to the findings of the greatest scholars in the fields I have covered then our interests are not joint.

In a recent letter you again ask permission to send my novel to Wetstein, even though I have shown you in his own words that he is a fanatical apologist for the Roman Church and no scholar at all. You have sent me a postcard from him to you in which he says, "Since Christianity is absolute truth, men in various times in various countries have come through reason or intuition to conclusions similar or identical with those of Christianity. Missionaries have found 'Christian notions' among natives in the remotest parts of the world." This Catholic casuistry, which notes to my novel fully develop, goes back to the earliest Christian beginnings. To say that Christianity is "absolute truth" is to make a statement so childish that the fact that any presumably intelligent man can say it in the middle of this century must be left to the psychologists.

To ask me to submit this novel to a fanatic and an apologist for the Roman Church is exactly analagous to asking some intelligent and fanatical Communist to make a judgment of your views. In either case the

924

judgment would be worthless. Nevertheless, I am willing with this provision, that a copy of his comments shall be delivered to me, with permission to make them public in any way I please, provided that I do not delete or change them, and fairly represent them.

I think another procedure would be more enlightened and intelligent. If you can bring forth proof from men internationally recognized as scholars in this field that my picture of Christian beginnings is unfair to the historical facts, I will revise the novel in every respect in which it is pointed out that I have been unfair. I shall be glad to let professors at Harvard, Yale, and Chicago name such scholars, and then you may submit the novel to as many of them as you please; and if it is found that I am more right than you, you will pay the reading fees; and if it is found that you are more right than I, I will pay them. If you do not regard this as fair, then I must suspect that fairness is not what you're after.

Since your first letters on this matter, after our discussion in your home, Angele and I have spent many hours going over and over it. That I am deeply distressed to find you taking such a position after our long and close relationship goes without saying. That I shall in any respect withdraw from the findings of the greatest scholars is unthinkable, even if the novels are never published.

He paused in his letter and turned again to the Rhode file, to see what the man actually had written: ". . . . whether or not it would be better if your protagonist's son should turn out to be a devout Christian and should burn his father's papers." ". . . . make him turn out to be a devout Christian and an upright man, burning his father's papers." ". . . . the more I think about it the more I believe you will commit literary hari-kiri if you publish this novel as it is." "No man in his senses under existing conditions is going to start a battle to destroy organized religions." "We haven't any idea of involving ourselves in controversy with the Roman Catholic Church . . . ."

Vridar put the file away, reflecting grimly that the Kinsey report, which had sold 250,000 copies, had been vigorously opposed by that Church. There was no reason to sit around day after day reading his letters; there was no reason to write him again. He belonged with those who resisted all the manifestations of deviation. To Angele he would say, "How can he ask me to do such a shameful and cowardly thing?" And he went on drinking.

One night, with Angele and two friends, he drove one wheel of his car off a canal bridge; and on leaving the car to see what the trouble was he pitched headlong into the canal. The current whipped him under the bridge. Though drunk he was soon aware that the air space between the water and the bridge above it was only an inch or two, and he struggled to get his mouth up to the air. He was making loud gurgling and blubbering sounds and clawing around him to find a way out, when a hand reached back under to seize him. Angele swore afterward that he had been clowning. Furious, he said, "You'll think I'm clowning when I die!" "You probably will be," she said. He was dragged out, halfdead, and hustled to a warm room and another bottle, and in his drenched clothes he paced the floor and drank until morning. At such times he murmured, "Move over, Scott Fitzgerald, and make room." He knew that he had gone pretty far into insanity and was approaching the point of no return: desperately he looked for a way out. One day he said to

Angele, "If we went to Europe again, would you be content to live on bread and cheese?"

"And walk barefoot in a rag!"

Before daylight one morning they were off, with Vridar turning at the last moment to thumb his nose in the direction of Rhode. They sat up two nights on dirty trains, eating nothing but stale sandwiches, but Angele's soul was singing like a child's. She found everything perfect on the ship, though their tiny third-class cabin on the *Ile de France* was so filled with plumbing and heating pipes that the two of them could barely stand in it when the door was closed. Several decks above, in first-class, Federal bureaucrats had handsome staterooms, and sat in luxurious chairs, with stewards trying to tempt them with delicacies.

Though a superb cook herself, Angele thought the food on this ship was straight out of wonderland. Even when they left the boat in a drizzling English rain under a sky of gloom, even when they found London a depressing area of fog and rain and bomb craters, and threadbare people, she loved every minute of it. She hated the Tower but had to be dragged out of the Museum.

In London they were fed and cared for by two gracious tactful Britons, whom they had never met but with whom Vridar had corresponded; and then they left the fogbound island for the Netherlands and Germany. Angele was like a child entering heaven when he took her to the cathedral in Cologne; the old churches here and in Bonn, Paris, Chartres, and over half of Europe, took her breath away. On entering Paris again there was for Vridar the old unmistakable odor of wetness and of moss on old stones; of bad sewage and the ugly stinking Seine; of wines spilled on sidewalks; of pastry shops, of the pigeons, of dirty old men fishing; but for Angele it was the bells, the spires of Notre Dame in morning light, the incredible treasures of the Louvre, the Left Bank, the Sorbonne, the Champs Elysées (to the end of which she walked alone one night in a rain)—all these, and the cafes and people and shops, and one letter from home. Vridar refused to talk about his woes, and he tried to hide from her his dark unhappy brooding, for he wanted the journey to be for her unalloyed joy. They went to Munich, to Salzburg, and on to Vienna, but this city depressed them horribly: the only persons there who seemed to be eating well were the Americans and the Russians. In the Tiergarten beasts and birds were so undernourished that Angele wept. Except the two ruling claques, the people everywhere were shabby, hungry, morose; a once-gay city had fallen under the blight of Stalin. After ten days they could stand it no longer and took a little old train across the magnificent landscape to southern Austria, where Vridar paused to see if he could write again. He found one constant delight during these months: he did not hear hysterical news commentators, who, imitating Winchell, kept the American people keyed to a sense of imminent disaster. He vowed that he would never listen to them again. He never did.

When crossing the ocean, he had tried to project himself into the black tortured soul of Hart Crane, in the moments before that poor lost child flung himself into midnight and the sea. He tried to imagine that he had done it, and to sense himself far out in the night, alone, facing death, as he watched the ship's lights vanish over the horizon. It was exactly the kind of thing he should not have been thinking of.

In London his first thought had been of Trevelyan, who had ordered Swinburne to leave the house after the poet had given Lady Trevelyan one of the *Comédie Humaine* novels. His thought on leaving London had been James Agate's words, "The English instinctively admire any person who has no talent and is modest about it." In Venice his first thought was of Monckton Milnes, who on his first visit to this city resolved to see it again at least once every five years. He looked at the ugly turgid water and remembered that Angele had brought fishhooks, fishlines, and plastic sheets to catch rain, in case of shipwreck!

Venice even more than Paris took her out of herself; and Rome almost as much as Venice. They rode the canal boats; looked with unbelief at the shabby gondolas and their sweating unromantic oarsmen; searched the Lido beach for shells; explored everything around Mark's square; and got lost in the amazing tangle of island streets. In Rome they occupied a small room high on the hill of the Via Sistina, and day by day explored a city about which Vridar had read a great deal. In the ruins of the Colosseum he had to fight back his nausea; in the ruins of the Forum, his tears. The magnificent dome of St. Peter's put them both in reverence before mankind at its noblest.

All the while here, as in other lands, he was striving to place will over emotion. Unwilling to put any fog on the sunshine of Angele's happiness, he went off by himself now and then; but he refused, even then, to look back at his own country, forcing himself to think of the acres of red tiled roofs in London and the flavor of Bass ale. He had said to Angele in London, "The English are so damned polite it's a wonder they can ever manage a copulation." He forced himself to think of such extraneous things as Emily Brontë's extremely small introverted handwriting, and Byron's large extroverted script; the curled up corpse of a woman six thousand years old; the Tower where so many with infinite time and pains had carved their names in stone; the two ravens standing where the gallows had stood.

Italy (he was now forced to be conscious of Wetstein) was an astonishing contrast of ugly poverty and arrogant wealth—the Basilica of St. Mary's with tons of gold imbedded in its ceiling—and the hideous old starved half-frozen women sitting all day in their rags trying to sell a few trinkets. Italy was a land of beggars, even around the Vatican—and Wetstein said beggars served a useful purpose! In Naples he saw so many people degraded below the animal level, and on Capri so much ostentation and wealth, that he wished another Vesuvius would bury it all. From a hotel on Rome's Via Veneto staggered a drunken American babbling about having recently seen Adenauer and a duke, who must now see Farouk or bust. Vridar said to Angele, "I see now that a part of obeisance to titles and rank is deference to Pa: the English have it bad, the Americans worse."

In a hotel in Naples an Italian-American woman said she had made the long journey to visit her people in the Boot, and had been so sickened by what she found there that she had remained not two weeks, as planned, but two days. Her people had legs that were cooked to the knees, and looked like sausages, from sitting close to tiny fires in bitter weather. Not more than three times in all their lives had they had a glass of cheap wine mixed with water. Her electric refrigerator in Philadelphia, she said, was worth more than the holdings of all her people in Italy.

927

Vridar had with him Lionel Trilling's words on Freud, that virtue consisted in making truth prevail against the resistance of society. That was it, Angele said; that was all of it. She then showed him an editorial from a picture journal called *Life,* in which a British historian had written that a workable diplomacy must rest on an assumption of original sin and universal guilt. They took the editorial with them when, after dark, they walked the ugly littered streets of Naples, toward the waterfront, to count the number of little old women sitting in freezing weather. In Catholic Spain and in Spanish Morocco they found such poverty, and such degradation of men, women, and children, as they had never known: the child-beggars were so scrawny, so almost-naked and filthy, and so dehumanized in their vicious obscene persistence that Angele fled to her room and sat for hours like one who had had a glimpse of hell.

After visiting Portugal they returned to Paris in mid-winter. Angele said, "Do we have to go home?" They were in a tiny hotel four blocks from the Opera. Vridar stood by a window, looking out at falling snow.

Yes, he said, they would have to go back and face it. He put her to bed to keep her warm, for there was almost no heat in the building; and then bundled up for a long walk. From the Rue Tronchet he headed for the Rue de Rivoli, which he followed to its end; then turning right he crossed the Seine and followed the broad Saint Michel until he came to the Sorbonne on his left and the Luxembourg gardens on his right; turned left and headed for the Jardin des Plantes and the river and followed the river back to the Louvre. It was a long walk but snow was falling all the way, and he loved deep white windless storm as he loved few things in life. He had wished to sense, if he could, alone, how it was going to be when he again faced the task of trying to find a publisher; of trying to write when there seemed no longer to be anything to write for; and of looking into the eyes of his brother again. Once more, in case they were never to return, he would slip to the Louvre for fifteen minutes of wonderstruck contemplation of Clouet's "Francis I," and then they would board a Dutch ship and be off.

The northern waters were wild this January: most of the passengers puked all the way over, but Vridar and Angele were good sailors: day after day they sat in the bar drinking Holland gin at ten cents a glass.

XX

During the passage home Vridar spent a part of his time trying more clearly to see the pattern of his life with his brother. A brilliant psychologist at his best, a genial and witty host, a husband of insights and charm, Marion was now lost, on what a poet had called the dark descent within. He still saw the few patients who came to him; outwardly, when walking the streets, he was still the professional man, brisk and incisive; but inwardly he was gone, and his going was a blow that Vridar found it almost impossible to face.

On the way home he refused to face it, but called to mind instead the lighter aspects of this amazing man. Marion all his life had proceeded on Rasputin's assumption that in seducing women he purified them; with tongue in cheek he had

928

said to Vridar, "My wife has taught me that sin is not what you do, but getting caught at it." One of his favorite stories concerned the oral examinations for his Doctor's degree: he said that after it was all over a famous professor took him aside, looked for a moment into his eyes, and said gently, "Do you know your own name?" Marion said, "I had thoroughly exposed all the professors in the department as impostors and frauds and they didn't like it: for four years they had taught me and I wasn't able to answer a single damned question." On entering the Army for War II Marion had taken an intelligence test. It was a test that he had given ten thousand times, and knew by heart. "After reading my answers, two majors and four captains walked round and round me, just looking at me, and I knew my goose was cooked. With an IQ above two hundred I went in as a colonel and came out as a corporal."

When Marion was in practice in Salt Lake City, he made one of his astonishing sardonic gestures: he gave a party in what he called Vridar's honor, at the principal hotel, and invited not only the president of the university, but some of the most self-righteous members of the faculty; and himself, as host, appeared late, and shamefully drunk. Vridar was so embarrassed that he had wanted to sink to the basement, when Marion, in plain sight of the full table, slipped his hand up under the dress of a pretty waitress and pinched her thigh. Afterward, when Vridar spoke of it, Marion growled, "You're so stupid that someone ought to pass a law to stop you from writing novels. Every one of them, from the president clear down to that roundfaced sniggering Mormon Elder, wanted to do exactly what I did, but didn't have the guts." Then, looking down his long nose at Vridar, he had used almost the words that Burton had addressed to his Isabel, "I'm in a bad way. I have to hate everybody except you and me." In the presence of his wife and of Angele, he would look at Vridar and say, "See the sadfaced impostor. I'm the one person in the world he loves more than all the others, and he hates himself for it but can do nothing about it. If ever I'm sick and he's across the world, he'll come to me. He'll come scowling and complaining and hating the hell out of me but he'll come, bringing more love than any but his kind of heart can hold. For I'm his son and his only son, he's my father and my only father. I hate him the the way the Christians hate God, and he loves me the way a man loves his first mistress."

The thing that dismayed Vridar, and went into him in deepest grief, was Marion's wish to destroy him. When pitched head over heels out of a tavern and hustled off to jail, Marion had told the officers that his name was Vridar Hunter. He gave the same name when, drunk, he ran off a highway and rolled his car over. Vridar was never to know how many times his brother had been treacherous against him, or whether there were treacheries blacker than a few he knew about. If he denounced him for it, Marion would say blandly, "Being more famous than I am, you can better afford it. Besides, writers are supposed to do such things." Vridar then would have to turn away to hide his mirth. But he had to turn away to hide his pain when Marion said, drunk and bitter, "My mother says I was born with two heads and all her life has hated me for it."

On the few occasions when they were alone together, Vridar would try to draw his brother out. He might say, "A writer named Malraux poses the question, What

929

is to be done with the soul if there is neither Christ nor God? He says self-examination does not teach us about man, but only about the man who is in the habit of examining himself." Marion had growled, "If that man is not now a Catholic he will be." Marion's contempt for most creative writers sank him below the level of speech. Or Vridar might say, "Hearst believed that all men are rascals more or less, that the secret of all loyalties is money. Pay a man enough, and you can spit in his face." Marion had said, "You always oversimplify things. All things are simpler than we suppose, but to get to them we have to push through the complexities that fear of truth has lost them in." Vridar might say, "A journal tells us that what ails 20th century poetry is summarized by a Netherlands poet, Koos Schuur: Me, me me and me and me and me, and me me me and me and me and me, and this world, this universe, this life, and me me me and me me me and me." With his most sardonic grin Marion had said, "All children are me me me and all poets are children. Look at you, for Christ's sake. Because the 20th century is too small for your ego you have gone to the past. Because your country's too small you've gone to Europe and the Middle East." From a desk drawer he yanked out a picture journal. "There," he said. "I use this to shame my paranoiacs." He was pointing to words by a writer named Hemingway. The words were about a story called *The Old Man and the Sea,* and the words said, "Don't you think it is a strange damn story that it should affect all of us (me especially) the way it does. I have had to read it now over two hundred times and every time it does something to me." Marion shoved the magazine back and said, "I read it. A lot of idiots called critics have been trying to explain it. He has a castration complex, and you never got over yours." Marion grinned. "Since I didn't idolize those parts, as you guys did, I've been able to give of them more freely. But this Hemingway story, does the guy know what he was doing?—when he goes out into the ancient symbol of the womb and the mother, and fishes something out of it? His father. He really worked him over, didn't he?"

Or Vridar might say, "Forel tells us that of one thing he was certain, the pernicious effect of metaphysical dogmas on mankind. Whether these dogmas proclaim God, religion, Weltanschauung, or a theory of the universe, they merely betray, he says, the vanity and shortsightedness of their creators and disciples, who imagine they can explain the universe within their own small self-contained systems. Their own small self-contained systems. What do you say to that?" And Marion had looked at him in his hard quick way and said, "When you try free association, what do you get?" Vridar said he got horrible fears and hatreds; some incestuous yearnings; doubt of his talent— "Yes, yes," said Marion impatiently. "All you writers cunningly and lovingly hide yourselves in folds of velvet, and people who call themselves critics spend their myopic lives trying to unfold you."

One day Vridar told his brother about a dream he had over and over. In the dream he stood just north of the first shack on their parents' ranch, listening with all his senses. He heard explosive but muffled sounds far overhead and saw a prodigious convulsion of the whole upper atmosphere. There were immense gray eruptions of what seemed to be billowing clouds and smoke but they were pale and wan like some strange atmosphere that had risen from innumerable graveyards or from all the Majdaneks of the earth. The world under this atmosphere was filled with light as from hidden fires, and the light was darkening, slowly. All this was terrifying, but a worse terror had come from what Vridar could feel but could not see—from a kind of stupendous engulfing loneliness, but more than that—an approaching menace, a vast and sinister thing, but with no threatening sounds, no apparitions. It was a sense of the end of something, even of the end of all things. It was a sense that all of death had gathered here. The most horrible part of it at this stage of the dream was the way all the familiar aspects of sky and earth were changing, until, though he recognized them, they were not what he had known all his life but were filled and darkened with an alien and incredibly sinister power—the power to blight and wither, consume and destroy. There was an odor that was strange and evil. But the thing that made him shake with fear was the absolute quiet. He had stood looking into the west, or up at the moving masses of wan unearthly light; and had listened, but there had been no sound. Then above the house something that had been hidden until this moment came slowly in sight. It was a strange blackness that resembled cloud or smoke, but was neither, for it was not of this world. It was two or three hundred feet above the earth. It moved out from its hiding place and then seemed not to move at all, but to lie there in the sky, its power complete and supreme; and some kind of atmosphere or spirit seemed to emanate from it, and this began to fill all the sky roundabout. The whole of earth and sky was being conquered by it, as a mind by loneliness, or a graveyard by night. Vridar had looked up and all hope had died within him.

Marion had stared at his brother several moments before he said, "What do you think it means?"

"I suppose the Freudian would say it is a guilt-dream, fear-dream, death-dream. I think it grows out of the novels I'm writing, for I dream it over and over."

"Is fear your demon?"

"It has always been. It is mankind's demon."

"I expect we'll both go insane before we die," Marion had said. "Remember when you stole that case of beer and lugged it out to the alfalfa field and we got drunk? That's about our highest achievement to date and not many have gone so high."

All his adult life Marion had been aloof, even cold, toward his brother, and as he began to deteriorate he developed a wish to destroy him. "I don't blame him for hating me," Vridar had said to Angele. "He has reason. The irony of it is that he hates me for the things I did for him that Christians would approve. It was our mother who estranged us, almost from birth."

Vridar had known that his brother was going downhill but had pretended to himself that it was not so. On his return from abroad he could no longer hide from it. He and Angele spent the weekend with Marion and his wife, and they all got drunk, as they always did when together; and Marion became violent in a wild way. He had written some novels and short stories (much of which, it seemed to Vridar, was pure lunacy) and he insisted on reading them aloud hour after hour. The next morning Vridar took home memory of his brother, standing with Mollie in the yard, looking haunted, lost, sick, and terribly alone.

931

That was on a Monday. A few days later a long distance call said that Marion had been stricken with a heart attack. Three hours past midnight Vridar managed to reach the doctor, who gave Marion not more than ten hours to live. Feeling that the world was going out from under him, Vridar entered his car with Angele and a bottle of whisky, and they drove through a black night until gray morning came. They had a cup of coffee and drove again. Vridar had loathed hospitals ever since he had run like a wild man up and down corridors to find a doctor for Neloa. When they entered this hospital, they came first to Mollie, in a hallway, weeping; and then to Prudence, sitting alone in an alcove. Vridar took the doctor and the cardiologist aside: the latter said it was the worst coronary he had ever known. They both said that Marion would die before the next morning. If Vridar had been told that the end of the world was imminent, he could not have felt deeper shock and horror. For how could it be! This was the one he had taken care of and fought for: how, then, could it be!

He was to learn from Mollie that while in the Army Marion had been committed and then discharged; and that since then he had lived in dread of having to ask, of his own will, to be locked up again. Vridar was stunned: it couldn't be, it couldn't be! Now, in the hospital, he knew that the Altar of Pity said that Marion should be allowed to die, but with all his fierce protective zeal, with the Guardian rising big and wild within him, Vridar wanted him to live. He looked at Marion, lying in a small room, with nurses around him and tubes down his nose and throat. He went to the bedside and clasped one of his brother's hands. He hadn't been so horribly full of this kind of sickness and loss since he turned away from the crematorium.

Marion had once asked his brother to collaborate with him on a book about marriage. After consulting with the doctor, Vridar bent low to Marion and told him that he must get well, that they would write the book. . . . It was a stupid, it was an incredible, thing to do: suddenly Marion was hurling the covers back and sitting up, with tubes falling from his nostrils, wild violent hands beating down and away all suggestion that he should go on in the nightmare of living and striving. Hastily moving away, Vridar turned once to look at his brother. He was never to look at him again.

In Mollie's home he poured himself a drink and waited. When the call came, he was at first so stunned he was paralyzed; and a few moments later flung himself down crying out of grief and horror, "My brother! My brother!..." It all had to come out of him then—all the bitter lonely hideous childhood that they had suffered together—in Annis, in Poplar, in Rigby, on the ranch—the whole black nightmarish vomit of it—it all had to come out as he chocked and strangled and fought to breathe...

It could never be now! These two should have been as close in fellowship as two men had ever been, who spent a long miserable childhood together, starving, suffering, trembling; who had shivered together in cold shacks, preparing their own simple food, making their own bed, scrubbing their own concrete floor; who had never run, who had never surrendered, yet who could never win! In his grief he was thinking of the rewards that went to the ruthless energy of evil...the heart-

932

break when death closed over unanswered questions . . . the doubts that had to endure. All night he spent with his grief, drinking, smoking, doubting, as he had doubted for Neloa, that this terrible thing could be; and all night he was aware of the gentle compassionate pressure of Angele's hand....

Little Marion had cared whether he was buried or burned---whether he had a funeral or was thrown to the winds in silence; but Mollie called for a Mormon funeral, and a Mormon bishop to preach a dull sermon. Vridar was sitting with the mourners when the casket was wheeled in. One end of the chapel was banked deep with flowers, many of them from Marion's former patients; and the casket was buried under a wealth of bloom. It was a former patient who sang the simple hymns weeping as he did so; it was a former patient who uttered the farewell, and he wept too. At the graveside the Legion took over. Then there was only the coffin there by a hole in the earth, and flowers banked all around.

"Marion is dead." In his breath Vridar murmured the words over and over but he could not believe them; and after he returned to his own home he climbed a hill and looked off in the direction of his brother's home, as though to see him there. He found it impossible to put away the thought that he could find him if he went to look for him; or the thought that he should go look for him. Only Neloa had gone into him so deep: how strange it was, how stupid, that he should break his heart over two persons who had caused him so much humiliation and pain! He knew now why he loathed the Prodigal Son story, for he had had two prodigals, whom he should have spurned when he discovered their real feelings toward him, yet over both of whom he would grieve to the day of his death. So it was with the mind, poor beaten-down thing, under the implacable tyranny of the emotions; so it was with Frazer's guns, and his own books and all books like them, against the deep sea-and-wind-powers of human aversion to truth and death!

Looking away towards Marion's home, and (just a little south of it) his grave, he would think, The things we might have said to one another will never be said; the fellowship that should have been will never be. In 1926 he had said to his brother, "We came together up out of nightmare, we should be friends. Can't we have a better relationship?" And coldly Marion had replied, "I like it this way." Never again had Vridar spoken of it. Angele had told him, to his amazement and confusion, that when she first entered Marion's home he had said to her, "Don't be surprised by anything you see between my brother and my wife." That could only be treachery: Marion knew all about his wife: no woman as simple as Mollie could have kept anything from a psychologist so able, so shrewd and cunning and persevering. It was about the same time that he had said to Angele in Salt Lake City, "Can I help it if my brother is the father of my son?" When she told Vridar what Marion had said, Angele had looked at him accusingly, as if expecting him to show guilt; and Vridar (he was to reflect afterward) must have stared at her as he might have stared had she said, "Your mother has told me that Joe is not your father." He had sunk to a chair, dazed, astounded, wondering what on earth his brother had meant. He knew that it meant a great deal, coming from Marion. He knew that Marion knew that Vridar would rather have died than have touched Mollie, even if that had been possible. So what had he meant? Was it the slyest *double entendre* ever spoken? Angele was to say, much later, that in her opinion Marion was only trying to break up their relationship. This explanation Vridar was never to accept. He had asked her, "Are you absolutely positive that is what he said?" She was absolutely positive: he had turned on her that sly evil wicked grin and said, "Can I help it if my brother is the father of my son?" "Did he italicize the second my?" "He said, 'Can I help it if my brother is the father of my *son?* That's the way life *is.* Don't you *see?'* "

The weeks following Marion's death were almost more than Vridar could endure: when deepest in the wish to kill himself, he would look at Angele and say, There she is, you love her, you have a duty to her, for she's as much of an orphan as Marion was! In despair he would smite himself such terrific blows that he would knock himself down; he would knock blood from his mouth or nose, and then, spent, would lie on his back and remember what Ernest Jones had written about Freud: "The theme of death, the dread of it and the wish for it, had always been a continual preoccupation of Freud's mind as far back as we know anything about it." And so it was with him! Jones said that Freud could not bear thought of death, unless to rejoin his mother: it was his brother whom Vridar wished to join. How well he knew now that the adult was only the child of the first ten or twelve years, and the child was the past! The thing about Freud, though, that had astonished him most was not his incestuous yearnings toward his mother, or his orphan-dread of death, or his extreme anxiety neurosis that forced him to be absurdly early (and Vridar too) to all appointments, or the failure of all his influential friends to get for him the Nobel award: it was his childish fooling around with occultism, telepathy, and numerology.

Day after day, refusing to write or read; week after week, drinking, smoking, grieving; month after month, tortured by the compulsive wish to go take care of the one whom in childhood he cared for, Vridar strove to see his relationship with Marion in all its aspects, suspecting that it was the diseased core of all that he was. In his basement he had Marion's office desk and chairs and rug, which Mollie had insisted that he should accept on a debt thirty years old; and he would sit in the chair behind the desk and look at the things Marion had looked at so many times; open a right drower in which Marion had kept a bottle---for in his last years he was often in an alcholic stupor when he met his patients; or at notepads on which Marion had written.

Silently the Wolf
The husband who talked to himself

During his years with Athene Vridar now and then had said, "Something is holding me back." Not until his brother's death could he force himself to see what it was. He should have known long ago, for when he first saw his own name in *Who's Who* he had slyly torn it out of the library copy and destroyed it; and when he was awarded a substantial prize, he had got wildly drunk and wept half the night (he knew now that it was because he had wanted Marion to have the prize). And now, bowing his head, Vridar would mutter, "There is nothing left for me but the shell. I have given. I have been one of the Givers. I have hated the

Alexanders and Caesars and Napoleons and Stalins and Hitlers because they were the Takers. I have given myself to the persons I have written about until I have no individuality left; to my brother, until, my wife says, I am taking on his vices; to the hope for a future for mankind, with my mind denying it all the way and my emotions over-riding my mind...."

Nothing in life---not anything about father or mother, wife or sister---could soften him inside and break him, until he fell all to pieces and had to go away to be alone---nothing like thought of his goddamned crosseyed woman-screwing failed insane brother! He understood now the mother's devotion to the imbecile son--- that there was no reason or logic or sense in it; that it went down deep where all the instincts were; and that his brother knew it all the time and took fullest advantage of it. And his brother would doublecross him again, as the prodigal son doublecrossed his father. Yes, he, the simple one, the fool; he, the over-submissive and over-giving one, to whom Angele had said so many times, "You must spend something on youself"---but he would not, not even for decent clothes; not even for a good meal without wondering about the two billion people who would never have a good meal; not for a good car without a sense of guilt: not for anything could he feel worthy, until all the Marions had, if not more than they should have, then as much as they needed. This in part explained in him what some called his reactionary tendencies: he could not see privileged groups, like big labor unions, big business, and big government, getting more than their share, when so many groups got less; for he had been taught to divide and give the better portion, and this was one of the deepest parts of his conscience. Here, he saw at last, was the Jesus symbol, in himself: he would understand why, on exploring Jerusalem's eastern hill, he could not keep the tears from coming. He was forced to under-stand, against all his mind and scruples and his sensitive sense of honor, that a person could be devoted, beyond his own physical interests, and his very self and all reason, to one whom in his heart he could not find worthy; to understand that he had spent so much of the father-mother in him on the brother-son that he had little left for his own sons; to understand how all his life he very possibly had been holding back on his own talent, hoping to see the brother-son advance beyond him. . . .

Until at last he could only bow his head in woe worse than death-sickness and think, It is too late now; it is too late for all these thing...even too late for me to climb to the summit of my own talent...too late for my brother and too late for me. Yes, his mother, with her tyrannical Reuben Rhode will, her great thrust of chin and her Puritan code, had driven deep into him the thought, and the principle and ideal to live by, that he was always to defend his brother, against failure no less than human tigers; encourage, support, and guide him, and keep him up and beyond him in the whole way of life. Vridar had been happy to find Marion with a much better car than his own; with twenty suits of clothes when he himself had only one; with Oriental rugs, when he didn't even have a home of his own---and with money for a two-dollar tip to a barmaid for two sixty-cent drinks. When Mollie said mean petty things about the quality of Vridar's house and its furnishings or his clothes, or about anything else that he owned, he had never resented it, for

Marion's possessions were one of his triumphs over Vridar, and Vridar was glad to have it so.

He would take from the desk a photograph of Marion and study it. The forehead was high and full, the eyes slate-gray and steady, the nose large and strong. The mouth was loose, sensual and weak. The hands, unlike Vridar's, were long, finely shaped, and powerful. Vridar had always been glad that his brother had some features better than his own, and he had been astonished to read in a letter from Wilford Pogue these words: "As a child he was very ugly, in a way that invited persecution....the powerful corrective glasses, which magnified his eyes to twice their size. These gave him a sinister look, which scared some people, made others hate him on sight and want to attack him....To him you seemed handsome and dashing and devilish with the women, always successful, while he was brutalized and repulsive....you were your mother's favorite....you were more successful in your work...."

It was all infernal nonsense, Vridar thought, shoving the long letter away from him: oh yes, he *was* the mother's favorite; but nobody else, to Vridar's knowledge, had ever thought Marion repulsive or ugly or sinister; and to say that Vridar was dashing and devilish with women was such a fantastic perversion of the facts that Vridar could only stare at the words and wonder about Pogue---an intelligent man with sharp insights who for years had been one of Marion's patients.

When after two months he seemed not to come out of the grief but to sink deeper, Angele, despairing, would put before him words which she hoped might touch him off to a return:

> It happened in every town, wherever she tried to identify herself with her schoolmates, wishing to become a part of that *real* world in which those others were so secure. Children love regimentation, mass-identity, fierce uniform standards of play and speech and dress [little blue boys!] With merciless cruelty they ostracize the one who is different [little boys blue!] '*Figlia di commedianti!*' was the cry Eleonora [Duse] heard on streets and playground where she was pointed out as a freak. She hated it. Going to school became a daily ordeal too cruel to be borne.

How well he and Marion had learned the lesson the great actress learned! But Marion was beyond the reach of all that now: sleep, brother, sleep!

She laid before him an article on Eugene O'Neill, which in his own words condemned him as a bellyaching child, a drunkard, a coward---a furious self-loathing trembling wreck of a man who shook so terribly he could not shave himself, yet struck attitudes and shouted to the Universe that he would tear down the curtain of Eternity. Another orphan, who belonged in the panels: who got drunk, one of O'Neill's wives said, to get the courage to face situations. So it had been with Marion; so it was and so it would be with millions: who was fool enough to say that fear was not the cancer in the human soul?

Among the letters that came after Marion's death was Diana's:

> I decided to write and allow the spirit of God to guide my thoughts. The Holy Ghost *is the* source of all comfort, truth and guidance from God to man.

You, brother, were also given the gift of the Holy Ghost at confirmation. Do turn back to Christ, as you once so humbly did, in prayer and thoughts. He is ever ready to help us poor weak mortals. I *know* for I have proven Him and *not* found him wanting.

Our brother learned (for he was seeking for the truth, and what is the truth---the word of God) that God is love. In other words one cannot hope to contact God unless one does it thru love—and humility. Both of those you used to have when you truly had a testimony in your heart that Christ lives and is the son of God. If you have completely lost humility before God (I can't believe you have) then get on your knees and pray....

The letter went on for pages. Vridar handed it to Angele, saying, "What a tower beyond tragedy ignorance can be for most people!" Athene wrote, too, and for Vridar her letter was just as pathetic. Long ago, she said, she had turned back to Christ---and since Athene had studied ancient Greek, and read it, Vridar imagined that she was one person who knew what the Christ-symbol meant. For years Athene had closed her letters to Vridar and Angele with pious exhortations: "Our love to you in Christ. May you be divinely illumined in recording the great mysteries of Being." She had written: "I am pursuing in spare time the study of the New Testament in original Greek. I am also studying it textually with an intellectually brilliant converted Jew, formerly of a strict Rabinical family in Poland and now head of New Testament at Eden Theological Seminary. I find that the revelation of Christianity does not come from reading scholarly tomes *about* what the Scripture *does* or *does not* reveal, but from humble, open-minded personal subjection to the text itself in meditation and prayer such as Gandhi, the greatest figure of modern India, practiced in twenty-four hours of silence every other day. I hope that each new day brings only right ideas, experiences, and decisions to both of you. In Christian love, Athene."

Vridar had read the letter to Angele, and said, "I trust that she and the Jew will keep their minds on the New Testament."

There was a letter from Mollie:

When you'd visit us and sometimes be pretty nasty with him, raking him over the coals for this and that, I'd ask him why you were so nasty and why he took so much and he'd say, 'Oh, he just has to spank his child once in a while. Does him good.' But I'd insist, 'Why don't you fight back?' He'd just look at me. 'Well, why in hell don't you fight back?' He'd answer, 'Well, I don't know what it might do to him if I became unruly. You see, he's been the Papa so long. The only time I feel like a man anyway is when I'm driving a truck.'

But in the last two years of his life he did say several times, 'You know, I'm going to quit letting that damned brother of mine say any damn thing he wants to say to me.' And then it came but the resistance was too strong. For you hurt him so deeply....

Annoyed, Vridar tossed the letter aside: his sister-in-law had a head well-stocked with misconceptions and nonsense. There was so much that she did not

937

know, or refused to see. Six months after Marion returned to Idaho, Vridar had a reputation far and wide as a lecher and libertine. When Angele wanted to look him up, her friends advised her against it, saying, "That guy has been thrown head over heels out of clubs around here. They say seduction is his principal business." Vridar, busy with his Federal projects, had been unaware of all that. Indeed, when Angele told him what his brother was like behind his professional front, and what Mollie was like behind hers, Vridar had been so enraged that he first abused her and quarreled with her, and when she in turn became furious and attacked him he had seized her by her hair and shaken her up and down, and blacked an eye. She had run screaming into the night to find a policeman. For months they had fought over this matter of what Marion and Mollie were, or were not. He remembered it now with deepest shame, for Angele had been right all the time! Vridar had been stubborn; it had taken a mountain of evidence to convince him: in his code of honor and his world a brother and a sister-in-law did not do some of the things which Angele had said they were doing. Even many years later Marion's treacheries were still following him: there was a high Federal official, one of Vridar's close friends, who suddenly cooled toward him; and when Vridar faced the man and demanded to know the reason he was astounded (on his faith in his brother he had placed no limits) to see the suspicion and hostility in this official's face and to hear him say, "Your brother came to me and said I should stay away from you because you were trying to destroy me." Vridar might have said, "Were you fool enough to believe it?" but his astonishment and hurt were too deep. He had turned away, feeling for his brother only compassion and pity.

Knowing that this whole complex matter of family was the heart of his books and of his long journey into the past, he tried week after week to send his mind like a net into the deep seas to dredge the things out of the darkness. He would crawl back under a spreading juniper and lie there, until Angele found him, his eyes open and staring, his mind numbed and sick, but busy. He would look back to his tortured childhood and wonder if it would not have been better for him to have been like other boys---to have grown up to be a farmer and a Mormon bishop. Who could say whether more of right and good was in the fanatical Diana, who spent endless hours on genealogy so that she could have those in her family lines "sealed" who died long ago; or in her free-thinking heretical adulterous brothers? He often thought of the last chapters in Taylor's *The Medieval Mind,* where it was shown how good could come out of conventional evil, or evil out of good; and he would feel again, with a sense of intolerable urgency, that mankind's great task was a reappraisal of all values and a redefining of all terms. When he asked Carl Noyce, "What in your opinion is the most significant contribution of this century?" Carl had said, "The enormous increase of demonstrable scientific hypotheses." He put the same question to Gary Colwell and got the reply, "Our progress in understanding the language we use." Vridar had no doubt that those were two great contributions.

When Angele routed him from the juniper, he would go to his study and sit there, drinking and feeling. Among the many clippings tacked to his walls were six magnicent photographs of Joan Blondell's shock and horror on seeing a fighter

938

named Walcott knocked out. A hundred times Vridar had studied the unfeigned emotion in her face. There was the face of Dave Langfeld, now divorced and married again, wealthy, fat and gross and smug; the cold face of Molotov, which he hated; the fanatical face of Sheen, which he loathed. Between Molotov and Sheen was a photo of a monstrous gorilla in the Chicago zoo. Back and forth Vridar would look at them, thinking, You can take the ape out of the trees and put pants on him and build a house around him, but you can't take him into the house. Angele would come in and look and say, "Poor gorilla, he's dead now: why couldn't it have been Molotov or Sheen?" She had brought with her a card on which she had typed the words: "I believe that man will not merely endure: he will prevail. He is immortal, not because he alone among creatures has an inexhaustible voice, but because he has a soul, a spirit capable of compassion and sacrifice and endurance."

Vridar said, "That's Faulkner accepting the Nobel award. That's the way precocious children talk."

Angele was curling her lips in the way she had when working up a fury. "So man is immortal because he is capable of sacrifice and endurance. So then is the elephant that bothers nobody but goes off into the swamp to die. So then is the mother quail, for I've seen her die for her babies." She squared off and looked at the faces on the wall. "Those men have a soul? Then why is there no sign of it in their faces?"

Vridar was looking at her with more than usual interest. So much of her had come into the light one day when she said that as a child she lived in deadly fear of her father, who had sworn to kidnap her. When she saw a car approaching her, she ran screaming to her grandmother. Still looking at her, while she studied the faces on the wall, he thought of that dark night when, convinced that a ewe had a baby somewhere up the mountain, she had run back and forth with a flashlight. For an hour he had watched the movement of the light in darkness, thinking, A poor little mother who has never had a baby, looking for a baby that was never there! He thought of that professor who had sneered at Vridar for his statement that he could learn about human beings by studying the lower animals: after the man had gone, Angele had thrown wide the doors and windows, saying, "The odor of self-righteousness! Can't you smell it?"

She now turned away from the wall to look at him. "Have you been drinking again?"

He hated to lie to her about it but during these weeks he sank so deep into alcoholism that with sly tricks he tried to deceive her. After drinking part of a bottle of whisky, he would pour two or three ounces of water into the bottle, to make it seem that he had drunk less than he had. He would slip outside with a bottle of sherry or Mexican whisky or sweet wine, all of which he detested, for they made him sick. If he was drinking in his study and heard her coming, he would quickly hide his glass, but he always looked foolish and guilty, for he had little skill in dissembling. He developed the idea that he had to drink if he was to catch up with his mail, and so would sit and write scores of letters that he had no need to write---and wrote them with such bitterness and anger, or with such sarcasm, or with such drunken foolish feebleness that he dared not send them. During these months after Marion's death he wrote hundreds of letters that he never sent. With a leer he would say to Angele, "I've dwelt so long on the notion of myself as important that I find it impossible to dislodge it without dislodging me." He would mutter, "Those blue death-mountains!" using John Gould Fletcher's words; or he would mutter Norman Macleod's words, "O let it all be equal to what I might have been before the mind accepted the dark descent within!" The dark descent within! How well he had said it!

"Vridar, please don't drink any more today."

"I won't," he said, but he knew that his promise was worthless.

XXI

So afraid for him that she would hide and weep, and so desperate that she looked everywhere for a way out of the darkness and back to the light, Angele wrote a letter to a director of a writers' conference, who had invited Vridar to participate, and laid it before him with the sharp command, "Sign here." He read it and then signed it, and she broke into tears on his shoulder.

He detested writers' conferences. In earlier years he had gone to two or three and had taken part in the preposterous mummery, observing each time that there were present a few writers who wanted to talk all the time, and forty or fifty registrants of all ages who thought that in writing there was a magical formula, if only they could lay their hands on it. Vridar had other reasons. He was morbidly shy. He despised the uncommon man's willingness to put himself on display, for a fee, before the common people, knowing that among those who came to him there probably was not one with enough talent to write a good book.

He told Angele to drive, and as soon as they were under way he read to her Fletcher's words, "I did not then suspect that the path to literary success in London, as elsewhere, lay less in merit than in cleverly handled contacts with the dominant figures of the day." He had known that, he said, a long time: all over Manhattan he had seen the second rate literary figures scratching one another's backs. He had read in their faces the bland assumption, You will grant me the significance I choose to feel for myself, and in return I shall not disturb yours. It was all part of the American drive toward ulcers, sleeping pills, endorsements, vulgar advertising, two cars and three television sets per family, deteriorating moral values, togetherness, and the wholesale glorification of mediocrities.

Often during these months he thought of Chris, as he had seen him the last time, slumped in his chair, a glass of whisky in his hand; muttering under his breath about the crass commerical spirit that had licked him, until, suddenly animated, he pulled himself forward, shot his gray brows halfway up his forehead, set his glass down, raised both hands, palms upward, and opened his eyes wide; only to subside slowly, like a thing dying, and resume his muttering, looking for all the world like a man in whom disillusionment was so thick and heavy that it cost him too much effort merely to raise his voice. Vridar caught a few words now and then about "a drooping old bird with all her feathers down" (meaning one Nettie

Darvan, book editor of a leading Manhattan newspaper); about Henry Wallace's century of the common man, with its "elite ruling class of whores." Chris, so far as Vridar could tell, had accepted the dark descent within.

He told Angele to bear in mind certain facts about writers, and she would not find it necessary to show astonishment---to remember what a great psychologist had said, that few of them, if indeed any, ever reached emotional (including sexual) maturity. You had to keep in mind the fact they were all orphans---that they were children—that they were vain envious posturing showoffs. He told her to remember, when looking at them, the question asked him in New York by a famous editor, "Did David Hawke lay his agent?"

A few days later there they were, among grown-up children, all of whom had passed their fortieth birthday. There was Lolly Otis, a novelist, married to a poet with a bulging forehead and the look of a mummy. Lolly was a charming woman who had a girlish way of turning to one side and looking down, with muted self-conscious laughter. She said her husband was simply dying to have heart trouble, but though he chased from doctor to doctor he could find none who agreed with him. He would sit around all day, Lolly said, with a rapt look on his face, holding his wrist, timing his pulse; and if he decided that he could hear murmurs or skipped beats, his face became angelic with happiness. Lolly's portrait of her man, drawn with laughter purling girlishly in her throat, was so amusing that it was impossible not to smile; but across the dinner table Vridar saw Angele's quick wink. The wink said, Does a woman love her man, who holds him up to ridicule? They got drunk with Lolly and staggered with her around the city, trying to find the sorority house in which the visiting geniuses were being cared for; and when at three in the morning they found it, Lolly missed the two steps leading down into her bedroom and pitched forward flat on her face. She picked herself up and said brightly, "That's the way Folker does when he gets drunk, except that he falls under the table." At breakfast, lunch, or dinner, Lolly loved to aim her malice at the Book-of-the-Month-Club or the Literary Guild judges; or deliberately to confuse Virginia Kirkus with Dorothy Canfield Fisher, both of whom she detested, but without venom, for there was more mother than meanness in her. She also took thrusts at the one she called Stiletto Martha.

Stiletto Martha was the dark thin sharply alert wife of Monty Bowles, a famous literary critic. Monty fascinated Angele. He was a man of middle height, rather thick and flabby, with graying hair, a round face with no outstanding feature, and appealing boyish eyes. He looked to Vridar like a man who had fought all his life against clothes. Angele's word for him was "cute." When looking at the man Vridar called to mind the fact that during the years when Bowles was a book editor, twice a well-known reviewer had asked to be allowed to review one of Vridar's books, and twice was told that the review was written and would soon appear, though no review ever appeared. To Angele he said, "This man, whom you find cute, has employed every known fertilizer to enrich his talent but has never got more than twenty bushels to the acre."

Bowles had the face of a slightly pockmarked and wistful mummy, who on being restored was not able to get used to the light. His eyes, so far as Vridar was able to tell, were blue, but when they looked at him he felt in them the kind of opaqueness that is seen in blind eyes. One evening the chairman of the conference gave a party to honor the celebrities; and Monty Bowles, after getting drunk enough to feel friendly toward the whole world, asked Lolly to dance with him. She declined. He then danced solo and in a sad plaintive voice sang old French ballads in cracked French. Watching him trying to have a little fun, a rumpled elderly man whose clothes looked as though they might fall off any moment, or at least slip down, Vridar felt tenderness for him; for even though he seemed to be a liar, he was without malice, almost guile---and an orphan, good Lord, if Vridar had ever seen one. Unlike so many in his profession, Bowles was not aggressive: if he told a story and you listened to it, he was pleased; and if you did not, he was not offended. Twice at the dinner table within the period of a week Vridar heard the man tell the same story: a student, he said, once asked him, In what category is the Bible?---fiction, non-fiction or what? "I asked him, Why? Are you intending to write one?" He then laughed immoderately, but his laughter died and his face sobered when he saw that no one was laughing with him. Vridar thought, He's not very clever and he suspects it.

All those present but Vridar and Angele (yes, and the sharp alert Martha) were too busy trying to possesss the stage and make quips and jests, or tell stories, to listen to, much less to appreciate, the wit or story of another. They were touched with that human disease which assumes that continuous talk is a sign of the knowledgeable and civilized life. Withdrawn, silent, but sharply observing, listening, studying, probing, Vridar now and then had a feeling of sinking, in his stomach and bowels: writers were such children, such childlike exhibitionists, such lost lonely little boys and girls! They said the most stupid things, as when a New York playwright said, "If the world's affairs were in the hands of artists, there would be neither dictatorships nor war."

By far the most aggressive one in this group was Davin Morris, a British poet. Like so many of the British he had contempt for the United States and its ways, but missed no chance to come over and fill his purse. He looked Vridar straight in the eye and said, "Have you ever been in Greece?" He had wanted to retort, "Not since you were in Peru" but he found it not easy to be mean to children. Davin was a tall man but instead of standing straight he humped forward, like one who had bashed his head too many times passing through six-foot doorways. He had eyes that could be full of humor and light, but that could turn ice-cold in a moment. He talked incessantly, about himself, and when stimulated by flattery he talked well: he was, Vridar made out, a man who knew a little about a lot of things, but not a great deal about anything. He was witty, sometimes dry, sometimes subtle, but so convinced of his cleverness that he never perceived that Vridar's many smiles of appreciation were now and then only a mechanical grimace, calculated to keep the man's opinion of himself in good order. Like so many writers, he talked, when not about himself, rather disparagingly about other writers: of a fellow poet, and a far more famous literary figure, he said that the man got up haggard and groaning each morning to gulp a handful of benzedrine, and crawled into bed late every night full of sleeping pills. "Until now," said Davin, "neither he nor his muse is much affected any more."

At lunch one day he said he was writing a fairy story. Two children dreamed and the next day the dream came true: there was a forest, with a unicorn—oh, but he might call it a unico; and nothing happened: there were words: a noun went along with an adverb at its heels; a fat verb or two rolled over: it was to be a take-off on S. P. Ollicut's latest opus. "How delightful!" someone murmured. Davin was the kind of man who kept leaping from fancy to fancy, feeling, it seemed likely to Vridar, that in speed he could quickly leave behind the occasional ineptness, and more probably overtake the few brilliants which in a long day of turning his superficial but restless mind inside out he hoped to find.

It was Lolly who loved to gossip in her malicious but charming way about other writers. She said that Ormond Stilson had written his Maisie story on gin, but now sat with his legs propped up, suffering horribly from gout, and a fairly drastic mitigation of his amour-propre: at his best he had never been, she said, more than an *ami de cour*. His present wife seemed devoted to him. Lolly let the laughter purl in her throat a moment and said, "I never met his second wife before she fell down and broke her neck." Bowles would now and then start to laugh, and at the moment of explosion throw his hands up to cover his eyes, after first shutting his eyes tight and looking tortured. Martha, with roached gray hair and bright alert eyes, sat across from Vridar. One day she tipped her iced tea over and three times explained (though nobody but Vridar and Angele ever listened to her) that it had not been her fault but the fault of the table. At the party Morris had stripped off his shirt (he wore no undershirt) and washed it in the kitchen sink, then loped upstairs to bring another shirt to the kitchen. His trousers were so short that he showed four inches of white sox when he walked. He talked of trees, flowers, painting, sculpture, Vienna, his poet friends, mountains in Greece, postwar Germany —but all the time he was talking about himself. He had an infectious laugh that Vridar found hard to resist, and a sly sense of fun that most of the others seemed to miss, or care nothing about. Vridar would never forget the way he looked at Bowles when Bowles said, of a book of short stories, that he had liked one, but the others had made him think of castration, of testicles scattered everywhere. There had then come his high tortured laugh. Looking at him, Vridar thought, You revealed a hell of a lot more that time than you intended to. It now occurred to Vridar that picturing Bowles in bed with a woman was beyond his imaginative powers. Later, he said to Angele, "No wonder he's devoted to authors of the lean athletic screwing."

When Angele and Vridar departed the scene, Angele kissed the women, who were startled, even astonished—but then, he perceived, pleased, too. It was Angele's way to kiss everybody she liked, and she liked nearly everybody.

Before leaving the city they went to the home of one of Vridar's old friends, a woman who had once been his student in the short story. She had read one of his novels about a long-ago time and had written him:

> For it was a delirious runaway upon the prairies of the infinite. Here
> are the oboes coming in to tell of Beethoven's sorrows and sufferings,

943

his poverty and loneliness. "O God, my Rock, my ALL, Thou unutterable, hear thy unhappy, thy most unhappy of mortals!" They are the tortured cries of the earth in its lonely labor pains.

It was a vibrantly living thing in every part of its flame. . . . In all of these was the primal pulse out of which the heart has come; in all of them were the energies and rhythms and harmonies . . . . And the strings, the horns and the exultant trumpets, the drums echo the vibrations of the tumult in the sea. And now can't you hear the first notes of the Scherzo and the Ode to Joy!

My God, man, it sounds as though you and Beethoven had lived contemporaneously and he had composed the music to your prose-poem. The price we have paid for a little beauty and a little good . . . . If we are only the blind driven down to the sea, it would be a senseless pain to look back upon the dark and bloody trail . . . . Here are the strings and trombones and drums changing from the rhythm of three bars to the rhythm of four bars in the exultant triumph of the spirit. . . .

The exultant triumph of the spirit, that was Mona Stackman. She had suffered half her life and was now taking drugs every fifteen minutes to keep her heart beating. Every time Vridar had seen her she had had, as now, only a jest for herself, a gay laugh, a humorous light in her eyes, and a good word for life. He had never known courage so free of self-pity. Her husband, a man of eighty-five, had lost his mind but was still physically vigorous. He came up to Vridar in his tall courtly way and bowing extended a hand saying, "I think I've not had the pleasure of meeting you. My name is John Stackman." Embarrassed, his wife spoke up: "Father, this is Vridar Hunter. You've known him thirty years." John turned to her a moment and then looked gravely at Vridar. He said, "I'm sure I've never seen this gentleman before." He went out to the yard. Mona said she had to keep him busy. He watered the plants and trees to death, flooded the lawns and the neighbors' cellars and the roadway. She had arranged with the city to have the water outside her house shut off each day, except for an hour or so. Vridar looked through a window and saw Stackman flooding the lawn. In a few minutes he came in and stood looking over at Vridar, then approached him with extended hand. "I think I've not had the pleasure of meeting you. My name is John Stackman."

After they left the city and turned homeward, Vridar thought of Mary Welsh Carlyle's cry, "Good Heavens! I often inwardly exclaim, and is *this* the Literary World? This rascal rout, this dirty rabble, destitute not only of high feeling or knowledge or intellect, but even of common honesty? The very best of them are ill-natured weaklings: they are not red-blooded *men* at all." He recalled Virginia Woolf's comments on *Ulysses*, ". . . puzzled, bored, irritated and disillusioned by a queasy undergraduate scratching his pimples. An illiterate, underbred book . . . egotistic, insistent, raw, striking and ultimately nauseating. And Tom, great Tom thinks this on a par with War and Peace! . . . A first rate writer respects writing too much to be tricky; startling; doing stunts. I'm reminded all the time of some callow board school boy, full of wits and powers, but so self-conscious and egotistical that he loses his head, becomes extravagant, mannered, uproarious, ill at ease, makes kindly people feel sorry for him and stern ones merely annoyed." Vridar had never known what to make of Virginia Woolf, who in both vanity and tricks, it seemed to him, was a match for Joyce. Some had written in superlatives of her brilliant mind, yet she could say, "It seems to me more and more clear that the only honest people are the artists." Of the work of Cervantes she had said that it was "scarcely conscious of serious meaning." She had said, "No creative writer can swallow another contemporary." "She wanted to," Vridar said, with a dry smirk at his wife, this woman who said of herself as a literary critic, "I think myself infallible." Poor Virginia!

It made an author wonder if in the whole field of literature there was anything he could touch and be sure of. How stupid of any writer to resent the malicious reviewers, when Balzac could put *Melmoth the Wanderer* side by side with Moliére and Goethe!

Vridar had received invitations to other conferences, and Angele begged him to go to one more. "Just one more," she said. He shuddered. At the conference he had just left the director was Ralph Izard, who looked like a soured monk from Mount Athos. One morning, when Vridar was talking to his class, Izard had slipped in, listened a few moments, then had risen to his feet to say that Vridar was wasting the time of these people and should at once proceed to the creative process. Trying to hide his amazement, and his anger at the worst affront he had ever had, Vridar picked up the line of what he had been saying; but after another five minutes Izard was again on his feet. This time his rebuke was sharper. At conferences which he directed, he said, instruction was raised above the informal and casual, to the high plane of the creative process. Would Vridar be good enough to make the creative process his subject? By this time Vridar was so blind with rage that he could hear the sound of it in his bowels. He was never to know how he managed to fill out the hour, or why he was so kind as never to speak of the matter to Izard. Angele said it was because the poor fellow so obviously was making the creative process a father-image.

Robin Welsh, director of the next conference, was as different from Izard as Abelard from Torquemada. Before midnight of the first day, Vridar and Angele were drunk with Robin and his wife—drunk with whisky and fellowship. When, alone with Vridar, Angele said they were both lovable, he agreed, and added: "They are simple in the way of big things, and lonely in the way of rare things." Then, with a grimace and a shrug: "But always bear in mind that love is not an adult characteristic."

Angele met in this city a famous folklorist, a little old woman, and on telling Vridar about her made a remark that he stored away: "I'm learning that people who are really superior are comfortable to be around." He had a small notebook, hidden away from her, in which he had written some of her most luminous sayings. In Rome she had said, "I don't think I'll send my nuns any holy pictures. They get so much holiness." She had meant the nuns where she had once been a student. In a moment of furious jealousy she had shouted at him, "I'm damned tired of a Narcissus who looks at himself all the time in the mirror of women!" Standing on a hill in Istanbul and looking away to the Golden Horn she had taken his hand and said, "Anywhere in the world the people are my people, if you are with me." He had said to her one day, "You're a poet, for the reason that children are, and

945

adults never." At this conference she was more the poet, because people of quality perceived the true nature of her and liked her.

She had brought a satchel of notes with her, and Vridar had brought a few books. On the long drive home they took turns at the wheel, and reading aloud. She was trying (he knew this but did not let her know that he knew it) to keep his mind off his brother and his sense of failure—and all this she did with such finesse that he marveled; as when, looking through some notes in a book, he found those that he did not recall having seen before, such as a card on Degas:

> To a person of his intellectual powers and originality, recognition by the Salon or from any official quarter was quite meaningless. His contempt for Manet, who was eager to receive the red ribbon of the Legion of Honor, was unbounded. It was not his nature to "belong." He was deeply suspicious of "schools" and "movements."

Vridar would read the words, a grin spreading over his face. So! If he did not seek acclaim; if he had only contempt even for the Nobel award in literature, after it had been given for political reasons to mediocrities; if he would not belong to groups and movements, or try to develop a cult, then why should he complain if nobody paid any attention to him!

He also grinned, and felt pretty silly, when he read a card at the top of which was the name

John James Audubon

> While he lived, it was a different story, and his struggles to complete a great work in the face of poverty and opposition have an epic quality about them, notwithstanding the vanity of the man, his unreasonable suspicions, and his inability to credit his rivals with honorable intentions.

Vridar read the card several times. One day, out of the blue, while drinking beer with her, he said, "So you think I'm as vain and suspicious as Audubon?" Quickly she replied, "As suspicious maybe, but you're not a vain person, really."

On another occasion he found, where he could hardly have missed them, Cezanne's words, "I am only a helpless pioneer on a lonely road." Or over the breakfast she would remember certain things they had seen in Amsterdam's museum, and then wonder aloud why a painting as fine as "The Night Watch" had destroyed Rembrandt's reputation and brought the remainder of his life down to the wretched level of poverty and heartbreak.

Now, while he drove, she read aloud from Dixon Wecter's *The Saga of American Society,* but suddenly broke off, exclaiming: she had found something good. It was Renan's statement about the leading families of Bonapartist society, that "their ignorance gives one a rough idea of the infinite."

"Wonderful!" Vridar cried, and shot a glance of admiration at the Wecter tome. He approved again when she read Lessing's words, "The iron pot longs to be lifted up by tongs of silver from the kitchen fire that it may think itself an urn." Or when she read Saki's words, "Government by democracy means government of the mentally unfit by the mentally mediocre tempered by the saving grace of snobbery."

No matter how much cologne he put on it, he said, the century of the common man reminded him of the contest in farting between Chaste Bumbell and his bride.

Angele said, "It's what Davin Morris told us, that all British writers, even those farthest to the left, are horrible snobs."

"Orphans," Vridar said. "We live in the age when millions of Kulaks were murdered; in the age of Belsen, Oswiecim, Majdanek, the sack of Nanking and Lidice; Buchenwald and Katyn; Roosevelt congratulating Stalin on his birthday; William O. Douglas shaking the hand of the Soviet ambassador just after the massacre of the Hungarians. But fear is the worm in the apple, not original sin, or the childish belief that man is born depraved."

"But aren't fear and original sin the same thing?"

He turned to look at her. "Well now," he said. "It's a nice bon mot maybe but I'd guess that fear begat the idea of sin, and that the idea of original sin is a tremendous rationalization. Poor Eve, with the berry half way to her lips."

After opening two cold beers she began to read from Reik's *Fragment of a Great Confession,* a probing of the Goethe and Reik psyches. "Man," she read, turning to a passage Vridar had marked, "is with all his senses and drives directed toward the outer world and he has much trouble recognizing it as such and making it serve his purposes and needs. He knows about himself only when he enjoys himself or suffers. Any comment?"

"Well, yes. I wonder why in hell Goethe never once suspected his incest problem."

"Would he have been happier if he had?"

"It's a matter of keeping the orphans from crying. Take Kant. He suffered so from theology as a child that in later life he avoided churches. Or did he? In fact, in the fog of a vast metaphysical system he built his own. Take Wallace: almost as great a man as Darwin, yet in his old age he went tottering into spiritualism. Take Truman. Weeks before he dropped the bomb on them the Japanese were begging for a truce. Stalin deliberately starved millions to death. Take Carl Noyce: he told me that we trampled over millions of young men in War II to build a better world. If we don't probe the damned male psyche and find the reasons for its disease, we'll have worse Belsens and Katyns and Hiroshimas."

When he fell silent, she said: "Go on probing."

He knew what she meant: she was determined to keep his mind off his brother.

"Probing? Let Reik probe. He says the original fear for the safety of one's self is usually a psychic reaction to repressed hatreds, which the ego can't accept, for the reason that the hatred is in conflict with one's principles. All right, I hated my father, I hated my mother, I hated the bullies in three schools; I hated the bigtalking thunderbolt-dropping deity of the Old Testament, and all the hairy shaggy old prophets with their mouths open howling at the heavens; and I hated—"

"Why not say that you hated just about everything?"

"No more than millions of people in the Western world hate. I felt as insecure as one holding to life with only fingertips. It's the same fear that forced Stalin and Hitler to murder millions. Do you think any person can ever feel secure if his emotional growing is stopped in childhood? Do you think a really matured intelligent adult male would murder millions in the name of a lunatic named Marx, or a ferocious father-image called God?"

"No, I don't think he would."

"Why don't the Reiks tell us who are crazy and who aren't? I suppose I'm insane, and so was my brother, so is my sister—three nuts produced by the Judean-Christian system. And there are millions like us."

"Have you thought of any person in the whole world who seems really adult?"

"Not a damned one. Nehru? Holy heaven! Eisenhower? A grandfatherly child. You'd think Freud must have been one, yet all his life he itched with petulant furies, tyrannies, tantrums, and the kind of mother-idolatry that has become bigger than Pa in Judaism. F. D. Roosevelt?—with his colossal vanity and conceit, his ten-year-old interest in sailing ships and stamp collecting and Hollywood phonies. When you think of him think of Tzar Alexander at the Congress of Vienna."

"Smuts?"

He knew she was teasing him. He had told her one day how a Dr. J. L. B. Smith had given a dedicated fifteen years to a search for the coelacanth, and that Smuts, a hero in American magazines, had refused to see him, much less to aid him.

"William A. Orton says that when men as different as Einstein, Franz Alexander and Osbert Sitwell agree that the world has reached a point of gross incredible moral decay—but what of it? Can you expect anything more than an age of whores and an era of gangsters in a world where children rule?"

He asked her to drive, and leaving the car went to the passenger side. "I have a slip of paper somewhere in this book," he said, "with the words on it of the former wife of a famous European novelist. Yes, here it is. Quote: 'The future may look back on this age and reflect that it had so little character and held that little so lightly. As a whore, I am minor in the company of millions who pimp and whore every day beyond the need of sustenance—selling their names for money, endorsing products, who have all the money that a thousand persons should have. I whore for bread and bed. They whore to get their names and faces before the public.' Does that say it? And remember that the whores she is talking about include not only those whose emotions smell of pus, but also a Columbia dean, a Columbia professor-poet, dear old Eleanor—"

"Yes, Cookie."

"Well, let's see, I have other attempts here to say it. Quote: 'Mr. Luce has a passion for glossy mediocrity and stereotypical order which derives from his obsession with mechanism . . . . the inevitable mockery accorded both by *Time* and *Life* to major talent . . . . In a word, *Time, Life,* and *Fortune* (*The New Yorker* can be tossed in with them) are the American Bloomsbury, our psychological bureaucracy, inhabited by well-paid artist-apes. In America art must pay off before it can be respecable . . . . The "sophisticated" tone of *Time* arises from nothing more than queasiness about the main march of human affections . . . . nurse a self-image of tweedy decorum and contented aplomb such as the "Men of Distinction" ads exhibit. So that *T.L.F.* constitute the Hollywood of the East Coast . . . . their dedication to the garish rhetoric of the machine . . . . The only practical problem that remains today is that of restoring human dimensions so that a merely human

948

order can become relevant and practical once more. It is obvious that, humbly envisaged, the machine could have helped to do this. But any rational hope in that quarter is now gone.' End of quote. Well, as you have said, it's going to be an immense toy-world for tall children with beards. Is Henry Luce the John the Baptist of the machine age? I see it this way: the machine has become triumphant, with the Judean-Christian corpse propped up alongside to make it look respectable."

"Fine! You've said it, don't spoil it, be still."

Pulling off the road she fetched two beers from the trunk; and he then fell into silence, brooding; unaware that she was glancing at him from time to time, unaware at first, of her voice when she spoke. She was asking him to go on probing, not because she wanted to hear again what she had already heard, but to keep him off the one subject that drew all his thoughts and emotions within the small shutter of despair and death. Arousing himself at last he said, a little angrily, "I wasn't thinking about him." He lied, and she knew that he lied.

Again he drew off the road. "Take the wheel," he said. When again she was driving he forced himself to thumb through a pile of notes. "You want to hear William Schlamm? He says the intellectuals of our time are the first working men in history who in their work have been removed from the labor of transforming things. He thinks that men denied mastery over matter will crave mastery over men. All sorts of persons, you see, have all sorts of explanations: it apparently occurs to none of them that the religious systems invented from the unconscious to make fear and loneliness tolerable have fixed the human race in childhood. The wish for power over men is chiefly the wish for power over father—or sometimes mother, sometimes both, sometimes a brother, or still another. Not in ten light-years would it occur to Schlamm and his kind that in fact we are only children, pretending we have an adult world. And I say to hell with it."

"But surely you can think of someone who is fairly adult? Picasso?"

He turned on her a dry cynical face, for he knew that again she was trying to tease him.

"Malraux? Edmund Wilson? Graham Greene? John O'Hara? John Steinbeck? Elvis Presley or Frank Sinatra or Richard Neuberger or Wayne Morse?"

"Why only male names?"

"Because it's a male world. All right: Suzanne LaFollette?—Edith Haggard?—Fleur Cowles?—the Duchess?"

"I detest the Duchess, but she's more adult than anyone you've named yet. Look, T. S. Eliot at seventy said all his stuff had been childish; and he has gone scurrying back into a dead Church to peer out and say that a rational order will never work. What child ever uttered with more devastating humor, not intended? W. H. Auden, with his ravaged face and sleeping pills, says we must abjure the open society and return to the closed. Can you more completely capitulate to fear? Meanwhile the sciences and their apostles, bishops, cardinals, and popes, have it within themselves to build as monstrous a tyranny as the Church in the Middle Ages, or the Communist; and I suspect they will."

"Have."

"All right, have. A hell of a lot I care any more."

949

They were now west of the Black Hills and heading for the great open spaces of Wyoming, with the Tetons beyond. They found cheap lodging, slept for seven hours, ate sandwiches and coffee, and with half a case of iced beer in the trunk were off again. Vridar began to talk about the Wind River, the Teton, and Sawtooth mountains. In all his life he had never talked to impress people, rarely to convince, only now and then to astonish, but chiefly to formulate—to bring all the mavericks of his thoughts and insights into corrals, where he could try to put his mark on them. He tapped the Reik book and spoke of Goethe's extraordinary powers of identification with the emotions of other people. That was true of him, too, he said; there was not much me me me left in me. There had not been much left in his brother: Marion had sunk so deep into so many patients ("I intend no pun") that at last he was only a shell full of alcohol and lunacy.

"Jesus and all the Christian fishes! He's back on incest. He says maybe Friederike unconsciously represented Goethe's sister, whose middle name was Friederike. How could a mind as able as Goethe's fumble all its life looking for a candle and never find it? Well, he at last married one as unlike his sister as possible; and so did I," said Vridar, looking over at his wife.

"I see that on page 215 I have marked this: 'I feel the same reluctance to read a book of my own.' I too. Waugh and Hemingway say they read their books hundreds of times—no one but a small child could, in the way of children reading comics until they wear them out. But no, it's not that: it's the same thing as my father chewing off his fingernails and swallowing them: fear has gone deep into persons who eat their nails, or keep reading their own books. You know, it's like the Margaret we met: she had a novel of eight hundred pages that a publisher was begging for but she wouldn't let it go. By this time no doubt she has eaten it."

"Or just reads it over and over."

"Most likely. What a picture of the child!"

"The orphan, Cookie."

"Yes, of course, the orphan. Well, here are the words that made my woman cry: What a blessing that not only the hunted but also the hunters get tired. And here's another I marked. Reik tells of a writer who so vividly imagined the tortures of a jealous husband that he wanted to choke his mistress to death."

Angele burst with laughter. "How wonderful!"

"You know, at the moment I'm thinking of a typical American narcissist glamor-woman who feeds on the illusion that men everywhere are jumping off towers or gulping poison because they haven't been to bed with her; and behind her in deep shadow stands a sadfaced moose-lipped son who when he talks mumbles out of his desolations, and makes facial contortions that would convulse a spider. Me me me, and me me me's flight from wives. Wasn't Goethe a fine fellow, though! The bum fled from Lilli, fled from Friederike and Lotte, fled from Frau von Stein—and by God he didn't even pause long enough to say goodbye to Frau and Lilli. The arts are full of men and women fleeing from their mates—their emotional ages ranging between six and twelve. We've had only one Robert and Elizabeth, thank God; how strange the way all of us turn away from the more adult people!

"Shall I give you Wolfe again?—to lose the earth you know for greater knowing;

to lose the life you have, for greater life; to leave the friends you loved, for greater loving; to find a land more kind than home, more large than earth—whereon the pillars of this earth are founded, toward which the conscience of the world is tending—a wind is rising, and the rivers flow. Who has ever phrased the child's lament better? Not even the children in the Bible.

"Look yonder, girl-woman: almost nowhere else in the world do rivers flow as well as there. Marion was right: I'm a lot like my father—a mountain man and river man. I'd like to give my typewriter away, and all my books, and with not even note paper or pencil go to the north of Alaska and live there with nobody but you, with this age of brutes and whores nothing but a memory."

He was looking out at the Wind River mountains. Beyond them were the Tetons, the Yellowstones, the Sawtooths, the Big Horns—four magnificent ranges, all endeared to him. Soon they were driving up Wind River; and looking south he said that a momument to Sacajawea was there. Looking north, he said that up there were three or four novels he would like to write. Had she ever been at the junction of Milk River and the Missouri? That would be a special spot for him, some day. Had she ever been at Travellers Rest, just out of Missoula, where the Lewis and Clark party rested, both going and coming?

"Well," he said, turning again to the book, "Reik says Goethe couldn't take women he respected, but only those he could look down on. In the Judean-Christian world there must be millions like him. I was not one. My response has been to the shy ready-to-flee quivering-with-intimations-of-rape kind. The aggressive ones like my mother, with hair on her chin and legs that could kick a cheese press to pieces, put me on the run. Herbert Silberer somewhere says that psychic impotence and fear of examinations are related. Well, all the way through school I had hideous dreams about examinations, which I always failed, always. I still have them. I still flunk Old English about twice a year."

"Cookie!" she said, and snickered.

"I do," he said. "Like Marion, I don't have much respect for an academic system that allowed me to get high degrees, and with high honors. Silberer—"

"This child needs another beer." She pulled off the highway. On leaving the car he stood a few moments to sniff the odors of Wyoming—of the Rocky Mountains plains areas. "Crow country," he said, returning from the trunk. "Crow Indian country. It reminds me of another novel I'd like to do some day. Silberer—"

"You're getting drunk," she said.

The rebuke silenced him and for fifty miles he pretended to sleep. Unable to get a response from him, she left the highway and stopped, and then slid across to him. Drawing him to her arms she said she was sorry; and he said, "It's all right. Of course I'm getting drunk. So are millions of others at this moment. Besides, I was afraid that I might be offending Monsieur Malraux."

She slid back to the wheel and started the engine; he poured whisky into two glasses. The beer was all gone, he said. Did she know that he had a tendency to put into his mouth almost anything that was handed to him? He would have been the easiest husband in the world to poison, for apparently he had never risen above the diaper level. Did she know that another strong tendency in him was to labor

951

long hours on holidays, when the nation went idle? "On Labor Day morning I heave myself up at daylight, and with both muscles and brain bulging I work like hell till after dark."

"Cookie!"

"Hadn't you observed it? What a virtue my mother made of toil! I tell you I have nightmares about a slothful world: the idea of a thirty-hour week fills me with such murderous furies that I seize a picture of Walter Reuther and say to it, I'd reuther cut you up in small pieces than see this nation—"

"Come-come!"

"It also makes a maniac of me to think of debt. My parents had such a horror of debt that they told their children never to owe anyone a single cent. I never have. Yet this nation will soon be in debt a thousand billions, leaving the burden to its grandchildren, who with still more infinite cunning will leave it to great-grand-children, who will add to it and with cunning multiplied again by four—but you talk. I'm so drunk now I'm stupid."

She was quiet a little while. Then: "I would talk of memories—of the first morning I looked out of the Suede hotel and saw the sunlight on Notre Dame; the first time we ate lunch in the ruins of the Parthenon—when did wine ever taste so good?; the small-boy awe in your face when you stared straight up at the vault of St. Peter's; the time we flew over the tower of Pisa just at dawn, with all the rest of the world gray, but the tower itself and the cathedral brilliant in morning light, and the grass all around like emerald velvet. Memory of the pigeons in Mark's square. Wind River? Nowhere else in the world had I known a wind so clean and exhilarating as the sun-warmed sea-and-earth-scented wind that washed over the hill and ruins of Pompeii: nowhere else had sunshine ever been so intimate, as though it had been designed for this spot, and all warmth and sunlight elsewhere were incidental, like the powdered sugar dust falling from a cookie."

Turned, he was looking at her profile. She had never liked to be viewed in pro-file but she seemed not to mind now, for she was halfdrunk, and sentimental with memories.

She went on: "That is what I thought until I stood in the ruins of the Acropolis. There again was a separate wonderful world with a sun and wind of its own. Again the past was so close that I felt myself a part of it—standing in the middle of the temple looking through the great doorway at a scene that seemed to have the depth of eternity. Nowhere since or before the blueness of the sky over Athens. Nowhere else the incredible intense blue of sky, with clouds a sharp true white."

"I've told you, damn it, you should write books. Let's have a coffee."

He entered a small cafe, taking with him two plastic cups, and returned with hot black coffee. "Crowheart," he said. "This place is called Crowheart. I suffer nostalgia as some suffer gout when I think of the thousands of names like this in the nation, and all the life that was in them and made them, now dead and gone. Crow country. Joe-Adam, the mountain and river man, would have loved this land, up there alone with his rifle on high mountains, with deer meat for supper.

"Did I ever tell you about a dream I had after Joe died? I had seen in a magazine a picture of a man kiling a leopard with a spear. I then dreamed of a huge and dreadful bull, with immense horns, bearing down on me. Somehow there was a break in the dream. Then the bull seemed to be lying close by a barn manger, and a woman who was Athene (who can now say I did not marry her because she was like my mother!) took a small penknife and thrusting between the bull's ribs pierced his heart. I was amazed that it could be done with such a small knife. The bull said, Ah, you have stabbed me! and looking at the face I saw the face of my father. I wish I could write stories as perfect as that one.

"All right, child-woman, let's have some more memories."

"No, Cookie. I think it's best for you to talk all these things out of you. Then you can write again." She turned to glance at him. "Have you ever realized that your mother made you head of the household?"

"The dream indicates that I have realized that. On her side was that all of it? One day not long ago she caught me alone a few moments, and seizing me with her mottled and veined but still strong hands she tried to draw me close; and looking up at me she said, You've always been my sweetheart. You know that, don't you? The word sweetheart for her doesn't mean lover; she doesn't know what a lover is. It means her dearest one. She was scowling, the question was sharp and angry, as though she had said, Deny it and I'll knock your stupid head off. She should have been a spider, then she could have eaten all her mates."

Angele glanced at him. She had never got used to the way the two sons talked about their parents. "I know the tone she used. The second time I ever saw her she scowled at me and said, You don't think my son intends to marry *you,* do you?"

"I can hear it. What woman was ever good enough for her manly little Vridar, God bless his mewling and pewling soul. What a dean of women she would have made! What a Mother Superior in a nunnery! But wait, I have it: What a Ma up there in the sky with the Hebrew Pa!

"Well, dear Ma and Pa, we have it—this shameful ingrown togetherness—almost with a lot of Judaic and Christian families as though they all slept in the same bed: the incest-yearning, father-son-hatred-ridden family, that produces the orphans—the orphans too strong to be children forever, too weak to be adults. Among all other animals the parent-child relationship is severed. Jews and Christians won't let it be severed. O Jesus no! My mother was determined to have her sons (her daughter?—never) build their homes on the ranch, close by her; and Rhode got nearly all of his right around him. And in this world of Jews and non-Jews, standing in the Bible up to their necks, the stupid asses wonder why they are so plagued with juvenile delinquency, gangsters, insanity, alcoholism, drug dopes, not to mention forty shrill insufferable news commentators all imitating Winchell."

Slyly teasing she said, "And you still can't think of an adult?"

He reached to the back seat for a magazine and opened it at pages showing the faces of George Gamow, Lionel Trilling, Paul Tillich, W. H. Auden, Thornton Wilder, Reinhold Niebuhr, Arthur T. Vanderbilt, Sumner Slichter, Walter Lippmann, Frank Lloyd Wright, J. Robert Oppenheimer, Sidney Hook, Russell Kirk, and Jacques Barzun. These had been chosen by the magazine's editors as typical American intelectuals of their time. He asked Angele to drive off the highway and stop. He then took the wheel, and told her to look at these faces, hard and searchingly, as one looking for a father, and tell him if there was a single one among the fourteen adult enough to please her.

Holding them this way and that way to the light, she studied them for twenty minutes or more, and then dismissed them one by one. Behind Auden's craggy face she said the little boy was visible, and he was gentle and tortured and lonely. Who could miss the petulant small-child impatience in Gamow, Hook, and Trilling? —the ape-philosopher boy in Wright or Tillich?—the little-lad zeal and naivete in Oppenheimer?—the round wondering adolscence in Kirk?—the overfed and over-grown amour-propre in Barzun? No, there was not one in the whole lot who looked any more like an adult than the father she had had, who was a child with a baseball and marbles in his pocket. She thought that possibly Wilder, Lippmann, and Vander-bilt came closest to being adult, but she didn't want any of them either. Vridar asked her to turn to another page and read what he had marked there: the face was that of the Jesuit son of John Foster Dulles, and these were the words she read aloud:

"It would not be enough to resolve to leave a theater in case you found yourself severely tempted. By that time you would already have incurred a serious danger of interiorly yielding to temptation, and the seeds of future temptation would already be implanted in your soul. Granted the normal tendencies of human nature, it is unlikely that an individual would be strong-minded enough to prevent these evils by leaving the theater as soon as the first signs of danger appeared."

Vridar said: "How old is the one who uttered those words?"

"It says thirty-seven here."

"Let's let your words stand without comment. Let them be the epitaph for our time."

When they were driving again Angele said, "There's something that always bothered me about your family. You say the most awful things about one another, yet you're all very close. In my family we're not close and we never talk about one another that way."

"Of course not. You're not Jews. What you're talking about is the essence of Jewishness. Like so many Christian families, mine is essentially Jewish. You know what the urine smells like after eating asparagus. Well, you can't stuff yourself with the Jewish holy books all the way up through the soft years when things outside your will shape you and be anything but a Jew. My father never once got his head up out of the Old Testament so that we could get a good look at him. Our parents shoved that book down our throats and then tied a noose around our necks to be sure we couldn't puke it out. But Marion and I at last vomited forth about everything, ex-cept Ecclesiastes and a few other morsels.

"Lorelei, if you had ever lived around Jews you'd know what I mean. No other people in the world will talk to one another in such abusive sneering insulting language; but raise a little finger against them and the clan will close ranks and stand as one man. Like a family of Jews we have all loathed one another—can you ever forget the distaste in the face of Jim Schwartz when he spoke of his sister or his nephew?—yet he left them a million or two each. The members of our family have been fond of one another, in a strange Old Testament diseased sort of way.

954

"There is a line by Tennyson that Landor said was worth whole volumes of poetry: The breaking heart that will not break. That's about where this schizoid Western world stands today.

"Look! The Tetons!"

XXII

One of Vridar's most sensuous delights was to sit propped against a big pine or fir tree, a bottle of old bourbon at his side, an interesting book on his lap, magnificent mountains towering above him, and his wife talking to the birds. They stopped to buy food, and when they reached the Tetons they searched over the area to find a spot for the night, where on an open campfire coffee could steam and bacon fry, their delicious odors mingling with the scent of conifers, mountain earth and stone, and pure mountain water. "Two things I've wanted to do in this life," he said, looking up at the peaks. "Go with Lewis and Clark to the ocean, and with someone like Leigh-Mallory climb to the summit of Everest."

Under the high spreading wings of a great tree he laid a fire, so that Angele could prepare the supper; and he then rummaged in the car to see what book he might read. He looked at and rejected a dozen, and settled at last on *The Writer in America* by Van Wyck Brooks. He scraped together a mound of pine cones, needles, and twigs, on top of which, against the bole, he placed the car robe, so that he could stretch out, reclining, in the way he loved, with a good book and a bottle, and a fire talking fifteen feet away. He had been breathing deep of all the clean mountain smells and wondering why most people by choice lived in big cities.

He had read the Brooks book and had marked a lot of passages, which he now intended to read to Angele, for the hell of it. Brooks, he said, speaking aloud, had worked up a case of seething disgust with contemporary American writing. "Listen. He says, 'Was judgment ever wilder in regard to values than when Dickens can be called "decadent" and Emerson a "fraud"? One might as well call the sun the source of darkness.' Certain critics, it seems, have been proclaiming that Poe is no good at all, and Browning had an inferior mind and spirit. I quote again: 'We have heard the poems of Matthew Arnold described as "chill-blained mittened musings" by one of the most eminent writers of the last three decades, as we have heard Milton called "donkey-eared, asinine, disgusting" by the celebrated poet who "chucked out" Virgil and Pindar.' That was Ezra Pound," Vridar said, looking over at Angele, who was greasing a skillet. "I quote some more of these delightful judgments. 'Have we not heard Wordsworth characterized as a "silly old sheep" and Meredith's *Modern Love* dismissed as "the flashy product of an unusual but vulgar cleverness working upon cheap emotion"?' And hasn't a famous writer, Brooks asks us, called one Hemingway the most important author since Shakespeare?"

"He sounds awfully upset," Angele said, rubbing her eyes in the smoke. "Doesn't he know that authors and critics have always been like that?"

"What he seems not to know, obviously, is that he is dealing with vain envious children who need a good hiding out in the woodshed. If he had known that, how

955

different his book might be! It's pretty damned childish to take any writer seriously when he speaks about another writer. Well, by God, here he is putting in a lusty blow or two for George Meredith, the same Meredith who bellyached until he was heard all over England; who said that if he, Meredith, was a novelist, Dickens was not---and all because the Dickens royalty checks were fifty times as big as his own. Do you suppose that Brooks knows that Sainte-Beuve, who dominated literary criticism in Europe for forty years, found almost nothing to admire in Balzac, Stendhal, and Flaubert, yet threw his critical hat in the air for an assortment of mediocre asses who were forgotten long ago? Has he any idea of the forces that join their anti-intellectual closed-society minds to make a literary reputation in our time?"

"Where has this man been living?"

"In New England, I imagine. Well, here's something that will tickle you like bugwalks. He says a poet named Ransom---that must be John Crowe---cited a poem by another poet, in which Ransom had found five supreme aesthetic effects, that made the reader think of these five collections—woman-love, here is American literary criticism at its profoundest, so lend an ear---these five collocations: 'rosy chocolate and gift umbrellas, chophouse chocolate and sham umbrellas, porcelain chocolate and fried umbrellas, mushy chocolate and frail umbrellas, Chinese chocolate and large umbrellas.' "

Suspecting that he was teasing her, Angele came over and knelt to read the words. Then meeting his eyes she said, "Is his picture in that book of poetry?"

"Oh, I would think so: he is one of the academic indestructibles: ipsa sibi obstat magnitudo, if I may sound learned for a moment."

Angele paid no attention, for she was staring at the poet's face. "This man wasn't spoofing," she said. "See what a nice little grandpa he is." Then she hastened to the fire and returned, saying, "I have some gilt umbrellas for you." What she had was a few bacon tidbits. He now opened his mouth like a nestling and she fed into it small lean morsels of bacon, spearing them with a sharpened pine twig. After accepting the last morsel, he seized her hand and kissed it.

"Nice umbrellas," he said. "Well, I see that I have here a page from a magazine which gives some of Robert Graves's adult animadversions: when this lad takes in after his competitors, he dips his spear in curare. Will you listen a moment to the oracle from Deyá?—and the next time we're in Palma we'd better run up and have a look at him. He says, 'What I like most about Eliot is that though one of his two hearts, the poetic one, has died and been given a separate funeral he continues to visit the grave wistfully and lay flowers on it.' "

"That's cute but it's pretty damned nasty."

"Oh, these writers are nasty children---the kind who push rusty old knives through helpless cats named Auden. Quote: 'Auden's is now the prescribed period style of the thirties, compounded of all the personal styles available; but he no longer borrows whole lines, as for his first volume, or even half-lines. It is a word here, a rhythm there, a rhetorical trophe, a simile, an ingenious rhyme, a classical reference, a metrical arrangement.' End of quote."

Angele had picked up the Williams book. "Is our Robert boy here?" She turned pages and suddenly cried out, "O my God! What a bitter scowling fellow!"

"He was pretty young then. Majorca has taken a part of the scowl off. As for Auden, one would think that after reading those words he would have chucked his Oxford professor-ship and blown his brains out. Well, back to Brooks.

"He is now saying, 'When certain critics say that Dreiser will not be read in another generation, one asks, But who of our time will be read?' Hunter!" Vridar said, looking over at his wife.

"Of course, doll," she said, banking twigs around the coffee pot. "If there are any adults, that is."

"Oh yes, adults. Now he's lamenting the neglect of O'Neill and Jeffers; and saying of Millay that she was ignored and snubbed for years before she died. Not by me. What lips my lips have kissed and where and why---"

"I guess the thing for all writers to do is die young."

"A lot of them have sense enough to do that. You know, nowhere do I find Mr. Brooks lamenting over Mr. Hunter, but he drops a large round tear for Fragonard, the painter, who died in Paris as obscurely, he says, as an artist ever died in New York---or lived in Cold Springs valley, he might have added, if he had not been dozing. If you'll pardon my dreadful French a moment, l'amour-propre est le plus grand de tous les flatteurs, said La Rochefoucauld. Self-love is what children are made of. Mr. Brooks seems not to know that the neglect, even the torture and killing, of its greatest minds and hearts has always been one of mankind's major sports. And what do you suppose he's asking now?---if Fitzgerald and Hemingway ever grew up!"

"All right, he's on the scent at last. How old did you say he is?"

"Seventy, anyway."

"And hasn't learned that Hemingway and Fitzgerald are only boys?"

"I'll astonish you even more, for I find another magazine page here, on which a novelist named Edward Dahlberg has an essay called Our Avant Garde Illiterates. He says—O my God!—he says, 'In the Faulkner and Caldwell fiction there is no difference between the sick stupidity of the protagonist and that of the author.' "

Angele said, "These writer children really play rough."

"The way boys do, out in back alleys. He says Faulkner has never learned how to write, and cites as proof, 'Twilight ran in like a violet dog.' "

"Must have been quite a dog," Angele said.

"Violet all over," Vridar said. "Dahlberg says he doesn't like what he calls 'that guttering infantile anthropomorphism' in such things as the 'bearded watching trees' and the 'sourceless suspurant moon.' "

"What kind of moon is that?"

"Haven't any idea. When I memorized the dictionary I stopped at L. Well, he's back on the slack gawk in the amorous scene, Time magazine's El Papa: that's what he says: Hemingway has no intellectual virility and is a slack gawk in an amorous scene. Dahlberg says it's hatred of women that dominates such writers: he smells the right odor but comes up with the wrong corpse. Have we time for one more drink?"

"A quick one."

He mixed another drink for her, poured straight bourbon for himself, and then washed the hot burning flavor and scent of mellow old bourbon all around his mouth and the back of his throat. And again he turned to Brooks.

"Well, here is our New England gentleman saying that Proust, Lawrence, Eliot, Yeats---he could have named a hundred more---all despised the things that have kept our society open. Brooks seems not to realize that an open society is only for adults: why does he think so many writers fled into the closed system of Communism? Doen't he understand that after Khrushchev kicked Pa Stalin into the mausoleum and called him a son of a bitch (which all but fools knew he was from the start), some of the prodigal sons came wailing back and got the fatted calf? This son who stayed home and plowed the fields and said Stalin was exactly what he turned out to be, what did this son get? The kind of rewards the Christians usually give to virtue."

Angele had come over to sit by him a few moments. She met his gaze, looked at the book, and again met his gaze, her face touched by amusement and pity. "Didn't you say Mr. Brooks is a famous literary critic?"

"Oh, very famous. He must have as many honorary degrees as Coolidge had. And here," said Vridar, striking a page with his forefinger, "right here he's telling us, with what I take to be astonishment, that some child named Graham Greene says perfect evil walks the world where perfect good can never walk again. If Greene goes on talking that way, he'll have more honorary degrees than Brooks has.

"I wish," Vridar said, closing the book, "that Brooks had learned this simple thing, that the Judean-Christian system has made the child-quest for security and welfare states inevitable; for if you won't let the children grow up, then, damn it, take care of them to their graves. No adult is interested in security, for he knows that it's his worst enemy."

"You must eat now," she said.

He got to his feet, still looking at the book and still talking. "Some egghead named Aldridge says that after War II tomorrow was lost. Another eight-year-old named Stein said the future isn't important any more. When such children are taken seriously in a world of the Panties Droppers, the Brassiere-with-French-Dressing, the Dagger-in-the-Abdomen School, the Adultery-in-the-Surf School, the Greene-astride-the-Isle-of-Patmos School, the---"

"Here," she said, and thrust at him a large paper plate of bacon, mushroom-omelette, buttermilk hotcakes with huckleberry jelly, olives, pickles, a stalk of crisp celery, and a large tin cup of black coffee. He sat, and she stooped to kiss his forehead. "After seeing the millions of starving people in such places as Egypt and the Arab refugee camps, anyone who can afford a plate of food like that, yet complains---"

"Oh, I know," he said quickly. "It's the Age of Bellyache and I'm determined to get in my part of it." He sampled the omelette, while thinking that in most American restaurants an omelette was a few eggs mixed together and fried in bacon grease. "Perfect!" he said, after digging out a mushroom. He drenched his hotcakes with butter and jelly, and turned to sniff the woodsmells, which a breeze was bring-

958

ing his way from the fire. During his hour and a half with the Brooks book he had been so absorbed, and so delighted along all the veins of his sense of irony, that he had forgotten his brother. Now, looking south and west, he saw that the sun was setting over the Divide; the flanks of the mountains on the eastern watersheds were immense basins filling with violet dusk. A lot of dogs were running there. Angele sat by him with her plate and coffee, and they ate and looked at the sunset.

"Brooks tells us," he said, with an effort bringing himself back to Brooks, "that in former times nobody had to bear the burden of freedom. Of course not. There was none. Everything was in Pa, and all his children were in a nursery called the closed society."

"Cookie, you think men will ever grow up?"

"I've no idea. The Greeks were growing up but the Jews got in the way. Brooks asks us if man is as base as certain writers say he is. It's the child looking for dung to stick his nose in, as it says in *Faust*." He looked round him. "Guess I'd better make our bed before dark."

"I'm not going to sleep on pine needles," she said. "I'm not the martyr type."

"You can curl up in the back seat."

On putting the plate aside he rolled over to hands and knees and examined the materials for the mattress. It was true that pine needles worked into bedding and through it, like tiny self-propelling daggers, and tormented a man all night. But he loved the smell of them. He now raked up three or four bushels, together with cones and twigs, and leveled the pile off; and over this he spread a blanket. He would have only the car robe over him, only one blanket under him. Should they drive on to Jackson? They could drive all night, for that matter. He left the tree and stared up through deepening dusk at the south Teton, thinking of Leigh-Mallory and Irvine, high on the ridge and then gone forever; and of the moment when he stood by his brother's grave, telling himself that in all the billions of trillions of years to come this act of consciousness would never occur again. Slipping his shoes and trousers off, he entered the blankets. After sitting by him a little while Angele kissed him goodnight and went to the car.

He was an unspeakably selfish man, he told himself: he would let her try to sleep on the back seat of a car because he wanted to spend a night by this mountain. But he would pay for it. All night he would turn from belly to side, from side to back, trying to escape the probes of a hundred needles. When morning came he felt thick and stupid, and made faces in the car mirror. Angele had told him that since Marion's death he had become more and more like him---he seemed to be trying to drink for both of them and to be insane for both of them. That was true, he thought, staring at his drawn aging face, his bald skull, his eyes full of alcohol and distaste, and untouched, this morning, by humor. He muttered, "Is this the curse of us, that we have never been able to be fathers, and being orphans must kneel forever on the stony ground of our gethsemane, praying to die who have never been able to live! What is this dark in us, and what is in the dark but ourselves, sentenced by tyrannies begotten by the Great Tyranny to be children all our days...."

Angele had said, "I dread the thought that your mother will die while you still live, for I could never stand you as your mother." He had had to smile at that;

959

and, remembering, he smiled now. Well, he had been so many people all the way down through the centuries that he was no longer a person, but only the shadow of a chameleon, in which the flame of irony was burning low. Trying to induce a more cheerful frame of mind he thought of Angele's story of the big Negro in a Manhattan coffee shop, to whom she had said "Merry Christmas!" one Christmas morning, when they both sat at a counter drinking coffee. At once the big fellow had risen and bowed to her and said, "Honey bun, how about a night in Harlem after I gits off work?"

Vridar went to a small mountain stream to bathe his face, hands, arms, and feet, using earth as soap. He was sick with hangover and brooding, and out of disgust came memory of Mira Jama's words, "What is man, when you come to think upon him, but a minutely set, ingenious machine for turning, with infinite artfulness, the red wine of Shiraz into urine?" He felt as if he had a bellyful of vomit that would not rise, but after drinking deep of water that tasted of snow and minerals he felt a little better. His arthritis was worse this morning. At home this affliction some-times gave him such intense pain that he would smite himself in a fury, or would say, "I'm taking this miserable failure down to drown him." With Angele crying after him he would hasten to the lake and thrust his head in, but pull it out to say, "When Rhode asked me if there is nothing after death, I said, Yes, God damn it, the whole universe." Angele had said, "You've told me that four or five times. You must think it is awfully clever." And gravely he had said, "Isn't it? You know, what have I done all my life but limp and pick at my nose? My mother sentenced me to failure when she made me my brother's conscience." "That's much better," Angele had said.

He now went to the car, where she sat combing her hair. Two hours later they ate breakfast in Jackson, then climbed the Divide to sit on the backbone of a continent and look around them. Science, he was thinking, had forced men to understand that even a mediocre mind could have designed a better world than this one; and this fact presented such a problem in rationalizing and face-saving (or God-saving) that theologians were beside themselves, and writers were entering the old dead outworn closed societies to surrender their minds and wills.

Slipping away from Angele, Vridar tried to look across mountain wilderness to Idaho, where his dead brother lay. Then, ashamed, he turned to the flowers. He gathered so many wild blossoms that when, at last, he turned the car down the mountain, toward home, Angele was almost lost under piles of mallow and gilia, gentian and paintbrush. He thought he heard her weeping. He supposed she had seen him when he thought he was alone, as he stared into the west, across Idaho.

XXIII

What good had it done him? he asked himself a few days later. What good had it done to go to two conferences and to imagine that he had found a gentle healing in the Wind River mountains and the Tetons, and all the magnificence of sky and earth? For he went on drinking. He seemed unable to get the disease out of his blood, the loss and grief out of his mind. Oh, he knew well enough what he should

960

be---a serene detached adult, quietly viewing the Age of Violence--- the age of gangsters and whores, and writing about it in the depths of all that he had suffered and learned. For there was something to write about here, when a thing named Mickey Cohen could swagger with nine armed bodyguards into the homes of Hollywood celebrities, and be welcomed, while Eisenhower was saying that the United States was the moral leader of the world! Yes, but he was sick of gangsters, sick of whores, sick of all the cheap punks and shoddy values; of the infantile tantrums and tyrannies in most of the world's leaders; and of all the dark closed societies based upon tyranny. He would read again Sisley Huddleston's words on France in *The Tragic Years*: "I thus gave great offense to people whose chief fault was a total lack of both realism and imagination. They were no different from the majority of our fellows who look on war from a secure corner, heedless of the suffering, the moral anguish of those who, less fortunate, cannot look on light-heartedly, as at some exciting game which does not concern them personally." How true it was, every word of it! He would read again Koestler's words, which hung from his wall: "As long as you don't feel ashamed to be alive while others are put to death; not guilty, sick, humiliated because you were spared, you will remain an accomplice by omission." How true it was, every word of it! Angele would then say to him, "But you forget so easily Cram's words in the Nock book, that only a few are human beings---that all but a few are the subhuman mass. It's so unreasonable to feel cast down because you have no publisher, as long as you insist on writing for adults. For look."

She put before him a paragraph that she had torn from a news magazine. He read:

> American children are being exposed to more and more crime and violence on television. That's the finding of a survey by the National Association for Better Radio and Television. In a single week, the survey found on early evening programs from seven TV stations: 161 murders, 60 "justifiable" homicides, 2 suicides, 192 attempted murders, 83 robberies, 15 kidnappings, 7 attempted lynchings, 6 dynamitings, 2 cases of arson, 2 of torture.

Thought of such depravity sickened him. Angele said, one were to write for the millions of people who sat evening after evening staring at these brutal representations of a brutal world---but he could no more write for them than he could shake the hands of the monsters who managed the gas-chambers, or the massacres in Katyn. As for writing books for adults, he had learned long ago that there was no living in it.

Sometimes he would sit all night in his study, looking at the books around him, reading again the words he had attached to walls; and one morning at daylight he found on his typewriter a note from Angele. The meaning of it went into him like the long slow blade of a knife. It said, "My darling, I sat up all night and cried and cried and cried, and then wrote this letter. I'm afraid that you'll not let me send it." Vridar glanced at the letter, again read the note; and with amazement and sickness and shame filling him he rose to his feet. He listened. Where was she now, this woman-child, whom he had put to such tortures with his despair? And what was this letter which she thought he would not let her send?

He did not pick it up at once (he was afraid to) but he leaned forward to look at the salutation. It was addressed to one of his former publishers, a man whom she had never met, but whom she had become fond of, because of his letters. Vridar looked down to her signature at the end. Then he read only the first sentence, because that was all he could stand at the moment. It said: "To whom does a wife pour out her anxiety and heartbreak when at last she must turn to someone and cry, How long---*how long* is a fine writer expected to stand up to the indifference of publishers and the hostility of critics?" Suddenly furious he wanted to shake a clenched fist at the world and shout, "To hell with it, Angele! To hell with all of it! The whole Goddamned shittaree of it isn't worth such a cry of desperation from you!" He glowered round him, and when his gaze fell on the one book in his study which he thought was the stupidest book there, he seized it and tore it in two. He hurled the two halves to the floor and kicked them to the wall. Turning, as he might have turned to face a gun, he read the next sentence: "Must I, the one person in the world who knows best his integrity and devotion to truth, sit by month after month and watch a fine mind being lost to alcohol and insanity?" "No," he muttered, as there filled him slowly a realization of what he was doing. "No, Angele, no. Poor dear!" he murmured, looking up toward her bedroom. Was she asleep now? ---or awake and wondering in the darkness of her despair and heartache? He took her note, kissed it, folded it, and started to place it in the shirt pocket over his heart. Then with an effort he went on reading: "Is there no publisher in the whole country willing to take a share of the responsibility of bringing to modern man a new and better faith in himself?"

He swung to the window and stood, looking out---looking over at the plunging white waters; at the male mallard on the lake that refused to desert its wounded mate, whose wing a hunter had broken; at the sagebrush on the mountainside, which for reasons that still eluded him he loved as some people roses; at the forest of locusts he had planted, that in springtime was a mass of white fragrant bloom--- how he loved it, how he loved it all! So why should there be in him this death-wish? He turned to read the titles on the spines of books, row on row, all the while trying to grasp the enormity of his cowardice. How had it been with Roger Bacon in the dungeon? Had he slept on a good bed and eaten good meals? Muttering again he said, "You've got your stupid mind so fouled with Mickey Cohens and Molotovs and the loathsome stuff on television and the malice of a few critics whose disease is their own self-loathing; you've so stuffed your soul with the horrors of concentration and slave camps, gas chambers, dictators and tyrants, wars and slaughters, barbarians and hypocrites that you've forgotten the few who under the morning star are climbing the hill with Hillel! You—" "Yes! Yes!" he cried angrily, as he always cried when the ruthless Critic-Censor in him bore down with more will than his shrinking nerves could stand. "Yes!" He said, "I'll be all right" but he was sane enough to know that he would never be all right again. Somehow, bringing powers in that he did not have, he would kick the living hell out of himself and get back to his work....

962

He bent forward to read again: "Must all the years of scholarly research and all the Spartan self-discipline...." But he could read no more. Not now. He folded the letter and putting it in the drawer of his desk carefully locked the drawer. He picked up the book he had torn in two, put the halves together, binding them across the spine with tape, and gently set the book on a shelf. How had this stupid book got into his study?---for he did not allow stupid books to come there. Turning to a wall he looked up at a panel of faces, his eyes quietly intent, like eyes that looked while the whole soul listened. He studied the Langfeld face, while thinking, What did the Hebrew Pa have that my Pa didn't have? An assortment of plagues and a louder voice. This conceit made him smile. Between the faces of Sheen and Molotov was a card now, with these words on it:

> But Winner's reason, as I see it, is little more than a rationalization of our deepest fears and insecurities—the fears and insecurities that underlie our racial feelings, our attitude toward art and artists, sex and difference, and our willingness to resort to reprisals and outright force in our efforts to put down any manifestations of deviation or discontent.

Under the words Angele had written: You're one of the manifestations. Well, Professor Burns had said a mouthful about a popular novel by someone named Cozzens. It *was* fear and a sense of insecurity under the thing called race prejudice ---under sex and difference; and the reprisals and force, on a large scale, were called war.

He looked around the walls to see what else Angele had tacked up, in the hope that an appeal to his sardonic sense of humor would shake him out of grief and back to work....Yes, there were other items, all from an incredible journal of editorials that called itself a news magazine. There was an editorial on a poet named Mac-Leish, who was quoted as having said, "Which means that in the conflict between God and Satan, in the struggle between good and evil, God stakes his supremacy as God upon man's fortitude and love....The justification of the injustice of the universe is not our blind acceptance of God's inexplicable will, nor our trust in God's love, his dark and incomprehensible love. . . ." What pathetic whimperings from the terrified children! And there, not far from it, was a solemn editorial about a book called *The Power of Prayer on Plants*: a Presbyterian named Loehr and his associates had prayed hard over two sealed jars of water, and then used them to water two plant- ings of seeds. Readers were gravely told that the seeds grew prodigiously, that had been watered with the water that had been prayed over! Doubting his senses, Vridar turned, and saw still a third item that she framed in a panel of fantastic nonsense: it was said that a frightened-child writer named Kafka "was hopelessly drawn to the letter k." Kierkegaard? Kafka Senior—Kafka Junior—K! Instead of snorting with wicked glee, as he might have done a few months or years ago, Vridar turned away, numbed by the senseless horror of it. The heritage of fear! It came to him now, in a small exploding sun deep in his brain, that fear was the basis of asceticism. Well, he had known that a long time but hadn't known that it ran so deep: there wasn't much difference between a man buried to his neck in desert sands, with insects drinking from his swollen scalp, and a man praying over a jar of sealed water.

963

Taking pen and paper, and a magazine to lay the paper on, he slipped quietly out of the house and away to his trees, where he hid. At once he plunged into an hour of free associations, as he had so often done---doodling away with all his might and talking aloud at the same time. After he had tried to empty mind and soul, and had shaken them like a tin pail turned bottomside up, he looked down at all the drawings and scratchings and abstracted the meanings. They were the meanings that he was already familiar with---he wanted to be an alcoholic because his brother was---go insane because his brother had gone---be a failure because his brother had died thinking himself a failure. It was all there, good God!---it had come flowing from his mind to his pen; and in the welter of it that had the precision of poison and the clarity of a hawk's rhythm, there were the words, as large and plain as the back of a river monster in a quiet pool, You're taking the Fitzgerald Road, you insufferable coward, and just ahead of you is the point of no return!

Well, in Marion's death he learned why the Jewish father gave the fatted calf to the prodigal son; why some of the nuns had eagerly knelt to lick up mucus; why the son had made not the slightest effort to escape the father, but had shouldered his cross and gone to golgotha; and the whole deep instinctual core of the mother's heart....

He went to a mountainside and rubbed between his palms the berries, leaves, and twigs of the buffalo bush (Angele found the scent of this plant sickening but he liked it); and went next to juniper and sage and crushed them between the heels of his hands and then rubbed his palms across his upper lip and over his face. It was afternoon when, feeling in a little better form with himself—feeling that he had enough mind and will left to complete his task, he turned toward the house, trying on the way to think of something that would put him in a lighter mood. In the Prado, during one of their journeys abroad, they looked at a roomful of naked Rubens women, and he had said to her, "Do you realize that no other man in history painted so many monstrously fat female bottoms?" She had said, "That's another of your little-farm-boy attitudes." In Venice he had said, "Have you observed that the face on American money is usually that of a father-image politician?" She had retorted, "Look at Italian money a while. There are many artists and scientists on it, so how can you say there is more childness in this Catholic country than in our own?"

He slipped into the house and to his study, and was astonished to find another letter on his typewriter. It was from Robin Welsh, the professor-poet-publisher they had met at a writers' conference; it said simply that if by any chance Vridar was having difficulty finding a publisher, then he would be glad to publish the novels, even if he had to set the type by hand on his own small press. Overcome, Vridar sank to a chair and read the letter again. After an hour or more he went softly upstairs and kneeling by the bed held his wife in his arms. "In the morning," he said, whispering, "I'll write again. . . ."

964

XXIV

He kept his promise. Rising from the table, he kissed Angele, as he always did after breakfast, and said, "I now have to explore the depths of that chamber of horrors known as St. Anthony. I'll be doing some strange things, and talking and dreaming strange things, but don't let it worry you. If only I could write books like Norman Vincent Peale's I'd have that kind of look on my face; but I have to write about father-hatred, which underwent a curious sea change and became mother-hatred. I don't suppose many people could understand this book I must write now, for they'd have to look deep into themselves first. You remember what William Bolitho said?—that of all the infamous murderers not one, except possibly Landru, but was a father-hater. If only we could lodge that fact in the minds of those who are so eager to be our leaders and manage our lives!"

He went to the head of the stairway and at once she rushed to him. Looking up at his eyes she said, "Darling, good luck!"

In his study he first looked at the rows of books and then touched, as some people touch a crucifix or an altar, the volumes by Henry Charles Lea. Looking and listening, to be sure that he had not been followed, he took one of Lea's books and pressed it to his cheek; then looked over a few moments at the face of Molotov; then laid a pile of notes on his desk and began to read and classify and write. Having learned that Jesus is every man, and that every man on his own level is Jesus; that Mary is every mother's frustration and bitterness over the father's tyranny; and that Christianity was put together all over the Roman world by fanatical and obsessed and terrified orphans, Vridar now passed to the later centuries. On the development of Christianity to the end of the 17th century he had read about six hundred learned tomes, by the ablest minds in the field; and had stood amazed again and again at the prejudices and prepossessions in most of them. For among the hundreds there was only one Henry Lea—only one who had, in such measure, detachment, adultness, and respect for the facts and the truths. There were no more than a dozen Henry Osborn Taylors. Of the Catholics who pretended to be scholars, there was not one, not a single one, whose mind did not abandon him when he approached El Papa to whom he had surrendered.

Many times Vridar had pondered Leuba's words, "The evils bred by the traditional conception of God may be called by the general name 'other worldliness.' It would be difficult to evaluate the harm done to humanity in the past by the conviction that the real destination of man is the world to come, and equally difficult to estimate the harm done by the conviction that for its ethical improvement society is dependent upon a personal God." What realms for speculation those words invited the reader to enter! The guns spoken of by Frazer had shot that child-notion to pieces, and out of the ruins had emerged a monstrous closed order called Communism; and, later, another thing called Existentialism; and everywhere the scurrying people in the ruins, whom a novelist had called the league of terrified Philistines. Terrified they were; and angry and desperate, like wasps disturbed and stinging; and determined, with any methods at hand, but chiefly with smear or suppression, to "put down any manifestations of deviation. . . ."

There were Bertrand Russell's words, "When you come to look at this argument from design, it is a most astonishing thing that people can believe that this world, with all the things that are in it, with all its defects, should be the best that omnipotence and omniscience have been able to produce in millions of years." Why hadn't he said in all of time? And why hadn't this great thinker realized that he was writing about children, so ensepulchered by deep and ancient fears that they dared not use their minds, or think at all about these things? Why had Rhode been so angry? Because he was so afraid.

"In a way," he said to Angele this evening, "you can almost hear, all over the earth, the guns firing—the guns Frazer spoke of; and you can almost smell the terrors in the people. It makes me feel sad, but elated, too: no great good may come of it but something better than what we have must. Russell says that among people at the present day he finds an indifference to truth that is dangerous. His lordship sounds a bit childish. All people but a few in all times have fled the truth, for they'd liefer meet a tiger on the road. Russell says there is not the faintest reason in history to suppose that Christianity offers a way out. We don't need a way out. We're standing in the ruins and we've got to rebuild them."

Had all those tens of thousands of Christians been mad who in the early centuries fled to the deserts? Mad with fear. Vridar thought it a mountainous irony that the Roman Church had canonized so many men who had been as crazy as bedbugs. There they went into the God-forsaken (literally) loneliness, to wrestle with Satan and endure the most hideous forms of self-mutilation and torture; there they stood naked in burning heat, with ten or twenty pounds of stones hanging from their scrotum, until both scrotum and testicles fell off! (Well, the Father would no longer be angry if he saw they were castrated!) Or they stood in the hot furnace of the earth with only their ridiculous heads above the sands; or in bogs to their necks, with blood-sucking insects swarming over their skulls.

Angele asked, "*Why* did they do it?"

"Fear of father. A wish to get on a hair shirt and escape his wrath and punishment. If it's true that I've wanted a hair shirt, I should be able to understand these men."

He had read a number of books about mysticism and asceticism, but still asked anyone who would listen, "What motivates the mystic?" Lippert had written, "The history of human ideas necessarily involves the formation of concepts with inherent contradictions and their toleration. They are the inevitable consequences of the first step. Later generations are satisfied with the truth of the traditional attributes. If, when man combines them, their contradictions come to light, he does not resolve them into the elements and subject them to proof. On the contrary, he only regards such contradictions as additional authority that it is a characteristic of a certain class of concepts to be able to combine attributes which the human mind cannot reconcile. This is the principle of mysticism."

Had Lippert gone to the heart of it? Theologians said that mysticism was not contrary to reason, but superior to it. To Angele Vridar said, "Listen a moment. Those thousands of hideous lunatics out in the desert are called mystics. You're a person of sharp insights, so put your mind on it."

It seemed to him that the fantastic flight of so many thousands of Christians to the desert had not been due primarily, as so many scholars believed, to the corruptness of Church leaders: he felt that it sprang from a father-son relationship (was the Church a father-surrogate?) that had been soured by the male's contempt for the female. The worst feature of Christianity, Bertrand Russell had said, was its attitude toward sexual matters. No man would ever be able to grasp more than a small notion of the hideous terrors and tortures that had been caused by the words, Thou shalt not suffer a witch to live. Far deeper and more shocking in its consequences had been the childish fable of Adam and Eve in the garden: the Judean-Christian systems had so humiliated and outraged and degraded women that in desperation they had striven, with appalling success, to conform their natures to the values and habits of men. All this had produced what one editor had called the bitch heroine; what another had called the mom-viper; and what still others in contempt called Mom. All the early Church leaders were dedicated ignorant fanatics. For all of them woman was the instrumentum diaboli. She was used by Satan himself, said Cyprian, to get possession of the souls of men. She ought to go about clad in mourning and ashes, her eyes overflowing with the tears of remorse, said Tertullian, "to make us forget that you have been man's destruction." Virginity, said Chrysostom, was as far above marriage as the heavens above the earth. Every married person on earth, said Ambrose, ought to blush; and Justin thundered, "Sexual activity is unnecessary to life!" What disgusting fanatics they had been, every single one of them!

Well, even Goethe had written, "When towards the Devil's house we tread woman's a thousand steps ahead." It was all so incredible. It was incredible, at least for Vridar, that such writers as Schopenhauer, Balzac, Molière, Strindberg, and a thousand more had held women in biting bitter contempt. Why? His eyes had bugged out when he read the words Maxwell Perkins, a famous editor, had written to Edward Bok, "You have practically confessed . . . to a rather low opinion of woman (an opinion to which I have no objection, since I share it). . . ." "Holy Saint Anthony!" Vridar would howl, and go storming to his typewriter. "I'll let a woman tell these horrors what stinkers they are, these mewling mom-boys vomiting their fear into their generations of vipers! I'll tell these obscene hypocrites, these ruttish goatish incestuous libidinous makers of whores and whorehouses—"

"Give it to them," Angele said.

"I tell you I can't stand these skinny naked Pa-supplicating psychotics who are headed for sainthood!"

"I can't either."

"On my wall now I have El Greco's Saint Jerome and John the Baptist, two of the most loathsome fanatics ever put on canvas. I look at them every morning before I write. And by the way, have you figured out what mysticism is?"

"It's what fear of women made of men."

His foolish dictionary said that mysticism was "the doctrine that the ultimate nature of reality or the divine essence may be known in an immediate insight differing from all ordinary sensation or ratiocination." Loehr said pompously that it was "man becoming one with God." For Silberer it was a shortcut in man's union

967

with divinity; for Harnack a mystic who was not a Catholic was a dilettante. Vridar had scores of definitions: in all but a few of them mysticism was union with the Father, or the perception of truth on a plane above that of reason. He liked Von Hartmann's best: "Mysticism is the filling of the consciousness with a content . . . out of the unconscious."

Angele said, "What makes you think all those fanatics were mystics? Maybe they were just plain simpletons."

"Asceticism is my problem, really, for it is the essence of the Christian, though not of the Judean, system." He could understand asceticism, being himself filled with it: over-submissiveness and self-denial had been two laws of life with him, and in this respect, if in no other, he said drily, he was a Christian. All those men who fled to the desert were scared to death. They were convinced that practically all the ills and evils of earth had been caused by women, for the reason that the Father's agents on earth were telling them so. Pondering the matter, Vridar would stare at the two El Grecos: they looked like two scrawny lunatics out of the Belsen camp.

He wrote on a card these words and placed them behind his typewriter, so that every morning he would see them when he came to his machine:

> It isn't conceivable that the concept of God as father could have emerged from a matriarchy, or from a patriarchy in which children were freed to mature and become adult.

Over and over he muttered, "Asceticism is our heritage of fear." Then he went off to a desert to try to project himself into the moods, the passions, the fear and despair, and the abject submissiveness, of the weird naked men who stood in bogs to let mosquitoes eat them alive; who buried themselves in the sands and allowed creatures to suck the juices from their skulls and feed at their eyelids; who immured themselves in tiny stone cells and lived and died with their loneliness, their lunacy, their fears and prayers and stink. All this he understood, for it was a part of him; but it outraged him and kept him furious, for he would never submit, never! He would never have a father or Father, or even a father-image any more, or be child-ish enough to apply the masculine pronouns to the universe or any aspect of it. He would be an adult, or if not an adult, he would struggle to free himself from the abominable suffocating strangling unclean association of parents, as long as he lived. He would stand free at last, and the Malrauxes could stay in their prison.

Returning from the desert, he hid under a tree and lying on his belly doodled in free associations; wrote thoughts down and rewrote and rewrote, and then allowed his dreams to rewrite them again. Was there a universal consciousness, of which human consciousness was a part? Weren't intelligence and emotion the same thing on different levels and in different perspectives? Was mysticism only an effort to thrust more fully into awareness, without the tiresome bother of orderly thinking? —or was it, more likely, the unconscious sublimation of schizophrenia?

"Ho-ho, see it there!" he would shout, and scribble furiously.

All right, then: men by the thousands cursed their lot and fled, with their hair standing up and their penis shrinking back into their body: the sons fleeing in terror from an idealized father whom they could neither respect nor love, having in them-

968

selves so little of love and respect with which to create his image. Probably most of them shook with horror at the thought of incest. "You agree with me that the horror of incest is in proportion to the strength of the repressed wish?" Yes, Angele said, she agreed. "Maxwell Perkins had a low opinion of women, did he? Five daughters and no son! All that meat and no potatoes! A small man who felt embarrassed when he watched male dancers. A man so short that he wore his hat in the shower!" Vridar had felt pity when he read Thomas Wolfe's cruel portrait of this tormented little man.

Yes, he understood the fanatics, and he understood that the desert was the only proper home for them. It was there that he found a small cave and walled himself in, with only a tiny aperture of light; and inside he sat, on a stone, his forearms across his knees. It cost him no effort to sense the loneliness and horror of it; but then suddenly he realized, with astonishment, that *there was the protection it offered, too!* He had not foreseen that. He understood now that a man in a cell had felt himself hidden, and removed forever from women—oh, the curse of them!—and from Father also, at least in this, that God, looking down, and seeing the starving naked praying fellow there would stop threatening to punish him! Vridar tried to pray, but gagged on the words and said, "No, Pa, I don't need you any more." He sniffed at the dry-cave odors; tried to see into a dim corner, wondering where day after day he would deposit his filth; stood up to look through the tiny hole of light and to try to sense how it was when after ten or twenty years one of the ascetics looked out and thought of the world he had left. But he knew how it was!—an overwhelming sweet rapturous flood of relief flowing over all his senses, for the blessedness of having put away forever the need to strive, to resist temptation, to appease an angry Father whose ingenious mind had contrived an infinite variety of punishments for him.

While thinking and feeling and listening, he thought he heard low soft music, like a gentle appoggiatura to the Ode to Joy. Did the monks in the cells hear music? He knew now that they had, a gentle sweet sad music that reached back into childhood! The poor frightened lads! He had thought he would remain in the cell two or three days or a week, to get under the full nightmare of it, the weeping and praying; but he knew after a few hours that it had not been nightmare at all, not at all. It had been peace. It had been peace based on spurious reasoning, and on a conception of women that only a scared-to-death boy could have; but it had been peace. Wryly amused to find how different it was from what he had expected, he said aloud, "I've half a mind to stay here! For never again could I be tortured by the death of a brother-son, or the venom of a critic, or the treachery of a friend. Never again would I have to sit for hours at a typewriter trying to tell with pity, but without palliation, with the full truth but without malice, the horrid shocking story of mankind back down the ages. . . ." Alone, thinking, feeling, and trying to elicit from the dark the answers to the questions that troubled him, he looked down over himself, recalling with shock and horror that tens of thousands of men in times past had unmanned themselves. It was not hard to understand that, if you first understood that fear had been the chief motivation in what men had done, all the way back, all the way up. Not love, not ambition, not greed, but fear. It was fear that forced the surrender of the son to the father. "Is there," he asked Angele, later, "any difference between the son who seeks martyrdom on the cross, saying that his father has sent him to die, and the one who flees to the desert to castrate himself?"

"I can see none," she said.

"The monks were orphans."

"They certainly weren't saints."

"Oh, but in a way they were. I had to immure myself before I could come to that." He picked up a dictionary. "Asceticism, it says, is the doctrine that the carnal or material world is evil or despicable, and that salvation is gained by mortification of the flesh. Salvation, I assume, is a refuge from father, and is deep in men."

"Salvation from incest maybe."

He looked at her a few moments, thinking. "That could easily be an aspect of it. Man's notion that woman threw him is the most astounding and the most craven subterfuge in all of history: unable to bear the burden of his feelings toward father or son, toward mother and sisters, he simply shoved the whole thing off on to woman! How like an angel! What a paragon he is!" He picked up a volume by Michelet. "Listen to this. 'When mankind has completely awakened from its prodigious dream of two thousand years, and can coolly and quietly take stock of Christian society in the Middle Ages, two astounding facts will become apparent, facts unique in the history of the world, viz. 1: *Adultery was one of its recognized institutions* (he italicizes some of his statements), normal, established, esteemed, sung and celebrated in all the monuments of literature, noble and bourgeois alike, in every poem and every *fabliau,* and, 2: *Incest is the ordinary condition of serfs.*"

Laying the book aside he said, "What I'd like to know is whether the father-son relationship improved among the serfs, with incest commonplace. I'd think it ought to have. Anyway, in the fourth century thousands fled to the desert; a few centuries later—"

"What were you doing out there in the desert?"

"Hiding from Pa. Maurice Utrillo, the orphan, got immured in the iron will of La Bonne Lucie. Braque escaped into cells which are now called cubism. I holed up in a cave, thinking of those who say that Christianity civilized Europe. What liars fear makes of men! Paganism did its best to civilize Christianity."

In this period, when with all his intuitive powers he projected himself into the desert ascetics, and looked deeper than any but the bravest dared look, he developed in his dreams severe castration pains; and again and again stood alone in a lonely place, with an enraged bull bearing down on him. He became, during certain hours, a ridiculous naked figure in a loincloth, or in nothing at all, eating hard stale bread dipped in water. He had let his hair grow long, and standing with his crust of bread he looked like a shaggy lunatic in from the desert.

The time had come, as he had known it must come, after he had got deep in his reading when he would have to risk everything and go close to, possibly even cross, the line of no return; for he would have to enter the Inquisition dungeon and spend some weeks there. He would have to feel and know for himself out of what the precious seed of freedom had been born, and what had nourished it. He dreaded the

970

writing of this book; but the moment the last testicle shriveled in the last monk, he brought out his piles of notes, and told Angele that he must go ahead, while he still had the will and the courage.

The notes for his novel covered four tables and a half-dozen chairs, in his study and in the room adjacent to it. Turning a wry grin on his wife he said, "Like Hebbel I'm about to disturb the sleep of the world."

XXV

The Middle Ages, glorified and glamorized by popular pro-Catholic journals, such as one called *Life,* were so corrupt and brutal and evil that time and again Vridar had found himself doubting the evidence. On a desk, attached to a panel of cardboard, and close enough to his eyes to be easily read, he had a number of statements which he tried to keep at the surface of consciousness. There were Rousset's words, "Misery that goes too deep arouses not compassion but repugnance and hatred." When in all of history had it gone deeper? The closest thing to it, known to him, were the atrocities under Hitler; and so he forced himself to take such a book as *War Crimes Trials The Belsen Trial* and look for hours at the photographs, and read the text. But you didn't have to read the text: the photographs told the whole story.

It was there in the faces of Irma Grese, Ilse Lothe, Hilde Lohbauer, Elisabeth Volkenrath, Herta Ehlert, Juana Bormann; it was there in the faces of Franz Hoessler, Otto Kulessa, Fritz Mathes, Ansgar Pichen, Franz Stofel, Walter Otto, Vladislav Ostrowski, Anna Hempel, Josef Kramer, Peter Weingartner. . . . These were not human beings, not one of them; they were degenerate apemen and apewomen. The story was in all their brutal stupid faces; and in all the other hideous incredible photographs of the dying and the dead—in the communal graves with their piles of bodies in which you could see nothing but bones; in the lorry piled high with forty or fifty bodies, which S. S. men were shown unloading and dumping into pits; in the vanload of corpses with Franz Hoessler standing at the side of it; in the compounds where the living could barely sit up, and the dead, long unburied, lay all around them; and in the most ghastly picture of all that showed a bulldozer shoving piles of the dead before it, all stark naked and nothing but bones. On the tractor sat a young man, smug and wellfed, smoking a cigarette. He was a German, but with different circumstances he could have been a man from any land.

Vridar forced himself to spend hours staring at these photographs, while with all the imagination he had he tried to reconstruct, in detail, the picture of this camp, and of all the other camps like it—to *see* the vanloads of Jews as they were brought up, to the gas chambers and the crematoria—the poor terrified helpless things!— not just this one vanload, not merely a few hundreds, but thousands of them, with millions of people. Millions! Like the universe, it was more than any mind could grasp. And in these concentration camps all over Germany were war prisoners— Hungarians and Czechs and Poles and Russians—starving to death on a pint of turnip soup a day; being kicked and beaten by their guards—by such as the horrible Irma Grese . . . taken out now and then to stand at parade, where doctors chose those

971

still strong enough to labor, who were moved over to the right, and those for the gas chambers, who were moved to the other side . . . those helpless trembling naked emaciated things standing there, in the complete power of these brutes—this was too much for any sanity to stand: anger boiled up in Vridar, and turned to deathly sick nausea, and he went away to puke and drain himself white. Wiping the slobber from his mouth, he would think, But the most horrible part of it—the *most horrible* —is the fact that it could just as easily have been the other way, with the fat wellfed ones standing trembling in the line, with the emaciated ones holding the power of death over them! For there were no heroes, there were no villians, in this subhuman mass motivated by fear.

Norman Cousins had said it but he hadn't said it strong enough: yes, this was in all men and all women, *except the very few who were human*—this brutal lusting over the helpless: yes, the taint was wide enough to cover all; but he should have gone on to say that all men and women must wipe off their faces the self-righteous smirks born of a diseased amour-propre, and dredge the lies and the fears out of their diseased systems, and face these things and themselves as participants in these things, and as accomplices by omission; or there would be more Belsens, Auschwitzes, Buchenwalds, Katyns, Warsaws. . . . They must face the fact that these things came from fear—that Hitler was a fear-diseased, fear-crazed, father-hating madman; that Irma Grese, as she herself admitted at her trial, had been a frightened child, who fled in fear . . . and so when she got the power she kicked the poor dying things with her heavy boots, whipped them with her riding crop, shot them with her pistol. Yes, but among these whom she tortured were some who, if the situation had been reversed, would have tortured her: this was the lesson that amour-propre refused to learn.

The whole thing went so deep into Vridar that it seemed to him that the book itself smelled of the terrors and stinks of Belsen. He told Angele that it seemed that way, and she sniffed the book and said, "It seems that way to me." She would not look at the photographs; she said she knew well enough, without looking, what the **human ape could do. The stench of the Belsen camp** had been such that one doctor confessed that he could not endure it for more than a few seconds at a time: for the unburied dead lay everywhere; and the living, too weak to move (for they were only hide and bones and hair), voided where they sat or lay. Several gas chambers and four crematoria could not handle the vanloads of Jews, and the war prisoners, that were hauled to them daily; and so great trenches were dug. All the while in Berlin was a father-hating madman who had brought the world to this; and in Downing Street and the White House and in other temples and courts were the cowards who had stood back and let him do it. And all over the world were the self-idealizing—no, the timid fearful people who refused to face the realities and look to the sources of their woes. "A few of us," Vridar said, "have to look for them and report what we see, even though they may never themselves have the courage to look; even though they may try to destroy us for looking."

He was looking for them every time he turned to the panel of cards before him. Under the words, "Wherefore, by their fruits ye shall know them" he had typed these words from the *Catholic Encyclopedia*: Her holiness appears in the fruits which she brings forth. But for healing, for gentleness, he had typed under the second line Schnitzler's, that the soul is a wide country. The 12th century, a scholar had said, marked the point in history when man had the highest idea of himself as a unit in a unified universe. "In other words," he said to Angele, "the closed society was really closed."

At the very top of this panel he had put Helen Waddell's candle in a cellar of darkness: For Damian there is Hildebrand's lightning-flash of genius, "My Holy Satan"! Just under it was Michelet's: The divine morning star, that has shed its sparkling beam on Socrates, Archimedes, Plato, and once and again inspired them to sublimer efforts, what is it now?—a devil, the great devil Lucifer. If Satan does this, we are bound to pay him homage, to admit that he may well be after all one of the aspects of God.

In the sense that he was the son, yes.

Angele had spent years in Catholic schools and knew the spirit of this Church. Vridar discussed with her all matters pertaining to it, that would appear in his novel. He had read widely in the history of the Roman Church, including many of the ablest Catholic historians. He had made a study of Thomas Aquinas, whose infinitely subtle sophistries had exhausted him.

Eckhardt in *Papacy and World Affairs* quoted a pope who had said that any person who in any manner harmed the Roman Church "is and shall be perpetually null, vain, invalid, iniquitous, unjust, condemned, reproved, frivolous." That took care of him, he told Angele; and she said, "If your novel is ever published you'll be the nullest invalidest person on earth. And terribly frivolous."

"Terribly. Well, Lord Acton—his lordship, bear in mind, was the greatest Catholic in England in his time—had the courage to say, 'The Papacy contrived murder on the largest and also on the most inhuman scale. They were not only wholesale assassins, but they made the principle of assassination a law of the Christian Church and a condition of salvation.' "

"Why didn't they excommunicate him?"

"No doubt he had the same thought. Maybe they were afraid he'd come forth with the evidence—such as the words of Pope Pius the Ninth, 'For we have to hold as of faith that no one can be saved outside the Apostolic Roman Church, that she is the one Ark of Salvation, that whoso does not enter her will perish in the flood.' After what the Church did to women they make it female!"

"Isn't that pretty hard on all the Chinese and the other billions who have never heard of it?"

"Ponder this. Professor Lepicier of the Papal College said, 'The naked fact that the Church of her own authority has tried heretics and condemned them to be delivered to death shows that she truly has the right of killing such men as are guilty of high treason to God. Who dares to say that the Church has erred in a matter so grave as that?' By such logic Hitler had a right to kill all the Jews, for who would dare to say that he erred in a matter as grave as that? By such logic—"

"Look, iniquitous, null, reproved and frivolous, haven't you made your point?"

"It's the terrors in me talking. I dream of Belsen—all around me I see these naked skeletons just sitting and breathing. I see the Jews piled five feet deep when the doors of the gas chambers are opened, with blood——"

"Shut up!"

"Don't shriek at me, you fool! I tell you to listen. They had blood all over them because they fought so desperately to get out. Can you think of such things and not be angry? Can you——"

But she had fled.

It was with the horrors of the Belsens and Buchenwalds and Katyns in him that he would read the quiet terrible words of Aquinas, that the Church abandons the heretic "to the secular judge to be cut off from this world and put to death"; the quiet terrible words of Cardinal Billot, as late as 1922: "We must say that material force is rightly employed to protect religion, to coerce those who disturb it, and generally speaking to remove those things which impede our spiritual aim: nay, that force can have no more noble use than this"; the quiet terrible words of Father Knox as late as 1927, when he said that all people who did not belong to the Roman Church "may just as well belong to no religious body at all. For it is necessary to salvation to hold the Catholic faith."

What pathetic children!—but what deadly unpitying adversaries!

It was plain to anyone who wanted the truth, and not merely his childish evasion of it, that the unspeakably brutal Inquisition would still be in full force if it had not been restrained. This kind of evil in men nobody could say was natural, nobody could say that this was innate: something terrible had happened in the apeman on the way up! Vridar could see no difference at all between the spirit and methods of the Roman Church, and of the Soviet tyranny, which he suspected of having copied the Church: they were both tyrannies, and for the *human* being they were both detestable. He shuddered when he thought of either one. To those who said to him, "Yes, but think of all the beauty!" he gave the stinging retort, "What price are you willing to pay for a cathedral?"

When he sat to write his book he felt a little like one sitting in a deathhouse. He had been trying for days to put all emotion away from him and to look at these matters with cold detachment; to shut his heart out and admit only his mind to the task. But the horrors filled his sleep and his dreams, and memories of dreams filled his waking hours. He was afraid to go with his protagonist into the dungeon. He was afraid that in this ordeal he would lose his mind beyond recall. When he told Angele that he was afraid, she knelt before him, weeping, and begged him to put his notes away.

"I can't," he said. "It's a book someone should have written long ago—for the few adults anyway, whose souls are wide country. What did Ellen Glasgow say?—'But I cannot hush. I have felt cruelty, and I shall never forget. Something deep down in me has, for the first time, awakened, something with a passionate, tormented hatred of merciless strength, with a heartbreaking pity for the abused and inarticulate, for all the helpless victims of life, everywhere.' For, you see, if my life has any meaning, if all that I shall have written is of any good, it is that, it is there."

"Cookie darling, please don't!"

"But somebody has to."

974

Yes, he had to write it. It was the one book of all the books in his life that he could least afford to evade—a book that would show the human being at his noblest, and the subhuman being at his basest. "Just watch me," he said. "Don't let any visitors, not even friends, not even relatives, look at me while I'm writing this. If you see me sinking out of sight, quote to me Catholic Hillaire Belloc, that the Roman Church must be divine, because 'no merely human institution conducted with such knavish imbecility would have lasted a fortnight.' Remind me of what the keeper said in the Tower of London, that they were *not* instruments of torture, but instruments of punishment. See to it that every morning I look at the paintings of at least ten cardinals and popes. Remind me that the great cathedrals, built largely with slave-labor in that age of knavish imbecility, cost more than I would ever pay. Let me not forget that Justice Douglas, a darling of various men who call themselves liberals, shook the hand of the Soviet ambassador and beamed on him, just after the massacre in Hungary. Ask me, Are Jesus and Satan the old Cain and Abel myth? Whisper to my mind the fact that Carlyle was sunk, sick, broken and bankrupt before he got through his book on Frederick. Tell me what d'Annunzio said to Duse. Repeat to me every morning and evening Koestler's words, that as long as you don't feel sick and guilty and ashamed to be alive, while those who are helpless are being put to death—"

"Why, then, you belong to what Cram called the subhuman."

"That's right. There's an inquisitor in your soul and your soul is hung with black cloth. Just keep telling me these things and I'll be all right. As a child I identified with mankind as a great and noble thing, and now I have to live a while with the symbol."

After the day's writing was done, he went to a thicket to sleep alone and to be alone with his scenes; and there he dreamed the same horrible dream over and over. He had climbed a very tall ladder to examine what seemed to be a church spire, that was set on top of another tall spire, standing in the earth. When he came to the top of the ladder a deathly black terror seized him, for he was afraid that he would fall. He could see in the depths below the ladder swaying, and all around him everywhere the piles of corpses, five and six deep, of the helpless people who in gas chambers had fought like blind animals to open the doors. They fought with such frenzy that they had killed those who fell under their feet, and had covered themselves with mucus and blood. His hands on the ladder seemed to clutch more and more feebly, as sweat poured off him and his senses almost blacked out. He did not know what he was supposed to do with the spire, unless to hurl it down; and he was not able to think about it, or with any but great effort touch it. He could think only of what would happen to him if he lost consciousness and fell; and so, desperately, he tried to free his feet, which seemed to be chained, and to descend to a more secure foothold. The spire above him waved with more and more menace, as it threatened to fall. The stench from the piles of the dead and the prison camps was so heavy that it had a gray color, like that of dead faces. Gasping and sweating and almost fainting, he slowly backed down the ladder, and collapsed when his feet touched earth. He then awakened, wet all over, and trembling with the terror of it. . . .

975

There were other dreams, including the death-dream of his childhood: he was on the homeplace, and at first sensed only utter stillness and a vast loneliness. Then slowly the sky was filled; he could not describe it more than to say that it was an overwhelming sinister darkening, filled with palpable menace; it came over the whole sky and the earth and was all around him. He knew that this was the horror of death and he cried out in his sleep. This was after---this and the other dreams--- he had gone with his protagonist into the dungeon, to live the life of one in black-ness and silence, with filth and the rats; while he was going with him into the chambers of terror, where the inquistors and the infernal machines waited. He suffered as he had not suffered since adolesence. Night after night he dreamed these dreams: sometimes he was standing in a church steeple, with the piles of the dead all around him; and sometimes he clung to the spire of a cathedral. He went through paintings to see if he could find these things: there were suggestions of them in some of Goya's work (in "The Colossus" and "The Snowstorm"); in Patinir's "The River Styx"; and in a few others; but no painting more than hinted of this dreadful darkening of sky and earth, that was the essence of death itself, and the dungeons of the Middle Ages. The whole universe had been filled with the stench and bones and heartbreaking supplications of the millions tortured and murdered by the father-haters....

Words that he had read under medieval drawings ran through his sleep all night—
Some had their hearts pulled out which the Papists gnawed with their teeth....Some had their right hands and feet crushed between red hot irons....Some their noses and breasts pulled off with red hot pincers....Some were torn in pieces by horses.

Every day he had to go over his notes and look at drawings with their captions; he had to familiarize himself with the interiors of the torture-chambers, and with all the methods used by the inquisitors. These included practially every form of torture that had been devised by man. The brutality of them was so unspeakable that now and then he felt that he must vomit---"Isaiah Garcino was literaly minced; Mary Raymondet had the flesh sliced from her bones piece by piece....Ann Charbonierre was transfixed upon a stake and left to die slowly....Holes were bored in Bartholomew Frasche's heels, ropes were passed through the open wounds, and in this way he was dragged to the dungeon where he died...."

He would stare at a drawing with the caption, "Tortures Inflicted on the Protestants by the Irish Papists in 1642." This hideous scene showed a huge brute cutting off the breasts of a naked woman; another naked woman being dragged by her heels from the tail of a horse; a man bound back downward across a cart, with a savage dog chewing at one arm while an apeman smote him across his belly and genitals; a man hung up, bound, with a fire under him....Such drawings were not exaggerations of fevered and fanatical imaginations: his wide readings in many authorities had made it plain that the human imagination could not possibly exag-gerate the horrors, all the way back through the centuries, and in his own time in China, Russia, Germany....He would study for a few minutes the face of Irma Grese, and then that of Anne Frank, the wistful and tragic child who was only one of the millions who fell before the idolized Brutes in the Age of Violence.

While he was writing the early parts of the novel, Angele felt quite cheerful about him. One afternoon, thinking himself hidden, he was sitting naked and stuffing flower petals up his nostrils and into his ears; he was rubbing the essence of various crushed flowers over his thighs, his pubic area, between his legs; he was scratching in his hair and looking over his body, like one searching for lice, when a loud astonished voice said, "What in the world are you doing now?"

He turned a sheepish face up to his wife and confessed that he had been working out a scene, in which a serf had taken a bath, the first in his life, and was trying to make himself smell sweet. "Did you know that in that time of knavish imbecility---which the most popular of all the picture journals for the common minds calls that time of singular sweetness---most of the people even in the upper classes seldom or never bathed, but smeared themselves with costly pastes, until they were encrusted layer on layer. What a joy to make love to such a woman! What a triumph when at last you have dug your way through all the layers of paste! See yon knight encased in armor, riding away to do battle with a shadow: what the popular novelists who write about him don't tell you is that you could have smelled him for ten miles; that usually the only fighting he ever did was with the lice chewing at his unwashed skin under the armor; that his lady-love---"

"Come-come!" said Angele, pulling flowers out of his nostrils and digging petals out of his ears.

Another time she found him stretched out on his belly, his shoulders propped on his elbows, his face fairly alive with contortions and grimaces; wrenchings and flutterings of his eyebrows; wrinklings of his nose and twitchings of his nostrils and involutions of his lips; and rolling and bugging and popping of his eyes---for he was in the preliminaries of a scene in which he was striving (he had rehearsed this a number of times) to project himself, with a positively uncontrollable carnal frenzy, into the soul and lecherous bloodlusting of a depraved priest about to rape a helpless child. Angele's cry this time was so shrill that his face turned rigid in a mask of revolting concupiscence, and staggering to his feet he hastened away, telling himself that he must look like a priest caught in the act.

On nothing in life, at least on nothing in his books, had he spent more time than on his effort to understand the raping priest and the murdering inquisitor. They were not normal human males: only an ignoramus would argue that. Was the Inquisitor a sadist? He would read: "Sadism being in part an expression of the will-to-power of the individual formulated specifically in sexual channels, may function in that form of persecution which takes shape in the imposition of disgusting tasks or moral humiliation." That, it seemed to him, said little or nothing at all. He would read, "I do not think there can be any doubt or question that a good deal of private or secret torturing of animals takes place in every civilized country." In every *civilized* country! Lady Astor at a meeting in Queen's Hall had spoken in support of the abolition of flogging, and had been hissed and booed by twenty-five hundred women. Wives and mothers, no doubt! He had learned that only a few, *only a very few,* persons in past times had opposed torture and tried to cry it down. He read, "It took Christianity a long time to realize that animals were entitled to legal protection against torture." In times past, and again now, he projected himself with all the intuitive powers he had into the soul of those who tortured, in secret and in

977

public, and came out always with the same meaning, that the core of it was a sense of fear, inadequacy and frustration, against some person or persons. He asked Angele what her feeling was about it and she said, "If I had the power to push a button and drop all such people ten light-years below purgatory I'd do it." She then reminded him of the man in an eastern Idaho city who had written him, "A grown female cat has live kittens inside her. I cut one open and proved it." Of the man about whom his wife said that, "He just loves to torture his little dog until it faints." Of the tall dark wealthy sheepman in the valley of whom his neighbors said that one of his hobbies was the torture of cats.

He wondered how much cruelty there would be if Christians (yes, and all other people) dared to do all the things that they had a buried wish to do. The sum of it, he had no doubt, would unhinge the mind and blot out the soul of any *human* being. What was the difference, except in degree, between the monsters who racked Cutbert Simson in the Tower of London, or tortured John Coustos in the Inquisition's chambers in Lisbon, or put William Lithgow on the rack, or flogged Jane Butterworth to death; between those who disemboweled by cutting open the belly and winding the intestines out on a winch, or who bound men and castrated them, not quickly, but with slow dull knives to prolong the pain; what was the difference, except in degree of horror, between such brutalities, and the malicious gloating to be read every month in many of the nation's journals? Man was a savage beast, yes, and had always been. He was brutal, he was cruel. But that men should deliberately torture the defenseless and the helpless; that they should have spent so much of their time and talent devising ways still more fiendish; and that these horrible black hellish passions, now denied the torture-chamber and the hypocritical cloak of religion, should show themselves so brazenly, and with such venomous glee, in journals that professed to be "sophisticated," and in so many of the "comics" and in so many of the television programs---what in the middle of the 20th century was a *human* being to think of it?

"That fear has depraved mankind," he said to Angele. "The past gives no other answer."

He was in the dungeon with his protagonist for nearly two months. During that time Angele thought she would lose her mind, for the reason that she thought he had lost his. When he was not sitting at his typewriter, she hardly knew him: he would come up from his study after hours there, drained of all energy and emotion, almost of all mind and will, his face pale and drawn, his eyes showing signs of tears that had been wiped away; and he would go outside, and flinging himself down by a juniper lie with his face in the sun, his eyes closed, his pulse slowed to fifty. Then, after lunch, he would go to his labors outside; but not once, not for a moment before he slept again could he free his mind of the horrors. "I think he's going to win," he would say to Angele, when passing her on the way to his study. "I think he's going to win through to a new position against the Wetsteins!" He had spent a good part of a lifetime reading about the past, he now knew it pretty well, but he was still unwilling to believe that the normal human male was at heart a monster of evil. It was long past time to look to the reasons. He had cast away, with scorn, and later with contempt, such childish explanations as original sin: those who hid

978

behind a reason so infantile were trying to hide from Koestler's words. The reason was to be found in the natural, not in the supernatural; in the earth and the things on the earth; in man and the things in man. A large part of the reason was to be found in the family relationship. "Dear fathers, dear mothers," he would say, passing Angele. "How they love us and how we love them. There's one in a dungeon, a symbol, who doesn't pretend to; he has the freedom to be human. Will the reviewers understand him?"

For weeks he lived with the inquisitors; he looked into their black eyes and studied them and their motives; and he saw that these men were afraid. They were afraid of Father, the idealized father, whom they had idealized because they were afraid of him. In their perverted cowardly terrified souls they hadn't the slightest interest in saving others for Heaven: their whole energy and passion was bent on keeping dire supernatural punishment from falling on their own heads. Did I, he asked, wreak my will on Marion, to please my father and mother? I badgered and tormented him, until he resolved to get a higher degree, and be a professor instead of a business man: between that, and torturing a heretic to "save his soul for the Father" there is no difference at all, except in the enormity of the evil. "See, Vridar," he said, coming up the stairway, "who saved his brother for Pa! And how did the brother die? An insane alcoholic. So let me stand side by side with the Inquisitors, and share their glory; for by sacrificing our brother we have turned away the father's wrath, his plagues and thunderbolts—as Abraham turned it away when he stood ready to cut the throat of his son! As it was turned away when he heard that in Israel one was hung on a cross for him, crying, Father, father, why have you forsaken me? When will people understand what these fables mean? When they're no longer afraid."

And then one day the ordeal was over, except for two rewritings, or three. He came up out of the basement, out of the dungeon, with the arm of "Hillel" across his shoulder, and the Morning Star singing. "I want a bushel of apples," he said, "for today a poor wounded tortured thing came out of a dungeon—out of Belsen and Buchenwald, out of Auschwitz and Katyn and the dark ages, out of the fear of father; and the morning star is singing. This wounded thing is hungry for apples and a cedar fire, gentleness and peace and healing...."

XXVI

Angele went to the city and returned with a bushel of Roman Beauty and Red Delicious apples, and he carried them to a spot by the lakeside, where he had arranged to build a small fire, of cedar, pine and sage wood. He had to get the smell of the Inquisition chambers and of Belsen out of his nostrils and his system; and he thought that possibly the scent of apples, and the no less delightful incense of burning sage and cedar, might do it. During his early childhood there had been an apple orchard, at the foot of the Butte in Annis, where he had wandered among currant, raspberry, and blackberry bushes, looking at and smelling the wonder of ripe fruit. An apple orchard had always been for him the loveliest thing in life, and the scent of apples the sweetest, whether on trees, or in the cellars dug in the earth, which the pioneers had used. His parents on the Snake River ranch had had

979

such a cellar, with apples in it in wintertime; and memory of the smell of apples in that cellar, in those winters before he first went to school, was, he sometimes thought, the most precious of all the memories of his early life. "Apples," he said, looking at their plump rosy faces, "are among the healers." He knelt by the basket to breathe of them.

He was sick; not only his brain and imagination but his nerves and bones were tired. He felt, he said, the way a female trout looked after a fishery attendant moved along its sides with thumb and finger to force the eggs out. His long look at the past; his agonizing adventure in self-discovery, which the intelligence of every man who was human owed to his spirit; his effort to foreshadow the next stage of civilization, in which freedom from fear would be achieved, not with social securities and economic guarantees, which were only another form of the nursery for children, but with liberation from the ancient bondage---all this had so exhausted him that in the little time he had left he wanted only gentleness and healing. "I have taken my turn on the cross," he said, "and it's a longer turn than most." Of those who read novels he did not imagine there were many whose knowledge was broad enough or whose insights were deep enough to allow them to understand why they were not adult. But it did not matter. Other writers would rise to fire at the mantled walls, aware, with Ellen Glasgow, that "moderation has never yet engineered an explosion, and it requires an explosion to overturn a mountain of prejudice."

"I don't have that faith," Angele said, sitting with him in fragrant woodsmoke and applesmell as evening came on. "I heard today over the radio that the children of this nation spend fifty-five million dollars a year just for bubble gum. Tell me this: what do the dedicated men like Robin Welsh get? No money for all their labor; not even gratitude."

"Honor," Vridar said. "If you have honor you have all the virtues. If you haven't it, you have none of them that count."

He got to his feet and went off to find wood, for he wanted a small pile of it before night closed in. It would be an open night though, he thought, looking up at the sky. The moon, the Old Woman, would be out in a little while. Returning with an armful of juniper and sage, he knelt and laid pieces on the fire. When he sat again he broke an apple open and began to eat, with the juices of it washing like the quintessence of cleanness down his throat.

"I've figured out what nostalgia is. It is a characteristic of those who are madly in love with life because they are afraid of death."

"But you don't tell me what pay the Robin Welshes get."

"Well, of course it's not the same kind of pay the whores get. Look, we've come up out of the slime, and finding how imperfect we are physically we try to make ourselves more beautiful. We've developed a little compassion, even though it is now so adulterated with self-pity; some sense of honor, the mother of all virtues, even though today you can't find much of it in the propaganda. We're in an overwhelming transition period, or a sinking deeper into the slime. Pa hasn't been buried yet but he's dead, with the orphans everywhere grieving over the corpse; and having lost him, the chief of their illusions and the main source of their terror, the people are running wild on the hills. The ape, long hidden under the accretions and bogus pieties, has come out stark and plain for what he is and for what he has been all the time. There he stands for all to see, in such as Khrushchev; and millions of terrified children look at him fearfully and say, But maybe he doesn't mean it. He has always meant it. There's no reason," he said, with a wry grin, "to try to explain Khrushchev as original sin. He's the ape who has thrown off all the decalogues and theologies and rationalizings with which people have tried to hide him, and we've got to get used to him. But mankind, I think, has enough courage and brains to build a better order, once it becomes adult. When there is even one who can suffer for truth as I have just seen one suffer, while all the Wetsteins try to break his will and spirit----"

"But only a child, and that was centuries ago! Where is there one now? You make me think of the reviewer who said one of your novels was too sexy. There is hardly any sex in it, but then we found out that he had just lost a testicle to cancer. Another reviewer---"

"They don't matter. One-testicled critics---"

"Oh, but they do matter! They can destroy authors, and have. And then there's the one who quotes the Pasternak character, who says, What you don't understand is that history as we know it now began with Christ, and that Christ's gospel is its foundation. So! All glory to the Chinese, the Egyptians, the Greeks, the Hebrews, the Romans! Twenty-five hundred years after the golden age of Greece the highest literary award is given to a book that doesn't show a glimmer of a notion of what Christ was!"

Vridar looked at the passion in her face and smiled. "Maybe he's right. If history as we know it now began with that symbol, that could be what's wrong with the world. But he doesn't matter either, nor all the funny little Bible-saturated boys who are writing essays about him."

"Then what does matter?"

"The precious few grains of gold that mankind pans from each century." He put pillows and blankets against a tree and lay back, with his hands holding two ripe apples under his nostrils. "Lorelei, I look at it this way. I had a teacher who taught me one simple thing, to respect the integrity of a fact, and the privileged position of a probability. That is all the more necesary, now that there is nothing known that is big enough for man to surrender to. Is that his tragedy? I think it will be his strength when at last he grows up. That is the meaning of science, after you've stripped away its myth and chased its cultists out of the room. What did Rimbaud say?---that even if, half-crazed in the end, he loses the understanding of his visions, he has seen them. Let him croak in his leap into those unutterable and innumerable things. Feeling what Allen Tate has called the illuminating intensity of awareness he might have said it better, but we know what he meant.

"Girl-child, we have today a lot of obscure dedicated people who won't be on the covers of magazines for the common man to gawk at; who won't be interviewed by tomurrow and tomurrow and tomurrow. But when the little bit of gold has been panned out of this century their traces will be there. Grain by grain they are adding to the body of knowledge, and to the freedom from fear, that will some day make the adult.

"Did I ever tell you that Jed Bridwell died a drunkard?---or Borg Swensen a dirty stinking sheepherder? Did I ever tell you of the time I carried Danny Mc-Givern out of the whorehouse and almost dropped him when I saw his flabby drunken Irish face smiling up at me with heavenly innocence? I thought, Father, O Father, where are you?--- for here is your child and he wants love. It was Danny who said that the world is full of Marions, every God damned one of whom hates the Vridars. The Marions want to be able to care for themselves, and the Vridars want to take care of them. There is a drive in every growing thing to become adult, but fear has made the older or more aggressive persons take tyrannical custody of the weaker. The heart of the Judean-Christian system is in the Vridar-Marion relationship." He now looked at her with a wry smile through woodsmoke, for he dared not be grave too long. He said, "Was it my fault if I had upleasant resemblances to the Hebrew Yahweh? I look back across my life—at the hideous childhood terror and loneliness; at all the bullies and the frenzies of fright; at the want of love and understanding, and I think of such as Maurice Utrillo, who was puking drunk and insane with hate and trying to hang himself before he was fourteen. The Dannys, the Marions, the Vridars, the Maurices--- you can see them all over this western world. The poor damn wretched lonely scared orphans."

They were silent a little while. Angele ate an apple and said at last, "One night in Boise you paced the floor and talked till morning. You said the answer to the question why men make war was in the past and you were going back to find it. You think it is fear?"

"Childness. The adult human male would never make war. Observe that I said human. Don't you think it an exquisite irony that of all U.S. presidents the past thirty years, the most adult has been Hoover, and for that reason the most detested? The child-dean of Columbia, named Barzun, thinks it is intellectualism that the grown-up children of this nation can't stand. When could children, ever? What the dean-child seems not to know is that he isn't adult, nor is anyone."

"And you can't think of anyone who is."

"I think there must be a few, quite a few. I would nominate Jung and a few others. Any adult is beautifully self-disciplined, and we see so little of that. I say again, just look around at all the people we know."

"Will you be adult before you die?"

"Holy bibles, no. I do think, though, that I have a fair idea of what adultness is. I don't think many people have even that. Take Ellen Glasgow's fine phrase, the illusion of disillusionment, and throw its light on the Gertrude Steins and the beatniks. The people were fooled by War I, were they? And came to their senses in Stein and the lost generation! They were fooled in War II, were they? People merely dig deeper into the old illusions, by routes and underground ways ever more dark and devious. If you disillusion the child and he can't set up some fancy rationalization, like original sin, or Existentialism, he has no choice but to become a whore or a gangster. The adult, I think, would have few illusions, and no bitterness. I think he would still feel fear, for fear may be as much a part of us as hunger. But as Harvard's McDougall has said, nearly all people repress fear as completely as they can, because to show it is thought to be a mark of inferiority."

Again they were silent. Angele bit into another apple, Vridar looked up through woodsmoke at a blue sky. Angele said:

"Ellen Glasgow tells us that she finished the course, she kept the faith. Would St. Paul think so?"

Vridar looked over at her, for he suspected that she was teasing him. "I don't seem able to care what St. Paul would think. For soon I must go, back down to the sea---"

"Nonsense. You'll see all your critics buried."

"It's decent to die when we should. So many foolish wrinkled old things, including Christians sure of heaven, cling to the twigs in wintertime. So many swan songs are croaked over and over."

Angele turned away to the house, saying she would be back in a few moments; and while she was gone Vridar took a swig of bourbon and recalled Jean Rostand's words. He had read to Angele what the distinguished French scientist had written: "The human race will die out just as dinosaurs and stegocephalia died out. ['That's one thing we shall owe to God,' Angele had said.] Little by little that small star which serves us as a sun will cease to light and to heat---every sort of life will by that time have ceased upon this earth and it, a wornout starlet, will go on ceaselessly revolving in boundless space. Nothing will survive of any human---or superhuman ---civilization, discoveries, philosphies, ideas, religions; there will not even remain of us as much as survives of Neanderthal man, some of whose bones, at least, are preserved in our museums. In this tiny corner of the universe, the petty adventure of the protoplasm will be forever erased. It is an adventure which, perhaps, even today, is fading out on other worlds. It is an adventure which perhaps may be played out again on other worlds where it will be sustained by the same illusions, will create the same torments, will be everywhere as absurd and as vain as with us, and just as irrevocably doomed from the beginning to final catastrophe and an infinity of darkness."

Vridar had thought that Rostand revealed his childness in his choice of such words as petty, absurd, vain, doomed, catastrophe. He had found Robin Welsh's statement more adult. The universe, Robin thought, "is essentially unknowable to human beings. It surely is not structured into some pet system; and even if it were, we could not know that. I think of it as non-rational rather than irrational: it has no consciousness in itself, it is blind to man. Rationality is a human concept; it can exist nowhere except in the thought of conscious beings. Whatever 'structure' of thought, meaning, insight there is anywhere is in man's consciousness. This consciousness doesn't know truth of something outside itself. It just is aware that there is an outside. To my mind, any of man's concepts that tend toward mysticism or irrationality (the current fad of the Beat for Zen, for example; the direction some artists have taken toward the Church, in the last generation) are silly; it is the child crying in the darkness for father or mother. But those concepts which tend toward rationality, toward judgment, do ennoble man in the sense that he has, at least, the fullest control of his destiny possible to him. Fortunately, through literature (the highest of the arts) and the other arts, we are sometimes able to record those moments of rational insight, with the quality of emotion---ecstasy, despair, etc.---associated with them, and thus for a moment assert the only true power of which we are capable, the power of awareness communicable to others."

"I like that," Vridar had said, pausing in his reading. "For we're all in a dark prison and tapping on walls and listening more than looking. The illumination of occasional awareness---that is, of our deepest insights---is the highest summit man has yet come to."

He had read again from Robin's letter: "Each is alone; full communication is not possible. The fullest communication attainable comes in those moments of insight, and can then be shared. Through the ages we have had some of these moments recorded; thus man in his aloneness is not absolutely alone. He isn't accompanied in the darkness by God or Will or Fate; but he is accompanied by the consciousness of such as Shakespeare and Donne and a lot of others. His own awarenesses are enriched; his moment becomes more intense as experience; and he thus provides some direction or meaning to his experience. The experience is not directed from outside himself, but, to some extent, he is able to direct it by consciousness of meaning.

"Thus, I am a philosophical pessimist in the sense that I think there is no future for the individual being, in some mystical sense. Dust to dust, and the unknowable miracle is that the dust is somehow alive, and that, through the long, long centuries, the dust is alive with consciousness. That this consciousness can occasionally respond to meaning and direction gives the only possible hope for man, and the only possible reason for wanting to be alive, to act, to do anything. But that is reason enough."

They had read Robin's statement a number of times and agreed with its essence. Vridar was wondering if that would be reason enough, in an adult world (it never could be in a child's world), when Angele returned with two bottles of beer and a piece of sharp cheese. She sat and looked at the white falling waters, with an expression on her face that Vridar thought of as the orphan-look. When at last she began to speak, she said that, to her, it seemed likely that mankind, obsessed with fear and with no apparent ability ever to become adult, would smother in an awful togetherness, like the poor things in the gas chambers piled five deep against the doors. Wasn't it horror of two world wars, and fear that a worse war might come, that motivated the present fantastic increase of world population?---as though by multiplying until they stood shoulder to shoulder people might somehow survive! Was fear going to make a Los Angeles of the whole earth? If so, what a nightmare it would be!

"I'd say that fear is the motivation. See all the billions of people like things that have crowded in out of a storm."

"That's what I'm thinking. I've heard you say you'd not willingly live your life again---"

"O God no."

"---if it had to be what it has been. Neither would I. Neither would any friend we have put the question to. Yet look, we belong to the elite, to the fortunate few. We've never seen the naked starving millions in India and China, but we've seen them in Egypt and Jordan and Spain and Italy and Mexico. If we and our friends, who are among the fortunate, don't find life worth living, then for all these others it can't be."

"Oh, but wait. It's the desperate digging need to keep alive that makes life worth living. Then all the senses are called to their full powers."

"So the moral is to starve and be happy. Who wants that kind of life?"

"Anybody whose whole soul is fixed on hunger. But there's another level. It doesn't take much mind, only a little adultness, to conceive of a world that is not obscenely, grotesquely over-populated---that doesn't stink of fear and superstitions ---that is not governed by children. Let an adult rational world have its chance. We can't expect to build much of a civilization with fear-obsessed and hate-obsessed children. As long as fear—"

"But can there ever be a time without it?"

"I don't see why not. Listen. The guns Frazer spoke of are firing all over the world, and will go on firing, until all the primitive citadels have been leveled. The hysteria of the so-called free world---what a joke that is!---tells us that the guns are firing. Otherwise why should there be such fantastic weeping and praying and rationalizing over Pasternak's mediocre book? Good God, even Benny Stillson, whom a lot of people call a literary critic, comes whooping along with the news that he has found half the Bible in it! Lorelei, there isn't much chance to build until the reactionary forces, saturated with atavism and its terrors, are got out of the way. They're damned frightened forces right now. They're giving incredible fees and acclaim and awards to those who keep praising and trying to ennoble the old atavisms. They try to destroy those who do not. It all reminds me of Rhode's fear-saturated question, Isn't there anything after death? Hell yes, I told him, the whole damned universe."

But Angele was shaking her head no. In technology, she said, man would go on improving---oh, the physical marvels to come were beyond belief! What a toy factory it would all be, and what fun the children would have killing themselves with their toys! Would there be a single adult tool in the whole world of it? Man didn't have in him the capacity to improve. Wasn't *that* the original sin? Man was no better, not by one jot, than he had been at the height of Egypt or Greece.

Vridar was chuckling. "That's good," he said. "I've been thinking that Stalin and Hitler have been our clearest images of original sin. But what you say may be it. Look, though: aren't you too depressed by all the ruins around you?---the hysteria of scared people in the ruins? This era of whores and gangsters will run its course. I don't suppose it's going to be a pretty sight for a long time, for the guns will go right on firing. The so-called human race will submerge itself in a night-marish mess of atavism, like a sick whale sinking into the ocean slime to die; or it will emerge into an adult order. I expect the few in each generation who are human will struggle against the forces that would hold them back.

"As for me and me---this over-submissive under-motivated psychically-unintegrated half-lunatic---I shall be going soon---back to that vastness out of which

985

consciousness came, back to the deepest-deep, back to the all-in-all that is you and I, eternally changing but ever the same; making us so lost and lonely, yet so utterly the wings of all that fly, the throat of all that sings, that none can die!"

She looked over at him with a wan smile and said, "Beautiful words, man-boy, but they are only a poet's words, a child's words. Full of the illusion of disillusionment you look up at the sky; but as you have said a hundred times, we can no more grasp the immensity there or its unhumanness than the dim feeble little microscopic consciousness of an insect as big as a match head can grasp the immensity of this dinky feeble little solar system."

"Fine!" he cried. "Keep talking."

"Look, there's a mallard duck on our lake dragging a broken wing. If the man who broke that wing were to look at that duck, it wouldn't matter any more to him than a wounded wren would to a tiger. Nor would that or a billion things like it matter to a billion men all over the world."

He was looking at her, for she was now speaking with passion.

"I've been reading the Glasgow autobiography too," she said. "Ellen says she had hoped her imagination would become less sensitive to the horrors of a world she never created. She says she wouldn't have created it. Neither would I. Men have spent more energy trying to rationalize the matter and make it look sane and decent than there is energy in the sea. The only people who can endure it and like it are those to whom it doesn't matter at all if to the end of its life a lovely mallard mother has to stay on one little pond, because a man who cares nothing for beauty broke her wing. Glasgow says a sensitive mind must always be an exile on earth. Haven't you been?—even from earliest childhood. What did you do when a book editor asked if it annoys you to see women in fur coats? Has that cynical stinker ever seen beasts suffering in traps?—or the way men club them to death, knocking their jaws off and their eyes out? He's the kind who can break wings and forget them.

"No, Cookie, no. A dozen times I've heard you read Koestler's words. Time and again I've seen you sick with nausea when reading about the past. The past is no worse—hell, I sometimes think it's better—than the time we're living in. You found nothing back there as black with evil as Stalin and Hitler—nobody more choked with ignorance than their dupes. Sure, the Inquisition was a horrible thing, but those stupid fanatics *did* think they were saving souls. Did Hitler have that much excuse when he crammed gas chambers full and shut the doors? Did Stalin have that much excuse when he murdered thousands of Polish officers?"

She looked at him gravely a few moments and said, "No, no, I can't go along with you. There not only isn't anything big enough to surrender to, there never will be."

"But you forget that it's not the adult, but the child, who wants to surrender. The concept of a divine Father can exist only in a world in which the people haven't been weaned from their parents. After a lifetime of reading and thinking I stand on this, that before in an act of final supreme vomit man turns on himself, having seen his face in the mirror for what it is, he should give himself a chance to grow up. The praise given to the golden age of Greece was for its adultness. The reverence for the Hebrew holy books has been for their childness. Inge was right: you can't mix the two."

He took an apple and, bursting it open, smelled of its sweetness. "Woman-child, I haven't much left to care with any more. There's not much left of me me me. It's the *who* that bothers the child, the *why* that bothers the adult—though I suspect that in an adult world the why would not bother either. But I'm not an adult, and I'm amused by all the grown persons like me who think they are. This child, girl-woman, must soon go back to the earth and the sky: all of it all of it this is I and this is I no more: neither the books nor the love, neither the faint thin line upon the shore: into the down-below, the up-above I shall go soon, leaving nothing of me, neither the moment nor the drop where I find the sea, leaving only the why."

She had turned to look at him and now came over. The stars were out. Dusk had passed into deepening night. He spread blankets and laid pillows, and they lay back and looked at the stars, which were not at all what they seemed to be. Nor were they, or life. Breathing the incense of sage and cedar and apple, listening to the deep earth-music of falling waters, smelling the evening breeze that came across greasewood and birch and columbine, they clasped hands and returned one another's pressure. After a little while he reached over the basket and spilled it, so that apples would be all around them in the grass and the night. Until morning they would be here, eating apples and drinking whisky, breathing woodsmoke and talking; until at last, still looking at the stars and thinking of light-years, and of the microscopic insect explaining the solar system in a mote of metaphysics, they would turn their faces to the cool waters and sleep.